PHYSICAL PROPERTIES OF CHEMICAL COMPOUNDS

A systematic tabular presentation of accurate data on the physical properties of 511 organic cyclic compounds compiled by R. R. Dreisbach of the Dow Chemical Co. These comprehensive and basic data were determined for specially prepared, high purity compounds. In addition to the precisely measured properties the author has calculated new values for many constants based upon his new experimental values.

Number fifteen of the Advances in Chemistry Series
Edited by the staff of *Industrial and Engineering Chemistry*

Published June 1955 by
AMERICAN CHEMICAL SOCIETY
1155 Sixteenth Street, N.W.
Washington, D. C.

Copyright 1955 by
AMERICAN CHEMICAL SOCIETY

CONTENTS

The physical properties covered in this book are listed below. Ranges covered are given in parentheses.

Parameters for various empirical equations are tabulated which permit accurate interpolation and extrapolation of the various properties within the ranges designated.

Where any of the values below are missing, it is because they have never been determined, or are patently inaccurate. Where the determined values do not conform to the formulas, they have been adjusted accordingly and labeled calculated.

To get full value out of this reference work, the editors recommend that the user take the time to become familiar with the section "Definition of the Symbols and Parameters Used, with the Methods of Calculating the Parameters."

Purity
Freezing point
Vapor pressure (25° C. to crit. temp.)
Liquid density (25° C., approx. 3 atm.)
Vapor density (25° C., approx. 3 atm.)
Refractive index (25° to approx. 60° C.)
Rate of change of boiling point
    with pressure (25° C. to crit. temp.)
Latent heat of fusion
Latent heat of evaporation (25° C., approx. 3 atm.)
Critical values
Compressibility (25° C., approx. 3 atm.)
Viscosity (approx. 0° to 100° C.)
Heat content (approx. 300° to 1000° K.)
Surface tension (20° to 40° C.)
Solubility (25° C.)

Introduction

THERE IS A CONTINUING NEED for reliable physical properties of pure chemical compounds by scientists and engineers. Many properties are already available in the literature but the reader often finds himself in doubt as to what extent they should be relied upon. Some of the data are obviously inconsistent, while in some cases it is apparent that precise determinations have been made on compounds of doubtful purity.

Some years ago, Mr. Dreisbach began a systematic compilation of reliable physical properties of pure compounds for his own use and for the use of his associates. As this work progressed, he became intrigued with the possibilities of correlating apparently unrelated properties through the use of well-known equations and others developed by himself. In this way he was able to cross-check calculated values with those carefully determined for this purpose and for the hydrocarbons in the well-known API Project 44. These relationships are now well enough understood so that it is possible to predict a large number of physical properties of a compound quite accurately from a few accurately determined properties.

This compilation of physical properties of organic compounds contains considerable data not hitherto published. It also includes parameters which can be used for interpolating and extrapolating the determined data for practically all the compounds listed.

It is in keeping with the long-established publishing program of The Dow Chemical Co. that these data are now made generally available to scientists and engineers everywhere.

H. S. NUTTING, Director
Central Research Index
The Dow Chemical Co.

Physical Properties
Of Chemical Compounds

R. R. Dreisbach

The Dow Chemical Co., Midland, Mich.

Definition of the Symbols and Parameters Used, with the
Methods of Calculating the Parameters

Mol. % Pur.: Mole % purity by weight.

F.P.: Freezing point, ° C.

F.P. 100%: Freezing point curve extrapolated to 100% purity.

B.P. 760 mm., 100 mm., etc.: Boiling points at these pressures, ° C.

P_{25}: Pressures at 25° C., in mm.

P_e: Pressure corresponding to temperature t_e in mm.

d^{20}, etc.: Density at 20° C., etc., g./ml.

a, b: Constants of Law of Rectilinear Diameters, $d_v + d_L = a + bt$
 d_v = density of the vapor, g./ml.; d_L = density of the liquid, g./ml.

n_D^{20}, etc.: Refractive index for the sodium line at 20° C., etc.

"C": Constant of the Eykman equation, $(n_D^2 - 1)/(n_D + 0.4) \times 1/d$ = "C"

MR (obs.): Molal refraction (obs.) = $(n_D^2 - 1)/(n_D^2 + 2) \times M/d$ = MR at 20° C.
 (M = mol. wt.)

MR (calc.): Molal refraction calculated from atomic refractive indices. See page 9.

3

$(n_D - d/2)$: Refractivity intercept equals refractive index minus one half the density, both at the same temperature, 20° C.

D: Dielectric constant run at a frequency of 10^5 (cycles/sec.) and at 25° C. unless otherwise noted. When reported as data of The Dow Chemical Co., error about ±0.005. Where Reference 5 is noted it was obtained by squaring the refractive index at 20° C.

A, B, C: Constants of the Antoine vapor pressure equation for the liquid state, giving P (pressure) in mm. and t (temperature) in ° C. This is in the range between the temperatures as indicated. These temperatures in general are the boiling point at 30 mm. to a T_R of 0.75 to 0.80. See method of obtaining A, B, C on page 6.
Antoine equation: $\log P = A - B/(t + C)$

A*, B*, K, c, t_k, t_x: Constants of the saturated vapor density equation
$\log d_v$(g./ml.) $= A^* - B^*/(t + C)$ to the temperature t_k
$\log d_v$(g./ml.) $= A^* - B^*/(t + C) + K/(1.1\ T_C - 273.2 - t) + c$
from temperature t_k to a reduced temperature, T_R, of 0.92
t_k = Temperature at which it is necessary to change from the simple vapor density equation to the corrected vapor density equation in the higher ranges, ° C.
$t_k = t_x + K/c$ and $t_x = (1.1\ T_C - 273.2)°$ C.

A* and B* where the latent heat at the atmospheric boiling point is available.
$V_g - V_L = (31381.7 \times \Delta H_v \times dt/dp)/T$

Where the latent heat is not available use
$M(\Delta H_v)/T_B = 21.0$ and from this $\Delta H_v = (T_B \times 21.0)/M$
The value 21.0 (or any other value as 21.4 say) is obtained from the nearest related compound which has a latent heat available. Then proceed as in case where latent heat is available for V_g value at B.P.

Since $d_v = 1/V_g$
$\log d_{v760} = A^* - B^*/(t_B + C)$ at 760 mm.
$\log d_{v30} = A^* - B^*/(t_{30} + C)$ at 30 mm.
Solve for A*, B*, since t and d_v at 760 mm. and 30 mm. and C are known.

A', B', C': Constants of the Antoine vapor pressure equation below 30 mm. pressure, covering the temperature range as indicated. See method of obtaining the constants on page 6.

A'*, B'*: Constants of the vapor density equation below 30 mm. These two values are obtained by using the boiling point at 30 mm. and the pressure at 25° C. (obtained from the values A', B', C') and assuming that at 25° C. the relationship PV/RT = 1. Then we have V_g at 25° C. $= RT/MP = 62{,}361 \times (25 + 273.2)/MP$.

Then $dv = 1/V_g$. Inserting these values of vapor density we then solve the two equations for the values of A'* and B'* as in the case of A* and B*.

Ac, Bc, Cc: Constants of the Antoine vapor pressure equation for the liquid state from $T_R = 0.75$ (or a higher T_R as indicated) to the critical temperature. See method of obtaining the constants on page 7.

Cryoscopic Constants, A°, B°: Cryoscopic constants for calculating mole % purity. See *J. Research Natl. Bur. Standards*, **35** (1945); RP 1676.

t_e ° C.: Temperature at which a mole of the vapor occupies 22.414 liters and the vapor is in equilibrium with the liquid, in ° C.

$$te = \frac{B^*}{(A^* - \log dv_e)} - C$$

dt/dp: Rate of change of boiling point with pressure, given by equation dt/dp = B/ [2.3026 × P × (A − log P)²]° C./mm.

ΔHm: Latent heat of fusion in cal./g.

ΔHv: Latent heat of vaporization at the temperature designated, cal./g.

t_e(d, e): The latent heat of vaporization at the temperature t_e as given by the equation $\Delta Hv = d - et$, and indicates the accuracy of this equation at the temperature t_e.

$\Delta Hv/T_e$: Molal latent heat of vaporization at t_e divided by T_e. (Equal to the molal entropy of vaporization at t_e.)

d, e; d', e': These are parameters of the latent heat of vaporization equation, ΔHv-(cal./g.) = d − et. This is valid between the temperatures indicated. It has been found that the latent heat between the boiling point at 30 mm. and the boiling point at 760 mm. is almost a linear function of the temperature. As seen in most cases this equation holds almost to the temperature t_e. Above and below this the latent heat is not linear with temperature except for short intervals.

d_o: Critical density, g./ml.

v_c: Critical volume, ml./g.

t_o: Critical temperature, ° C. See also page 7.

P_o mm.: Critical pressure in mm. Where this was not obtained from the literature it is calculated as follows (The Thomson method, private communication from George W. Thomson): The critical temperature is inserted in the Antoine equation, using the A, B, and C values to calculate the critical pressure.
This value is too low. This is then multiplied by 1.07 and is assumed to be the critical pressure. In the great majority of cases, this will agree with determined values to within ±3%. For high boiling compounds this value must be decreased, since in most cases there is somewhat irregular drift with increasing temperature, so this should be continually lowered as the boiling point becomes increasingly higher.

PV/RT: Compressibility at the temperature designated.
z = PV/RT
where P = pressure in mm., V = volume in ml./mole, and R = 62361.

ΔHc: Heat of combustion, kcal./mole, gas at constant pressure, 298.16° K. or 25° C.

ΔHf: Heat of formation, kcal./mole, liquid at 298.16° K. or 25° C.

ΔFf: Free energy of formation, kcal./mole, liquid at 298.16° K. or 25° C.

η: Kinematic viscosity in centistokes, at temperature designated. The kinematic viscosity is given by the equation
log η = A^v + B^v/T
between the temperatures indicated to an accuracy of 1% or better.

B.P. ° C., 30 mm.; dt/dp; ΔHv; PV/RT: These values at 30 mm. are calculated from the Antoine equation using A, B, and C. It has been found that at 30 mm. in almost all Cox Chart Families the ratio PV/RT is negligibly different from one. This, then, has been taken as one point (the other point being the B.P. at 760 mm.) from which to calculate A* and B*, always assuming the compressibility as 1.0000 at 30 mm.

c_p: Specific heat at constant pressure at temperature designated, cal./g. ° K.

c_v: Specific heat at constant volume at temperature designated, cal./g. ° K.

f, g, h, f′, g′, h′: Parameters of the heat content equation for the liquid for the temperature ranges designated, ° K.

c_p (liquid) $= f + gT + hT^2$

m, n, o, m′, n′, o′: Parameters of the heat content equation for the vapor for the temperature ranges designated, ° K.

c_p (vapor) $= m + nT + oT^2$

γ: Surface tension in dynes/cm., at temperature designated.

[P]: Parachor at the temperature designated:

$M(\gamma)^{1/4}/(d_L - d_v) = [P]$

[P] Sugd.: Parachor from atomic and structural values as given by Sugden. See Table. The parachor value for oxygen as hydroxyl (alcohols) in these tables is taken as 15. Sugden gives the values of 20 for oxygen and 30 for oxygen in esters, which does not seem to work for alcohols and phenols.

Exp. L.l.; Exp. L.u.: Explosion limits lower and upper range, % by wt.

Dispersion: Specific dispersion, $10^4(n_F - n_C)/d$, ml./g. at 25° C.

n_F, n_C = refractive index for F and C lines.

d = density, g./ml.

Flash and Fire Points, ° C.: Cleveland open cup (ASTM D 92-46) if not otherwise designated. Closed cup (ASTM D 56-36) will be designated as such.

M Spec.: Mass Spectrograph.

Ultra V.: Ultraviolet.

X-Ray Dif.: X-Ray Diffraction.

Infrared: Infrared Spectrograph.

Solubility at 25° C., in solvents as designated.

Explanation of the methods used for calculating the various parameters in the foregoing:

A, B, C: The A, B, and C constants, except where given by the API reports, are calculated by means of the Thomson method [*Chem. Revs.*, **38**, 1–39 (1946)] using the determined boiling points at three different pressures. The three formulas for this are as follows:

$(y_3 - y_2)/(y_2 - y_1) \cdot (t_2 - t_1)/(t_3 - t_2) = 1 - (t_3 - t_1)/(t_3 + C)$

$B = (y_3 - y_1)/(t_3 - t_1) \cdot (t_1 + C)(t_3 + C)$ and

$A = y_1 + B/(t_1 + C)$

where y_1, y_2, and y_3 are equal to log P_1, log P_2, and log P_3 at temperatures t_1, t_2, and t_3. Unless the data for the three points are *very* accurate the C value can be considerably in error. As a check on this method an empirical formula developed by Thomson (private communication from George W. Thomson) will give a much better value of C if the data are much in error. This formula is $C = 239 - 0.19t_B$. The A and B values can then be readily determined from the two points given, since they are much less critical.

A′, B′, C′ (for pressures below 30 mm.): Applicable when molar heats of vaporization are available at 25° C. and the Antoine equation can be used to obtain the boiling point at 30 mm. Let A, B, C be the constants of the usual Antoine equation valid above 30 mm. and let A′, B′, C′ be the constants of the Antoine equation sought for below 30 mm. These two equations are taken to give the same value of the pressure-temperature slope at 30 mm.

log 30 $= A - B/(t_1 + C) = A' - B'/(t_1 + C')$

$B/(t_1 + C)^2 = B'/(t_1 + C')^2$

Since PV/RT may be assumed to be 1.0000 at t_1, the temperature corresponding to 30 mm., and is also 1.0000 at 25° C., the molar heat of vaporization at 25° C., $M\Delta Hv_2$, is given by

$M\Delta Hv_2 = 2.3026 \ RB' \ [(t_2 + 273.2)/(t_2 + C')]^2$

where $t_2 = 25°$ C. To solve for A', B', C' let

$g_2 = M\Delta Hv_2/2.3026 \ R(t_2 + 273.2)^2 = M\Delta Hv_2/406883$ if $t_2 = 25°$ C.

Also $g_2 = B'/(t_2 + C')^2$

Since t_1, t_2 and all values on left hand side of equations above are known then B' and C' are readily obtained as follows:

$[B'/(t_2 + C')^2][(t_1 + C')^2/B'] = g_2 \ (t_1 + C')^2/B' = $ say, h^2

Then $C' = (t_1 - ht_2)/(h - 1)$ and $B' = g_2(t_2 + C')^2$

Also $B' = B[(t_1 + C')/(t_1 + C)]^2$

$A' = \log 30 + B'/(t_1 + C')$ since $P_1 = 30$ mm.

These formulas were developed with the aid of George Thomson.

When heats of vaporization at 25° C. are not known:

In this case the C' value is estimated and A' and B' are calculated from known data. It was noticed that C' has a value approximately 18 higher than C when latent heats at 25° C. are known. By adding this increment to C we have C', then B' from the relation for the first case

$B' = B[(t_{30} + C')/(t_{30} + C)]^2$

and then A' as in first case.

Ac, Bc, Cc: This method was developed by George Thomson [*Chem. Revs.*, **38**, No. 1, 23 (1946)] and is similar to the one for obtaining A', B', C'. It is assumed that the parameters A, B, C of the Antoine equation are good to a T_R 0.75 or a higher reduced temperature, and this temperature corresponds to the 25° C. in the case of A', B', C', and the critical point corresponds to the 30 mm. point.

$B/(t_1 + C)^2 \cdot (t_c - t_1)/(y_c - y_1) = 1 + (t_c - t_1)/(t_1 + Cc)$

and $Bc = (y_c - y_1)/(t_c - t_1) \cdot (t_1 + Cc)(t_c + Cc); \ Ac = B/(t_c + Cc) + y_c$

where t_1 ° C. = T_R 0.75, t_c ° C. = critical temperature

$y_1 = \log P$ at t_1, $y_c = \log P_c$

The first equation is used to evaluate Cc, the second, Bc, and the third, Ac.

Association: The association in the vapor phase of organic acids seems to vary inversely as the temperature for some acids, at least for part of the range. In part of the range, and also apparently for some acids over the whole range, the association is fairly constant. The association is given in these sheets by the formula $M_x = p - rt$. For instance, for acetic acid this formula would be $M_x = 2.225 - 0.004085 \ t$ from 0° C. to 100° C. From 100° C. to a T_R of 0.92, $M_x = 1.85$. That is to say, the vapor density as calculated by the A*, B* formula would have to be multiplied by this correction factor to take care of the association. Further, if the reciprocal of the density is used as calculated to give vapor volume, it would be necessary to divide by 1.85 to get the actual vapor volume.

t_c: Where the critical temperature has not been determined, it is calculated by Watson's equation:

$T_c/T_c = 0.283(M/d_s)^{0.18}$

where d_s = liquid density, g./ml. at the boiling point, and M = molecular weight. This is used for all hydrocarbons and halohydrocarbons.

f, g, h, m, n, o, etc.: For a short temperature range the equation $C_p = f + gT + hT^2$ reproduces almost exactly determined data. The parameters were set up on the IBM machines using eight determined values where that many or more were available.

The IBM machines were used to set up the Antoine constants from determined data. A preliminary C value was obtained from the equation $C = 239. - 0.19t_B$. A and B were then obtained and new C values either side of the first C used and new A and B values found. In each case above, the boiling points at the experimental pressures were calculated and compared with the determined boiling points.

Actually the value of C was generally obtained from $C = 239. - 0.19t_B$, since the determined values must be *very very* accurate to give better values of C.

Cox Chart Families

1. Alkyl and halo benzenes
2. Styrenes
3. Thiaalkyl benzenes
4. Thiophenes
5. Alkyl naphthalenes
6. Tetrahydronaphthalenes
7. Decahydronaphthalenes
8. Aromatic phenols
9. Thiophenols
10. Aromatic amines
11. Nitrobenzenes
12. Aromatic alcohols (Phenyl ethyl alcohols)
13. Aromatic ketones
14. Aromatic esters
15. Cyclopentanes
16. Cyclopentenes
17. Thiacyclopentanes
18. Thiacyclopropanes
19. Cyclohexanes
20. Cyclohexenes
21. Thiacyclohexanes
22. Miscellaneous

Atomic Refractive Indices Used for Computing Molecular Refractive Index

All values are for the sodium line.

Carbon singly bound and alone	2.592	NO as nitrites	5.91
Carbon singly bound	2.418	NO as nitrosoamine	5.37
Carbon double bond	1.733	NO$_2$ as alkyl nitrite	7.44
Carbon triple bond	2.398	NO$_2$ as alkyl nitrate	7.59
Carbon conjugated	1.27	NO$_2$ as nitro paraffin	6.72
Hydrogen	1.100	NO$_2$ as nitro aromatic	7.30
Oxygen—hydroxyl	1.525	NO$_2$ as nitramine	7.51
Oxygen—ethereal	1.643	Fluorine	0.95*
Oxygen—ketonic	2.211	Chlorine	5.967
Oxygen—as ester	1.64	Bromine	8.865
		Iodine	13.900
Sulfur—as SH	7.69		
Sulfur—as RSR	7.97		
Sulfur—as RCNS	7.91		
Sulfur—as RSSR	8.11		

Nitrogen

as aliphatic primary amine	2.45
as aromatic primary amine	3.21
as aliphatic secondary amine	2.65
as aromatic secondary amine	3.59
as aliphatic tertiary amine	3.00
as aromatic tertiary amine	4.36
as hydroxylamine	2.48
as hydrazine	2.47
as aliphatic cyanide	3.05
as aromatic cyanide	3.79
as aliphatic oxime	3.93
as primary amide	2.65
as secondary amide	2.27
as tertiary amide	2.71

* This value for one fluorine atom attached to carbon.   The value 1.1 is to be used for each fluorine atom in polyfluorides.

Atomic and Structural Constants for Calculation of Parachor

	Sugden		Sugden
CH$_2$	39.0	Br	68.0
C	4.8	I	91.0
H	17.1	Single bond	..
O	20.0	Double bond	23.2
O (Alcohol)	15.0	Triple bond	46.6
O$_2$ (Ester)	60.0	3-Membered ring	16.7
N	12.5	4-Membered ring	11.6
N (Nitrile)	14.4	5-Membered ring	8.5
S	48.2	6-Membered ring	6.1
F	25.7	7-Membered ring	..
Cl	54.3	Aliphatic alcohol...subtract	6.0

TABLE I. ALKYL AND HALO BENZENES

No. 1

NAME	Benzene	STRUCTURAL FORMULA

Mole % Pur. 99.996	Ref. 2	Molecular Formula C_6H_6	Molecular Weight 78.108	

		Ref.			Ref.				Ref.
F.P. °C	5.533	2	dt/dP			f	270 to	0.2605	4
F.P. 100%			°C/mm			g	350 °K	0.0_331	4
B.P. °C			25°C	0.2276	5	h		0.0_669	4
760 mm	80.100	2	BP	0.04272	2				
100	26.075	2	t_e	0.0355	5	f'	to		
30	2.30	4	30 mm	0.5949	4	g'	°K		
10	-15.7	5	ΔHm cal/g	30.09	2	h'			
1	-45.	5	ΔHv cal/g			m	300 to	-0.1030	4
Pressure			25°C	103.57	2	n	700 °K	0.0014	4
mm 25°C	95.18	5	30 mm	108.19	4	o		-0.0_671	4
t_e	964.4	5	BP	94.14	2				
Density			t_e	92.65	5	m'	700 to	0.445	4
g/ml 20°C	0.87901	2	t_e (d, e)	92.71	5	n'	1100 °K	0.0_394	4
d_4^t 25	0.87370	2	ΔHv/T_e	20.03	5	o'		-0.0_634	4
30	0.86837	4	d 25 to	107.85	5	Surface tension			
a	0.90025	4	e 90 °C	0.1711	5	dynes/cm. 20°C		28.88	2
b	-0.00105	4	d' 0 to	108.79	5	γ	30	27.49	2
Ref. Index			e' 25 °C	0.2088	5		40	26.14	2
n_D 20°C	1.50112	2	d_c g/ml	0.300	2	Parachor [P]			
25	1.49792	2	v_c ml/g	3.333	2		20°C	206.06	4
30	1.49468	4	t_c °C	289.45	2		30	206.10	4
"C"	0.7500	4	P_c mm	36936.	2		40	206.11	4
MR (Obs.)	26.1835	2	PV/RT				Sugd.	207.1	5
MR (Calc.)			25°C	0.9922	4	Exp. L.1.%/wt.		1.8	3'
(nD-d/2)	1.06162	2	30 mm	1.0000	5	u.		7.7	3'
Dielectric	2.283	1	BP	0.9658	4	Dispersion		189.2	2
A 0 to	6.90565	2	t_e	0.9596	5	Flash Point °C #		-11.	3^2
B 160 °C	1211.033	2	t_c	0.274	5	Fire Point			
C	220.79	2	ΔHc kcal/m	757.52	2	M. Spec.		Yes	1
A* 15 to	1.19411	4	ΔHf	11.718	2	Ultra V.		Yes	1
B* 150 °C	1127.9	4	ΔFf	29.756	2	X-Ray Dif.		Yes	1
K	25.0	4	Viscosity			Infrared		99.	1
c	-0.13147	4	centistokes			Solubility in +			
t_k 150 °C	155.	4	η 20 °C	0.7427	1	Acetone		∞	
t_x 245 °C	345.8	5	30	0.6592	1	Carbon tet.		∞	
A' to			50	0.5156	1	Benzene		∞	
B' °C			70	0.4148	1	Ether		∞	
C'			B^v 25 to	523.4	4	n-Heptane		∞	
A'* to			A^v 80 °C	$\bar{2}$.09290	4	Ethanol		∞	
B'* °C			(B^v) to			Water #		0.174	1
Ac 160 to	7.42912	5	(A^v) °C			Water in		7.0	1
Bc t_c °C	1628.32	5				#		0.226	3
Cc	279.56	5	c_p liq. 300°K	0.4178	3^2				
Cryos. A°	0.01523	2	320	0.4315	3^2				
consts. B°	0.0032	2	c_p vap. 300°K	0.2516	2				
t_e °C	88.04	5	400	0.3424	2				
			c_v vap.						

T_R = 0.77 T_c # closed cup   + grams/100 grams solvent

REFERENCES: 1-Dow 2-API 3-Lit. 4-Calc. from det. data 5-Calc. by formula

SOURCE: API

PURIFICATION: API

LITERATURE REFERENCES: 3 J.A.C.S. 73, 1573 (1951); 3' Chem. Met. Eng. 44-12, 733 (1947); 3^2 Timmermans

11

No. 2

NAME	Toluene	STRUCTURAL FORMULA
	Methylbenzene	

Mole % Pur. 99.999	Ref. 2	Molecular Formula C_7H_8	Molecular Weight 92.134

		Ref.			Ref.				Ref.
F.P. °C	-94.991	2	dt/dP			f	5 to	0.3971	4
F.P. 100%			°C/mm			g	110 °K	-0.0_359	4
B.P. °C			25°C	0.6808	4	h		0.0_521	4
760 mm	110.625	2	BP	0.0463	2	f'	to		
100	51.944	4	t_e	0.0360	5	g'	°K		
30	26.04	4	30 mm	0.6487	4	h'			
10	6.37	5	ΔHm cal/g	17.17	2				
1	-26.1 ?	5	ΔHv cal/g			m	300 to	-0.0654	4
Pressure			25°C	98.55	2	n	700 °K	0.0013	4
mm 25°C	28.437	4	30 mm	97.9	5	o		-0.0_655	4
t_e	1048.2	4	BP	86.80	2				
			t_e	84.73	5	m'	700 to	0.0471	4
Density			t_e (d, e)	85.17	5	n'	1100 °K	0.0_398	4
g/ml 20°C	0.86694	2	ΔHv/T_e	19.74	5	o'		-0.0_635	4
d_4^d 25	0.86230	2				Surface tension			
30	0.85757	4	d 25 to	101.98	5	dynes/cm. 20°C		28.53	2
a	0.88547	4	e 130 °C	0.1372	5	γ 30		27.32	2
b	-0.0_3924	4	d' to			40		26.15	2
Ref. Index			e' °C						
n_D 20°C	1.49693	2	d_c g/ml	0.288	2	Parachor [P]			
25	1.49414	2	v_c ml/g	3.473	2	20°C		245.63	4
30	1.49129	4	t_c °C	320.8	2	30		245.68	4
"C"	0.7545	4	P_c mm	30400.	2	40		245.71	4
MR (Obs.)	31.095	2	PV/RT			Sugd.		246.1	5
MR (Calc.)	30.925	2	25°C	0.9968	4	Exp. L.1.%/wt.		1.24	3'
(nD-d/2)	1.06346	2	30 mm	0.9966	4	u.		19.3	3'
Dielectric	2.379	3	BP	0.9613	4	Dispersion		184.7	2
A 20 to	6.95334	2	t_e	0.9522	5	Flash Point °C		4.44‡	3'
B 200 °C	1343.943	2	t_c	0.263	4	Fire Point			
C	219.377	2	ΔHc kcal/m	901.50	2	M Spec.		Yes	1
A* 20 to	1.27923	4	ΔHf	2.867	2	Ultra V.		Yes	1
B* 175 °C	1252.3	4	ΔFf	27.282	2	X-Ray Dif.			
K	23.	5	Viscosity			Infrared		865.	1
c	-0.11760	5	centistokes			Solubility in +			
t_k 175 to	175.	5	η 20 °C	0.67778	1	Acetone		∞	
t_x 270 °C	380.0	5	40	0.56457	1	Carbon tet.		∞	
A' to			60	0.45825	1	Benzene		∞	
B' °C			80	0.39119	1	Ether		∞	
C'						n-Heptane		∞	
A'* to			B^v 40 to	440.66	4	Ethanol		∞	
B'* °C			A^v 90 °C	$\overline{2}.34476$	4	Water		7.3	1
			(B^v) to			Water in		0.055	1
Ac 200 to	7.45657	4	(A^v) °C						
Bc t_c °C	1796.9	4							
Cc	284.62	4	c_p liq. °K						
Cryos. A°	0.02508	2	c_p vap.300°K	0.2708	2				
consts. B°	0.0019	2	400	0.3609	2				
t_e °C	122.34	5	c_v vap.						

‡ closed cup   + grams/100 grams solvent

REFERENCES: 1-Dow 2-API 3-Lit. 4-Calc. from det. data 5-Calc. by formula

SOURCE:	API
PURIFICATION:	API

LITERATURE REFERENCES: 3 NBS 514; 3' Nat. Fire Prot. Assoc. 325 (1949)

TABLE I. ALKYL AND HALO BENZENES

No. 3

NAME	Ethylbenzene		STRUCTURAL FORMULA

Structural formula: benzene ring with C_2H_5

Mole % Pur.	99.995	Ref. 2	Molecular Formula C_8H_{10}	Molecular Weight 106.160

		Ref.			Ref.				Ref.
F.P. °C	-94.975	2	dt/dP			f	to		
F.P. 100%			°C/mm			g	___ °K		
			25°C	1.8286	5	h			
B.P. °C			BP	0.04898	2				
760 mm	136.186	2	t_e	0.0360	5	f'	to		
100	74.10	2	30 mm	0.6866	4	g'	___ °K		
30	46.69	4	ΔHm cal/g	20.63	2	h'			
10	25.77	5	ΔHv cal/g			m	300 to	-0.0734	4
1	-9.2	5	25°C	95.11	2	n	600 °K	0.0014	4
Pressure			30 mm	93.00	4	o		-0.0_661	4
mm 25°C	9.571	5	BP	81.00	2				
t_e	1128.	5	t_e	78.97	5	m'	700 to	0.0675	4
Density			t_e (d, e)	78.94	2	n'	1000 °K	0.0_399	4
g/ml 20°C	0.86702	2	ΔHv/T_e	19.74	5	o'		-0.0_635	4
d_4^t 25	0.86264	2	d 45 to	99.26	4	Surface tension			
30	0.85826	4	e 160 °C	0.1341	4	dynes/cm. 20°C	29.04	2	
a	0.88453	4	d' 15 to	97.54	4	ɤ 30	27.93	2	
b	-0.0_387	4	e' 45 °C	0.0973	4	40	26.79	2	
Ref. Index			d_c g/ml	0.29	2	Parachor [P]			
n_D 20°C	1.49588	2	v_c ml/g	3.448	2	20°C	284.3	4	
25	1.49320	2	t_c °C	346.4	2	30	284.4	4	
30	1.4904	4	P_c mm	28120.	2	40	284.3	4	
"C"	0.7528	4	PV/RT			Sugd.	285.1	5	
MR (Obs.)	35.761	2	25°C	1.0000	5	Exp. L.l.%/wt.			
MR (Calc.)	35.543	5	30 mm	1.0000	5	u.			
(nD-d/2)	1.06237	2	BP	0.9652	4	Dispersion	174.7	2	
Dielectric	2.238	5	t_e	0.9547	5	Flash Point °C	15.0	3	
A 45 to	6.95719	2	t_c	0.266	2	Fire Point			
B 190 °C	1424.255	2	ΔHc kcal/m	1048.53	2	M. Spec.	Yes	1	
C	213.206	2	ΔHf	-2.977	2	Ultra V.	Yes	1	
A* 45 to	1.32502	5	ΔFf	28.614	2	X-Ray Dif.			
B* 160 °C	1331.16	5	Viscosity			Infrared	507.	1	
K			centistokes			Solubility in +			
c			η 20 °C	0.7823	2	Acetone	∞		
t_k to			40	0.6305	2	Carbon tet.	∞		
t_x °C			60	0.525	2	Benzene	∞		
A' 20 to	7.32525	5	80	0.447	2	Ether	∞		
B' 45 °C	1622.0	5				n-Heptane	∞		
C'	230.7	5	B^v 20 to	413.1	4	Ethanol	∞		
			A^v 90 °C	$\overline{2}$.48073	4	Water	0.020	1	
A'* 25 to	1.69224	5	(B^v) 90 to	408.5	4	Water in	0.114	1	
B'* 45 °C	1522.4	5	(A^v) 150 °C	$\overline{2}$.49428	4				
Ac 190 to	7.3729	5	c_p liq. °K						
Bc t_c °C	1779.0	5							
Cc	260.6	5	c_p vap.300°K	0.29088	2				
Cryos. A°	0.03471	2	400	0.38395	2				
consts. B°	0.0029	2	c_v vap.						
t_e °C	151.52	5							

$T_R = 0.75 T_c$ + grams/100 grams solvent

REFERENCES: 1-Dow   2-API   3-Lit.   4-Calc. from det. data   5-Calc. by formula

SOURCE: API

PURIFICATION: API

LITERATURE REFERENCES: 3 Nat. Fire Prot. Assoc. 325 (1949)

No. 4

NAME	o-Xylene					STRUCTURAL FORMULA		
	1,2-Dimethylbenzene							

| Mole % Pur. 99.999 | Ref. 2 | Molecular Formula C_8H_{10} | | Molecular Weight 106.160 | | | | |

		Ref.			Ref.			Ref.
F.P. °C	-25.182	2	dt/dP			f | to		
F.P. 100%			°C/mm			g | °K		
B.P. °C			25°C	2.545	5	h |		
760 mm	144.411	2	BP	0.0497	2			
100	81.31	2	t_e	0.0359	5	f' | to		
30	53.38	4	30 mm	0.7002	4	g' | °K		
10	32.0	5				h' |		
1	-3.7	5	ΔHm cal/g	30.61	2			
Pressure			ΔHv cal/g			m | 300 to	-0.0055	4
mm 25°C	6.688	5	25°C	97.79	2	n | 700 °K	0.0012	4
t_e	1149.	5	30 mm	95.05	4	o |	-0.0₆44	4
Density			BP	82.90	2			
g/ml 20°C	0.88020	2	t_e	80.75	5	m' | 700 to	0.0701	4
d_4^t 25	0.87596	2	t_e (d,e)	80.72	5	n' | 1100 °K	0.0₃97	4
30	0.87172	4	ΔHv/T_e	19.75	5	o' |	-0.0₆34	4
a	0.89715	2	d | 50 to	102.17	4	Surface tension		
b	-0.0₃846	4	e | 160 °C	0.1334	4	dynes/cm. 20°C	30.03	2
Ref. Index			d' | 10 to	100.21	4	γ 30	28.93	2
n_D 20°C	1.50545	2	e' | 50 °C	0.0967	4	40	27.84	2
25	1.50295	2	d_c g/ml	0.28	2	Parachor [P]		
30	1.50025	4	v_c ml/g	3.58	2	20°C	282.4	4
"C"	0.7550	4	t_c °C	359.0	2	30	282.5	4
MR (Obs.)	35.800	2	P_c mm	27360.	2	40	282.5	4
MR (Calc.)	35.543	5				Sugd.	285.1	5
(nD-d/2)	1.06535	2	PV/RT					
Dielectric	2.266	5	25°C	1.0000	5	Exp. L.1.%/wt.	3.66	3
			30 mm	1.0000	5	u.	17.0	3
A | 50 to	6.99891	2	BP	0.9630	4	Dispersion	180.1	2
B | 200 °C	1474.679	2	t_e	0.9518	5	Flash Point °C	27.0	5
C	213.686	2	t_c	0.26	2	Fire Point		
A* | 50 to	1.36031	5	ΔHc kcal/m	1045.94	2	M Spec.	Yes	1
B* | 170 °C	1380.0	5	ΔHf	-5.841	2	Ultra V.	Yes	1
K			ΔFf	26.370	2	X-Ray Dif.		
c						Infrared		
t_k | to			Viscosity			Solubility in +		
t_x | °C			centistokes			Acetone	∞	
A' | 25 to	7.35638	5	η 20 °C	0.919	2	Carbon tet.	∞	
B' | 55 °C	1671.8	5	40	0.724	2	Benzene	∞	
C'	231.0	5	60	0.592	2	Ether	∞	
			80	0.497	2	n-Heptane	∞	
A'* 25 to	1.71752	5	B^v | 25 to	449.07	4	Ethanol	∞	
B'* 55 °C	1570.59	5	A^v | 90 °C	2.42593	4	Water		
			(B^v) | 90 to	436.36	4	Water in		
Ac | 200 to	7.4175	5	(A^v) | 150 °C	2.45900	4			
Bc | t_c °C	1842.1	5						
Cc	262.4	5	c_p liq. °K					
Cryos. A°	0.02659	2	c_p vap.300°K	0.30162	2			
consts. B°	0.0030	2	400	0.38649	2			
t_e °C	160.74	5	c_v vap.					

$T_R = 0.75\,T_c$

+ grams/100 grams solvent

REFERENCES: 1-Dow 2-API 3-Lit. 4-Calc. from det. data 5-Calc. by formula

SOURCE:	API
PURIFICATION:	API

LITERATURE REFERENCES: 3 Nat. Fire Prot. Assoc. 325 (1949)

TABLE I. ALKYL AND HALO BENZENES

No. 5

NAME	m-Xylene	STRUCTURAL FORMULA
	1,3-Dimethylbenzene	

Mole % Pur. 99.997	Ref. 2	Molecular Formula C_8H_{10}	Molecular Weight 106.160	CH$_3$ / CH$_3$

		Ref.			Ref.				Ref.
F.P. °C	-47.872	2	dt/dP			f	to		
F.P. 100%			°C/mm			g	°K		
B.P. °C			25°C	2.0725	5	h			
760 mm	139.103	2	BP	0.04903	2				
100	76.82	2	t_e	0.0358	5	f'	to		
30	49.23	4				g'	°K		
10	28.14	5	30 mm	0.6917	4	h'			
1	-7.2	5	ΔHm cal/g	26.04	2				
Pressure			ΔHv cal/g			m	300 to	-0.0307	4
mm 25°C	8.363	5	25°C	96.03	2	n	600 °K	0.0012	4
t_e	1135.	5	30 mm	93.77	4	o		-0.0$_6$46	4
Density			BP	82.0	2				
g/ml 20°C	0.86417	2	t_e	79.96	5	m'	700 to	0.0489	4
d_4^t 25	0.85990	2	t_e (d,e)	79.95	5	n'	1000 °K	0.0010	4
30	0.85563	4	ΔHv/T_e	19.84	5	o'		-0.0$_6$36	4
a	0.88124	4	d 50 to	100.22	4	Surface tension			
b	-0.0$_3$85	4	e 150 °C	0.1310	4	dynes/cm. 20°C		28.63	2
Ref. Index			d' 15 to	98.35	4	γ	30	27.54	2
n_D 20°C	1.49722	2	e' 50 °C	0.0931	4		40	26.44	2
25	1.49464	2	d_c g/ml	0.27	2	Parachor [P]			
30	1.49200	4	v_c ml/g	3.67	2		20°C	284.2	4
"C"	0.7573	4	t_c °C	346.0	2		30	284.2	4
MR (Obs.)	35.961	2	P_c mm	26600.	2		40	284.2	4
MR (Calc.)	35.543	5	PV/RT				Sugd.	285.1	5
(nD-d/2)	1.06514	2	25°C	1.0000	5	Exp. L.1.%/vol.		1.1	3
Dielectric	2.242	5	30 mm	1.0000	5	u.		7.0	3
A 45 to	7.00908	2	BP	0.9643	4	Dispersion		180.6	2
B 195 °C	1462.266	2	t_e	0.9537	5	Flash Point °C	23.2		5
C	215.105	2	t_c	0.27	2	Fire Point			
A* 45 to	1.37298	5	ΔHc kcal/m	1045.52	2	M. Spec.	Yes		1
B* 165 °C	1367.45	5	ΔHf	-6.075	2	Ultra V.	Yes		1
K			ΔFf	25.730	2	X-Ray Dif.			
c			Viscosity			Infrared	943.		1
t_k to			centistokes			Solubility in $^+$			
t_x °C			η 20 °C	0.714	2	Acetone	∞		
A' 25 to	7.36810	5	40	0.581	2	Carbon tet.	∞		
B' 50 °C	1658.23	5	60	0.488	2	Benzene	∞		
C'	232.3	5	80	0.419	2	Ether	∞		
A'* 25 to	1.73078	5	B^v 20 to	392.6	4	n-Heptane	∞		
B'* 50 °C	1556.9	5	A^v 90 °C	$\overline{2}$.51059	4	Ethanol	∞		
Ac 195 to	7.4281	5	(B^v) 90 to	396.7	4	Water			
Bc t_c °C	1824.1	5	(A^v) 150 °C	$\overline{2}$.49933	4	Water in			
Cc	262.8	5	c_p liq. °K						
Cryos. A°	0.02741	2	c_p vap.300°K	0.28881	2				
consts. B°	0.0027	2	400	0.37707	2				
t_e °C	154.72	5	c_v vap.						

$T_R = 0.75\,T_c$

$^+$ grams/100 grams solvent

REFERENCES: 1-Dow 2-API 3-Lit. 4-Calc. from det. data 5-Calc. by formula

SOURCE: API

PURIFICATION: API

LITERATURE REFERENCES: 3 Nat. Fire Prot. Assoc. 325

No. 6

NAME	p-Xylene				STRUCTURAL FORMULA
	1,4-Dimethylbenzene				

Mole % Pur. 99.999	Ref. 2	Molecular Formula C_8H_{10}		Molecular Weight 106.160		

		Ref.				Ref.				Ref.
F.P. °C	13.263	2	dt/dP °C/mm			f		to		
F.P. 100%			25°C	1.979	5	g		°K		
B.P. °C			BP	0.04917	2	h				
760 mm	138.351	2	t_e	0.036	5	f'		to		
100	75.931	2				g'		°K		
30	48.31	4	30 mm	0.6922	4	h'				
10	27.2	5	ΔHm cal/g	38.53	2					
1	-8.1	5	ΔHv cal/g			m		300 to	-0.0210	4
Pressure			25°C	95.40	2	n		600 °K	0.0011	4
mm 25°C	8.816	5	30 mm	93.18	4	o			-0.0_640	4
t_e	1129.	5	BP	81.20	2					
Density			t_e	79.17	5	m'		700 to	0.0417	4
g/ml 20°C	0.86105	2	t_e (d, e)	79.15	5	n'		1000 °K	0.0010	4
d_4^t 25	0.85669	2	ΔHv/T_e	19.68	5	o'			-0.0_636	4
30	0.85233	4	d 50 to	99.61	4	Surface tension				
a	0.87848	4	e 150 °C	0.1330	4	dynes/cm. 20°C			28.31	2
b	-0.0_387	4	d' 15 to	97.78	4	γ		30	27.22	2
Ref. Index			e' 50 °C	0.0952	4			40	26.13	2
n_D 20°C	1.49581	2	d_c g/ml	0.29	2	Parachor [P]				
25	1.49325	2	v_c ml/g	3.48	2			20°C	284.4	4
30	1.49037	2	t_c °C	345.0	2			30	284.5	4
"C"	0.7580	4	P_c mm	25840.	2			40	284.6	4
MR (Obs.)	36.005	2	PV/RT					Sugd.	285.1	5
MR (Calc.)	35.543	5	25°C	1.0000	5	Exp. L.l.%/vol.			1.1	3
(nD-d/2)	1.06530	2	30 mm	1.0000	5	u.			7.0	3
Dielectric	2.237	5	BP	0.9613	4	Dispersion			182.1	2
A 45 to	6.99052	2	t_e	0.9504	5	Flash Point °C			23.0	5
B 190 °C	1453.430	2	t_c	0.25	2	Fire Point				
C	215.307	2	ΔHc kcal/m	1045.69	2	M Spec.			Yes	1
A* 45 to	1.36044	5	ΔHf	-5.838	2	Ultra V.			Yes	1
B* 165 °C	1360.12	5	ΔFf	26.310	2	X-Ray Dif.				
K			Viscosity			Infrared			944.	1
c			centistokes			Solubility in +				
t_k to			η 20 °C	0.748	2	Acetone			∞	
t_x °C			40	0.602	2	Carbon tet.			∞	
A' 25 to	7.32611	5	60	0.502	2	Benzene			∞	
B' 50 °C	1635.74	5	80	0.428	2	Ether			∞	
C'	231.4	5	B^V 20 to	409.7	4	n-Heptane			∞	
A'* 25 to	1.69080	5	A^V 90 °C	$\bar{2}.47135$	4	Ethanol			∞	
B'* 50 °C	1535.29	5	(B^V) 90 to	419.5	4	Water				
Ac 190 to	7.4096	5	(A^V) 150 °C	$\bar{2}.44420$	4	Water in				
Bc t_c °C	1814.3	5	c_p liq. °K							
Cc	263.0	5								
Cryos. A°	0.02509	2	c_p vap.300°K	0.28721	2					
consts. B°	0.0028	2	400	0.37396	2					
t_e °C	153.79	5	c_v vap.							
$T_R = 0.75 T_c$						+ grams/100 grams solvent				

REFERENCES: 1-Dow 2-API 3-Lit. 4-Calc. from det. data 5-Calc. by formula

SOURCE:	API
PURIFICATION:	API

LITERATURE REFERENCES: 3 Nat. Fire Prot. Assoc. 325 (1949)

TABLE I. ALKYL AND HALO BENZENES

No. 7

NAME	n-Propylbenzene	STRUCTURAL FORMULA
		⌬ C_3H_7

Mole % Pur. 99.72	Ref. 2	Molecular Formula C_9H_{12}	Molecular Weight 120.186

		Ref.			Ref.					Ref.
F.P. °C	-99.50	2	dt/dP			f		to		
F.P. 100%			°C/mm			g	$\lfloor$ _ _ _ $\rfloor$ °K			
			25°C	4.652	5	h				
B.P. °C			BP	0.05143	2					
760 mm	159.217	2	t_e	0.036	5	f'		to		
100	94.056	2	30 mm	0.7204	4	g'	$\lfloor$ _ _ _ $\rfloor$ °K			
30	65.28	4				h'				
10	43.34	5	ΔHm cal/g	16.97	2					
1	6.7	5				m	$\lceil$ 300 to	-0.0433	4
			ΔHv cal/g			n	$\lfloor$ 600 °K	0.0013	4
Pressure			25°C	91.93	2	o		-0.0$_6$57	4
mm 25°C	3.438	5	30 mm	87.65	4				
t_e	1196.	5	BP	76.00	2	m'	$\lceil$ 700 to	0.0713	4
			t_e	73.73	5	n'	$\lfloor$ 1000 °K	0.0010	4
Density			t_e (d, e)	73.69	5	o'		-0.0$_6$36	4
g/ml 20°C	0.86204	2							
d_4^t 25	0.85780	2	ΔHv/T_e	19.65	5	Surface tension			
30	0.85356	4	d $\lceil$ 60 to	95.74	4	dynes/cm. 20°C	28.99	2
a	0.87899	4	e $\lfloor$ 180 °C	0.1240	4	δ 30	27.91	2
b	-0.0$_3$847	4	d' $\lceil$ 15 to	94.59	4	40	26.81	2
			e' $\lfloor$ 60 °C	0.1063	4				
Ref. Index						Parachor [P]		
n_D 20°C	1.49202	2	d_c g/ml	0.28	2	20°C	323.5	4
25	1.48951	2	v_c ml/g	3.66	2	30	323.6	4
30	1.48683	4	t_c °C	365.	2	40	323.6	4
"C"	0.7520	4	P_c mm	23560.	2	Sugd.	324.1	5
MR (Obs.)	40.450	2	PV/RT			Exp. L.l.%/wt.		
MR (Calc.)	40.161	5	25°C	1.0000	5	u.		
(nD-d/2)	1.061	5	30 mm	1.0000	5	Dispersion	166.4	2
Dielectric	2.226	5	BP	0.9654	4	Flash Point °C	39.0	5
A $\lceil$ 65 to	6.95142	2	t_e	0.9532	5	Fire Point		
B $\lfloor$ 205 °C	1491.297	2	t_c	0.26	2	M. Spec.	Yes	1
C	207.140	2	ΔHc kcal/m	1195.12	2	Ultra V.	Yes	1
A* $\lceil$ 65 to	1.35159	5	ΔHf	-9.178	2	X-Ray Dif.		
B* $\lfloor$ 190 °C	1394.52	5	ΔFf	29.600	2	Infrared	781.	1
K			Viscosity			Solubility in +		
c			centistokes			Acetone	∞	
t_k $\lceil$ to			η 20 °C	0.9944	2	Carbon tet.	∞	
t_x $\lfloor$ °C			40	0.7770	2	Benzene	∞	
			60	0.633	2	Ether	∞	
A' $\lceil$ 25 to	7.26890	5	80	0.529	2	n-Heptane	∞	
B' $\lfloor$ 65 °C	1669.28	5	B^v $\lceil$ 25 to	461.7	4	Ethanol	∞	
C'	222.9	5	A^v $\lfloor$ 90 °C	$\overline{2}$.41616	4	Water		
A'* 25 to	1.68569	5	$(B^v)\vert 100$ to	428.8	4	Water in		
B'* 65 °C	1571.68	5	$(A^v)\vert 160$ °C	$\overline{2}$.50526	4			
Ac $\lceil$ 205 to	7.3599	5	c_p liq. °K					
Bc $\lfloor$ t_c °C	1847.0	5						
Cc	253.7	5	c_p vap 300°K	0.30777	2			
Cryos. A°	0.034	2	p 400	0.39938	2			
consts. B°	0.003	2	c_v vap.					
t_e °C	177.85	5						

$T_R = 0.75\, T_c$

+ grams/100 grams solvent

REFERENCES: 1-Dow   2-API   3-Lit.   4-Calc. from det. data   5-Calc. by formula

SOURCE: API

PURIFICATION: API

LITERATURE REFERENCES:

No. 8

NAME	Isopropylbenzene					STRUCTURAL FORMULA		
	Cumene							

Mole % Pur. 99.9996   Ref. 2   Molecular Formula C_9H_{12} Molecular Weight 120.186

Structural formula: benzene ring with $CH(CH_3)_2$

		Ref.				Ref.				Ref.
F.P. °C	-96.035	2	dt/dP °C/mm				f	to		
F.P. 100%			25°C	3.5187	5		g	°K		
B.P. °C			BP	0.05074	2		h			
760 mm	152.392	2	t_e	0.0361	5		f'	to		
100	88.13	2	30 mm	0.7095	4		g'	°K		
30	59.79	4	ΔHm cal/g	14.15	2		h'			
10	38.19	5					m	300to	-0.0657	4
1	2.1	5	ΔHv cal/g				n	600°K	0.0014	4
Pressure			25°C	89.77	2		o		-0.0$_6$68	4
mm 25°C	4.655	5	30 mm	86.14	4		m'	700to	0.0403	4
t_e	1176.	5	BP	74.60	2		n'	1000°K	0.0011	4
Density			t_e	72.44	5		o'		-0.0$_6$42	4
g/ml 20°C	0.86179	2	t_e (d, e)	72.40	5		Surface tension			
d_4^t 25	0.85751	2	ΔHv/T_e	19.64	5		dynes/cm. 20°C	28.20		2
30	0.85323	4	d 60 to	93.58	4		ɣ 30	27.17		2
a	0.87890	4	e 170 °C	0.1246	4		40	26.09		2
b	-0.0$_3$854	4	d' 15 to	92.38	4		Parachor [P]			
Ref. Index			e' 60 °C	0.1045	4		20°C	321.4		4
n_D 20°C	1.49146	2	d_c g/ml	0.28	2		30	321.6		4
25	1.48892	2	v_c ml/g	3.66	2		40	321.6		4
30	1.48628	4	t_c °C	363.	2		Sugd.	324.1		5
"C"	0.7512	4	P_c mm	23560.	2		Exp. L.1.%/wt.			
MR (Obs.)	40.422	2	PV/RT				u.			
MR (Calc.)	40.161	5	25°C	1.0000	5		Dispersion	165.4		2
(nD-d/2)	1.06055	2	30 mm	1.0000	5		Flash Point °C	39.		3
Dielectric	2.224	5	BP	0.9653	4		Fire Point			
A 60 to	6.93666	2	t_e	0.9535	5		M Spec.	Yes		1
B 200 °C	1460.793	2	t_c	0.26	2		Ultra V.			
C	207.777	2	ΔHc kcal/m	1194.19	2		X-Ray Dif.			
A* 60 to	1.34442	5	ΔHf	-9.848	2		Infrared	782.		1
B* 180 °C	1365.87	5	ΔFf	29.708	2		Solubility in +			
K			Viscosity				Acetone	∞		
c			centistokes				Carbon tet.	∞		
t_k to			η 10 °C	1.054	2		Benzene	∞		
t_x °C			20	0.918	2		Ether	∞		
A' 25 to	7.25827	5	40	0.724	2		n-Heptane	∞		
B' 60 °C	1637.97	5	60	0.591	2		Ethanol	∞		
C'	223.5	5	B^v 10 to	467.1	4		Water			
A'* 25 to	1.67854	5	A^v 70 °C	2.36973	4		Water in			
B'* 60 °C	1541.00	5	(B^v) to							
Ac 200 to	7.3445	5	(A^v) °C							
Bc t_c °C	1809.9	5	c_p liq. °K							
Cc	253.6	5	c_p vap.300°K	0.30345	2					
Cryos. A°	0.028	2	400	0.39938	2					
consts. B°	0.003	2	c_v vap.							
t_e °C	170.05	5								

$T_R = 0.75 T_c$

+ grams/100 grams solvent

REFERENCES: 1-Dow 2-API 3-Lit. 4-Calc. from det. data 5-Calc. by formula

SOURCE: API

PURIFICATION: API

LITERATURE REFERENCES: 3 Nat. Fire Prot. Assoc. 325 (1949)

TABLE I.   ALKYL AND HALO BENZENES

19

No. 9

NAME	1, 2, 3 - Trimethylbenzene	STRUCTURAL FORMULA
	Hemimellitene	

CH₃
CH₃
CH₃

Mole % Pur. 99.99	Ref. 2	Molecular Formula C_9H_{12}	Molecular Weight 120.186

		Ref.			Ref.					Ref.
F.P. °C	-25.375	2	dt/dP °C/mm			f		to		
F.P. 100%			25°C	9.734	5	g		°K		
B.P. °C			BP	0.05263	2	h				
760 mm	176.084	2	t_e	0.0360	5	f'		to		
100	109.13	2				g'		°K		
30	79.41	4	30 mm	0.7454	4	h'				
10	56.68	5	ΔHm cal/g	16.64	2					
1	18.6	5	ΔHv cal/g			m	300 to	0.0291	4
			25°C	97.56	2	n	600°K	0.0010	4
Pressure			30 mm	91.93	4	o		-0.0₆27	4
mm 25°C	1.548	5	BP	79.60	2				
t_e	1234.	5	t_e	77.07	5	m'	700 to	0.0424	4
Density			t_e (d, e)	77.99	5	n'	1000°K	0.0010	4
g/ml 20°C	0.89438	2	ΔHv/T_e	19.72	5	o'		-0.0₆37	4
d_4^t 25	0.89044	2	d 80 to	102.06	4	Surface tension			
30	0.88650	4	e 200 °C	0.1275	4	dynes/cm. 20°C	31 27	2
a	0.91014	4	d' 15 to	100.15	4	δ 30	30.25	2
b	-0.0₃787	4	e' 80 °C	0.1035	4	40	29.20	2
Ref. Index			d_c g/ml	0.28	2	Parachor [P]		
n_D 20°C	1.51393	2	v_c ml/g	3.66	2	20°C	317.8	4
25	1.51150	2	t_c °C	395.	2	30	318.0	4
30	1.50900	4	P_c mm	23560.	2	40	318.0	4
"C"	0.7546	4	PV/RT			Sugd.	324.1	5
MR (Obs.)	40.451	2	25°C	1.0000	5	Exp. L. 1.%/wt.		
MR (Calc.)	40.161	5	30 mm	1.0000	5	u.		
(nD-d/2)	1.06674	2	BP	0.9583	4	Dispersion	175.7	2
Dielectric	2.292	5	t_e	0.9444	5	Flash Point °C	51.0	5
A 75 to	7.04082	2	t_c	0.26	2	Fire Point		
B 230 °C	1593.958	2	ΔHc kcal/m	1190.96	2	M. Spec.		
C	207.078	2	ΔHf	-14.013	2	Ultra V.		
A* 75 to	1.43482	5	ΔFf	25.679	2	X-Ray Dif.		
B* 205 °C	1495.51	5				Infrared	1310.	1
K			Viscosity			Solubility in +		
c			centistokes			Acetone	∞	
t_k to			η °C			Carbon tet.	∞	
t_x °C						Benzene	∞	
A' 25 to	7.37775	5				Ether	∞	
B' 80 °C	1792.86	5	B^v to			n-Heptane	∞	
C'	224.4	5	A^v °C			Ethanol	∞	
A'* 25 to	1.78176	5	(B^v) to			Water		
B'* 80 °C	1691.49	5	(A^v) °C			Water in		
Ac 230 to	7.4536	5						
Bc t_c °C	1973.5	5	c_p liq. °K					
Cc	256.1	5						
Cryos. A°	0.0164	2	c_p vap.300°K	0.30819	2			
consts. B°	0.003	2	400	0.39023	2			
t_e °C	196.51	5	c_v vap.					

$T_R = 0.75\,T_c$

+ grams/100 grams solvent

REFERENCES: 1-Dow 2-API 3-Lit.   4-Calc. from det. data 5-Calc. by formula

SOURCE:	API
PURIFICATION:	API
LITERATURE REFERENCES:	

No. 10

NAME	1,2,4-Trimethylbenzene	STRUCTURAL FORMULA
	Pseudocumene	

Mole % Pur. 99.70	Ref. 2	Molecular Formula C_9H_{12}	Molecular Weight 120.186

		Ref.
F.P. °C	-43.80	2
F.P. 100%		
B.P. °C		
760 mm	169.351	2
100	103.36	2
30	74.056	4
10	51.64	5
1	14.1	5
Pressure mm 25°C	2.0980	5
t_e	1208.	5
Density g/ml 20°C	0.87582	2
d_4^t 25	0.87180	2
30	0.86778	4
a	0.89190	4
b	-0.0$_3$803	4
Ref. Index		
n_D 20°C	1.50484	2
25	1.50237	2
30	1.49988	4
"C"	0.7580	4
MR (Obs.)	40.691	2
MR (Calc.)	40.161	5
(nD-d/2)	1.06693	2
Dielectric	2.264	5
A $\mid$ 70 to	7.04383	2
B $\underline{\lfloor 220}$ °C	1573.267	2
C	208.564	2
A* $\mid$ 70 to	1.45156	5
B* $\underline{\lfloor 200}$ °C	1478.15	5
K		
c		
t_k to		
t_x °C		
A' $\mid$ 25 to	7.38166	5
B' $\underline{\lfloor 75}$ °C	1770.01	5
C'	225.7	5
A'* 25 to	1.78795	5
B'* 75 °C	1668.69	5
Ac $\mid$220 to	7.4565	5
Bc $\underline{\lfloor t_c}$ °C	1944.8	5
Cc	256.2	5
Cryos. A°	0.0282	2
consts. B°	0.0028	2
t_e °C	188.55	5

$T_R = 0.75\,T_c$

		Ref.
dt/dP °C/mm		
25°C	7.351	5
BP	0.0519	2
t_e	0.0360	5
30 mm	0.7350	4
ΔHm cal/g	24.54	2
ΔHv cal/g		
25°C	95.33	2
30 mm	90.43	4
BP	78.00	2
t_e	75.59	5
t_e (d, e)	75.50	5
ΔHv/T_e	19.68	5
d $\mid$ 70 to	100.08	4
e $\mid$ 190 °C	0.1304	4
d' $\mid$ 15 to	97.83	4
e' $\mid$ 70 °C	0.1000	4
d_c g/ml	0.28	2
v_c ml/g	3.57	2
t_c °C	381.5	2
P_c mm	24320.	2
PV/RT		
25°C	1.0000	5
30 mm	1.0000	5
BP	0.9540	4
t_e	0.9403	5
t_c	0.255	5
ΔHc kcal/m	1189.92	2
ΔHf	-14.785	2
ΔFf	24.462	2
Viscosity centistokes		
η 20 °C	1.154	2
30	0.936	2
B^v $\mid$ to		
A^v $\mid$ °C		
(B^v) $\mid$ to		
(A^v) $\mid$ °C		
c_p liq. °K		
c_p vap.300°K	0.31018	2
400	0.39189	2
c_v vap.		

			Ref.
f	to		
g	$\mid$ _ _ °K_		
h			
f'	to		
g'	$\mid$ _ _ °K_		
h'			
m	$\mid$ 300 to	0.0292	4
n	$\mid$ 600 °K	0.0010	4
o		-0.0$_6$30	4
m'	$\mid$ 700 to	0.0432	4
n'	$\mid$1000 °K	0.0010	4
o'		-0.0$_6$37	4
Surface tension dynes/cm. 20°C		29.71	2
γ 30		28.67	2
40		27.66	2
Parachor [P]			
20°C		320.4	4
30		320.5	4
40		320.6	4
Sugd.		324.1	5
Exp. L.1.%/wt.			
u.			
Dispersion		177.9	2
Flash Point °C		46.0	5
Fire Point			
M Spec.			
Ultra V.			
X-Ray Dif.			
Infrared		897.	1
Solubility in +			
Acetone		∞	
Carbon tet.		∞	
Benzene		∞	
Ether		∞	
n-Heptane		∞	
Ethanol		∞	
Water			
Water in			

+ grams/100 grams solvent

REFERENCES: 1-Dow 2-API 3-Lit. 4-Calc. from det. data 5-Calc. by formula

SOURCE:	API
PURIFICATION:	API
LITERATURE REFERENCES:	

TABLE I. ALKYL AND HALO BENZENES

No. 11

NAME	1,3,5-Trimethylbenzene			STRUCTURAL FORMULA
	Mesitylene			

Structural formula:

$$H_3C \underset{}{\overset{CH_3}{\bigotimes}} CH_3$$

Mole % Pur. 99.96	Ref. 2	Molecular Formula C_9H_{12}	Molecular Weight 120.186

		Ref.			Ref.					Ref.
F.P. °C	-44.720	2	dt/dP °C/mm			f		to		
F.P. 100%			25°C	6.266	5	g		°K		
			BP	0.05100	2	h				
B.P. °C			t_e	0.0357	5	f'		to		
760 mm	164.716	2	30 mm	0.7253	4	g'		°K		
100	99.75	2	ΔHm cal/g	19.14	2	h'				
30	70.85	4				m	300 to	0.0031		4
10	48.72	5	ΔHv cal/g			n	600 °K	0.0011		4
1	11.6	5	25°C	94.40	2	o		-0.0₆33		4
Pressure			30 mm	89.95	4					
mm 25°C	2.486	5	BP	77.60	2	m'	700 to	0.0450		4
t_e	1193.	5	t_e	75.28	5	n'	1000 °K	0.0010		4
Density			t_e (d, e)	75.19	5	o'		-0.0₆37		4
g/ml 20°C	0.86518	2	ΔHv/T_e	19.83	5	Surface tension				
d_4^t 25	0.86111	2				dynes/cm. 20°C		28.83		2
30	0.85704	4	d 70 to	99.27	4	γ 30		27.79		2
a	0.88145	4	e 185 °C	0.1316	4	40		26.75		2
b	-0.0₃813	4	d' 15 to	96.83	4					
			e' 70 °C	0.0971	4	Parachor [P]				
Ref. Index						20°C		321.9		4
n_D 20°C	1.49937	2	d_c g/ml	0.28	2	30		322.0		4
25	1.49684	2	v_c ml/g	3.57	2	40		322.0		4
30	1.49429	4	t_c °C	369.	2	Sugd.		324.1		5
"C"	0.7595	4	P_c mm	24320.	2					
MR (Obs.)	40.813	2	PV/RT			Exp. L.l.%/wt.				
MR (Calc.)	40.161	5	25°C	1.0000	5	u.				
(nD-d/2)	1.06678	2	30 mm	1.0000	5	Dispersion		177.5		2
Dielectric	2.248	5	BP	0.9531	4	Flash Point °C		43.0		5
A 70 to	7.07436	2	t_e	0.9398	5	Fire Point				
B 210 °C	1569.622	2	t_c	0.260	2	M. Spec.		Yes		1
C	209.578	2	ΔHc kcal/m	1189.41	2	Ultra V.		Yes		1
A* 70 to	1.48804	5	ΔHf	-15.184	2	X-Ray Dif.				
B* 200 °C	1475.78	5	ΔFf	24.832	2	Infrared		898.		1
K			Viscosity			Solubility in +				
c			centistokes			Acetone		∞		
t_k to			η °C			Carbon tet.		∞		
t_x °C						Benzene		∞		
A' 25 to	7.42169	5				Ether		∞		
B' 70 °C	1770.47	5				n-Heptane		∞		
C'	227.0	5	B^v to			Ethanol		∞		
A'* 25 to	1.82870	5	A^v °C			Water				
B'* 70 °C	1668.82	5	(B^v) to			Water in				
Ac 210 to	7.4868	5	(A^v) °C							
Bc t_c °C	1935.7	5								
Cc	256.0	5	c_p liq. °K							
Cryos. A°	0.022	2	c_p vap.300°K	0.30037	2					
consts. B°	0.003	2	400	0.38615	2					
t_e °C	183.05	5	c_v vap.							

$T_R = 0.75 T_c$

+ grams/100 grams solvent

REFERENCES:	1-Dow 2-API 3-Lit. 4-Calc. from det. data 5-Calc. by formula
SOURCE:	API
PURIFICATION:	API
LITERATURE REFERENCES:	

No. 12

NAME	o-Ethyltoluene	STRUCTURAL FORMULA
	2-Ethyl-1-methylbenzene	

Mole % Pur. 99.76	Ref. 2	Molecular Formula C_9H_{12}	Molecular Weight 120.186

		Ref.			Ref.				Ref.
F.P. °C	-80.833	2	dt/dP °C/mm			f	to		
F.P. 100%			25°C	6.143	5	g	°K		
B.P. °C			BP	0.05163	2	h			
760 mm	165.150	2	t_e	0.0360	5	f'	to		
100	99.58	2	30 mm	0.7279	4	g'	°K		
30	70.54	4	ΔHm cal/g	21.13	2	h'			
10	48.39	5	ΔHv cal/g			m	300 to	-0.0058	4
1	11.5	5	25°C	94.90	2	n	600 °K	0.0012	4
Pressure			30 mm	89.47	4	o		-0.0$_6$48	4
mm 25°C	2.522	5	BP	77.30	2	m'	700 to	0.0670	4
t_e	1203.	5	t_e	74.93	5	n'	1000 °K	0.0010	4
Density			t_e (d, e)	74.86	5	o'		-0.0$_6$37	4
g/ml 20°C	0.88069	2	ΔHv/T_e	19.69	5	Surface tension			
d_4^t 25	0.87657	2	d 70 to	98.55	4	dynes/cm. 20°C		30.20	2
30	0.87245	4	e 180 °C	0.1286	4	γ	30	29.13	2
a	0.89716	4	d' 15 to	97.88	4		40	28.11	2
b	-0.0$_3$823	4	e' 70 °C	0.1192	4	Parachor [P]			
Ref. Index			d_c g/ml	0.28	2		20°C	319.9	4
n_D 20°C	1.50456	2	v_c ml/g	3.66	2		30	320.0	4
25	1.50208	2	t_c °C	380.	2		40	320.2	4
30	1.49951	4	P_c mm	23560.	2		Sugd.	324.1	5
"C"	0.75339	4	PV/RT			Exp. L.1.%/wt.			
MR (Obs.)	40.447	2	25°C	1.0000	5	u.			
MR (Calc.)	40.161	5	30 mm	1.0000	5	Dispersion		172.1	2
(nD-d/2)	1.06422	2	BP	0.9591	4	Flash Point °C		43.0	5
Dielectric	2.265	5	t_e	0.9459	5	Fire Point			
A 70 to	7.00314	2	t_c	0.26	2	M Spec.		Yes	1
B 215 °C	1535.374	2	ΔHc kcal/m	1193.54	2	Ultra V.			
C	207.3	2	ΔHf	-11.110	2	X-Ray Dif.			
A* 70 to	1.40772	5	ΔFf	27.973	2	Infrared		550.	1
B* 195 °C	1439.76	5	Viscosity			Solubility in +			
K			centistokes			Acetone		∞	
c			η °C			Carbon tet.		∞	
t_k to						Benzene		∞	
t_x °C						Ether		∞	
A' 25 to	7.22202	5				n-Heptane		∞	
B' 70 °C	1659.41	5	B^v to			Ethanol		∞	
C'	218.3	5	A^v °C			Water			
A'* 25 to	1.64102	5	(B^v) to			Water in			
B'* 70 °C	1564.17	5	(A^v) °C						
Ac 215 to	7.4134	5	c_p liq. °K						
Bc t_c °C	1900.3	5							
Cc	254.7	5	c_p vap.300°K	0.31568	2				
Cryos. A°	0.0346	2	400	0.40354	2				
consts. B°	0.003	2	c_v vap.						
t_e °C	184.11	5							

$T_R = 0.75 T_c$ + grams/100 grams solvent

REFERENCES: 1-Dow   2-API   3-Lit.   4-Calc. from det. data   5-Calc. by formula

SOURCE: API

PURIFICATION: API

LITERATURE REFERENCES:

TABLE I. ALKYL AND HALO BENZENES

23

No. 13

NAME	m-Ethyltoluene			STRUCTURAL FORMULA
	3-Ethyl-1-methylbenzene			CH_3

Mole % Pur. 99.77	Ref. 2	Molecular Formula C_9H_{12}	Molecular Weight 120.186	C_2H_5

		Ref.			Ref.				Ref.
F.P. °C	-95.55	2	dt/dP			f	to		
F.P. 100%			°C/mm			g	°K		
B.P. °C			25°C	5.268	5	h			
760 mm	161.305	2	BP	0.05111	2	f'	to		
100	96.36	2	t_e	0.0359	5	g'	°K		
30	67.58	4	30 mm	0.7216	4	h'			
10	45.60	5	ΔHm cal/g	15.14	2				
1	8.9	5	ΔHv cal/g			m	300 to	-0.0283	4
Pressure			25°C	93.30	2	n	600 °K	0.0013	4
mm 25°C	2.991	5	30 mm	88.70	2	o		-0.0$_6$50	4
t_e	1190.	5	BP	76.60	2				
Density			t_e (d, e)	74.32	5	m'	700 to	0.0814	4
g/ml 20°C	0.86452	2		74.24	5	n'	1000 °K	0.0$_3$97	4
d_4^t 25	0.86040	2	$\Delta Hv/T_e$	19.73	5	o'		-0.0$_6$33	4
30	0.85628	4	d 65 to	97.42	4	Surface tension			
a	0.88099	4	e 180 °C	0.1291	4	dynes/cm. 20°C		29.07	2
b	-0.0$_3$823	4	d' 15 to	96.00	4	γ	30	27.97	2
Ref. Index			e' 65 °C	0.1081	4		40	26.89	2
n_D 20°C	1.49661	2	d_c g/ml	0.28	2	Parachor [P]			
25	1.49408	2	v_c ml/g	3.66	2		20°C	322.8	4
30	1.49145	4	t_c °C	363.	2		30	322.8	4
"C"	0.7561	4	P_c mm	23560.	2		40	322.7	4
MR (Obs.)	40.652	2	PV/RT				Sugd.	324.1	5
MR (Calc.)	40.161	5	25°C	1.0000	5	Exp. L. l. %/wt.			
(nD-d/2)	1.06434	2	30 mm	1.0000	5	u.			
Dielectric	2.240	5	BP	0.9576	5	Dispersion		173.1	2
A 65 to	7.01582	2	t_e	0.9448	5	Flash Point °C		41.0	5
B 210 °C	1529.184	2	t_c	0.26	2	Fire Point			
C	208.509	2	ΔHc kcal/m	1192.80	2	M. Spec.		Yes	1
A* 65 to	1.42613	5	ΔHf	-11.670	2	Ultra V.			
B* 190 °C	1434.72	5	ΔFf	26.977	2	X-Ray Dif.			
K			Viscosity			Infrared		551.	1
c			centistokes			Solubility in +			
t_k to			η °C			Acetone		∞	
t_x °C						Carbon tet.		∞	
A' 25 to	7.29569	5				Benzene		∞	
B' 70 °C	1687.63	5				Ether		∞	
C'	222.5	5	B^v to			n-Heptane		∞	
A'* 25 to	1.71135	5	A^v °C			Ethanol		∞	
B'* 70 °C	1589.9	5	(B^v) to			Water			
Ac 210 to	7.4264	5	(A^v) °C			Water in			
Bc t_c °C	1889.8	5	c_p liq. °K						
Cc	254.9	5	c_p vap 300°K	0.30444	2				
Cryos. A°	0.029	2	400	0.39522	2				
consts. B°	0.003	2	c_v vap.						
t_e °C	179.59	5							
T_R = 0.75 T_c						+ grams/100 grams solvent			

REFERENCES: 1-Dow   2-API   3-Lit.   4-Calc. from det. data   5-Calc. by formula

SOURCE:	API
PURIFICATION:	API
LITERATURE REFERENCES:	

No. 14

NAME	p-Ethyltoluene	STRUCTURAL FORMULA
	4-Ethyl-1-methylbenzene	CH_3 / C_2H_5

Mole % Pur. 99.94	Ref. 2	Molecular Formula C_9H_{12}	Molecular Weight 120.186

		Ref.			Ref.					Ref.
F.P. °C	-62.350	2	dt/dP °C/mm			f		to °K		
F.P. 100%			25°C	5.261	5	g				
B.P. °C			BP	0.0515	2	h				
760 mm	161.989	2	t_e	0.0361	5	f'		to °K		
100	96.62	2	30 mm	0.7253	4	g'				
30	67.68	4	ΔHm cal/g	25.29	2	h'				
10	45.59	5	ΔHv cal/g			m		300 to	-0.0199	4
1	8.6	5	25°C	92.70	2	n		600 °K	0.0012	4
Pressure			30 mm	88.30	4	o			-0.0$_6$45	4
mm 25°C	3.015	5	BP	76.40	2					
t_e	1195.	5	t_e	74.12	5	m'		700 to	0.0269	4
Density			t_e (d, e)	74.06	5	n'		1000 °K	0.0011	4
g/ml 20°C	0.86118	2	$\Delta Hv/T_e$	19.63	5	o'			-0.0$_6$42	4
d_4^t 25	0.85702	2	d | 65 to	96.84	4	Surface tension				
30	0.85286	4	e | 185 °C	0.1262	4	dynes/cm. 20°C			28.84	2
a	0.87781	4	d' | 15 to	95.28	4	γ		30	27.73	2
b	-0.0$_3$831	4	e' | 65 °C	0.1031	4			40	26.69	2
Ref. Index			d_c g/ml	0.28	2	Parachor [P]				
n_D 20°C	1.49500	2	v_c ml/g	3.66	2			20°C	323.4	4
25	1.49244	2	t_c °C	363.	2			30	323.4	4
30	1.48981	2	P_c m.m	23560.	2			40	323.5	4
"C"	0.7567	4	PV/RT					Sugd.	324.1	5
MR (Obs.)	40.699	2	25°C	1.0000	5	Exp. L.l.%/wt.				
MR (Calc.)	40.161	5	30 mm	1.0000	5	u.				
(nD-d/2)	1.06440	2	BP	0.9591	4	Dispersion			173.6	2
Dielectric	2.235	5	t_e	0.9462	5	Flash Point °C			42.0	5
A | 65 to	6.99802	2	t_c	0.26	2	Fire Point				
B | 210 °C	1527.113	2	ΔHc kcal/m	1192.47	2	M Spec.			Yes	1
C	208.921	2	ΔHf	-11.920	2	Ultra V.				
A* | 65 to	1.40451	5	ΔFf	27.041	2	X-Ray Dif.				
B* | 190 °C	1431.45	5	Viscosity			Infrared			552.	1
K			centistokes			Solubility in +				
c			η 20 °C	0.819	2	Acetone			∞	
t_k | to			40	0.658	2	Carbon tet.			∞	
t_x | °C			60	0.548	2	Benzene			∞	
A' | 25 to	7.30339	5	80	0.470	2	Ether			∞	
B' | 70 °C	1700.72	5				n-Heptane			∞	
C'	224.2	5	B^v | 25 to	404.1	4	Ethanol			∞	
A'* 25 to	1.71657	5	A^v | 90 °C	2.52790	4	Water				
B'* 70 °C	1601.72	5	(B^v) | to			Water in				
Ac | 210 to	7.4095	5	(A^v) | °C							
Bc | t_c °C	1889.3	5	c_p liq. °K							
Cc	255.7	5								
Cryos. A°	0.0344	2	c_p vap.300°K	0.30303	2					
consts. B°	0.003	2	400	0.39272	2					
t_e °C	180.57	5	c_v vap.							
T_R = 0.75 T_c						+ grams/100 grams solvent				

REFERENCES: 1-Dow 2-API 3-Lit. 4-Calc. from det. data 5-Calc. by formula

SOURCE: API

PURIFICATION: API

LITERATURE REFERENCES:

TABLE I. ALKYL AND HALO BENZENES

No. 15

NAME	n-Butylbenzene					STRUCTURAL FORMULA

Mole % Pur. 99.91	Ref. 2	Molecular Formula	$C_{10}H_{14}$	Molecular Weight 134.212	

		Ref.			Ref.					Ref.
F.P. °C	-87.970	2	dt/dP			f		to		
F.P. 100%			°C/mm			g		°K		
B.P. °C			25°C	13.413	5	h				
760 mm	183.270	2	BP	0.05358	2					
100	115.28	2	t_e	0.0364	5	f'		to		
30	85.21	4	30 mm	0.7535	4	g'		°K		
10	62.2	5	ΔHm cal/g	19.55	2	h'				
1	23.8	5	ΔHv cal/g			m	300 to	-0.0373	4
Pressure			25°C	90.47	5	n	600 °K	0.0013	4
mm 25°C	1.0849	5	30 mm	84.14	4	o		-0.0_657	4
t_e	1245.	5	BP	71.82	5	m'	700 to	0.0738	4
Density			t_e	69.24	5	n'	1000 °K	0.0010	4
g/ml 20°C	0.86013	2	t_e (d, e)	69.16	5	o'		-0.0_637	4
d_4^t 25	0.85607	2	$\Delta Hv/T_e$	19.45	5	Surface tension			
30	0.85201	4	d 85 to	94.84	5	dynes/cm. 20°C	29.19	5
a	0.87637	4	e 205 °C	0.1256	5	δ 30	28.10	5
b	-0.0_3812	4	d' 10 to	93.10	5	40	27.05	5
Ref. Index			e' 85 °C	0.1052	5	Parachor [P]			
n_D 20°C	1.48979	2	d_c g/ml	0.268	5	20°C		
25	1.48742	2	v_c ml/g	3.735	5	30		
30	1.48502	4	t_c °C	386.1	5	40		
"C"	0.7502	4	P_c mm	21210.	5	Sugd.	362.7	5
MR (Obs.)	45.096	2	PV/RT			Exp. L.1.%/wt.			
MR (Calc.)	44.779	5	25°C	1.0000	5	u.		
(nD-d/2)	1.05972	2	30 mm	1.0000	5	Dispersion	159.3	2
Dielectric	2.220	5	BP	0.9529	5	Flash Point °C	57.0	5
A 85 to	6.98317	2	t_e	0.9367	5	Fire Point		
B 220 °C	1577.965	2	t_c	0.258	5	M. Spec.	Yes	1
C	201.378	2	ΔHc kcal/m	1341.80	2	Ultra V.		
A* 85 to	1.43384	5	ΔHf	-15.28	2	X-Ray Dif.		
B* 215 °C	1484.01	5	ΔFf	34.62	2	Infrared	168.	1
K			Viscosity			Solubility in +		
c			centistokes			Acetone	∞	
t_k to			η 20 °C	1.203	2	Carbon tet.	∞	
t_x °C			40	0.925	2	Benzene	∞	
A' 25 to	7.33005	5	60	0.741	2	Ether	∞	
B' 85 °C	1783.05	5	80	0.611	2	n-Heptane	∞	
C'	219.4	5	B^v 25 to	498.1	4	Ethanol	∞	
A'* 25 to	1.78452	5	A^v 90 °C	$\overline{2}.37586$	4	Water		
B'* 85 °C	1684.34	5	(B^v)100 to	458.3	4	Water in		
Ac 220 to	7.38707	5	(A^v)160 °C	$\overline{2}.48529$	4			
Bc t_c °C	1937.9	5	c_p liq. °K					
Cc	247.1	5	c_p vap.300°K	0.3136	2			
Cryos. A°	0.0385	2	400	0.4079	2			
consts. B°			c_v vap.					
t_e °C F	204.47	5						

$T_R = 0.75\ T_c$

+ grams/100 grams solvent

REFERENCES: 1-Dow   2-API   3-Lit.   4-Calc. from det. data   5-Calc. by formula

SOURCE: API

PURIFICATION: API

LITERATURE REFERENCES:

No. 16

NAME	Isobutylbenzene		STRUCTURAL FORMULA

$CH_2CH(CH_3)_2$

Mole % Pur. 99.87	Ref. 2	Molecular Formula $C_{10}H_{14}$	Molecular Weight 134.212	

		Ref.				Ref.				Ref.
F.P. °C	-51.48	2	dt/dP °C/mm				f	to °K		
F.P. 100%			25°C	7.948	5		g			
B.P. °C			BP	0.05319	2		h			
760 mm	172.759	2	t_e	0.0373	5		f'	to °K		
100	105.42	2					g'			
30	75.73	4	30 mm	0.7431	4		h'			
10	53.11	5	ΔHm cal/g	22.28	2					
1	15.3	5					m	to °K		
Pressure			ΔHv cal/g				n			
mm 25°C	1.930	5	25°C	85.84	5		o			
t_e	1197.	5	30 mm	80.87	4					
			BP	68.08	5		m'	to °K		
Density			t_e	65.82	5		n'			
g/ml 20°C	0.85321	2	t_e (d, e)	65.53	5		o'			
d_4^t 25	0.84907	2	ΔHv/T_e	18.99	5		Surface tension			
30	0.84492	4	d 75 to	90.85	5		dynes/cm. 20°C	28.26	5
a	0.86978	4	e 190 °C	0.1318	5		ɤ 30	27.18	5
b	-0.0₃828	4	d' 10 to	88.29	5		40	26.12	5
Ref. Index			e' 75 °C	0.0980	5		Parachor [P]		
n_D 20°C	1.48646	2	d_c g/ml	0.274	5		20°C		
25	1.48400	2	v_c ml/g	3.651	5		30		
30	1.48456	4	t_c °C	368.8	5		40		
"C"	0.7515	4	P_c mm	19757.	5		Sugd.	362.7	5
MR (Obs.)	45.198	2	PV/RT				Exp. L.1.%/wt.		
MR (Calc.)	44.779	5	25°C	1.0000	5		u.		
(nD-d/2)	1.05986	2	30 mm	1.0000	5		Dispersion	160.5	2
Dielectric	2.209	5	BP	0.9397	5		Flash Point °C	49.0	5
A 75 to	6.93033	2	t_e	0.9250	5		Fire Point		
B 210 °C	1526.384	2	t_c	0.26	5		M Spec.	Yes	2
C	204.171	2	ΔHc kcal/m				Ultra V.	Yes	2
A* 75 to	1.41008	5	ΔHf	-16.70	2		X-Ray Dif.		
B* 210 °C	1439.51	5	ΔFf				Infrared	169.	1
K			Viscosity				Solubility in +		
c			centistokes				Acetone	∞	
t_k to			η °C				Carbon tet.	∞	
t_x °C							Benzene	∞	
A' 25 to	7.27388	5					Ether	∞	
B' 75 °C	1724.77	5					n-Heptane	∞	
C'	221.8	5	B^v to				Ethanol	∞	
A'* 25 to	1.73207	5	A^v °C				Water		
B'* 75 °C	1626.00	5	(B^v) to				Water in		
Ac 210 to	7.3324	5	(A^v) °C						
Bc t_c °C	1876.1	5							
Cc	249.0	5	c_p liq. °K						
Cryos. A°	0.0306	2	c_p vap. °K						
consts. B°									
t_e °C F	192.08	5	c_v vap.						

$T_R = 0.75 T_c$ + grams/100 grams solvent

REFERENCES: 1-Dow   2-API   3-Lit.   4-Calc. from det. data   5-Calc. by formula

SOURCE:	API
PURIFICATION:	API
LITERATURE REFERENCES:	

TABLE I. ALKYL AND HALO BENZENES

27

No. 17

NAME	sec-Butylbenzene	STRUCTURAL FORMULA
	2-Phenylbutane	$CH_3CHC_2H_5$

Mole % Pur. 99.93	Ref. 2	Molecular Formula $C_{10}H_{14}$	Molecular Weight 134.212

		Ref.				Ref.				Ref.
F.P. °C	-75.470	2	dt/dP				f	to		
F.P. 100%			°C/mm				g	___ °K		
			25°C	8.167	5		h			
B.P. °C			BP	0.05313	2					
760 mm	173.305	2	t_e	0.0368	5		f'	to		
100	105.98	2					g'	___ °K		
30	76.27	4	30 mm	0.7441	4		h'			
10	53.6	5	ΔHm cal/g	17.51	2		m	to		
1	15.7	5	ΔHv cal/g				n	___ °K		
Pressure			25°C	85.90	5		o			
mm 25°C	1.877	5	30 mm	81.00	4					
t_e	1215.	5	BP	69.11	5		m'	to		
Density			t_e	66.89	5		n'	___ °K		
g/ml 20°C	0.86207	2	t_e (d, e)	66.67	5		o'			
d_4^t 25	0.85797	2	ΔHv/T_e	19.25	5		Surface tension			
30	0.85387	4	d 75 to	90.35	5		dynes/cm. 20°C	29.46	5
a	0.87848	4	e 200 °C	0.1225	5		δ 30	28.35	5
b	-0.0₃82	4	d' 10 to	88.29	5		40	27.27	5
Ref. Index			e' 75 °C	0.0956	5		Parachor [P]		
n_D 20°C	1.49020	2	d_c g/ml	0.263	5		20°C		
25	1.48779	2	v_c ml/g	3.805	5		30		
30	1.48539	4	t_c °C	372.0	5		40		
"C"	0.7492	4	P_c mm	20480.	5		Sugd.	362.7	5
MR (Obs.)	45.027	2	PV/RT				Exp. L.1.%/wt.		
MR (Calc.)	44.779	5	25°C	1.0000	5		u.		
(nD-d/2)	1.05916	2	30 mm	1.0000	5		Dispersion	158.7	2
Dielectric	2.221	5	BP	0.9503	5		Flash Point °C	49.0	5
A 75 to	6.95097	2	t_e	0.9360	5		Fire Point		
B 210 °C	1540.174	2	t_c	0.26	5		M. Spec.	Yes	1
C	205.101	2	ΔHc kcal/m				Ultra V.	Yes	1
A* 75 to	1.41125	5	ΔHf	-15.89	2		X-Ray Dif.		
B* 210 °C	1447.55	5	ΔFf				Infrared	Yes	1
K			Viscosity				Solubility in +		
c			centistokes				Acetone	∞	
t_k to			η °C				Carbon tet.	∞	
t_x °C							Benzene	∞	
A' 25 to	7.29582	5					Ether	∞	
B' 75 °C	1740.35	5					n-Heptane	∞	
C'	222.8	5	B^v to				Ethanol	∞	
A'* 25 to	1.75224	5	A^v °C				Water		
B'* 75 °C	1640.73	5	(B^v) to				Water in		
Ac 210 to	7.3566	5	(A^v) °C						
Bc t_c °C	1896.0	5	c_p liq. °K						
Cc	250.6	5							
Cryos. A°	0.0303	2	c_p vap. °K						
consts. B°									
t_e °C F	193.236	5	c_v vap.						

$T_R = 0.75 T_c$ + grams/100 grams solvent

REFERENCES: 1-Dow 2-API 3-Lit. 4-Calc. from det. data 5-Calc. by formula

SOURCE:	API
PURIFICATION:	API

LITERATURE REFERENCES:

No. 18

NAME	tert-Butylbenzene	STRUCTURAL FORMULA
	2-Phenyl-2-methylpropane	$C(CH_3)_3$

Mole % Pur. 99.94	Ref. 2	Molecular Formula $C_{10}H_{14}$		Molecular Weight 134.212

		Ref.			Ref.					Ref.
F.P. °C	-57.850	2	dt/dP			f		to		
F.P. 100%			°C/mm			g		°K		
			25°C	6.969	5	h				
B.P. °C			BP	0.05269	2					
760 mm	169.119	2	t_e	0.0368	5	f'		to		
100	102.45	2	30 mm	0.7351	4	g'		°K		
30	73.08	4	ΔHm cal/g	14.93	2	h'				
10	50.7	5								
1	13.3	5	ΔHv cal/g			m		to		
			25°C	85.35	5	n		°K		
Pressure			30 mm	80.51	4	o				
mm 25°C	2.214	5	BP	68.61	5					
t_e	1204.	5	t_e	66.22	5	m'		to		
			t_e (d, e)	66.21	5	n'		°K		
Density						o'				
g/ml 20°C	0.86650	2	ΔHv/T_e	19.25	5	Surface tension				
d^t_4 25	0.86240	2	d | 75 to	89.55	5	dynes/cm. 20°C	30.07	5
30	0.85826	4	e |190 °C	0.1238	5	ɤ	30	28.94	5
a	0.88291	4	d' | 10 to	87.86	5		40	27.84	5
b	-0.0₃821	4	e' | 75 °C	0.1007	5	Parachor [P]		
Ref. Index							20°C	
n_D 20°C	1.49266	2	d_c g/ml	0.274	5		30	
25	1.49024	2	v_c ml/g	3.651	5		40	
30	1.48784	4	t_c °C	366.6	5		Sugd.	362.7	5
"C"	0.7488	4	P_c mm	20423.	5			
MR (Obs.)	44.988	2	PV/RT			Exp. L.1.%/wt.		
MR (Calc.)	44.779	2	25°C	1.0000	5	u.		
(nD-d/2)	1.05941	2	30 mm	1.0000	5	Dispersion	159.0	2
Dielectric	2.228	5	BP	0.9534	5	Flash Point °C	46.0	5
A | 70 to	6.92050	2	t_e	0.9376	5	Fire Point		
B |205 °C	1504.572	2	t_c	0.26	5			
C	203.328	2	ΔHc kcal/m			M Spec.	Yes	1
A* | 70 to	1.38485	5	ΔHf			Ultra V.	Yes	1
B* |205 °C	1413.60	5	ΔFf			X-Ray Dif.		
K			Viscosity			Infrared	Yes	2
c			centistokes			Solubility in +		
t_k | to			η °C			Acetone	∞	
t_x | °C						Carbon tet.	∞	
A' | 25 to	7.26343	5				Benzene	∞	
B' | 75 °C	1700.12	5				Ether	∞	
C'	220.7	5	B^v | to			n-Heptane	∞	
A'* 25 to	1.72508	5	A^v | °C			Ethanol	∞	
B'* 75 °C	1602.63	5	(B^v) | to			Water		
Ac |205 to	7.3229	5	(A^v) | °C			Water in		
Bc | t_c °C	1852.7	5	c_p liq. °K					
Cc	248.3	5						
Cryos. A°	0.02175	2	c_p vap. °K					
consts. B°								
t_e °C F	188.52	5	c_v vap.					
T_R = 0.75 T_c						+ grams/100 grams solvent		

REFERENCES: 1-Dow 2-API 3-Lit. 4-Calc. from det. data 5-Calc. by formula

SOURCE: API

PURIFICATION: API

LITERATURE REFERENCES:

TABLE I. ALKYL AND HALO BENZENES

29

No. 19

| NAME | o-Propyltoluene | STRUCTURAL FORMULA |
| | 1-Methyl-2-propylbenzene | |

| Mole % Pur. | Ref. | Molecular Formula $C_{10}H_{14}$ | Molecular Weight 134.212 |

		Ref.			Ref.			Ref.
F.P. °C	-60.2	2	dt/dP °C/mm			f | to g | __°K		
F.P. 100%			25°C	14.407	5	h |		
B.P. °C			BP	0.0536	2	f' | to		
760 mm	184.80	2	t_e	0.0363	5	g' | __°K		
100	116.7	4	30 mm	0.7559	4	h' |		
30	86.5	4	ΔHm cal/g			m | to		
10	63.5	5				n | __°K		
1	24.9	5	ΔHv cal/g			o |		
Pressure			25°C	90.88	5	m' | to		
mm 25°C	1.006	5	30 mm	84.50	4	n' | __°K		
t_e	1251.	5	BP	72.16	5	o' |		
Density			t_e	69.73	5	Surface tension		
g/ml 20°C	0.8744	2	t_e (d, e)	69.46	5	dynes/cm. 20°C	31.18	5
d_4^t 25	0.8705	2	ΔHv/T_e	19.52	5	𝛾 30	30.08	5
30	0.8666	4	d | 85 to	95.38	5	40	29.01	5
a	0.8900	4	e | 210 °C	0.1256	5			
b	-0.0₃78	4	d' | 20 to	93.47	5	Parachor [P]		
Ref. Index			e' | 85 °C	0.1036	5	20°C		
n_D 20°C	1.4998	2	d_c g/ml	0.274	5	30		
25	1.4974	2	v_c ml/g	3.651	5	40		
30	1.4952	4	t_c °C	391.5	5	Sugd.	362.7	5
"C"	0.7524	4	P_c mm	22164.	5			
MR (Obs.)	45.13	2	PV/RT			Exp. L.1.%/wt.		
MR (Calc.)	44.779	5	25°C	1.0000	5	u.		
(nD-d/2)	1.0626	2	30 mm	1.0000	5	Dispersion	166.	2
Dielectric	2.249	5	BP	0.9516	5	Flash Point °C		
A | 85 to	7.0023	2	t_e	0.9378	5	Fire Point		
B | 225 °C	1594.00	2	t_c			M. Spec.		
C	201.95	2	ΔHc kcal/m			Ultra V.		
A* | 85 to	1.44886	5	ΔHf			X-Ray Dif.		
B* | 215 °C	1498.70	5	ΔFf			Infrared		
K			Viscosity			Solubility in +		
c			centistokes			Acetone		
t_k | to			η °C			Carbon tet.		
t_x | °C						Benzene		
A' | 25 to	7.3504	5				Ether		
B' | 85 °C	1801.2	5				n-Heptane		
C'	220.1	5	B^v | to			Ethanol		
A'* 25 to	1.8028	5	A^v | °C			Water		
B'* 85 °C	1701.7	5	(B^v) | to			Water in		
Ac | 225 to	7.4062	5	(A^v) | °C					
Bc | t_c °C	1957.8	5	c_p liq. °K					
Cc	248.2	5						
Cryos. A°			c_p vap. °K					
consts. B°								
t_e °C	206.24	5	c_v vap.					

$T_R = 0.75 T_c$

+ grams/100 grams solvent

REFERENCES: 1-Dow 2-API 3-Lit. 4-Calc. from det. data 5-Calc. by formula

SOURCE: API

PURIFICATION: API

LITERATURE REFERENCES:

No. 20

NAME	m-Propyltoluene				STRUCTURAL FORMULA	
	1-Methyl-3-propylbenzene					

| Mole % Pur. | Ref. | Molecular Formula $C_{10}H_{14}$ | | Molecular Weight 134.212 | | |

		Ref.			Ref.			Ref.
F.P. °C			dt/dP			f | to		
F.P. 100%			°C/mm			g | °K		
B.P. °C			25°C	12.788	5	h |		
760 mm	181.80	2	BP	0.0530	2			
100	114.24	2	t_e	0.0361	5	f' | to		
30	84.3	4	30 mm	0.7507	4	g' | °K		
10	61.4	5	ΔHm cal/g			h' |		
1	23.1	5	ΔHv cal/g			m | to		
Pressure			25°C	90.03	5	n | °K		
mm 25°C	1.144	5	30 mm	84.02	4	o |		
t_e	1245.	5	BP	71.98	5			
Density			t_e	69.56	5	m' | to		
g/ml 20°C	0.8610	2	t_e (d, e)	69.39	5	n' | °K		
d_4^t 25	0.8570	2	ΔHv/T_e	19.61	5	o' |		
30	0.8530	4	d | 85 to	94.42	5	Surface tension		
a	0.8770	4	e |210 °C	0.1234	5	dynes/cm. 20°C	29.31	5
b	-0.0₃80	4	d' | 10 to	92.56	5	γ 30	28.23	5
Ref. Index			e' | 85 °C	0.1014	5	40	27.19	5
n_D 20°C	1.4936	2	d_c g/ml	0.285	5	Parachor [P]		
25	1.4912	2	v_c ml/g	3.509	5	20°C		
30	1.4887	4	t_c °C	384.4	5	30		
"C"	0.7549	4	P_c mm	21715.	5	40		
MR (Obs.)	45.35	2	PV/RT			Sugd.	362.7	5
MR (Calc.)	44.779	5	25°C	1.0000	5	Exp. L.1.%/wt.		
(nD-d/2)	1.0631	2	30 mm	1.0000	5	u.		
Dielectric	2.231	5	BP	0.9538	5	Dispersion	166.	2
A | 85 to	7.0160	2	t_e	0.9397	5	Flash Point °C	56.0	5
B |220 °C	1591.00	2	t_c	0.25	5	Fire Point		
C	202.95	2	ΔHc kcal/m			M Spec.		
A* | 85 to	1.46228	5	ΔHf	-18.02	2	Ultra V.		
B* |215 °C	1495.25	5	ΔFf			X-Ray Dif.		
K			Viscosity			Infrared		
c			centistokes			Solubility in +		
t_k | to			η °C			Acetone	∞	
t_x | °C						Carbon tet.	∞	
A' | 25 to	7.36495	5				Benzene	∞	
B' | 85 °C	1797.78	5	B^v | to			Ether	∞	
C'	221.0	5	A^v | °C			n-Heptane	∞	
A'* 25 to	1.81809	5	(B^v) | to			Ethanol	∞	
B'* 85 °C	1698.10	5	(A^v) | °C			Water		
Ac | 220 to	7.4200	5	c_p liq. °K			Water in		
Bc | t_c °C	1951.1	5						
Cc	248.4	5	c_p vap. °K					
Cryos. A°								
consts. B°			c_v vap.					
t_e °C F	202.82	5						
T_R = 0.75 T_c						+ grams/100 grams solvent		

REFERENCES: 1-Dow   2-API   3-Lit.   4-Calc. from det. data   5-Calc. by formula

SOURCE: API

PURIFICATION: API

LITERATURE REFERENCES:

TABLE I. ALKYL AND HALO BENZENES

31

No. 21

NAME	p-Propyltoluene	STRUCTURAL FORMULA
	1-Methyl-4-propylbenzene	

Mole % Pur.	Ref.	Molecular Formula $C_{10}H_{14}$	Molecular Weight 134.212	

Structural formula: benzene ring with CH_3 at top and C_3H_7 at bottom.

		Ref.			Ref.			Ref.
F.P. °C	-63.6	2	dt/dP			f to		
F.P. 100%			°C/mm			g °K		
B.P. °C			25°C	13.0743	5	h		
760 mm	183.30	2	BP	0.0535	2			
100	115.12	2	t_e	0.0365	5	f' to		
30	84.9	4	30 mm	0.7562	4	g' °K		
10	61.9	5	ΔHm cal/g			h'		
1	23.3	5				m to		
Pressure			ΔHv cal/g			n °K		
mm 25°C	1.122	5	25°C	89.73	5	o		
t_e	1244.	5	30 mm	83.72	4			
Density			BP	71.47	5	m' to		
g/ml 20°C	0.8584	2	t_e	69.02	5	n' °K		
d_4^t 25	0.8544	2	t_e (d, e)	68.83	5	o'		
30	0.8504	4	ΔHv/T_e	19.39	5	Surface tension		
a	0.8744	4	d 85 to	94.30	5	dynes/cm. 20°C	28.96	5
b	-0.0_380	4	e 210 °C	0.1245	5	ɣ 30	27.89	5
Ref. Index			d' 10 to	92.23	5	40	26.85	5
n_D 20°C	1.4919	2	e' 85 °C	0.1002	5			
25	1.4895	2	d_c g/ml	0.274	5	Parachor [P]		
30	1.4870	4	v_c ml/g	3.651	5	20°C		
"C"	0.7548	4	t_c °C	386.1	5	30		
MR (Obs.)	45.35	2	P_c mm	21162.	5	40		
MR (Calc.)	44.779	5	PV/RT			Sugd.	362.7	5
(nD-d/2)	1.0627	2	25°C	1.0000	5	Exp. L.l.%/wt.		
Dielectric	2.226	5	30 mm	1.0000	5	u.		
A 85 to	6.9926	2	BP	0.9505	5	Dispersion	166.	2
B 220 °C	1589.00	2	t_e	0.9358	5	Flash Point °C	57.0	5
C	203.15	2	t_c	0.25	5	Fire Point		
A* 85 to	1.44319	5	ΔHc kcal/m			M. Spec.		
B* 215 °C	1494.44	5	ΔHf	-18.06	2	Ultra V.		
K			ΔFf			X-Ray Dif.		
c						Infrared		
t_k to			Viscosity			Solubility in +		
t_x °C			centistokes			Acetone	∞	
A' 25 to	7.34008	5	η °C			Carbon tet.	∞	
B' 85 °C	1795.52	5				Benzene	∞	
C'	221.3	5	B^v to			Ether	∞	
A'* 25 to	1.7923	5	A^v °C			n-Heptane	∞	
B'* 85 °C	1695.51	5	(B^v) to			Ethanol	∞	
Ac 220 to	7.39734	5	(A^v) °C			Water		
Bc t_c °C	1951.2	5	c_p liq. °K			Water in		
Cc	249.0	5						
Cryos. A°			c_p vap. °K					
consts. B°								
t_e °C F	204.51	5	c_v vap.					

$T_R = 0.75\,T_c$ + grams/100 grams solvent

REFERENCES: 1-Dow   2-API   3-Lit.   4-Calc. from det. data   5-Calc. by formula

SOURCE: API

PURIFICATION: API

LITERATURE REFERENCES:

No. 22

NAME	o-Isopropyltoluene (o-Cymene)		STRUCTURAL FORMULA
	1-Methyl-2-isopropylbenzene		

Mole % Pur. 99.94 | Ref. 2 | Molecular Formula $C_{10}H_{14}$ | Molecular Weight 134.212

		Ref.				Ref.			Ref.
F.P. °C	-71.540	2	dt/dP				f | to		
F.P. 100%			°C/mm				g | °K		
			25°C	10.0750	5		h		
B.P. °C			BP	0.0529	2				
760 mm	178.15	2	t_e	0.0369	5		f' | to		
100	110.19	2					g' | °K		
30	80.2	4	30 mm	0.7507	4		h'		
10	57.3	5	ΔHm cal/g	17.81	2				
1	19.1	5					m | to		
			ΔHv cal/g				n | °K		
Pressure			25°C	87.64	5		o		
mm 25°C	1.491	5	30 mm	82.12	4				
t_e	1226.	5	BP	69.83	5		m' | to		
			t_e	67.43	5		n' | °K		
Density			t_e (d, e)	67.26	5		o'		
g/ml 20°C	0.8766	2	ΔHv/T_e	19.18	5				
d_4^t 25	0.8726	2					Surface tension		
30	0.8684	4	d | 80 to	92.18	5		dynes/cm. 20°C	31.49	5
a	0.8930	4	e | 200 °C	0.1254	5		ɣ 30	30.33	5
b	-0.0₃82	4	d' | 10 to	90.15	5		40	29.19	5
			e' | 80 °C	0.1001	5				
Ref. Index							Parachor [P]		
n_D 20°C	1.5006	2	d_c g/ml	0.274	5		20°C		
25	1.4982	2	v_c ml/g	3.651	5		30		
30	1.4957	4	t_c °C	381.2	5		40		
"C"	0.7514	4	P_c mm	20964.	5		Sugd.	362.7	5
MR (Obs.)	45.08	2	PV/RT				Exp. L.1.%/wt.		
MR (Calc.)	44.779	5	25°C	1.0000	5		u.		
(nD-d/2)	1.0623	2	30 mm	1.0000	5		Dispersion	166.	2
Dielectric	2.252	5	BP	0.9489	5		Flash Point °C	53.0	5
			t_e	0.9338	5		Fire Point		
A | 80 to	6.9427	2	t_c	0.25	5				
B |220 °C	1549.00	2					M Spec.		
C	203.20	2	ΔHc kcal/m				Ultra V.	Yes	2
			ΔHf	-18.19	2		X-Ray Dif.		
A* | 80 to	1.40222	5	ΔFf				Infrared		
B* |210 °C	1456.87	5	Viscosity						
K			centistokes				Solubility in +		
c			η °C				Acetone	∞	
t_k | to							Carbon tet.	∞	
t_x | °C							Benzene	∞	
A' | 25 to	7.28703	5					Ether	∞	
B' | 80 °C	1750.32	5					n-Heptane	∞	
C'	221.1	5	B^V | to				Ethanol	∞	
			A^V | °C				Water		
A'* 25 to	1.74286	5	(B^V) | to				Water in		
B'* 80 °C	1651.27	5	(A^V) | °C						
Ac | 220 to	7.3473	5	c_p liq. °K						
Bc | t_c °C	1908.2	5							
Cc	249.4	5							
Cryos. A°	0.0296	2	c_p vap. °K						
consts. B°									
t_e °C F	198.7	5	c_v vap.						

$T_R = 0.75 T_c$ + grams/100 grams solvent

REFERENCES: 1-Dow   2-API   3-Lit.   4-Calc. from det. data   5-Calc. by formula

SOURCE: API

PURIFICATION: API

LITERATURE REFERENCES:

TABLE I. ALKYL AND HALO BENZENES

No. 23

NAME	m-Isopropyltoluene (m-Cymene)	STRUCTURAL FORMULA
	1-Methyl-3-isopropylbenzene	

STRUCTURAL FORMULA

CH_3

$CH(CH_3)_2$

Mole % Pur. 99.93	Ref. 2	Molecular Formula $C_{10}H_{14}$	Molecular Weight 134.212

		Ref.				Ref.				Ref.
F.P. °C	-63.745	2	dt/dP				f	to		
F.P. 100%			°C/mm				g	°K		
			25°C	8.858	5		h			
B.P. °C			BP	0.0533	2					
760 mm	175.14	2	t_e	0.0369	5		f'	to		
100	107.58	2					g'	°K		
30	77.8	4	30 mm	0.7463	4		h'			
10	55.0	5	ΔHm cal/g	24.36	2		m	to		
1	17.1	5					n	°K		
Pressure			ΔHv cal/g				o			
mm 25°C	1.715	5	25°C	86.66	5					
t_e	1219.	5	30 mm	81.47	4		m'	to		
			BP	69.31	5		n'	°K		
Density			t_e	67.01	5		o'			
g/ml 20°C	0.8610	2	t_e (d, e)	66.79	5		Surface tension			
d_4^t 25	0.8570	2	ΔHv/T_e	19.20	5		dynes/cm. 20°C	29.31	5
30	0.8530	4	d 80 to	91.18	5		γ 30	28.23	5
a	0.8770	4	e 200 °C	0.1249	5		40	27.18	5
b	-0.0₃80	4	d' 10 to	89.12	5		Parachor [P]		
			e' 80 °C	0.0983	5		20°C		
Ref. Index			d_c g/ml	0.274	5		30		
n_D 20°C	1.4930	2	v_c ml/g	3.651	5		40		
25	1.4906	2	t_c °C	374.9	5		Sugd.	362.7	
30	1.4881	4	P_c mm	20504.	5				
"C"	0.7541	4	PV/RT				Exp. L.1.%/wt.		
MR (Obs.)	45.30	2	25°C	1.0000	5		u.		
MR (Calc.)	44.779	5	30 mm	1.0000	5		Dispersion	166.	2
(nD-d/2)	1.0625	2	BP	0.9490	5		Flash Point °C	50.0	5
Dielectric	2.229	5	t_e	0.9350	5		Fire Point		
A 75 to	6.9428	2	t_c	0.25	5		M. Spec.	Yes	1
B 215 °C	1540.00	2	ΔHc kcal/m				Ultra V.	Yes	1
C	203.98	2	ΔHf	-18.69	2		X-Ray Dif.		
A* 75 to	1.40344	5	ΔFf				Infrared		
B* 205 °C	1447.88	5	Viscosity				Solubility in +		
K			centistokes				Acetone	∞	
c			η 25 °C	1.0210	1		Carbon tet.	∞	
t_k to			40	0.8454	1		Benzene	∞	
t_x °C			60	0.6826	1		Ether	∞	
A' 25 to	7.2871	5	80	0.5688	1		n-Heptane	∞	
B' 80 °C	1740.2	5	B^v 30 to	475.95	4		Ethanol	∞	
C'	221.7	5	A^v 90 °C	2.40742	4		Water		
A'* 25 to	1.7439	5	(B^v) to				Water in		
B'* 80 °C	1641.1	5	(A^v) °C						
Ac 215 to	7.3474	5	c_p liq. °K						
Bc t_c °C	1895.8	5							
Cc	249.6	5	c_p vap. °K						
Cryos. A°	0.0375	2							
consts. B°			c_v vap.						
t_e °C F	195.31	5							

$T_R = 0.75\ T_C$

+ grams/100 grams solvent

REFERENCES: 1-Dow 2-API 3-Lit. 4-Calc. from det. data 5-Calc. by formula

SOURCE:	API
PURIFICATION:	API

LITERATURE REFERENCES:

No. 24

NAME	p-Isopropyltoluene (p-Cymene)	STRUCTURAL FORMULA
	1-Methyl-4-isopropylbenzene	

Mole % Pur. 99.95 | Ref. 2 | Molecular Formula $C_{10}H_{14}$ | Molecular Weight 134.212

Structural formula: benzene ring with CH_3 at top and $CH(CH_3)_2$ at bottom.

		Ref.				Ref.				Ref.
F.P. °C	-67.935	2	dt/dP °C/mm				f | to			
F.P. 100%			25°C	9.504	5		g | °K			
B.P. °C			BP	0.0537	5		h |			
760 mm	177.10	2	t_e	0.0371	5		f'	to		
100	109.12	4	30 mm	0.7499	4		g' | °K			
30	79.16	4					h' |			
10	56.3	5	ΔHm cal/g	17.20	2					
1	18.2	5	ΔHv cal/g				m | to			
			25°C	87.14	5		n | °K			
Pressure			30 mm	81.71	4		o |			
mm 25°C	1.590	5	BP	69.31	5					
t_e	1222.	5	t_e	66.95	5		m' | to			
			t_e (d,e)	66.72	5		n' | °K			
Density			ΔHv/T_e	19.09	5		o' |			
g/ml 20°C	0.8573	2					Surface tension			
d_4^t 25	0.8533	2	d | 80 to	91.74	5		dynes/cm. 20°C	28.81	5
30	0.8493	4	e | 200 °C	0.1266	5		γ 30	27.74	5
a	0.8733	4	d' | 15 to	89.65	5		40	26.71	5
b	-0.0_380	4	e' | 80 °C	0.1003	5		Parachor [P]		
Ref. Index			d_c g/ml	0.266	5		20°C		
n_D 20°C	1.4909	2	v_c ml/g	3.762	5		30		
25	1.4885	4	t_c °C	377.1	5		40		
30	1.4859	4	P_c mm	20165.	5		Sugd.	362.7	5
"C"	0.7543	4	PV/RT				Exp. L.1.%/wt.		
MR (Obs.)	45.33	2	25°C	1.0000	5		u.		
MR (Calc.)	44.779	5	30 mm	1.0000	5		Dispersion	166.	2
(nD-d/2)	1.0623	2	BP	0.9473	5		Flash Point °C	47.	3
Dielectric	2.243	3'	t_e	0.9327	5		Fire Point		
A | 80 to	6.9260	2	t_c	0.25	5		M Spec.	Yes	1
B |215 °C	1538.00	2					Ultra V.	Yes	2
C	203.10	2	ΔHc kcal/m				X-Ray Dif.		
A* | 80 to	1.38851	5	ΔHf	-18.73	2		Infrared	Yes	2
B* |215 °C	1446.72	5	ΔFf						
K			Viscosity				Solubility in +		
c			centistokes				Acetone	∞	
t_k | to			η 25 °C	0.9296	1		Carbon tet.	∞	
t_x | °C			40	0.7777	1		Benzene	∞	
A' | 25 to	7.2693	5	60	0.6352	1		Ether	∞	
B' | 80 °C	1737.9	5	80	0.5335	1		n-Heptane	∞	
C'	220.9	5	B^v | 30 to	452.67	4		Ethanol	∞	
			A^v | 90 °C	2.44552	4		Water		
A'* | 25 to	1.7261	5	(B^v) | to				Water in		
B'* | 80 °C	1639.2	5	(A^v) | °C						
Ac | 215 to	7.3297	5	c_p liq. °K						
Bc | t_c °C	1893.7	5							
Cc	248.9	5							
Cryos. A°	0.02758	2	c_p vap. °K						
consts. B°									
t_e °C F	197.52	5	c_v vap.						

$T_R = 0.75 T_c$ + grams/100 grams solvent

REFERENCES: 1-Dow 2-API 3-Lit. 4-Calc. from det. data 5-Calc. by formula

SOURCE: API

PURIFICATION: API

LITERATURE REFERENCES: 3 Nat. Fire Prot. Assoc. 325 (1949); 3' NBS 514

TABLE I.   ALKYL AND HALO BENZENES   35

No. 25

NAME	1,2-Diethylbenzene	STRUCTURAL FORMULA
	o-Diethylbenzene	

Mole % Pur. 99.95	Ref. 2	Molecular Formula $C_{10}H_{14}$	Molecular Weight 134.212

		Ref.
F.P. °C	-31.240	2
F.P. 100%		
B.P. °C		
760 mm	183.423	2
100	115.65	4
30	85.66	4
10	62.8	5
1	24.4	5
Pressure mm 25°C	1.042	5
t_e	1248.	5
Density g/ml 20°C	0.87996	2
d_4^t 25	0.87592	2
30	0.87186	4
a	0.89612	4
b	-0.0$_3$808	4
Ref. index n_D 20°C	1.50346	2
25	1.50106	2
30	1.49846	4
"C"	0.7524	4
MR (Obs.)	45.122	2
MR (Calc.)	44.779	5
(nD-d/2)	1.06348	2
Dielectric	2.260	5
A 85 to	6.99016	2
B 225 °C	1577.894	2
C	200.554	2
A* 85 to	1.43869	5
B* 215 °C	1483.61	5
K		
c		
t_k to		
t_x °C		
A' 20 to	7.3375	5
B' 85 °C	1783.0	5
C'	218.6	5
A'* 20 to	1.7927	5
B'* 85 °C	1684.8	5
Ac 225 to	7.3918	5
Bc t_c °C	1937.3	5
Cc	246.4	5
Cryos. A° consts. B°	0.0299	2
t_e °C	204.65	5
$T_R = 0.75\,T_c$		

		Ref.
dt/dP °C/mm		
25°C	13.873	5
BP	0.05340	2
t_e	0.0362	5
30 mm	0.7516	4
ΔHm cal/g	25.93	2
ΔHv cal/g		
25°C	91.10	5
30 mm	84.57	4
BP	72.21	5
t_e	69.62	5
t_e (d, e)	69.53	5
ΔHv/T_e	19.55	5
d 85 to	95.39	5
e 210 °C	0.1264	5
d' 20 to	93.79	5
e' 85 °C	0.1077	5
d_c g/ml	0.274	5
v_c ml/g	3.65	5
t_c °C	389.6	5
P_c mm	22177.	5
PV/RT		
25°C	1.0000	5
30 mm	1.0000	5
BP	0.9540	5
t_e	0.9384	5
t_c		
ΔHc kcal/m		
ΔHf	-16.94	2
ΔFf		
Viscosity centistokes		
η °C		
B^v to		
A^v °C		
(B^v) to		
(A^v) °C		
c_p liq. °K		
c_p vap. °K		
c_v vap.		

		Ref.
f to		
g °K		
h		
f' to		
g' °K		
h'		
m to		
n °K		
o		
m' to		
n' °K		
o'		
Surface tension dynes/cm. 20°C	31.98	5
γ 30	30.82	5
40	29.69	5
Parachor [P] 20°C		
30		
40		
Sugd.	362.7	5
Exp. L.1.%/wt. u.		
Dispersion	165.9	2
Flash Point °C	57.0	5
Fire Point		
M. Spec.	Yes	2
Ultra V.		
X-Ray Dif.		
Infrared	Yes	2
Solubility in +		
Acetone	∞	
Carbon tet.	∞	
Benzene	∞	
Ether	∞	
n-Heptane	∞	
Ethanol	∞	
Water		
Water in		

+ grams/100 grams solvent

REFERENCES: 1-Dow 2-API 3-Lit. 4-Calc. from det. data 5-Calc. by formula

SOURCE: API

PURIFICATION: API

LITERATURE REFERENCES:

No. 26

NAME	1,3-Diethylbenzene		STRUCTURAL FORMULA
	m-Diethylbenzene		

Mole % Pur. 99.93	Ref. 2	Molecular Formula	$C_{10}H_{14}$	Molecular Weight 134.212

		Ref.			Ref.			Ref.
F.P. °C	-83.920	2	dt/dP °C/mm			f	to °K	
F.P. 100%			25°C	12.828	5	g		
B.P. °C			BP	0.05293	2	h		
760 mm	181.102	2	t_e	0.0360	5	f'	to °K	
100	113.87	2	30 mm	0.7465	4	g'		
30	84.09	4	ΔHm cal/g	19.59	2	h'		
10	61.3	5	ΔHv cal/g			m	to °K	
1	23.2	5	25°C	90.72	5	n		
Pressure			30 mm	84.40	4	o		
mm 25°C	1.131	5	BP	72.23	5	m'	to °K	
t_e	1245.	5	t_e	69.74	5	n'		
Density			t_e (d,e)	69.60	5	o'		
g/ml 20°C	0.86394	2	ΔHv/T_e	19.69	5	Surface tension		
d_4^t 25	0.85993	2	d 85 to	94.96	5	dynes/cm. 20°C	29.71	5
30	0.85590	4	e 210 °C	0.1255	5	γ 30	28.62	5
a	0.87998	4	d' 10 to	93.40	5	40	27.56	5
b	-0.0₃802	4	e' 85 °C	0.1069	5	Parachor [P]		
Ref. Index			d_c g/ml	0.287	5	20°C		
n_D 20°C	1.49552	2	v_c ml/g	3.485	5	30		
25	1.49310	2	t_c °C	383.9	5	40		
30	1.49050	4	P_c mm	21894.	5	Sugd.	362.7	5
"C"	0.7550	4	PV/RT			Exp. L.1.%/wt.		
MR (Obs.)	45.344	2	25°C	1.0000	5	u.		
MR (Calc.)	44.779	5	30 mm	1.0000	5	Dispersion	166.6	2
(nD-d/2)	1.06355	2	BP	0.9557	5	Flash Point °C	56.0	5
Dielectric	2.236	5	t_e	0.9413	5	Fire Point		
A 85 to	7.00601	2	t_c	0.25	5	M Spec.	Yes	1
Б 1220 °C	1576.261	2	ΔHc kcal/m			Ultra V.	Yes	1
C	201.004	2	ΔHf	-17.44	2	X-Ray Dif.		
A* 85 to	1.45233	5	ΔFf			Infrared	Yes	2
B* 215 °C	1481.17	5	Viscosity			Solubility in +		
K			centistokes			Acetone	∞	
c			η °C			Carbon tet.	∞	
t_k to						Benzene	∞	
t_x °C						Ether	∞	
A' 25 to	7.35433	5				n-Heptane	∞	
B' 85 °C	1781.13	5	B^v to			Ethanol	∞	
C'	219.0	5	A^v °C			Water		
A'* 25 to	1.81036	5	(B^v) to			Water in		
B'* 85 °C	1682.99	5	(A^v) °C					
Ac 220 to	7.4071	5	c_p liq. °K					
Bc t_c °C	1931.7	5						
Cc	246.0	5	c_p vap. °K					
Cryos. A°	0.0369	2						
consts. B°			c_v vap.					
t_e °C F	202.03	5						

$T_R = 0.75 T_c$ + grams/100 grams solvent

REFERENCES: 1-Dow   2-API   3-Lit.   4-Calc. from det. data   5-Calc. by formula

SOURCE: API

PURIFICATION: API

LITERATURE REFERENCES:

TABLE I. ALKYL AND HALO BENZENES

No. 27

NAME	1,4-Diethylbenzene	STRUCTURAL FORMULA
	p-Diethylbenzene	

		Ref.	Molecular Formula $C_{10}H_{14}$	Molecular Weight 134.212	
Mole % Pur. 99.93		2			

		Ref.			Ref.				Ref.
F.P. °C	-42.850	2	dt/dP °C/mm			f	to °K		
F.P. 100%			25°C	13.785	5	g			
B.P. °C			BP	0.05351	2	h			
760 mm	183.752	2	t_e	0.0363	5	f'	to °K		
100	115.80	2	30 mm	0.7541	4	g'			
30	85.71	4				h'			
10	62.7	5	ΔHm cal/g	18.85	2	m	to °K		
1	24.2	5	ΔHv cal/g			n			
Pressure			25°C	90.59	5	o			
mm 25°C	1.054	5	30 mm	84.31	4				
t_e	1247.	5	BP	71.98	5	m'	to °K		
Density			t_e	69.53	5	n'			
g/ml 20°C	0.86196	2	t_e (d,e)	69.31	5	o'			
d_4^t 25	0.85794	2	ΔHv/T_e	19.51	5	Surface tension			
30	0.85390	4	d 85 to	95.08	5	dynes/cm. 20°C	29.44	5
a	0.87804	4	e 210 °C	0.1257	5	ɣ 30	28.36	5
b	-0.0₃804	4	d' 10 to	93.18	5	40	27.30	5
Ref. Index			e' 85 °C	0.1035	5	Parachor [P]		
n_D 20°C	1.49483	2	d_c g/ml	0.281	5	20°C		
25	1.49245	2	v_c ml/g	3.563	5	30		
30	1.48981	4	t_c °C	387.3	5	40		
"C"	0.7556	4	P_c mm	21528.	5	Sugd. 362.7		5
MR (Obs.)	45.394	2	PV/RT			Exp. L.l.%/wt.		
MR (Calc.)	44.779	5	25°C	1.0000	5	u.		
(nD-d/2)	1.06385	2	30 mm	1.0000	5	Dispersion	167.9	2
Dielectric	2.235	5	BP	0.9518	5	Flash Point °C	57.0	5
A 85 to	7.00054	2	t_e	0.9376	5	Fire Point		
B 225 °C	1589.273	2	t_c	0.25	5	M. Spec.	Yes	1
C	202.019	2	ΔHc kcal/m			Ultra V.	Yes	1
A* 85 to	1.44865	5	ΔHf	-17.47	2	X-Ray Dif.		
B* 215 °C	1494.38	5	ΔFf			Infrared	Yes	2
K			Viscosity			Solubility in +		
c			centistokes			Acetone	∞	
t_k to			η °C			Carbon tet.	∞	
t_x °C						Benzene	∞	
A' 25 to	7.34852	5				Ether	∞	
B' 85 °C	1795.83	5				n-Heptane	∞	
C'	220.1	5	B^v to			Ethanol	∞	
A'* 25 to	1.80161	5	A^v °C			Water		
B'* 85 °C	1696.49	5	(B^v) to			Water in		
Ac 225 to	7.4037	5	(A^v) °C					
Bc t_c °C	1949.7	5	c_p liq. °K					
Cc	247.7	5	c_p vap. °K					
Cryos. A°	0.0240	2						
consts. B°			c_v vap.					
t_e °C F	205.02	5						

$T_R = 0.75 T_c$ + grams/100 grams solvent

REFERENCES: 1-Dow 2-API 3-Lit. 4-Calc. from det. data 5-Calc. by formula

SOURCE:	API
PURIFICATION:	API
LITERATURE REFERENCES:	

No. 28

| NAME | 2-Ethyl-1,3-dimethylbenzene | STRUCTURAL FORMULA |
| | 2-Ethyl-m-xylene | |

| Mole % Pur. | Ref. | Molecular Formula $C_{10}H_{14}$ | Molecular Weight 134.212 | |

		Ref.			Ref.				Ref.
F.P. °C	-16.28	2	dt/dP °C/mm			f | to			
F.P. 100%			25°C	18.615	5	g | °K			
B.P. °C			BP	0.0561	2	h |			
760 mm	190.01	2	t_e	0.0360	5				
100	121.55	2	30 mm	0.7624	4	f' | to			
30	91.16	4	ΔHm cal/g			g' | °K			
10	67.9	5	ΔHv cal/g			h' |			
1	28.9	5	25°C	92.78	5	m | to			
Pressure			30 mm	85.95	4	n | °K			
mm 25°C	0.762	5	BP	73.72	5	o |			
t_e	1267.	5	t_e	71.11	5.	m' | to			
Density			t_e (d, e)	70.99	5	n' | °K			
g/ml 20°C	0.8904	2	ΔHv/T_e	19.67	5	o' |			
d_4^t 25	0.8864	2	d | 90 to	97.23	5	Surface tension			
30	0.8824	4	e | 210 °C	0.1237	5	dynes/cm. 20°C	33.52	5
a	0.9064	4	d' | 10 to	95.36	5	γ 30	32.33	5
b	-0.0380	4	e' | 90 °C	0.1033	5	40	31.17	5
Ref. Index			d_c g/ml	0.301	5	Parachor [P]		
n_D 20°C	1.5107	2	v_c ml/g	3.324	5	20°C		
25	1.5085	2	t_c °C	401.0	5	30		
30	1.5054	4	P_c mm	23271.	5	40		
"C"	0.7536	4	PV/RT			Sugd.	362.7	5
MR (Obs.)	45.13	2	25°C	1.0000	5	Exp. L.1.%/wt.		
MR (Calc.)	44.779	5	30 mm	1.0000	5	u.		
(nD-d/2)	1.0655	2	BP	0.9536	5	Dispersion	170.	2
Dielectric	2.282	5	t_e	0.9382	5	Flash Point °C	62.0	5
A | 90 to	7.0440	2	t_c	0.247	5	Fire Point		
B | 235 °C	1632.0	2	ΔHc kcal/m			M Spec.	Yes	2
C	202.0	2	ΔHf	-19.84	2	Ultra V.	Yes	2
A* | 90 to	1.4840	5	ΔFf			X-Ray Dif.		
B* | 220 °C	1534.9	5	Viscosity			Infrared		
K			centistokes			Solubility in +		
c			η °C			Acetone	∞	
t_k | to						Carbon tet.	∞	
t_x | °C						Benzene	∞	
A' | 25 to	7.3947	5				Ether	∞	
B' | 90 °C	1844.1	5				n-Heptane	∞	
C'	220.5	5	B^V | to			Ethanol	∞	
			A^V | °C			Water		
A'* 25 to	1.8432	5	(B^V) | to			Water in		
B'* 90 °C	1743.5	5	(A^V) | °C					
Ac | 235 to	7.4493	5	c_p liq. °K					
Bc | t_c °C	2003.1	5						
Cc	248.9	5	c_p vap. °K					
Cryos. A° consts. B°			c_v vap.					
t_e °C F	212.07	5						

T_R = 0.75 T_c + grams/100 grams solvent

REFERENCES: 1-Dow 2-API 3-Lit. 4-Calc. from det. data 5-Calc. by formula

SOURCE: API

PURIFICATION: API

LITERATURE REFERENCES:

TABLE I. ALKYL AND HALO BENZENES

No. 29

| NAME | 2-Ethyl-1,4-dimethylbenzene | STRUCTURAL FORMULA |
| | 2-Ethyl-p-xylene | |

Structural formula: benzene ring with CH_3 (top), C_2H_5 (upper right), CH_3 (bottom)

| Mole % Pur. | Ref. | Molecular Formula $C_{10}H_{14}$ | Molecular Weight 134.212 | |

		Ref.			Ref.				Ref.
F.P. °C	-53.68	2	dt/dP			f	to		
F.P. 100%			°C/mm			g	°K		
B.P. °C			25°C	15.480	5	h			
760 mm	186.91	2	BP	0.0533	2				
100	118.46	2	t_e	0.0363	5	f'	to		
30	88.10	4	30 mm	0.7615	4	g'	°K		
10	64.9	5	ΔHm cal/g			h'			
1	25.9	5							
Pressure			ΔHv cal/g			m	to		
mm 25°C	0.937	5	25°C	90.78	5	n	°K		
t_e	1255.	5	30 mm	84.60	4	o			
Density			BP	72.46	5				
g/ml 20°C	0.8772	2	t_e	70.02	5	m'	to		
d_4^t 25	0.8732	2	t_e (d, e)	69.79	5	n'	°K		
30	0.8692	4	$\Delta Hv/T_e$	19.51	5	o'			
a	0.8932	4	d 90 to	95.43	5	Surface tension			
b	-0.0380	4	e 210 °C	0.1229	5	dynes/cm. 20°C	31.58	5
Ref. index			d' 10 to	93.23	5	γ 30	30.44	5
n_D 20°C	1.5043	2	e' 90 °C	0.0979	5	40	29.33	5
25	1.5020	2	d_c g/ml	0.291	5	Parachor [P]			
30	1.4994	4	v_c ml/g	3.431	5	20°C			
"C"	0.7560	4	t_c °C	394.4	5	30			
MR (Obs.)	45.33	2	P_c mm	22328.	5	40			
MR (Calc.)	44.779	5				Sugd.	362.7	5
(nD-d/2)	1.0657	2	PV/RT			Exp. L.l.%/wt.			
Dielectric	2.263	5	25°C	1.0000	5	u.			
A 90 to	7.0301	2	30 mm	1.0000	5	Dispersion	171.	2
B 230 °C	1622.0	2	BP	0.9506	5	Flash Point °C	60.0	5
C	204.0	2	t_e	0.9364	5	Fire Point			
A* 90 to	1.4748	5	t_c	0.247	5	M. Spec.	Yes	2
B* 220 °C	1525.51	5	ΔHc kcal/m			Ultra V.	Yes	2
K			ΔHf	-20.38	2	X-Ray Dif.		
c			ΔFf			Infrared		
t_k to			Viscosity			Solubility in +		
t_x °C			centistokes			Acetone	∞	
			η °C			Carbon tet.	∞	
A' 25 to	7.3799	5				Benzene	∞	
B' 90 °C	1832.8	5				Ether	∞	
C'	222.0	5	B^v to			n-Heptane	∞	
A'* 25 to	1.8282	5	A^v °C			Ethanol	∞	
B'* 90 °C	1731.3	5	(B^v) to			Water		
Ac 230 to	7.4373	5	(A^v) °C			Water in		
Bc t_c °C	1992.4	5	c_p liq. °K					
Cc	250.7	5						
Cryos. A°			c_p vap. °K					
consts. B°								
t_e °C F	208.58	5	c_v vap.					

$T_R = 0.75 T_c$ + grams/100 grams solvent

REFERENCES: 1-Dow 2-API 3-Lit. 4-Calc. from det. data 5-Calc. by formula

SOURCE: API

PURIFICATION: API

LITERATURE REFERENCES:

No. 30

NAME	3-Ethyl-1,2-dimethylbenzene	STRUCTURAL FORMULA
	3-Ethyl-o-xylene	

| Mole % Pur. | | Ref. | Molecular Formula | $C_{10}H_{14}$ | Molecular Weight | 134.212 | |

		Ref.				Ref.				Ref.
F.P. °C	-49.5	2	dt/dP				f		to	
F.P. 100%			°C/mm				g		°K	
			25°C	22.337	5		h			
B.P. °C			BP	0.0554	2					
760 mm	193.91	2	t_e	0.0360	5		f'		to	
100	125.02	2					g'		°K	
30	94.42	4	30 mm	0.7676	4		h'			
10	71.0	5	ΔHm cal/g							
1	31.7	5					m		to	
			ΔHv cal/g				n		°K	
Pressure			25°C	94.24	5		o			
mm 25°C	0.625	5	30 mm	86.90	4					
t_e	1276.	5	BP	74.42	5		m'		to	
			t_e	71.74	5		n'		°K	
Density			t_e (d, e)	71.59	5		o'			
g/ml 20°C	0.8921	2								
d_4^t 25	0.8881	2	ΔHv/T_e	19.66	5		Surface tension			
30	0.8841	4	d	95 to	98.74		dynes/cm. 20°C	33.78	5
			e	220 °C	0.1254	5	Y	30	32.58	5
a	0.9081	4	d'	10 to	96.88	5		40	31.42	5
b	-0.0380	4	e'	95 °C	0.1057	5				
							Parachor [P]			
Ref. Index			d_c g/ml	0.301	5			20°C	
n_D 20°C	1.5117	2	v_c ml/g	3.326	5			30	
25	1.5095	2	t_c °C	406.9	5			40	
30	1.5068	4	P_c mm	23460.	5		Sugd.	362.7	5
"C"	0.7535	4								
MR (Obs.)	45.12	2	PV/RT				Exp. L.1.%/wt.			
MR (Calc.)	44.779	2	25°C	1.0000	5		u.			
(nD-d/2)	1.0656	2	30 mm	1.0000	5		Dispersion	170.	2
Dielectric	2.285	5	BP	0.9526	5		Flash Point °C	65.0	5
			t_e	0.9370	5		Fire Point			
A 95 to	7.0488	2	t_c	0.247	5					
B 235 °C	1646.0	2					M Spec.	Yes	1
C	201.0	2	ΔHc kcal/m				Ultra V.	Yes	2
			ΔHf	-19.84	2		X-Ray Dif.		
A* 95 to	1.4871	5	ΔFf				Infrared		
B* 225 °C	1548.8	5								
K			Viscosity				Solubility in +			
c			centistokes				Acetone	∞	
t_k	to		η °C				Carbon tet.	∞	
t_x	°C						Benzene	∞	
A' 25 to	7.3998	5					Ether	∞	
B' 95 °C	1859.9	5					n-Heptane	∞	
C'	219.6	5	B^v	to			Ethanol	∞	
			A^v	°C			Water		
A'* 25 to	1.8470	5	(B^v)	to			Water in		
B'* 95 °C	1759.4	5	(A^v)	°C					
Ac 235 to	7.4535	5							
Bc t_c °C	2019.5	5	c_p liq. °K						
Cc	248.1	5	c_p vap. °K						
Cryos. A°									
consts. B°			c_v vap.						
t_e °C F	216.47	5							

$T_R = 0.75 T_c$ + grams/100 grams solvent

REFERENCES: 1-Dow 2-API 3-Lit. 4-Calc. from det. data 5-Calc. by formula

SOURCE: API

PURIFICATION: API

LITERATURE REFERENCES:

TABLE I. ALKYL AND HALO BENZENES

NAME	4-Ethyl-1,2-dimethylbenzene	STRUCTURAL FORMULA
	4-Ethyl-o-xylene	

Mole % Pur.	Ref.	Molecular Formula $C_{10}H_{14}$	Molecular Weight 134.212	

		Ref.			Ref.				Ref.
F.P. °C	-67.0	2	dt/dP			f	to		
F.P. 100%			°C/mm			g	°K		
			25°C	18.567	5	h			
B.P. °C			BP	0.0563	2				
760 mm	189.75	2	t_e	0.0359	5	f'	to		
100	121.4	2				g'	°K		
30	91.06	4	30 mm	0.7614	4	h'			
10	67.8	5	ΔHm cal/g						
1	28.9	5				m	to		
			ΔHv cal/g			n	°K		
Pressure			25°C	92.84	5	o			
mm 25°C	0.764	5	30 mm	86.01	4				
t_e	1267.	5	BP	73.77	5	m'	to		
			t_e	71.22	5	n'	°K		
Density			t_e (d,e)	71.03	5	o'			
g/ml 20°C	0.8745	2							
d_4^t 25	0.8706	2	ΔHv/T_e	19.71	5	Surface tension			
30	0.8667	4				dynes/cm. 20°C	31.19	5
a	0.8901	4	d 90 to	97.31	5	𝛾 30	30.09	5
b	-0.0₃78	4	e 220 °C	0.1241	5	40	29.02	5
			d' 10 to	95.43	5				
Ref. Index			e' 90 °C	0.1034	5	Parachor [P]		
n_D 20°C	1.5031	2				20°C		
25	1.5009	2	d_c g/ml	0.297	5	30		
30	1.4983	4	v_c ml/g	3.368	5	40		
"C"	0.7567	4	t_c °C	398.6	5	Sugd.	362.7	5
MR (Obs.)	45.38	2	P_c mm	22888.	5			
MR (Calc.)	44.779	5	PV/RT			Exp. L.1.%/wt.		
(nD-d/2)	1.0658	2	25°C	1.0000	5	u.		
Dielectric	2.259	5	30 mm	1.0000	5	Dispersion	171.	2
			BP	0.9536	5	Flash Point °C	71.0	5
A 90 to	7.0493	2	t_e	0.9390	5	Fire Point		
B 230 °C	1633.0	2	t_c	0.247	5			
C	202.0	2	ΔHc kcal/m			M. Spec.	Yes	2
			ΔHf	-20.38	2	Ultra V.	Yes	2
A* 90 to	1.48840	5	ΔFf			X-Ray Dif.		
B* 220 °C	1535.60	5				Infrared		
K			Viscosity			Solubility in +		
c			centistokes			Acetone	∞	
t_k to			η °C			Carbon tet.	∞	
t_x °C						Benzene	∞	
A' 25 to	7.40035	5				Ether	∞	
B' 90 °C	1845.24	5				n-Heptane	∞	
C'	220.5	5	B^v to			Ethanol	∞	
			A^v °C			Water		
A'* 25 to	1.84891	5	(B^v) to			Water in		
B'* 90 °C	1744.65	5	(A^v) °C					
Ac 230 to	7.4540	5						
Bc t_c °C	2002.0	5	c_p liq. °K					
Cc	248.4	5						
Cryos. A°			c_p vap. °K					
consts. B°								
t_e °C F	211.78	5	c_v vap.					

$T_R = 0.75 T_c$ + grams/100 grams solvent

REFERENCES: 1-Dow 2-API 3-Lit. 4-Calc. from det. data 5-Calc. by formula

SOURCE: API

PURIFICATION: API

LITERATURE REFERENCES:

No. 32

NAME	4-Ethyl-1,3-dimethylbenzene	STRUCTURAL FORMULA
	4-Ethyl-m-xylene	

| Mole % Pur. | Ref. | Molecular Formula $C_{10}H_{14}$ | Molecular Weight 134.212 | |

		Ref.			Ref.				Ref.
F.P. °C	-62.90	2	dt/dP °C/mm			f	to		
F.P. 100%			25°C	17.066	5	g	°K		
B.P. °C			BP	0.0555	2	h			
760 mm	188.41	2	t_e	0.0361	5	f'	to		
100	120.04	2	30 mm	0.7613	4	g'	°K		
30	89.69	4	ΔHm cal/g			h'			
10	66.5	5							
1	27.5	5	ΔHv cal/g			m	to		
Pressure			25°C	91.88	5	n	°K		
mm 25°C	0.840	5	30 mm	85.37	4	o			
t_e	1262.	5	BP	73.21	5				
Density			t_e	70.70	5	m'	to		
g/ml 20°C	0.8763	2	t_e (d,e)	70.52	5	n'	°K		
d_4^t 25	0.8723	2	ΔHv/T_e	19.63	5	o'			
30	0.8683	4	d 90 to	96.42	5	Surface tension			
a	0.8923	4	e 210 °C	0.1232	5	dynes/cm. 20°C	31.45	5
b	-0.0380	4	d' 10 to	94.40	5	30	30.31	5
Ref. Index			e' 90 °C	0.1007	5	40	29.21	5
n_D 20°C	1.5038	2	d_c g/ml	0.294	5	Parachor [P]		
25	1.5016	2	v_c ml/g	3.398	5	20°C		
30	1.4990	4	t_c °C	396.4	5	30		
"C"	0.7562	4	P_c mm	22611.	5	40		
MR (Obs.)	45.34	2	PV/RT			Sugd.	362.7	5
MR (Calc.)	44.779	5	25°C	1.0000	5	Exp. L.1.%/wt.		
(nD-d/2)	1.0656	2	30 mm	1.0000	5	u.		
Dielectric	2.261	5	BP	0.9526	5	Dispersion	171.	2
A 90 to	7.0427	2	t_e	0.9380	5	Flash Point °C	61.0	5
B 230 °C	1629.0	2	t_c	0.247	5	Fire Point		
C	203.0	2	ΔHc kcal/m			M Spec.	Yes	2
A* 90 to	1.4840	5	ΔHf	-20.38	2	Ultra V.	Yes	2
B* 220 °C	1531.9	5	ΔFf			X-Ray Dif.		
K			Viscosity			Infrared		
c			centistokes			Solubility in +		
t_k to			η °C			Acetone	∞	
t_x °C						Carbon tet.	∞	
A' 25 to	7.3933	5				Benzene	∞	
B' 90 °C	1840.7	5				Ether	∞	
C'	221.4	5	B^v to			n-Heptane	∞	
A'* 25 to	1.8416	5	A^v °C			Ethanol	∞	
B'* 90 °C	1739.7	5	(B^v) to			Water		
Ac 230 to	7.4486	5	(A^v) °C			Water in		
Bc t_c °C	1998.6	5	c_p liq. °K					
Cc	249.5	5						
Cryos. A°			c_p vap. °K					
consts. B°								
t_e °C F	210.27	5	c_v vap.					

$T_R = 0.75 T_c$ + grams/100 grams solvent

REFERENCES: 1-Dow 2-API 3-Lit. 4-Calc. from det. data 5-Calc. by formula

SOURCE: API

PURIFICATION: API

LITERATURE REFERENCES:

TABLE I. ALKYL AND HALO BENZENES

NAME	5-Ethyl-1,3-dimethylbenzene	STRUCTURAL FORMULA
	5-Ethyl-m-xylene	

| Mole
% Pur. 99.89 | Ref.
2 | Molecular
Formula $C_{10}H_{14}$ | Molecular
Weight 134.212 | |

Structural formula: CH_3 / H_5C_2 ring CH_3

		Ref.			Ref.			Ref.
F.P. °C	-84.325	2	dt/dP			f $\quad$ to		
F.P. 100%			°C/mm			g $\quad$ °K		
B.P. °C			25°C	14.007	5	h		
760 mm	183.75	2	BP	0.0542	2			
100	116.06	2	t_e	0.0360	5	f' $\quad$ to		
30	86.01	4	30 mm	0.7539	4	g' $\quad$ °K		
10	63.0	5				h'		
1	24.4	5	ΔHm cal/g	15.94	2			
			ΔHv cal/g			m $\quad$ to		
Pressure			25°C	90.48	5	n $\quad$ °K		
mm 25°C	1.0389	5	30 mm	84.47	4	o		
t_e	1251.	5	BP	72.64	5			
Density			t_e	70.19	5	m' $\quad$ to		
g/ml 20°C	0.8648	2	t_e (d,e)	70.06	5	n' $\quad$ °K		
$d_4^t \quad 25$	0.8608	2	$\Delta Hv/T_e$	19.70	5	o'		
$\quad 30$	0.8568	4	d $\quad$ 85 to	94.88	5	Surface tension		
a	0.8808	4	e $\quad$ 205 °C	0.1211	5	dynes/cm. 20°C	29.83	5
b	-0.0_380	4	d' $\quad$ 10 to	92.95	5	δ $\qquad$ 30	28.74	5
Ref. Index			e' $\quad$ 85 °C	0.0985	5	$\qquad$ 40	27.68	5
$n_D \quad 20°C$	1.4981	2	d_c g/ml	0.293	5	Parachor [P]		
$\quad 25$	1.4958	2	v_c ml/g	3.416	5	20°C		
$\quad 30$	1.4931	4	t_c °C	387.8	5	30		
"C"	0.7579	4	P_c mm	22208.	5	40		
MR (Obs.)	45.50	2				Sugd.	362.7	5
MR (Calc.)	44.779	5	PV/RT			Exp. L.1.%/wt.		
(nD-d/2)	1.0657	2	25°C	1.0000	5	u.		
Dielectric	2.244	5	30 mm	1.0000	5	Dispersion	172.	2
A $\quad$ 85 to	7.0459	2	BP	0.9548	5	Flash Point °C	57.0	5
B $\quad$ 225 °C	1615.0	2	t_e	0.9405	5	Fire Point		
C	204.0	2	t_c	0.247	5	M. Spec.	Yes	2
A* $\quad$ 85 to	1.4878	5	ΔHc kcal/m			Ultra V.	Yes	2
B* $\quad$ 215 °C	1517.7	5	ΔHf	-20.86	2	X-Ray Dif.		
K			ΔFf			Infrared		
c			Viscosity			Solubility in $^+$		
$t_k \quad$ to			centistokes			Acetone	∞	
$t_k \quad$ °C			η $\quad$ °C			Carbon tet.	∞	
t_x						Benzene	∞	
A' $\quad$ 25 to	7.3967	5				Ether	∞	
B' $\quad$ 85 °C	1824.9	5				n-Heptane	∞	
C'	222.3	5	$B^v \quad$ to			Ethanol	∞	
A'* $\quad$ 25 to	1.8468	5	$A^v \quad$ °C			Water		
B'* $\quad$ 85 °C	1723.9	5	$(B^v) \quad$ to			Water in		
Ac $\quad$ 225 to	7.4518	5	$(A^v) \quad$ °C					
Bc $\quad t_c$ °C	1979.9	5	c_p liq. °K					
Cc	249.7	5						
Cryos. A°	0.0302	2	c_p vap. °K					
consts. B°								
t_e °C $\quad$ F	205.02	5	c_v vap.					

$T_R = 0.75\ T_c$ $\qquad$ $^+$ grams/100 grams solvent

REFERENCES: 1-Dow 2-API 3-Lit. 4-Calc. from det. data 5-Calc. by formula

SOURCE: $\qquad$ API

PURIFICATION: $\qquad$ API

LITERATURE REFERENCES:

NAME	1, 2, 3, 4 - Tetramethylbenzene	STRUCTURAL FORMULA
	Prehnitene	

Mole % Pur.	Ref.	Molecular Formula $C_{10}H_{14}$	Molecular Weight 134.212	

		Ref.				Ref.			Ref.
F.P. °C	-6.25	2	dt/dP				f | to		
F.P. 100%			°C/mm				g | °K		
B.P. °C			25°C	36.540	5		h |		
760 mm	205.04	2	BP	0.0553	2				
100	134.64	2	t_e	0.0362	5		f' | to		
30	103.36	4	30 mm	0.7850	4		g' | °K		
10	79.4	5	ΔHm cal/g	19.97	2		h' |		
1	39.2	5	ΔHv cal/g				m | to		
Pressure			25°C	97.71	5		n | °K		
mm 25°C	0.369	5	30 mm	89.15	4		o |		
t_e	1302.	5	BP	76.09	5				
Density			t_e	73.20	5		m' | to		
g/ml 20°C	0.9052	2	t_e (d, e)	73.01	5		n' | °K		
d_4^t 25	0.9015	2	ΔHv/T_e	19.56	5		o' |		
30	0.8978	4	d |100 to	102.43	5		Surface tension		
a	0.9200	4	e |230 °C	0.1285	5		dynes/cm. 20°C	35.81	5
b	-0.0₃74	4	d' | 10 to	100.44	5		ɣ 30	34.65	5
Ref. Index			e' |100 °C	0.1092	5		40	33.52	5
n_D 20°C	1.5203	2	d_c g/ml	0.308	5		Parachor [P]		
25	1.5181	2	v_c ml/g	3.246	5		20°C		
30	1.5155	4	t_c °C	426.9	5		30		
"C"	0.7540	4	P_c mm	24553.	5		40		
MR (Obs.)	45.10	2	PV/RT				Sugd.	362.7	5
MR (Calc.)	44.779	5	25°C	1.0000	5		Exp. L.1.%/wt.		
(nD-d/2)	1.0677	2	30 mm	1.0000	5		u.		
Dielectric	2.311		BP	0.9489	5		Dispersion	174.	2
A |100 to	7.0584	2	t_e	0.9320	5		Flash Point °C	73.0	5
B |250 °C	1689.10	2	t_c	0.245	5		Fire Point		
C	199.28	2	ΔHc kcal/m				M Spec.		
A* |100 to	1.4934	5	ΔHf	-23.04	2		Ultra V.		
B* |240 °C	1591.6	5	ΔFf				X-Ray Dif.		
K			Viscosity				Infrared	Yes	2
c			centistokes				Solubility in +		
t_k | to			η °C				Acetone	∞	
t_x | °C							Carbon tet.	∞	
A' | 25 to	7.4100	5					Benzene	∞	
B' |100 °C	1908.6	5					Ether	∞	
C'	218.3	5	B^v | to				n-Heptane	∞	
A'* 25 to	1.8524	5	A^v | °C				Ethanol	∞	
B'*100 °C	1807.4	5	(B^v) | to				Water		
Ac |250 to	7.4638	5	(A^v) | °C				Water in		
Bc | t_c °C	2074.7	5	c_p liq. °K						
Cc	248.1	5							
Cryos. A°	0.0190	2	c_p vap. °K						
consts. B°									
t_e °C F	229.02	5	c_v vap.						

T_R = 0.75 T_c + grams/100 grams solvent

REFERENCES: 1-Dow 2-API 3-Lit. 4-Calc. from det. data 5-Calc. by formula

SOURCE:	API
PURIFICATION:	API
LITERATURE REFERENCES:	

TABLE I. ALKYL AND HALO BENZENES

No. 35

NAME	1, 2, 3, 5 - Tetramethylbenzene	STRUCTURAL FORMULA
	Isodurene	

| Mole % Pur. 99.92 | Ref. 2 | Molecular Formula $C_{10}H_{14}$ | Molecular Weight 134.212 | |

		Ref.			Ref.			Ref.
F. P. °C	-23.685	2	dt/dP.			f	to	
F. P. 100%			°C/mm			g	°K	
			25°C	27.330	5	h		
B. P. °C			BP	0.055	2			
760 mm	198.00	2	t_e	0.036	5	f'	to	
100	128.79	2				g'	°K	
30	98.00	4	30 mm	0.7728	4	h'		
10	74.4	5	ΔHm cal/g					
1	34.8	5				m	to	
			ΔHv cal/g			n	°K	
Pressure			25°C	95.71	5	o		
mm 25°C	0.5033	5	30 mm	88.00	4			
t_e	1289.	5	BP	75.57	5	m'	to	
			t_e	72.79	5	n'	°K	
Density			t_e (d, e)	72.70	5	o'		
g/ml 20°C	0.8903	2	ΔHv/T_e	19.76	5			
d_4^t 25	0.8865	2				Surface tension		
30	0.8827	4	d 100 to	100.17	5	dynes/cm. 20°C	33.51	5
a	0.9055	4	e 220 °C	0.1243	5	ɣ 30	32.38	5
b	-0.0376	4	d' 20 to	98.35	5	40	31.28	5
Ref. Index			e' 100 °C	0.1057	5			
n_D 20°C	1.5130	2				Parachor [P]		
25	1.5107	2	d_c g/ml	0.308	5	20°C		
30	1.5074	4	v_c ml/g	3.25	5	30		
"C"	0.7568	4	t_c °C	413.6	5	40		
			P_c mm	24119.	5	Sugd.	362.7	5
MR (Obs.)	45.31	2	PV/RT			Exp. L. l. %/wt.		
MR (Calc.)	44.779	5	25°C	1.0000	5	u.		
(nD-d/2)	1.0678	2	30 mm	1.0000	5	Dispersion	174.	2
Dielectric	2.289	5	BP	0.9538	5	Flash Point °C	68.0	5
A 95 to	7.0769	2	t_e	0.9374	5	Fire Point		
B 240 °C	1674.00	2	t_c	0.247	5			
C	200.94	2	ΔHc kcal/m			M. Spec.		
A* 95 to	1.50994	5	ΔHf	-23.54	2	Ultra V.		
B* °C	1575.28	5	ΔFf			X-Ray Dif.		
K						Infrared		
c			Viscosity			Solubility in +		
t_k to			centistokes			Acetone	∞	
t_x °C			η °C			Carbon tet.	∞	
A' 25 to	7.42969	5				Benzene	∞	
B' 95 °C	1891.57	5				Ether	∞	
C'	219.8	5	B^v to			n-Heptane	∞	
A'* 25 to	1.87408	5	A^v °C			Ethanol	∞	
B'* 95 °C	1790.24	5	(B^v) to			Water		
Ac 240 to	7.48236	5	(A^v) °C			Water in		
Bc t_c °C	2052.4	5						
Cc	248.4	5	c_p liq. °K					
Cryos. A°	0.023	2	c_p vap. °K					
consts. B°								
t_e °C	221.09	5	c_v vap.					
T_R = 0.75 T_c						+ grams/100 grams solvent		

REFERENCES: 1-Dow 2-API 3-Lit. 4-Calc. from det. data 5-Calc. by formula

SOURCE:	API
PURIFICATION:	API

LITERATURE REFERENCES:

NAME	1, 2, 4, 5 - Tetramethylbenzene	STRUCTURAL FORMULA
	Durene	

Mole % Pur. 99.86	Ref. 2	Molecular Formula $C_{10}H_{14}$	Molecular Weight 134.212

		Ref.			Ref.				Ref.
F.P. °C	79.240	2	dt/dP °C/mm			f	to		
F.P. 100%			25°C	25.964	5	g	°K		
B.P. °C			BP	0.054	2	h			
760 mm	196.80	2	t_e	0.0358	5	f'	to		
100	127.77	2	30 mm	0.7709	4	g'	°K		
30	97.1	4	ΔHm cal/g	37.40	2	h'			
10	73.5	5	ΔHv cal/g			m	to		
1	34.0	5	25°C	95.35	5	n	°K		
Pressure			30 mm	87.78	4	o			
mm 25°C	0.532	5	BP	75.34	5				
t_e	1287.	5	t_e	72.69	5	m'	to		
Density			t_e (d, e)	72.48	5	n'	°K		
g/ml 20°C	0.8875+	2	$\Delta Hv/T_e$	19.79	5	o'			
d_4^t 25	0.8837+	2	d	95 to	99.88	5	Surface tension		
30	0.8799	4	e	220 °C	0.1247	5	dynes/cm. 20°C	33.09	5
a	0.9027	4	d'	10 to	97.97	5	Ȣ 30	31.97	5
b	-0.0376	4	e'	95 °C	0.1051	5	40	30.88	5
Ref. Index			d_c g/ml	0.306	5	Parachor [P]		
n_D 20°C	1.5116	2	v_c ml/g	3.268	5	20°C		
25	1.5093	2	t_c °C	411.4	5	30		
30	1.5073	4	P_c mm	24037.	5	40		
"C"	0.7579	4	PV/RT			Sugd.	362.7	5
MR (Obs.,	45.35	2	25°C	1.0000	5	Exp. L.1.%/wt.		
MR (Calc.)	44.779	5	30 mm	1.0000	5	u.		
(nD-d/2)	1.0678	2	BP	0.9531	5	Dispersion	174.	2
Dielectric	2.285	5	t_e	0.9383	5	Flash Point °C	67.0	5
A 95 to	7.0790	2	t_c	0.247	5	Fire Point		
B 240 °C	1671.0	2	ΔHc kcal/m			M Spec.	Yes	2
C	201.23	2	ΔHf	-23.58	2	Ultra V.		
A* 95 to	1.5118	5	ΔFf			X-Ray Dif.	Yes	1
B* 230 °C	1572.1	5	Viscosity			Infrared	Yes	2
K			centistokes			Solubility in +		
c			η °C			Acetone	∞	
t_k to						Carbon tet.	∞	
t_x °C						Benzene	∞	
A' 25 to	7.4319	5				Ether	∞	
B' 100 °C	1888.21	5				n-Heptane	∞	
C'	220.0	5	B^v to			Ethanol	∞	
A'* 25 to	1.8767	5	A^v °C			Water		
B'*100 °C	1786.8	5	(B^v) to			Water in		
Ac 240 to	7.4845	5	(A^v) °C					
Bc t_c °C	2048.2	5	c_p liq. °K					
Cc	248.5	5	c_p vap. °K					
Cryos. A° consts. B°	0.02034	2	c_v vap.					
t_e °C F	219.73	5						

$T_R = 0.75 T_c$ + undercooled liquid   + grams/100 grams solvent

REFERENCES: 1-Dow 2-API 3-Lit. 4-Calc. from det. data 5-Calc. by formula

SOURCE: API

PURIFICATION: API

LITERATURE REFERENCES:

TABLE I. ALKYL AND HALO BENZENES

No. 37

| NAME | n-Pentylbenzene | | STRUCTURAL FORMULA |
| | n-Amylbenzene | | C_5H_{11} |

| Mole % Pur. | Ref. | Molecular Formula $C_{11}H_{16}$ | Molecular Weight 148.238 |

		Ref.				Ref.					Ref.
F.P. °C	-75.	2	dt/dP °C/mm				f	to °K			
F.P. 100%			25°C	40.259	5		g				
B.P. °C			BP	0.055	2		h				
760 mm	205.4	2	t_e	0.0359	5		f'	to °K			
100	135.42	4	30 mm	0.7796	4		g'				
30	104.34	4					h'				
10	80.6	5	ΔHm cal/g				m	300 to	-0.0312	4	
1	40.7	5	ΔHv cal/g				n	600 °K	0.0013	4	
Pressure			25°C	90.34	5		o		-0.0$_6$56	4	
mm 25°C	0.328	5	30 mm	81.70	5		m'	700 to	0.0804	4	
t_e	1307.	5	BP	69.52	5		n'	1000 °K	0.0010	4	
Density			t_e	66.77	5		o'		-0.0$_6$37	4	
g/ml 20°C	0.8585	2	t_e (d, e)	66.63	5		Surface tension				
d_4^t 25	0.8546	2	ΔHv/T_e	19.69	5		dynes/cm. 20°C	29.41	5	
30	0.8507	4					ठ 30	28.35	5	
a	0.8741	4	d 105 to	94.28	5		40	27.33	5	
b	-0.0$_3$78	4	e 230 °C	0.1205	5		Parachor [P]			
Ref. Index			d' 20 to	93.06	5		20°C			
n_D 20°C	1.4878	2	e' 105 °C	0.1088	5		30			
25	1.4855	2	d_c g/ml	0.284	5		40			
30	1.4830	4	v_c ml/g	3.518	5		Sugd.	402.1	5
"C"	0.7487	4	t_c °C	405.9	5		Exp. L.1.%/wt.			
MR (Obs.)	49.73	2	P_c mm	19894.	5		u.			
MR (Calc.)	49.397	5	PV/RT				Dispersion	154.	2
(nD-d/2)	1.0585	2	25°C	1.0000	5		Flash Point °C			
Dielectric	2.213		30 mm	1.0000	5		Fire Point			
A 105 to	7.04709	4	BP	0.9518	5		M. Spec.			
B 270 °C	1670.68	4	t_e	0.9348	5		Ultra V.			
C	195.6	5	t_c	0.245	5		X-Ray Dif.			
A* 105 to	-1.52337	5	ΔHc kcal/m	1488.72	2		Infrared			
B* 240 °C	1573.86	5	ΔHf				Solubility in +			
K			ΔFf				Acetone	∞		
c			Viscosity centistokes				Carbon tet.	∞		
t_k to			η 20 °C	1.553	2		Benzene	∞		
t_x °C			40	1.157	2		Ether	∞		
A' 25 to	7.39800	5	60	0.913	2		n-Heptane	∞		
B' 105 °C	1887.82	5	80	0.741	2		Ethanol	∞		
C'	214.5	5	B^v 30 to	535.16	4		Water			
A'* 25 to	1.88781	5	A^v 90 °C	2.35464	4		Water in			
B'* 105 °C	1789.21	5	(B^v) 90 to	537.68	4		Viscosity centistokes			
Ac 270 to	7.69926	5	(A^v) 160 °C	2.35272	4		100°C	0.617	2
Bc t_c °C	2333.3	5	c_p liq. °K				110	0.570	2
Cc	280.3	5					150	0.420	2
Cryos. A°			c_p vap.300°K	0.3210	2					
consts. B°			400	0.4161	2					
t_e °C F	229.43	5	c_v vap.							

$T_R = 0.80 T_c$ + grams/100 grams solvent

REFERENCES: 1-Dow 2-API 3-Lit. 4-Calc. from det. data 5-Calc. by formula

SOURCE: API

PURIFICATION: API

LITERATURE REFERENCES:

No. 38

NAME	(1-Methylbutyl)benzene	STRUCTURAL FORMULA
	2-Phenylpentane	$CH_3CH(CH_2)_2CH_3$

Mole % Pur.	Ref.	Molecular Formula $C_{11}H_{16}$	Molecular Weight 148.238

		Ref.				Ref.			Ref.
F.P. °C			dt/dP				f	to	
F.P. 100%			°C/mm				g	°K	
B.P. °C			25°C	21.082	5		h		
760 mm	193.	2	BP	0.0544	5				
100	123.9	5	t_e	0.0364	5		f'	to	
30	93.4	5	30 mm	0.7664	5		g'	°K	
10	70.	5					h'		
1	31.	5	ΔHm cal/g						
Pressure			ΔHv cal/g				m	to	
mm 25°C	0.6636	5	25°C	85.21	5		n	°K	
t_e	1271.	5	30 mm	78.34	5		o		
Density			BP	66.63	5				
g/ml 20°C	0.8585	2	t_e	64.13	5		m'	to	
d_4^t 25	0.8546	2	t_e (d,e)	64.99	5		n'	°K	
30	0.8507	4	ΔHv/T_e	19.46	5		o'		
a	0.8741	4	d 95 to	89.31	5		Surface tension		
b	-0.0378	4	e 215 °C	0.1175	5		dynes/cm. 20°C	29.41	5
Ref. Index			d' 20 to	87.72	5		30	28.35	5
n_D 20°C	1.4876	2	e' 95 °C	0.1005	5		40	27.32	5
25	1.4853	2	d_c g/ml	0.276	5		Parachor [P]		
30	1.4829	4	v_c ml/g	3.618	5		20°C		
"C"	0.7485	4	t_c °C	388.6	5		30		
MR (Obs.)	49.71	2	P_c mm	18930.	5		40		
MR (Calc.)	49.397	5	PV/RT				Sugd.	402.1	5
(nD-d/2)	1.0584	2	25°C	1.0000	5		Exp. L.1.%/wt.		
Dielectric	2.213	5	30 mm	1.0000	5		u.		
A 90 to	6.99955	5	BP	0.9507	5		Dispersion	151.	2
B 230 °C	1614.5	5	t_e	0.9346	5		Flash Point °C		
C	199.	5	t_c	0.246	5		Fire Point		
A* 90 to	1.48726	5	ΔHc kcal/m				M Spec.		
B* 225 °C	1519.7	5	ΔHf				Ultra V.		
K			ΔFf				X-Ray Dif.		
c			Viscosity				Infrared		
t_k to			centistokes				Solubility in +		
t_x °C			η °C				Acetone		
A' 20 to	7.34746	5					Carbon tet.		
B' 90 °C	1824.3	5					Benzene		
C'	217.4	5	B^v to				Ether		
A'* 20 to	1.84150	5	A^v °C				n-Heptane		
B'* 90 °C	1725.6	5	(B^v) to				Ethanol		
Ac 230 to	7.37304	5	(A^v) °C				Water		
Bc t_c °C	1950.6	5	c_p liq. °K				Water in		
Cc	241.5	5							
Cryos. A°			c_p vap. °K						
consts. B°									
t_e °C	215.45	5	c_v vap.						

$T_R = 0.76 T_c$ + grams/100 grams solvent

REFERENCES: 1-Dow 2-API 3-Lit. 4-Calc. from det. data 5-Calc. by formula

SOURCE: API

PURIFICATION: API

LITERATURE REFERENCES:

TABLE I. ALKYL AND HALO BENZENES

NAME	(1-Ethylpropyl)benzene	STRUCTURAL FORMULA
	3-Phenylpentane	$CH(C_2H_5)_2$

Mole % Pur.	Ref.	Molecular Formula $C_{11}H_{16}$	Molecular Weight 148.238

		Ref.			Ref.			Ref.
F.P. °C			dt/dP			f | to		
F.P. 100%			°C/mm			g | ___ °K		
			25°C	19.325	5	h |		
B.P. °C			BP	0.0542	5			
760 mm	191.	2	t_e	0.0364	5	f' | to		
100	122.2	5	30 mm	0.7631	5	g' | ___ °K		
30	91.7	5				h' |		
10	68.5	5	ΔHm cal/g			m | to		
1	29.5	5	ΔHv cal/g			n | ___ °K		
Pressure			25°C	84.70	5	o |		
mm 25°C	0.7282	5	30 mm	77.99	5			
t_e	1265.	5	BP	66.34	5	m' | to		
Density			t_e	63.84	5	n' | ___ °K		
g/ml 20°C	0.860	2	t_e (d, e)	63.73	5	o' |		
d_4^t 25	0.856	2	ΔHv/T_e	19.46	5	Surface tension		
30	0.852	4	d | 90 to	88.75	5	dynes/cm. 20°C	29.61	5
a	0.876	4	e | 215 °C	0.1174	5	γ 30	28.52	5
b	-0.0₃8	4	d' | 20 to	87.22	5	40	27.47	5
Ref. Index			e' | 90 °C	0.1006	5			
n_D 20°C	1.4877	2	d_c g/ml	0.269	5	Parachor [P]		
25	1.4854	2	v_c ml/g	3.722	5	20°C		
30	1.4829	4	t_c °C	385.4	5	30		
"C"	0.7473	4	P_c mm	18975.	5	40		
MR (Obs.)	49.6	2				Sugd.	402.1	5
MR (Calc.)	49.397	5	PV/RT			Exp. L.1.%/wt.		
(nD-d/2)	1.0577	2	25°C	1.0000	5	u.		
Dielectric	2.213	5	30 mm	1.0000	5	Dispersion	149.	2
A | 90 to	6.99268	5	BP	0.9514	5	Flash Point °C		
B | 230 °C	1603.6	5	t_e	0.9351	5	Fire Point		
C	199.	5	t_c	0.246	5			
A* | 90 to	1.48192	5	ΔHc kcal/m			M. Spec.		
B* | 220 °C	1509.2	5	ΔHf			Ultra V.		
K			ΔFf			X-Ray Dif.		
c						Infrared		
t_k | to			Viscosity			Solubility in +		
t_x | °C			centistokes			Acetone		
A' | 20 to	7.34016	5	η °C			Carbon tet.		
B' | 90 °C	1812.0	5				Benzene		
C'	217.3	5				Ether		
			B^v | to			n-Heptane		
A'* 20 to	1.83553	5	A^v | °C			Ethanol		
B'* 90 °C	1713.6	5	(B^v) | to			Water		
Ac | 230 to	7.4304	5	(A^v) | °C			Water in		
Bc | t_c °C	1998.7	5	c_p liq. °K					
Cc	248.6	5						
Cryos. A°			c_p vap. °K					
consts. B°								
t_e °C	213.19	5	c_v vap.					

$T_R = 0.76 T_c$ \+ grams/100 grams solvent

REFERENCES: 1-Dow 2-API 3-Lit. 4-Calc. from det. data 5-Calc. by formula

SOURCE: API

PURIFICATION: API

LITERATURE REFERENCES:

No. 40

NAME	(2-Methylbutyl)benzene					STRUCTURAL FORMULA			
	2-Methyl-1-phenylbutane								

$CH_2CH(CH_3)C_2H_5$

| Mole % Pur. | Ref. | Molecular Formula $C_{11}H_{16}$ | | Molecular Weight 148.238 | | | | | |

		Ref.			Ref.				Ref.
F.P. °C			dt/dP			f		to	
F.P. 100%			°C/mm			g		°K	
			25°C	25.131	5	h			
B.P. °C			BP	0.0548	5				
760 mm	197.	2	t_e	0.0364	5	f'		to	
100	127.4	5	30 mm	0.7729	5	g'		°K	
30	96.6	5	ΔHm cal/g			h'			
10	73.0	5							
1	34.	5	ΔHv cal/g			m		to	
Pressure			25°C	86.22	5	n		°K	
mm 25°C	0.5501	5	30 mm	79.06	5	o			
t_e	1280.	5	BP	67.30	5				
Density			t_e	64.67	5	m'		to	
g/ml 20°C	0.859	2	t_e (d,e)	64.61	5	n'		°K	
d_4^t 25	0.855	2	$ΔHv/T_e$	19.44	5	o'			
30	0.851	4	d | 95 to	90.37	5	Surface tension			
a	0.875	4	e | 220 °C	0.1171	5	dynes/cm. 20°C	29.48		5
b	-0.038	4	d' | 20 to	88.73	5	γ	30	28.39	5
Ref. Index			e' | 95 °C	0.1001	5		40	27.34	5
n_D 20°C	1.486	2	d_c g/ml	0.269	5	Parachor [P]			
25	1.484	2	v_c ml/g	3.722	5	20°C			
30	1.481	4	t_c °C	393.6	5	30			
"C"	0.7458	4	P_c mm	19113.	5	40			
MR (Obs.)	49.6	2	PV/RT			Sugd.	402.1		5
MR (Calc.)	49.397	5	25°C	1.0000	5	Exp. L.l.%/wt.			
(nD-d/2)	1.056	2	30 mm	1.0000	5	u.			
Dielectric	2.208	5	BP	0.9504	5	Dispersion	153.		2
A | 95 to	7.01336	5	t_e	0.9329	5	Flash Point °C			
B |235 °C	1636.5	5	t_c	0.246	5	Fire Point			
C	199.	5	ΔHc kcal/m			M Spec.			
A* | 95 to	1.49919	5	ΔHf			Ultra V.			
B* |230 °C	1541.2	5	ΔFf			X-Ray Dif.			
K			Viscosity			Infrared			
c			centistokes			Solubility in +			
t_k | to			η °C			Acetone			
t_x | °C						Carbon tet.			
A' | 20 to	7.36214	5				Benzene			
B' |95 °C	1849.2	5				Ether			
C'	217.6	5	B^v | to			n-Heptane			
A'* 20 to	1.85353	5	A^v | °C			Ethanol			
B'* 95 °C	1749.7	5	(B^v)| to			Water			
Ac |235 to	7.4502	5	(A^v)| °C			Water in			
Bc| t_c °C	2036.3	5	c_p liq. °K						
Cc	249.0	5							
Cryos. A°			c_p vap. °K						
consts. B°									
t_e °C	219.96	5	c_v vap.						

$T_R = 0.76 T_c$

+ grams/100 grams solvent

REFERENCES: 1-Dow   2-API   3-Lit.   4-Calc. from det. data   5-Calc. by formula

SOURCE:	API
PURIFICATION:	API

LITERATURE REFERENCES:

TABLE I. ALKYL AND HALO BENZENES

No. 41

NAME	Isopentylbenzene		STRUCTURAL FORMULA
	3-Methyl-1-phenylbutane		$CH_2CH_2CH(CH_3)_2$

Mole % Pur.	Ref.	Molecular Formula $C_{11}H_{16}$	Molecular Weight 143.238

		Ref.			Ref.			Ref.
F.P. °C			dt/dP			f | to		
F.P. 100%			°C/mm			g | ___ °K		
			25°C	27.302	5	h |		
B.P. °C			BP	0.0549	5			
760 mm	198.9	2	t_e	0.0364	5	f' | to		
100	129.1	5	30 mm	0.7760	5	g' | ___ °K		
30	98.1	5	ΔHm cal/g			h' |		
10	74.5	5						
1	35.	5	ΔHv cal/g			m | to		
			25°C	86.70	5	n | ___ °K		
Pressure			30 mm	79.39	5	o |		
mm 25°C	0.5036	5	BP	67.51	5			
t_e	1285.	5	t_e	64.96	5	m' | to		
Density			t_e (d, e)	64.77	5	n' | ___ °K		
g/ml 20°C	0.856	2	ΔHv/T_e	19.44	5	o' |		
d_4^t 25	0.852	2	d | 95 to	90.97	5	Surface tension		
30	0.848	4	e |225 °C	0.1179	5	dynes/cm. 20°C	29.07	5
a	0.872	4	d' | 20 to	89.20	5	γ 30	27.99	5
b	-0.0₃8	4	e' | 25 °C	0.0999	5	40	26.95	5
Ref. Index			d_c g/ml	0.269	5			
n_D 20°C	1.484	2	v_c ml/g	3.722	5	Parachor [P]		
25	1.482	2	t_c °C	395.8	5	20°C		
30	1.479	4	P_c mm	19070.	5	30		
"C"	0.7455	4				40		
MR (Obs.)	49.6	2	PV/RT			Sugd.	402.1	5
MR (Calc.)	49.397	5	25°C	1.0000	5	Exp. L.1.%/wt.		
(nD-d/2)	1.056	2	30 mm	1.0000	5	u.		
Dielectric	2.202	5	BP	0.9487	5	Dispersion		
A |100 to	7.01996	5	t_e	0.9327	5	Flash Point °C		
B |235 °C	1646.9	5	t_c	0.246	5	Fire Point		
C	199.	5	ΔHc kcal/m			M. Spec.		
A* |100 to	1.50402	5	ΔHf			Ultra V.		
B* |230 °C	1551.2	5	ΔFf			X-Ray Dif.		
K			Viscosity			Infrared		
c			centistokes			Solubility in +		
t_k | to			η °C			Acetone		
t_x | °C						Carbon tet.		
A' | 20 to	7.36916	5				Benzene		
B' |100 °C	1861.0	5	B^v | to			Ether		
C'	217.7	5	A^v | °C			n-Heptane		
A'* 20 to	1.85931	5	(B^v)| to			Ethanol		
B'*100 °C	1761.1	5				Water		
Ac |235 to	7.4574	5	(A^v)| °C			Water in		
Bc | t_c °C	2048.7	5	c_p liq. °K					
Cc | — —	249.1	5	c_p vap. °K					
Cryos. A°								
consts. B°								
t_e °C	222.10	5	c_v vap.					

$T_R = 0.76 T_c$ + grams/100 grams solvent

REFERENCES: 1-Dow 2-API 3-Lit. 4-Calc. from det. data 5-Calc. by formula

SOURCE:	API
PURIFICATION:	API

LITERATURE REFERENCES:

No. 42

NAME	(1,1-Dimethylpropyl)benzene	STRUCTURAL FORMULA
	2-Methyl-2-phenylbutane	$(CH_3)_2 C C_2H_5$

Mole % Pur.	Ref.	Molecular Formula $C_{11}H_{16}$	Molecular Weight 148.238

	Ref.			Ref.				Ref.
F.P. °C		dt/dP			f		to	
F.P. 100%		°C/mm			g		°K	
B.P. °C		25°C	20.517	5	h			
760 mm	192.38	2	BP	0.0543	5			
100	123.39	5	t_e	0.0364	5	f'	to	
30	92.9	5	30 mm	0.7654	5	g'	°K	
10	69.5	5	ΔHm cal/g			h'		
1	31.	5	ΔHv cal/g			m	to	
Pressure		25°C	85.05	5	n	°K		
mm 25°C	0.6831	5	30 mm	78.23	5	o		
t_e	1269.	5	BP	66.61	5			
Density		t_e	64.06	5	m'	to		
g/ml 20°C	0.8748	2	t_e (d,e)	64.00	5	n'	°K	
d_4^t 25	0.8709	2	ΔHv/T_e	19.46	5	o'		
30	0.8670	4				Surface tension		
a	0.8904	4	d 90 to	89.07	5	dynes/cm. 20°C	31.70	5
b	-0.0378	4	e 215 °C	0.1167	5	ɣ 30	30.59	5
Ref. Index		d' 25 to	87.56	5	40	29.50	5
n_D 20°C	1.4958	2	e' 90 °C	0.1005	5	Parachor [P]		
25	1.4935	2	d_c g/ml	0.269	5	20°C		
30	1.4910	4	v_c ml/g	3.722	5	30		
"C"	0.7461	4	t_c °C	390.3	5	40		
MR (Obs.)	49.48	2	P_c mm	19639.	5	Sugd.	402.1	5
MR (Calc.)	49.397	5	PV/RT			Exp. L.1.%/wt.		
(nD-d/2)	1.0584	2	25°C	1.0000	5	u.		
Dielectric	2.237	5	30 mm	1.0000	5	Dispersion	151.	2
A 90 to	6.99742	5	BP	0.9518	5	Flash Point °C		
B 230 °C	1611.1	5	t_e	0.9348	5	Fire Point		
C	199.	5	t_c	0.246	5	M Spec.		
A* 90 to	1.48553	5	ΔHc kcal/m			Ultra V.		
B* 220 °C	1516.4	5	ΔHf			X-Ray Dif.		
K		ΔFf			Infrared		
c		Viscosity			Solubility in +		
t_k to		centistokes			Acetone		
t_x °C		η °C			Carbon tet.		
A' 15 to	7.34520	5				Benzene		
B' 90 °C	1820.5	5				Ether		
C'	217.4	5	B^V to			n-Heptane		
A'* 15 to	1.83965	5	A^V °C			Ethanol		
B'* 90 °C	1721.8	5	(B^V) to			Water		
Ac 230 to	7.43445	5	(A^V) °C			Water in		
Bc t_c °C	2009.0	5	c_p liq. °K					
Cc	249.2	5						
Cryos. A°		c_p vap. °K					
consts. B°							
t_e °C	214.75	5	c_v vap.					

$T_R = 0.76 T_c$

+ grams/100 grams solvent

REFERENCES: 1-Dow 2-API 3-Lit. 4-Calc. from det. data 5-Calc. by formula

SOURCE: API

PURIFICATION: API

LITERATURE REFERENCES:

TABLE I. ALKYL AND HALO BENZENES

No. 43

NAME	(1, 2-Dimethylpropyl)benzene		STRUCTURAL FORMULA
	3-Methyl-2-phenylbutane		$CH_3 CHCH(CH_3)_2$

Mole % Pur.	Ref.	Molecular Formula $C_{11}H_{16}$	Molecular Weight 148.238

		Ref.			Ref.				Ref.
F.P. °C			dt/dP			f	to		
F.P. 100%			°C/mm			g	°K		
B.P. °C			25°C	16.966	5	h			
760 mm	188.	2	BP	0.0539	5				
100	119.6	5	t_e	0.0364	5	f'	to		
30	89.3	5	30 mm	0.7582	5	g'	°K		
10	66.2	5	ΔHm cal/g			h'			
1	28.	5	ΔHv cal/g			m	to		
Pressure			25°C	83.95	5	n	°K		
mm 25°C	0.8370	5	30 mm	77.46	5	o			
t_e	1258.	5	BP	65.87	5				
Density			t_e	63.43	5	m'	to		
g/ml 20°C	0.870	2	t_e (d, e)	63.31	5	n'	°K		
d_4^t 25	0.866	2	$ΔHv/T_e$	19.47	5	o'			
30	0.862	4				Surface tension			
a	0.886	4	d | 90 to	87.94	5	dynes/cm. 20°C	31.01	5
b	-0.0₃8	4	e | 220 °C	0.1174	5	ɤ 30	29.89	5
Ref. Index			d' | 20 to	86.47	5	40	28.79	5
n_D 20°C	1.486	2	e' | 90 °C	0.1009	5	Parachor [P]		
25	1.484	2	d_c g/ml	0.269	5	20°C		
30	1.481	4	v_c ml/g	3.722	5	30		
"C"	0.7363	4	t_c °C	382.9	5	40		
MR (Obs.)	48.9	2	P_c mm	19223.	5	Sugd.	402.1	5
MR (Calc.)	49.397	5	PV/RT			Exp. L.1.%/wt.		
(nD-d/2)	1.051	2	25°C	1.0000	5	u.		
Dielectric	2.208	5	30 mm	1.0000	5	Dispersion	152.	2
A | 90 to	6.98241	5	BP	0.9520	5	Flash Point °C		
B | 225 °C	1587.3	5	t_e	0.9361	5	Fire Point		
C	199.	5	t_c	0.246	5	M. Spec.		
A* | 90 to	1.47359	5	ΔHc kcal/m			Ultra V.		
B* | 220 °C	1493.4	5	ΔHf			X-Ray Dif.		
K			ΔFf			Infrared		
c			Viscosity			Solubility in +		
t_k | to			centistokes			Acetone		
t_x °C			η °C			Carbon tet.		
						Benzene		
A' | 20 to	7.32924	5				Ether		
B' | 90 °C	1793.6	5				n-Heptane		
C'	217.2	5	B^v | to			Ethanol		
A'* 20 to	1.82664	5	A^v | °C			Water		
B'* 90 °C	1695.7	5	(B^v)| to			Water in		
Ac | 225 to	7.4181	5	(A^v)| °C					
Bc | t_c °C	1978.7	5	c_p liq. °K					
Cc	248.4	5						
Cryos. A°			c_p vap. °K					
consts. B°								
t_e °C	209.81	5	c_v vap.					

$T_R = 0.76 T_c$ + grams/100 grams solvent

REFERENCES: 1-Dow 2-API 3-Lit. 4-Calc. from det. data 5-Calc. by formula

SOURCE:	API
PURIFICATION:	API
LITERATURE REFERENCES:	

No. 44

NAME	(2,2-Dimethylpropyl)benzene	STRUCTURAL FORMULA
	Neopentylbenzene	

$CH_2 C(CH_3)_3$

Mole % Pur.	Ref.	Molecular Formula $C_{11}H_{16}$	Molecular Weight 148.238

		Ref.			Ref.					Ref.
F.P. °C			dt/dP °C/mm			f	to		
F.P. 100%			25°C	15.563	5	g	°K		
B.P. °C			BP	0.0537	5	h			
760 mm	186.	2	t_e	0.0363	5	f'	to		
100	117.9	5	30 mm	0.7549	5	g'	°K		
30	87.7	5	ΔHm cal/g			h'			
10	64.7	5	ΔHv cal/g			m	to		
1	26.	5	25°C	83.45	5	n	°K		
Pressure			30 mm	77.11	5	o			
mm 25°C	0.9179	5	BP	65.54	5				
t_e	1253.	5	t_e	63.13	5	m'	to		
Density			t_e (d, e)	63.00	5	n'	°K		
g/ml 20°C	0.858	2	$ΔHv/T_e$	19.47	5	o'			
d^t_4 25	0.854	2	d | 85 to	87.43	5	Surface tension			
30	0.850	4	e | 210 °C	0.1177	5	dynes/cm. 20°C	29.34	5
a	0.874	4	d' | 20 to	85.97	5	γ 30	28.26	5
b	-0.0₃8	4	e' | 85 °C	0.1011	5	40	27.20	5
Ref. Index			d_c g/ml	0.269	5	Parachor [P]		
n_D 20°C	1.488	2	v_c ml/g	3.722	5	20°C		
25	1.486	2	t_c °C	378.1	5	30		
30	1.483	4	P_c mm	18762.	5	40		
"C"	0.7495	4	PV/RT			Sugd.	402.1	5
MR (Obs.)	49.8	2	25°C	1.0000	5	Exp. L.1.%/wt.		
MR (Calc.)	49.397	5	30 mm	1.0000	5	u.		
(nD-d/2)	1.055	2	BP	0.9522	5	Dispersion		
Dielectric	2.214	5	t_e	0.9366	5	Flash Point °C		
A | 85 to	6.97560	5	t_c	0.246	5	Fire Point		
B | 220 °C	1576.5	5	ΔHc kcal/m			M Spec.		
C	199.	5	ΔHf			Ultra V.		
A* | 85 to	1.46828	5	ΔFf			X-Ray Dif.		
B* | 220 °C	1483.0	5				Infrared		
K			Viscosity			Solubility in +		
c			centistokes			Acetone		
t_k | to			η °C			Carbon tet.		
t_x | °C						Benzene		
A' | 20 to	7.32200	5				Ether		
B' | 85 °C	1781.4	5				n-Heptane		
C'	217.1	5	B^v | to			Ethanol		
A'* 20 to	1.82081	5	A^v | °C			Water		
B'* 85 °C	1683.9	5	(B^v) | to			Water in		
Ac | 220 to	7.4101	5	(A^v) | °C					
Bc | t_c °C	1963.4	5	c_p liq. °K					
Cc	247.8	5						
Cryos. A°			c_p vap. °K					
consts. B°								
t_e °C	207.55	5	c_v vap.					

$T_R = 0.76 T_c$ + grams/100 grams solvent

REFERENCES: 1-Dow   2-API   3-Lit.   4-Calc. from det. data   5-Calc. by formula

SOURCE: API

PURIFICATION: API

LITERATURE REFERENCES:

TABLE I. ALKYL AND HALO BENZENES

55

No. 45

NAME	1-n-Butyl-2-methylbenzene	STRUCTURAL FORMULA
	o-Butyltoluene	

Structural formula: C_4H_9, CH_3 (benzene ring)

Mole % Pur.	Ref.	Molecular Formula $C_{11}H_{16}$	Molecular Weight 148.238

		Ref.			Ref.				Ref.
F.P. °C			dt/dP			f	to		
F.P. 100%			°C/mm			g	___ °K		
B.P. °C			25°C	40.898	5	h			
760 mm	208.	2	BP	0.0558	5				
100	137.0	5	t_e	0.0364	5	f'	to		
30	105.52	5	30 mm	0.7908	5	g'	___ °K		
10	81.4	5	ΔHm cal/g			h'			
1	41.	5							
Pressure			ΔHv cal/g			m	to		
mm 25°C	0.3274	5	25°C	89.03	5	n	___ °K		
t_e	1307.	5	30 mm	81.05	5	o			
Density			BP	69.04	5	m'	to		
g/ml 20°C	0.871	2	t_e (d, e)	66.26	5	n'	___ °K		
d_4^t 25	0.867	2		66.18	5	o'			
30	0.863	4	$ΔHv/T_e$	19.43	5	Surface tension			
a	0.887	4	d 105 to	93.41	5	dynes/cm. 20°C	31.16	5
b	-0.0₃8	4	e 235 °C	0.1172	5	γ 30	30.03	5
Ref. Index			d' 25 to	91.51	5	40	28.93	5
n_D 20°C	1.496	2	e' 105 °C	0.0991	5				
25	1.494	2	d_c g/ml	0.269	5	Parachor [P]			
30	1.491	4	v_c ml/g	3.722	5	20°C			
"C"	0.7496	4	t_c °C	411.0	5	30			
MR (Obs.)	49.7	2	P_c mm	19867.	5	40			
MR (Calc.)	49.397	5	PV/RT			Sugd.	402.1	5
(nD-d/2)	1.060	2	25°C	1.0000	5	Exp. L. l. %/wt.			
Dielectric	2.238	5	30 mm	1.0000	5	u.			
A 105 to	7.05183	5	BP	0.9478	5	Dispersion			
B 245 °C	1697.6	5	t_e	0.9294	5	Flash Point °C			
C	199.	5	t_c	0.245	5	Fire Point			
A* 105 to	1.53094	5	ΔHc kcal/m			M. Spec.			
B* 240 °C	1600.6	5	ΔHf			Ultra V.			
K			ΔFf			X-Ray Dif.			
c						Infrared			
t_k to			Viscosity			Solubility in +			
t_x °C			centistokes			Acetone			
A' 25 to	7.40304	5	η °C			Carbon tet.			
B' 105 °C	1918.2	5				Benzene			
C'	218.2	5	B_v to			Ether			
A'* 25 to	1.88724	5	A_v °C			n-Heptane			
B'* 105 °C	1816.8	5	(B^v) to			Ethanol			
Ac 245 to	7.4916	5	(A^v) °C			Water			
Bc t_c °C	2112.3	5				Water in			
Cc	250.5	5	c_p liq. °K						
Cryos. A°			c_p vap. °K						
consts. B°									
t_e °C	232.36	5	c_v vap.						

$T_R = 0.76 T_c$ + grams/100 grams solvent

REFERENCES: 1-Dow 2-API 3-Lit. 4-Calc. from det. data 5-Calc. by formula

SOURCE:	API
PURIFICATION:	API
LITERATURE REFERENCES:	

No. 46

NAME	1-n-Butyl-3-methylbenzene			STRUCTURAL FORMULA
	m-n-Butyltoluene			C_4H_9

Mole % Pur.	Ref.	Molecular Formula $C_{11}H_{16}$	Molecular Weight 148.238	CH_3

		Ref.			Ref.			Ref.
F.P. °C			dt/dP			f | to		
F.P. 100%			°C/mm			g | °K		
B.P. °C			25°C	35.775	5	h |		
760 mm	205.	2	BP	0.0555	5			
100	134.4	5	t_e	0.0364	5	f' | to		
30	103.1	5				g' | °K		
10	79.1	5	30 mm	0.7859	5	h' |		
1	39.	5	ΔHm cal/g					
Pressure			ΔHv cal/g			m | to		
mm 25°C	0.3775	5	25°C	88.26	5	n | °K		
t_e	1300.	5	30 mm	80.50	5	o |		
Density			BP	68.45	5			
g/ml 20°C	0.859	2	t_e	65.82	5	m' | to		
d_4^t 25	0.855	2	t_e (d, e)	65.62	5	n' | °K		
30	0.851	4	ΔHv/T_e	19.43	5	o' |		
a	0.875	4	d | 105 to	92.68	5	Surface tension		
b	-0.0₃8	4	e | 230 °C	0.1182	5	dynes/cm. 20°C	29.48	5
Ref. Index			d' | 20 to	90.75	5	ɣ 30	28.39	5
n_D 20°C	1.491	2	e' | 105 °C	0.0994	5	40	27.34	5
25	1.489	2	d_c g/ml	0.269	5	Parachor [P]		
30	1.486	4	v_c ml/g	3.722	5	20°C		
"C"	0.7530		t_c °C	404.7	5	30		
MR (Obs.)	50.0	2	P_c mm	19350.	5	40		
MR (Calc.)	49.397	5	PV/RT			Sugd.	402.1	5
(nD-d/2)	1.062	2	25°C	1.0000	5	Exp. L.1.%/wt.		
Dielectric	2.223	5	30 mm	1.0000	5	u.		
A | 100 to	7.04127	5	BP	0.9471	5	Dispersion		
B | 240 °C	1680.8	5	t_e	0.9305	5	Flash Point °C		
C	199.	5	t_c	0.245	5	Fire Point		
A* | 100 to	1.5220	5	ΔHc kcal/m			M Spec.		
B* | 235 °C	1584.2	5	ΔHf			Ultra V.		
K			ΔFf			X-Ray Dif.		
c			Viscosity			Infrared		
t_k | to			centistokes			Solubility in +		
t_x | °C			ɳ °C			Acetone		
A' | 20 to	7.3918	5				Carbon tet.		
B' | 100 °C	1899.3	5				Benzene		
C'	218.0	5	B^V | to			Ether		
A'* 20 to	1.87797	5	A^V | °C			n-Heptane		
B'* 100 °C	1798.3	5	(B^V) | to			Ethanol		
Ac | 240 to	7.4796	5	(A^V) | °C			Water		
Bc | t_c °C	2089.6	5	c_p liq. °K			Water in		
Cc	249.7	5						
Cryos. A°			c_p vap. °K					
consts. B°								
t_e °C	228.98	5	c_v vap.					
T_R = 0.76 T_c						+ grams/100 grams solvent		

REFERENCES: 1-Dow   2-API   3-Lit.   4-Calc. from det. data   5-Calc. by formula

SOURCE:	API
PURIFICATION:	API
LITERATURE REFERENCES:	

TABLE I. ALKYL AND HALO BENZENES

NAME	1-n-Butyl-4-methylbenzene	STRUCTURAL FORMULA
	p-n-Butyltoluene	

Mole % Pur.	Ref.	Molecular Formula $C_{11}H_{16}$	Molecular Weight 148.238	

		Ref.			Ref.			Ref.
F. P. °C			dt/dP			f ⎜ to		
F. P. 100%			°C/mm			g ⎜ °K		
B. P. °C			25°C	39.114	5	h ⎜		
760 mm	207.	2	BP	0.0557	5	f' ⎜ to		
100	136.2	5	t_e	0.0364	5	g' ⎜ °K		
30	104.7	5	30 mm	0.7892	5	h' ⎜		
10	80.6	5	ΔHm cal/g			m ⎜ to		
1	40.	5	ΔHv cal/g			n ⎜ °K		
Pressure			25°C	88.77	5	o ⎜		
mm 25°C	0.3433	5	30 mm	80.86	5	m' ⎜ to		
t_e	1305.	5	BP	68.75	5	n' ⎜ °K		
Density			t_e	66.10	5	o' ⎜		
g/ml 20°C	0.857	2	t_e (d, e)	65.88	5	Surface tension		
d_4^t 25	0.853	2	ΔHv/T_e	19.43	5	dynes/cm. 20°C	29.20	5
30	0.849	4	d ⎜ 105 to	93.27	5	γ 30	28.13	5
a	0.873	4	e ⎜ 235 °C	0.1185	5	40	27.08	5
b	-0.0₃8	4	d' ⎜ 25 to	91.25	5			
Ref. Index			e' ⎜ 105 °C	0.0992	5	Parachor [P]		
n_D 20°C	1.490	2	d_c g/ml	0.269	5	20°C		
25	1.488	2	v_c ml/g	3.722	5	30		
30	1.484	4	t_c °C	407 2	5	40		
"C"	0.7533	4	P_c mm	19335.	5	Sugd.	402.1	5
MR (Obs.)	50.0	2	PV/RT			Exp. L.l.%/wt.		
MR (Calc.)	49.397	5	25°C	1.0000	5	u.		
(nD-d/2)	1.062	2	30 mm	1.0000	5	Dispersion		
Dielectric	2.220	5	BP	0.9463	5	Flash Point °C		
A ⎜ 105 to	7.04830	5	t_e	0.9297	5	Fire Point		
B ⎜ 250 °C	1692.0	5	t_c	0.245	5	M. Spec.		
C	199.	5	ΔHc kcal/m			Ultra V.		
A* ⎜ 105 to	1.52804	5	ΔHf			X-Ray Dif.		
B* ⎜ 240 °C	1595.1	5	ΔFf			Infrared		
K			Viscosity			Solubility in ⁺		
c			centistokes			Acetone		
t_k ⎜ to			η °C			Carbon tet.		
t_x ⎜ °C						Benzene		
A' ⎜ 25 to	7.39928	5				Ether		
B' ⎜ 105 °C	1911.9	5	B^v ⎜ to			n-Heptane		
C'	218.1	5	A^v ⎜ °C			Ethanol		
A'* 25 to	1.88414	5	(B^v)⎜ to			Water		
B'* 105 °C	1810.6	5	(A^v)⎜ °C			Water in		
Ac ⎜ 250 to	7.5313	5	c_p liq. °K					
Bc ⎜ t_c °C	2154.2	5						
Cc ⎜	256.7	5						
Cryos. A°			c_p vap. °K					
consts. B°								
t_e °C	231.23	5	c_v vap.					

T_R = 0.77 T_c

⁺ grams/100 grams solvent

REFERENCES: 1-Dow 2-API 3-Lit. 4-Calc. from det. data 5-Calc. by formula

SOURCE:	API
PURIFICATION:	API
LITERATURE REFERENCES:	

No. 48

NAME	1-sec-Butyl-2-methylbenzene	STRUCTURAL FORMULA
	o-sec-Butyltoluene	$CH_3 CHC_2H_5$ CH_3

Mole % Pur.	Ref.	Molecular Formula $C_{11}H_{16}$	Molecular Weight 148.238

		Ref.				Ref.						Ref.
F.P. °C			dt/dP				f		to			
F.P. 100%			°C/mm				g		°K			
			25°C	24.052	5		h					
B.P. °C			BP	0.0547	5							
760 mm	196.	2	t_e	0.0364	5		f'		to			
100	126.6	5	30 mm	0.7713	5		g'		°K			
30	95.8	5	ΔHm cal/g				h'					
10	72.3	5										
1	33.	5	ΔHv cal/g				m		to			
Pressure			25°C	85.97	5		n		°K			
mm 25°C	0.5765	5	30 mm	78.88	5		o					
t_e	1278.	5	BP	66.98	5							
Density			t_e	64.54	5		m'		to			
g/ml 20°C	0.873	2	t_e (d,e)	64.27	5		n'		°K			
d_4^t 25	0.869	2	ΔHv/T_e	19.45	5		o'					
30	0.865	4					Surface tension					
a	0.889	4	d	95	to	90.25	5	dynes/cm. 20°C	31.44	5
b	-0.038	4	e	220	°C	0.1187	5	γ	30	30.31	5
Ref. Index			d'	20	to	88.47	5		40	29.20	5
n_D 20°C	1.497	2	e'	95	°C	0.1002	5				
25	1.495	2	d_c g/ml			0.269	5	Parachor [P]		
30	1.492	4	v_c ml/g			3.722	5	20°C		
"C"	0.7494	4	t_c °C			394.6	5	30		
MR (Obs.)	49.7	2	P_c mm			19565.	5	40		
MR (Calc.)	49.397	2	PV/RT					Sugd.	402.1	5
(nD-d/2)	1.060	2	25°C			1.0000	5	Exp. L.1.%/wt.		
Dielectric	2.241	5	30 mm			1.0000	5	u.		
			BP			0.9482	5	Dispersion	160.	2
A	95 to	7.00990	5	t_e			0.9333	5	Flash Point °C		
B	235 °C	1631.0	5	t_c			0.246	5	Fire Point		
C		199.	5	ΔHc kcal/m					M Spec.		
				ΔHf					Ultra V.		
A*	95 to	1.49634	5	ΔFf					X-Ray Dif.		
B*	225 °C	1535.9	5						Infrared		
K				Viscosity							
c				centistokes					Solubility in +		
t_k	to			η °C					Acetone		
t_x	°C								Carbon tet.		
A'	20 to	7.35847	5						Benzene		
B'	95 °C	1843.0	5						Ether		
C'		217.6	5						n-Heptane		
A'*	20 to	1.85051	5	B^v		to			Ethanol		
B'*	95 °C	1743.7	5	A^v		°C			Water		
				(B^v)		to			Water in		
Ac	235 to	7.4467	5	(A^v)		°C					
Bc	t_c °C	2031.5	5	c_p liq. °K							
Cc		249.3	5								
Cryos. A°				c_p vap. °K							
consts. B°											
t_e °C	218.83	5	c_v vap.							

T_R = 0.76 T_c

+ grams/100 grams solvent

REFERENCES: 1-Dow 2-API 3-Lit. 4-Calc. from det. data 5-Calc. by formula

SOURCE:	API
PURIFICATION:	API
LITERATURE REFERENCES:	

TABLE I. ALKYL AND HALO BENZENES

59

No. 49

NAME	1-sec-Butyl-3-methylbenzene	STRUCTURAL FORMULA
	m-sec-Butyltoluene	CH₃CHC₂H₅

Mole % Pur.	Ref.	Molecular Formula $C_{11}H_{16}$	Molecular Weight 148.238

		Ref.			Ref.					Ref.
F.P. °C			dt/dP			f	to			
F.P. 100%			°C/mm			g	°K			
			25°C	22.030	5	h				
B.P. °C			BP	0.0545	5					
760 mm	194.	2	t_e	0.0364	5	f'	to			
100	124.8	5	30 mm	0.7680	5	g'	°K			
30	94.2	5	ΔHm cal/g			h'				
10	70.8	5								
1	32.	5	ΔHv cal/g			m	to			
Pressure			25°C	85.46	5	n	°K			
mm 25°C	0.6332	5	30 mm	78.52	5	o				
t_e	1273.	5	BP	66.73	5					
			t_e	64.26	5	m'	to			
Density			t_e (d, e)	64.07	5	n'	°K			
g/ml 20°C	0.858	2	ΔHv/T_e	19.45	5	o'				
d_4^t 25	0.854	2								
30	0.850	4	d | 95 to	89.64	5	Surface tension				
			e | 220 °C	0.1181	5	dynes/cm. 20°C	29.34	5
a	0.874	4	d' | 20 to	87.97	5	γ 30	28.26	5
b	-0.0₃8	4	e' | 95 °C	0.1004	5	40	27.21	5
Ref. Index										
n_D 20°C	1.490	2	d_c g/ml	0.269	5	Parachor [P]				
25	1.488	2	v_c ml/g	3.722	5	20°C				
30	1.485	4	t_c °C	389.3	5	30				
"C"	0.7524	4	P_c mm	18993.	5	40				
						Sugd.	402.1	5
MR (Obs.)	50.0	2	PV/RT							
MR (Calc.)	49.397	5	25°C	1.0000	5	Exp. L.1.%/wt.				
(nD-d/2)	1.062	2	30 mm	1.0000	5	u.				
Dielectric	2.220	5	BP	0.9497	5	Dispersion	161.	2
			t_e	0.9341	5	Flash Point °C				
A | 95 to	7.00299	5	t_c	0.246	5	Fire Point				
B | 230 °C	1620.0	5								
C	199.	5	ΔHc kcal/m			M. Spec.				
			ΔHf			Ultra V.				
A* | 95 to	1.49044	5	ΔFf			X-Ray Dif.				
B* | 225 °C	1525.2	5				Infrared				
K			Viscosity							
c			centistokes			Solubility in +				
t_k | to			η °C			Acetone				
t_x | °C						Carbon tet.				
A' | 20 to	7.35112	5				Benzene				
B' | 95 °C	1830.6	5				Ether				
C'	217.5	5	B^v | to			n-Heptane				
			A^v | °C			Ethanol				
A'* 20 to	1.84449	5	(B^v)| to			Water				
B'* 95 °C	1731.6	5	(A^v)| °C			Water in				
Ac | 230 to	7.4393	5								
Bc | t_c °C	2016.2	5	c_p liq. °K							
Cc |	248.6	5								
Cryos. A°			c_p vap. °K							
consts. B°										
t_e °C	216.57	5	c_v vap.							

$T_R = 0.76 T_c$ + grams/100 grams solvent

REFERENCES: 1-Dow 2-API 3-Lit. 4-Calc. from det. data 5-Calc. by formula

SOURCE:	API
PURIFICATION:	API
LITERATURE REFERENCES:	

No. 50

NAME	1-sec-Butyl-4-methylbenzene		STRUCTURAL FORMULA
	p-sec-Butyltoluene		$CH_3 CH C_2H_5$

| Mole % Pur. | Ref. | Molecular Formula $C_{11}H_{16}$ | | Molecular Weight 148.238 | | | |

		Ref.			Ref.				Ref.
F.P. °C			dt/dP			f		to	
F.P. 100%			°C/mm			g		°K	
B.P. °C			25°C	25.131	5	h			
760 mm	197.	2	BP	0.0548	5				
100	127.4	5	t_e	0.0364	5	f'		to	
30	96.6	5	30 mm	0.7729	5	g'		°K	
10	73.0	5	ΔHm cal/g			h'			
1	34.	5	ΔHv cal/g			m		to	
Pressure			25°C	86.22	5	n		°K	
mm 25°C	0.5501	5	30 mm	79.06	5	o			
t_e	1280.	5	BP	67.30	5				
Density			t_e	64.68	5	m'		to	
g/ml 20°C	0.866	2	t_e (d,e)	64.61	5	n'		°K	
d_4^t 25	0.862	2	ΔHv/T_e	19.44	5	o'			
30	0.858	4	d 95 to	90.37	5	Surface tension			
a	0.882	4	e 220 °C	0.1171	5	dynes/cm. 20°C	30.45	5	
b	-0.0₃8	4	d' 25 to	88.73	5	j 30	29.34	5	
Ref. Index			e' 95 °C	0.1001	5	40	28.26	5	
n_D 20°C	1.493	2	d_c g/ml	0.269	5	Parachor [P]			
25	1.491	2	v_c ml/g	3 72	5	20°C			
30	1.488	4	t_c °C	394.8	5	30			
"C"	0.7497	4	P_c mm	19355.	5	40			
MR (Obs.)	49.8	2	PV/RT			Sugd.	402.1	5	
MR (Calc.)	49.397	5	25°C	1.0000	5	Exp. L.1.%/wt.			
(nD-d/2)	1.060	2	30 mm	1.0000	5	u.			
Dielectric	2.229	5	BP	0.9504	5	Dispersion	158.	2	
A 95 to	7.01336	5	t_e	0.9329	5	Flash Point °C			
B 235 °C	1636.5	5	t_c	0.246	5	Fire Point			
C	199.	5	ΔHc kcal/m			M Spec.			
A* 95 to	1.49919	5	ΔHf			Ultra V.			
B* 230 °C	1541.2	5	ΔFf			X-Ray Dif.			
K			Viscosity			Infrared			
c			centistokes			Solubility in +			
t_k to			η °C			Acetone			
t_x °C						Carbon tet.			
A' 20 to	7.36214	5				Benzene			
B' 95 °C	1849.2	5				Ether			
C'	217.6	5	B^v to			n-Heptane			
A'* 20 to	1.85353	5	A^v °C			Ethanol			
B'* 95 °C	1749.7	5	(B^v) to			Water			
Ac 235 to	7.4527	5	(A^v) °C			Water in			
Bc t_c °C	2039.6	5	c_p liq. °K						
Cc	249.4	5							
Cryos. A°			c_p vap. °K						
consts. B°									
t_e °C	219.96	5	c_v vap.						

$T_R = 0.76 T_c$

+ grams/100 grams solvent

REFERENCES: 1-Dow 2-API 3-Lit. 4-Calc. from det. data 5-Calc. by formula

SOURCE: API

PURIFICATION: API

LITERATURE REFERENCES:

TABLE I. ALKYL AND HALO BENZENES

No. 51

NAME	o-Isobutyltoluene	STRUCTURAL FORMULA
	1-Isobutyl-2-methylbenzene	$CH_2CH(CH_3)_2$ CH_3

Mole % Pur.	Ref.	Molecular Formula $C_{11}H_{16}$	Molecular Weight 148.238

		Ref.			Ref.						Ref.
F.P. °C			dt/dP			f		to			
F.P. 100%			°C/mm			g		°K			
B.P. °C			25°C	24.052	5	h					
760 mm	196.	2	BP	0.0547	5						
100	126.6	5	t_e	0.0364	5	f'		to			
30	95.8	5	30 mm	0.7713	5	g'		°K			
10	72.3	5	ΔHm cal/g			h'					
1	33.	5	ΔHv cal/g			m		to			
Pressure			25°C	85.97	5	n		°K			
mm 25°C	0.5765	5	30 mm	78.88	5	o					
t_e	1278.	5	BP	66.98	5	m'		to			
Density			t_e	64.54	5	n'		°K			
g/ml 20°C	0.8649	2	t_e (d, e)	64.27	5	o'					
d_4^t 25	0.8610	2	$\Delta Hv/T_e$	19.44	5	Surface tension					
30	0.8571	4	d 95 to	90.25	5	dynes/cm. 20°C		30.29	5		
a	0.8805	4	e 220 °C	0.1187	5	γ 30		29.21	5		
b	-0.0378	4	d' 20 to	88.47	5	40		28.16	5		
Ref. Index			e' 95 °C	0.1002	5	Parachor [P]					
n_D 20°C	1.4935	2	d_c g/ml	0.269	5	20°C					
25	1.4912	2	v_c ml/g	3.72	5	30					
30	1.4887	4	t_c °C	393.8	5	40					
"C"	0.7514	4	P_c mm	19408.	5	Sugd.		402.1	5		
MR (Obs.)	49.85	2	PV/RT			Exp. L.1.%/wt.					
MR (Calc.)	49.397	5	25°C	1.0000	5	u.					
(nD-d/2)	1.0610	2	30 mm	1.0000	5	Dispersion		162.	2		
Dielectric	2.231	5	BP	0.9482	5	Flash Point °C					
A 95 to	7.00990	5	t_e	0.9333	5	Fire Point					
B 235 °C	1631.0	5	t_c	0.246	5	M. Spec.					
C	199.	5	ΔHc kcal/m			Ultra V.					
A* 95 to	1.49634	5	ΔHf			X-Ray Dif.					
B* 230 °C	1535.9	5	ΔFf			Infrared					
K			Viscosity			Solubility in +					
c			centistokes			Acetone					
t_k to			η °C			Carbon tet.					
t_x °C						Benzene					
A' 20 to	7.35847	5				Ether					
B' 95 °C	1843.0	5				n-Heptane					
C'	217.6	5	B^v to			Ethanol					
A'* 20 to	1.85051	5	A^v °C			Water					
B'* 95 °C	1743.6	5	(B^v) to			Water in					
Ac 235 to	7.4469	5	(A^v) °C								
Bc t_c °C	2031.1	5	c_p liq. °K								
Cc	249.2	5	c_p vap. °K								
Cryos. A°											
consts. B°			c_p vap. °K								
t_e °C	218.83	5	c_v vap.								
$T_R = 0.76 T_c$						+ grams/100 grams solvent					

REFERENCES: 1-Dow 2-API 3-Lit. 4-Calc. from det. data 5-Calc. by formula

SOURCE: API

PURIFICATION: API

LITERATURE REFERENCES:

No. 52

NAME	1-Isobutyl-3-methylbenzene			STRUCTURAL FORMULA
	m-Isobutyltoluene			$CH_2CH(CH_3)_2$

| Mole % Pur. | Ref. | Molecular Formula $C_{11}H_{16}$ | Molecular Weight 148.238 | |

		Ref.				Ref.				Ref.
F.P. °C			dt/dP °C/mm				f		to	
F.P. 100%			25°C	22.030	5		g		°K	
B.P. °C			BP	0.0545	5		h			
760 mm	194.	2	t_e	0.0364	5		f'		to	
100	124.8	5					g'		°K	
30	94.2	5	30 mm	0.7680	5		h'			
10	70.8	5	ΔHm cal/g							
1	32.	5	ΔHv cal/g				m		to	
Pressure			25°C	85.46	5		n		°K	
mm 25°C	0.6332	5	30 mm	78.52	5		o			
t_e	1273.	5	BP	66.73	5					
Density			t_e	64.26	5		m'		to	
g/ml 20°C	0.8536	2	t_e (d, e)	64.07	5		n'		°K	
d_4^t 25	0.8497	2	$ΔHv/T_e$	19.45	5		o'			
30	0.8458	4	d | 95 to	89.64	5		Surface tension			
a	0.8692	4	e | 215 °C	0.1181	5		dynes/cm. 20°C	28.74	5	
b	-0.0378	4	d' | 20 to	87.97	5		30	27.70	5	
Ref. Index			e' | 95 °C	0.1004	5		40	26.69	5	
n_D 20°C	1.4888	2	d_c g/ml	0.269	5		Parachor [P]			
25	1.4865	2	v_c ml/g	3.72	5		20°C			
30	1.4840	4	t_c °C	389.1	5		30			
"C"	0.7545	4	P_c mm	18962.	5		40 Sugd.	402.1	5	
MR (Obs.)	50.10	2	PV/RT				Exp. L.1.%/wt.			
MR (Calc.)	49.397	5	25°C	1.0000	5		u.			
(nD-d/2)	1.0620	2	30 mm	1.0000	5		Dispersion	163.	2	
Dielectric	2.217	5	BP	0.9497	5		Flash Point °C			
A | 95 to	7.00299	5	t_e	0.9341	5		Fire Point			
B | 230 °C	1620.0	5	t_c	0.246	5		M Spec.			
C	199.	5	ΔHc kcal/m				Ultra V.			
A* | 95 to	1.49044	5	ΔHf				X-Ray Dif.			
B* | 225 °C	1525.2	5	ΔFf				Infrared			
K			Viscosity				Solubility in +			
c			centistokes				Acetone			
t_k | to			η °C				Carbon tet.			
t_x | °C							Benzene			
A' | 20 to	7.35112	5					Ether			
B' | 95 °C	1830.5	5					n-Heptane			
C'	217.5	5	B^v | to				Ethanol			
A'* 20 to	1.84449	5	A^v | °C				Water			
B'* 95 °C	1731.6	5	(B^v) | to				Water in			
Ac | 230 to	7.4392	4	(A^v) | °C							
Bc | t_c °C	2016.0	5	c_p liq. °K							
Cc	248.6	5	c_p vap. °K							
Cryos. A° consts. B°										
t_e °C	216.57	5	c_v vap.							

$T_R = 0.76 T_c$ + grams/100 grams solvent

REFERENCES: 1-Dow 2-API 3-Lit. 4-Calc. from det. data 5-Calc. by formula

SOURCE:	API
PURIFICATION:	API
LITERATURE REFERENCES:	

TABLE I. ALKYL AND HALO BENZENES

No. 53

NAME	1-Isobutyl-4-methylbenzene	STRUCTURAL FORMULA
	p-Isobutyltoluene	$CH_2CH(CH_3)_2$

Mole % Pur.	Ref.	Molecular Formula $C_{11}H_{16}$	Molecular Weight 148.238	CH_3

		Ref.			Ref.			Ref.
F.P. °C			dt/dP			f	to	
F.P. 100%			°C/mm			g	___ °K	
B.P. °C			25°C	24.052	5	h		
760 mm	196.	2	BP	0.0547	5	f'	to	
100	126.6	5	t_e	0.0364	5	g'	___ °K	
30	95.8	5	30 mm	0.7713	5	h'		
10	72.3	5	ΔHm cal/g			m	to	
1	33.	5	ΔHv cal/g			n	___ °K	
Pressure			25°C	85.97	5	o		
mm 25°C	0.5765	5	30 mm	78.88	5	m'	to	
t_e	1278.	5	BP	66.97	5	n'	___ °K	
Density			t_e	64.53	5	o'		
g/ml 20°C	0.8517	2	t_e (d, e)	64.26	5	Surface tension		
d_4^t 25	0.8478	2	ΔHv/T_e	19.44	5	dynes/cm. 20°C	28.49	5
30	0.8439	4	d 95 to	90.26	5	ɤ 30	27.46	5
a	0.8673	4	e 220 °C	0.1188	5	40	26.45	5
b	-0.0₃78	4	d' 20 to	88.47	5	Parachor [P]		
Ref. Index			e' 95 °C	0.1002	5	20°C		
n_D 20°C	1.4874	2	d_c g/ml	0.269	5	30		
25	1.4851	2	v_c ml/g	3.72	5	40		
30	1.4829	4	t_c °C	391.6	5	Sugd.	402.1	5
"C"	0.7546	4	P_c mm	18953.	5	Exp. L. l. %/wt.		
MR (Obs.)	50.09	2	PV/RT			u.		
MR (Calc.)	49.397	5	25°C	1.0000	5	Dispersion		
(nD-d/2)	1.0616	2	30 mm	1.0000	5	Flash Point °C		
Dielectric	2.212	5	BP	0.9482	5	Fire Point		
A 95 to	7.00990	5	t_e	0.9333	5	M. Spec.		
B 230 °C	1631.0	5	t_c	0.246	5	Ultra V.		
C	199.	5	ΔHc kcal/m			X-Ray Dif.		
A* 95 to	1.49634	5	ΔHf			Infrared		
B* 230 °C	1535.9	5	ΔFf			Solubility in +		
K			Viscosity			Acetone		
c			centistokes			Carbon tet.		
t_k to			η °C			Benzene		
t_x °C						Ether		
A' 20 to	7.35847	5				n-Heptane		
B' 95 °C	1843.0	5	B^v to			Ethanol		
C'	217.6	5	A^v °C			Water		
A'* 20 to	1.85051	5	(B^v) to			Water in		
B'* 95 °C	1743.6	5	(A^v) °C					
Ac 230 to	7.4463	5	c_p liq. °K					
Bc t_c °C	2028.9	5						
Cc	248.7	5	c_p vap. °K					
Cryos. A°								
consts. B°			c_v vap.					
t_e °C	218.83	5						

$T_R = 0.76 T_c$ + grams/100 grams solvent

REFERENCES: 1-Dow 2-API 3-Lit. 4-Calc. from det. data 5-Calc. by formula
SOURCE: API
PURIFICATION: API
LITERATURE REFERENCES:

No. 54

NAME	1-tert-Butyl-2-methylbenzene	STRUCTURAL FORMULA
	o-tert-Butyltoluene	$C(CH_3)_3$ CH_3

Mole % Pur.	Ref.	Molecular Formula	$C_{11}H_{16}$	Molecular Weight 148.238

		Ref.
F.P. °C	-50.32	2
F.P. 100%		
B.P. °C		
760 mm	200.45	2
100	130.43	5
30	99.38	5
10	75.6	5
1	35.9	5
Pressure mm 25°C	0.4680	5
t_e	1289.	5
Density g/ml 20°C	0.8897	2
d^t_4 25	0.8858	2
30	0.8819	4
a	0.9053	4
b	-0.0$_3$78	4
Ref. Index n_D 20°C	1.5076	2
25	1.5053	2
30	1.5028	4
"C"	0.7500	4
MR (Obs.)	49.63	2
MR (Calc.)	49.397	5
(nD-d/2)	1.0628	2
Dielectric	2.273	5
A | 100 to	7.02535	5
B |_240 °C	1655.5	5
C	199.	5
A*| 100 to	1.50872	5
B*|_235 °C	1559.6	5
K		
c		
t_k | to		
t_x | °C		
A' | 25 to	7.37489	5
B' |_100 °C	1870.7	5
C'	217.8	5
A'* | 25 to	1.86402	5
B'* | 100 °C	1770.5	5
Ac | 240 to	7.4646	5
Bc | t_c °C	2065.2	5
Cc	250.5	5
Cryos. A°		
consts. B°		
t_e °C	223.85	5

$T_R = 0.76 T_c$

		Ref.
dt/dP °C/mm		
25°C	29.241	5
BP	0.0551	5
t_e	0.0364	5
30 mm	0.7785	5
ΔHm cal/g		
ΔHv cal/g		
25°C	87.10	5
30 mm	79.67	5
BP	67.82	5
t_e	65.21	5
t_e (d, e)	65.08	5
$\Delta Hv/T_e$	19.45	5
d | 100 to	91.33	5
e |_225_ °C	0.1173	5
d' | 25 to	89.59	5
e' | 100 °C	0.0998	5
d_c g/ml	0.269	5
v_c ml/g	3.72	5
t_c °C	404.2	5
P_c mm	20417.	5
PV/RT		
25°C	1.0000	5
30 mm	1.0000	5
BP	0.9490	5
t_e	0.9320	5
t_c	0.246	5
ΔHc kcal/m		
ΔHf		
ΔFf		
Viscosity centistokes η °C		
B^v | to		
A^v | °C		
(B^v) | to		
(A^v) | °C		
c_p liq. °K		
c_p vap. °K		
c_v vap.		

			Ref.
f		to °K	
g			
h			
f'		to °K	
g'			
h'			
m		to °K	
n			
o			
m'		to °K	
n'			
o'			
Surface tension dynes/cm. 20°C	33.92		5
γ 30	32.75		5
40	31.60		5
Parachor [P] 20°C			
30			
40			
Sugd.	402.1		5
Exp. L.1.%/wt. u.			
Dispersion			
Flash Point °C			
Fire Point			
M Spec.			
Ultra V.			
X-Ray Dif.			
Infrared			
Solubility in +			
Acetone			
Carbon tet.			
Benzene			
Ether			
n-Heptane			
Ethanol			
Water			
Water in			

+ grams/100 grams solvent

REFERENCES: 1-Dow 2-API 3-Lit. 4-Calc. from det. data 5-Calc. by formula

SOURCE: API

PURIFICATION: API

LITERATURE REFERENCES:

No. 55

NAME	1-tert-Butyl-3-methylbenzene	STRUCTURAL FORMULA
	m-tert-Butyltoluene	$C(CH_3)_3$ ... CH_3

Mole % Pur.	Ref.	Molecular Formula $C_{11}H_{16}$	Molecular Weight 148.238

Column 1

		Ref.
F.P. °C	-41.370	2
F.P. 100%		
B.P. °C		
760 mm	189.26	2
100	120.69	5
30	90.35	5
10	67.2	5
1	28.4	5
Pressure mm 25°C	0.7890	5
t_e	1261.	5
Density g/ml 20°C	0.8657	2
d_4^t 25	0.8618	2
30	0.8579	4
a	0.8813	4
b	$-0.0_3 78$	4
Ref. Index n_D 20°C	1.4944	2
25	1.4921	2
30	1.4895	4
"C"	0.7516	4
MR (Obs.)	49.88	2
MR (Calc.)	49.397	5
(nD-d/2)	1.0616	2
Dielectric	2.233	5
A 90 to	6.98672	5
B 225 °C	1594.2	5
C	199.	5
A* 90 to	1.47761	5
B* 220 °C	1500.3	5
K		
c		
t_k to		
t_x °C		
A' 15 to	7.33382	5
B' 90 °C	1801.4	5
C'	217.2	5
A'* 15 to	1.83036	5
B'* 90 °C	1703.3	5
Ac 225 to	7.4224	5
Bc t_c °C	1986.6	5
Cc	248.5	5
Cryos. A° consts. B°		
t_e °C	211.23	5

Column 2

		Ref.
dt/dP °C/mm		
25°C	17.929	5
BP	0.0540	5
t_e	0.0364	5
30 mm	0.7603	5
ΔHm cal/g		
ΔHv cal/g		
25°C	84.27	5
30 mm	77.68	5
BP	66.00	5
t_e	63.58	5
t_e (d, e)	63.40	5
ΔHv/T_e	19.46	5
d 90 to	88.36	5
e 215 °C	0.1181	5
d' 15 to	86.88	5
e' 90 °C	0.1008	5
d_c g/ml	0.269	5
v_c ml/g	3.72	5
t_c °C	384.5	5
P_c mm	19225.	5
PV/RT		
25°C	1.0000	5
30 mm	1.0000	5
BP	0.9507	5
t_e	0.9353	5
t_c	0.246	5
ΔHc kcal/m		
ΔHf		
ΔFf		
Viscosity centistokes η °C		
B^v to		
A^v °C		
(B^v) to		
(A^v) °C		
c_p liq. °K		
c_p vap. °K		
c_v vap.		

Column 3

			Ref.
f to			
g °K			
h			
f' to			
g' °K			
h'			
m to			
n °K			
o			
m' to			
n' °K			
o'			
Surface tension dynes/cm. 20°C	30.41		5
γ 30	29.32		5
40	28.27		5
Parachor [P] 20°C			
30			
40			
Sugd.	402.1		5
Exp. L.1.%/wt. u.			
Dispersion			
Flash Point °C			
Fire Point			
M. Spec.			
Ultra V.			
X-Ray Dif.			
Infrared			
Solubility in +			
Acetone			
Carbon tet.			
Benzene			
Ether			
n-Heptane			
Ethanol			
Water			
Water in			

$T_R = 0.76 T_c$

+ grams/100 grams solvent

REFERENCES: 1-Dow 2-API 3-Lit. 4-Calc. from det. data 5-Calc. by formula

SOURCE: API

PURIFICATION: API

LITERATURE REFERENCES:

No. 56

NAME	1-tert-Butyl-4-methylbenzene	STRUCTURAL FORMULA
	p-tert-Butyltoluene	$C(CH_3)_3$ ... CH_3

Mole % Pur.	Ref.	Molecular Formula $C_{11}H_{16}$	Molecular Weight 148.238

Column 1

	Value	Ref.
F.P. °C	-52.515	2
F.P. 100%		
B.P. °C		
760 mm	192.76	2
100	123.72	5
30	93.16	5
10	69.8	5
1	30.7	5
Pressure mm 25°C	0.6710	5
t_e	1270.	5
Density g/ml 20°C	0.8612	2
d_4^t 25	0.8573	2
30	0.8534	4
a	0.8768	4
b	-0.0378	4
Ref. Index n_D 20°C	1.4918	2
25	1.4895	2
30	1.4871	4
"C"	0.7522	4
MR (Obs.)	49.92	2
MR (Calc.)	49.397	5
(nD-d/2)	1.0612	2
Dielectric	2.225	5
A 90 to	6.99872	5
B 230 °C	1613.2	5
C	199.	5
A* 90 to	1.48683	5
B* 225 °C	1518.5	5
K		
c		
t_k to		
t_x °C		
A' 15 to	7.34658	5
B' 90 °C	1822.9	5
C'	217.4	5
A'* 15 to	1.84078	5
B'* 90 °C	1724.1	5
Ac 230 to	7.4344	5
Bc t_c °C	2008.5	5
Cc	248.7	5
Cryos. A°		
consts. B°		
t_e °C	215.18	5
$T_R = 0.76 T_c$		

Column 2

	Value	Ref.
dt/dP °C/mm		
25°C	20.865	5
BP	0.0544	5
t_e	0.0364	5
30 mm	0.7660	5
ΔHm cal/g		
ΔHv cal/g		
25°C	85.15	5
30 mm	78.30	5
BP	66.57	5
t_e	64.09	5
t_e (d, e)	63.93	5
ΔHv/T_e	19.45	5
d 90 to	89.27	5
e 220 °C	0.1178	5
d' 15 to	87.66	5
e' 90 °C	0.1005	5
d_c g/ml	0.269	5
v_c ml/g	3.72	5
t_c °C	388.7	5
P_c mm	19185.	5
PV/RT 25°C	1.0000	5
30 mm	1.0000	5
BP	0.9503	5
t_e	0.9345	5
t_c	0.246	5
ΔHc kcal/m		
ΔHf		
ΔFf		
Viscosity centistokes η °C		
B^v to		
A^v °C		
(B^v) to		
(A^v) °C		
c_p liq. °K		
c_p vap. °K		
c_v vap.		

Column 3

	Value	Ref.
f to / g °K / h		
f' to / g' °K / h'		
m to / n °K / o		
m' to / n' °K / o'		
Surface tension dynes/cm. 20°C	29.78	5
γ 30	28.71	5
40	27.67	5
Parachor [P] 20°C		
30		
40		
Sugd.	402.1	5
Exp. L.1.%/wt. u.		
Dispersion	170.	2
Flash Point °C		
Fire Point		
M Spec.		
Ultra V.		
X-Ray Dif.		
Infrared		
Solubility in +		
Acetone		
Carbon tet.		
Benzene		
Ether		
n-Heptane		
Ethanol		
Water		
Water in		

+ grams/100 grams solvent

REFERENCES: 1-Dow 2-API 3-Lit. 4-Calc. from det. data 5-Calc. by formula

SOURCE: API

PURIFICATION: API

LITERATURE REFERENCES:

TABLE I.   ALKYL AND HALO BENZENES

67

No. 57

NAME	1-Ethyl-2-n-propylbenzene		STRUCTURAL FORMULA

STRUCTURAL FORMULA

C_2H_5
C_3H_7

Mole % Pur.	Ref.	Molecular Formula $C_{11}H_{16}$	Molecular Weight 148.238

		Ref.			Ref.			Ref.
F.P. °C			dt/dP			f | to		
F.P. 100%			°C/mm			g | °K		
B.P. °C			25°C	32.748	5	h		
760 mm	203.	2	BP	0.0553	5			
100	132.7	5	t_e	0.0364	5	f' | to		
30	101.5	5	30 mm	0.7827	5	g' | °K		
10	77.6	5	ΔHm cal/g			h'		
1	38.	5						
Pressure			ΔHv cal/g			m | to		
mm 25°C	0.4148	5	25°C	87.75	5	n | °K		
t_e	1295.	5	30 mm	80.14	5	o		
Density			BP	68.17	5			
g/ml 20°C	0.8744	2	t_e	65.54	5	m' | to		
d_4^t 25	0.8705	2	t_e (d, e)	65.37	5	n' | °K		
30	0.8666	4	ΔHv/T_e	19.44	5	o'		
a	0.8900	4	d | 100 to	92.10	5	Surface tension		
b	-0.0₃78	4	e | 230 °C	0.1179	5	dynes/cm. 20°C	31.65	5
			d' | 25 to	90.24	5	γ 30	30.53	5
Ref. Index			e' | 100 °C	0.0996	5	40	29.45	5
n_D 20°C	1.4992	2	d_c g/ml	0.269	5	Parachor [P]		
25	1.4969	2	v_c ml/g	3.72	5	20°C		
30	1.4945	4	t_c °C	405.2	5	30		
"C"	0.7512	4	P_c mm	19960.	5	40		
MR (Obs.)	49.79	2	PV/RT			Sugd.	402.1	5
MR (Calc.)	49.397	5	25°C	1.0000	5	Exp. L. l. %/wt.		
(nD-d/2)	1.0620	2	30 mm	1.0000	5	u.		
Dielectric	2.248	5	BP	0.9478	5	Dispersion		
A | 100 to	7.03426	5	t_e	0.9310	5	Flash Point °C		
B | 240 °C	1669.7	5	t_c	0.245	5	Fire Point		
C	199.	5	ΔHc kcal/m			M. Spec.		
A* | 100 to	.1.51649	5	ΔHf			Ultra V.		
B* | 235 °C	1573.5	5	ΔFf			X-Ray Dif.		
K						Infrared		
c			Viscosity			Solubility in +		
t_k | to			centistokes			Acetone		
t_x | °C			η °C			Carbon tet.		
A' | 25 to	7.38436	5				Benzene		
B' | 100 °C	1886.7	5				Ether		
C'	217.9	5	B^v | to			n-Heptane		
A'* 25 to	1.87181	5	A^v | °C			Ethanol		
B'* 100 °C	1786.1	5	(B^v)| to			Water		
Ac | 240 to	7.4731	5	(A^v)| °C			Water in		
Bc | t_c °C	2079.6	5	c_p liq. °K					
Cc	250.2	5						
Cryos. A°			c_p vap. °K					
consts. B°								
t_e °C	226.72	5	c_v vap.					

$T_R = 0.76 T_c$

+ grams/100 grams solvent

REFERENCES: 1-Dow   2-API   3-Lit.   4-Calc. from det. data   5-Calc. by formula

SOURCE:	API
PURIFICATION:	API

LITERATURE REFERENCES:

No. 58

NAME	1-Ethyl-3-n-propylbenzene		STRUCTURAL FORMULA

C_2H_5

C_3H_7

Mole % Pur.	Ref.	Molecular Formula $C_{11}H_{16}$	Molecular Weight 148.238

		Ref.			Ref.					Ref.
F.P. °C			dt/dP			f	| to			
F.P. 100%			°C/mm			g	| °K			
			25°C	29.975	5	h				
B.P. °C			BP	0.0551	5					
760 mm	201.	2	t_e	0.0364	5	f'	| to			
100	130.9	5	30 mm	0.7795	5	g'	| °K			
30	99.8	5	ΔHm cal/g			h'				
10	76.1	5								
1	36.	5	ΔHv cal/g			m	| to			
Pressure			25°C	87.24	5	n	| °K			
mm 25°C	0.4558	5	30 mm	79.78	5	o				
t_e	1290.	5	BP	67.88	5					
Density			t_e	65.25	5	m'	| to			
g/ml 20°C	0.8607	2	t_e (d,e)	65.12	5	n'	| °K			
d_4^t 25	0.8568	2	ΔHv/T_e	19.43	5	o'				
30	0.8529	4				Surface tension				
a	0.8763	4	d | 100 to	91.51	5	dynes/cm. 20°C		29.71	5
b	-0.0378	4	e | 225 °C	0.1176	5	γ	30	28.65	5
Ref. Index			d' | 25 to	89.73	5		40	27.61	5
n_D 20°C	1.4930	2	e' | 100 °C	0.0998	5				
25	1.4907	2				Parachor [P]			
30	1.4882	4	d_c g/ml	0.269	5	20°C			
"C"	0.7543	4	v_c ml/g	3.72	5	30			
MR (Obs.)	50.05	2	t_c °C	400.1	5	40			
MR (Calc.)	49.397	5	P_c mm	19415.	5	Sugd.	402.1	5	
(nD-d/2)	1.0626	2	PV/RT			Exp. L.l.%/wt.			
Dielectric	2.229	5	25°C	1.0000	5	u.			
			30 mm	1.0000	5	Dispersion			
A | 100 to	7.02727	5	BP	0.9488	5	Flash Point °C			
B | 240 °C	1658.6	5	t_e	0.9316	5	Fire Point			
C	199.	5	t_c	0.245	5				
			ΔHc kcal/m			M Spec.			
A* | 100 to	1.51071	5	ΔHf			Ultra V.			
B* | 230 °C	1562.7	5	ΔFf			X-Ray Dif.			
K			Viscosity			Infrared			
c			centistokes			Solubility in +			
t_k | to			η °C			Acetone			
t_x | °C						Carbon tet.			
A' | 25 to	7.37693	5				Benzene			
B' | 100 °C	1874.2	5				Ether			
C'	217.8	5	B^V | to			n-Heptane			
A'* 25 to	1.86569	5	A^V | °C			Ethanol			
B'* 100 °C	1773.9	5	(B^V)| to			Water			
Ac | 240 to	7.4639	5	(A^V)| °C			Water in			
Bc | t_c °C	2062.6	5	c_p liq. °K						
Cc	249.4	5							
Cryos. A°			c_p vap. °K						
consts. B°									
t_e °C	224.47	5	c_v vap.						

$T_R = 0.76 T_c$ ⁺grams/100 grams solvent

REFERENCES: 1-Dow 2-API 3-Lit. 4-Calc. from det. data 5-Calc. by formula

SOURCE:	API
PURIFICATION:	API
LITERATURE REFERENCES:	

TABLE I. ALKYL AND HALO BENZENES 69

No. 59

NAME	1-Ethyl-4-n-propylbenzene		STRUCTURAL FORMULA

STRUCTURAL FORMULA
C_2H_5

C_3H_7

Mole % Pur.	Ref.	Molecular Formula $C_{11}H_{16}$	Molecular Weight 148.238

		Ref.			Ref.				Ref.
F.P. °C			dt/dP			f	to		
F.P. 100%			°C/mm			g	°K		
B.P. °C			25°C	35.774	5	h			
760 mm	205.	2	BP	0.0555	5				
100	134.4	5	t_e	0.0364	5	f'	to		
30	103.1	5	30 mm	0.7859	5	g'	°K		
10	79.1	5	ΔHm cal/g			h'			
1	39.	5	ΔHv cal/g			m	to		
Pressure			25°C	88.26	5	n	°K		
mm 25°C	0.3775	5	30 mm	80.50	5	o			
t_e	1300.	5	BP	68.46	5				
Density			t_e	65.83	5	m'	to		
g/ml 20°C	0.8594	2	t_e (d, e)	65.62	5	n'	°K		
d_4^t 25	0.8555	2	ΔHv/T_e	19.43	5	o'			
30	0.8516	4	d ⎸105 to	92.68	5	Surface tension			
a	87.50	4	e ⎸230 °C	0.1182	5	dynes/cm. 20°C	29.53	5
b	-0.0378	4	d' ⎸25 to	90.75	5	δ 30	28.47	5
Ref. Index			e' ⎸105 °C	0.0994	5	40	27.44	5
n_D 20°C	1.4921	2	d_c g/ml	0.269	5	Parachor [P]		
25	1.4898	2	v_c ml/g	3.72	5	20°C		
30	1.4874	2	t_c °C	405.4	5	30		
"C"	0.7542	4	P_c mm	19495.	5	40		
MR (Obs.)	50.05	2	PV/RT			Sugd.	402.1	5
MR (Calc.)	49.397	5	25°C	1.0000	5	Exp. L.l.%/wt.		
(nD-d/2)	1.0624	2	30 mm	1.0000	5	u.		
Dielectric	2.226		BP	0.9471	5	Dispersion		
A ⎸100 to	7.04127	5	t_e	0.9305	5	Flash Point °C		
B ⎸250 °C	1680.8	5	t_c	0.245	5	Fire Point		
C	199.	5	ΔHc kcal/m			M. Spec.		
A* ⎸100 to	1.52201	5	ΔHf			Ultra V.		
B* ⎸240 °C	1584.2	5	ΔFf			X-Ray Dif.		
K			Viscosity			Infrared		
c			centistokes			Solubility in +		
t_k ⎸ to			η °C			Acetone		
t_x ⎸ °C						Carbon tet.		
A' ⎸25 to	7.39181	5				Benzene		
B' ⎸100 °C	1899.3	5				Ether		
C'	218.0	5	B^v ⎸ to			n-Heptane		
A'* 25 to	1.87797	5	A^v ⎸ °C			Ethanol		
B'* 100 °C	1798.3	5	(B^v)⎸ to			Water		
Ac ⎸250 to	7.5235	5	(A^v)⎸ °C			Water in		
Bc ⎸t_c °C	2141.0	5	c_p liq. °K					
Cc	256.7	5						
Cryos. A°			c_p vap. °K					
consts. B°								
t_e °C	228.98	5	c_v vap.					

T_R = 0.77 T_c + grams/100 grams solvent

REFERENCES: 1-Dow 2-API 3-Lit. 4-Calc. from det. data 5-Calc. by formula

SOURCE: API

PURIFICATION: API

LITERATURE REFERENCES:

No. 60

NAME	1-Ethyl-2-isopropylbenzene	STRUCTURAL FORMULA
	o-Ethylcumene	

Mole % Pur.	Ref.	Molecular Formula $C_{11}H_{16}$	Molecular Weight 148.238	

Structural formula: benzene ring with C_2H_5 and $CH(CH_3)_2$ substituents.

		Ref.				Ref.							Ref.
F.P. °C			dt/dP				f		to				
F.P. 100%			°C/mm				g		°K				
B.P. °C			25°C	21.082	5		h						
760 mm	193.	2	BP	0.0544	5								
100	123.9	5	t_e	0.0364	5		f'		to				
30	93.4	5	30 mm	0.7664	5		g'		°K				
10	70.0	5	ΔHm cal/g				h'						
1	31.	5	ΔHv cal/g				m		to				
Pressure			25°C	85.21	5		n		°K				
mm 25°C	0.6636	5	30 mm	78.34	5		o						
t_e	1271.	5	BP	66.64	5								
Density			t_e	64.15	5		m'		to				
g/ml 20°C	0.888	2	t_e (d, e)	64.01	5		n'		°K				
d_4^t 25	0.884	2	ΔHv/T_e	19.46	5		o'						
30	0.880	4	d 95 to	89.30	5		Surface tension					
a	0.904	4	e 220 °C	0.1174	5		dynes/cm. 20°C			33.66	5
b	-0.0₃8	4	d' 20 to	87.72	5		30			32.46	5
Ref. Index			e' 95 °C	0.1005	5		40			31.30	5
n_D 20°C	1.508	2	d_c g/ml	0.269	5		Parachor [P]					
25	1.506	2	v_c ml/g	3.72	5		20°C					
30	1.503	4	t_c °C	392.8	5		30					
"C"	0.7519	4	P_c mm	19989.	5		40					
MR (Obs.)	49.8	2	PV/RT				Sugd.	402.1	5
MR (Calc.)	49.397	5	25°C	1.0000	5		Exp. L.1.%/wt.					
(nD-d/2)	1.064	2	30 mm	1.0000	5		u.					
Dielectric	2.274	5	BP	0.9506	5		Dispersion	160.				2
A 90 to	6.99955	5	t_e	0.9345	5		Flash Point °C					
B 235 °C	1614.5	5	t_c	0.246	5		Fire Point					
C	199.	5	ΔHc kcal/m				M Spec.					
A* 90 to	1.48738	5	ΔHf				Ultra V.					
B* 225 °C	1519.8	5	ΔFf				X-Ray Dif.					
K			Viscosity				Infrared					
c			centistokes				Solubility in +					
t_k to			η °C				Acetone					
t_x °C							Carbon tet.					
A' 15 to	7.34746	5					Benzene					
B' 90 °C	1824.3	5					Ether					
C'	217.4	5	B^v to				n-Heptane					
A'* 15 to	1.84150	5	A^v °C				Ethanol					
B'* 90 °C	1725.5	5	(B^v) to				Water					
Ac 235 to	7.2793	5	(A^v) °C				Water in					
Bc t_c °C	1865.3	5	c_p liq. °K									
Cc	231.3	5										
Cryos. A°			c_p vap. °K									
consts. B°												
t_e °C	215.45	5	c_v vap.									

$T_R = 0.76 T_c$ + grams/100 grams solvent

REFERENCES: 1-Dow 2-API 3-Lit. 4-Calc. from det. data 5-Calc. by formula

SOURCE:	API
PURIFICATION:	API

LITERATURE REFERENCES:

TABLE I. ALKYL AND HALO BENZENES

No. 61

NAME	1-Ethyl-3-isopropylbenzene m-Ethylcumene		STRUCTURAL FORMULA
Mole % Pur.	Ref.	Molecular Formula $C_{11}H_{16}$ Molecular Weight 148.238	C_2H_5 , $CH(CH_3)_2$

		Ref.			Ref.				Ref.
F.P. °C			dt/dP			f	to		
F.P. 100%			°C/mm			g	°K		
			25°C	20.194	5	h			
B.P. °C			BP	0.0543	5				
760 mm	192.0	2	t_e	0.0364	5	f'	to		
100	123.1	5				g'	°K		
30	92.6	5	30 mm	0.7648	5	h'			
10	69.2	5	ΔHm cal/g						
1	30.	5	ΔHv cal/g			m	to		
Pressure			25°C	84.96	5	n	°K		
mm 25°C	0.6948	5	30 mm	78.17	5	o			
t_e	1268.	5	BP	66.46	5	m'	to		
Density			t_e	63.97	5	n'	°K		
g/ml 20°C	0.859	2	t_e (d, e)	63.83	5	o'			
d_4^t 25	0.855	2	ΔHv/T_e	19.45	5	Surface tension			
30	0.851	4	d 90 to	89.06	5	dynes/cm. 20°C	29.48	5
a	0.875	4	e 215 °C	0.1177	5	ɤ 30	28.39	5
b	-0.0₃8	4	d' 15 to	87.47	5	40	27.34	5
Ref. Index			e' 90 °C	0.1005	5				
n_D 20°C	1.492	2	d_c g/ml	0.269	5	Parachor [P]			
25	1.490	2	v_c ml/g	3.72	5	20°C			
30	1.487	4	t_c °C	386.7	5	30			
"C"	0.7544	4	P_c mm	18967.	5	40			
MR (Obs.)	50.1	2	PV/RT				Sugd.	402.1	5
MR (Calc.)	49.397	5	25°C	1.0000	5	Exp. L.1.%/wt.			
(nD-d/2)	1.062	2	30 mm	1.0000	5	u.			
Dielectric	2.226	5	BP	0.9507	5	Dispersion	161.	2
A 90 to	6.99611	5	t_e	0.9345	5	Flash Point °C			
B 230 °C	1609.1	5	t_c	0.246	5	Fire Point			
C	199.	5	ΔHc kcal/m			M. Spec.			
A* 90 to	1.48510	5	ΔHf			Ultra V.			
B* 220 °C	1514.7	5	ΔFf			X-Ray Dif.			
K			Viscosity			Infrared			
c			centistokes			Solubility in			
t_k to			η °C			Acetone			
t_x °C						Carbon tet.			
A' 20 to	7.34381	5				Benzene			
B' 90 °C	1818.2	5				Ether			
C'	217.4	5	B^v to			n-Heptane			
A'* 20 to	1.83850	5	A^v °C			Ethanol			
B'* 90 °C	1719.6	5	(B^v) to			Water			
Ac 230 to	7.4329	5	(A^v) °C			Water in			
Bc t_c °C	2003.0	5	c_p liq. °K						
Cc	248.4	5							
Cryos. A°			c_p vap. °K						
consts. B°									
t_e °C	214.32	5	c_v vap.						
$T_R = 0.76 T_c$						grams/100 grams solvent			

REFERENCES: 1-Dow 2-API 3-Lit. 4-Calc. from det. data 5-Calc. by formula

SOURCE: API

PURIFICATION: API

LITERATURE REFERENCES:

No. 62

NAME	1-Ethyl-4-isopropylbenzene		STRUCTURAL FORMULA
	p-Ethylcumene		

Structural formula: C_2H_5 ... $CH(CH_3)_2$

Mole % Pur.	Ref.	Molecular Formula $C_{11}H_{16}$		Molecular Weight 148.238	

		Ref.				Ref.					Ref.
F.P. °C			dt/dP				f	to			
F.P. 100%			°C/mm				g	°K			
			25°C	24.693	5		h				
B.P. °C			BP	0.0547	5						
760 mm	196.6	2	t_e	0.0364	5		f'	to			
100	127.1	5	30 mm	0.7723	5		g'	°K			
30	96.3	5	ΔHm cal/g				h'				
10	72.7	5									
1	33.	5	ΔHv cal/g				m	to			
			25°C	86.12	5		n	°K			
Pressure			30 mm	78.98	5		o				
mm 25°C	0.5605	5	BP	67.19	5						
t_e	1279.	5	t_e	64.62	5		m'	to			
			t_e (d, e)	64.49	5		n'	°K			
Density							o'				
g/ml 20°C	0.8585	2	ΔHv/T_e	19.44	5		Surface tension				
d_4^t 25	0.8546	2					dynes/cm. 20°C		29.41	5
30	0.8507	4	d 95 to	90.30	5		γ 30		28.35	5
a	0.8741	4	e 220 °C	0.1176	5		40		27.32	5
b	-0.0378	4	d' 15 to	88.63	5						
			e' 95 °C	0.1001	5		Parachor [P]				
Ref. Index			d_c g/ml	0.269	5		20°C				
n_D 20°C	1.4923	2	v_c ml/g	3.72	5		30				
25	1.4900	2	t_c °C	393.6	5		40				
30	1.4875	4	P_c mm	19206.	5		Sugd.	402.1		5
"C"	0.7553	4	PV/RT				Exp. L. l.%/wt.				
MR (Obs.)	50.12	2	25°C	1.0000	5		u.				
MR (Calc.)	49.397	5	30 mm	1.0000	5		Dispersion	163.		2
(nD-d/2)	1.0630	2	BP	0.9498	5		Flash Point °C				
Dielectric	2.227	5	t_e	0.9331	5		Fire Point				
A 95 to	7.01198	5	t_c	0.246	5		M Spec.				
B 235 °C	1634.3	5	ΔHc kcal/m				Ultra V.				
C	199.	5	ΔHf				X-Ray Dif.				
A* 95 to	1.49804	5	ΔFf				Infrared				
B* 230 °C	1539.1	5	Viscosity				Solubility in +				
K			centistokes				Acetone				
c			η °C				Carbon tet.				
t_k to							Benzene				
t_x °C							Ether				
A' 20 to	7.36068	5					n-Heptane				
B' 95 °C	1846.7	5	B^v to				Ethanol				
C'	217.6	5	A^v °C				Water				
A'* 20 to	1.85233	5	(B^v) to				Water in				
B'* 95 °C	1747.3	5	(A^v) °C								
Ac 235 to	7.4491	5	c_p liq. °K								
Bc t_c °C	2034.4	5									
Cc	249.0	5	c_p vap. °K								
Cryos. A°											
consts. B°			c_v vap.								
t_e °C	219.51	5									

$T_R = 0.76 T_c$ + grams/100 grams solvent

REFERENCES: 1-Dow   2-API   3-Lit.   4-Calc. from det. data   5-Calc. by formula

SOURCE:	API
PURIFICATION:	API
LITERATURE REFERENCES:	

TABLE I. ALKYL AND HALO BENZENES 73

No. 63

NAME	1,2-Dimethyl-3-n-propylbenzene	STRUCTURAL FORMULA
	3-Propyl-o-xylene	

Mole % Pur.	Ref.	Molecular Formula $C_{11}H_{16}$	Molecular Weight 148.238	

		Ref.				Ref.				Ref.
F.P. °C			dt/dP				f	to		
F.P. 100%			°C/mm				g	°K		
			25°C	46.159	5		h			
B.P. °C			BP	0.0560	5					
760 mm	210.7	2	t_e	0.0364	5		f'	to		
100	139.4	5	30 mm	0.7951	5		g'	°K		
30	107.7	5	ΔHm cal/g				h'			
10	83.5	5					m	to		
1	43.	5	ΔHv cal/g				n	°K		
Pressure			25°C	89.72	5		o			
mm 25°C	0.2878	5	30 mm	81.54	5					
t_e	1314.	5	BP	69.44	5		m'	to		
Density			t_e	66.66	5		n'	°K		
g/ml 20°C	0.8864	2	t_e (d, e)	66.54	5		o'			
d_4^t 25	0.8825	2	$\Delta Hv/T_e$	19.43	5		Surface tension			
30	0.8786	4	d 105 to	94.20	5		dynes/cm. 20°C	33.42	5
a	0.9020	4	e 235 °C	0.1175	5		δ 30	32.26	5
b	-0.0₃78	4	d' 20 to	92.20	5		40	31.13	5
Ref. Index			e' 105 °C	0.0989	5		Parachor [P]		
n_D 20°C	1.5075	2	d_c g/ml	0.269	5		20°C		
25	1.5053	2	v_c ml/g	3.72	5		30		
30	1.5027	4	t_c °C	418.0	5		40		
"C"	0.7526	4	P_c mm	20645.	5		Sugd.	402.1	5
MR (Obs.)	49.81	2	PV/RT				Exp. L. 1.%/wt.		
MR (Calc.)	49.397	5	25°C	1.0000	5		u.		
(nD-d/2)	1.0643	2	30 mm	1.0000	5		Dispersion	166.	2
Dielectric	2.273	5	BP	0.9467	5		Flash Point °C		
A 105 to	7.06138	5	t_e	0.9284	5		Fire Point		
B 250 °C	1712.8	5	t_c	0.245	5		M. Spec.		
C	199.	5	ΔHc kcal/m				Ultra V.		
A* 105 to	1.53914	5	ΔHf				X-Ray Dif.		
B* 245 °C	1615.4	5	ΔFf				Infrared		
K			Viscosity				Solubility in +		
c			centistokes				Acetone		
t_k to			η °C				Carbon tet.		
t_x °C							Benzene		
A' 20 to	7.41319	5					Ether		
B' 105 °C	1935.4	5					n-Heptane		
C'	218.3	5	B^v to				Ethanol		
A'* 20 to	1.89564	5	A^v °C				Water		
B'* 105 °C	1833.4	5	(B^v) to				Water in		
Ac 250 to	7.5021	5	(A^v) °C						
Bc t_c °C	2133.5	5	c_p liq. °K						
Cc	251.4	5							
Cryos. A°			c_p vap. °K						
consts. B°									
t_e °C	235.41	5	c_v vap.						

$T_R = 0.76\,T_c$ + grams/100 grams solvent

REFERENCES: 1-Dow 2-API 3-Lit. 4-Calc. from det. data 5-Calc. by formula

SOURCE: API

PURIFICATION: API

LITERATURE REFERENCES:

NAME	1,2-Dimethyl-4-n-propylbenzene	STRUCTURAL FORMULA

4-Propyl-o-xylene

Mole % Pur.	Ref.	Molecular Formula $C_{11}H_{16}$	Molecular Weight 148.238

Structural formula: benzene ring with CH_3, CH_3, C_3H_7

		Ref.			Ref.				Ref.
F.P. °C			dt/dP			f	to		
F.P. 100%			°C/mm			g	°K		
			25°C	42.555	5	h			
B.P. °C			BP	0.0558	5				
760 mm	208.9	2	t_e	0.0364	5	f'	to		
100	137.8	5	30 mm	0.7922	5	g'	°K		
30	106.2	5	ΔHm cal/g			h'			
10	82.1	5							
1	42.	5	ΔHv cal/g			m	to		
			25°C	89.26	5	n	°K		
Pressure			30 mm	81.21	5	o			
mm 25°C	0.3138	5	BP	69.11	5				
t_e	1310.	5	t_e	66.41	5	m'	to		
Density			t_e (d,e)	66.23	5	n'	°K		
g/ml 20°C	0.8715	2	ΔHv/T_e	19.43	5	o'			
d_4^t 25	0.8676	2	d 105 to	93.73	5	Surface tension			
30	0.8637	4	e 235 °C	0.1178	5	dynes/cm. 20°C	31.23	5
a	0.8871	4	d' 20 to	91.74	5	30	30.13	5
b	-0.0₃78	4	e' 105 °C	0.0991	5	40	29.05	5
Ref. Index			d_c g/ml	0.269	5	Parachor [P]		
n_D 20°C	1.5000	2	v_c ml/g	3.72	5	20°C		
25	1.4978	2	t_c °C	413.0	5	30		
30	1.4953	4	P_c mm	20053.	5	40		
"C"	0.7549	4				Sugd.	402.1	5
MR (Obs.)	50.03	2	PV/RT			Exp. L.1.%/wt.		
MR (Calc.)	49.397	5	25°C	1.0000	5	u.		
(nD-d/2)	1.0642	2	30 mm	1.0000	5	Dispersion	168.	2
Dielectric	2.250	5	BP	0.9466	5	Flash Point °C		
A 105 to	7.05501	5	t_e	0.9294	5	Fire Point		
B 250 °C	1702.6	5	t_c	0.245	5	M Spec.		
C	199.	5	ΔHc kcal/m			Ultra V.		
A* 105 to	1.53322	5	ΔHf			X-Ray Dif.		
B* 240 °C	1605.3	5	ΔFf			Infrared		
K			Viscosity			Solubility in +		
t_c			centistokes			Acetone		
t_k to			η °C			Carbon tet.		
t_x °C						Benzene		
A' 20 to	7.40642	5				Ether		
B' 105 °C	1923.9	5	B^v to			n-Heptane		
C'	218.3	5	A^v °C			Ethanol		
A'* 20 to	1.89005	5	(B^v) to			Water		
B'* 105 °C	1822.2	5	(A^v) °C			Water in		
Ac 250 to	7.4947	5	c_p liq. °K					
Bc t_c °C	2118.7	5						
Cc	250.7	5	c_p vap. °K					
Cryos. A°								
consts. B°			c_v vap.					
t_e °C	233.38	5						
$T_R = 0.76 T_c$						+ grams/100 grams solvent		

REFERENCES: 1-Dow   2-API   3-Lit.   4-Calc. from det. data   5-Calc. by formula

SOURCE:	API
PURIFICATION:	API

LITERATURE REFERENCES:

TABLE I. ALKYL AND HALO BENZENES

No. 65

| NAME | 1,3-Dimethyl-2-n-propylbenzene | STRUCTURAL FORMULA |
| | 2-Propyl-m-xylene | |

Structural formula shown with ring: CH_3, C_3H_7, CH_3

| Mole % Pur. | Ref. | Molecular Formula | $C_{11}H_{16}$ | Molecular Weight 148.238 |

		Ref.			Ref.				Ref.
F.P. °C			dt/dP			f	to		
F.P. 100%			°C/mm			g	°K		
			25°C	40.190	5	h			
B.P. °C			BP	0.0557	5				
760 mm	207.6	2	t_e	0.0364	5	f'	to		
100	136.7	5	30 mm	0.7902	5	g'	°K		
30	105.2	5				h'			
10	81.1	5	ΔHm cal/g			m	to		
1	41.	5				n	°K		
			ΔHv cal/g			o			
Pressure			25°C	88.93	5				
mm 25°C	0.3335	5	30 mm	80.97	5	m'	to		
t_e	1306.	5	BP	68.92	5	n'	°K		
Density			t_e	66.21	5	o'			
g/ml 20°C	0.8856	2	t_e (d, e)	66.06	5	Surface tension			
d_4^t 25	0.8817	2	ΔHv/T_e	19.43	5	dynes/cm. 20°C	33.30	5
30	0.8778	4				ɤ 30	32.14	5
a	0.9012	4	d 105 to	93.36	5	40	31.01	5
b	-0.0378	4	e 235 °C	0.1177	5	Parachor [P]			
			d' 20 to	91.41	5	20°C			
Ref. Index			e' 105 °C	0.0992	5	30			
n_D 20°C	1.5063	2				40			
25	1.5041	2	d_c g/ml	0.269	5	Sugd.	402.1	5
30	1.5015	4	v_c ml/g	3.72	5				
"C"	0.7516	4	t_c °C	413.5	5	Exp. L.1.%/wt.			
MR (Obs.)	49.76	2	P_c mm	20509.	5	u.			
MR (Calc.)	49.397	5	PV/RT			Dispersion	166.	2
(nD-d/2)	1.0635	2	25°C	1.0000	5	Flash Point °C			
Dielectric	2.269	5	30 mm	1.0000	5	Fire Point			
A 105 to	7.05042	5	BP	0.9470	5				
B 250 °C	1695.4	5	t_e	0.9293	5	M. Spec.			
C	199.	5	t_c	0.245	5	Ultra V.			
A* 105 to	1.53012	5	ΔHc kcal/m			X-Ray Dif.			
B* 240 °C	1598.5	5	ΔHf			Infrared			
K			ΔFf			Solubility in +			
c			Viscosity			Acetone			
t_k to			centistokes			Carbon tet.			
t_x °C			η °C			Benzene			
A' 20 to	7.40154	5				Ether			
B' 105 °C	1915.7	5				n-Heptane			
C'	218.2	5	B^v to			Ethanol			
A'* 20 to	1.88600	5	A^v °C			Water			
B'* 105 °C	1814.3	5	(B^v) to			Water in			
Ac 250 to	7.4908	5	(A^v) °C						
Bc t_c °C	2112.7	5	c_p liq. °K						
Cc	251.1	5							
Cryos. A°			c_p vap. °K						
consts. B°									
t_e °C	231.91	5	c_v vap.						

$T_R = 0.76 T_c$

+ grams/100 grams solvent

REFERENCES: 1-Dow 2-API 3-Lit. 4-Calc. from det. data 5-Calc. by formula

SOURCE: _____ API

PURIFICATION: _____ API

LITERATURE REFERENCES:

No. 66

NAME	1,3-Dimethyl-4-n-propylbenzene	STRUCTURAL FORMULA
	4-Propyl-m-xylene	

| Mole % Pur. | Ref. | Molecular Formula $C_{11}H_{16}$ | Molecular Weight 148.238 | |

		Ref.			Ref.				Ref.
F.P. °C			dt/dP			f	to		
F.P. 100%			°C/mm			g	°K		
B.P. °C			25°C	38.437	5	h			
760 mm	206.6	2	BP	0.0556	5				
100	135.8	5	t_e	0.0364	5	f'	to		
30	104.4	5				g'	°K		
10	80.3	5	30 mm	0.7885	5	h'			
1	40.	5	ΔHm cal/g						
Pressure			ΔHv cal/g			m	to		
mm 25°C	0.3497	5	25°C	88.67	5	n	°K		
t_e	1304.	5	30 mm	80.79	5	o			
Density			BP	68.77	5				
g/ml 20°C	0.8723	2	t_e	66.05	5	m'	to		
d_4^t 25	0.8684	2	t_e (d, e)	65.93	5	n'	°K		
30	0.8645	4	ΔHv/T_e	19.43	5	o'			
a	0.8879	4	d | 105 to	93.07	5	Surface tension			
b	-0.0378	4	e | 230 °C	0.1176	5	dynes/cm. 20°C	31.34	5
Ref. Index			d' | 20 to	91.15	5	ɣ 30	30.24	5
n_D 20°C	1.4998	2	e' | 105 °C	0.0993	5	40	29.16	5
25	1.4976	2	d_c g/ml	0.269	5	Parachor [P]			
30	1.4950	4	v_c ml/g	3.72	5	20°C			
"C"	0.7539	4	t_c °C	409.9	5	30			
MR (Obs.)	49.97	2	P_c mm	20000.	5	40			
MR (Calc.)	49.397	5	PV/RT			Sugd.	402.1	5
(nD-d/2)	1.0637	2	25°C	1.0000	5	Exp. L.1.%/wt.			
Dielectric	2.249	5	30 mm	1.0000	5	u.			
A | 105 to	7.04689	5	BP	0.9475	5	Dispersion	166.	2
B |245 °C	1689.8	5	t_e	0.9297	5	Flash Point °C			
C	199.	5	t_c	0.245	5	Fire Point			
A* | 105 to	1.52717	5	ΔHc kcal/m			M Spec.			
B* |240 °C	1593.1	5	ΔHf			Ultra V.			
K			ΔFf			X-Ray Dif.			
c						Infrared			
t_k | to			Viscosity			Solubility in +			
t_x | °C			centistokes			Acetone			
A' | 20 to	7.39779	5	η °C			Carbon tet.			
B' |105 °C	1909.4	5				Benzene			
C'	218.1	5				Ether			
A'* 20 to	1.88289	5				n-Heptane			
B'* 105 °C	1808.2	5				Ethanol			
			B^v | to			Water			
Ac |245 to	7.4867	5	A^v | °C			Water in			
Bc | t_c °C	2103.8	5	(B^v)| to						
Cc	250.5	5	(A^v)| °C						
Cryos. A°			c_p liq. °K						
consts. B°			c_p vap. °K						
t_e °C	230.78	5	c_v vap.						

$T_R = 0.76 T_c$

+ grams/100 grams solvent

REFERENCES: 1-Dow 2-API 3-Lit. 4-Calc. from det. data 5-Calc. by formula

SOURCE: API

PURIFICATION: API

LITERATURE REFERENCES:

TABLE I. ALKYL AND HALO BENZENES 77

No. 67

NAME	1,3-Dimethyl-5-n-propylbenzene	STRUCTURAL FORMULA
	5-propyl-m-xylene	

Mole % Pur.	Ref.	Molecular Formula $C_{11}H_{16}$	Molecular Weight 148.238	

STRUCTURAL FORMULA

$$H_7C_3 \diagdown \bigcirc \diagup CH_3 \quad CH_3$$

		Ref.			Ref.			Ref.
F.P. °C	-59.1	2	dt/dP			f to		
F.P. 100%			°C/mm			g °K		
			25°C	31.671	5	h		
B.P. °C			BP	0.0552	5			
760 mm	202.24	2	t_e	0.0364	5	f' to		
100	132.0	5				g' °K		
30	100.8	5	30 mm	0.7815	5	h'		
10	77.0	5	ΔHm cal/g					
1	37.	5				m to		
			ΔHv cal/g			n °K		
Pressure			25°C	87.56	5	o		
mm 25°C	0.4299	5	30 mm	80.00	5			
t_e	1293.	5	BP	68.17	5	m' to		
Density			t_e	65.41	5	n' °K		
g/ml 20°C	0.8607	2	t_e (d, e)	65.42	5	o'		
d_4^t 25	0.8568	2	ΔHv/T_e	19.43	5	Surface tension		
30	0.8529	4	d 100 to	91.76	5	dynes/cm. 20°C	29.71	5
a	0.8763	4	e 230 °C	0.1166	5	δ 30	28.65	5
b	-0.0378	4	d' 20 to	90.05	5	40	27.61	5
Ref. Index			e' 100 °C	0.0996	5	Parachor [P]		
n_D 20°C	1.4952	2	d_c g/ml	0.269	5	20°C		
25	1.4930	2	v_c ml/g	3.72	5	30		
30	1.4904	4	t_c °C	401.8	5	40		
"C"	0.7575	4	P_c mm	19452.	5	Sugd.	402.1	5
MR (Obs.)	50.24	2	PV/RT			Exp. L.1.%/wt.		
MR (Calc.)	49.397	5	25°C	1.0000	5	u.		
(nD-d/2)	1.0648	2	30 mm	1.0000	5	Dispersion	168.	2
Dielectric	2.236	5	BP	0.9499	5	Flash Point °C		
A 100 to	7.03160	5	t_e	0.9311	5	Fire Point		
B 240 °C	1665.5	5	t_c	0.246	5			
C	199.	5	ΔHc kcal/m			M. Spec.		
A* 100 to	1.51448	5	ΔHf			Ultra V.		
B* 235 °C	1569.5	5	ΔFf			X-Ray Dif.		
K						Infrared		
c			Viscosity			Solubility in +		
t_k to			centistokes			Acetone		
t_x °C			η °C			Carbon tet.		
A' 20 to	7.38153	5				Benzene		
B' 100 °C	1882.0	5				Ether		
C'	217.9	5	B^v to			n-Heptane		
A'* 20 to	1.86948	5	A^v °C			Ethanol		
B'* 100 °C	1781.5	5	(B^v) to			Water		
Ac 240 to	7.4686	5	(A^v) °C			Water in		
Bc t_c °C	2071.0	5	c_p liq. °K					
Cc	249.5	5						
Cryos. A°			c_p vap. °K					
consts. B°								
t_e °C	225.87	5	c_v vap.					

$T_R = 0.76 T_c$ + grams/100 grams solvent

REFERENCES: 1-Dow 2-API 3-Lit. 4-Calc. from det. data 5-Calc. by formula

SOURCE: API

PURIFICATION: API

LITERATURE REFERENCES:

No. 68

NAME	1,4-Dimethyl-2-n-propylbenzene	STRUCTURAL FORMULA
	2-Propyl-p-xylene	

| Mole % Pur. | Ref. | Molecular Formula $C_{11}H_{16}$ | Molecular Weight 148.238 | |

		Ref.				Ref.				Ref.
F.P. °C			dt/dP °C/mm				f	to °K		
F.P. 100%			25°C	34.680	5		g			
B.P. °C			BP	0.0554	5		h			
760 mm	204.3	2	t_e	0.0364	5		f'	to °K		
100	133.8	5	30 mm	0.7848	5		g'			
30	102.5	5	ΔHm cal/g				h'			
10	78.6	5	ΔHv cal/g				m	to °K		
1	38.	5	25°C	88.08	5		n			
Pressure			30 mm	80.37	5		o			
mm 25°C	0.3902	5	BP	68.42	5		m'	to °K		
t_e	1298.	5	t_e	65.74	5		n'			
Density			t_e (d, e)	65.61	5		o'			
g/ml 20°C	0.8717	2	ΔHv/T_e	19.44	5		Surface tension			
d_4^t 25	0.8678	2	d 100 to	92.41	5		dynes/cm. 20°C	31.26	5	
30	0.8639	4	e 230 °C	0.1174	5		ɣ 30	30.15	5	
a	0.8873	4	d' 20 to	90.57	5		40	29.08	5	
b	-0.0₃78	4	e' 100 °C	0.0995	5		Parachor [P]			
Ref. Index			d_c g/ml	0.269	5		20°C			
n_D 20°C	1.4999	2	v_c ml/g	3.72	5		30			
25	1.4977	2	t_c °C	406.6	5		40			
30	1.4951	4	P_c mm	19909.	5		Sugd.	402.1	5	
"C"	0.7546	4	PV/RT				Exp. L.1.%/wt.			
MR (Obs.)	50.03	2	25°C	1.0000	5		u.			
MR (Calc.)	49.397	2	30 mm	1.0000	5		Dispersion	168.	2	
(nD-d/2)	1.0640	2	BP	0.9481	5		Flash Point °C			
Dielectric	2.250	5	t_e	0.9307	5		Fire Point			
A 100 to	7.03881	5	t_c	0.246	5		M Spec.			
B 245 °C	1676.9	5	ΔHc kcal/m				Ultra V.			
C	199.	5	ΔHf				X-Ray Dif.			
A* 100 to	1.51999	5	ΔFf				Infrared			
B* 235 °C	1580.4	5	Viscosity				Solubility in +			
K			centistokes				Acetone			
c			η °C				Carbon tet.			
t_k to							Benzene			
t_x °C							Ether			
A' 20 to	7.38920	5					n-Heptane			
B' 100 °C	1894.8	5	B^v to				Ethanol			
C'	218.0	5	A^v °C				Water			
A'* 20 to	1.87581	5	(B^v) to				Water in			
B'* 100 °C	1794.0	5	(A^v) °C							
Ac 245 to	7.4776	5	c_p liq. °K							
Bc t_c °C	2087.7	5								
Cc	250.2	5	c_p vap. °K							
Cryos. A° consts. B°			c_v vap.							
t_e °C	228.19	5								

$T_R = 0.76 T_c$ + grams/100 grams solvent

REFERENCES: 1-Dow   2-API   3-Lit.   4-Calc. from det. data   5-Calc. by formula

SOURCE: API

PURIFICATION: API

LITERATURE REFERENCES:

TABLE I. ALKYL AND HALO BENZENES

NAME	1, 2-Dimethyl-3-isopropylbenzene	STRUCTURAL FORMULA
	2, 3-Dimethylcumene	

Structural formula: benzene ring with CH_3, CH_3, $CH(CH_3)_2$ substituents

Mole % Pur.	Ref.	Molecular Formula $C_{11}H_{16}$	Molecular Weight 148.238

		Ref.				Ref.				Ref.
F.P. °C			dt/dP				f $\quad$ to			
F.P. 100%			°C/mm				g $\quad$ °K			
B.P. °C			25°C	32.180	5		h			
760 mm	202.6	2	BP	0.0553	5		f' $\quad$ to			
100	132.3	5	t_e	0.0364	5		g' $\quad$ °K			
30	101.1	5	30 mm	0.7821	5		h'			
10	77.3	5	ΔHm cal/g				m $\quad$ to			
1	37.	5	ΔHv cal/g				n $\quad$ °K			
Pressure			25°C	87.65	5		o			
mm 25°C	0.4226	5	30 mm	80.07	5					
t_e	1294.	5	BP	68.07	5		m' $\quad$ to			
Density			t_e	65.49	5		n' $\quad$ °K			
g/ml 20°C	0.888	2	t_e (d, e)	65.28	5		o'			
d_4^t 25	0.884	2	ΔHv/T_e	19.44	5		Surface tension			
30	0.880	4	d $\quad$ 100 to	92.02	5		dynes/cm. 20°C	33.66	5
a	0.904	4	e $\quad$ 230 °C	0.1182	5		ƴ $\quad$ 30	32.46	5
b	-0.0₃8	4	d' $\quad$ 20 to	90.14	5		40	31.30	5
Ref. Index			e' $\quad$ 100 °C	0.0996	5					
n_D 20°C	1.508	2	d_c g/ml	0.269	5		Parachor [P]			
25	1.506	2	v_c ml/g	3.72	5		20°C			
30	1.503	4	t_c °C	406.3	5		30			
"C"	0.7519	4	P_c mm	20296.	5		40			
MR (Obs.)	49.8	2					Sugd.	402.1	5
MR (Calc.)	49.397	5	PV/RT				Exp. L.1.%/wt.			
(nD-d/2)	1.064	2	25°C	1.0000	5		u.			
Dielectric	2.274	5	30 mm	1.0000	5		Dispersion	166.·	2
A 100 to	7.03286	5	BP	0.9474	5		Flash Point °C			
B 245 °C	1667.5	5	t_e	0.9310	5		Fire Point			
C	199.	5	t_c	0.245	5		M. Spec.			
A* 100 to	1.51552	5	ΔHc kcal/m				Ultra V.			
B* 235 °C	1571.4	5	ΔHf				X-Ray Dif.			
K			ΔFf				Infrared			
c			Viscosity				Solubility in +			
t_k to			centistokes				Acetone			
t_x °C			η °C				Carbon tet.			
A' 20 to	7.38287	5					Benzene			
B' 100 °C	1884.2	5					Ether			
C'	217.9	5	B^v to				n-Heptane			
A'* 20 to	1.87058	5	A^v °C				Ethanol			
B'* 100 °C	1783.7	5	(B^v) to				Water			
Ac 245 to	7.4704	5	(A^v) °C				Water in			
Bc t_c °C	2076.8	5	c_p liq. °K							
Cc	250.3	5								
Cryos. A°			c_p vap. °K							
consts. B°										
t_e °C	226.27	5	c_v vap.							

$T_R = -0.76\,T_c$

+ grams/100 grams solvent

REFERENCES: 1-Dow 2-API 3-Lit. 4-Calc. from det. data 5-Calc. by formula

SOURCE: $\qquad$ API

PURIFICATION: $\qquad$ API

LITERATURE REFERENCES:

NAME	1,2-Dimethyl-4-isopropylbenzene	STRUCTURAL FORMULA
	3,4-Dimethylcumene	

Mole % Pur.	Ref.	Molecular Formula $C_{11}H_{16}$	Molecular Weight 148.238

Structural formula: benzene ring with CH_3, CH_3 and $CH(CH_3)_2$ substituents

		Ref.				Ref.				Ref.
F.P. °C			dt/dP °C/mm			f		to	
F.P. 100%			25°C	31.044	5	g		°K	
B.P. °C			BP	0.0552	5	h			
760 mm	201.8	2	t_e	0.0364	5	f'		to	
100	131.6	5	30 mm	0.7807	5	g'		°K	
30	100.5	5	ΔHm cal/g			h'			
10	76.7	5	ΔHv cal/g			m		to	
1	37.	5	25°C	87.44	5	n		°K	
Pressure			30 mm	79.92	5	o			
mm 25°C	0.4391	5	BP	68.00	5	m'		to	
t_e	1292.	5	t_e	65.38	5	n'		°K	
Density			t_e (d, e)	65.23	5	o'			
g/ml 20°C	0.8699	2	ΔHv/T_e	19.44	5	Surface tension			
d_4^t 25	0.8660	2	d 100 to	91.74	5	dynes/cm. 20°C	31.00	5
30	0.8621	4	e 225 °C	0.1176	5	γ 30	29.90	5
a	0.8855	4	d' 20 to	89.94	5	40	28.83	5
b	-0.0378	4	e' 100 °C	0.0997	5	Parachor [P]		
Ref. Index			d_c g/ml	0.269	5	20°C		
n_D 20°C	1.4993	2	v_c ml/g	3.72	5	30		
25	1.4971	2	t_c °C	402.8	5	40		
30	1.4945	4	P_c mm	19765.	5	Sugd.	402.1	5
"C"	0.7553	4	PV/RT			Exp. L.1.%/wt.		
MR (Obs.)	50.06	2	25°C	1.0000	5	u.		
MR (Calc.)	49.397	5	30 mm	1.0000	5	Dispersion	167.	2
(nD-d/2)	1.0644	2	BP	0.9484	5	Flash Point °C		
Dielectric	2.248	5	t_e	0.9315	5	Fire Point		
A 100 to	7.03006	5	t_c	0.246	5	M Spec.		
B 240 °C	1663.	5	ΔHc kcal/m			Ultra V.		
C	199.	5	ΔHf			X-Ray Dif.		
A* 100 to	1.51274	5	ΔFf			Infrared		
B* 235 °C	1566.9	5	Viscosity			Solubility in +		
K			centistokes			Acetone		
c			η °C			Carbon tet.		
t_k to						Benzene		
t_x °C						Ether		
A' 20 to	7.37990	5				n-Heptane		
B' 100 °C	1879.1	5				Ethanol		
C'	217.9	5	B^v to			Water		
A'* 20 to	1.86814	5	A^v °C			Water in		
B'* 100 °C	1778.8	5	(B^v) to					
Ac 240 to	7.4665	5	(A^v) °C					
Bc t_c °C	2068.8	5	c_p liq. °K					
Cc	249.7	5	c_p vap. °K					
Cryos. A°								
consts. B°								
t_e °C	225.37	5	c_v vap.					

$T_R = 0.76 T_C$ + grams/100 grams solvent

REFERENCES: 1-Dow 2-API 3-Lit. 4-Calc. from det. data 5-Calc. by formula

SOURCE:	API
PURIFICATION:	API
LITERATURE REFERENCES:	

TABLE I. ALKYL AND HALO BENZENES

NAME	1,3-Dimethyl-2-isopropylbenzene	STRUCTURAL FORMULA
	2,6-Dimethylcumene	

Mole % Pur.	Ref.	Molecular Formula $C_{11}H_{16}$	Molecular Weight 148.238	

		Ref.			Ref.			Ref.
F.P. °C			dt/dP			f | to		
F.P. 100%			°C/mm			g | °K		
B.P. °C			25°C	27.435	5	h |		
760 mm	199.	2	BP	0.0549	5			
100	129.2	5	t_e	0.0364	5	f' | to		
30	98.2	5	30 mm	0.7762	5	g' | °K		
10	75.	5	ΔHm cal/g			h' |		
1	35.	5	ΔHv cal/g			m | to		
Pressure			25°C	86.73	5	n | °K		
mm 25°C	0.5010	5	30 mm	79.41	5	o |		
t_e	1285.	5	BP	67.51	5			
Density			t_e	64.99	5	m' | to		
g/ml 20°C	0.890	2	t_e (d,e)	64.77	5	n' | °K		
d_4^t 25	0.886	2	ΔHv/T_e	19.45	5	o' |		
30	0.882	4	d | 100 to	91.01	5	Surface tension		
a	0.906	4	e | 225 °C	0.1181	5	dynes/cm. 20°C	33.97	5
b	-0.038	4	d' | 20 to	89.23	5	γ 30	32.76	5
Ref. Index			e' | 100 °C	0.0999	5	40	31.59	5
n_D 20°C	1.509	2	d_c g/ml	0.269	5	Parachor [P]		
25	1.507	2	v_c ml/g	3.72	5	20°C		
30	1.504	4	t_c °C	401.6	5	30		
"C"	0.7516	4	P_c mm	20251.	5	40		
MR (Obs.)	49.7	2	PV/RT			Sugd.	402.1	5
MR (Calc.)	49.397	5	25°C	1.0000	5	Exp. L.1.%/wt.		
(nD-d/2)	1.064	2	30 mm	1.0000	5	u.		
Dielectric	2.277	5	BP	0.9483	5	Dispersion	165.	2
A | 100 to	7.02030	5	t_e	0.9324	5	Flash Point °C		
B | 240 °C	1647.5	5	t_c	0.246	5	Fire Point		
C	199.	5	ΔHc kcal/m			M. Spec.		
A* | 100 to	1.50470	5	ΔHf			Ultra V.		
B* | 235 °C	1551.9	5	ΔFf			X-Ray Dif.		
K			Viscosity			Infrared		
c			centistokes			Solubility in +		
t_k | to			η °C			Acetone		
t_x | °C						Carbon tet.		
A' | 20 to	7.36952	5				Benzene		
B' | 100 °C	1861.6	5	B^v | to			Ether		
C'	217.7	5	A^v | °C			n-Heptane		
A'* 20 to	1.85960	5	(B^v) | to			Ethanol		
B'* 100 °C	1761.8	5	(A^v) | °C			Water		
Ac | 240 to	7.4588	5				Water in		
Bc | t_c °C	2054.6	5	c_p liq. °K					
Cc	250.2	5	c_p vap. °K					
Cryos. A°								
consts. B°								
t_e °C	222.21	5	c_v vap.					

T_R = 0.76 T_c

+ grams/100 grams solvent

REFERENCES: 1-Dow 2-API 3-Lit. 4-Calc. from det. data 5-Calc. by formula

SOURCE: API

PURIFICATION: API

LITERATURE REFERENCES:

No. 72

| NAME | 1,3-Dimethyl-4-isopropylbenzene | STRUCTURAL FORMULA |
| | 2,4-Dimethylcumene | |

Molecular Formula $C_{11}H_{16}$ Molecular Weight 148.238

Structural formula: benzene ring with CH_3, CH_3, $CH(CH_3)_2$

		Ref.			Ref.					Ref.
F.P. °C			dt/dP °C/mm			f	|	to		
F.P. 100%			25°C	27.568	5	g	|	°K		
B.P. °C			BP	0.0549	5	h	|			
760 mm	199.1	2	t_e	0.0364	5					
100	129.3	5	30 mm	0.7764	5	f'	|	to		
30	98.3	5	ΔHm cal/g			g'	|	°K		
10	75.	5	ΔHv cal/g			h'	|			
1	35.	5	25°C	86.76	5					
Pressure			30 mm	79.43	5	m	|	to		
mm 25°C	0.4984	5	BP	67.57	5	n	|	°K		
t_e	1285.	5	t_e	64.98	5	o	|			
Density			t_e (d, e)	64.84	5					
g/ml 20°C	0.873	2	ΔHv/T_e	19.44	5	m'	|	to		
d_4^t 25	0.869	2				n'	|	°K		
30	0.865	4	d | 100 to	91.00	5	o'	|			
a	0.889	4	e | 225 °C	0.1177	5	Surface tension				
b	-0.038	4	d' | 20 to	89.26	5	dynes/cm. 20°C		31.44	5
Ref. Index			e' | 100 °C	0.0999	5	γ 30		30.31	5
n_D 20°C	1.500	2	d_c g/ml	0.269	5	40		29.20	5
25	1.498	2	v_c ml/g	3.72	5	Parachor [P]			
30	1.495	4	t_c °C	398.9	5	20°C			
"C"	0.7536	4	P_c mm	19659.	5	30			
MR (Obs.)	49.9	2	PV/RT			40			
MR (Calc.)	49.397	5	25°C	1.0000	5	Sugd.	402.1	5
(nD-d/2)	1.064	2	30 mm	1.0000	5	Exp. L.1.%/wt.			
Dielectric	2.250	5	BP	0.9490	5	u.			
A | 100 to	7.02065	5	t_e	0.9321	5	Dispersion	166.	2
B | 240 °C	1648.1	5	t_c	0.245	5	Flash Point °C			
C	199.	5	ΔHc kcal/m			Fire Point			
A* | 100 to	1.50536	5	ΔHf			M Spec.			
B* | 235 °C	1552.6	5	ΔFf			Ultra V.			
K			Viscosity			X-Ray Dif.			
c			centistokes			Infrared			
t_k | to			η °C			Solubility in +			
t_x | °C						Acetone			
A' | 20 to	7.36989	5				Carbon tet.			
B' | 100 °C	1862.3	5				Benzene			
C'	217.7	5	B^V | to			Ether			
A'* 20 to	1.85990	5	A^V | °C			n-Heptane			
B'* 100 °C	1762.4	5	(B^V)| to			Ethanol			
Ac | 240 to	7.4587		(A^V)| °C			Water			
Bc | t_c °C	2052.8	5	c_p liq. °K			Water in			
Cc	249.7	5	c_p vap. °K						
Cryos. A°			c_v vap.						
consts. B°									
t_e °C	222.33	5							

$T_R = 0.76\,T_c$

grams/100 grams solvent

REFERENCES: 1-Dow 2-API 3-Lit. 4-Calc. from det. data 5-Calc. by formula

SOURCE: API

PURIFICATION: API

LITERATURE REFERENCES:

TABLE I. ALKYL AND HALO BENZENES

83

No. 73

NAME	1,3-Dimethyl-5-isopropylbenzene	STRUCTURAL FORMULA
	3,5-Dimethylcumene	

Mole % Pur.	Ref.	Molecular Formula $C_{11}H_{16}$	Molecular Weight 148.238	$(CH_3)_2HC$ —⟨⟩— CH_3 (with CH_3)

		Ref.			Ref.				Ref.
F.P. °C			dt/dP			f	| to		
F.P. 100%			°C/mm			g	| °K		
B.P. °C			25°C	23.041	5	h	|		
760 mm	194.5	2	BP	0.0543	5				
100	125.5	5	t_e	0.0362	5	f'	| to		
30	94.9	5	30 mm	0.7674	5	g'	| °K		
10	71.5	5	ΔHm cal/g			h'	|		
1	32.	5	ΔHv cal/g			m	| to		
Pressure			25°C	85.90	5	n	| °K		
mm 25°C	0.6023	5	30 mm	78.88	5	o	|		
t_e	1276.	5	BP	67.19	5				
Density			t_e	64.69	5	m'	| to		
g/ml 20°C	0.862	2	t_e (d,e)	64.53	5	n'	| °K		
d_4^t 25	0.858	2	ΔHv/T_e	19.56	5	o'	|		
30	0.854	4	d 95 to	90.00	5	Surface tension			
a	0.878	4	e | 220 °C	0.1173	5	dynes/cm. 20°C	29.89	5
b	-0.0₃8	4	d' | 20 to	88.41	5	γ 30	28.79	5
Ref. Index			e' | 95 °C	0.1006	5	40	27.73	5
n_D 20°C	1.495	2	d_c g/ml	0.269	5	Parachor [P]		
25	1.493	2	v_c ml/g	3.72	5	20°C		
30	1.490	4	t_c °C	390.7	5	30		
"C"	0.7560	4	P_c mm	19373.	5	40		
MR (Obs.)	50.2	2	PV/RT			Sugd.	402.1	5
MR (Calc.)	49.397	5	25°C	1.0000	5	Exp. L.l.%/wt.		
(nD-d/2)	1.064	2	30 mm	1.0000	5	u.		
Dielectric	2.235	5	BP	0.9513	5	Dispersion	168.	2
A | 95 to	7.02030	5	t_e	0.9356	5	Flash Point °C		
B |230 °C	1628.9	5	t_c	0.246	5	Fire Point		
C	199.	5	ΔHc kcal/m			M. Spec.		
A* | 95 to	1.50482	5	ΔHf			Ultra V.		
B* |225 °C	1533.2	5	ΔFf			X-Ray Dif.		
K			Viscosity			Infrared		
c			centistokes			Solubility in +		
t_k | to			η °C			Acetone		
t_x | °C						Carbon tet.		
A' | 20 to	7.36952	5				Benzene		
B' |95 °C	1840.6	5				Ether		
C'	217.5	5	B_v | to			n-Heptane		
A'* 20 to	1.86233	5	A_v | °C			Ethanol		
B'* 95 °C	1741.5	5	(B^v)| to			Water		
Ac| 230 to	7.4568	5	(A^v)| °C			Water in		
Bc| t_c °C	2026.3	5	c_p liq. °K					
Cc	248.6	5						
Cryos. A°			c_p vap. °K					
consts. B°								
t_e °C	217.14	5	c_v vap.					

$T_R = 0.76 T_c$

+ grams/100 grams solvent

REFERENCES: 1-Dow 2-API 3-Lit. 4-Calc. from det. data 5-Calc. by formula

SOURCE: API

PURIFICATION: API

LITERATURE REFERENCES:

No.   74

NAME	1,4-Dimethyl-2-isopropylbenzene	STRUCTURAL FORMULA
	2,5-Dimethylcumene	

Mole % Pur. | Ref. | Molecular Formula $C_{11}H_{16}$ | Molecular Weight 148.238

STRUCTURAL FORMULA

CH_3
$CH(CH_3)_2$
CH_3

		Ref.				Ref.				Ref.
F.P. °C			dt/dP				f | | to			
F.P. 100%			°C/mm				g | | °K			
B.P. °C			25°C	24.264	5		h |			
760 mm	196.2	2	BP	0.0547	5					
100	126.7	5	t_e	0.0364	5		f' | | to			
30	96.0	5					g' | | °K			
10	72.	5	30 mm	0.7716	5		h' |			
1	33.	5	ΔHm cal/g							
Pressure			ΔHv cal/g				m | | to			
mm 25°C	0.5711	5	25°C	86.02	5		n | | °K			
t_e	1278.	5	30 mm	78.91	5		o |			
Density			BP	67.14	5					
g/ml 20°C	0.8738	2	t_e	64.58	5		m' | | to			
d_4^t 25	0.8699	2	t_e (d, e)	64.45	5		n' | | °K			
30	0.8660	4	ΔHv/T_e	19.45	5		o' |			
a	0.8894	4	d | 95 to	90.18	5		Surface tension			
b	-0.0₃78	4	e | 220 °C	0.1175	5		dynes/cm. 20°C	31.56	5
Ref. Index			d' | 20 to	88.52	5		γ 30	30.45	5
n_D 20°C	1.5010	2	e' | 95 °C	0.1002	5		40	29.36	5
25	1.4988	2	d_c g/ml	0.269	5		Parachor [P]			
30	1.4963	4	v_c ml/g	3.72	5		20°C			
"C"	0.7543	4	t_c °C	395.6	5		30			
MR (Obs.)	49.98	2	P_c mm	19721.	5		40			
MR (Calc.)	49.397	5	PV/RT				Sugd.	402.1	5
(nD-d/2)	1.0641	2	25°C	1.0000	5		Exp. L.1.%/wt.			
Dielectric	2.253	5	30 mm	1.0000	5		u.			
			BP	0.9499	5		Dispersion	168.	2
A | 95 to	7.01059	5	t_e	0.9332	5		Flash Point °C			
B | 235 °C	1632.1	5	t_c	0.246	5		Fire Point			
C	199.	5	ΔHc kcal/m				M Spec.			
A* | 95 to	1.49691	5	ΔHf				Ultra V.			
B* | 230 °C	1537.0	5	ΔFf				X-Ray Dif.			
K							Infrared			
c			Viscosity				Solubility in +			
t_k | to			centistokes				Acetone			
t_x | °C			η °C				Carbon tet.			
A' | 20 to	7.35920	5					Benzene			
B' | 95 °C	1844.2	5					Ether			
C'	217.6	5	B^v | to				n-Heptane			
			A^v | °C				Ethanol			
A'* 20 to	1.85111	5	(B^v) | to				Water			
B'* 95 °C	1744.9	5	(A^v) | °C				Water in			
Ac | 235 to	7.4483	5	c_p liq. °K							
Bc | t_c °C	2034.2	5								
Cc	249.5	5	c_p vap. °K							
Cryos. A°										
consts. B°			c_v vap.							
t_e °C	219.06	5								

$T_R = 0.76 T_c$

+ grams/100 grams solvent

REFERENCES: 1-Dow   2-API   3-Lit.   4-Calc. from det. data   5-Calc. by formula

SOURCE: API

PURIFICATION: API

LITERATURE REFERENCES:

TABLE I. ALKYL AND HALO BENZENES

No. 75

NAME	2,3-Diethyl-1-methylbenzene	STRUCTURAL FORMULA
	2,3-Diethyltoluene	

Mole % Pur.	Ref.	Molecular Formula $C_{11}H_{16}$	Molecular Weight 148.238

		Ref.			Ref.				Ref.
F.P. °C			dt/dP			f	to		
F.P. 100%			°C/mm			g	___ °K		
			25°C	38.437	5	h			
B.P. °C			BP	0.0556	5				
760 mm	206.6	2	t_e	0.0364	5	f'	to		
100	135.8	5	30 mm	0.7885	5	g'	___ °K		
30	104.4	5				h'			
10	80.	5	ΔHm cal/g			m	to		
1	40.	5	ΔHv cal/g			n	___ °K		
Pressure			25°C	88.67	5	o			
mm 25°C	0.3497	5	30 mm	80.79	5				
t_e	1304.	5	BP	68.78	5	m'	to		
Density			t_e	66.07	5	n'	___ °K		
g/ml 20°C	0.8910	2	t_e (d, e)	65.94	5	o'			
d_4^t 25	0.8871	2	ΔHv/T_e	19.43	5				
30	0.8832	4				Surface tension			
a	0.9066	4	d 105 to	93.06	5	dynes/cm. 20°C	34.12	5	
b	-0.0₃78	4	e 230 °C	0.1175	5	γ 30	32.94	5	
Ref. Index			d' 20 to	91.15	5	40	31.79	5	
n_D 20°C	1.5105	2	e' 105 °C	0.0993	5				
25	1.5083	2	d_c g/ml	0.269	5	Parachor [P]			
30	1.5057	4	v_c ml/g	3.72	5	20°C			
"C"	0.7528	4	t_c °C	413.0	5	30			
MR (Obs.)	49.80	2	P_c mm	20668.	5	40			
MR (Calc.)	49.397	5				Sugd.	402.1	5	
(nD-d/2)	1.0650	2	PV/RT			Exp. L.l.%/wt.			
Dielectric	2.282	5	25°C	1.0000	5	Exp. u.			
A 105 to	7.04689	5	30 mm	1.0000	5	Dispersion	166.	2	
B 250 °C	1689.8	5	BP	0.9475	5	Flash Point °C			
C	199.	5	t_e	0.9297	5	Fire Point			
A* 105 to	1.52717	5	t_c	0.245	5	M. Spec.			
B* 240 °C	1593.1	5	ΔHc kcal/m			Ultra V.			
K			ΔHf			X-Ray Dif.			
c			ΔFf			Infrared			
t_k to			Viscosity			Solubility in +			
t_x °C			centistokes			Acetone			
A' 20 to	7.39779	5	η °C			Carbon tet.			
B' 105 °C	1909.4	5				Benzene			
C'	218.1	5				Ether			
A'* 20 to	1.88289	5	B^v to			n-Heptane			
B'* 105 °C	1808.2	5	A^v °C			Ethanol			
Ac 250 to	7.4868	5	(B^v) to			Water			
Bc t_c °C	2106.3	5	(A^v) °C			Water in			
Cc	251.1	5	c_p liq. °K						
Cryos. A°			c_p vap. °K						
consts. B°									
t_e °C	230.78	5	c_v vap.						

$T_R = 0.76 T_c$ + grams/100 grams solvent

REFERENCES: 1-Dow 2-API 3-Lit. 4-Calc. from det. data 5-Calc. by formula

SOURCE: API

PURIFICATION: API

LITERATURE REFERENCES:

No. 76

NAME	2,4-Diethyl-1-methylbenzene			STRUCTURAL FORMULA
	2,4-Diethyltoluene			

Mole % Pur.	Ref.	Molecular Formula $C_{11}H_{16}$		Molecular Weight 148.238	

		Ref.			Ref.			Ref.
F.P. °C			dt/dP			f	to	
F.P. 100%			°C/mm			g	°K	
B.P. °C			25°C	35.774	5	h		
760 mm	205.0	2	BP	0.0555	5			
100	134.4	5	t_e	0.0364	5	f'	to	
30	103.1	5	30 mm	0.7859	5	g'	°K	
10	79.	5				h'		
1	39.	5	ΔHm cal/g					
Pressure			ΔHv cal/g			m	to	
mm 25°C	0.3775	5	25°C	88.26	5	n	°K	
t_e	1300.	5	30 mm	80.50	5	o		
			BP	68.46	5			
Density			t_e	65.84	5	m'	to	
g/ml 20°C	0.8748	2	t_e (d,e)	65.63	5	n'	°K	
d_4^t 25	0.8709	2	ΔHv/T_e	19.44	5	o'		
30	0.8670	4	d 105 to	92.67	5	Surface tension		
a	0.8904	4	e 230 °C	0.1181	5	dynes/cm. 20°C	31.71	5
b	-0.0$_3$78	4	d' 20 to	90.75	5	γ 30	30.59	5
Ref. Index			e' 105 °C	0.0994	5	40	29.50	5
n_D 20°C	1.5027	2	d_c g/ml	0.269	5	Parachor [P]		
25	1.5005	2	v_c ml/g	3.72	5	20°C		
30	1.4979	4	t_c °C	408.1	5	30		
"C"	0.7558	4	P_c mm	20042.	5	40		
MR (Obs.)	50.07	2	PV/RT			Sugd.	402.1	5
MR (Calc.)	49.397	5	25°C	1.0000	5	Exp. L.1.%/wt.		
(nD-d/2)	1.0653	2	30 mm	1.0000	5	u.		
Dielectric	2.258	5	BP	0.9471	5	Dispersion	168.	2
A 100 to	7.04127	5	t_e	0.9305	5	Flash Point °C		
B 245 °C	1680.8	5	t_c	0.245	5	Fire Point		
C	199.	5	ΔHc kcal/m			M Spec.		
A* 100 to	1.52201	5	ΔHf			Ultra V.		
B* 240 °C	1584.2	5	ΔFf			X-Ray Dif.		
K			Viscosity			Infrared		
c			centistokes			Solubility in +		
t_k to			η °C			Acetone		
t_x °C						Carbon tet.		
A' 20 to	7.39181	5				Benzene		
B' 100 °C	1899.3	5				Ether		
C'	218.0	5	B^v to			n-Heptane		
A'* 20 to	1.87797	5	A^v °C			Ethanol		
B'* 100 °C	1798.3	5	(B^v) to			Water		
Ac 245 to	7.48035	5	(A^v) °C			Water in		
Bc t_c °C	2092.9	5	c_p liq. °K					
Cc	250.4	5	c_p vap. °K					
Cryos. A° consts. B°								
t_e °C	228.98	5	c_v vap.					

$T_R = 0.76 T_c$

+ grams/100 grams solvent

REFERENCES: 1-Dow 2-API 3-Lit. 4-Calc. from det. data 5-Calc. by formula

SOURCE:	API
PURIFICATION:	API

LITERATURE REFERENCES:

TABLE I. ALKYL AND HALO BENZENES

87

No. 77

| NAME | 2,5-Diethyl-1-methylbenzene | STRUCTURAL FORMULA |
| | 2,5-Diethyltoluene | |

Structural formula:

| Mole % Pur. | Ref. | Molecular Formula $C_{11}H_{16}$ | Molecular Weight 148.238 |

		Ref.			Ref.			Ref.
F.P. °C			dt/dP			f | to		
F.P. 100%			°C/mm			g | __ __°K		
			25°C	39.303	5	h |		
B.P. °C			BP	0.0557	5			
760 mm	207.1	2	t_e	0.0364	5	f' | to		
100	136.3	5	30 mm	0.7893	5	g' | __ __°K		
30	104.8	5	ΔHm cal/g			h' |		
10	81.	5						
1	40.	5	ΔHv cal/g			m | to		
Pressure			25°C	88.80	5	n | __ __°K		
mm 25°C	0.3415	5	30 mm	80.88	5	o |		
t_e	1305.	5	BP	68.78	5			
Density			t_e	66.13	5	m' | to		
g/ml 20°C	0.8758	2	t_e (d, e)	65.91	5	n' | __ __°K		
d_4^t 25	0.8719	2	ΔHv/T_e	19.43	5	o' |		
30	0.8680	4				Surface tension		
a	0.8914	4	d | 105 to	93.29	5	dynes/cm. 20°C	31.85	5
b	-0.0₃78	4	e | 230 °C	0.1183	5	ঠ 30	30.73	5
			d' | 20 to	91.28	5	40	29.64	5
Ref. Index			e' | 105 °C	0.0992	5			
n_D 20°C	1.5034	2	d_c g/ml	0.269	5	Parachor [P]		
25	1.5012	2	v_c ml/g	3.72	5	20°C		
30	1.4912	4	t_c °C	411.2	5	30		
"C"	0.7560	4	P_c mm	20141.	5	40		
MR (Obs.)	50.07	2				Sugd.	402.1	5
MR (Calc.)	49.397	5	PV/RT			Exp. L.1.%/wt.		
(nD-d/2)	1.0655	2	25°C	1.0000	5	u.		
			30 mm	1.0000	5	Dispersion	169.	2
Dielectric	2.260	5	BP	0.9463	5			
A | 105 to	7.04866	5	t_e	0.9295	5	Flash Point °C		
B | 245 °C	1692.6	5	t_c	0.245	5	Fire Point		
C	199.	5	ΔHc kcal/m			M. Spec.		
A* | 105 to	1.52863	5	ΔHf			Ultra V.		
B* | 240 °C	1595.8	5	ΔFf			X-Ray Dif.		
K						Infrared		
c			Viscosity			Solubility in +		
t_k | to			centistokes			Acetone		
t_x | °C			η °C			Carbon tet.		
A' | 20 to	7.39967	5				Benzene		
B' | 105 °C	1912.6	5				Ether		
C'	218.1	5	B^v | to			n-Heptane		
A'* 20 to	1.88445	5	A^v | °C			Ethanol		
B'* 105 °C	1811.3	5	(B^v) | to			Water		
Ac | 245 to	7.4881	5	(A^v) | °C			Water in		
Bc | t_c °C	2107.2	5						
Cc	250.6	5	c_p liq. °K					
Cryos. A°								
consts. B°			c_p vap. °K					
t_e °C	231.35	5	c_v vap.					

$T_R = 0.76 T_C$

+ grams/100 grams solvent

REFERENCES: 1-Dow 2-API 3-Lit. 4-Calc. from det. data 5-Calc. by formula

SOURCE: API

PURIFICATION: API

LITERATURE REFERENCES:

No. 78

NAME	2,6-Diethyl-1-methylbenzene	STRUCTURAL FORMULA
	2,6-Diethyltoluene	

Structural formula: CH_3, H_5C_2 — ring — C_2H_5

Mole % Pur.	Ref.	Molecular Formula $C_{11}H_{16}$	Molecular Weight 148.238

		Ref.			Ref.			Ref.
F.P. °C			dt/dP °C/mm			f | to °K		
F.P. 100%			25°C	42.390	5	g |		
B.P. °C			BP	0.0558	5	h |		
760 mm	208.8	2	t_e	0.0364	5	f' | to °K		
100	137.7	5	30 mm	0.7921	5	g' |		
30	106.2	5	ΔHm cal/g			h' |		
10	82.	5	ΔHv cal/g			m | to °K		
1	41.	5	25°C	89.24	5	n |		
Pressure mm 25°C	0.3151	5	30 mm	81.19	5	o |		
t_e	1309.	5	BP	69.15	5	m' | to °K		
Density g/ml 20°C	0.8907	2	t_e	66.39	5	n' |		
d_4^t 25	0.8868	2	t_e (d,e)	66.28	5	o' |		
30	0.8829	4	ΔHv/T_e	19.43	5	Surface tension dynes/cm. 20°C	34.07	5
a	0.9063	4	d | 105 to	93.65	5	γ 30	32.89	5
b	-0.0378	4	e | 235 °C	0.1173	5	40	31.75	5
Ref. Index n_D 20°C	1.5106	2	d' | 20 to	91.71	5	Parachor [P]		
25	1.5084	2	e' | 105 °C	0.0991	5	20°C	34.07	5
30	1.5058	4	d_c g/ml	0.269	5	30	32.89	5
"C"	0.7532	4	v_c ml/g	3.72	5	40	31.75	5
MR (Obs.)	49.83	2	t_c °C	416.1	5	Sugd.	402.1	5
MR (Calc.)	49.397		P_c mm	20737.	5	Exp. L.1.%/wt. u.		
(nD-d/2)	1.0652	2	PV/RT			Dispersion	166.	2
Dielectric	2.282	5	25°C	1.0000	5	Flash Point °C		
A | 105 to	7.05466	5	30 mm	1.0000	5	Fire Point		
B | 250 °C	1702.1	5	BP	0.9472	5	M Spec.		
C	199.	5	t_e	0.9291	5	Ultra V.		
A* | 105 to	1.53338	5	t_c	0.245	5	X-Ray Dif.		
B* | 245 °C	1605.0	5	ΔHc kcal/m			Infrared		
K			ΔHf			Solubility in +		
c			ΔFf			Acetone		
t_k | to °C			Viscosity centistokes η °C			Carbon tet.		
t_x |						Benzene		
A' | 20 to	7.40605	5				Ether		
B' | 105 °C	1923.3	5				n-Heptane		
C'	218.2	5	B^V | to			Ethanol		
A'* 20 to	1.88973	5	A^V | °C			Water		
B'* 105 °C	1821.7	5	(B^V) | to			Water in		
Ac | 250 to	7.4950	5	(A^V) | °C					
Bc | t_c °C	2121.1	5	c_p liq. °K					
Cc	251.3	5	c_p vap. °K					
Cryos. A° consts. B°			c_v vap.					
t_e °C	233.26	5						
T_R = 0.76 T_C						+ grams/100 grams solvent		

REFERENCES: 1-Dow 2-API 3-Lit. 4-Calc. from det. data 5-Calc. by formula

SOURCE: API

PURIFICATION: API

LITERATURE REFERENCES:

No. 79

NAME	3,4-Diethyl-1-methylbenzene	STRUCTURAL FORMULA
	3,4-Diethyltoluene	

Mole % Pur.	Ref.	Molecular Formula $C_{11}H_{16}$	Molecular Weight 148.238

Structural formula: benzene ring with CH_3, C_2H_5, C_2H_5 substituents

		Ref.			Ref.				Ref.
F.P. °C			dt/dP			f	to		
F.P. 100%			°C/mm			g	$\llcorner$ $\underline{\quad}$ °K		
B.P. °C			25°C	33.619	5	h			
760 mm	203.6	2	BP	0.0554	5				
100	133.2	5	t_e	0.0364	5	f'	to		
30	101.9	5	30 mm	0.7837	5	g'	$\llcorner$ $\underline{\quad}$ °K		
10	78.	5	ΔHm cal/g			h'			
1	38.	5				m	to		
Pressure			ΔHv cal/g			n	$\llcorner$ $\underline{\quad}$ °K		
mm 25°C	0.4034	5	25°C	87.90	5	o			
t_e	1297.	5	30 mm	80.24	5				
Density			BP	68.34	5	m'	to		
g/ml 20°C	0.8762	2	t_e	65.64	5	n'	$\llcorner$ $\underline{\quad}$ °K		
d_4^t 25	0.8723	2	t_e (d, e)	65.55	5	o'			
30	0.8684	4	$\Delta Hv/T_e$	19.44	5				
a	0.8918	4	d 100 to	92.18	5	Surface tension			
b	-0.0378	4	e 230 °C	0.1171	5	dynes/cm. 20°C	31.91		5
Ref. Index			d' 20 to	90.39	5	γ 30	30.79		5
n_D 20°C	1.5039	2	e' 100 °C	0.0995	5	40	29.69		5
25	1.5017	2							
30	1.4991	4	d_c g/ml	0.269	5	Parachor [P]			
"C"	0.7563	4	v_c ml/g	3.72	5	20°C			
MR (Obs.)	49.83	2	t_c °C	406.3	5	30			
MR (Calc.)	49.397	5	P_c mm	20046.	5	40			
(nD-d/2)	1.0652	2	PV/RT			Sugd.	402.1		5
Dielectric	2.262	5	25°C	1.0000	5	Exp. L.1.%/wt.			
A 100 to	7.03636	5	30 mm	1.0000	5	u.			
B 245 °C	1673.	5	BP	0.9487	5	Dispersion	166.		2
C	199.	5	t_e	0.9310	5	Flash Point °C			
A* 100 to	1.51792	5	t_c	0.245	5	Fire Point			
B* 235 °C	1576.6	5	ΔHc kcal/m			M. Spec.			
K			ΔHf			Ultra V.			
c			ΔFf			X-Ray Dif.			
t_k to			Viscosity			Infrared			
t_x °C			centistokes			Solubility in +			
A' 20 to	7.38659	5	η °C			Acetone			
B' 100 °C	1890.4	5				Carbon tet.			
C'	218.0	5				Benzene			
A'* 20 to	1.87366	5	B^v to			Ether			
B'* 100 °C	1789.7	5	A^v °C			n-Heptane			
			(B^v) $\underline{\quad}$ to			Ethanol			
Ac 245 to	7.4757	5	(A^v) °C			Water			
Bc t_c °C	2084.2	5				Water in			
Cc	250.4	5	c_p liq. °K						
Cryos. A°			c_p vap. °K						
consts. B°									
t_e °C F	227.4	5	c_v vap.						

$T_R = 0.76\,T_c$

+ grams/100 grams solvent

REFERENCES: 1-Dow 2-API 3-Lit. 4-Calc. from det. data 5-Calc. by formula

SOURCE: API

PURIFICATION: API

LITERATURE REFERENCES:

No. 80

NAME	3, 5-Diethyl-1-methylbenzene					STRUCTURAL FORMULA		
	3, 5-Diethyltoluene							

CH_3, H_5C_2, C_2H_5

Mole % Pur.		Ref.	Molecular Formula $C_{11}H_{16}$		Molecular Weight 148.238			

		Ref.				Ref.			Ref.
F.P. °C	-74.12	2	dt/dP				f	to	
F.P. 100%			°C/mm				g	°K	
			25°C		29.570	5	h		
B.P. °C			BP		0.0551	5			
760 mm	200.70	2	t_e		0.0364	5	f'	to	
100	130.7	5	30 mm		0.7790	5	g'	°K	
30	100.0	5					h'		
10	76.	5	ΔHm cal/g						
1	36.	5	ΔHv cal/g				m	to	
Pressure			25°C		87.16	5	n	°K	
mm 25°C	0.4625	5	30 mm		79.72	5	o		
t_e	1289.	5	BP		67.84	5			
Density			t_e		65.21	5	m'	to	
g/ml 20°C	0.8630	2	t_e (d, e)		65.09	5	n'	°K	
d_4^t 25	0.8591	2	ΔHv/T_e		19.44	5	o'		
30	0.8552	4	d 100 to		91.42	5	Surface tension		
a	0.8786	4	e 225 °C		0.1175	5	dynes/cm. 20°C	30.03	5
b	-0.0378	4	d' 20 to		89.66	5	ɣ 30	28.96	5
Ref. Index			e' 100 °C		0.0998	5	40	27.91	5
n_D 20°C	1.4969	2	d_c g/ml		0.269	5	Parachor [P]		
25	1.4947	2	v_c ml/g		3.72	5	20°C		
30	1.4921	4	t_c °C		400.1	5	30		
"C"	0.7579	4	P_c mm		19489.	5	40		
MR (Obs.)	50.26	2	PV/RT				Sugd.	402.1	5
MR (Calc.)	49.357	5	25°C		1.0000	5	Exp. L.1.%/wt.		
(nD-d/2)	1.0654	2	30 mm		1.0000	5	u.		
Dielectric	2.241	5	BP		0.9489	5	Dispersion	168.	2
A 100 to	7.02622	5	t_e		0.9319	5	Flash Point °C		
B 240 °C	1656.9	5	t_c		0.245	5	Fire Point		
C	199.	5	ΔHc kcal/m				M Spec.		
A* 100 to	1.50957	5	ΔHf				Ultra V.		
B* 235 °C	1561.0	5	ΔFf				X-Ray Dif.		
K			Viscosity				Infrared		
c			centistokes				Solubility in +		
t_k to			η °C				Acetone		
t_x °C							Carbon tet.		
A' 20 to	7.37581	5					Benzene		
B' 100 °C	1872.2	5					Ether		
C'	217.8	5	B^v to				n-Heptane		
A'* 20 to	1.86478	5	A^v °C				Ethanol		
B'* 100 °C	1772.1	5	(B^v) to				Water		
Ac 240 to	7.4640	5	(A^v) °C				Water in		
Bc t_c °C	2062.1	5	c_p liq. °K						
Cc	249.6	5							
Cryos. A°			c_p vap. °K						
consts. B°									
t_e °C F	224.13	5	c_v vap.						

$T_R = 0.76 T_c$ + grams/100 grams solvent

REFERENCES: 1-Dow   2-API   3-Lit.   4-Calc. from det. data   5-Calc. by formula

SOURCE: API

PURIFICATION: API

LITERATURE REFERENCES:

TABLE I. ALKYL AND HALO BENZENES

No. 81

NAME	2-Ethyl-1,3,5-trimethylbenzene	STRUCTURAL FORMULA

Structural formula: benzene ring with CH_3 (top), C_2H_5, H_3C, CH_3

Mole % Pur.	Ref.	Molecular Formula $C_{11}H_{16}$	Molecular Weight 148.238

		Ref.				Ref.					Ref.
F.P. °C	-15.5	2	dt/dP				f		to		
F.P. 100%			°C/mm				g		°K		
B.P. °C			25°C	49.824	5		h				
760 mm	212.4	2	BP	0.0562	5						
100	140.9	5	t_e	0.0364	5		f'		to		
30	109.1	5	30 mm	0.7979	5		g'		°K		
10	85.	5	ΔHm cal/g				h'				
1	44.	5	ΔHv cal/g				m		to		
Pressure			25°C	90.16	5		n		°K		
mm 25°C	0.2654	5	30 mm	81.86	5		o				
t_e	1318.	5	BP	69.60	5						
Density			t_e	66.90	5		m'		to		
g/ml 20°C	0.883	2	t_e (d,e)	66.64	5		n'		°K		
d_4^t 25	0.879	2	ΔHv/T_e	19.42	5		o'				
30	0.875	4	d 110 to	94.80	5	Surface tension					
a	0.899	4	e 240 °C	0.1187	5	dynes/cm. 20°C	32.91	5			
b	-0.0₃8	4	d' 20 to	92.63	5	ɣ 30	31.73	5			
Ref. Index			e' 110 °C	0.0988	5	40	30.59	5			
n_D 20°C	1.5074	2	d_c g/ml	0.269	5	Parachor [P]					
25	1.5052	2	v_c ml/g	3.72	5	20°C					
30	1.5025	4	t_c °C	419.2	5	30					
"C"	0.7554	4	P_c mm	20438.	5	40 Sugd.	402.1	5			
MR (Obs.)	50.0	2	PV/RT			Exp. L.1.%/wt.					
MR (Calc.)	49.397	5	25°C	1.0000	5	u.					
(nD-d/2)	1.0659	2	30 mm	1.0000	5	Dispersion	171.	2			
Dielectric	2.272	5	BP	0.9447	5	Flash Point °C					
A 110 to	7.06742	5	t_e	0.9278	5	Fire Point					
B 255 °C	1722.4	5	t_c	0.244	5	M. Spec.					
C	199.	5	ΔHc kcal/m			Ultra V.					
A* 110 to	1.54426	5	ΔHf			X-Ray Dif.					
B* 245 °C	1624.8	5	ΔFf			Infrared					
K			Viscosity			Solubility in +					
c			centistokes			Acetone					
t_k to			η °C			Carbon tet.					
t_x °C						Benzene					
A' 20 to	7.41961	5				Ether					
B' 110 °C	1946.3	5				n-Heptane					
C'	218.4	5	B^v to			Ethanol					
A'* 20 to	1.90096	5	A^v °C			Water					
B'* 110 °C	1844.0	5	(B^v) to			Water in					
Ac 255 to	7.5078	5	(A^v) °C								
Bc t_c °C	2143.4	5	c_p liq. °K								
Cc	251.2	5									
Cryos. A°			c_p vap. °K								
consts. B°											
t_e °C F	237.32	5	c_v vap.								

$T_R = 0.76 T_C$

+ grams/100 grams solvent

REFERENCES: 1-Dow 2-API 3-Lit. 4-Calc. from det. data 5-Calc. by formula

SOURCE: API

PURIFICATION: API

LITERATURE REFERENCES:

NAME	3-Ethyl-1,2,4-trimethylbenzene	STRUCTURAL FORMULA

Structural formula: CH_3, CH_3, C_2H_5, CH_3 on benzene ring

Mole % Pur.	Ref.	Molecular Formula $C_{11}H_{16}$	Molecular Weight 148.238

		Ref.				Ref.				Ref.
F.P. °C			dt/dP				f | to			
F.P. 100%			°C/mm				g | __ °K			
B.P. °C			25°C	60.204	5		h |			
760 mm	216.6	2	BP	0.0565	5					
100	144.6	5	t_e	0.0364	5		f' | to			
30	112.5	5	30 mm	0.8046	5		g' | __ °K			
10	88.	5	ΔHm cal/g				h' |			
1	47.	5								
Pressure			ΔHv cal/g				m | to			
mm 25°C	0.2170	5	25°C	91.25	5		n | __ °K			
t_e	1328.	5	30 mm	82.63	5		o |			
Density			BP	70.26	5					
g/ml 20°C	0.895	2	t_e	67.53	5		m' | to			
d_4^t 25	0.891	2	t_e (d,e)	67.24	5		n' | __ °K			
30	0.887	4	ΔHv/T_e	19.43	5		o' |			
a	0.911	4	d | 110 to	96.01	5		Surface tension		
b	-0.0₃8	4	e | 240 °C	0.1189	5		dynes/cm. 20°C	34.74	5
			d' | 20 to	93.71	5		ɤ 30	33.51	5
Ref. Index			e' | 110 °C	0.0984	5		40	32.32	5
n_D 20°C	1.5133	2							
25	1.5111	2	d_c g/ml	0.269	5		Parachor [P]		
30	1.5083	4	v_c ml/g	3.72	5		20°C		
			t_c °C	427.1	5		30		
"C"	0.7533	5	P_c mm	21022.	5		40		
MR (Obs.)	49.8	2					Sugd.	402.1	5
MR (Calc.)	49.397	5	PV/RT						
(nD-d/2)	1.0658	2	25°C	1.0000	5		Exp. L.1.%/wt.		
			30 mm	1.0000	5		u.		
Dielectric	2.290	5	BP	0.9436	5		Dispersion	171.	2
A | 110 to	7.08241	5	t_e	0.9266	5		Flash Point °C		
B |_260_°C	1746.2	5	t_c	0.244	5		Fire Point		
C	199.	5	ΔHc kcal/m				M Spec.		
			ΔHf				Ultra V.		
A* | 110 to	1.55670	5	ΔFf				X-Ray Dif.		
B* |_250_°C	1647.9	5					Infrared		
K			Viscosity				Solubility in +		
c	__		centistokes				Acetone		
t_k | to			η °C				Carbon tet.		
t_x | °C							Benzene		
A' | 20 to	7.43554	5					Ether		
B' |_110_°C	1973.1	5					n-Heptane		
C'	218.6	5	B^v | to				Ethanol		
A'* 20 to	1.91420	5	A^v | °C				Water		
B'* 110 °C	1870.1	5	(B^v) | to				Water in		
Ac | 260 to	7.5241	5	(A^v) | °C						
Bc |_t_c_°C	2174.2	5	c_p liq. °K						
Cc	252.1	5							
Cryos. A°			c_p vap. °K						
consts. B°									
t_e °C F	242.06	5	c_v vap.						

T_R = 0.76 T_C + grams/100 grams solvent

REFERENCES: 1-Dow 2-API 3-Lit. 4-Calc. from det. data 5-Calc. by formula
SOURCE: API
PURIFICATION: API
LITERATURE REFERENCES:

TABLE I. ALKYL AND HALO BENZENES

No. 83

NAME	4-Ethyl-1, 2, 3-trimethylbenzene		STRUCTURAL FORMULA

Mole % Pur.	Ref.	Molecular Formula $C_{11}H_{16}$	Molecular Weight 148.238

		Ref.			Ref.				Ref.
F.P. °C			dt/dP			f	to		
F.P. 100%			°C/mm			g	°K		
B.P. °C			25°C	71.535	5	h			
760 mm	220.4	2	BP	0.0569	5	f'	to		
100	147.9	5	t_e	0.0364	5	g'	°K		
30	115.6	5	30 mm	0.8106	5	h'			
10	91.	5	ΔHm cal/g			m	to		
1	49.	5	ΔHv cal/g			n	°K		
Pressure			25°C	92.23	5	o			
mm 25°C	0.1807	5	30 mm	83.34	5	m'	to		
t_e	1338.	5	BP	71.01	5	n'	°K		
Density			t_e	68.09	5	o'			
g/ml 20°C	0.9019	2	t_e (d, e)	67.95	5	Surface tension			
d_4^t 25	0.8980	2	ΔHv/T_e	19.43	5	dynes/cm. 20°C	35.82	5
30	0.8941	4	d 115 to	96.96	5	γ 30	34.60	5
a	0.9175	5	e 245 °C	0.1177	5	40	33.40	5
b	-0.0378	5	d' 20 to	94.68	5	Parachor [P]			
Ref. Index			e' 115 °C	0.0981	5	20°C			
n_D 20°C	1.5180	2	d_c g/ml	0.269	5	30			
25	1.5158	2	v_c ml/g	3.72	5	40			
30	1.5133	4	t_c °C	434.3	5	Sugd.	402.1	5
"C"	0.7540	4	P_c mm	21563.	5	Exp. L.1.%/wt.			
MR (Obs.)	49.81	2	PV/RT			u.			
MR (Calc.)	49.397	5	25°C	1.0000	5	Dispersion	171.	2
(nD-d/2)	1.0670	2	30 mm	1.0000	5	Flash Point °C			
Dielectric	2.304	5	BP	0.9444	5	Fire Point			
A 115 to	7.09606	5	t_e	0.9254	5	M. Spec.			
B 265 °C	1767.9	5	t_c	0.242	5	Ultra V.			
C	199.	5	ΔHc kcal/m			X-Ray Dif.			
A* 115 to	1.56826	5	ΔHf			Infrared			
B* 255 °C	1669.1	5	ΔFf			Solubility in +			
K			Viscosity			Acetone			
c			centistokes			Carbon tet.			
t_k to			η °C			Benzene			
t_x °C						Ether			
A' 20 to	7.45005	5				n-Heptane			
B' 115 °C	1997.7	5				Ethanol			
C'	218.8	5	B^v to			Water			
			A^v °C			Water in			
A'* 20 to	1.92628	5	(B^v) to						
B'*115 °C	1894.0	5	(A^v) °C						
Ac 265 to	7.5397	5	c_p liq. °K						
Bc t_c °C	2203.0	5							
Cc	252.9	5	c_p vap. °K						
Cryos. A°									
consts. B°			c_v vap.						
t_e °C F	246.35	5							

$T_R = 0.76 T_c$ + grams/100 grams solvent

REFERENCES: 1-Dow 2-API 3-Lit. 4-Calc. from det. data 5-Calc. by formula

SOURCE:	API
PURIFICATION:	API
LITERATURE REFERENCES:	

No. 84

NAME	5-Ethyl-1,2,3-trimethylbenzene					STRUCTURAL FORMULA

Mole % Pur.	Ref.	Molecular Formula $C_{11}H_{16}$		Molecular Weight 148.238		

		Ref.			Ref.				Ref.
F.P. °C			dt/dP °C/mm			f | | to			
F.P. 100%			25°C	58.039	5	g | | __ °K_			
B.P. °C			BP	0.0565	5	h |			
760 mm	215.8	2	t_e	0.0364	5				
100	143.9	5				f' | | to			
30	111.9	5	30 mm	0.8033	5	g' | | __ °K_			
10	87.	5	ΔHm cal/g			h' |			
1	46.	5	ΔHv cal/g			m | | to			
Pressure			25°C	91.04	5	n | | __ °K_			
mm 25°C	0.2256	5	30 mm	82.48	5	o |			
t_e	1327.	5	BP	70.20	5				
Density			t_e	67.42	5	m' | | to			
g/ml 20°C	0.8863	2	t_e (d, e)	67.20	5	n' | | __ °K_			
d_4^t 25	0.8824	2	ΔHv/T_e	19.43	5	o' |			
30	0.8785	4				Surface tension			
a	0.9019	4	d | 110 to	95.70	5	dynes/cm. 20°C	33.41	5
b	-0.0₃78	4	e | 240 °C	0.1182	5	γ 30	32.24	5
Ref. Index			d' | 20 to	93.50	5	40	31.11	5
n_D 20°C	1.5101	2	e' | 110 °C	0.0985	5			
25	1.5079	2	d_c g/ml	0.269	5	Parachor [P]		
30	1.5053	4	v_c ml/g	3.72	5	20°C		
"C"	0.7563	4	t_c °C	425.1	5	30		
MR (Obs.)	50.03	2	P_c mm	20822.	5	40		
MR (Calc.)	49.397	5	PV/RT			Sugd.	402.1	5
(nD-d/2)	1.0670	2	25°C	1.0000	5	Exp. L.1.%/wt.		
Dielectric	2.280	5	30 mm	1.0000	5	u.		
A | 110 to	7.07954	5	BP	0.9447	5	Dispersion	172.	2
B | 260 °C	1741.6	5	t_e	0.9271	5	Flash Point °C		
C	199.	5	t_c	0.244	5	Fire Point		
A* | 110 to	1.55391	5	ΔHc kcal/m			M Spec.		
B* | 250 °C	1643.3	5	ΔHf			Ultra V.		
K			ΔFf			X-Ray Dif.		
c						Infrared		
t_k | to			Viscosity			Solubility in +		
t_x | °C			centistokes			Acetone		
A' | 20 to	7.43249	5	η °C			Carbon tet.		
B' | 110 °C	1968.0	5				Benzene		
C'	218.6	5				Ether		
A'* 20 to	1.91167	5	B^v | to			n-Heptane		
B'* 110 °C	1865.1	5	A^v | °C			Ethanol		
Ac | 260 to	7.5215	5	(B^v) | to			Water		
Bc | t_c °C	2168.6	5	(A^v) | °C			Water in		
Cc	251.9	5	c_p liq. °K					
Cryos. A°								
consts. B°			c_p vap. °K					
t_e °C F	241.16	5	c_v vap.					

$T_R = 0.76 T_c$ + grams/100 grams solvent

REFERENCES: 1-Dow   2-API   3-Lit.   4-Calc. from det. data   5-Calc. by formula
SOURCE: API
PURIFICATION: API
LITERATURE REFERENCES:

TABLE I. ALKYL AND HALO BENZENES

95

No. 85

NAME	5-Ethyl-1,2,4-trimethylbenzene	STRUCTURAL FORMULA

Mole % Pur.	Ref.	Molecular Formula $C_{11}H_{16}$	Molecular Weight 148.238

		Ref.			Ref.			Ref.
F.P. °C	-13.5	2	dt/dP			f | to		
F.P. 100%			°C/mm			g | °K		
B.P. °C			25°C	51.191	5	h		
760 mm	213.0	2	BP	0.0562	5			
100	141.4	5	t_e	0.0364	5	f' | to		
30	109.6	5				g' | °K		
10	85.	5	30 mm	0.7988	5	h'		
1	44.	5	ΔHm cal/g			m | to		
Pressure			ΔHv cal/g			n | °K		
mm 25°C	0.2578	5	25°C	90.32	5	o		
t_e	1319.	5	30 mm	81.97	5			
Density			BP	69.76	5	m' | to		
g/ml 20°C	0.883	2	t_e	66.98	5	n' | °K		
d_4^t 25	0.879	2	t_e (d, e)	66.81	5	o'		
30	0.875	4	ΔHv/T_e	19.42	5	Surface tension		
a	0.899	4	d | 110 to	94.90	5	dynes/cm. 20°C	32.91	5
b	-0.0$_3$8	4	e | 240 °C	0.1180	5	8 30	31.73	5
Ref. Index			d' | 20 to	92.79	5	40	30.59	5
n_D 20°C	1.5075	2	e' | 110 °C	0.0987	5	Parachor [P]		
25	1.5053	2	d_c g/ml	0.269	5	20°C		
30	1.5026	4	v_c ml/g	3.72	5	30		
"C"	0.7555	4	t_c °C	420.0	5	40		
MR (Obs.)	50.0	2	P_c mm	20458.	5	Sugd.	402.1	5
MR (Calc.)	49.397	5	PV/RT			Exp. L.1.%/wt.		
(nD-d/2)	1.0660	2	25°C	1.0000	5	u.		
Dielectric	2.273	5	30 mm	1.0000	5	Dispersion	173.	2
A | 110 to	7.06955	5	BP	0.9456	5	Flash Point °C		
B | 255 °C	1725.8	5	t_e	0.9276	5	Fire Point		
C	199.	5	t_c	0.244	5	M. Spec.		
A* | 110 to	1.54611	5	ΔHc kcal/m			Ultra V.		
B* | 250 °C	1628.1	5	ΔHf			X-Ray Dif.		
K			ΔFf			Infrared		
c			Viscosity			Solubility in +		
t_k | to			centistokes			Acetone		
t_x | °C			η °C			Carbon tet.		
A' | 20 to	7.42187	5				Benzene		
B' | 110 °C	1950.1	5				Ether		
C'	218.4	5	B^v | to			n-Heptane		
A'* 20 to	1.90284	5	A^v | °C			Ethanol		
B'* 110 °C	1847.7	5	(B^v)| to			Water		
Ac | 255 to	7.5107	5	(A^v)| °C			Water in		
Bc | t_c °C	2148.3	5	c_p liq. °K					
Cc	251.4	5						
Cryos. A°			c_p vap. °K					
consts. B°								
t_e °C F	238.0	5	c_v vap.					

$T_R = 0.76 T_c$

+ grams/100 grams solvent

REFERENCES: 1-Dow 2-API 3-Lit. 4-Calc. from det. data 5-Calc. by formula

SOURCE: API

PURIFICATION: API

LITERATURE REFERENCES:

NAME	6-Ethyl-1,2,4-trimethylbenzene	STRUCTURAL FORMULA

Mole % Pur.	Ref.	Molecular Formula	$C_{11}H_{16}$	Molecular Weight 148.238

		Ref.			Ref.				Ref.
F.P. °C			dt/dP			f	| to		
F.P. 100%			°C/mm			g	| °K		
			25°C	51.191	5	h	|		
B.P. °C			BP	0.0562	5				
760 mm	213.0	2	t_e	0.0364	5	f'	| to		
100	141.4	5	30 mm	0.7988	5	g'	| °K		
30	109.6	5	ΔHm cal/g			h'	|		
10	85.	5							
1	44.	5	ΔHv cal/g			m	| to		
Pressure			25°C	90.32	5	n	| °K		
mm 25°C	0.2578	5	30 mm	81.97	5	o	|		
t_e	1319.	5	BP	69.77	5				
			t_e	66.99	5	m'	| to		
Density			t_e (d, e)	66.82	5	n'	| °K		
g/ml 20°C	0.8897	2	ΔHv/T_e	19.43	5	o'	|		
d_4^t . 25	0.8858	2				Surface tension			
30	0.8819	4	d | 110 to	94.89	5	dynes/cm. 20°C	33.92	5
a	0.9053	4	e | 240 °C	0.1180	5	30	32.75	5
b	-0.0₃78	4	d' | 20 to	92.79	5	40	31.60	5
Ref. Index			e' | 110 °C	0.0987	5	Parachor [P]		
n_D 20°C	1.5118	2	d_c g/ml	0.269	5	20°C		
25	1.5096	2	v_c ml/g	3.72	5	30		
30	1.5070	4	t_c °C	421.8	5	40		
"C"	0.7557	4	P_c mm	20844.	5	Sugd.	402.1	5
MR (Obs.)	49.98	2	PV/RT			Exp. L.1.%/wt.		
MR (Calc.)	49.397	5	25°C	1.0000	5	u.		
(nD-d/2)	1.0670	2	30 mm	1.0000	5	Dispersion	172.	2
Dielectric	2.286	5	BP	0.9456	5	Flash Point °C		
A | 110 to	7.06955	5	t_e	0.9276	5	Fire Point		
B | 255 °C	1725.8	5	t_c	0.244	5	M Spec.		
C	199.	5	ΔHc kcal/m			Ultra V.		
A* | 110 to	1.54611	5	ΔHf			X-Ray Dif.		
B* | 250 °C	1628.1	5	ΔFf			Infrared		
K			Viscosity			Solubility in +		
c			centistokes			Acetone		
t_k | to			η °C			Carbon tet.		
t_x | °C						Benzene		
A' | 20 to	7.42187	5				Ether		
B' | 110 °C	1950.1	5	B^v | to			n-Heptane		
C'	218.4	5	A^v | °C			Ethanol		
A'* 20 to	1.90284	5	(B^v) | to			Water		
B'* 110 °C	1847.7	5	(A^v) | °C			Water in		
Ac | 255 to	7.51125	5	c_p liq. °K					
Bc | t_c °C	2150.2	5						
Cc |	251.8	5	c_p vap. °K					
Cryos. A°								
consts. B°			c_v vap.					
t_e °C F	238.0	5						

$T_R = 0.76 T_c$

+ grams/100 grams solvent

REFERENCES: 1-Dow   2-API   3-Lit.   4-Calc. from det. data   5-Calc. by formula

SOURCE: API

PURIFICATION: API

LITERATURE REFERENCES:

TABLE I. ALKYL AND HALO BENZENES 97

No. 87

NAME	Pentamethylbenzene					STRUCTURAL FORMULA		
Mole % Pur.		Ref.	Molecular Formula $C_{11}H_{16}$		Molecular Weight 148.238			

Structural formula: pentamethylbenzene (benzene ring with five CH_3 groups)

		Ref.			Ref.			Ref.
F.P. °C	54.3	2	dt/dP			f | to		
F.P. 100%			°C/mm			g | °K		
			25°C	120.66	5	h |		
B.P. °C			BP	0.0578	5			
760 mm	231.8	2	t_e	0.0364	5	f' | to		
100	157.9	5				g' | °K		
30	125.0	5	30 mm	0.8285	5	h' |		
10	100.	5	ΔHm cal/g					
1	57.	5				m | to		
Pressure			ΔHv cal/g			n | °K		
mm 25°C	0.1038	5	25°C	95.21	5	o |		
t_e	1366.	5	30 mm	85.50	5			
			BP	72.85	5	m' | to		
Density			t_e	69.82	5	n' | °K		
g/ml 20°C	0.917 ≠	2	t_e (d, e)	69.60	5	o' |		
d_4^t 25	0.913 ≠	2	ΔHv/T_e	19.44	5			
30	0.909	4				Surface tension		
a	0.933	4	d | 125 to	100.30	5	dynes/cm. 20°C	38.28	5
b	-0.0₃8	4	e | 260 °C	0.1184	5	γ 30	36.96	5
			d' | 20 to	97.64	5	40	35.68	5
Ref. Index			e' | 125 °C	0.0971	5			
n_D 20°C	1.527 ≠	2				Parachor [P]		
25	1.525 ≠	2	d_c g/ml	0.269	5	20°C		
30	1.522	4	v_c ml/g	3.72	5	30		
"C"	0.7536	4	t_c °C	452.1	5	40		
			P_c mm	22419.	5	Sugd.	402.1	5
MR (Obs.)	49.8 ≠	2	PV/RT			Exp. L.].%/wt.		
MR (Calc.)	49.397	2	25°C	1.0000	5	u.		
(nD-d/2)	1.068 ≠	2	30 mm	1.0000	5	Dispersion	174.	2
Dielectric	2.332	5	BP	0.9414	5	Flash Point °C		
A | 125 to	7.13756	5	t_e	0.9220	5	Fire Point		
B | 280 °C	1833.8	5	t_c	0.241	5	M. Spec.		
C	199.	5	ΔHc kcal/m			Ultra V.		
A* | 125 to	1.60312	5	ΔHf			X-Ray Dif.		
B* | 270 °C	1733.2	5	ΔFf			Infrared		
K								
c			Viscosity			Solubility in +		
t_k | to			centistokes			Acetone		
t_x | °C			η °C			Carbon tet.		
A' | 20 to	7.49417	5				Benzene		
B' | 125 °C	2072.1	5				Ether		
C'	219.4	5	B^v | to			n-Heptane		
A'* 20 to	1.96339	5	A^v | °C			Ethanol		
B'* 125 °C	1966.5	5	(B^v) | to			Water		
Ac | 280 to	7.5838	5	(A^v) | °C			Water in		
Bc | t_c °C	2284.2	5						
Cc	254.4	5	c_p liq. °K					
Cryos. A° consts. B°			c_p vap. °K					
t_e °C	259.20	5	c_v vap.					

$T_R = 0.76 T_c$ ≠ for undercooled liquid   + grams/100 grams solvent

REFERENCES: 1-Dow 2-API 3-Lit. 4-Calc. from det. data 5-Calc. by formula

SOURCE: API

PURIFICATION: API

LITERATURE REFERENCES:

No. 88

NAME	n-Hexylbenzene		STRUCTURAL FORMULA
	1-Phenylhexane		C_6H_{13}

Mole % Pur.	Ref.	Molecular Formula $C_{12}H_{18}$	Molecular Weight 162.264

		Ref.			Ref.				Ref.
F.P. °C	-61.0	2	dt/dP			f		to	
F.P. 100%			°C/mm			g		°K	
B.P. °C			25°C	116.663	5	h			
760 mm	226.1	2	BP	0.056	2				
100	154.5	5	t_e	0.0351	5	f'		to	
30	122.4	4	30 mm	0.8065	4	g'		°K	
10	97.7	5	ΔHm cal/g			h'			
1	56.2	5	ΔHv cal/g			m		300 to	-0.0265	4
Pressure			25°C	88.83	5	n		600 °K	0.0013	4
mm 25°C	0.1051	5	30 mm	79.20	5	o			-0.0$_6$55	4
t_e	1370.	5	BP	68.00	5				
Density			t_e	65.22	5	m'		700 to	0.0839	4
g/ml 20°C	0.8575	2	t_e (d,e)	65.12	5	n'		1000 °K	0.0011	4
d_4^t 25	0.8537	2	ΔHv/T_e			o'			-0.0$_6$37	4
30	0.8499	4	d 122 to	92.42	5	Surface tension			
a	0.8727	4	e 250 °C	0.1080	5	dynes/cm. 20°C	29.53	5
b	-0.0$_3$76	4	d' 20 to	91.30	5	γ 30	28.49	5
Ref. Index			e' 122 °C	0.0988	5	40	27.49	5
n_D 20°C	1.4864	2	d_c g/ml	0.278	5	Parachor [P]		
25	1.4842	2	v_c ml/g	3.59	5	20°C		
30	1.4820	4	t_c °C	423.6	5	30		
"C"	0.7480	4	P_c mm	19160.	5	40		
MR (Obs.)	54.37	2	PV/RT			Sugd.	441.1	5
MR (Calc.)	54.015	5	25°C	1.0000	5	Exp. L.l.%/wt.		
(nD-d/2)	1.0577	2	30 mm	1.0000	5	u.		
Dielectric	2.209	5	BP	0.9536	5	Dispersion	149.	2
A 120 to	7.18284	5	t_e	0.9363	5	Flash Point °C		
B 290 °C	1813.74	5	t_c	0.245	5	Fire Point		
C	195.5	5	ΔHc kcal/m	1635.65	2	M Spec.		
A* 120 to	1.67370	5	ΔHf gas	-13.15	2	Ultra V.		
B* 265 °C	1709.72	5	ΔFf			X-Ray Dif.		
K			Viscosity			Infrared		
c			centistokes			Solubility in +		
t_k to			η 20 °C	1.953	2.	Acetone	∞	
t_x °C			40	1.419	2	Carbon tet.	∞	
A' 20 to	7.54230	5	60	1.098	2	Benzene	∞	
B' 125 °C	2049.47	5	80	0.876	2	Ether	∞	
C'	215.5	5	B^v 30 to	579.33	4	n-Heptane	∞	
A'* 20 to	2.05771	5	A^v 90 °C	$\overline{2}$.21362	4	Ethanol	∞	
B'* 125 °C	1947.20	5	(B^v) 90 to	597.74	4	Water		
Ac 290 to	7.88933	5	(A^v) 160 °C	$\overline{2}$.25968	4	Water in		
Bc t_c °C	2561.8	5				Viscosity		
Cc	286.7	5	c_p liq. °K			centistokes		
Cryos. A°						100°C	0.72	2
consts. B°			c_p vap.300°K	0.32712	2	110	0.66	2
			400	0.42295	2	150	0.47	2
t_e °C F	252.77	5	c_v vap.					

$T_R = 0.81 T_C$ + grams/100 grams solvent

REFERENCES: 1-Dow 2-API 3-Lit. 4-Calc. from det. data 5-Calc. by formula

SOURCE: API

PURIFICATION: API

LITERATURE REFERENCES:

TABLE I. ALKYL AND HALO BENZENES   99

No. 89

NAME	o-Diisopropylbenzene	STRUCTURAL FORMULA
	1,2-Diisopropylbenzene	$CH(CH_3)_2$ $CH(CH_3)_2$

Mole % Pur. 99.6	Ref. 3	Molecular Formula $C_{12}H_{18}$	Molecular Weight 162.264

		Ref.				Ref.				Ref.
F.P. °C	-56.68	3'	dt/dP				f	to		
F.P. 100%			°C/mm				g	°K		
B.P. °C			25°C	35.166	5		h			
760 mm	203.75	3	BP	0.05496	4					
100	133.73	3	t_e	0.0360	5		f'	to		
30	102.6	4	30 mm	0.7820	4		g'	°K		
10	78.7	5	ΔHm cal/g				h'			
1	38.6	5					m	to		
Pressure			ΔHv cal/g				n	°K		
mm 25°C	0.384	5	25°C	80.62	5		o			
t_e	1302.	5	30 mm	73.72	4					
Density			BP	63.05	5		m'	to		
g/ml 20°C	0.87707	3	t_e	60.65	5		n'	°K		
d_4^t 25	0.87320	5	t_e (d,e)	60.54	5		o'			
30	0.86932	5	$ΔHv/T_e$	19.65	5		Surface tension			
a	0.89255	5	d 100 to	84.53	5		dynes/cm. 20°C	32.31	5
b	-0.0₃77	5	e 230 °C	0.1054	5		𝛾 30	31.19	5
Ref. Index			d' 20 to	82.85	5		40	30.09	5
n_D 20°C	1.49603	3	e' 100 °C	0.0890	5		Parachor [P]		
25	1.4940	5	d_c g/ml	0.278	5		20°C		
30	1.4916	5	v_c ml/g	3.592	5		30		
"C"	0.7449	4	t_c °C	395.8	5		40		
MR (Obs.)	54.229	4	P_c mm	18348.	5		Sugd.	441.1	5
MR (Calc.)	54.015	5	PV/RT				Exp. L.1.%/wt.		
(nD-d/2)	1.0575	4	25°C	1.0000	5		u.		
Dielectric	2.238	5	30 mm	1.0000	5		Dispersion	157.	3
A 100 to	7.07875	4	BP	0.9510	5		Flash Point °C	77.	3
B 260 °C	1694.92	4	t_e	0.9346	5		Fire Point		
C	200.0	4	t_c	0.25	5		M. Spec.	Yes	3
A* 100 to	1.59289	5	ΔHc kcal/m				Ultra V.	Yes	3
B* 240 °C	1596.2	5	ΔHf				X-Ray Dif.		
K			ΔFf				Infrared	Yes	3
c			Viscosity				Solubility in +		
t_k to			centistokes				Acetone	∞	
t_x °C			η °C				Carbon tet.	∞	
A' 20 to	7.43165	5					Benzene	∞	
B' 100 °C	1915.2	5					Ether	∞	
C'	219.1	5	B^v to				n-Heptane	∞	
A'* 20 to	1.9561	5	A^v °C				Ethanol	∞	
B'* 100 °C	1813.6	5	(B^v)				Water		
Ac 260 to	7.73507	5	(A^v) °C				Water in		
Bc t_c °C	2354.6	5	c_p liq. °K						
Cc	282.4	5							
Cryos. A°	0.0221	3	c_p vap. °K						
consts. B°									
t_e °C F	227.57	5	c_v vap.						

$T_R = 0.80 T_c$	+ grams/100 grams solvent

REFERENCES: 1-Dow 2-API 3-Lit. 4-Calc. from det. data 5-Calc. by formula

SOURCE: LIT.

PURIFICATION: LIT.

LITERATURE REFERENCES: 3 JACS 70, 935 (1948) Melpolder, Woodbridge, Headington;
3' NFPA 325

No. 90

NAME	m-Diisopropylbenzene		STRUCTURAL FORMULA
	1, 3-Diisopropylbenzene		$CH(CH_3)_2$

Mole % Pur. 99.6	Ref. 3	Molecular Formula $C_{12}H_{18}$	Molecular Weight 162.264	$CH(CH_3)_2$

		Ref.				Ref.					Ref.
F.P. °C	-63.13	3	dt/dP				f		to		
F.P. 100%			°C/mm				g		°K		
B.P. °C			25°C	34.526	5		h				
760 mm	203.18	3	BP	0.0548	4						
100	133.29	3	t_e	0.0359	5		f'		to		
30	102.20	4	30 mm	0.7806	4		g'		°K		
10	78.4	5	ΔHm cal/g				h'				
1	38.4	5									
Pressure			ΔHv cal/g				m		to		
mm 25°C	0.3915	5	25°C	80.57	5		n		°K		
t_e	1302.	5	30 mm	73.69	4		o				
Density			BP	63.12	5						
g/ml 20°C	0.85593	3	t_e	60.65	5		m'		to		
d_4^t 25	0.85200	5	t_e (d, e)	60.64	5		n'		°K		
30	0.84806	5	ΔHv/T_e	19.68	5		o'				
a	0.87165	5	d 100 to	84.39	5		Surface tension				
b	-0.0379	5	e 230 °C	0.1047	5		dynes/cm. 20°C		29.31	5
Ref. Index			d' 20 to	82.80	5		γ	30	28.25	5
n_D 20°C	1.4883	3	e' 100 °C	0.0891	5			40	27.21	5
25	1.4854	5	d_c g/ml	0.278	5		Parachor [P]				
30	1.4830	5	v_c ml/g	3.592	5		20°C				
"C"	0.7510	4	t_c °C	391.2	5		30				
MR (Obs.)	54.616	4	P_c mm	17617.	5		40				
MR (Calc.)	54.015	5	PV/RT				Sugd.		441.1	5
(nD-d/2)	1.06086	4	25°C	1.0000	5		Exp. L.1.%/wt.				
Dielectric	2.215	5	30 mm	1.0000	5		u.				
A 100 to	7.08134	4	BP	0.9526	5		Dispersion		155.	3
B 260 °C	1693.57	4	t_e	0.9353	5		Flash Point °C				
C	200.0	4	t_c	0.25	5		Fire Point				
A* 100 to	1.59497	5	ΔHc kcal/m				M Spec.		Yes	3
B* 240 °C	1594.7	5	ΔHf				Ultra V.		Yes	3
K			ΔFf				X-Ray Dif.				
c			Viscosity				Infrared		Yes	3
t_k to			centistokes				Solubility in +				
t_x °C			η °C				Acetone		∞		
A' 20 to	7.43441	5					Carbon tet.		∞		
B' 100 °C	1913.7	5					Benzene		∞		
C'	219.0	5					Ether		∞		
			B^V to				n-Heptane		∞		
A'* 20 to	1.95916	5	A^V °C				Ethanol		∞		
B'* 100 °C	1812.1	5	(B^V) to				Water				
Ac 260 to	7.49727	5	(A^V) °C				Water in				
Bc t_c °C	2062.4	5	c_p liq. °K								
Cc	241.3	5									
Cryos. A°	0.0385	3	c_p vap. °K								
consts. B°											
t_e °C F	226.93	5	c_v vap.								

$T_R = 0.80 T_c$

+ grams/100 grams solvent

REFERENCES: 1-Dow 2-API 3-Lit. 4-Calc. from det. data 5-Calc. by formula

SOURCE: LIT.

PURIFICATION: LIT.

LITERATURE REFERENCES: 3 JACS 70, 935 (1948) Melpolder, Woodbridge, Headington

TABLE I. ALKYL AND HALO BENZENES

No. 91

NAME	p-Diisopropylbenzene	STRUCTURAL FORMULA
	1,4-Diisopropylbenzene	$CH(CH_3)_2$

| Mole % Pur. 99.8 | Ref. 3 | Molecular Formula | $C_{12}H_{18}$ | Molecular Weight 162.264 | |

Structural formula: benzene ring with $CH(CH_3)_2$ groups at para positions.

		Ref.				Ref.					Ref.
F.P. °C	-17.07	3	dt/dP				f	to			
F.P. 100%			°C/mm				g	°K			
B.P. °C			25°C	47.246	5		h				
760 mm	210.37	3	BP	0.0557	4		f'	to			
100	139.43	4	t_e	0.0361	5		g'	°K			
30	107.87	5	30 mm	0.7923	4		h'				
10	83.7	5	ΔHm cal/g				m	to			
1	43.	5	ΔHv cal/g				n	°K			
			25°C	82.37	5		o				
Pressure			30 mm	74.82	4						
mm 25°C	0.2798	5	BP	63.79	5		m'	to			
t_e	1317.	5	t_e	61.28	5		n'	°K			
Density			t_e (d, e)	61.13	5		o'				
g/ml 20°C	0.85676	3	ΔHv/T_e	19.56	5		Surface tension				
d_4^t 25	0.85290	5	d 105 to	86.43	5		dynes/cm. 20°C	29.42	5		
30	0.84903	5	e 240 °C	0.1076	5		ɤ 30	28.38	5		
a	0.87220	5	d' 20 to	84.65	5		40	27.36	5		
b	-0.0377	5	e' 105 °C	0.0911	5		Parachor [P]				
Ref. Index							20°C				
n_D 20°C	1.48983	3	d_c g/ml	0.278	5		30				
25	1.4875	5	v_c ml/g	3.60	5		40				
30	1.4851	5	t_c °C	401.6	5		Sugd.	441.1	5		
"C"	0.7533	4	P_c mm	17688.	5						
MR (Obs.)	54.772	4	PV/RT				Exp. L.l.%/wt.				
MR (Calc.)	54.015	5	25°C	1.0000	5		u.				
(nD-d/2)	1.06145	4	30 mm	1.0000	5		Dispersion	157.	3		
Dielectric	2.219	5	BP	0.9483	5		Flash Point °C	81.0	5		
A 105 to	7.08043	5	t_e	0.9313	5		Fire Point				
B 270 °C	1718.36	4	t_c	0.25	5		M. Spec.	Yes	3		
C	198.8	4	ΔHc kcal/m				Ultra V.	Yes	3		
A* 105 to	1.59339	5	ΔHf				X-Ray Dif.				
B* 245 °C	1619.8	5	ΔFf				Infrared	Yes	3		
K			Viscosity				Solubility in +				
c			centistokes				Acetone	∞			
t_k to			η °C				Carbon tet.	∞			
t_x °C							Benzene	∞			
A' 15 to	7.43344	5					Ether	∞			
B' 105 °C	1941.7	5					n-Heptane	∞			
C'	218.1	5	B^v to				Ethanol	∞			
A'* 15 to	1.95531	5	A^v °C				Water				
B'* 105 °C	1839.8	5	(B^v) to				Water in				
Ac 270 to	7.66556	5	(A^v) °C								
Bc t_c °C	2311.7	5	c_p liq. °K								
Cc	273.9	5									
Cryos. A°	0.0292	3	c_p vap. °K								
consts. B°											
t_e °C F	235.03	5	c_v vap.								

$T_R = 0.80 T_C$

+ grams/100 grams solvent

REFERENCES: 1-Dow 2-API 3-Lit. 4-Calc. from det. data 5-Calc. by formula

SOURCE: LIT.

PURIFICATION: LIT.

LITERATURE REFERENCES: 3 JACS 70, 935 (1948) Melpolder, Woodbridge, Headington

No. 92

NAME	n-Heptylbenzene	STRUCTURAL FORMULA
	1-Phenylheptane	C_7H_{15}

Mole % Pur.	Ref.	Molecular Formula $C_{13}H_{20}$	Molecular Weight 176.290		

		Ref.				Ref.				Ref.
F.P. °C	-48.	2	dt/dP °C/mm			f		to		
F.P. 100%			25°C	296.174	5	g		__ °K		
B.P. °C			BP	0.0580	2	h				
760 mm	245.5	2	t_e	0.0355	5	f'		to		
100	171.27	5	30 mm	0.8361	4	g'		__ °K		
30	138.03	4	ΔHm cal/g			h'				
10	112.5	5	ΔHv cal/g							
1	69.4	5	25°C	86.98	5	m		300 to	-0.0225	4
Pressure			30 mm	75.99	5	n		600 °K	0.0013	4
mm 25°C	0.0389	5	BP	64.68	5	o			-0.0$_6$55	4
t_e	1413.	5	t_e	61.78	5	m'		700 to	0.0865	4
Density			t_e (d,e)	61.61	5	n'		1000 °K	0.0011	4
g/ml 20°C	0.8567	2	ΔHv/T_e	19.88	5	o'			-0.0$_6$37	4
d_4^t 25	0.8530	2	d	140 to	90.52	5	Surface tension				
30	0.8493	4	e	270 °C	0.1053	5	dynes/cm. 20°C	29.63	5
a	0.8715	4	d'	15 to	89.41	5	30	28.62	5
b	-0.0$_3$74	4	e'	140 °C	0.09717	5	40	27.63	5
Ref. Index			d_c g/ml	0.274	5	Parachor [P]				
n_D 20°C	1.4854	2	v_c ml/g	3.647	5	20°C				
25	1.4832	2	t_c °C	439.7	5	30				
30	1.4810	4	P_c mm	17191.	5	40				
"C"	0.7469	4	PV/RT			Sugd.	480.1	5
MR (Obs.)	59.01	2	25°C	1.0000	5	Exp. L. l.%/wt.				
MR (Calc.)	58.633	5	30 mm	1.0000	5	u.				
(nD-d/2)	1.0570	2	BP	0.9462	5	Dispersion	145.	2
Dielectric	2.1987	5	t_e	0.9268	5	Flash Point °C				
A | 135 to	7.19114	5	t_c	0.246	5	Fire Point				
B | 305 °C	1885.77	5	ΔHc kcal/m	1782.58	2	M Spec.				
C	192.0	5	ΔHf			Ultra V.				
A* | 135 to	1.71535	5	ΔFf			X-Ray Dif.				
B* | 285 °C	1782.46	5	Viscosity			Infrared				
K			centistokes			Solubility in +				
c			η 20 °C	2.43	2	Acetone	∞	
t_k | to			40	1.722	2	Carbon tet.	∞	
t_x | °C			60	1.305	2	Benzene	∞	
A' | 15 to	7.55112	5	80	1.025	2	Ether		
B' | 140 °C	2130.86	5	B^V | 30 to	623.11	4	n-Heptane		
C'	212.8	5	A^V | 90 °C	$\overline{2}$.24654	4	Ethanol	∞	
A'* 15 to	2.09472	5	(B^V) | 100 to	611.17	4	Water		
B'* 140 °C	2027.85	5				Water in		
Ac | 305 to	7.79109	5	(A^V) | 160 °C	$\overline{2}$.28011	4			
Bc | t_c °C	2528.2	5	c_p liq. °K			Viscosity		
Cc	270.4	5				centistokes		
Cryos. A°			c_p vap.300°K	0.33229	2	100°C	0.831	2
consts. B°			400	0.42867	2	110	0.750	2
t_e °C F	274.65	5	c_v vap.			150	0.530	2

$T_R = 0.81 T_c$

+ grams/100 grams solvent

REFERENCES: 1-Dow 2-API 3-Lit. 4-Calc. from det. data 5-Calc. by formula

SOURCE:	API
PURIFICATION:	API
LITERATURE REFERENCES:	

TABLE I. ALKYL AND HALO BENZENES

No. 93

NAME	n-Octylbenzene	STRUCTURAL FORMULA
	1-Phenyloctane	C_8H_{17}

Mole % Pur.	Ref.	Molecular Formula $C_{14}H_{22}$	Molecular Weight 190.316

		Ref.				Ref.				Ref.
F.P. °C	-36.	2	dt/dP				f	to		
F.P. 100%			°C/mm				g	___ °K		
B.P. °C			25°C	904.1	5		h			
760 mm	264.5	2	BP	0.060	5					
100	187.9	5	t_e	0.0365	5		f'	to		
30	153.8	5	30 mm	0.8572	5		g'	___ °K		
10	127.6	5	ΔHm cal/g				h'			
1	84.	5								
Pressure			ΔHv cal/g				m	300 to	-0.0192	4
mm 25°C	0.0115	5	25°C	88.98	5		n	600 °K	0.0013	4
t_e	1427.	5	30 mm	74.03	5		o		-0.0_654	4
Density			BP	60.92	5					
g/ml 20°C	0.8562	2	t_e	57.64	5		m'	700 to	0.0913	4
d_4^t 25	0.8525	2	t_e (d, e)	57.29	5		n'	1000 °K	0.0011	4
d_4^t 30	0.8488	4	$ΔHv/T_e$	19.30	5		o'		-0.0_637	4
a	0.8710	4	d 155 to	92.24	5		Surface tension			
b	-0.0_374	4	e 295 °C	0.1184	5		dynes/cm. 20°C		29.74	5
			d' 20 to	91.88	5		ɤ 30		28.73	5
Ref. Index			e' 155 °C	0.1160	5		40		27.74	5
n_D 20°C	1.4845	2	d_c g/ml	0.271	5		Parachor [P]			
25	1.4824	2	v_c ml/g	3.689	5		20°C			
30	1.4800	4	t_c °C	453.5	5		30			
"C"	0.7460	4	P_c mm	14897.	5		40			
MR (Obs.)	63.65	2						Sugd.	519.1	5
MR (Calc.)	63.251	5	PV/RT				Exp. L.l.%/wt.			
(nD-d/2)	1.0564	2	25°C	1.0000	5		u.			
Dielectric	2.204	5	30 mm	1.0000	5		Dispersion	142.		2
A 155 to	7.11415	5	BP	0.9267	5		Flash Point °C			
B 320 °C	1881.7	5	t_e	0.9025	5		Fire Point			
C	180.	5	t_c	0.246	5		M. Spec.			
A* 155 to	1.7001	5	ΔHc kcal/m	1929.50	2		Ultra V.			
B* 300 °C	1792.2	5	ΔHf				X-Ray Dif.			
K			ΔFf				Infrared			
c			Viscosity				Solubility in +			
t_k to			centistokes				Acetone	∞		
t_x °C			η 20 °C	2.99	2		Carbon tet.	∞		
A' 25 to	7.4693	5	40	2.07	2		Benzene	∞		
B' 155 °C	2126.3	5	60	1.539	2		Ether	∞		
C'	201.	5	80	1.190	2		n-Heptane	∞		
A'* 25 to	2.0498	5	B^v 30 to	664.89	4		Ethanol	∞		
B'* 155 °C	2029.2	5	A^v 90 °C	2.19306	4		Water			
			(B^v) 100 to	663.48	4		Water in			
Ac 320 to	7.85374	5	(A^v) 160 °C	2.20308	4		Viscosity			
Bc t_c °C	2690.	5					centistokes			
Cc	277.	5	c_p liq. °K				100°C	0.952		2
Cryos. A°							110	0.86		2
consts. B°			c_p vap 300°K	0.33665	2		150	0.59		2
			400	0.43354	2					
t_e °C F	295.22	5	c_v vap.							

$T_R = 0.81 T_c$ + grams/100 grams solvent

REFERENCES: 1-Dow 2-API 3-Lit. 4-Calc. from det. data 5-Calc. by formula

SOURCE: API

PURIFICATION: API

LITERATURE REFERENCES:

No. 94

NAME	n-Nonylbenzene	STRUCTURAL FORMULA
	1-Phenylnonane	C_9H_{19}

Mole % Pur.	Ref.	Molecular Formula $C_{15}H_{24}$	Molecular Weight 204.342	

		Ref.			Ref.					Ref.
F.P. °C	-24.	2	dt/dP			f		to		
F.P. 100%			°C/mm			g		°K		
B.P. °C			25°C	2291.0	5	h				
760 mm	282.0	2	BP	0.0613	5					
100	203.6	5	t_e	0.0363	5	f'		to		
30	168.5	5	30 mm	0.8830	5	g'		°K		
10	141.5	5	ΔHm cal/g			h'				
1	96.	5	ΔHv cal/g			m	300 to	-0.0163	4
Pressure			25°C	86.97	5	n	600 °K	0.0014	4
mm 25°C	0.0043	5	30 mm	71.62	5	o		-0.0₆54	4
t_e	1472.	5	BP	59.04	5	m'	700 to	0.0905	4
Density			t_e	55.80	5	n'	1000 °K	0.0011	4
g/ml 20°C	0.8558	2	t_e (d, e)	55.39	5	o'		-0.0₆38	4
d_4^t 25	0.8522	2	ΔHv/T_e	19.39	5	Surface tension			
30	0.8486	4	d	165 to	90.28	5	dynes/cm. 20°C	29.85	5
a	0.8702	4	e	315 °C	0.1108	5	30	28.86	5
b	-0.0₃72	4	d'	25 to	89.64	5	40	27.89	5
Ref. Index			e'	165 °C	0.1070	5	Parachor [P]		
n_D 20°C	1.4838	2	d_c g/ml		0.269	5	20°C		
25	1.4817	2	v_c ml/g		3.719	5	30		
30	1.4781	4	t_c °C		467.5	5	40		
"C"	0.7434	4	P_c mm		13956.	5	Sugd.	558.1	5
MR (Obs.)	68.29	2	PV/RT				Exp. L.1.%/wt.		
MR (Calc.)	67.869	5	25°C	1.0000	5	u.		
(nD-d/2)	1.0559	2	30 mm	1.0000	5	Dispersion	139.	2
Dielectric	2.202	5	BP	0.9238	5	Flash Point °C		
A	165 to	7.19041	5	t_e	0.8993	5	Fire Point		
B	330 °C	1991.0	5	t_c	0.235	5	M Spec.		
C		180.	5	ΔHc kcal/m	2076.43	2	Ultra V.		
A*	165 to	1.7956	5	ΔHf			X-Ray Dif.		
B*	325 °C	1898.6	5	ΔFf			Infrared		
K				Viscosity			Solubility in	+	
c			.	centistokes			Acetone	∞	
t_k	to			η 20 °C	3.66	2	Carbon tet.	∞	
t_x	°C			40	2.47	2	Benzene	∞	
A'	25 to	7.5503	5	60	1.800	2	Ether	∞	
B'	165 °C	2249.8	5	80	1.370	2	n-Heptane	∞	
C'		202.	5	B^v 30 to	707.9	4	Ethanol	∞	
A'*	25 to	2.1508	5	A^v 90 °C	Σ.1324	4	Water		
B'*	165 °C	2149.8	5	(B^v) 100 to	676.90	4	Water in		
Ac	330 to	7.9653	5	(A^v) 160 °C	Σ.22006	4	Viscosity		
Bc	t_c °C	2863.	5	c_p liq. °K			centistokes		
Cc		282.	5				100°C	1.082	2
Cryos. A°				c_p vap.300°K	0.34046	2	110	0.970	2
consts. B°				400	0.43775	2	150	0.660	2
t_e °C F	314.95	5	c_v vap.						
T_R = 0.82 T_c						+ grams/100 grams solvent		

REFERENCES: 1-Dow 2-API 3-Lit. 4-Calc. from det. data 5-Calc. by formula

SOURCE:	API
PURIFICATION:	API

LITERATURE REFERENCES:

TABLE I. ALKYL AND HALO BENZENES

NAME	n-Decylbenzene	STRUCTURAL FORMULA
	1-Phenyldecane	

$C_{10}H_{21}$

Mole % Pur.	Ref.	Molecular Formula $C_{16}H_{26}$	Molecular Weight 218.368

		Ref.			Ref.					Ref.
F.P. °C	-14.38	2	dt/dP			f		to		
F.P. 100%			°C/mm			g		°K		
B.P. °C			25°C	6155.8	5	h				
760 mm	300.	2	BP	0.0625	5					
100	220.	5	t_e	0.0360	5	f'		to		
30	184.	5	30 mm	0.9087	5	g'		°K		
10	156.	5	ΔHm cal/g			h'				
1	109.	5	ΔHv cal/g			m		300 to	-0.0146	4
Pressure			25°C	85.43	5	n		600 °K	0.0014	4
mm 25°C	0.0015	5	30 mm	69.70	5	o			$-0.0_6 54$	4
t_e	1518.	5	BP	57.67	5					
Density			t_e	54.34	5	m'		700 to	0.0927	4
g/ml 20°C	0.85553	2	t_e (d, e)	54.03	5	n'		1000 °K	0.0011	4
d_4^t 25	0.85189	2	ΔHv/T_e	19.50	5	o'			$-0.0_6 38$	4
30	0.84825	4	d 185 to	88.70	5	Surface tension				
a	0.87009	4	e 335 °C	0.1034	5	dynes/cm. 20°C			29.95	5
b	$-0.0_3 73$	4	d' 25 to	87.91	5	४		30	28.94	5
Ref. Index			e' 185 °C	0.0991	5			40	27.96	5
n_D 20°C	1.48319	2	d_c g/ml			Parachor [P]				
25	1.48112	2	v_c ml/g					20°C		
30	1.47999	4	t_c °C	480.7	5			30		
"C"	0.7465	4	P_c mm	12912.	5			40		
MR (Obs.)	72.920	2	PV/RT					Sugd.	597.1	5
MR (Calc.)	72.487	5	25°C	1.0000	5	Exp. L. 1.%/wt.				
(nD-d/2)	1.05542	2	30 mm	1.0000	5			u.		
Dielectric	2.200	5	BP	0.9230	5	Dispersion			136.6	2
A 185 to	7.27177	5	t_e	0.8964	5	Flash Point °C				
B 345 °C	2107.7	5	t_c			Fire Point				
C	180.	5	ΔHc kcal/m	2223.35	2	M. Spec.				
A* 185 to	1.8937	5	ΔHf			Ultra V.				
B* 345 °C	2012.2	5	ΔFf			X-Ray Dif.				
K			Viscosity			Infrared				
c			centistokes			Solubility in +				
t_k to			η 20 °C	4.44	2	Acetone		∞		
t_x °C			40	2.92	2	Carbon tet.		∞		
A' 25 to	7.6368	5	60	2.09	2	Benzene		∞		
B' 185 °C	2381.6	5	80	1.566	2	Ether		∞		
C'	203.	5	B^V 30 to	748.3	4	n-Heptane		∞		
A'* 25 to	2.2551	5	A^V 90 °C	$\overline{2}.07607$	4	Ethanol		∞		
B'* 185 °C	2278.7	5	(B^V) 100 to	705.98	4	Water				
Ac to			(A^V) 160 °C	$\overline{2}.19509$	4	Water in				
Bc t_c °C						Viscosity				
Cc			c_p liq. °K			centistokes				
Cryos. A°						100°C		1.222	2
consts. B°			c_p vap.300°K	0.34373	2	110		1.09	2
t_e °C F	335.25	5	400	0.44146	2	150		0.730	2
			c_v vap.							

$T_R = 0.82 T_c$

+ grams/100 grams solvent

REFERENCES: 1-Dow 2-API 3-Lit. 4-Calc. from det. data 5-Calc. by formula

SOURCE: API

PURIFICATION: API

LITERATURE REFERENCES:

No. 96

NAME	n-Undecylbenzene	STRUCTURAL FORMULA
	1-Phenylundecane	

Mole % Pur.	Ref.	Molecular Formula $C_{17}H_{28}$	Molecular Weight 232.394

benzene ring — $C_{11}H_{23}$

Column 1

		Ref.
F.P. °C	-5.	2
F.P. 100%		
B.P. °C		
760 mm	316.	2
100	234.	5
30	197.	5
10	169.	5
1	121.	5
Pressure mm 25°C	0.0_360	5
t_e	1525.	5
Density g/ml 20°C	0.8553	2
d_4^t 25	0.8517	2
30	0.8481	4
a	0.8697	4
b	-0.0_372	4
Ref. Index n_D 20°C	1.4828	2
25	1.4807	2
30	1.4784	4
"C"	0.7443	5
MR (Obs.)	77.57	2
MR (Calc.)	77.105	5
(nD-d/2)	1.0552	2
Dielectric	2.199	5
A ⌐195 to	7.34672	5
B ⌊375 °C	2215.1	5
C	180.	5
A* ⌐195 to	1.9853	5
B* ⌊360 °C	2116.9	5
K		
c		
t_k ⌐ to		
t_x ⌊ °C		
A' ⌐25 to	7.7165	5
B' ⌊195 °C	2503.0	5
C'	204.	5
A'* ⌐25 to	2.3523	5
B'* ⌊195 °C	2397.5	5
Ac ⌐ to		
Bc ⌊t_c °C		
Cc		
Cryos. A°		
consts. B°		
t_e °C F	353.29	5

Column 2

		Ref.
dt/dP °C/mm		
25°C	15222.	5
BP	0.0635	5
t_e	0.0357	5
30 mm	0.9308	5
ΔHm cal/g		
ΔHv cal/g 25°C	83.73	5
30 mm	67.82	5
BP	56.26	5
t_e	52.94	5
t_e (d, e)	52.63	5
ΔHv/T_e	19.64	5
d ⌐195 to	87.05	5
e ⌊350 °C	0.0974	5
d' ⌐25 to	86.04	5
e' ⌊195 °C	0.0923	5
d_c g/ml	0.265	5
v_c ml/g	3.778	5
t_c °C	492.3	5
P_c mm	12059.	5
PV/RT 25°C	1.0000	5
30 mm	1.0000	5
BP	0.9217	5
t_e	0.8949	5
t_c	0.226	5
ΔHc kcal/m	2370.27	2
ΔHf		
ΔFf		
Viscosity centistokes		
η 20 °C	5.34	2
40	3.43	2
60	2.41	2
80	1.779	2
B^V ⌐30 to	788.49	4
A^V ⌊90 °C	$\bar{2}.01777$	4
(B^V) ⌐100 to	743.02	4
(A^V) ⌊160 °C	$\bar{2}.14737$	4
c_p liq. °K		
c_p vap.300°K	0.34661	2
400	0.44467	2
c_v vap.		

Column 3

			Ref.
f ⌐ to			
g ⌊ °K			
h			
f' ⌐ to			
g' ⌊ °K			
h'			
m ⌐300 to	-0.0123		4
n ⌊600 °K	0.0014		4
o	-0.0_654		4
m' ⌐700 to	0.0971		4
n' ⌊1000 °K	0.0011		4
o'	-0.0_637		4
Surface tension dynes/cm. 20°C	30.04		5
y 30	29.04		5
40	28.07		5
Parachor [P] 20°C			
30			
40			
Sugd.	636.1		5
Exp. L.1.%/wt. u.			
Dispersion	134.		2
Flash Point °C			
Fire Point			
M Spec.			
Ultra V.			
X-Ray Dif.			
Infrared			
Solubility in +			
Acetone			
Carbon tet.			
Benzene			
Ether			
n-Heptane			
Ethanol			
Water			
Water in			
Viscosity centistokes 100°C	1.371		2
110	1.22		2
150	0.80		2

+ grams/100 grams solvent

REFERENCES:	1-Dow 2-API 3-Lit. 4-Calc. from det. data 5-Calc. by formula
SOURCE:	API
PURIFICATION:	API
LITERATURE REFERENCES:	

TABLE I. ALKYL AND HALO BENZENES

No. 97

NAME	n-Dodecylbenzene	STRUCTURAL FORMULA
	1-Phenyldodecane	

STRUCTURAL FORMULA: $C_{12}H_{25}$ (on benzene ring)

Mole % Pur.	Ref.	Molecular Formula $C_{18}H_{30}$	Molecular Weight 246.420

		Ref.			Ref.					Ref.
F.P. °C	3.	2	dt/dP °C/mm			f		to		
F.P. 100%			25°C	36477.	5	g		_ _ _°K		
B.P. °C			BP	0.0643	5	h				
760 mm	331.	2	t_e	0.0354	5	f'		to		
100	248.	5	30 mm	0.9508	5	g'		_ _ _°K		
30	210.	5	ΔHm cal/g			h'				
10	181.	5	ΔHv cal/g			m		300 to	-0.0103	4
1	132.	5	25°C	82.09	5	n		600 °K	0.0014	4
Pressure			30 mm	66.09	5	o			-0.0_654	4
mm 25°C	0.0_324	5	BP	54.98	5	m'		700 to	0.0978	4
t_e	1600.	5	t_e	51.68	5	n'		1000 °K	0.0011	4
Density			t_e (d,e)	51.38	5	o'			-0.0_637	4
g/ml 20°C	0.8551	2	$\Delta Hv/T_e$	19.79	5	Surface tension				
d_4^t 25	0.8516	2	d	210 to	85.43	5	dynes/cm. 20°C	30.12	5
30	0.8481	4	e	360 °C	0.0920	5	γ		30	29.14	5
a	0.8691	4	d'	25 to	84.25	5			40	28.19	5
b	-0.0_37	4	e'	210 °C	0.0864	5					
Ref. Index			d_c g/ml	0.263	5	Parachor [P]				
n_D 20°C	1.4824	2	v_c ml/g	3.798	5			20°C		
25	1.4803	2	t_c °C	503.6	5			30		
30	1.4782	4	P_c mm	11383.	5			40		
"C"	0.7439	4	PV/RT					Sugd.	675.1	5
MR (Obs.)	82.21	2	25°C	1.0000	5	Exp. L.l.%/wt.				
MR (Calc.)	81.723	5	30 mm	1.0000	5	u.				
(nD-d/2)	1.0549	2	BP	0.9211	5	Dispersion		132.		2
Dielectric	2.198	5	t_e	0.8940	5	Flash Point °C				
A 210 to	7.41934	5	t_c			Fire Point				
B 385 °C	2319.2	5	ΔHc kcal/m	2517.19	2	M. Spec.				
C	180.	5	ΔHf			Ultra V.				
A* 210 to	2.0722	5	ΔFf			X-Ray Dif.				
B* 380 °C	2217.9	5				Infrared				
K			Viscosity centistokes			Solubility in +				
c			η 20 °C	6.39	2	Acetone				
t_k to			40	4.06	2	Carbon tet.				
t_x °C			60	2.76	2	Benzene				
A' 25 to	7.7937	5	80	2.01	2	Ether				
B' 210 °C	2620.6	5	B^v 50 to	795.64	4	n-Heptane				
C'	205.	5	A^v 105 °C	$\overline{2}.05305$	4	Ethanol				
A'* 25 to	2.44602	5	(B^v) 105 °C	774.13	4	Water				
B'* 210 °C	2512.7	5	(A^V) 160 °C	$\overline{2}.11015$	4	Water in				
Ac to			c_p liq. °K			Viscosity centistokes				
Bc t_c °C							100°C	1.531	2.
Cc			c_p vap.300°K	0.34920	2		110	1.350	2
Cryos. A°			400	0.44753	2		150	0.870	2
consts. B°			c_v vap.						
t_e °C F	370.21	5							

+ grams/100 grams solvent

REFERENCES: 1-Dow 2-API 3-Lit. 4-Calc. from det. data 5-Calc. by formula
SOURCE: API
PURIFICATION: API
LITERATURE REFERENCES:

No. 98

NAME	n-Tridecylbenzene	STRUCTURAL FORMULA
	1-Phenyltridecane	$C_{13}H_{27}$ (benzene ring)

Mole % Pur.	Ref.	Molecular Formula $C_{19}H_{32}$	Molecular Weight 260.446

Column 1

Property	Value	Ref.
F.P. °C	10.	2
F.P. 100%		
B.P. °C		
760 mm	346.	5
100	262.	5
30	223.	5
10	194.	5
1	143.	5
Pressure mm 25°C	0.0_494	5
t_e	1642.	5
Density g/ml 20°C	0.8550	2
d_4^t 25	0.8515	2
30	0.8480	4
a	0.8690	4
b	-0.0_37	4
Ref. Index n_D 20°C	1.4821	2
25	1.4800	2
30	1.4779	4
"C"	0.7436	4
MR (Obs.)	86.85	2
MR (Calc.)	86.341	5
(nD-d/2)	1.0546	2
Dielectric	2.197	5
A |225 to	7.49437	5
B |405 °C	2626.7	5
C	180.	5
A* |225 to	2.1594	5
B* |390 °C	2321.9	5
K		
c		
t_k | to		
t_x | °C		
A' | 25 to	7.87345	5
B' |225 °C	2742.1	5
C'	205.	5
A'* 25 to	2.54109	5
B'* 225 °C	2631.8	5
Ac | to		
Bc | t_c °C		
Cc		
Cryos. A°		
consts. B°		
t_e °C F	387.12	5

$T_R = 0.86\,T_c$

Column 2

Property	Value	Ref.
dt/dP °C/mm 25°C	89602.	5
BP	0.0652	5
t_e	0.0363	5
30 mm	0.9702	5
ΔHm cal/g		
ΔHv cal/g 25°C	80.69	5
30 mm	64.62	5
BP	53.99	5
t_e	50.63	5
t_e (d, e)	50.43	5
ΔHv/T_e	19.97	5
d | 225 to	83.95	5
e | 380 °C	0.0866	5
d' | 25 to	82.72	5
e' | 225 °C	0.0811	5
d_c g/ml	0.262	5
v_c ml/g	3.820	5
t_c °C	513.7	5
P_c mm	10190.	5
PV/RT 25°C	1.0000	5
30 mm	1.0000	5
BP	0.9221	5
t_e	0.8938	5
t_c	0.206	5
ΔHc kcal/m	2664.12	2
ΔHf		
ΔFf		
Viscosity centistokes η 20 °C	7.60	2
40	4.65	2
60	3.15	2
80	2.26	2
B^V | 50 to	831.92	4
A^V | 105 °C	2.00154	4
(B^V) | 105 °C	805.22	4
(A^V) | 160 °C	2.07479	4
c_p liq. °K		
c_p vap.300°K	0.35147	2
400	0.45007	2
c_v vap.		

Column 3

Property	Value	Ref.
f | to		
g | °K		
h		
f' | to		
g' | °K		
h'		
m | 300 to	-0.0086	4
n | 600 °K	0.0014	4
o	-0.0_654	4
m' | 700 to	0.0989	4
n' | 1000 °K	0.0011	4
o'	-0.0_638	4
Surface tension dynes/cm. 20°C	30.20	5
γ 30	29.22	5
40	28.27	5
Parachor [P] 20°C		
30		
40		
Sugd.	714.1	5
Exp. L.1.%/wt. u.		
Dispersion	130.	2
Flash Point °C		
Fire Point		
M Spec.		
Ultra V.		
X-Ray Dif.		
Infrared		
Solubility in +		
Acetone		
Carbon tet.		
Benzene		
Ether		
n-Heptane		
Ethanol		
Water		
Water in		
Viscosity centistokes 100°C	1.701	2
110	1.50	2
150	0.95	2

+ grams/100 grams solvent

REFERENCES: 1-Dow 2-API 3-Lit. 4-Calc. from det. data 5-Calc. by formula

SOURCE: API

PURIFICATION: API

LITERATURE REFERENCES:

No. 99

NAME	n-Tetradecylbenzene	STRUCTURAL FORMULA
	1-Phenyltetradecane	
Mole % Pur. / Ref.	Molecular Formula $C_{20}H_{34}$; Molecular Weight 274.472	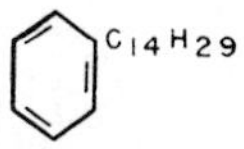

		Ref.
F.P. °C	16.	2
F.P. 100%		
B.P. °C 760 mm	359.	2
100	274.	5
30	235.	5
10	204.	5
1	153.	5
Pressure mm 25°C	0.0_441	5
t_e	1679.	5
Density g/ml 20°C	0.8549	2
d^t_4 25	0.8514	2
30	0.8479	4
a	0.8689	4
b	-0.0_37	4
Ref. Index n_D 20°C	1.4818	2
25	1.4797	2
30	1.4776	4
"C"	0.7432	4
MR (Obs.)	91.49	2
MR (Calc.)	90.959	5
(nD-d/2)	1.0543	2
Dielectric	2.196	5
A 235 to	7.56143	5
B 410 °C	2522.8	5
C	180.	5
A* 235 to	2.2384	5
B* 410 °C	2414.6	5
K		
c		
t_k to		
t_x °C		
A' 25 to	7.94474	5
B' 235 °C	2850.7	5
C'	206.	5
A'* 25 to	2.62769	5
B'* 235 °C	2738.3	5
Ac to		
Bc t_c °C		
Cc		
Cryos. A°		
consts. B°		
t_e °C F	401.78	5

		Ref.
dt/dP °C/mm 25°C	1.99×10^5	5
BP	0.0658	5
t_e	0.0347	5
30 mm	0.9866	5
ΔHm cal/g		
ΔHv cal/g 25°C	79.11	5
30 mm	63.09	5
BP	52.88	5
t_e	49.54	5
t_e (d, e)	49.37	5
$\Delta Hv/T_e$	20.14	5
d 235 to	82.34	5
e 390 °C	0.0821	5
d' 25 to	81.02	5
e' 235 °C	0.0764	5
d_c g/ml	0.261	5
v_c ml/g	3.833	5
t_c °C	521.4	5
P_c mm	9100.	5
PV/RT 25°C	1.0000	5
30 mm	1.0000	5
BP	0.9226	5
t_e	0.8941	5
t_c	0.193	5
ΔHc kcal/m	2811.04	2
ΔHf		
ΔFf		
Viscosity centistokes η 20 °C	8.98	2
40	5.36	2
60	3.57	2
80	2.53	2
B^v 50 to	865.10	4
A^v 105 °C	$\bar{3}.95632$	4
(B^v) 105 to	829.69	4
(A^v) 160 °C	$\bar{2}.05232$	4
c_p liq. °K		
c_p vap. 300°K	0.35355	2
400	0.45236	2
c_v vap.		

			Ref.
f	to		
g	°K		
h			
f'	to		
g'	°K		
h'			
m	300 to	-0.0070	4
n	600 °K	0.0014	4
o		-0.0_653	4
m'	700 to	0.0986	4
n'	1000 °K	0.0011	4
o'		-0.0_638	4
Surface tension dynes/cm. 20°C		30.27	5
γ 30		29.30	5
40		28.34	5
Parachor [P] 20°C			
30			
40			
Sugd.		753.1	5
Exp. L.1.%/wt. u.			
Dispersion		129.	2
Flash Point °C			
Fire Point			
M. Spec.			
Ultra V.			
X-Ray Dif.			
Infrared			
Solubility in +			
Acetone			
Carbon tet.			
Benzene			
Ether			
n-Heptane			
Ethanol			
Water			
Water in			
Viscosity centistokes 100°C		1.881	2
110		1.65	2
150		1.03	2

$T_R = 0.87\ T_c$

+ grams/100 grams solvent

REFERENCES: 1-Dow 2-API 3-Lit. 4-Calc. from det. data 5-Calc. by formula

SOURCE: API

PURIFICATION: API

LITERATURE REFERENCES:

No. 100

NAME	n-Pentadecylbenzene	STRUCTURAL FORMULA
	1-Phenylpentadecane	

Mole % Pur.	Ref.	Molecular Formula $C_{21}H_{36}$	Molecular Weight 288.498

$C_{15}H_{31}$

		Ref.				Ref.					Ref.
F.P. °C	22.	2	dt/dP				f		to		
F.P. 100%			°C/mm				g		°K		
B.P. °C			25°C	4.83×10^5	5		h				
760 mm	373.	2	BP	0.0665	5						
100	287.	5	t_e	0.0343	5		f'		to		
30	247.	5	30 mm	1.0036	5		g'		°K		
10	216.	5	ΔHm cal/g				h'				
1	163.	5	ΔHv cal/g				m		300 to	-0.0055	4
Pressure			25°C	77.92	5		n		600 °K	0.0014	4
mm 25°C	0.0_416	5	30 mm	61.90	5		o			-0.0_654	4
t_e	1720.4	5	BP	52.11	5						
Density			t_e	48.74	5		m'		700 to	0.1012	4
g/ml 20°C	0.8548‡	2	t_e (d, e)	48.65	5		n'		1100 °K	0.0011	4
d_4^t 25	0.8513‡	2	ΔHv/T_e	20.36	5		o'			-0.0_638	4
30	0.8478	4	d 245 to	81.08	5		Surface tension				
a	0.8688	4	e 415 °C	0.0777	5		dynes/cm. 20°C			30.34	5
b	-0.0_37	4	d' 25 to	79.73	5		γ		30	29.36	5
Ref. Index			e' 245 °C	0.0722	5				40	28.40	5
n_D 20°C	1.4815‡	2	d_c g/ml	0.260	5		Parachor [P]				
25	1.4794‡	2	v_c ml/g	3.847	5				20°C		
30	1.4773	4	t_c °C	530.4	5				30		
"C"	0.7429	4	P_c mm	8050.	5				40		
MR (Obs.)	96.13‡	2	PV/RT						Sugd.	792.1	5
MR (Calc.)	95.577	5	25°C	1.0000	5		Exp. L.1.%/wt.				
(nD-d/2)	1.0541‡	2	30 mm	1.0000	5		u.				
Dielectric	2.195	5	BP	0.9241	5		Dispersion			127.	2
A 245 to	7.63586	5	t_e	0.8951	5		Flash Point °C				
B 420 °C	2629.5	5	t_c	0.178	5		Fire Point				
C	180.	5	ΔHc kcal/m	2957.96	2		M Spec.				
A* 245 to	2.3220	5	ΔHf				Ultra V.				
B* 420 °C	2517.2	5	ΔFf				X-Ray Dif.				
K			Viscosity				Infrared				
c			centistokes				Solubility in +				
t_k to			η 20 °C	10.54	2		Acetone				
t_x °C			40	6.15	2		Carbon tet.				
A' 25 to	8.02386	5	60	4.02	2		Benzene				
B' 245 °C	2971.3	5	80	2.81	2		Ether				
C'	207.	5	B^V 50 to	896.13	4		n-Heptane				
			A^V 105 °C	3.91476	4		Ethanol				
A'* 25 to	2.72051	5	(B^V) 105 to	851.15	4		Water				
B'* 245 °C	2856.7	5	(A^V) 160 °C	2.03411	4		Water in				
Ac to			c_p liq. °K				Viscosity				
Bc t_c °C							centistokes				
Cc			c_p vap.300°K	0.35539	2				100°C	2.07	2
Cryos. A°			400	0.45442	2				110	1.80	2
consts. B°			c_v vap.						150	1.11	2
t_e °C F	417.58	5									

‡ for undercooled liquid   + grams/100 grams solvent

REFERENCES: 1-Dow   2-API   3-Lit.   4-Calc. from det. data   5-Calc. by formula
SOURCE: API
PURIFICATION: API
LITERATURE REFERENCES:

TABLE I. ALKYL AND HALO BENZENES   111

No. 101

NAME	n-Hexadecylbenzene	STRUCTURAL FORMULA
	1-Phenylhexadecane	

Mole % Pur.	Ref.	Molecular Formula $C_{22}H_{38}$	Molecular Weight 302.524	$C_{16}H_{33}$ (benzene ring)

		Ref.			Ref.				Ref.
F.P. °C	27.	2	dt/dP			f	to		
F.P. 100%			°C/mm			g	°K		
B.P. °C			25°C	1.05×10^6	5	h			
760 mm	385.	2	BP	0.0670	5	f'	to		
100	298.	5	t_e	0.0339	5	g'	°K		
30	258.	5	30 mm	1.0177	5	h'			
10	226.	5	ΔHm cal/g			m	300 to	-0.0096	4
1	173.	5	ΔHv cal/g			n	600 °K	0.0014	4
Pressure			25°C	76.53	5	o		-0.0_658	4
mm 25°C	0.0_572	5	30 mm	60.61	5	m'	700 to	0.1042	4
t_e	1756.	5	BP	51.23	5	n'	1000 °K	0.0011	4
Density			t_e	47.84	5	o'		-0.0_637	4
g/ml 20°C	$0.8547^{\neq}$	2	t_e (d, e)	47.84	5	Surface tension			
d_4^t 25	$0.8512^{\neq}$	2	$\Delta Hv/T_e$	20.55	5	dynes/cm. 20°C		30.40	5
30	0.8477	4	d 260 to	79.58	5	ŏ 30		29.41	5
a	0.8687	4	e 430 °C	0.0736	5	40		28.45	5
b	-0.0_37	4	d' 25 to	78.24	5	Parachor [P]			
Ref. Index			e' 260 °C	0.0684	5	20°C			
n_D 20°C	$1.4813^{\neq}$	2	d_c g/ml	0.259	5	30			
25	$1.4792^{\neq}$	2	v_c ml/g	3.861	5	40			
30	1.4771	4	t_c °C	537.0	5	Sugd.		831.1	5
"C"	0.7427	4	P_c mm	7190.	5	Exp. L.1.%/wt.			
MR (Obs.)	$100.77^{\neq}$	2	PV/RT			u.			
MR (Calc.)	100.195	5	25°C	1.0000	5	Dispersion		$126.^{\neq}$	2
(nD-d/2)	$1.0539^{\neq}$	2	30 mm	1.0000	5	Flash Point °C			
Dielectric	2.194	5	BP	0.9258	5	Fire Point			
A 260 to	7.70156	5	t_e	0.8961	5	M. Spec.			
B 440 °C	2723.7	5	t_c	0.166	5	Ultra V.			
C	180.	5	ΔHc kcal/m	3104.89	2	X-Ray Dif.			
A* 260 to	2.3976	5	ΔHf			Infrared			
B* 440 °C	2607.8	5	ΔFf			Solubility in +			
K			Viscosity			Acetone			
c			centistokes			Carbon tet.			
t_k to			η 40 °C	7.03	2	Benzene			
t_x °C			60	4.52	2	Ether			
A' 25 to	8.0937	5	80	3.12	2	n-Heptane			
B' 260 °C	3077.7	5	100	2.27	2	Ethanol			
C'	208.	5	B^v 50 to	929.87	4	Water			
A'* 25 to	2.80424	5	A^v 105 °C	$\overline{3}.86442$	4	Water in			
B'* 260 °C	2961.2	5	(B^v) 105 to	887.55	4	Viscosity			
Ac to			(A^v) 160 °C	$\overline{3}.97830$	4	centistokes			
Bc t_c °C			c_p liq. °K			110°C		1.97	2
Cc						150		1.19	2
Cryos. A°			c_p vap.300°K	0.35706	2				
consts. B°			400	0.45629	2				
t_e °C F	431.1	5	c_v vap.						

≠ for undercooled liquid	+ grams/100 grams solvent

REFERENCES: 1-Dow 2-API 3-Lit. 4-Calc. from det. data 5-Calc. by formula

SOURCE: API

PURIFICATION: API

LITERATURE REFERENCES:

No. 102

NAME	n-Heptadecylbenzene	STRUCTURAL FORMULA
	1-Phenylheptadecane	$C_{17}H_{35}$
Mole % Pur.	Ref. Molecular Formula $C_{23}H_{40}$	Molecular Weight 316.550

		Ref.				Ref.					Ref.
F.P. °C	32.	2	dt/dP				f	to			
F.P. 100%			°C/mm				g	°K			
B.P. °C			25°C	9.3×10^{6}	5		h				
760 mm	397.	2	BP	0.06747	4						
100	309.5	5	t_e	0.03387	5		f'	to			
30	269.5	5	30 mm	1.0110	5		g'	°K			
10	238.5	5	ΔHm cal/g				h'				
1	186.	5	ΔHv cal/g				m	to			
Pressure			25°C	87.69	5		n	°K			
mm 25°C	0.0_668	5	30 mm	60.97	5		o				
t_e	$1786._6$	5	BP	50.32	5						
Density			t_e	46.60	5		m'	to			
g/ml 20°C	$0.8546^{\neq}$	2	t_e (d,e)	46.34	5		n'	°K			
d_4^t 25	$0.8512^{\neq}$	2	ΔHv/T_e	20.55	5		o'				
30	0.8478	4	d 270 to	83.49	5		Surface tension				
a	0.8682	4	e 430 °C	0.0836	5		dynes/cm. 20°C	30.45	5
b	-0.0_368	4	d' 25 to	90.42	5		γ	30	29.49	5
Ref. Index			e' 270 °C	0.1093	5			40	28.56	5
n_D 20°C	$1.4810^{\neq}$	2	d_c g/ml				Parachor [P]				
25	$1.4790^{\neq}$	2	v_c ml/g				20°C				
30	1.4769	4	t_c °C	545.6	5		30				
"C"	0.7423	4	P_c mm	7973.	5		40				
MR (Obs.)	$105.42^{\neq}$	2	PV/RT				Sugd.	870.1	5
MR (Calc.)	104.809	5	25°C	1.0000	5		Exp. L.1.%/wt.				
(nD-d/2)	$1.0537^{\neq}$	2	30 mm	1.0000	5		u.				
Dielectric	2.193	5	BP	0.9247	5		Dispersion	$125.^{\neq}$	2
A 270 to	7.55602	4	t_e	0.8945	5		Flash Point °C				
B 465°C	2580.7	4	t_c				Fire Point				
C	155.	5	ΔHc kcal/m				M Spec.				
A* 270 to	2.27692	5	ΔHf				Ultra V.				
B* 450°C	2474.5	5	ΔFf				X-Ray Dif.				
K			Viscosity				Infrared				
c			centistokes				Solubility in +				
t_k to			η °C				Acetone				
t_x °C							Carbon tet.				
A' 25 to	7.9390	5					Benzene				
B' 270 °C	2916.1	5					Ether				
C'	181.7	5	B^v to				n-Heptane				
A'* 25 to	2.6900	5	A^v °C				Ethanol				
B'* 270 °C	2816.9	5	(B^v) to				Water				
Ac to			(A^v) °C				Water in				
Bc t_c °C			c_p liq. °K								
Cc											
Cryos. A°			c_p vap. °K								
consts. B°											
t_e °C F	444.6	5	c_v vap.								

≠ for undercooled liquid   + grams/100 grams solvent

REFERENCES: 1-Dow   2-API   3-Lit.   4-Calc. from det. data   5-Calc. by formula

SOURCE: API

PURIFICATION: API

LITERATURE REFERENCES:

TABLE I. ALKYL AND HALO BENZENES 113

No. 103

NAME	n-Octadecylbenzene	STRUCTURAL FORMULA
	1-Phenyloctadecane	

Mole % Pur. | Ref. | Molecular Formula $C_{24}H_{42}$ | Molecular Weight 330.576

Structural formula: benzene ring with $C_{18}H_{37}$

		Ref.			Ref.				Ref.
F.P. °C	36.	2	dt/dP			f	to		
F.P. 100%			°C/mm			g	°K		
B.P. °C			25°C	1.97×10^{7}	5	h			
760 mm	408.	2	BP	0.06812	4				
100	319.5	5	t_e	0.0337	5	f'	to		
30	279.0	5	30 mm	1.0255	5	g'	°K		
10	247.5	5	ΔHm cal/g			h'			
1	194.	5	ΔHv cal/g			m	to		
Pressure			25°C	86.02	5	n	°K		
mm 25°C	0.0_632	5	30 mm	59.58	5	o			
t_e	1815.	5	BP	49.27	5				
Density			t_e	45.52	5	m'	to		
g/ml 20°C	$0.8546^{\neq}$	2	t_e (d, e)	45.35	5	n'	°K		
d_4^t 25	$0.8511^{\neq}$	2	ΔHv/T_e	20.61	5	o'			
30	0.8476	4				Surface tension			
a	0.8686	4	d 280 to	81.88	5	dynes/cm. 20°C	30.51	5
b	-0.0_37	4	e 445 °C	0.0799	5	Ɣ 30	29.52	5
Ref. Index			d' 25 to	88.62	5	40	28.56	5
n_D 20°C	$1.4809^{\neq}$	2	e' 280 °C	0.1041	5	Parachor [P]		
25	$1.4788^{\neq}$	2	d_c g/ml			20°C		
30	1.4767	4	v_c ml/g			30		
"C"	0.7422	4	t_c °C	549.3	5	40		
MR (Obs.)	$110.06^{\neq}$	2	P_c mm	7207.	5	Sugd.	909.1	5
MR (Calc.)	109.427	5	PV/RT			Exp. L.1.%/wt.		
(nD-d/2)	$1.0535^{\neq}$	2	25°C	1.0000	5	u.		
Dielectric	2.193	5	30 mm	1.0000	5	Dispersion	$124.^{\neq}$	2
A 280 to	7.60357	4	BP	0.9247	5	Flash Point °C		
B 470 °C	2658.9	4	t_e	0.8936	5	Fire Point		
C	155.	5	t_c			M. Spec.		
A* 280 to	2.33666	5	ΔHc kcal/m			Ultra V.		
B* 460 °C	2550.76	5	ΔHf			X-Ray Dif.		
K			ΔFf			Infrared		
c			Viscosity			Solubility in +		
t_k to			centistokes			Acetone		
t_x °C			η °C			Carbon tet.		
A' 25 to	7.98954	5				Benzene		
B' 280 °C	3004.5	5				Ether		
C'	182.3	5	B^v to			n-Heptane		
A'* 25 to	2.7534	5	A^v °C			Ethanol		
B'* 280 °C	2903.7	5	(B^v) to			Water		
Ac to			(A^v) °C			Water in		
Bc t_c °C			c_p liq. °K					
Cc								
Cryos. A°			c_p vap. °K					
consts. B°								
t_e °C F	457.0	5	c_v vap.					

≠ for undercooled liquid   + grams/100 grams solvent

REFERENCES: 1-Dow   2-API   3-Lit.   4-Calc. from det. data   5-Calc. by formula

SOURCE: API

PURIFICATION: API

LITERATURE REFERENCES:

No. 104

NAME	n-Nonadecylbenzene		STRUCTURAL FORMULA
	1-Phenylnonadecane		

$C_{19}H_{39}$

Mole % Pur.	Ref.	Molecular Formula $C_{25}H_{44}$	Molecular Weight 344.602

	Ref.			Ref.			Ref.
F.P. °C	40.	2	dt/dP °C/mm			f | to	
F.P. 100%			25°C	4.21×10^{7}	5	g | °K	
B.P. °C			BP	0.06875	4	h |	
760 mm	419.	2	t_e	0.0335	5	f' | to	
100	329.5	5	30 mm	1.0398	5	g' | °K	
30	288.5	5	ΔHm cal/g			h' |	
10	256.6	5				m | to	
1	202.	5	ΔHv cal/g			n | °K	
Pressure			25°C	84.50	5	o |	
mm 25°C	$0.0_6 144$	5	30 mm	58.33	5		
t_e	1844.9^6	5	BP	48.34	5	m' | to	
Density			t_e	44.61	5	n' | °K	
g/ml 20°C	$0.8545^{\neq}$	2	t_e (d, e)	44.48	5	o' |	
d_4^t 25	$0.8511^{\neq}$	2	ΔHv/T_e	20.70	5	Surface tension	
30	0.8477	4	d | 290 to	80.429	5	dynes/cm. 20°C	30.55	5
a	0.8681	4	e | 455 °C	0.0766	5	γ 30	29.59	5
b	$-0.0_3 68$	4	d' | 25 to	86.987	5	40	28.65	5
Ref. Index			e' | 290 °C	0.0993	5	Parachor [P]	
n_D 20°C	$1.4807^{\neq}$	2	d_c g/ml			20°C	
25	$1.4786^{\neq}$	2	v_c ml/g			30	
30	1.4766	4	t_c °C	557.1	5	40	
"C"	0.7420	4	P_c mm	6843.	5	Sugd. 948.1	5
MR (Obs.)	$114.70^{\neq}$	2	PV/RT			Exp. L.1.%/wt.	
MR (Calc.)	114.045	5	25°C	1.0000	5	u.	
(nD-d/2)	$1.0534^{\neq}$	2	30 mm	1.0000	5	Dispersion	$123.^{\neq}$	2
Dielectric	2.192	5	BP	0.9245	5	Flash Point °C	
A | 290 to	7.65210	4	t_e	0.8929	5	Fire Point	
B | 480 °C	2738.7	4	t_c			M Spec.	
C	155.	5	ΔHc kcal/m			Ultra V.	
A* | 290 to	2.3962	5	ΔHf			X-Ray Dif.	
B* | 470 °C	2628.4	5	ΔFf			Infrared	
K			Viscosity			Solubility in +	
c			centistokes			Acetone	
t_k | to			η °C			Carbon tet.	
t_x | °C						Benzene	
A' | 25 to	8.0411	5				Ether	
B' | 290 °C	3094.6	5				n-Heptane	
C'	182.9	5	B^v | to			Ethanol	
A'* | 25 to	2.8170	5	A^v | °C			Water	
B'* 290 °C	2992.3	5	(B^v) | to			Water in	
Ac | to			(A^v) | °C				
Bc | t_c °C			c_p liq. °K				
Cc			c_p vap. °K				
Cryos. A°			c_v vap.				
consts. B°							
t_e °C F	469.4	5					

≠ for undercooled liquid   + grams/100 grams solvent

REFERENCES: 1-Dow 2-API 3-Lit. 4-Calc. from det. data 5-Calc. by formula

SOURCE:　　　　　　API

PURIFICATION:　　　　API

LITERATURE REFERENCES:

TABLE I. ALKYL AND HALO BENZENES

No. 105

NAME	n-Eicosylbenzene	STRUCTURAL FORMULA
	1-Phenyleicosane	$C_{20}H_{41}$

Mole % Pur.	Ref.	Molecular Formula $C_{26}H_{46}$	Molecular Weight 358.628	

		Ref.			Ref.				Ref.
F.P. °C	44.	2	dt/dP			f	to		
F.P. 100%			°C/mm			g	°K		
			25°C	8.49×10^7	5	h			
B.P. °C			BP	0.06929	4				
760 mm	429.	2	t_e	0.0333	5	f'	to		
100	338.7	5				g'	°K		
30	297.2	5	30 mm	1.0525	5	h'			
10	264.9	5	ΔHm cal/g						
1	209.	5				m	to		
			ΔHv cal/g			n	°K		
Pressure			25°C	82.96	5	o			
mm 25°C	$0.0_7 70$	5	30 mm	57.10	5				
t_e	1873.	5	BP	47.45	5	m'	to		
			t_e	43.71	5	n'	°K		
Density			t_e (d, e)	43.66	5	o'			
g/ml 20°C	$0.8545^{\neq}$	2	ΔHv/T_e	20.79	5				
d_4^t 25	$0.8511^{\neq}$	2				Surface tension			
30	0.8477	4	d 295 to	78.87	5	dynes/cm. 20°C		30.60	5
			e 470 °C	0.0732	5	8	30	29.64	5
a	0.8681	4	d' 25 to	85.33	5		40	28.70	5
b	$-0.0_3 68$	4	e' 295 °C	0.0950	5				
						Parachor [P]			
Ref. Index			d_c g/ml			20°C			
n_D 20°C	$1.4805^{\neq}$	2	v_c ml/g			30			
25	$1.4785^{\neq}$	2	t_c °C	561.9	5	40			
30	1.4764	2	P_c mm	6350.	5	Sugd.	987.1		5
"C"	0.7417	4	PV/RT			Exp. L.1.%/wt.			
MR (Obs.)	$119.34^{\neq}$	2	25°C	1.0000	5	u.			
MR (Calc.)	118.663	5	30 mm	1.0000	5	Dispersion	$122.^{\neq}$		2
(nD-d/2)	$1.0533^{\neq}$	2	BP	0.9254	5				
Dielectric	2.192	5	t_e	0.8932	5	Flash Point °C			
A 295 to	7.69708	4	t_c			Fire Point			
B 500 °C	2812.7	4				M. Spec.			
C	155.	5	ΔHc kcal/m			Ultra V.			
A* 295 to	2.4510	5	ΔHf			X-Ray Dif.			
B* 480 °C	2699.8	5	ΔFf			Infrared			
K			Viscosity			Solubility in +			
c			centistokes			Acetone			
t_k to			η °C			Carbon tet.			
t_x °C						Benzene			
A' 25 to	8.0889	5				Ether			
B' 295 °C	3178.3	5	B^v to			n-Heptane			
C'	183.5	5	A^v °C			Ethanol			
A'* 25 to	2.8767	5	(B^v) to			Water			
B'* 295 °C	3074.6	5	(A^v) °C			Water in			
Ac to			c_p liq. °K						
Bc t_c °C									
Cc									
Cryos. A°			c_p vap. °K						
consts. B°									
t_e °C F	480.72	5	c_v vap.						

≠ for undercooled liquid   + grams/100 grams solvent

REFERENCES: 1-Dow 2-API 3-Lit. 4-Calc. from det. data 5-Calc. by formula

SOURCE:	API
PURIFICATION:	API

LITERATURE REFERENCES:

No. 106

NAME	n-Heneicosylbenzene	STRUCTURAL FORMULA
	1-Phenylheneicosane	$C_{21}H_{43}$

Mole % Pur.	Ref.	Molecular Formula $C_{27}H_{48}$		Molecular Weight 372.654

		Ref.			Ref.					Ref.
F.P. °C	48.	2	dt/dP °C/mm			f | to			
F.P. 100%			25°C	1.73×10^8	5	g | — °K			
B.P. °C			BP	0.06981	4	h |			
760 mm	439.	2	t_e	0.0331	5				
100	347.9	5	30 mm	1.0649	5	f' | to			
30	305.9	5				g' | — °K			
10	273.2	5	ΔHm cal/g			h' |			
1	217.	5							
Pressure			ΔHv cal/g			m | to			
mm 25°C	0.0_734	5	25°C	81.54	5	n | — °K			
t_e	1901.5_7	5	30 mm	55.98	5	o |			
Density			BP	46.59	5				
g/ml 20°C	$0.8545^{\neq}$	2	t_e	42.85	5	m' | to			
d_4^t 25	$0.8510^{\neq}$	2	t_e (d, e)	42.85	5	n' | — °K			
30	0.8475	4	ΔHv/T_e	20.87	5	o' |			
a	0.8685	4	d | 305 to	77.58	5	Surface tension			
b	-0.0_370	4	e | 480 °C	0.0706	5	dynes/cm. 20°C	30.65	5
Ref. Index			d' | 25 to	83.82	5	ɣ 30	29.65	5
n_D 20°C	$1.4804^{\neq}$	2	e' | 305 °C	0.0910	5	40	28.69	5
25	$1.4783^{\neq}$	2	d_c g/ml						
30	1.4762	4	v_c ml/g			Parachor [P]			
"C"	0.7416	4	t_c °C	564.4	5	20°C			
MR (Obs.)	$123.98^{\neq}$	2	P_c mm	5723.	5	30			
MR (Calc.)	123.281	5	PV/RT			40			
(nD-d/2)	$1.0532^{\neq}$	2	25°C	1.0000	5	Sugd.	1026.1	5
Dielectric	2.192	5	30 mm	1.0000	5	Exp. L.l.%/wt.			
A | 305 to	7.74293	4	BP	0.9254	5	u.			
B | 500 °C	2888.1	4	t_e	0.8932	5	Dispersion	$121.^{\neq}$	2
C	155.	5	t_c			Flash Point °C			
A* | 305 to	2.5064	5	ΔHc kcal/m			Fire Point			
B* | 500 °C	2772.8	5	ΔHf			M Spec.			
K			ΔFf			Ultra V.			
c						X-Ray Dif.			
t_k | to			Viscosity			Infrared			
t_x | °C			centistokes			Solubility in +			
A' | 25 to	8.1377	5	η °C			Acetone			
B' | 305 °C	3263.5	5				Carbon tet.			
C'	184.0	5				Benzene			
A'* 25 to	2.9368	5	B^v | to			Ether			
B'* 305 °C	3158.4	5	A^v | °C			n-Heptane			
Ac | to			(B^v) | to			Ethanol			
Bc | t_c °C			(A^v) | °C			Water			
Cc			c_p liq. °K			Water in			
Cryos. A°			c_p vap. °K						
consts. B°									
t_e °C F	492.	5	c_v vap.						

$\neq$ for undercooled liquid   + grams/100 grams solvent

REFERENCES: 1-Dow 2-API 3-Lit. 4-Calc. from det. data 5-Calc. by formula

SOURCE:	API
PURIFICATION:	API
LITERATURE REFERENCES:	

No. 107

NAME	n-Docosylbenzene	STRUCTURAL FORMULA
	1-Phenyldocosane	$C_{22}H_{45}$

Mole % Pur.	Ref.	Molecular Formula $C_{28}H_{50}$	Molecular Weight 386.680		

		Ref.			Ref.			Ref.
F.P. °C	51.	2	dt/dP			f | to		
F.P. 100%			°C/mm			g | __ °K		
B.P. °C			25°C	3.32×10^8	5	h |		
760 mm	448.	2	BP	0.07026	4			
100	356.2	5	t_e	0.0329	5	f' | to		
30	313.8	5	30 mm	1.0759	5	g' | __ °K		
10	280.7	5	ΔHm cal/g			h' |		
1	224.	5	ΔHv cal/g			m | to		
Pressure			25°C	80.08	5	n | __ °K		
mm 25°C	0.0_717	5	30 mm	54.86	5	o |		
t_e	1927.	5	BP	45.75	5			
Density			t_e	42.04	5	m' | to		
g/ml 20°C	$0.8544^{\neq}$	2	t_e (d, e)	42.07	5	n' | __ °K		
d_4^t 25	$0.8510^{\neq}$	2	ΔHv/T_e	20.97	5	o' |		
30	0.8476	4	d | 310 to	76.18	5	Surface tension		
a	0.8680	4	e | 490 °C	0.0679	5	dynes/cm. 20°C	30.68	5
b	-0.0_368	4	d' | 25 to	82.27	5	γ 30	29.71	5
Ref. Index			e' | 310 °C	0.0873	5	40	28.77	5
n_D 20°C	$1.4802^{\neq}$	2	d_c g/ml			Parachor [P]		
25	$1.4782^{\neq}$	2	v_c ml/g			20°C		
30	1.4761	4	t_c °C	570.4	5	30		
"C"	0.7414	4	P_c mm	5467.	5	40		
MR (Obs.)	$128.62^{\neq}$	2	PV/RT			Sugd.	1065.1	5
MR (Calc.)	127.899	5	25°C	1.0000	5	Exp. L.1.%/wt.		
(nD-d/2)	$1.0531^{\neq}$	2	30 mm	1.0000	5	u.		
Dielectric	2.191	5	BP	0.9256	5	Dispersion	$120.^{\neq}$	2
A | 310 to	7.78494	4	t_e	0.8933	5	Flash Point °C		
B |515 °C	2957.2	4	t_c			Fire Point		
C	155.	5	ΔHc kcal/m			M. Spec.		
A*| 310 to	2.55799	5	ΔHf			Ultra V.		
B*| 510 °C	2839.7	5	ΔFf			X-Ray Dif.		
K			Viscosity			Infrared		
c			centistokes			Solubility in +		
t_k | to			η °C			Acetone		
t_x | °C						Carbon tet.		
A' | 25 to	8.1823	5				Benzene		
B' |310 °C	3341.5	5	B^v | to			Ether		
C'	184.5	5	A^v | °C			n-Heptane		
A'* 25 to	2.9927	5	(B^v)| to			Ethanol		
B'* 310 °C	3235.2	5	(A^v)| °C			Water		
Ac | to						Water in		
Bc | t_c °C			c_p liq. °K					
Cc								
Cryos. A°			c_p vap. °K					
consts. B°								
t_e °C F	502.15	5	c_v vap.					

$\neq$ for undercooled liquid   + grams/100 grams solvent

REFERENCES: 1-Dow   2-API   3-Lit.   4-Calc. from det. data   5-Calc. by formula

SOURCE: API

PURIFICATION: API

LITERATURE REFERENCES:

No. 108

NAME	n-Tricosylbenzene	STRUCTURAL FORMULA
	1-Phenyltricosane	

$C_{23}H_{47}$

Mole % Pur.	Ref.	Molecular Formula $C_{29}H_{52}$	Molecular Weight 400.706

		Ref.			Ref.					Ref.
F.P. °C	54.	2	dt/dP °C/mm			f | to				
F.P. 100%			25°C	6.43×10^8	5	g | °K				
B.P. °C			BP	0.07070	4	h |				
760 mm	457.	2	t_e	0.0327	5	f' | to				
100	364.5	5	30 mm	1.0867	5	g' | °K				
30	321.7	5	ΔHm cal/g			h' |				
10	288.3	5								
1	231.	5	ΔHv cal/g			m | to				
Pressure			25°C	78.74	5	n | °K				
mm 25°C	0.0_887	5	30 mm	53.84	5	o |				
t_e	$1953.$	5	BP	44.97	5					
Density			t_e	41.29	5	m' | to				
g/ml 20°C	$0.8544^{\neq}$	2	t_e (d, e)	41.35	5	n' | °K				
d_4^t 25	$0.8510^{\neq}$	2	ΔHv/T_e	21.06	5	o' |				
30	0.8476	4								
a	0.8680	5	d | 320 to	74.93	5	Surface tension dynes/cm. 20°C	30.72	5		
b	-0.0_368	5	e | 490 °C	0.0656	5	𝛾 30	29.75	5		
Ref. Index			d' | 25 to	80.84	5	40	28.81	5		
n_D 20°C	$1.4801^{\neq}$	2	e' | 320 °C	0.0839	5					
25	$1.4781^{\neq}$	2	d_c g/ml			Parachor [P]				
30	1.4760	4	v_c ml/g			20°C				
"C"	0.7412	4	t_c °C	574.3	5	30				
MR (Obs.)	$133.26^{\neq}$		P_c mm	5077.	5	40				
MR (Calc.)	132.517	5	PV/RT			Sugd.	1104.1	5		
(nD-d/2)	$1.0530^{\neq}$	2	25°C	1.0000	5	Exp. L.1.%/wt.				
Dielectric	2.191	5	30 mm	1.0000	5	u.				
A | 320 to	7.82768	4	BP	0.9260	5	Dispersion	$119.^{\neq}$	2		
B | 520 °C	3027.5	4	t_e	0.8937	5	Flash Point °C				
C	155.	5	t_c			Fire Point				
A* | 320 to	2.6094	5	ΔHc kcal/m			M Spec.				
B* | 510 °C	2907.5	5	ΔHf			Ultra V.				
K			ΔFf			X-Ray Dif.				
c			Viscosity			Infrared				
t_k | to			centistokes			Solubility in +				
t_x | °C			𝜂 °C			Acetone				
A' | 25 to	8.2278	5				Carbon tet.				
B' | 320 °C	3421.	5				Benzene				
C'	185.0	5	B^v | to			Ether				
A'* 25 to	3.0489	5	A^v | °C			n-Heptane				
B'* 320 °C	3313.4	5	(B^v) | to			Ethanol				
Ac | to			(A^v) | °C			Water				
Bc | t_c °C			c_p liq. °K			Water in				
Cc										
Cryos. A°			c_p vap. °K							
consts. B°										
t_e °C F	512.3	5	c_v vap.							

$\neq$ for undercooled liquid

+ grams/100 grams solvent

REFERENCES: 1-Dow 2-API 3-Lit. 4-Calc. from det. data 5-Calc. by formula

SOURCE: API

PURIFICATION: API

LITERATURE REFERENCES:

TABLE I. ALKYL AND HALO BENZENES

No. 109

NAME	n-Tetracosylbenzene	STRUCTURAL FORMULA
	1-Phenyltetracosane	

Mole % Pur.   Ref.   Molecular Formula $C_{30}H_{54}$ Molecular Weight 414.732

$C_{24}H_{49}$

		Ref.			Ref.			Ref.
F.P. °C	57.	2	dt/dP			f $\quad$ to		
F.P. 100%			°C/mm			g $\quad$ °K		
			25°C	1.26×10^9	5	h		
B.P. °C			BP	0.07111	4			
760 mm	466.	2	t_e	0.03248	5	f' $\quad$ to		
100	372.8	5	30 mm	1.0973	5	g' $\quad$ °K		
30	329.7	5	ΔHm cal/g			h'		
10	295.9	5						
1	238.	5	ΔHv cal/g			m $\quad$ to		
Pressure			25°C	77.51	5	n $\quad$ °K		
mm 25°C	$0.0_8 44$	5	30 mm	52.90	5	o		
t_e	1980.	5	BP	44.28	5	m' $\quad$ to		
Density			t_e	40.61	5	n' $\quad$ °K		
g/ml 20°C	$0.8544^{\neq}$	2	t_e (d, e)	40.71	5	o'		
$d_4^t \quad 25$	$0.8510^{\neq}$	2	ΔHv/T_e	21.17	5	Surface tension		
30	0.8476	4	d $\quad$ 330 to	73.74	5	dynes/cm. 20°C	30.75	5
a	0.8680	5	e $\quad$ 500 °C	0.0632	5	$\gamma \quad$ 30	29.79	5
b	-0.0_368	5	d' $\quad$ 25 to	79.53	5	40	28.84	5
Ref. Index			e' $\quad$ 330 °C	0.0808	5	Parachor [P]		
$n_D \quad 20°C$	$1.4800^{\neq}$	2	d_c g/ml	0.2175	5	20°C		
25	$1.4780^{\neq}$	2	v_c ml/g	4.5972	5	30		
30	1.4760	4	t_c °C	578.2	5	40		
"C"	0.7411	4	P_c mm	4717.	5	Sugd.	1143.1	5
MR (Obs.)	$137.90^{\neq}$	2	PV/RT			Exp. L. l.%/wt.		
MR (Calc.)	137.135	5	25°C	1.0000	5	u.		
(nD-d/2)	$1.0529^{\neq}$	2	30 mm	1.0000	5	Dispersion	$118.^{\neq}$	2
Dielectric	2.190		BP	0.9266	5	Flash Point °C		
A $\lceil$ 330 to	7.87118	4	t_e	0.8945	5	Fire Point		
B $\lfloor$ 530 °C	3099.0	4	t_c			M. Spec.		
C	155.	5	ΔHc kcal/m			Ultra V.		
A* 330 to	2.6606	5	ΔHf			X-Ray Dif.		
B* 525 °C	2976.3	5	ΔFf			Infrared		
K			Viscosity			Solubility in $^+$		
c			centistokes			Acetone		
$t_k \lceil \quad$ to			$\eta \quad$ °C			Carbon tet.		
$t_x \lfloor \quad$ °C						Benzene		
A' $\lceil$ 25 to	8.2740	5				Ether		
B' $\lfloor$ 330 °C	3501.8	5				n-Heptane		
C'	185.5	5	$B^v \lceil \quad$ to			Ethanol		
A'* 25 to	3.1056	5	$A^v \lfloor \quad$ °C			Water		
B'* 330 °C	3393.	5	$(B^v)| \quad$ to			Water in		
Ac $\lceil \quad$ to			$(A^v)| \quad$ °C					
Bc $\lfloor t_c$ °C			c_p liq. °K					
Cc								
Cryos. A°			c_p vap. °K					
consts. B°								
t_e °C $\quad$ F	522.45	5	c_v vap.					

$\neq$ for undercooled liquid $\qquad\qquad\qquad$ $^+$ grams/100 grams solvent

REFERENCES: 1-Dow 2-API 3-Lit. 4-Calc. from det. data 5-Calc. by formula

SOURCE: API

PURIFICATION: API

LITERATURE REFERENCES:

No. 110

NAME	n-Pentacosylbenzene	STRUCTURAL FORMULA
	1-Phenylpentacosane	

$C_{25}H_{51}$

Mole % Pur.	Ref.	Molecular Formula $C_{31}H_{56}$	Molecular Weight 428.758

		Ref.			Ref.				Ref.
F.P. °C	59.	2	dt/dP °C/mm			f	to		
F.P. 100%			25°C	2.3×10^9	5	g	°K		
B.P. °C			BP	0.07146	4	h			
760 mm	474.	2	t_e	0.0323	5	f'	to		
100	380.3	5	30 mm	1.1066	5	g'	°K		
30	336.8	5	ΔHm cal/g			h'			
10	302.7	5	ΔHv cal/g			m	to		
1	244.	5	25°C	76.21	5	n	°K		
Pressure mm 25°C	$0.0_8 24$	5	30 mm	51.94	5	o			
t_e	2004.	5	BP	43.59	5	m'	to		
Density g/ml 20°C	$0.8544^{\neq}$	2	t_e	39.89	5	n'	°K		
d_4^t 25	$0.8510^{\neq}$	2	t_e (d, e)	40.09	5	o'			
30	0.8476	4	ΔHv/T_e	21.26	5	Surface tension dynes/cm. 20°C		30.79	5
a	0.8680	4	d 335 to	72.45	5	30		29.82	5
b	$-0.0_3 68$	4	e 515 °C	0.0609	5	40		28.88	5
Ref. Index			d' 25 to	78.16	5				
n_D 20°C	$1.4799^{\neq}$	2	e' 335 °C	0.0778	5	Parachor [P]			
25	$1.4779^{\neq}$	2	d_c g/ml			20°C			
30	1.4758	4	v_c ml/g			30			
"C"	0.7410	4	t_c °C	581.1	5	40			
MR (Obs.)	$142.54^{\neq}$	2	P_c mm	4384.	5	Sugd.	1182.1		5
MR (Calc.)	141.753	5	PV/RT			Exp. L.1.%/wt.			
(nD-d/2)	$1.0527^{\neq}$	2	25°C	1.0000	5	u.			
Dielectric	2.190	5	30 mm	1.0000	5	Dispersion		$118.^{\neq}$	2
A 335 to	7.91049	4	BP	0.9279	5	Flash Point °C			
B 540 °C	3163.7	4	t_e	0.8950	5	Fire Point			
C	155.	5	t_c			M Spec.			
A* 335 to	2.7081	5	ΔHc kcal/m			Ultra V.			
B* 530 °C	3038.6	5	ΔHf			X-Ray Dif.			
K			ΔFf			Infrared			
c			Viscosity			Solubility in +			
t_k to			centistokes			Acetone			
t_x °C			η °C			Carbon tet.			
A' 25 to	8.3158	5				Benzene			
B' 335 °C	3574.9	5				Ether			
C'	186.0	5				n-Heptane			
A'* 25 to	3.1575	5	B^v to			Ethanol			
B'* 335 °C	3464.9	5	A^v °C			Water			
Ac to			(B^v) to			Water in			
Bc t_c °C			(A^v) °C						
Cc			c_p liq. °K						
Cryos. A° consts. B°			c_p vap. °K						
t_e °C F	531.47	5	c_v vap.						

≠ for undercooled liquid   + grams/100 grams solvent

REFERENCES:	1-Dow	2-API	3-Lit.	4-Calc. from det. data	5-Calc. by formula

SOURCE:	API
PURIFICATION:	API
LITERATURE REFERENCES:	

TABLE I.   ALKYL AND HALO BENZENES   121

No. 111

NAME	n-Hexacosylbenzene		STRUCTURAL FORMULA
	1-Phenylhexacosane		

$C_{26}H_{53}$

Mole % Pur.	Ref.	Molecular Formula $C_{32}H_{58}$	Molecular Weight 442.784

		Ref.			Ref.				Ref.
F.P. °C	62.	2	dt/dP			f | to			
F.P. 100%			°C/mm			g | °K			
			25°C	4.23×10^9	5	h |			
B.P. °C			BP	0.07180	4				
760 mm	482.	2	t_e	0.0321	5	f' | to			
100	388.	5	30 mm	1.1156	5	g' | °K			
30	344.	5	ΔHm cal/g			h' |			
10	309.	5							
1	250.	5	ΔHv cal/g			m | to			
Pressure			25°C	75.01	5	n | °K			
mm 25°C	$0.0_8 13$	5	30 mm	51.06	5	o |			
t_e	2029.	5	BP	42.93	5				
Density				39.29	5	m' | to			
g/ml 20°C	0.8543‡	2	t_e (d, e)	39.49	5	n' | °K			
d_4^t 25	0.8510‡	2	$\Delta Hv/T_e$	21.38	5	o' |			
30	0.8477	4				Surface tension			
a	0.8675	4	d | 345 to	71.29	5	dynes/cm. 20°C	30.81	5
b	-0.0_3 66	4	e | 540 °C	0.0588	5	ɣ 30	29.87	5
Ref. Index			d' | 25 to	76.89	5	40	28.95	5
n_D 20°C	1.4798‡	2	e' | 345 °C	0.0751	5	Parachor [P]			
25	1.4778‡	2	d_c g/ml			20°C			
30	1.4768	4	v_c ml/g			30			
"C"	0.7409	4	t_c °C	586.7	5	40			
MR (Obs.)	147.18‡	2	P_c mm	4225.	5	Sugd.	1221.1	5
MR (Calc.)	146.371	5	PV/RT			Exp. L.l.%/wt.			
(nD-d/2)	1.0526‡	2	25°C	1.0000	5	u.			
Dielectric	2.190	5	30 mm	1.0000	5	Dispersion	117.‡	2
A | 345 to	7.95042	4	BP	0.9285	5	Flash Point °C			
B | 550 °C	3229.3	4	t_e	0.8961	5	Fire Point			
C	155.	5	t_c			M. Spec.			
A* | 345 to	2.75494	5	ΔHc kcal/m			Ultra V.			
B* | 550 °C	3101.4	5	ΔHf			X-Ray Dif.			
K			ΔFf			Infrared			
c			Viscosity			Solubility in +			
t_k | to			centistokes			Acetone			
t_x | °C			η °C			Carbon tet.			
A' | 25 to	8.3582	5				Benzene			
B' | 345 °C	3649.0	5				Ether			
C'	186.4	5	B^v | to			n-Heptane			
			A^v | °C			Ethanol			
A'* 25 to	3.2098	5	(B^v)| to			Water			
B'* 345 °C	3538.0	5				Water in			
Ac | to			(A^v)| °C						
Bc | t_c °C			c_p liq. °K						
Cc									
Cryos. A°			c_p vap. °K						
consts. B°									
t_e °C F	540.49	5	c_v vap.						

‡ for undercooled liquid   + grams/100 grams solvent

REFERENCES: 1-Dow 2-API 3-Lit.   4-Calc. from det. data 5-Calc. by formula

SOURCE: API

PURIFICATION: API

LITERATURE REFERENCES:

No. 112

NAME	n-Heptacosylbenzene				STRUCTURAL FORMULA			
	1-Phenylheptacosane							

Structural formula: $C_{27}H_{55}$ (benzene ring)

Mole % Pur.	Ref.	Molecular Formula $C_{33}H_{60}$		Molecular Weight 456.810				

		Ref.				Ref.				Ref.
F.P. °C	64.	2	dt/dP °C/mm				f | | to		
F.P. 100%			25°C	6.43×10^{10}	5		g | | °K		
B.P. °C			BP	0.07045	4		h |		
760 mm	490.	2	t_e	0.0321	5		f' | | to		
100	397.4	5	30 mm	1.0984	5		g' | | °K		
30	354.	5	ΔHm cal/g				h' |		
10	320.3	5							
1	262.	5	ΔHv cal/g				m | | to		
Pressure			25°C	84.23	5		n | | °K		
mm 25°C	$0.0_{10}71$	5	30 mm	51.97	5		o |		
t_e	1972.	5	BP	42.07	5				
Density			t_e	38.21	5		m' | | to		
g/ml 20°C	0.8543‡	2	t_e (d, e)	36.03	5		n' | | °K		
d_4^t 25	0.8510‡	2	ΔHv/T_e	21.32	5		o' |		
30	0.8477	4					Surface tension		
a	0.8675	4	d | 355 to	77.74	5		dynes/cm. 20°C	30.84	5
b	-0.0₃66	4	e | 540 °C	0.0728	5		ɣ 30	29.90	5
			d' | 25 to	86.68	5		40	28.98	5
Ref. Index			e' | 355 °C	0.0980	5				
n_D 20°C	1.4797‡	2	d_c g/ml				Parachor [P]		
25	1.4777‡	2	v_c ml/g				20°C		
30	1.4758	4	t_c °C	585.	5		30		
"C"	0.7408	4	P_c mm	3577.	5		40		
MR (Obs.)	151.82‡	2					Sugd.	1260.1	5
MR (Calc.)	150.989	5	PV/RT				Exp. L.1.%/wt.		
(nD-d/2)	1.0526‡	2	25°C	1.0000	5		u.		
Dielectric	2.190	5	30 mm	1.0000	5		Dispersion	117.‡	2
A | 355 to	7.99100	4	BP	0.9026	5		Flash Point °C		
B | 550 °C	3219.4	4	t_e	0.8657	5		Fire Point		
C	140.	5	t_c				M Spec.		
A* | 355 to	2.86032	5	ΔHc kcal/m				Ultra V.		
B* | 550 °C	3120.	5	ΔHf				X-Ray Dif.		
K			ΔFf				Infrared		
c			Viscosity				Solubility in +		
t_k | to			centistokes				Acetone		
t_x | °C			η °C				Carbon tet.		
A' | 25 to	8.4014	5					Benzene		
B' | 355 °C	3637.8	5					Ether		
C'	171.	5	B^v | to				n-Heptane		
			A^v | °C				Ethanol		
A'* 25 to	3.2762	5	(B^v) | to				Water		
B'* 355 °C	3536.7	5	(A^v) | °C				Water in		
Ac | to			c_p liq. °K						
Bc | t_c °C									
Cc			c_p vap. °K						
Cryos. A°									
consts. B°			c_v vap.						
t_e °C	545.5	5							

‡ for undercooled liquid   + grams/100 grams solvent

REFERENCES: 1-Dow 2-API 3-Lit. 4-Calc. from det. data 5-Calc. by formula

SOURCE: API

PURIFICATION: API

LITERATURE REFERENCES:

TABLE I. ALKYL AND HALO BENZENES

No. 113

NAME	n-Octacosylbenzene	STRUCTURAL FORMULA
	1-Phenyloctacosane	

Structural Formula: (benzene ring) $C_{28}H_{57}$

Mole % Pur.	Ref.	Molecular Formula $C_{34}H_{62}$	Molecular Weight 470.836

		Ref.			Ref.				Ref.
F.P. °C	66.	2	dt/dP			f	| to		
F.P. 100%			°C/mm			g	| _ _ °K		
B.P. °C			25°C	1.26×10^{11}	5	h	|		
760 mm	498.	2	BP	0.07077	4				
100	405.	5	t_e	0.0319	5	f'	| to		
30	361.	5	30 mm	1.1073	5	g'	| _ _ °K		
10	327.	5	ΔHm cal/g			h'	|		
1	268.	5	ΔHv cal/g			m	| to		
Pressure			25°C	83.04	5	n	| _ _ °K		
m.m 25°C	$0.0_{10}36$	5	30 mm	51.16	5	o	|		
t_e	2001.	5	BP	41.52	5	m'	| to		
Density			t_e	37.65	5	n'	| _ _ °K		
g/ml 20°C	$0.8543^{\neq}$	2	t_e (d, e)	37.53	5	o'	|		
d_4^t 25	$0.8510^{\neq}$	2	ΔHv/T_e	21.41	5	Surface tension			
30	0.8477	4	d | 360 to	76.58	5	dynes/cm. 20°C		30.87	5
a	0.8675	4	e | 550 °C	0.0704	5	γ	30	29.93	5
b	-0.0_366	4	d' | 25 to	85.41	5		40	29.01	5
Ref. Index			e' | 360 °C	0.0948	5	Parachor [P]			
n_D 20°C	$1.4796^{\neq}$	2	d_c g/ml			20°C			
25	$1.4776^{\neq}$	2	v_c ml/g			30			
30	1.4757	4	t_c °C	588.8	5	40			
"C"	0.7407	4	P_c mm	3333.	5	Sugd. 1299.1			5
MR (Obs.)	$156.46^{\neq}$	2	PV/RT			Exp. L.1.%/wt.			
MR (Calc.)	155.607	4	25°C	1.0000	5	u.			
(nD-d/2)	$1.0524^{\neq}$	2	30 mm	1.0000	5	Dispersion		$116.^{\neq}$	2
Dielectric	2.189	5	BP	0.9037	5	Flash Point °C			
A | 360 to	8.03223	4	t_e	0.8687	5	Fire Point			
B | 560 °C	3286.6	4	t_c			M. Spec.			
C	140.	5	ΔHc kcal/m			Ultra V.			
A* | 360 to	2.89990	5	ΔHf			X-Ray Dif.			
B* | 560 °C	3180.	5	ΔFf			Infrared			
K			Viscosity			Solubility in +			
c			centistokes			Acetone			
t_k | to			η °C			Carbon tet.			
t_x | °C						Benzene			
A' | 25 to	8.4452	5				Ether			
B' | 360 °C	3713.8	5				n-Heptane			
C'	172.	5	B^v | to			Ethanol			
A'* 25 to	3.3291	5	A^v | °C			Water			
B'* 360 °C	3611.7	5	(B^v)| to			Water in			
Ac | to			(A^v)| °C						
Bc | t_c °C			c_p liq. °K						
Cc									
Cryos. A°			c_p vap. °K						
consts. B°									
t_e °C	554.7	5	c_v vap.						

$\neq$ for undercooled liquid   + grams/100 grams solvent

REFERENCES: 1-Dow 2-API 3-Lit. 4-Calc. from det. data 5-Calc. by formula

SOURCE: API

PURIFICATION: API

LITERATURE REFERENCES:

No. 114

NAME	n-Nonacosylbenzene		STRUCTURAL FORMULA
	1-Phenylnonacosane		$C_{29}H_{59}$

Mole % Pur.	Ref.	Molecular Formula $C_{35}H_{64}$	Molecular Weight 484.862

		Ref.				Ref.					Ref.
F.P. °C	68.	2	dt/dP				f	$\mid$	to		
F.P. 100%			°C/mm				g	$\mid$	°K		
B.P. °C			25°C	2.29×10^{11}	5		h	$\mid$			
760 mm	505.	2	BP	0.07104	4						
100	411.	4	t_e	0.0306	5		f'	$\mid$	to		
30	368.	5	30 mm	1.1149	5		g'	$\mid$	°K		
10	333.	4	ΔHm cal/g				h'	$\mid$			
1	274.	5									
			ΔHv cal/g				m	$\mid$	to		
Pressure			25°C	81.78	5		n	$\mid$	°K		
mm 25°C	$0.0_{10}19$	5	30 mm	50.32	5		o	$\mid$			
t_e	2110.	5	BP	42.69	5						
Density				38.47	5		m'	$\mid$	to		
g/ml 20°C	0.8543$^{\neq}$	2	t_e				n'	$\mid$	°K		
d_4^t 25	0.8509$^{\neq}$	2	t_e (d, e)	39.33	5		o'	$\mid$			
30	0.8475	4	ΔHv/T_e	22.24	5						
a	0.8679	4	d $\mid$ 365 to	70.82	5		Surface tension				
b	-0.0_368	4	e $\mid$ 555 °C	0.0557	5		dynes/cm. 20°C		30.90	5
			d' $\mid$ 25 to	34.07	5		ɤ		30	29.93	5
Ref. Index			e' $\mid$ 365 °C	0.0918	5				40	28.98	5
n_D 20°C	1.4796$^{\neq}$	2	d_c g/ml				Parachor [P]				
25	1.4775$^{\neq}$	2	v_c ml/g				20°C				
30	1.4756	4	t_c °C	591.	5		30				
"C"	0.7407	4	P_c mm	3098.	5		40				
MR (Obs.)	161.10$^{\neq}$	2	PV/RT						Sugd.	1338.1	5
MR (Calc.)	160.235	5	25°C	1.0000	5		Exp. L.1.%/wt.				
(nD-d/2)	1.0524$^{\neq}$	2	30 mm	1.0000	5		u.				
Dielectric	2.189	5	BP	0.9433	5		Dispersion		116.$^{\neq}$	2
A $\mid$ 365 to	8.06885	4	t_e	0.9045	5		Flash Point °C				
B $\mid$ 570°C	3346.3	4	t_c				Fire Point				
C	140.	5	ΔHc kcal/m				M Spec.				
A* $\mid$ 365 to	2.92902	5	ΔHf				Ultra V.				
B* $\mid$ 570°C	3240.	5	ΔFf				X-Ray Dif.				
K							Infrared				
c			Viscosity				Solubility in +				
t_k $\mid$ to			centistokes				Acetone				
t_x $\mid$ °C			ɳ °C				Carbon tet.				
A' $\mid$ 25 to	8.48413	5					Benzene				
B' $\mid$ 365°C	3781.2	5					Ether				
C'	172.	5	B^V $\mid$ to				n-Heptane				
A'* 25 to	3.37707	5	A^V $\mid$ °C				Ethanol				
B'* 365°C	3678.1	5	(B^V) $\mid$ to				Water				
Ac $\mid$ to			(A^V) $\mid$ °C				Water in				
Bc $\mid$ t_c °C			c_p liq. °K								
Cc											
Cryos. A°			c_p vap. °K								
consts. B°											
t_e °C	565.3	5	c_v vap.								

≠ for undercooled liquid	+ grams/100 grams solvent

REFERENCES: 1-Dow 2-API 3-Lit. 4-Calc. from det. data 5-Calc. by formula

SOURCE:	API
PURIFICATION:	API

LITERATURE REFERENCES:

TABLE I. ALKYL AND HALO BENZENES 125

NAME	n-Triacontylbenzene	STRUCTURAL FORMULA
	1-Phenyltriacontane	$C_{30}H_{61}$

Mole % Pur.	Ref.	Molecular Formula $C_{36}H_{66}$	Molecular Weight 498.888

		Ref.			Ref.			Ref.
F.P. °C	70.	2	dt/dP			f	to	
F.P. 100%			°C/mm			g	°K	
			25°C	4.2×10^{11}	5	h		
B.P. °C			BP	0.07130	4			
760 mm	512.	2	t_e	0.0313	5	f'	to	
100	418.	5	30 mm	1.1224	5	g'	°K	
30	374.	5	ΔHm cal/g			h'		
10	339.	5	ΔHv cal/g			m	to	
1	279.	5	25°C	80.59	5	n	°K	
Pressure			30 mm	49.54	5	o		
mm 25°C	$0.0_{10}1$	5	BP	40.73	5			
t_e	2060.	5	t_e	36.73	5	m'	to	
Density			t_e (d, e)	36.96	5	n'	°K	
g/ml 20°C	0.8543‡	2	$\Delta Hv/T_e$	21.71	5	o'		
d_4^t 25	0.8509‡	2				Surface tension		
30	0.8475	4	d ⌐ 375 to	73.38	5	dynes/cm. 20°C	30.92	5
a	0.8679	4	e ⌊ 570 °C	0.0638	5	γ 30	29.95	5
b	-0.0₃68	4	d' ⌐ 25 to	82.81	5	40	29.00	5
Ref. Index			e' ⌊ 375 °C	0.0890	5	Parachor [P]		
n_D 20°C	1.4795‡	2	d_c g/ml			20°C		
25	1.4775‡	2	v_c ml/g			30		
30	1.4755	4	t_c °C	590.8	5	40		
"C"	0.7405	4	P_c mm	2781.	5	Sugd.	1377.1	5
MR (Obs.)	165.74‡	2	PV/RT			Exp. L.1.%/wt.		
MR (Calc.)	164.853	5	25°C	1.0000	5	u.		
(nD-d/2)	1.0523‡	2	30 mm	1.000	5	Dispersion	115.‡	2
Dielectric	2.189	5	BP	0.9138	5	Flash Point °C		
A ⌐375 to	8.10600	4	t_e	0.8772	5	Fire Point		
B ⌊580 °C	3406.8	4	t_c			M. Spec.		
C	140.	5	ΔHc kcal/m			Ultra V.		
A* ⌐375 to	2.98945	5	ΔHf			X-Ray Dif.		
B* ⌊570 °C	3300.	5	ΔFf			Infrared		
K			Viscosity			Solubility in ⁺		
c			centistokes			Acetone		
t_k ⌐ to			η °C			Carbon tet.		
t_x ⌊ °C						Benzene		
A' ⌐ 25 to	8.52362	5				Ether		
B' ⌊375 °C	3849.6	5	B^v ⌐ to			n-Heptane		
C'	172.	5	A^v ⌊ °C			Ethanol		
A'* 25 to	3.4254	5	(B^v) ⌐ to			Water		
B'* 375 °C	3745.6	5	(A^v) ⌊ °C			Water in		
Ac ⌐ to								
Bc ⌊ t_c °C			c_p liq. °K					
Cc								
Cryos. A°			c_p vap. °K					
consts. B°								
t_e °C	570.9	5	c_v vap.					

‡ for undercooled liquid   ⁺ grams/100 grams solvent

REFERENCES: 1-Dow 2-API 3-Lit. 4-Calc. from det. data 5-Calc. by formula

SOURCE: API

PURIFICATION: API

LITERATURE REFERENCES:

No. 116

NAME	n-Hentriacontylbenzene	STRUCTURAL FORMULA
	1-Hentriacontane	$C_{31}H_{63}$

Mole % Pur.	Ref.	Molecular Formula $C_{37}H_{68}$	Molecular Weight 512.914

		Ref.			Ref.			Ref.
F.P. °C	72.	2	dt/dP °C/mm			f | to		
F.P. 100%			25°C	7.74×10^{11}	5	g | °K		
B.P. °C			BP	0.07155	4	h |		
760 mm	519.	2	t_e	0.0316	5	f' | to		
100	425.	5	30 mm	1.1297	5	g' | °K		
30	380.	5	ΔHm cal/g			h' |		
10	345.	5				m | to		
1	285.	5	ΔHv cal/g			n | °K		
Pressure			25°C	79.48	5	o |		
mm 25°C	$0.0_{11}56$	5	30 mm	48.81	5	m' | to		
t_e	2037.	5	BP	39.49	5	n' | °K		
Density			t_e	35.59	5	o' |		
g/ml 20°C	0.8543≠	2	t_e (d, e)	35.59	5	Surface tension		
d_4^t 25	0.8509≠	2	ΔHv/T_e	21.46	5	dynes/cm. 20°C	30.95	5
30	0.8475	4	d | 380 to	74.30	5	ɣ 30	29.97	5
a	0.8679	4	e | 580 °C	0.06705	5	40	29.02	5
b	-0.0_368	4	d' | 25 to	81.64	5	Parachor [P]		
Ref. Index			e' | 380 °C	0.0863	5	20°C		
n_D 20°C	1.4794≠	2	d_c g/ml			30		
25	1.4774≠	2	v_c ml/g			40		
30	1.4754	4	t_c °C	591.	5	Sugd.	1416.1	5
"C"	0.7404	2	P_c mm	2508.	5	Exp. L.1.%/wt.		
MR (Obs.)	170.38≠	2	PV/RT			u.		
MR (Calc.)	169.471	5	25°C	1.0000	5	Dispersion	115.≠	2
(nD-d/2)	1.0523≠	2	30 mm	1.0000	5	Flash Point °C		
Dielectric	2.189	5	BP	0.8987	5	Fire Point		
A | 380 to	8.14368	4	t_e	0.8607	5	M Spec.		
B | 580 °C	3468.2		t_c			Ultra V.		
C	140.	5	ΔHc kcal/m			X-Ray Dif.		
A* | 380 to	3.05729	5	ΔHf			Infrared		
B* | 580 °C	3370.	5	ΔFf			Solubility in +		
K			Viscosity			Acetone		
c			centistokes			Carbon tet.		
t_k | to			η °C			Benzene		
t_x | °C						Ether		
A' | 25 to	8.56367	5				n-Heptane		
B' | 380 °C	3919.0	5				Ethanol		
C'	173.	5	B^v | to			Water		
A'* | 25 to	3.47392	5	A^v | °C			Water in		
B'* 380 °C	3814.1	5	(B^v) | to					
Ac | to			(A^v) | °C					
Bc | t_c °C			c_p liq. °K					
Cc								
Cryos. A°			c_p vap. °K					
consts. B°								
t_e °C	577.4	5	c_v vap.					

≠ for undercooled liquid   + grams/100 grams solvent

REFERENCES: 1-Dow 2-API 3-Lit. 4-Calc. from det. data 5-Calc. by formula

SOURCE: API

PURIFICATION: API

LITERATURE REFERENCES:

TABLE I. ALKYL AND HALO BENZENES

No. 117

| NAME | n-Dotriacontylbenzene | STRUCTURAL FORMULA |
| | 1-Phenyldotriacontane | |

| Mole
% Pur. | Ref. | Molecular
Formula $C_{38}H_{70}$ | Molecular
Weight 526.940 | $C_{32}H_{65}$ |

		Ref.			Ref.			Ref.
F.P. °C	74.	2	dt/dP			f | to		
F.P. 100%			°C/mm			g | - - °K		
			25°C	1.32×10^{12}	5	h |		
B.P. °C			BP	0.07176	5			
760 mm	525.	2	t_e	0.0310	5	f' | to		
100	430.	4	30 mm	1.1359	5	g' | - - °K		
30	386.	5	ΔHm cal/g			h' |		
10	351.	4	ΔHv cal/g			m | to		
1	290.	5	25°C	78.28	5	n | - - °K		
Pressure			30 mm	48.04	5	o |		
mm 25°C	$0.0_{11}33$	5	BP	39.60	5	m' | to		
t_e	2091.7^{11}	5	t_e	35.66	5	n' | - - °K		
Density			t_e (d, e)	35.95	5	o' |		
g/ml 20°C	$0.8543^{\neq}$	2	ΔHv/T_e	21.89	5	Surface tension		
d_4^t 25	$0.8509^{\neq}$	2	d | 385 to	71.74	5	dynes/cm. 20°C	30.97	5
30	0.8475	4	e | 580 °C	0.0607	5	δ 30	30.00	5
a	0.8679	4	d' | 25 to	80.38	5	40	29.05	5
b	-0.0_368	4	e' | 385 °C	0.0839	5			
Ref. Index			d_c g/ml			Parachor [P]		
n_D 20°C	$1.4794^{\neq}$	2	v_c ml/g			20°C		
25	$1.4773^{\neq}$	2	t_c °C	597.7	5	30		
30	1.4754	2	P_c mm	2526.	5	40		
"C"	0.7404	4	PV/RT			Sugd.	1455.1	5
MR (Obs.)	$175.02^{\neq}$	2	25°C	1.0000	5	Exp. L.l.%/wt.		
MR (Calc.)	174.089	5	30 mm	1.0000	5	u.		
(nD-d/2)	$1.0522^{\neq}$	2	BP	0.9148	5	Dispersion	$114.^{\neq}$	2
Dielectric	2.189	5	t_e	0.8758	5	Flash Point °C		
A | 385 to	8.17642	4	t_c			Fire Point		
B | 585 °C	3521.6	4	ΔHc kcal/m			M. Spec.		
C	140.	5	ΔHf			Ultra V.		
A* | 385 to	3.08707	5	ΔFf			X-Ray Dif.		
B* | 570 °C	3420.	5	Viscosity			Infrared		
K			centistokes			Solubility in +		
c			η °C			Acetone		
t_k | to						Carbon tet.		
t_x | °C						Benzene		
A' | 25 to	8.59848	5				Ether		
B' | 385 °C	3979.3	5	B_v | to			n-Heptane		
C'	173.	5	A_v | °C			Ethanol		
A'* | 25 to	3.51752	5	(B^v) | to			Water		
B'* | 385 °C	3873.7	5	(A^v) | °C			Water in		
Ac | to			c_p liq. °K					
Bc | t_c °C								
Cc |			c_p vap. °K					
Cryos. A°								
consts. B°								
t_e °C	585.2	5	c_v vap.					

$\neq$ for undercooled liquid   + grams/100 grams solvent

REFERENCES: 1-Dow 2-API 3-Lit. 4-Calc. from det. data 5-Calc. by formula

| SOURCE: | API |
| PURIFICATION: | API |

LITERATURE REFERENCES:

No. 118

NAME	n-Tritriacontylbenzene	STRUCTURAL FORMULA
	1-Phenyltritriacontane	$C_{33}H_{67}$

Mole % Pur.	Ref.	Molecular Formula $C_{39}H_{72}$	Molecular Weight 540.966

		Ref.				Ref.					Ref.
F.P. °C	75.	2	dt/dP				f		to		
F.P. 100%			°C/mm				g	°K			
B.P. °C			25°C	2.46×10^{12}	5		h				
760 mm	532.	2	BP	0.07199	4						
100	437.	5	t_e	0.0310	5		f'		to		
30	392.	5	30 mm	1.1430	5		g'	°K			
10	357.	5	ΔHm cal/g				h'				
1	295.	5	ΔHv cal/g				m		to		
Pressure			25°C	77.31	5		n	°K			
mm 25°C	$0.0_{11}17$	5	30 mm	47.40	5		o				
t_e	2094.	5	BP	38.80	5						
Density			t_e	34.85	5		m'		to		
g/ml 20°C	0.8543‡	2	t_e (d,e)	35.06	5		n'	°K			
d_4^t 25	0.8509‡	2	ΔHv/T_e	21.78	5		o'				
30	0.8475	4	d 390 to	71.46	5		Surface tension				
a	0.8679	4	e 585 °C	0.0614	5		dynes/cm. 20°C		30.99	5
b	-0.0_368	4	d' 25 to	79.34	5		γ 30		30.02	5
Ref. Index			e' 390 °C	0.0815	5		40		29.07	5
n_D 20°C	1.4793‡	2	d_c g/ml				Parachor [P]				
25	1.4773‡	2	v_c ml/g				20°C				
30	1.4753	2	t_c °C	596.	5		30				
"C"	0.7403	4	P_c mm	2199.	5		40				
MR (Obs.)	179.66‡	2	PV/RT				Sugd.	1494.1		5
MR (Calc.)	178.707	5	25°C	1.0000	5		Exp. L.1.%/wt.				
(nD-d/2)	1.0522‡	2	30 mm	1.0000	5		u.				
Dielectric	2.188	5	BP	0.9077	5		Dispersion	114.‡		2
A 390 to	8.21513	4	t_e	0.8694	5		Flash Point °C				
B 590 °C	3584.7	4	t_c				Fire Point				
C	140.	5	ΔHc kcal/m				M Spec.				
A* 390 to	3.13377	5	ΔHf				Ultra V.				
B* 590 °C	3480.	5	ΔFf				X-Ray Dif.				
K			Viscosity				Infrared				
c			centistokes				Solubility in +				
t_k to			η °C				Acetone				
t_x °C							Carbon tet.				
A' 25 to	8.63962	5					Benzene				
B' 390 °C	4050.6	5					Ether				
C'	174.	5	B^v to				n-Heptane				
A'* 25 to	3.56644	5	A^v °C				Ethanol				
B'* 390 °C	3944.0	5	(B^v) to				Water				
Ac to			(A^v) °C				Water in				
Bc t_c °C			c_p liq. °K								
Cc											
Cryos. A°			c_p vap. °K								
consts. B°											
t_e °C	592.5	5	c_v vap.								

‡ for undercooled liquid

+ grams/100 grams solvent

REFERENCES: 1-Dow 2-API 3-Lit. 4-Calc. from det. data 5-Calc. by formula

SOURCE: API

PURIFICATION: API

LITERATURE REFERENCES:

TABLE I. ALKYL AND HALO BENZENES

129

No. 119

NAME	n-Tetratriacontylbenzene	STRUCTURAL FORMULA
	1-Phenyltetratriacontane	

$C_{34}H_{69}$ (benzene ring)

Mole % Pur.	Ref.	Molecular Formula $C_{40}H_{74}$	Molecular Weight 554.992

		Ref.				Ref.					Ref.
F.P. °C	77.	2	dt/dP °C/mm			f	to				
F.P. 100%			25°C	4.23×10^{12}	5	g	_ _ °K				
B.P. °C			BP	0.07218	4	h					
760 mm	538.	2	t_e	0.0314	5	f'	to				
100	442.	5	30 mm	1.1490	5	g'	_ _ °K				
30	397.	5	ΔHm cal/g			h'					
10	362.	5	ΔHv cal/g			m	to				
1	300.	5	25°C	76.24	5	n	_ _ °K				
Pressure mm 25°C	$0.0_{12}99$	5	30 mm	46.72	5	o					
t_e	2068.	5	BP	37.56	5	m'	to				
Density g/ml 20°C	0.8543	2	t_e	33.67	5	n'	_ _ °K				
d_4^t 25	0.8509	2	t_e (d, e)	33.66	5	o'					
30	0.8475	4	ΔHv/T_e	21.46	5	Surface tension dynes/cm. 20°C	32.67	5			
a	0.8679	4	d 395 to	72.53	5	δ 30	31.64	5			
b	-0.0_368	4	e 595 °C	0.0650	5	40	30.63	5			
Ref. Index			d' 25 to	78.22	5	Parachor [P]					
n_D 20°C	1.4792	2	e' 395 °C	0.0793	5	20°C					
25	1.4772	2	d_c g/ml			30					
30	1.4752	4	v_c ml/g			40					
"C"	0.7402	4	t_c °C			Sugd.	1553.1	5			
MR (Obs.)	184.30	2	P_c mm								
MR (Calc.)	183.323	5	PV/RT			Exp. L.1.%/wt.					
(nD-d/2)	1.0521	2	25°C	1.0000	5	u.					
Dielectric	2.188	5	30 mm	1.0000	5	Dispersion	113.	2			
A 400 to	8.24877	4	BP	0.8915	5	Flash Point °C					
B 610 °C	3639.5	4	t_e	0.8534	5	Fire Point					
C	140.	5	t_c			M. Spec.					
A* 400 to	3.19216	5	ΔHc kcal/m			Ultra V.					
B* 600 °C	3540.	5	ΔHf			X-Ray Dif.					
K			ΔFf			Infrared					
c			Viscosity centistokes			Solubility in +					
t_k to			η °C			Acetone					
t_x °C						Carbon tet.					
A' 25 to	8.67538	5				Benzene					
B' 400 °C	4112.5	5				Ether					
C'	174.	5	B_v to			n-Heptane					
A'* 25 to	3.61032	5	A_v °C			Ethanol					
B'* 400 °C	4005.2	5	(B^v) to			Water					
Ac to			(A^v) °C			Water in					
Bc t_c °C											
Cc			c_p liq. °K								
Cryos. A° consts. B°			c_p vap. °K								
t_e °C	598.	5	c_v vap.								

≠ for undercooled liquid   + grams/100 grams solvent

REFERENCES: 1-Dow 2-API 3-Lit. 4-Calc. from det. data 5-Calc. by formula

SOURCE: API

PURIFICATION: API

LITERATURE REFERENCES:

No. 120

NAME	n-Pentatriacontylbenzene	STRUCTURAL FORMULA
	1-Phenylpentatriacontane	

$C_{35}H_{71}$

Mole % Pur.	Ref.	Molecular Formula $C_{41}H_{76}$	Molecular Weight 569.018

		Ref.			Ref.			Ref.
F.P. °C	79.	2	dt/dP			f | to		
F.P. 100%			°C/mm			g | °K		
B.P. °C			25°C	7.31×10^{12}	5	h |		
760 mm	544.	2	BP	0.07236	4			
100	448.	5	t_e	0.0307	5	f' | to		
30	403.	5	30 mm	1.1549	5	g' | °K		
10	367.	5				h' |		
1	305.	5	ΔHm cal/g					
Pressure			ΔHv cal/g			m | to		
mm 25°C	$0.0_{12}56$	5	25°C	75.24	5	n | °K		
t_e	2128.	5	30 mm	46.08	5	o |		
Density			BP	37.81	5			
g/ml 20°C	0.8543≠	2	t_e	33.83	5	m' | to		
d_4^t 25	0.8509≠	2	t_e (d, e)	34.18	5	n' | °K		
30	0.8475	4	ΔHv/T_e	21.89	5	o' |		
a	0.8679	4	d | 400 to	69.72	5	Surface tension		
b	-0.0₃68	4	e | 590 °C	0.0586	5	dynes/cm. 20°C	31.04	5
	-0.0_368	4	d' | 25 to	77.16	5	γ 30	30.06	5
Ref. Index			e' | 400 °C	0.0771	5	40	29.11	5
n_D 20°C	1.4792≠	2	d_c g/ml			Parachor [P]		
25	1.4772≠	2	v_c ml/g			20°C		
30	1.4752	2	t_c °C			30		
"C"	0.7402	4	P_c mm			40		
MR (Obs.)	188.95≠	2	PV/RT			Sugd.	1572.1	5
MR (Calc.)	187.943	5	25°C	1.0000	5	Exp. L.1.%/wt.		
(nD-d/2)	1.0521≠	2	30 mm	1.0000	5	u.		
Dielectric	2.188	5	BP	0.9089	5	Dispersion	113.≠	2
A | 400 to	8.28283	4	t_e	0.8702	5	Flash Point °C		
B | 610 °C	3695.0	4	t_c			Fire Point		
C	140.	5	ΔHc kcal/m			M Spec.		
A* | 400 to	3.21872	5	ΔHf			Ultra V.		
B* | 600 °C	3590.	5	ΔFf			X-Ray Dif.		
K			Viscosity			Infrared		
c			centistokes			Solubility in +		
t_k | to			η °C			Acetone		
t_x | °C						Carbon tet.		
A' | 25 to	8.7116	5				Benzene		
B' | 400 °C	4175.2	5	B^v | to			Ether		
C'	174.	5	A^v | °C			n-Heptane		
						Ethanol		
A'* 25 to	3.6544	5	(B^v) | to			Water		
B'* 400 °C	4067.1	5	(A^v) | °C			Water in		
Ac | to			c_p liq. °K					
Bc | t_c °C								
Cc								
Cryos. A°			c_p vap. °K					
consts. B°								
t_e °C	606.	5	c_v vap.					

≠ for undercooled liquid   + grams/100 grams solvent

REFERENCES: 1-Dow   2-API   3-Lit.   4-Calc. from det. data   5-Calc. by formula

SOURCE: API

PURIFICATION: API

LITERATURE REFERENCES:

TABLE I. ALKYL AND HALO BENZENES

No. 121

NAME	n-Hexatriacontylbenzene	STRUCTURAL FORMULA
	1-Phenylhexatriacontane	

Mole % Pur.	Ref.	Molecular Formula $C_{42}H_{78}$	Molecular Weight 583.044

Structural formula: benzene ring with $C_{36}H_{73}$

		Ref.			Ref.				Ref.
F.P. °C	80.	2	dt/dP			f	to		
F.P. 100%			°C/mm			g	°K		
B.P. °C			25°C	1.16×10^{13}	5	h			
760 mm	549.	2	BP	0.07250	4				
100	453.	5	t_e	0.0311	5	f'	to		
30	407.	5	30 mm	1.1597	5	g'	°K		
10	372.	5	ΔHm cal/g			h'			
1	309.	5	ΔHv cal/g			m	to		
Pressure			25°C	74.14	5	n	°K		
mm 25°C	$0.0_{12}35$	5	30 mm	45.39	5	o			
t_e	2097.	5	BP	36.56	5				
Density			t_e	32.73	5	m'	to		
g/ml 20°C	$0.8542^{\neq}$	2	t_e (d, e)	32.77	5	n'	°K		
d_4^t 25	$0.8509^{\neq}$	2	$\Delta Hv/T_e$	21.61	5	o'			
30	0.8476	4				Surface tension			
a	0.8674	4	d 405 to	70.71	5	dynes/cm. 20°C	31.04	5
b	$-0.0_{3}66$	4	e 610 °C	0.0622	5	γ 30	30.09	5
Ref. Index			d' 25 to	76.02	5	40	29.17	5
n_D 20°C	$1.4791^{\neq}$	2	e' 405 °C	0.0752	5				
25	$1.4771^{\neq}$	2	d_c g/ml			Parachor [P]			
30	1.4752	4	v_c ml/g			20°C			
"C"	0.7401	4	t_c °C			30			
			P_c mm			40			
MR (Obs.)	$193.59^{\neq}$	2	PV/RT			Sugd.	1611.1	5
MR (Calc.)	192.561	5	25°C	1.0000	5	Exp. L.1.%/wt.			
(nD-d/2)	$1.0520^{\neq}$	2	30 mm	1.0000	5	u.			
Dielectric	2.188	5	BP	0.8917	5	Dispersion	$113.^{\neq}$	2
A 405 to	8.31154	4	t_e	0.8536	5	Flash Point °C			
B 610 °C	3741.8	4	t_c			Fire Point			
C	140.	5	ΔHc kcal/m			M. Spec.			
A* 405 to	3.26943	5	ΔHf			Ultra V.			
B* 600 °C	3640.	5	ΔFf			X-Ray Dif.			
K			Viscosity			Infrared			
c			centistokes			Solubility in +			
t_k to			η °C			Acetone			
t_x °C						Carbon tet.			
A' 25 to	8.74211	5				Benzene			
B' 405 °C	4228.1	5				Ether			
C'	174.	5	B^v	to		n-Heptane			
A'* 25 to	3.6930	5	A^v °C			Ethanol			
B'* 405 °C	4119.3	5	(B^v) to			Water			
Ac to			(A^v) °C			Water in			
Bc t_c °C									
Cc			c_p liq. °K						
Cryos. A°			c_p vap. °K						
consts. B°									
t_e °C	610.	5	c_v vap.						

$\neq$ for undercooled liquid $+$ grams/100 grams solvent

REFERENCES: 1-Dow 2-API 3-Lit. 4-Calc. from det. data 5-Calc. by formula

SOURCE: API

PURIFICATION: API

LITERATURE REFERENCES:

No. 122

NAME	Fluorobenzene	STRUCTURAL FORMULA
	Phenyl fluoride	

Mole % Pur.	Ref.	Molecular Formula C_6H_5F	Molecular Weight 96.100

		Ref.				Ref.			Ref.
F.P. °C	-41.9	3	dt/dP °C/mm			f		to °K	
F.P. 100%			25°C	0.2800	4	g			
B.P. °C			BP	0.0423	4	h			
760 mm	85.1	3'	t_e	0.0344	5	f'		to °K	
100	31.3	5	30 mm	0.5990	4	g'			
30	7.5	5	ΔHm cal/g			h'			
10	-10.7	5	ΔHv cal/g			m		to °K	
1	-41.	5	25°C	88.35	5	n			
Pressure			30 mm	90.64	5	o			
mm 25°C	74.33	4	BP	80.09	4	m'		to °K	
t_e	986.4	5	t_e	78.89	5	n'			
Density			t_e (d, e)	78.92	5	o'			
g/ml 20°C	1.0225	3'	ΔHv/T_e	20.66	5	Surface tension			
d_4^t 25	1.0165	4	d | 5 to	91.65	5	dynes/cm. 20°C	27.51		5
30	1.0104	3'	e | 95 °C	0.1358	5	γ 30	26.23		5
a	1.0463	4	d' | to			40	24.98		5
b	-0.00118	4	e' | °C						
Ref. Index			d_c g/ml	0.3541	3'	Parachor [P]			
n_D 20°C	1.46837	3	v_c ml/g	2.824	3'	20°C			
25	1.46553	4	t_c °C	286.65	3'	30			
30	1.46256	4	P_c mm	33912.	3'	40			
"C"	0.6052	4	PV/RT			Sugd.	215.3		5
MR (Obs.)	26.020	4	25°C	0.9999	5	Exp. L.1.%/wt.			
MR (Calc.)	26.229	5	30 mm	1.0000	5	u.			
(nD-d/2)	0.9571	4	BP	0.9725	4	Dispersion			
Dielectric	5.42	3²	t_e	0.9663	5	Flash Point °C			
A | 0 to	7.04659	3'	t_c			Fire Point			
B |145 °C	1283.5	3'	ΔHc kcal/m			M Spec.			
C	223.	5	ΔHf			Ultra V.			
A* | 0 to	1.41361	5	ΔFf			X-Ray Dif.			
B* |105 °C	1197.6	5	Viscosity			Infrared	Yes		1
K			centistokes			Solubility in +			
c			η °C			Acetone	∞		
t_k | to						Carbon tet.	∞		
t_x | °C						Benzene	∞		
A' | to						Ether	∞		
B' | °C			B^v | to			n-Heptane	∞		
C'			A^v | °C			Ethanol	∞		
A'* | to			(B^v)| to			Water			
B'* °C			(A^v)| °C			Water in			
Ac|145 to	7.0756	4	c_p liq. °K						
Bc| t_c °C	1305.	4							
Cc	226.	4							
Cryos. A°			c_p vap. °K						
consts. B°									
t_e °C	-93.7	5	c_v vap.						

$T_R = 0.75 T_c$

+ grams/100 grams solvent

REFERENCES: 1-Dow   2-API   3-Lit.   4-Calc. from det. data   5-Calc. by formula

SOURCE: 3, 3'

PURIFICATION: 3, 3'

LITERATURE REFERENCES: 3 Timmermans; 3' Young; 3² NBS Circ. 514

TABLE I. ALKYL AND HALO BENZENES

No. 123

NAME	Benzotrifluoride			STRUCTURAL FORMULA		
	a,a,a-Trifluorotoluene					

| Mole % Pur. 99.95 | Ref. 1 | Molecular Formula $C_7H_5F_3$ | | Molecular Weight 146.11 | | |

		Ref.				Ref.					Ref.
F.P. °C	-29.11	1	dt/dP °C/mm				f	to °K			
F.P. 100%			25°C	0.5104	5		g				
B.P. °C			BP	0.04468	4		h				
760 mm	102.06	1	t_e	0.03547	5		f'	to °K			
100	45.30	4	30 mm	0.6302	4		g'				
30	20.2	4	ΔHm cal/g	22.04	4		h'				
10	1.0	5	ΔHv cal/g				m	to °K			
1	-30.6	5	25°C	61.48	5		n				
Pressure			30 mm	61.90	5		o				
mm 25°C	38.55	5	BP	53.82	5		m'	to °K			
t_e	1019.5	5	t_e	52.80	5		n'				
Density			t_e (d, e)	52.80	5		o'				
g/ml 20°C	1.18838	1	ΔHv/T_e	20.01	5		Surface tension				
d_4^t 25	1.18129	1	d 15 to	63.89	5		dynes/cm. 20°C	23.41	1		
30	1.17351	4	e 120 °C	0.0987	5		30	22.34	1		
a	1.21665	4	d' to				40	21.28	1		
b	-0.00143	4	e' °C				Parachor [P]				
Ref. Index			d_c g/ml	0.427	5		20°C	270.5	4		
n_D 20°C	1.41458	1	v_c ml/g	2.34	5		30	270.6	4		
25	1.41225	1	t_c °C	289.5	5		40	270.8	4		
30	1.39991	1	P_c mm	26698.	5		Sugd.	271.9	5		
"C"	0.4642	4	PV/RT				Exp. L.1.%/wt.				
MR (Obs.)	30.762	4	25°C	1.0000	5		u.				
MR (Calc.)	30.475	5	30 mm	1.0000	5		Dispersion				
(nD-d/2)	0.82039	4	BP	0.9587	5		Flash Point °C				
Dielectric	9.035	1	t_e	0.9504	5		Fire Point				
A 0 to	7.00708	1	t_c	0.26	5		M. Spec.				
B 150 °C	1331.3	1	ΔHc kcal/m				Ultra V.				
C	220.58	1	ΔHf				X-Ray Dif.				
A* 10 to	1.56264	5	ΔFf				Infrared				
B* 125 °C	1248.0	5	Viscosity				Solubility in +				
K			centistokes				Acetone	∞			
c			η 20 °C	0.4878	1		Carbon tet.	∞			
t_k to			40	0.4039	1		Benzene	∞			
t_x °C			60	0.3441	1		Ether	∞			
A' to			80	0.2979	1		n-Heptane	∞			
B' °C			B^v 20 to	365.61	4		Ethanol	∞			
C'			A^v 90 °C	2.43894	4		Water	Decomp.	1		
A'* to			(B^v) to				Water in	Decomp.	1		
B'* °C			(A^v) °C								
Ac 150 to	7.42586	5	c_p liq. °K								
Bc t_c °C	1658.7	5									
Cc	263.5	5	c_p vap. °K								
Cryos. A° consts. B°	0.02732	1									
t_e °C	112.35	5	c_v vap.								

$T_R = 0.75\,T_c$ + grams/100 grams solvent

REFERENCES: 1-Dow   2-API   3-Lit.   4-Calc. from det. data   5-Calc. by formula

SOURCE: Dow, Lit.

PURIFICATION: Dow distillation, Lit.

LITERATURE REFERENCES: 3 JACS 73, 91 (1951) Potter and Saylor

No. 124

NAME	Chlorobenzene			STRUCTURAL FORMULA

Mole % Pur. 99.98	Ref. 1	Molecular Formula C_6H_5Cl	Molecular Weight 112.557

		Ref.				Ref.				Ref.
F.P. °C	-45.58	1	dt/dP				f | to			
F.P. 100%			°C/mm				g | °K			
			25°C		1.4794	4	h |			
B.P. °C			BP		0.0489	4				
760 mm	131.70	1	t_e		0.0364	5	f' | to			
100	69.8	4					g' | °K			
30	42.4	4	30 mm		0.6842	4	h' |			
10	21.6	5	ΔHm cal/g							
1	-13.	5	ΔHv cal/g				m | to			
Pressure			25°C		90.31	4	n | °K			
mm 25°C	11.75	4	30 mm		85.66	4	o |			
t_e	1109.	5	BP		74.39	3				
Density			t_e		72.74	5	m' | to			
g/ml 20°C	1.10578	1	t_e (d, e)		72.74	5	n' | °K			
d_4^t 25	1.10037	1	ΔHv/T_e		19.52	5	o' |			
30	1.09477	4	d | 40 to		90.99	5	Surface tension			
a	1.12743	4	e | 150 °C		0.1248	5	dynes/cm. 20°C	33.19	1
b	-0.00109	4	d' | 0 to		89.35	5	30	31.98	1
Ref. Index			e' | 40 °C		0.0864	5	40	30.77	1
n_D 20°C	1.52406	1	d_c g/ml		0.3654	3	Parachor [P]			
25	1.52138	1	v_c ml/g		2.737	3	20°C	244.33	4
30	1.51837	4	t_c °C		359.2	3	30	244.51	4
"C"	0.6216	4	P_c mm		33926.	3	40	244.62	4
MR (Obs.)	31.17	4	PV/RT				Sugd.	244.3	5
MR (Calc.)	31.174	5	25°C		1.0000	5	Exp. L.1.%/wt.	6.6 ≠	3³
(nD-d/2)	0.97120	4	30 mm		0.99992	5	u.	29. #	3³
Dielectric	5.621	3²	BP		0.9604	5	Dispersion			
A | 40 to	6.94504	4	t_e		0.9499	5	Flash Point °C	29.	3³
B |200 °C	1413.12	4	t_c		0.265	4	Fire Point			
C	216.0	4	ΔHc kcal/m				M Spec.	Yes	1
A* | 40 to	1.34982	4	ΔHf				Ultra V.	Yes	1
B* |205 °C	1321.8	4	ΔFf				X-Ray Dif.			
K	34.2	4	Viscosity				Infrared	240.	1
c	-0.16067	4	centistokes				Solubility in +			
t_k |205 to	207.2	4	η 20 °C		0.7232	1	Acetone	∞	
t_x |310 °C	420.	5	40		0.5837	1	Carbon tet.	∞	
A' | 0 to	7.49823	4	60		0.4858	1	Benzene	∞	
B' | 40 °C	1654.0	4	80		0.4139	1	Ether	∞	
C'	232.3	5	B^v | 30 to		412.87	4	n-Heptane	∞	
A'* | 0 to	1.89473	5	A^v | 90 °C		2.44796	4	Ethanol	∞	
B'* | 40 °C	1527.4	5	(B^v) | to				Water	0.050	1
Ac |200 to	7.58977	4	(A^v) | °C				Water in	4.4	1
Bc | t_c °C	2001.9	4	c_p liq $_{293.2}$ °K		0.3186	3'				
Cc	295.3	4								
Cryos. A°			c_p vap. °K							
consts. B°										
t_e °C	146.24	4	c_v vap.							

T_R = 0.75 T_c ≠ 100°C   # 150°C   + grams/100 grams solvent

REFERENCES: 1-Dow   2-API   3-Lit.   4-Calc. from det. data   5-Calc. by formula

SOURCE: Dow

PURIFICATION: Distillation

LITERATURE REFERENCES: 3 Young;   3' Timmermans;   3² NBS 514;   3³ NFPA 325

TABLE I. ALKYL AND HALO BENZENES

NAME	o-Dichlorobenzene	STRUCTURAL FORMULA
	1,2-Dichlorobenzene	

Mole % Pur. 99.85	Ref. 1	Molecular Formula $C_6H_4Cl_2$	Molecular Weight 147.006

		Ref.			Ref.				Ref.
F.P. °C	-17.0	1	dt/dP			f	to		
F.P. 100%			°C/mm			g	°K		
B.P. °C			25°C	11.490	5	h			
760 mm	180.46	4	BP	0.0538	5				
100	112.4	4	t_e	0.03715	5	f'	to		
30	82.4	4	30 mm	0.7506	4	g'	°K		
10	59.6	5	ΔHm cal/g	21.70	1	h'			
1	21.	5	ΔHv cal/g			m	to		
Pressure			25°C	81.61	5	n	°K		
mm 25°C	1.282	5	30 mm	75.92	5	o			
t_e	1221.5	5	BP	63.88	5	m'	to		
Density			t_e	61.63	5	n'	°K		
g/ml 20°C	1.30570	1	t_e (d, e)	61.38	5	o'			
d_4^t 25	1.30015	1	ΔHv/T_e	19.11	5	Surface tension			
30	1.29457	4	d 80 to	85.91	5	dynes/cm. 20°C	37.18	1
a	1.32790	4	e 200 °C	0.1221	5	δ 30	36.02	1
b	-0.00111	4	d' 15 to	84.09	5	40	34.92	1
Ref. Index			e' 80 °C	0.0992	5	Parachor [P]		
n_D 20°C	1.55154	1	d_c g/ml	0.408	5	20°C		
25	1.54920	1	v_c ml/g	2.449	5	30		
30	1.54650	4	t_c °C	424.1	5	40		
"C"	0.5521	1	P_c mm	30800.	5	Sugd.	281.1	5
MR (Obs.)	35.94	4	PV/RT			Exp. L.1.%/wt.		
MR (Calc.)	36.041	5	25°C	1.0000	5	u.		
(nD-d/2)	0.8985	5	30 mm	1.0000	5	Dispersion		
Dielectric	9.93	1	BP	0.9423	5	Flash Point °C	93.3	1
A 80 to	6.92400	4	t_e	0.9261	5	Fire Point		
B 250 °C	1538.3	4	t_c	0.255	5	M. Spec.	Yes	1
C	200.0	4	ΔHc kcal/m			Ultra V.		
A* 80 to	1.43584	5	ΔHf			X-Ray Dif.		
B* 220 °C	1450.9	5	ΔFf			Infrared	351.	1
K			Viscosity			Solubility in +		
c			centistokes			Acetone	∞	
t_k to			η 20 °C	1.0656	1	Carbon tet.	∞	
t_x °C			40	0.8288	1	Benzene	∞	
A' 15 to	7.26715	5	60	0.6636	1	Ether	∞	
B' 80 °C	1738.2	5	80	0.5729	1	n-Heptane	∞	
C'	217.8	5	B^v 30 to	443.51	4	Ethanol	∞	
A'* 15 to	1.76521	5	A^v 90 °C	$\overline{2}$.50238	4	Water		
B'* 80 °C	1641.1	5	(B^v) to			Water in	2.1	1
Ac 250 to	7.33302	5	(A^v) °C					
Bc t_c °C	1928.2	5	c_p liq. 20 °C	0.275	1			
Cc	253.8	5	40	0.298	1			
Cryos. A°	0.02215	1	c_p vap. °K					
consts. B°								
t_e °C	200.9	5	c_v vap.					

$T_R = 0.75 T_c$

+ grams/100 grams solvent

REFERENCES: 1-Dow 2-API 3-Lit. 4-Calc. from det. data 5-Calc. by formula

SOURCE: Dow

PURIFICATION: Distillation

LITERATURE REFERENCES:

No. 126

NAME	m-Dichlorobenzene	STRUCTURAL FORMULA
	1,3-Dichlorobenzene	

Mole % Pur. 99.04	Ref. 1	Molecular Formula $C_6H_4Cl_2$	Molecular Weight 147.006

		Ref.				Ref.			Ref.
F.P. °C	-24.76	1	dt/dP				f	to	
F.P. 100%			°C/mm				g	°K	
B.P. °C			25°C	8.061		5	h		
760 mm	173.08	1	BP	0.0534		5			
100	105.57	4	t_e	0.0372		5	f'	to	
30	75.9	4					g'	°K	
10	53.3	5	30 mm	0.7419		4	h'		
1	16.	5	ΔHm cal/g						
Pressure			ΔHv cal/g				m	to	
mm 25°C	1.889	5	25°C	78.96		5	n	°K	
t_e	1214.	5	30 mm	74.02		5	o		
			BP	62.79		5			
Density			t_e	60.61		5	m'	to	
g/ml 20°C	1.28844	1	t_e (d, e)	60.48		5	n'	°K	
d_4^t 25	1.28280	1	ΔHv/T_e	19.11		5	o'		
30	1.27712	4					Surface tension		
a	1.31101	4	d | 75 to	82.79		5	dynes/cm. 20°C	36.84	5
b	-0.00113	4	e | 190 °C	0.1156		5	γ 30	35.56	5
			d' | 25 to	81.38		5	40	34.32	5
Ref. Index			e' | 75 °C	0.0969		5	Parachor [P]		
n_D 20°C	1.54586	1	d_c g/ml	0.410		5	20°C		
25	1.54337	1	v_c ml/g	2.44		5	30		
30	1.54076	4	t_c °C	410.8		1	40		
"C"	0.5543	4	P_c mm	29112.		5	Sugd.	281.1	5
MR (Obs.)	36.14	4	PV/RT				Exp. L.1.%/wt.		
MR (Calc.)	36.041	5	25°C	1.0000		5	u.		
(nD-d/2)	0.90197	5	30 mm	1.0000		5	Dispersion		
Dielectric	5.04	3	BP	0.9510		5	Flash Point °C	72.0	5
A | 75 to	6.88045	4	t_e	0.9354		5	Fire Point		
B | 240 °C	1496.2	4	t_c	0.255		5	M Spec.	Yes	1
C	201.	5	ΔHc kcal/m				Ultra V.		
A* | 75 to	1.38472	5	ΔHf				X-Ray Dif.		
B* | 205 °C	1406.2	5	ΔFf				Infrared	352.	1
K			Viscosity				Solubility in +		
c			centistokes				Acetone	∞	
t_k | to			η °C				Carbon tet.	∞	
t_x | °C							Benzene	∞	
A' | 10 to	7.22086	5					Ether	∞	
B' | 75 °C	1690.7	5					n-Heptane	∞	
C'	218.4	5	B^v | to				Ethanol	∞	
A'* 15 to	1.72298	5	A^v | °C				Water		
B'* 75 °C	1594.3	5	(B^v) | to				Water in		
Ac | 240 to	7.28934	5	(A^v) | °C						
Bc | t_c °C	1878.8	5	c_p liq. °K						
Cc	254.2	5							
Cryos. A°			c_p vap. °K						
consts. B°									
t_e °C F	193.11	5	c_v vap.						

$T_R = 0.75 T_c$ + grams/100 grams solvent

REFERENCES:	1-Dow 2-API 3-Lit. 4-Calc. from det. data 5-Calc. by formula
SOURCE:	Dow
PURIFICATION:	Distillation
LITERATURE REFERENCES:	3 NBS Circ. 514

TABLE I. ALKYL AND HALO BENZENES

No. 127

NAME	p-Dichlorobenzene	STRUCTURAL FORMULA
	1,4-Dichlorobenzene	

Mole % Pur. 99.91	Ref. 1	Molecular Formula $C_6H_4Cl_2$	Molecular Weight 147.006

		Ref.			Ref.				Ref.
F.P. °C	53.1	1	dt/dP			f	to		
F.P. 100%			°C/mm			g	___ °K		
			25°C	8.595	5	h			
B.P. °C			BP	0.0534	5				
760 mm	174.21	1	t_e	0.0371	5	f'	to		
100	106.73	4	30 mm	0.7426	4	g'	___ °K		
30	77.06	4	ΔHm cal/g	30.434	1	h'			
10	54.5	5	ΔHv cal/g			m	to		
1	16.7	5	25°C	79.49	5	n	___ °K		
Pressure			30 mm	74.44	5	o			
mm 25°C	1.759	5	BP	63.04	5				
t_e	1213.	5	t_e	60.85	5	m'	to		
Density			t_e (d, e)	60.69	5	n'	___ °K		
g/ml 55 C	1.24750	1	$\Delta Hv/T_e$	19.06	5	o'			
d_4^t 60	1.24166	1				Surface tension			
65	1.23581	4	d 75 to	83.48	5	dynes/cm 60 C	31.33	1
a 55°C	1.31159	4	e 190 °C	0.1173	5	ɣ 70	30.42	1
b	-0.00116	4	d' 20 to	81.92	5	117	25.44	3
Ref. Index			e' 75 °C	0.0970	5				
n_D 55°C	1.52849	1	d_c g/ml	0.395	5	Parachor [P]			
60	1.52586	4	v_c ml/g	2.53	5	60°C	280.1	4
65	1.52319	5	t_c °C	411.6	1	70	280.7	4
"C" 55°C	0.5554	4	P_c mm	29300.	5	117	281.3	4
MR (Obs.) 55°	36.323	4				Sugd.	281.1	5
MR (Calc.)	36.041	5	PV/RT			Exp. L.l.%/wt.			
(nD-d/2)55°	0.90474	5	25°C	1.0000	5	u.			
Dielectric 55°	2.465	1	30 mm	1.0000	5	Dispersion			
			BP	0.9481	5	Flash Point °C	68.3	1
A 75 to	6.89797	4	t_e	0.9330	5	Fire Point	140.5	1
B 240 °C	1507.3	4	t_c	0.268	5				
C	201.	4	ΔHc kcal/m			M. Spec.	Yes	1
A* 75 to	1.40489	5	ΔHf			Ultra V.	Yes	1
B* 205 °C	1418.0	5	ΔFf			X-Ray Dif.	Yes	1
K			Viscosity			Infrared	353.	1
c			centistokes			Solubility in +			
t_k to			η °C			Acetone	∞	
t_x °C						Carbon tet.	∞	
A' 0 to	7.23948	5				Benzene	∞	
B' 75 °C	1703.2	5				Ether	∞	
C'	218.	5	B^v to			n-Heptane	∞	
A'* 15 to	1.74063	5	A^v °C			Ethanol	∞	
B'* 75 °C	1606.6	5	(B^v) to			Water		
Ac 240 to	7.30658	5	(A^v) °C			Water in		
Bc t_c °C	1889.6	5	c_p liq. °K					
Cc	254.	5	c_p vap. °K					
Cryos. A°	0.02116	1						
consts. B°								
t_e °C F	194.2	5	c_v vap.					

$T_R = 0.75 T_c$

+ grams/100 grams solvent

REFERENCES: 1-Dow 2-API 3-Lit. 4-Calc. from det. data 5-Calc. by formula

SOURCE: Dow

PURIFICATION: Distillation

LITERATURE REFERENCES: 3 Timmermans

No. 128

NAME	1,2,4-Trichlorobenzene		STRUCTURAL FORMULA

Mole % Pur. 99.93	Ref. 1	Molecular Formula $C_6H_3Cl_3$	Molecular Weight 181.455

		Ref.			Ref.			Ref.
F.P. °C	16.92	1	dt/dP °C/mm			f | to		
F.P. 100%	16.95	1	25°C	47.094	5	g | °K		
B.P. °C			BP	0.0561	4	h |		
760 mm	213.48	1	t_e	0.0361	5	f' | to		
100	141.68	4	30 mm	0.8089	4	g' | °K		
30	109.52	4	ΔHm cal/g	21.53	4	h' |		
10	84.8	5	ΔHv cal/g			m | to		
1	43.1	5	25°C	71.12	5	n | °K		
Pressure			30 mm	66.10	5	o |		
mm 25°C	0.2907	5	BP	57.43	5	m' | to		
t_e	1324.	5	t_e	55.38	5	n' | °K		
Density			t_e (d, e)	55.34	5	o' |		
g/ml 20°C	1.45420	1	$\Delta Hv/T_e$	19.64	5	Surface tension		
d_4^t 25	1.44829	1	d | 110 to	75.23	5	dynes/cm. 20°C	39.10	1
30	1.44237	4	e | 240 °C	0.0834	5	30	37.98	1
a	1.47784	4	d' | 20 to	72.60	5	40	36.86	1
b	-0.00118	4	e' | 110 °C	0.0594	5	Parachor [P]		
Ref. Index			d_c g/ml	0.471	5	20°C	312.0	4
n_D 20°C	1.57168	1	v_c ml/g	2.12	5	30	312.3	4
25	1.56933	1	t_c °C	461.8	5	40	312.5	4
50	1.55765	1	P_c mm	29900.	5	Sugd.	318.7	5
"C"	0.5127	4	PV/RT			Exp. L.1.%/wt.		
MR (Obs.)	41.038	4	25°C	1.0000	5	u.		
MR (Calc.)	40.908	5	30 mm	1.0000	5	Dispersion		
(nD-d/2)	0.84458	4	BP	0.9476	5	Flash Point °C	110.	3
Dielectric	3.945	1	t_e	0.9299	5	Fire Point	None	1
A |110 to	7.19508	1	t_c	0.25	5	M Spec.		
B |280 °C	1827.0	1	ΔHc kcal/m			Ultra V.		
C	210.	1	ΔHf			X-Ray Dif.		
A* | 25 to	1.74692	5	ΔFf			Infrared		
B* |110 °C	1721.8	5	Viscosity			Solubility in +		
K			centistokes			Acetone		
c			η 20 °C	1.4225	1	Carbon tet.		
t_k | to			40	1.0252	1	Benzene		
t_x | °C			60	0.7915	1	Ether		
A' | 20 to	7.5553	5	80	0.6402	1	n-Heptane		
B' |110 °C	2064.4	5	B^v | 30 to	565.53	4	Ethanol		
C'	230.1	5	A^v | 90 °C	2.20516	4	Water		
A'* 25 to	2.1092	5	(B^v) | to			Water in		
B'* 110 °C	1953.3	5	(A^v) | °C					
Ac |280 to	7.19792	5	c_p liq. °K					
Bc | t_c °C	1829.7	5						
Cc	210.4	5	c_p vap. °K					
Cryos. A° consts. B°	0.02338	1	c_v vap.					
t_e °C F	238.54	5						
T_R = 0.75 T_c						+ grams/100 grams solvent		

REFERENCES: 1-Dow 2-API 3-Lit. 4-Calc. from det. data 5-Calc. by formula

SOURCE: 3, Dow

PURIFICATION: Dow distillation, crystallization

LITERATURE REFERENCES: 3 Prod. Dev. Bull. CB-3, Solvay Proc. Div.

TABLE I. ALKYL AND HALO BENZENES

No. 129

NAME	o-Chlorotoluene	STRUCTURAL FORMULA
	1-Chloro-2-methylbenzene	

Mole % Pur.		Ref.	Molecular Formula C_7H_7Cl		Molecular Weight 126.583	

		Ref.			Ref.					Ref.
F.P. °C	-35.1	3	dt/dP			f	to		
F.P. 100%			°C/mm			g	$°K$		
			25°C	4.478	5	h			
B.P. °C			BP	0.0517	4				
760 mm	159.15	3	t_e	0.0367	5	f'	to		
100	93.61	4	30 mm	0.7242	4	g'	$°K$		
30	64.69	4				h'			
10	42.6	5	ΔHm cal/g	15.80	3				
1	5.8	5				m	to		
			ΔHv cal/g			n	$°K$		
Pressure			25°C	86.15	5	o			
mm 25°C	3.619	5	30 mm	82.49	5				
t_e	1179.	5	BP	70.87	5	m'	to		
			t_e	68.83	5	n'	$°K$		
Density			t_e (d, e)	68.64	5	o'			
g/ml 20°C	1.08245	4							
d_4^t 25	1.07762	3	$\Delta Hv/T_e$	19.34	5	Surface tension			
30	1.07273	3				dynes/cm. 15°C	33.99	3
			d 65 to	90.45	5	γ 20	33.44	3
a	1.10178	4	e 175 °C	0.1230	5	30	32.33	3
b	-0.0₃967	4	d' 15 to	88.45	5			
			e' 65 °C	0.0922	5	Parachor [P]		
Ref. Index						20°C	281.3	4
n_D 20°C	1.52680	1	d_c g/ml	0.348	5	30	281.4	4
25	1.52221	1	v_c ml/g	2.869	5	40	281.4	4
30	1.51760	4	t_c °C	385.9	5	Sugd.	283.3	5
"C"	0.6382	4	P_c mm	28862.	5			
MR (Obs.)	35.473	4	PV/RT			Exp. L.1.%/wt.		
MR (Calc.)	35.792	5	25°C	1.0000	5	u.		
(nD-d/2)	0.9856	4	30 mm	1.0000	5	Dispersion		
Dielectric	4.73	3	BP	0.9532	5	Flash Point °C		
A 65 to	6.94763	4	t_e	0.9409	5	Fire Point		
B 220 °C	1497.2	4	t_c	0.255	5			
C	209.0	5				M. Spec.		
A* 65 to	1.38854	5	ΔHc kcal/m			Ultra V.	Yes	3
B* 200 °C	1404.8	5	ΔHf			X-Ray Dif.		
K			ΔFf			Infrared	Yes	3
c			Viscosity			Solubility in +		
t_k to			centistokes			Acetone	∞	
t_x °C			η °C			Carbon tet.	∞	
A' 0 to	7.29227	5				Benzene	∞	
B' 65 °C	1691.79	5				Ether	∞	
C'	226.2	5	B^v to			n-Heptane	∞	
			A^v °C			Ethanol	∞	
A'* 10 to	1.72744	5	(B^v) to			Water		
B'* 65 °C	1591.85	5				Water in		
Ac 220 to	7.3637	5	(A^v) °C					
Bc t_c °C	1876.5	5	c_p liq. 0°C	0.315	3			
Cc	260.4	5						
Cryos. A°			c_p vap. °K					
consts. B°								
t_e °C F	177.27	5	c_v vap.					
$T_R = 0.75 T_c$						+ grams/100 grams solvent		

REFERENCES: 1-Dow 2-API 3-Lit. 4-Calc. from det. data 5-Calc. by formula

SOURCE:	3
PURIFICATION:	3

LITERATURE REFERENCES: 3 Characteristics der Corps Chim. Purs. et Tech. editor Dunod, Paris, France

NAME	3,4-Dichlorotoluene	STRUCTURAL FORMULA
	3,4-Dichloro-1-methylbenzene	

Mole % Pur. 99.93	Ref. 1	Molecular Formula $C_7H_6Cl_2$	Molecular Weight 161.032

		Ref.				Ref.				Ref.
F.P. °C	-15.25	1	dt/dP				f	to		
F.P. 100%			°C/mm				g	°K		
			25°C	42.149	5		h			
B.P. °C			BP	0.0563	4					
760 mm	208.92	1	t_e	0.0369	5		f'	to		
100	137.47	4	30 mm	0.7916	4		g'	°K		
30	105.87	4					h'			
10	81.8	5	ΔHm cal/g	15.85	4					
1	41.4	5	ΔHv cal/g				m	to		
Pressure			25°C	82.78	5		n	°K		
mm 25°C	0.315	5	30 mm	74.67	5		o			
t_e	1303.	5	BP	62.92	5					
Density			t_e	60.39	5		m'	to		
g/ml 20°C	1.25256	1	t_e (d, e)	60.12	5		n'	°K		
d_4^t 25	1.24751	1	ΔHv/T_e	19.20	5		o'			
30	1.24245	4	d | 105 to	86.74	5		Surface tension			
a	1.27276	4	e | 230 °C	0.1140	5		dynes/cm. 20°C	36.50	1
b	-0.00101	4	d' | 25 to	85.28	5		ɣ 30	35.61	1
Ref. Index			e' | 105 °C	0.1003	5		40	34.58	1
n_D 20°	1.54712	1	d_c g/ml	0.407	5		Parachor [P]			
25	1.54494	1	v_c ml/g	2.456	5		20°C	316.0	4
50	1.53368	1	t_c °C	451.2	5		30	316.8	4
"C"	0.5714	4	P_c mm	27986.	5		40	316.7	4
MR (Obs.)	40.780	4	PV/RT				Sugd.	320.5	5
MR (Calc.)	40.659	4	25°C	1.0000	5		Exp. L.1.%/wt.			
(nD-d/2)	0.92084	4	30 mm	1.0000	5		u.			
Dielectric	8.970	1	BP	0.9427	5		Dispersion			
A | 105 to	6.97925	4	t_e	0.9246	5		Flash Point °C			
B | 270 °C	1655.44	4	t_c	0.245	5		Fire Point			
C	195.0	4	ΔHc kcal/m				M Spec.			
A* | 105 to	1.50376	5	ΔHf				Ultra V.			
B* | 245 °C	1562.5	5	ΔFf				X-Ray Dif.			
K			Viscosity				Infrared			
c			centistokes				Solubility in +			
t_k | to			η 20 °C	1.2542	1		Acetone	∞		
t_x | °C			40	0.9403	1		Carbon tet.	∞		
A' | 25 to	7.32588	5	60	0.7447	1		Benzene	∞		
B' | 05 °C	1870.60	5	80	0.6121	1		Ether	∞		
C'	214.0	5	B^v | 30 to	515.64	4		n-Heptane	∞		
A'* 25 to	1.85124	5	A^v | 90 °C	2.32692	4		Ethanol	∞		
B'* 105 °C	1772.11	5	(B^v) | to				Water			
Ac | 270 to	7.3839	5	(A^v) | °C				Water in 30°C	0.0026	1
Bc | t_c °C	2053.3	5	c_p liq. °K						
Cc	247.9	5								
Cryos. A° consts. B°	0.01932	1	c_p vap. °K							
t_e °C F	233.4	5	c_v vap.							
$T_R = 0.75 T_c$							+ grams/100 grams solvent			

REFERENCES: 1-Dow 2-API 3-Lit. 4-Calc. from det. data 5-Calc. by formula

SOURCE: Dow

PURIFICATION: Distillation

LITERATURE REFERENCES:

TABLE I. ALKYL AND HALO BENZENES

No. 131

| NAME | 2,4-Dichlorobenzyl chloride | STRUCTURAL FORMULA |
| | α,2,4-Trichlorotoluene | |

Structural formula: CH$_2$Cl, Cl (benzene ring) Cl

| Mole % Pur. 99.53 | Ref. 1 | Molecular Formula C$_7$H$_5$Cl$_3$ | Molecular Weight 195.481 | |

		Ref.			Ref.			Ref.
F.P. °C	-2.60	1	dt/dP			f | to		
F.P. 100%			°C/mm			g | °K		
			25°C	290.43	5	h |		
B.P. °C			BP	0.0591	4			
760 mm	248.03	1	t$_e$	0.0368	5	f' | to		
100	172.57	1				g' | °K		
30	138.87	4	30 mm	0.8471	4	h' |		
10	113.0	5	ΔHm cal/g	16.08	4			
1	69.4	5	ΔHv cal/g			m | to		
Pressure			25°C	77.57	5	n | °K		
mm 25°C	0.04012	5	30 mm	67.92	5	o |		
t$_e$	1383.	5	BP	56.71	5			
Density			t$_e$	54.15	5	m' | to		
g/ml 20°C	1.40683	1	t$_e$ (d, e)	53.77	5	n' | °K		
d$_4^t$ 25	1.40139	1	ΔHv/T$_e$	19.25	5	o' |		
30	1.39595	4	d | 140 to	82.19	5	Surface tension		
a	1.42859	4	e | 270 °C	0.1027	5	dynes/cm. 20°C	41.32	.1
b	-0.00109	4	d' | 25 to	79.69	5	ɤ 30	40.19	1
Ref. Index			e' | 140 °C	0.0848	5	40	39.06	1
n$_D$ 20°C	1.57606	1	d$_c$ g/ml			Parachor [P]		
25	1.57383	1	v$_c$ ml/g			20°C	352.3	4
50	1.56271	1	t$_c$ °C	498.1	5	30	352.6	4
"C"	0.5338	4	P$_c$ mm	28460.	5	40	352.8	4
MR (Obs.)	47.035	4	PV/RT			Sugd.	357.7	5
MR (Calc.)	46.258	5	25°C	1.0000	5	Exp. L.l.%/wt.		
(nD-d/2)	0.87265	4	30 mm	1.0000	5	u.		
Dielectric	6.290	1	BP	0.9256	5	Dispersion		
A | 140 to	7.14735	1	t$_e$	0.9039	5	Flash Point °C		
B | 305 °C	1881.38	1	t$_c$			Fire Point		
C	192.93	1	ΔHc kcal/m			M. Spec.		
A* | 140 to	1.75073	5	ΔHf			Ultra V.		
B* | 290 °C	1789.19	5	ΔFf			X-Ray Dif.		
K			Viscosity			Infrared		
c			centistokes			Solubility in +		
t$_k$ | to			η 20 °C	2.6000	1	Acetone		
t$_x$ | °C			40	1.6617	1	Carbon tet.		
A' | 20 to	7.50457	5	60	1.1876	1	Benzene		
B' | 140 °C	2125.90	.5	100	0.9084	1	Ether		
C'	213.8	5	B^v | 30 to	510.93	4	n-Heptane		
A'* 25 to	2.09119	5	A^v | 110 °C	2.58923	4	Ethanol		
B'* 140 °C	2022.0	5	(B^v)| to			Water		
Ac | 305 to	7.5540	5	(A^v)| °C			Water in		
Bc | t$_c$ °C	2308.4	5	c$_p$ liq. °K					
Cc	246.6	5	c$_p$ vap. °K					
Cryos. A°	0.02274	1	c$_v$ vap.					
consts. B°								
t$_e$ °C F	276.64	5						

$T_R = 0.75 T_c$

+ grams/100 grams solvent

REFERENCES: 1-Dow 2-API 3-Lit. 4-Calc. from det. data 5-Calc. by formula

SOURCE: Dow

PURIFICATION: Dow

LITERATURE REFERENCES:

No. 132

NAME	o-Chlorobenzotrichloride				STRUCTURAL FORMULA	
	o, a, a, a -Tetrachlorotoluene					

Mole % Pur. 99.98	Ref. 1	Molecular Formula $C_7H_4Cl_4$	Molecular Weight 229.930	

		Ref.				Ref.				Ref.
F.P. °C	29.37	1	dt/dP				f	to		
F.P. 100%			°C/mm				g	°K		
B.P. °C			25°C	461.466	5		h			
760 mm	264.27	1	BP	0.0621	4					
100	185.01	4	t_e	0.0384	5		f'	to		
30	149.67	4	30 mm	0.8878	4		g'	°K		
10	122.6	5	ΔHm cal/g	14.32	1		h'			
1	77.0	5	ΔHv cal/g				m	to		
Pressure			25°C	66.04	5		n	°K		
mm 25°C	0.0252	5	30 mm	58.02	5		o			
t_e	1398.	5	BP	47.90	5					
Density			t_e	45.55	5		m'	to		
g/ml 20°C	1.51870	1	t_e (d, e)	45.19	5		n'	°K		
d_4^t 25	1.51312	1	ΔHv/T_e	18.43	5		o'			
30	1.50754	1	d | 150 to	71.24	5		Surface tension			
a	1.54102	4	e | 290 °C	0.0883	5		dynes/cm. 20°C	42.34	1
b	-0.00112	4	d' | 25 to	67.65	5		ɣ 30	41.16	1
Ref. Index			e' | 150 °C	0.0643	5		40	40.03	1
n_D 20°C	1.58362	1	d_c g/ml				Parachor [P]		
25	1.58142	1	v_c ml/g				20°C	386.2	4
30	1.57032	1	t_c °C	511.0	5		30	386.3	4
"C"	0.5005	4	P_c mm	24455.	5		40	386.5	4
MR (Obs.)	50.628	4	PV/RT				Sugd.	388.8	5
MR (Calc.)	50.393	5	25°C	1.0000	5		Exp. L. 1.%/wt.		
(nD-d/2)	0.82427	5	30 mm	1.0000	5		u.		
Dielectric	8.989	1	BP	0.9100	5		Dispersion		
A |150 to	7.11794	4	t_e	0.8844	5		Flash Point °C		
B |315 °C	1951.37	4	t_c	0.23	5		Fire Point		
C	196.27	4	ΔHc kcal/m				M Spec.		
A* |150 to	1.80509	5	ΔHf				Ultra V.		
B* |305 °C	1863.73	5	ΔFf				X-Ray Dif.		
K			Viscosity				Infrared		
c			centistokes				Solubility in +		
t_k to			η 20 °C	5.4408	1		Acetone		
t_x °C			40	3.16736	1		Carbon tet.		
A' | 15 to	7.47331	5	60	2.10212	1		Benzene		
B' |150 °C	2205.	5	80	1.50080	1		Ether		
C'	218.1	5	B^v | 30 to	897.09	4		n-Heptane		
A'* 20 to	2.11803	5	A^v | 90 °C	3.63643	4		Ethanol		
B'*150 °C	2096.2	5	(B^v) | to				Water	Decomp.	1
Ac |315 to	7.5302	5	(A^v) | °C				Water in	Decomp.	1
Bc | t_c °C	2395.6	5	c_p liq. °K						
Cc	251.5	5							
Cryos. A°	0.01813	1	c_p vap. °K						
consts. B°									
t_e °C F	294.96	5	c_v vap.						

$T_R = 0.75 T_c$ + grams/100 grams solvent

REFERENCES: 1-Dow 2-API 3-Lit. 4-Calc. from det. data 5-Calc. by formula

SOURCE: Dow

PURIFICATION: Distillation

LITERATURE REFERENCES:

TABLE I. ALKYL AND HALO BENZENES

No. 133

NAME	3,4-Dichlorobenzotrichloride		STRUCTURAL FORMULA

Mole % Pur. 99.68	Ref. 1	Molecular Formula $C_7H_3Cl_5$	Molecular Weight 264.379

		Ref.			Ref.			Ref.
F.P. °C	25.82	1	dt/dP			f | to		
F.P. 100%			°C/mm			g | °K		
			25°C	2136.9	5	h |		
B.P. °C			BP	0.0634	4			
760 mm	283.14	1	t_e	0.0386	5	f' | to		
100	202.89	4	30 mm	0.8918	4	g' | °K		
30	167.30	4	ΔHm cal/g	15.23	5	h' |		
10	140.1	5	ΔHv cal/g			m | to		
1	95.	5	25°C	68.15	5	n | °K		
Pressure			30 mm	54.52	5	o |		
mm 25°C	0.00459	5	BP	43.60	5			
t_e	1436.	5	t_e	40.88	5	m' | to		
Density			t_e (d, e)	40.48	5	n' | °K		
g/ml 20°C	1.59134	1	ΔHv/T_e	18.34	5	o' |		
d_4^t 25.	1.58544	1	d | 165 to	70.29	5	Surface tension		
30	1.57954	4	e | 310 °C	0.0943	5	dynes/cm. 20°C	41.70	1
a	1.61494	4	d' | 25 to	70.55	5	ɣ 30	40.58	1
b	-0.00118	4	e' | 165 °C	0.0958	5	40	39.50	1
Ref. Index			d_c g/ml			Parachor [P]		
n_D 20°C	1.58860	1	v_c ml/g			20°C	422.2	4
25	1.58643	1	t_c °C	524.0	5	30	422.5	4
30	1.57550	1	P_c mm	21355.	5	40	422.8	4
"C"	0.4815	4	PV/RT			Sugd.	432.1	5
MR (Obs.)	55.958	4	25°C	1.0000	5.	Exp. L.1.%/wt.		
MR (Calc.)	55.260	5	30 mm	1.0000	5	u.		
(nD-d/2)	0.79293	4	BP	0.9075	5	Dispersion		
Dielectric			t_e	0.8756	5	Flash Point °C		
A | 165 to	6.98524	4	ΔHc kcal/m			Fire Point		
B | 390 °C	1868.905	4	ΔHf			M. Spec.		
C	172.0	1	ΔFf			Ultra V.		
A* | 165 to	1.74321	5	Viscosity			X-Ray Dif.		
B* | 330 °C	1792.43	5	centistokes			Infrared		
K			η 20 °C	4.5369	1	Solubility in +		
c			40	2.6711	1	Acetone		
t_k | to			60	1.8034	1	Carbon tet.		
t_x | °C			80	1.3221	1	Benzene		
A' | 25 to	7.33225	5				Ether		
B' | 165 °C	2111.80	5	B^v | 30 to	844.66	4	n-Heptane		
C'	193.4	5	A^v | 90 °C	3.72982	4	Ethanol		
A'* 25 to	2.05561	5	(B^v)| to			Water		
B'* 165 °C	2018.0	5	(A^v)| °C			Water in		
Ac | 330 to	7.4091	5	c_p liq. °K					
Bc | t_c °C	2321.3	5						
Cc	230.	5						
Cryos. A°	0.02267	1	c_p vap. °K					
consts. B°								
t_e °C F	316.2	5	c_v vap.					

$T_R = 0.76 T_c$ + grams/100 grams solvent

REFERENCES: 1-Dow   2-API   3-Lit.   4-Calc. from det. data   5-Calc. by formula

SOURCE: Dow

PURIFICATION: Distillation

LITERATURE REFERENCES:

No. 134

NAME	1-Chloro-2-ethylbenzene	STRUCTURAL FORMULA
	o-Chloroethylbenzene	

Mole % Pur. 99.61	Ref. 1	Molecular Formula C_8H_9Cl	Molecular Weight 140.609

		Ref.				Ref.				Ref.
F.P. °C	-83.32	1	dt/dP				f | to			
F.P. 100%			°C/mm				g | °K			
			25°C	11.216	5		h |			
B.P. °C			BP	0.0529	4					
760 mm	178.43	1	t_e	0.0361	5		f' | to			
100	111.34	4	30 mm	0.7434	4		g' | °K			
30	81.67	4	ΔHm cal/g				h' |			
10	59.0	5	ΔHv cal/g				m | to			
1	21.	5	25°C	85.59	5		n | °K			
Pressure			30 mm	79.80	5		o |			
mm 25°C	1.309	5	BP	68.14	5					
t_e	1236.	5	t_e	65.89	5		m' | to			
Density			t_e (d, e)	65.65	5		n' | °K			
g/ml 20°C	1.05690	1	ΔHv/T_e	19.62	5		o' |			
d_4^t 25	1.05228	1	d | 80 to	89.65	5		Surface tension			
30	1.04763	4	e | 200 °C	0.1206	5		dynes/cm. 20°C	34.44	5
a	1.07538	4	d' | 25 to	88.14	5		γ 30	33.25	5
b	-0.0₃925	4	e' | 80 °C	0.1021	5		40	32.09	5
Ref. Index			d_c g/ml	0.346	5		Parachor [P]		
n_D 20°C	1.52175	1	v_c ml/g	2.89	5		20°C		
25	1.51905	1	t_c °C	399.8	5		30		
30	1.51688	1	P_c mm	26384.	5		40		
"C"	0.6478	4	PV/RT				Sugd.	322.3	5
MR (Obs.)	40.558	4	25°C	1.0000	5		Exp. L.1.%/wt.		
MR (Calc.)	40.410	5	30 mm	1.0000	5		u.		
(nD-d/2)	0.99330	4	BP	0.9540	5		Dispersion		
Dielectric			t_e	0.9405	5		Flash Point °C	57.0	5
A | 80 to	6.98169	4	t_c	0.255	5		Fire Point		
B | 230 °C	1556.0	4	ΔHc kcal/m				M Spec.		
C	201.0	5	ΔHf				Ultra V.	Yes	1
A* | 80 to	1.45261	5	ΔFf				X-Ray Dif.		
B* | 210 °C	1462.1	5	Viscosity				Infrared	515.	1
K			centistokes				Solubility in +		
c			η °C				Acetone	∞	
t_k | to							Carbon tet.	∞	
t_x | °C							Benzene	∞	
A' | 0 to	7.32848	5					Ether	∞	
B' | 80 °C	1758.2	5	B^v | to				n-Heptane	∞	
C'	218.8	5	A^v | °C				Ethanol	∞	
A'* 10 to	1.80780	5	(B^v) | to				Water		
B'* 80 °C	1661.06	5	(A^v) | °C				Water in		
Ac | 230 to	7.3867	5	c_p liq. °K						
Bc | t_c	1926.1	5							
Cc	250.	5	c_p vap. °K						
Cryos. A°									
consts. B°									
t_e °C F	199.02	5	c_v vap.						

$T_R = 0.75 T_c$ + grams/100 grams solvent

REFERENCES: 1-Dow   2-API   3-Lit.   4-Calc. from det. data   5-Calc. by formula

SOURCE:	Dow
PURIFICATION:	Distillation

LITERATURE REFERENCES:

TABLE I. ALKYL AND HALO BENZENES

No. 135

NAME	1-Chloro-3-ethylbenzene	STRUCTURAL FORMULA
	m-Chloroethylbenzene	

Mole % Pur. 98.83	Ref. 1	Molecular Formula C_8H_9Cl	Molecular Weight 140.609

		Ref.			Ref.				Ref.
F.P. °C	-55.04	1	dt/dP			f	to		
F.P. 100%			°C/mm			g	___ °K		
B.P. °C			25°C	14.250	5	h			
760 mm	183.77	1	BP	0.0534	5				
100	116.04	4	t_e	0.0362	5	f'	to		
30	86.07	4	30 mm	0.7511	5	g'	___ °K		
10	63.2	5	ΔHm cal/g			h'			
1	24.9	5	ΔHv cal/g			m	to		
Pressure			25°C	87.32	5	n	___ °K		
mm 25°C	1.010	5	30 mm	80.96	5	o			
t_e	1248.	5	BP	69.06	5				
Density			t_e	66.65	5	m'	to		
g/ml 20°C	1.05294	1	t_e (d, e)	66.48	5	n'	___ °K		
d_4^t 25	1.04826	1	ΔHv/T_e	19.60	5	o'			
30	1.04356	4	d 85 to	91.43	5	Surface tension			
a	1.07166	4	e 200 °C	0.1217	5	dynes/cm. 20°C	33.93	5	
b	-0.0_3936	4	d' 25 to	89.93	5	γ 30	32.74	5	
Ref. Index			e' 85 °C	0.1043	5	40	31.58	5	
n_D 20°C	1.51949	1	d_c g/ml	0.343	5	Parachor [P]			
25	1.51707	1	v_c ml/g	2.914	5	20°C			
30	1.51464	1	t_c °C	406.9	5	30			
"C"	0.64760	4	P_c mm	26376.	5	40			
MR (Obs.)	40.563	4	PV/RT			Sugd.	322.3	5	
MR (Calc.)	40.586	4	25°C	1.0000	5	Exp. L.1.%/wt.			
(nD-d/2)	0.99302	4	30 mm	1.0000	5	u.			
Dielectric			BP	0.9532	5	Dispersion			
A 85 to	6.99082	5	t_e	0.9381	5	Flash Point °C	62.0	5	
B 235 °C	1577.3	5	t_c	0.255	5	Fire Point			
C	200.	5	ΔHc kcal/m			M. Spec.			
A* 85 to	1.46007	5	ΔHf			Ultra V.	Yes	1	
B* 220 °C	1483.3	5	ΔFf			X-Ray Dif.			
K			Viscosity			Infrared	1084.	1	
c			centistokes			Solubility in +			
t_k to			η °C			Acetone	∞		
t_x °C						Carbon tet.	∞		
A' 0 to	7.33818	5				Benzene	∞		
B' 85 °C	1782.3	5				Ether	∞		
C'	218.	5	B^v to			n-Heptane	∞		
A'* 10 to	1.81406	5	A^v °C			Ethanol	∞		
B'* 85 °C	1684.44	5	(B^v) to			Water			
Ac 235 to	7.3954	5	(A^v) °C			Water in			
Bc t_c °C	1950.5	5							
Cc	249.	5	c_p liq. °K						
Cryos. A°			c_p vap. °K						
consts. B°									
t_e °C F	205.0	5	c_v vap.						

$T_R = 0.75\,T_C$ + grams/100 grams solvent

REFERENCES: 1-Dow 2-API 3-Lit. 4-Calc. from det. data 5-Calc. by formula

SOURCE: Dow

PURIFICATION: Distillation

LITERATURE REFERENCES:

NAME	1-Chloro-4-ethylbenzene		STRUCTURAL FORMULA
	p-Chloroethylbenzene		
Mole % Pur. 99.86	Ref. 1	Molecular Formula C_8H_9Cl	Molecular Weight 140.609

		Ref.				Ref.				Ref.
F.P. °C	-62.57	1	dt/dP °C/mm				f	to		
F.P. 100%			25°C	14.459	5		g	°K		
B.P. °C			BP	0.0535	4		h			
760 mm	184.42	1	t_e	0.0363	5		f'	to		
100	116.47	4	30 mm	0.7531	4		g'	°K		
30	86.42	4	ΔHm cal/g	15.72	1		h'			
10	63.5	5								
1	25.1	5	ΔHv cal/g				m	to		
Pressure			25°C	87.29	5		n	°K		
mm 25°C	0.9957	5	30 mm	80.90	5		o			
t_e	1250.	5	BP	69.01	5		m'	to		
Density			t_e (d, e)	66.58	5		n'	°K		
g/ml 20°C	1.04553	1		66.41	5		o'			
d_4^t 25	1.04083	1	ΔHv/T_e	19.55	5		Surface tension			
30	1.03611	4	d	85 to	91.39	5	dynes/cm. 20°C	32.78	1
a	1.06433	4	e	205 °C	0.1214	5	γ	30	31.68	1
b	-0.0₃941	4	d'	25 to	89.89	5		40	30.64	1
Ref. Index			e'	85 °C	0.1041	5	Parachor [P]			
n_D 20°C	1.51751	1	d_c g/ml	0.337	5		20°C	321.8	4
25	1.51517	1	v_c ml/g	2.967	5		30	322.0	4
30	1.51260	1	t_c °C	406.8	5		40	322.2	4
"C"	0.6498	4	P_c mm	25926.	5		Sugd.	321.9	5
MR (Obs.)	40.736	4	PV/RT				Exp. L.1.%/wt.			
MR (Calc.)	40.410	5	25°C	1.0000	5		u.			
(nD-d/2)	1.09475	4	30 mm	1.0000	5		Dispersion			
Dielectric	6.049	1	BP	0.9531	5		Flash Point °C	62.0	5
A	85 to	6.98309	4	t_e	0.9380	5		Fire Point		
B	235 °C	1577.0	4	t_c	0.255	5		M Spec.		
C		200.	4	ΔHc kcal/m				Ultra V.	Yes	1
A*	85 to	1.45161	5	ΔHf				X-Ray Dif.		
B*	220 °C	1482.84	5	ΔFf				Infrared	516.	1
K				Viscosity				Solubility in +		
c				centistokes				Acetone	∞	
t_k	to			η	°C			Carbon tet.	∞	
t_x	°C							Benzene	∞	
A'	0 to	7.32997	5					Ether	∞	
B'	85 °C	1781.96	5					n-Heptane	∞	
C'		218.0	5	B^v	to			Ethanol		
A'*	10 to	1.80553	5	A^v	°C			Water		
B'*	85 °C	1684.02	5	(B^v)	to			Water in		
Ac	235 to	7.38761	5	(A^v)	°C					
Bc	t_c °C	1950.2	5	c_p liq. °K						
Cc		248.9	5							
Cryos. A°	0.02519	1	c_p vap. °K							
consts. B°										
t_e °C F	205.8	5	c_v vap.							

$T_R = 0.75 T_c$

+ grams/100 grams solvent

REFERENCES: 1-Dow 2-API 3-Lit. 4-Calc. from det. data 5-Calc. by formula

SOURCE: Dow

PURIFICATION: Distillation

LITERATURE REFERENCES:

TABLE I. ALKYL AND HALO BENZENES

NAME	2,5-Dichloro-p-xylene	STRUCTURAL FORMULA

Mole % Pur. 99.86	Ref. 1	Molecular Formula $C_8H_8Cl_2$	Molecular Weight 175.058

		Ref.				Ref.					Ref.
F.P. °C	68.24	1	dt/dP				f		to		
F.P. 100%			°C/mm				g		_ _ °K		
			25°C	107.26		5	h				
B.P. °C			BP	0.0559		4					
760 mm	224.32	4	t_e	0.0352		5	f'		to		
100	152.84	4	30 mm	0.8036		4	g'		_ _ °K		
30	120.88	4					h'				
10	96.3	5	ΔHm cal/g	25.85		4	m		to		
1	55.	5	ΔHv cal/g				n		_ _ °K		
Pressure			25°C	82.02		5	o				
mm 25°C	0.1147	5	30 mm	73.12		5					
t_e	1365.	5	BP	61.97		5	m'		to		
Density			t_e	60.73		5	n'		_ _ °K		
g/ml 20°C			t_e (d, e)	59.30		5	o'				
d_4^t 25			ΔHv/T_e	20.29		5	Surface tension				
30			d 120 to	86.33		5	dynes/cm. 20°C				
a			e 250 °C	0.1078		5	δ 30				
b			d' 25 to	84.34		5	40				
Ref. Index			e' 120 °C	0.0928		5	Parachor [P]				
n_D 20°C			d_c g/ml				20°C				
25			v_c ml/g				30				
30			t_c °C				40				
"C"			P_c mm				Sugd.	359.5		5	
MR (Obs.)			PV/RT				Exp. L.1.%/wt.				
MR (Calc.)	45.277	5	25°C	1.0000		5	u.				
(nD-d/2)			30 mm	1.0000		5	Dispersion				
Dielectric			BP	0.9400		5	Flash Point °C				
A 120 to	7.16727	4	t_e	0.9399		5	Fire Point				
B 300 °C	1797.4	4	t_c				M. Spec.				
C	195.	4	ΔHc kcal/m				Ultra V.				
A* 120 to	1.71859	5	ΔHf				X-Ray Dif.				
B* 275 °C	1702.2	5	ΔFf				Infrared				
K			Viscosity				Solubility in +				
c			centistokes				Acetone				
t_k ⌐ to			η 120 °C	0.5533		1	Carbon tet.				
t_x °C			130	0.5114		1	Benzene				
A' 25 to	7.52575	5	140⧣	0.4785		1	Ether				
B' 120 °C	2031.0	5	150⧣	0.4448		1	n-Heptane				
C'	215.	5	B^v 120 to	517.02		4	Ethanol				
A'* 25 to	2.07549	5	A^v 160 °C	2.42647		4	Water				
B'* 120 °C	1929.3	5	(B^v) to				Water in				
Ac to			(A^v) °C								
Bc ⌐t_c °C			c_p liq. °K								
Cc											
Cryos. A°	0.01955	1	c_p vap. °K								
consts. B°											
t_e °C F	250.76	5	c_v vap.								

⧣ some sublimation   + grams/100 grams solvent

REFERENCES: 1-Dow   2-API   3-Lit.   4-Calc. from det. data   5-Calc. by formula

SOURCE: Dow

PURIFICATION: Distillation

LITERATURE REFERENCES:

No. 138

NAME	o-Chlorocumene	STRUCTURAL FORMULA

1-Chloro-2-isopropylbenzene

CH(CH₃)₂ / Cl

Mole % Pur. 100.0	Ref. 1	Molecular Formula $C_9H_{11}Cl$	Molecular Weight 154.635

		Ref.				Ref.					Ref.
F.P. °C	-74.42	1	dt/dP				f		to		
F.P. 100%			°C/mm				g		°K		
			25°C	19.850	5		h				
B.P. °C			BP	0.0541	4						
760 mm	191.08	1	t_e	0.0363	5		f'		to		
100	122.43	4	30 mm	0.7614	4		g'		°K		
30	92.05	4	ΔHm cal/g				h'				
10	68.8	5	ΔHv cal/g				m		to		
1	30.0	5	25°C	81.70	5		n		°K		
Pressure			30 mm	75.06	5		o				
mm 25°C	0.705	5	BP	63.80	5						
t_e	1267.	5	t_e	61.48	5		m'		to		
Density			t_e (d,e)	61.27	5		n'		°K		
g/ml 20°C	1.03414	1	ΔHv/T_e	19.54	5		o'				
d_4^t 25	1.02950	1	d | 90 to	85.52	5		Surface tension				
30	1.02484	4	e | 210 °C	0.1137	5		dynes/cm. 20°C	34.08	5
a	1.05270	4	d' | 25 to	84.18	5		γ 30	32.87	5
b	-0.0₃928	4	e' | 90 °C	0.0991	5		40	31.70	5
Ref. Index			d_c g/ml	0.333	5		Parachor [P]		
n_D 20°C	1.51678	1	v_c ml/g	3.003	5		20°C		
25	1.51437	1	t_c °C	403.5	5		30		
30	1.51189	4	P_c mm	23024.	5		40		
"C"	0.6561	4					Sugd.	361.3	5
MR (Obs.)	45.24	4	PV/RT				Exp. L.1.%/wt.		
MR (Calc.)	45.189	5	25°C	1.0000	5		u.		
(nD-d/2)	0.99962	4	30 mm	1.0000	5		Dispersion		
Dielectric			BP	0.9513	5		Flash Point °C		
A | 90 to	6.99207	4	t_e	0.9360	5		Fire Point		
B |235 °C	1599.61	4	t_c	0.253	5		M Spec.		
C	198.00	4	ΔHc kcal/m				Ultra V.		
A* | 90 to	1.49897	5	ΔHf				X-Ray Dif.		
B* |230 °C	1505.37	5	ΔFf				Infrared		
K			Viscosity				Solubility in +		
c			centistokes				Acetone		
t_k | to			η °C				Carbon tet.		
t_x | °C							Benzene		
A' | 0 to	7.33951	5					Ether		
B' | 90 °C	1807.5	5					n-Heptane		
C'	216.3	5	B^v | to				Ethanol		
A'* | 10 to	1.85437	5	A^v | °C				Water		
B'* | 90 °C	1709.8	5	(B^v) | to				Water in		
Ac | 235 to	7.39236	5	(A^v) | °C						
Bc | t_c °C	1964.5	5	c_p liq. °K						
Cc	244.8	5	c_p vap. °K						
Cryos. A°									
consts. B°			c_v vap.						
t_e °C F	213.28	5							

$T_R = 0.75 T_c$ + grams/100 grams solvent

REFERENCES: 1-Dow 2-API 3-Lit.   4-Calc. from det. data 5-Calc. by formula

SOURCE: Dow

PURIFICATION: Distillation

LITERATURE REFERENCES:

TABLE I. ALKYL AND HALO BENZENES

No. 139

NAME	p-Chlorocumene	STRUCTURAL FORMULA
	1-Chloro-4-isopropylbenzene	

| Mole % Pur. 99.98 | Ref. 1 | Molecular Formula $C_9H_{11}Cl$ | Molecular Weight 154.635 | |

		Ref.			Ref.			Ref.
F.P. °C	-12.27	1	dt/dP			f	to	
F.P. 100%			°C/mm			g	°K	
			25°C	26.774	5	h		
B.P. °C			BP	0.0550	4			
760 mm	198.30	1	t_e	0.0367	5	f'	to	
100	128.49	4	30 mm	0.7739	4	g'	°K	
30	97.61	4	ΔHm cal/g			h'		
10	74.0	5				m	to	
1	34.5	5	ΔHv cal/g			n	°K	
Pressure			25°C	83.41	5	o		
mm 25°C	0.5117	5	30 mm	76.10	5			
t_e	1274.	5	BP	64.48	5	m'	to	
Density			t_e	61.66	5	n'	°K	
g/ml 20°C	1.02078	1	t_e (d, e)	61.42	5	o'		
d_4^t 25	1.01622	1	ΔHv/T_e	19.29	5	Surface tension		
30	1.01165	4	d 95 to	87.71	5	dynes/cm. 20°C	32.36	5
a	1.03902	4	e 220 °C	0.1189	5	γ 30	31.21	5
b	-0.0₃912	4	d' 25 to	85.93	5	40	30.10	5
Ref. Index			e' 95 °C	0.1007	5	Parachor [P]		
n_D 20°C	1.51174	1	d_c g/ml	0.340	5	20°C		
25	1.50938	1	v_c ml/g	2.94	5	30		
30	1.50678	4	t_c °C	412.0	5	40		
"C"	0.6585	4	P_c mm	22454.	5	Sugd.	361.3	5
MR (Obs.)	45.46	4	PV/RT			Exp. L.1.%/wt.		
MR (Calc.)	45.028	5	25°C	1.0000	5	u.		
(nD-d/2)	1.00127	4	30 mm	1.0000	5	Dispersion		
Dielectric			BP	0.9431	5	Flash Point °C	72.0	5
A 95 to	6.98784	5	t_e	0.9261	5	Fire Point		
B 240 °C	1623.51	5	t_c	0.24	5	M. Spec.	Yes	1
C	197.00	5	ΔHc kcal/m			Ultra V.		
A* 95 to	1.50326	5	ΔHf			X-Ray Dif.		
B* 240 °C	1532.23	5	ΔFf			Infrared	788.	1
K			Viscosity			Solubility in +		
c			centistokes			Acetone	∞	
t_k to			η °C			Carbon tet.	∞	
t_x °C						Benzene	∞	
A' 0 to	7.33502	5				Ether	∞	
B' 95 °C	1834.52	5	B^v to			n-Heptane	∞	
C'	215.6	5	A^v °C			Ethanol	∞	
A'* 15 to	1.84670	5	(B^v) to			Water		
B'* 95 °C	1736.32	5	(A^v) °C			Water in		
Ac 240 to	7.3880	5	c_p liq. °K					
Bc t_c °C	1992.7	5						
Cc	244.2	5	c_p vap. °K					
Cryos. A°								
consts. B°			c_v vap.					
t_e °C F	221.13	5						

T_R = 0.75 T_c + grams/100 grams solvent

REFERENCES:	1-Dow 2-API 3-Lit. 4-Calc. from det. data 5-Calc. by formula
SOURCE:	Dow
PURIFICATION:	Distillation
LITERATURE REFERENCES:	

No. 140

NAME	Bromobenzene			STRUCTURAL FORMULA

Mole % Pur. 99.97	Ref. 1	Molecular Formula C_6H_5Br	Molecular Weight 157.016

		Ref.			Ref.				Ref.
F.P. °C	-30.82	1	dt/dP			f	to		
F.P. 100%			°C/mm			g	°K		
			25°C	3.887	5	h			
B.P. °C			BP	0.05177	4				
760 mm	156.06	1	t_e	0.03711	4	f'	to		
100	90.54	1	30 mm	0.7218	4	g'	°K		
30	61.70	4				h'			
10	42.07	4	ΔHm cal/g	16.18	4				
1	3.7	4	ΔHv cal/g			m	to		
Pressure			25°C	69.23	5	n	°K		
mm 25°C	4.182	5	30 mm	65.50	5	o			
t_e	1165.0	4	BP	56.25	4				
Density			t_e	54.77	4	m'	to		
g/ml 20°C	1.49500	1	t_e (d, e)	54.50	5	n'	°K		
d_4^t 25	1.48824	4	ΔHv/T_e	19.24	5	o'			
30	1.48148	4	d | 60 to	71.61	4	Surface tension			
a	1.52203	4	e | 175 °C	0.0991	4	dynes/cm. 20°C	36.34	3'
b	-0.00135	4	d' | 15 to	71.77	5	y 30	35.11	5
Ref. Index			e' | 60 °C	0.1016	5	40	33.84	5
n_D 20°C	1.55972	1	d_c g/ml	0.4853	3	Parachor [P]			
25	1.55709	1	v_c ml/g	2.061	3	20°C	258.4	5
30	1.55426	1	t_c °C	397.	3	30		
"C"	0.4890	4	P_c mm	33912.	3	40		
MR (Obs.)	33.97	4	PV/RT			Sugd.	258.0	5
MR (Calc.)	34.38	5	25°C	1.0000	5	Exp. L.1.%/wt.			
(nD-d/2)	0.81297	4	30 mm	1.0000	5	u.			
Dielectric	5.308	1	BP	0.9491	4	Dispersion			
A | 60 to	6.91444	1	t_e	0.9370	5	Flash Point °C			
B |190 °C	1474.06	1	t_c	0.3026	3	Fire Point			
C	209.4	1	ΔHc kcal/m			M Spec.			
A* | 60 to	1.44788	4	ΔHf			Ultra V.			
B* |200 °C	1380.0	4	ΔFf			X-Ray Dif.	Yes	1
K	37.	4	Viscosity			Infrared	Yes	1
c	-0.14394	4	centistokes			Solubility in +			
t_k |200 to	207.	4	η °C			Acetone			
t_x |340 °C	464.	5				Carbon tet.			
A' | 0 to	7.35311	5				Benzene			
B' | 60 °C	1696.4	5				Ether			
C'	227.	5	B^V | to			n-Heptane			
A'* | 10 to	1.88241	5	A^V | °C			Ethanol			
B'* | 60 °C	1596.3	5	(B^V) | to			Water			
Ac |190 to	7.35936	4	(A^V) | °C			Water in			
Bc | t_c °C	1853.57	4	c_p liq. °K						
Cc	258.2	4							
Cryos. A°	0.02039	1	c_p vap. °K						
consts. B°									
t_e °C	173.67	4	c_v vap.						

+ grams/100 grams solvent

REFERENCES: 1-Dow 2-API 3-Lit. 4-Calc. from det. data 5-Calc. by formula

SOURCE: Dow

PURIFICATION: Distillation

LITERATURE REFERENCES: 3 Young; 3' Timmermans

TABLE I. ALKYL AND HALO BENZENES

No. 141

NAME	o-Dibromobenzene					STRUCTURAL FORMULA		
	1,2-Dibromobenzene							

| Mole % Pur. 99.80 | Ref. 1 | Molecular Formula | $C_6H_4Br_2$ | Molecular Weight 235.924 | | | | |

		Ref.				Ref.				Ref.
F.P. °C	7.13	1	dt/dP				f	to		
F.P. 100%			°C/mm				g	°K		
B.P. °C			25°C	69.635	5		h			
760 mm	225.46	1	BP	0.0585	4		f'	to		
100	150.81	4	t_e	0.0381	5		g'	°K		
30	117.55	4	30 mm	0.8352	4		h'			
10	92.1	5	ΔHm cal/g	12.80	4		m	to		
1	49.2	5	ΔHv cal/g				n	°K		
Pressure			25°C	55.83	5		o			
mm 25°C	0.1927	5	30 mm	51.33	5		m'	to		
t_e	1312.	5	BP	43.15	5		n'	°K		
Density			t_e	41.44	5		o'			
g/ml 20°C	1.98429	1	t_e (d, e)	41.19	5		Surface tension			
d_4^t 25	1.97670	1	ΔHv/T_e	18.64	5		dynes/cm. 20°C	43.02	1
30	1.96910	4	d 115 to	60.24	5		δ 30	41.80	1
a	2.01465	4	e 250 °C	0.0758	5		40	40.64	1
b	-0.00152	4	d' 25 to	57.05	5		Parachor [P]			
Ref. Index			e' 115 °C	0.0486	5		20°C	304.5	4
n_D 20°C	1.61553	1	d_c g/ml	0.644	5		30	304.6	4
25	1.60909	1	v_c ml/g	1.55	5		40	305.2	4
30	1.59716	1	t_c °C	486.6	5		Sugd.	308.9	5
"C"	0.4026	1	P_c mm	31591.	5				
MR (Obs.)	41.518	4	PV/RT				Exp. L.1.%/wt.		
MR (Calc.)	41.837	5	25°C	1.0000	5		u.		
(nD-d/2)	0.62339	4	30 mm	1.0000	5		Dispersion		
Dielectric	7.793	1	BP	0.9199	5		Flash Point °C		
A 115 to	7.10265	4	t_e	0.8992	5		Fire Point		
B 295 °C	1825.77	4	t_c	0.245	5		M. Spec.		
C	207.0	4	ΔHc kcal/m				Ultra V.		
A* 120 to	1.80879	5	ΔHf				X-Ray Dif.		
B* 280 °C	1735.	5	ΔFf				Infrared		
K			Viscosity				Solubility in +		
c			centistokes				Acetone	∞	
t_k to			η 20 °C	1.4686	1		Carbon tet.	∞	
t_x °C			40	1.0520	1		Benzene	∞	
A' 20 to	7.45706	5	60	0.8062	1		Ether	∞	
B' 120 °C	2063.06	5	80	0.6470	1		n-Heptane	∞	
C'	227.4	5	B^v 30 to	583.85	4		Ethanol	∞	
A'* 20 to	2.12281	5	A^v 90 °C	2.15788	4		Water		
B'* 120 °C	1952.59	5	(B^v) to				Water in		
Ac 295 to	7.52773	5	(A^v) °C						
Bc t_c °C	2279.0	5	c_p liq. °K						
Cc	266.1	5							
Cryos. A°	0.01901	1	c_p vap. °K						
consts. B°									
t_e °C F	251.19	5	c_v vap.						

T_R = 0.75 T_c + grams/100 grams solvent

REFERENCES: 1-Dow 2-API 3-Lit. 4-Calc. from det. data 5-Calc. by formula

SOURCE: Dow

PURIFICATION: Distillation

LITERATURE REFERENCES:

No. 142

NAME	o-Bromotoluene	STRUCTURAL FORMULA

	1-Bromo-2-methylbenzene	

Mole % Pur. 99.96	Ref. 1	Molecular Formula C_7H_7Br	Molecular Weight 171.042

		Ref.			Ref.			Ref.
F.P. °C	-27.73	1	dt/dP			f to		
F.P. 100%			°C/mm			g °K		
B.P. °C			25°C	11.0514	5	h		
760 mm	181.69	1	BP	0.0546	5			
100	112.66	4	t_e	0.0376	5	f' to		
30	82.27	4				g' °K		
10	59.1	5	30 mm	0.7603	5	h'		
1	20.5	5	ΔHm cal/g	14.17	4			
Pressure			ΔHv cal/g			m to		
mm 25°C	1.358	5	25°C	68.84	5	n °K		
t_e	1228.	5	30 mm	64.36	5	o		
Density			BP	54.49	5	m' to		
g/ml 20°C	1.42322	1	t_e	52.58	5	n' °K		
d_4^t 25	1.41774	1	t_e (d, e)	52.41	5	o'		
30	1.41223	4	ΔHv/T_e	18.90	5	Surface tension		
a	1.44514	4	d 85 to	72.52	5	dynes/cm. 20°C	35.85	1
b	-0.00110	4	e 200 °C	0.0993	5	γ 30	34.79	1
			d' 25 to	70.79	5	40	33.68	1
Ref. Index			e' 85 °C	0.0782	5	Parachor [P]		
n_D 20°C	1.55650	1	d_c g/ml	0.468	5	20°C	294.1	4
25	1.55412	1	v_c ml/g	2.138	5	30	294.1	4
30	1.54187	1	t_c °C	419.7	5	40	294.0	4
"C"	0.5109	4	P_c mm	28151.	5	Sugd.	297.0	5
MR (Obs.)	38.662	4	PV/RT			Exp. L.1.%/wt.		
MR (Calc.)	38.690	5	25°C	1.0000	5	. u.		
(nD-d/2)	0.84489	4	30 mm	1.0000	5	Dispersion		
Dielectric			BP	0.9439	5	Flash Point °C		
A 80 to	6.90847	4	t_e	0.9277	5	Fire Point		
B 245 °C	1549.39	4	t_c	0.24	5	M Spec.		
C	203.0	4	ΔHc kcal/m			Ultra V.		
A* 80 to	1.47860	5	ΔHf			X-Ray Dif.		
B* 215 °C	1458.88	5	ΔFf			Infrared		
K			Viscosity			Solubility in +		
c			centistokes			Acetone		
t_k to			η 20 °C	1.0045	1	Carbon tet.	∞	
t_x °C			40	0.7706	1	Benzene	∞	
A' 20 to	7.25065	5	60	0.6189	1	Ether	∞	
B' 80 °C	1750.76	5	80	0.5131	1	n-Heptane		
C'	221.0	5	B^V 30 to	488.48	4	Ethanol		
A'* 20 to	1.81035	5	A^V 90 °C	$\overline{2}$.42771	4	Water		
B'* 80 °C	1651.40	5	(B^V) to			Water in		
Ac 245 to	7.3209	5	(A^V) °C					
Bc t_c °C	1942.3	5						
Cc	256.8	5	c_p liq. °K					
Cryos. A°	0.02025	1	c_p vap. °K					
consts. B°								
t_e °C F	202.69	5	c_v vap.					

$T_R = 0.75 T_c$ + grams/100 grams solvent

REFERENCES: 1-Dow   2-API   3-Lit.   4-Calc. from det. data   5-Calc. by formula

SOURCE: Dow

PURIFICATION: Distillation

LITERATURE REFERENCES:

TABLE I. ALKYL AND HALO BENZENES

No. 143

NAME	p-Bromotoluene	STRUCTURAL FORMULA
	1-Bromo-4-methylbenzene	

Mole % Pur. 99.94	Ref. 1	Molecular Formula C_7H_7Br	Molecular Weight 171.042

		Ref.				Ref.						Ref.
F.P. °C	24.84	1	dt/dP				f		to			
F.P. 100%			°C/mm				g		°K			
			25°C	12.934	5		h					
B.P. °C			BP	0.0541	4							
760 mm	184.35	1	t_e	0.0368	5		f'		to			
100	115.62	4	30 mm	0.7631	4		g'		°K			
30	85.18	4					h'					
10	61.9	5	ΔHm cal/g	20.71	4							
1	22.9	5					m		to			
			ΔHv cal/g				n		°K			
Pressure			25°C	69.50	5		o					
mm 25°C	1.149	5	30 mm	65.18	5							
t_e	1243.	5	BP	55.87	5		m'		to			
Density			t_e	54.02	5		n'		°K			
g/ml 25 °C	1.39953	1	t_e (d, e)	53.86	5		o'					
d_4^t 30	1.39339	1	ΔHv/T_e	19.29	5							
35	1.38729	1	d 85 to	73.18	5		Surface tension					
a	1.43023	4	e 200 °C	0.0939	5		dynes/cm. 20°C	35.47		1		
b	-0.00123	4	d' 25 to	71.29	5		δ 30	34.16		1		
Ref. Index			e' 85 °C	0.0718	5		40	33.04		1		
n_D 25 °C	1.54768	1	d_c g/ml	0.456	5		Parachor [P]					
30	1.54433	1	v_c ml/g	2.193	5		20°C	296.95		4		
50	1.53700	1	t_c °C	419.7	5		30	296.77		4		
"C"	0.5119	4	P_c mm	28949.	5		40	296.93		4		
MR (Obs.)	38.78	4	PV/RT				Sugd.	297.0		5		
MR (Calc.)	38.690	5	25°C	1.0000	5		Exp. L. l. %/wt.					
(nD-d/2)	0.74792	4	30 mm	1.0000	5		u.					
Dielectric	5.829	1	BP	0.9482	5		Dispersion					
A 85 to	7.00762	4	t_e	0.9332	5		Flash Point °C					
B 250 °C	1612.35	4	t_c	0.253	5		Fire Point					
C	206.36	4	ΔHc kcal/m				M. Spec.					
A* 85 to	1.56345	5	ΔHf				Ultra V.					
B* 215 °C	1516.72	5	ΔFf				X-Ray Dif.					
K			Viscosity				Infrared					
c			centistokes				Solubility in +					
t_k to			η 30 °C	0.78163	1		Acetone					
t_x °C			40	0.69285	1		Carbon tet.					
A' 25 to	7.35604	5	60	0.56238	1		Benzene					
B' 85 °C	1821.91	5	80	0.47080	1		Ether	∞		3		
C'	224.7	5					n-Heptane					
A'* 25 to	1.90860	5	B^v 30 to	464.06	4		Ethanol					
B'* 85 °C	1719.24	5	A^v 90 °C	2.35897	4		Water solid phase	0.011		1		
Ac 250 to	7.4238	5	(B^v) to				Water in					
Bc t_c °C	2011.3	5	(A^v) °C									
Cc	259.3	5	c_p liq. °K									
Cryos. A°												
consts. B°			c_p vap. °K									
t_e °C F	205.69	5	c_v vap.									

T_R = 0.75 T_c + grams/100 grams solvent

REFERENCES: 1-Dow   2-API   3-Lit.   4-Calc. from det. data   5-Calc. by formula

SOURCE: Dow

PURIFICATION: Distillation, absorption

LITERATURE REFERENCES: 3 Lange

No. 144

NAME	1-Bromo-2-ethylbenzene	STRUCTURAL FORMULA
	o-Bromoethylbenzene	

| Mole % Pur. 99.93 | Ref. 1 | Molecular Formula C_8H_9Br | Molecular Weight 185.068 | |

Structural formula: benzene ring with C_2H_5 and Br substituents

		Ref.			Ref.				Ref.
F.P. °C	-67.92	1	dt/dP			f	to		
F.P. 100%	-67.89	1	°C/mm			g	°K		
B.P. °C			25°C	26.06	5	h			
760 mm	199.30	1	BP	0.0556	4				
100	128.76	4	t_e	0.0374	5	f'	to		
30	97.61	4	30 mm	0.7803	4	g'	°K		
10	73.8	5	ΔHm cal/g			h'			
1	34.1	5	ΔHv cal/g						
Pressure			25°C	68.99	5	m	to		
mm 25°C	0.5311	5	30 mm	63.07	5	n	°K		
t_e	1263.	5	BP	52.75	5	o			
Density			t_e	50.70	5	m'	to		
g/ml 20°C	1.35483	1	t_e (d, e)	50.45	5	n'	°K		
d_4^t 25	1.34917	1	ΔHv/T_e	18.95	5	o'			
30	1.34345	4	d 95 to	72.98	5	Surface tension			
a	1.37772	4	e 215 °C	0.1015	5	dynes/cm. 20°C	35.02	1
b	-0.00114	4	d' 25 to	71.02	5	ɤ 30	33.98	1
Ref. Index			e' 95 °C	0.0815	5	40	32.95	1
n_D 20°C	1.54856	1	d_c g/ml	0.444	5	Parachor [P]		
25	1.54624	1	v_c ml/g	2.34	5	20°C	332.3	4
30	1.53429	1	t_c °C	427.4	5	30	332.6	4
"C"	0.5295	4	P_c mm	25030.	5	40	332.6	4
MR (Obs.)	43.419	4	PV/RT			Sugd.	336.0	5
MR (Calc.)	43.308	5	25°C	1.0000	5	Exp. L. 1.%/wt.		
(nD-d/2)	0.87112	4	30 mm	1.0000	5	u.		
Dielectric	4.580		BP	0.9346	5	Dispersion		
A 95 to	6.96150	4	t_e	0.9167	5	Flash Point °C		
B 250 °C	1621.24	4	t_c	0.250	5	Fire Point		
C	198.0	4	ΔHc kcal/m			M Spec.		
A* 95 to	1.56782	5	ΔHf			Ultra V.		
B* 235 °C	1533.46	5	ΔFf			X-Ray Dif.		
K			Viscosity			Infrared		
c			centistokes			Solubility in +		
t_k to			η 20 °C	1.1677	1	Acetone	∞	
t_x °C			40	0.8794	1	Carbon tet.	∞	
A' 10 to	7.30702	5	60	0.6969	1	Benzene	∞	
B' 95 °C	1831.9	5	80	0.5737	1	Ether	∞	
C'	216.6	5	B^v 30 to	513.03	4	n-Heptane	∞	
A'* 15 to	1.89534	5	A^v 90 °C	2.30616	4	Ethanol	∞	
B'* 95 °C	1733.0	5	(B^v) to			Water	0.0039	1
Ac 250 to	7.3664	5	(A^v) °C			Water in		
Bc t_c °C	2006.3	5	c_p liq. °K					
Cc	248.6	5						
Cryos. A° consts. B°	0.01811	1	c_p vap. °K					
t_e °C F	222.0	5	c_v vap.					

$T_R = 0.75\,T_c$

+ grams/100 grams solvent

REFERENCES: 1-Dow   2-API   3-Lit.   4-Calc. from det. data   5-Calc. by formula

SOURCE: Dow

PURIFICATION: Distillation

LITERATURE REFERENCES:

TABLE I. ALKYL AND HALO BENZENES

No. 145

| NAME | 1-Bromo-4-ethylbenzene | STRUCTURAL FORMULA |
| | p-Bromoethylbenzene | |

Structural formula: C_2H_5 on benzene ring with Br

| Mole % Pur. 100.0 | Ref. 1 | Molecular Formula C_8H_9Br | Molecular Weight 185.068 |

		Ref.			Ref.				Ref.
F.P. °C	-43.47	1	dt/dP			f | to		
F.P. 100%			°C/mm			g | °K		
			25°C	38.511	5	h |		
B.P. °C			BP	0.0555	4			
760 mm	205.07	4	t_e	0.0370	5	f' | to		
100	134.69	4	30 mm	0.7799	4	g' | °K		
30	103.57	5				h' |		
10	79.8	5	ΔHm cal/g					
1	40.	5	ΔHv cal/g			m | to		
			25°C	72.40	5	n | °K		
Pressure			30 mm	65.15	5	o |		
mm 25°C	0.3424	5	BP	54.17	5			
t_e	1277.	5	t_e	51.95	5	m' | to		
Density			t_e (d, e)	51.67	5	n' | °K		
g/ml 20°C	1.34226	1	$\Delta Hv/T_e$	19.17	5	o' |		
d_4^t 25	1.33653	1				Surface tension		
30	1.33079	4	d | 105 to	76.35	5	dynes/cm. 20°C	35.27	5
a	1.36518	4	e | 220 °C	0.1082	5	γ 30	34.08	5
b	-0.00115	4	d' | 25 to	74.71	5	40	32.92	5
Ref. Index			e' | 105 °C	0.0923	5	Parachor [P]		
n_D 20°C	1.54475	1				20°C		
25	1.54228	1	d_c g/ml	0.434	5	30		
30	1.53981	4	v_c ml/g	2.305	5	40		
"C"	0.5311	4	t_c °C	433.9	5	Sugd.	336.0	5
			P_c mm	25545.	5			
MR (Obs.)	43.73	4	PV/RT			Exp. L. 1.%/wt.		
MR (Calc.)	43.308	5	25°C	1.0000	5	u.		
(nD-d/2)	0.87401	4	30 mm	1.0000	5	Dispersion		
Dielectric			BP	0.9338	5	Flash Point °C		
A | 105 to	6.98209	4	t_e	0.9150	5	Fire Point		
B | 260 °C	1632.60	4	t_c	0.290	5	M. Spec.		
C	193.	4	ΔHc kcal/m			Ultra V.		
A* | 105 to	1.58901	5	ΔHf			X-Ray Dif.		
B* | 240 °C	1546.76	5	ΔFf			Infrared	510.	1
K			Viscosity			Solubility in +		
c			centistokes			Acetone	∞	
t_k | to			η 20 °C	1.0545	1	Carbon tet.	∞	
t_x | °C			40	0.8119	1	Benzene	∞	
A' | 15 to	7.32890	5	60	0.6574	1	Ether	∞	
B' | 105 °C	1844.79	5	80	0.5485	1	n-Heptane	∞	
C'	212.	5	B_v | 30 to	471.03	4	Ethanol	∞	
A'* 20 to	1.91928	5	A_v | 90 °C	2.40558	4	Water		
B'* 105 °C	1748.3	5	(B^v) | to			Water in		
Ac | 260 to	7.3807	5	(A^v) | °C					
Bc | t_c °C	2011.2	5	c_p liq. °K					
Cc	242.	5						
Cryos. A°	0.01336	1	c_p vap. °K					
consts. B°								
t_e °C F	228.2	5	c_v vap.					

$T_R = 0.75 T_c$

+ grams/100 grams solvent

REFERENCES: 1-Dow 2-API 3-Lit. 4-Calc. from det. data 5-Calc. by formula

SOURCE: Dow

PURIFICATION: Distillation

LITERATURE REFERENCES:

No. 146

NAME	o-Bromocumene		STRUCTURAL FORMULA
	1-Bromo-2-isopropylbenzene		

Mole % Pur. 99.9	Ref. 1	Molecular Formula $C_9H_{11}Br$	Molecular Weight 199.904

		Ref.				Ref.					Ref.
F.P. °C	-59.27	1	dt/dP				f		to		
F.P. 100%			°C/mm				g		°K		
			25°C	45.454	5		h				
B.P. °C			BP	0.0563	4						
760 mm	210.24	4	t_e	0.0374	5		f'		to		
100	138.77	4					g'		°K		
30	107.13	4	30 mm	0.7929	4		h'				
10	83.0	5	ΔHm cal/g								
1	42.5	5					m		to		
			ΔHv cal/g				n		°K		
Pressure			25°C	67.09	5		o				
mm 25°C	0.2899	5	30 mm	60.45	5						
t_e	1284.	5	BP	50.21	5		m'		to		
Density			t_e	48.10	5		n'		°K		
g/ml 20°C	1.30195	1	t_e (d, e)	47.84	5		o'				
d_4^t 25	1.29636	1	ΔHv/T_e	18.96	5		Surface tension				
30	1.29076	5	d	105 to	71.10	5	dynes/cm. 20°C	35.58	5
a	1.32431	4	e	225 °C	0.0994	5	7	30	34.37	5
b	-0.00112	4	d'	25 to	69.11	5		40	33.20	5
Ref. Index			e'	105 °C	0.0808	5	Parachor [P]				
n_D 20°C	1.54084	1	d_c g/ml	0.447	5	20°C				
25	1.53853	1	v_c ml/g	2.237	5	30				
30	1.53592	4	t_c °C	427.5	5	40				
"C"	0.5438	4	P_c mm	22157.	5	Sugd. 375.0	5
MR (Obs.)	48.07	4	PV/RT				Exp. L. 1.%/wt.				
MR (Calc.)	47.926	5	25°C	1.0000	5	u.				
(nD-d/2)	0.89035	4	30 mm	1.0000	5	Dispersion				
Dielectric			BP	0.9294	5	Flash Point °C				
A 105 to	6.99354	4	t_e	0.9097	5	Fire Point				
B 255 °C	1666.7	4	t_c	0.244	5	M Spec.				
C	195.	4	ΔHc kcal/m				Ultra V.				
A* 105 to	1.63505	5	ΔHf				X-Ray Dif.				
B* 245 °C	1580.8	5	ΔFf				Infrared	1354.	1
K			Viscosity				Solubility in +				
			centistokes				Acetone	∞	
t_k to			η °C				Carbon tet.	∞	
t_x °C							Benzene	∞	
A' 15 to	7.34107	5					Ether	∞	
B' 105 °C	1883.32	5					n-Heptane	∞	
C'	214.	5	B^v to				Ethanol	∞	
A'* 20 to	1.95932	5	A^v °C				Water	0.0013	1
B'* 105 °C	1784.6	5	(B^v) to				Water in		
Ac 255 to	7.3931	5	(A^v) °C						
Bc t_c °C	2043.	5							
Cc	243.	5	c_p liq. °K						
Cryos. A°			c_p vap. °K						
consts. B°									
t_e °C F	234.0	5	c_v vap.						

$T_R = 0.75\,T_c$ ⁺grams/100 grams solvent

REFERENCES: 1-Dow 2-API 3-Lit. 4-Calc. from det. data 5-Calc. by formula

SOURCE: Dow

PURIFICATION: Distillation

LITERATURE REFERENCES:

TABLE I. ALKYL AND HALO BENZENES

No. 147

NAME	p-Bromocumene	STRUCTURAL FORMULA
	1-Bromo-4-isopropylbenzene	$CH(CH_3)_2$

| Mole % Pur. 99.95 | Ref. 1 | Molecular Formula $C_9H_{11}Br$ | Molecular Weight 199.904 | |

		Ref.			Ref.				Ref.
F.P. °C	-22.37	1	dt/dP			f	to		
F.P. 100%	-22.35	1	°C/mm			g	°K		
B.P. °C			25°C	65.79	5	h			
760 mm	219.02	1	BP	0.0571	5				
100	146.37	4	t_e	0.0373	5	f'	to		
30	114.12	4	30 mm	0.8091	4	g'	°K		
10	89.45	5	ΔHm cal/g	10.46	4	h'			
1	48.1	5	ΔHv cal/g			m	to		
Pressure			25°C	68.24	5	n	°K		
mm 25°C	0.1969	5	30 mm	61.44	5	o			
t_e	1305.	5	BP	51.23	5	m'	to		
Density			t_e	49.05	5	n'	°K		
g/ml 20°C	1.28535	1	t_e (d, e)	48.81	5	o'			
d_4^t 25	1.27995	1	$\Delta Hv/T_e$	18.96	5	Surface tension			
30	1.27454	4	d 115 to	72.55	5	dynes/cm. 20°C	33.20	1
a	1.30695	4	e 240 °C	0.0973	5	ϑ 30	32.19	1
b	-0.00108	4	d' 25 to	70.15	5	40	31.19	1
Ref. Index			e' 115 °C	0.0763	5			
n_D 20°C	1.53617	1	d_c g/ml	0.419	5	Parachor [P]		
25	1.53378	1	v_c ml/g	2.38	5	20°C	373.3	4
30	1.52233	1	t_c °C	438.9	5	30	373.6	4
"C"	0.5464	4	P_c mm	22384.	5	40	373.9	4
MR (Obs.)	48.508	4	PV/RT			Sugd.	375.0	5
MR (Calc.)	48.126	5	25°C	1.0000	5	Exp. L.1.%/wt.		
(nD-d/2)	0.89350	4	30 mm	1.0000	5	u.		
Dielectric	5.503	1	BP	0.9278	5	Dispersion		
A 115 to	7.04407	4	t_e	0.9073	5	Flash Point °C		
B 260 °C	1732.0	4	t_c			Fire Point		
C	197.0	5	ΔHc kcal/m			M. Spec.		
A* 115 to	1.67846	5	ΔHf			Ultra V.		
B* 255 °C	1643.81	5	ΔFf			X-Ray Dif.		
K			Viscosity			Infrared		
c			centistokes			Solubility in +		
t_k to			η 20 °C	1.3148	1	Acetone	∞	
t_x °C			40	0.9713	1	Carbon tet.	∞	
A' 25 to	7.39479	5	60	0.7621	1	Benzene	∞	
B' 115 °C	1957.11	5	80	0.6218	1	Ether	∞	
C'	216.6	5	B^v 30 to	535.69	4	n-Heptane	∞	
A'* 25 to	2.00476	5	A^v 90 °C	2.27699	4	Ethanol	∞	
B'* 115 °C	1855.29	5	(B^v) to			Water		
Ac 260 to	7.44774	5	(A^v) °C			Water in		
Bc t_c °C	2121.4	5	c_p liq. °K					
Cc	245.9	5						
Cryos. A°	0.01707	1	c_p vap. °K					
consts. B°								
t_e °C F	243.9	5	c_v vap.					

$T_R = 0.75\, T_C$

+ grams/100 grams solvent

REFERENCES: 1-Dow 2-API 3-Lit. 4-Calc. from det. data 5-Calc. by formula

SOURCE: Dow

PURIFICATION: Distillation

LITERATURE REFERENCES:

No. 148

NAME	Iodobenzene				STRUCTURAL FORMULA		

Mole % Pur.	Ref.	Molecular Formula C_6H_5I		Molecular Weight 204.020			

		Ref.				Ref.				Ref.
F.P. °C	-31.27	3[2]	dt/dP				f	to		
F.P. 100%			°C/mm			g	°K		
B.P. °C			25°C	14.533	5	h			
760 mm	188.33	3	BP	0.0554	4				
100	118.27	4	t_e	0.0372	5	f'	to		
30	87.46	4	30 mm	0.7708	4	g'	°K		
10	64.0	5				h'			
1	24.9	5	ΔHm cal/g	11.426	3				
Pressure			ΔHv cal/g			m	to		
mm 25°C	1.009	5	25°C	58.09	4	n	°K		
t_e	1270.	5	30 mm	54.79	4	o			
Density			BP	46.27	3[1]				
g/ml 20°C	1.8308	3[1]	t_e	44.47	4	m'	to		
d_4^t 25	1.8229	4	t_e (d, e)	44.38	5	n'	°K		
30	1.8149	3[1]	ΔHv/T_e	18.73	4	o'			
a	1.8624	4	d | 85 to	62.18	5	Surface tension			
b	-0.00158	4	e | 200 °C	0.0845	5	dynes/cm. 20°C	41.45	3[4]
Ref. Index			d' | 25 to	59.66	5	γ 40	38.69	3[4]
n_D 20°C	1.6200	3[5]	e' | 85 °C	0.0629	5	60	35.94	3[4]
25	1.6172	5	d_c g/ml	0.5814	3[1]	Parachor [P]			
30	1.6142	5	v_c ml/g	1.720	3[1]	20°C	282.8	4
"C"	0.4393	4	t_c °C	448.	3[1]	30	282.8	4
MR (Obs.)	39.15	4	P_c mm	33912.	3[1]	40	282.6	4
MR (Calc.)	39.582	5	PV/RT			Sugd.	281.0	5
(nD-d/2)	0.7046	4	25°C	1.0000	5	Exp. L. 1.%/wt.			
Dielectric	20° 4.63	3[3]	30 mm	1.0000	5	u.			
			BP	0.9579	5	Dispersion			
A | 85 to	6.89506	4	t_e	0.9421	5				
B |270 °C	1562.87	4	t_c	0.2646	4	Flash Point °C			
C	201.0	5	ΔHc kcal/m			Fire Point			
A* | 85 to	1.51165	5	ΔHf			M Spec.			
B* |230 °C	1464.48	5	ΔFf			Ultra V.			
K	41.	4				X-Ray Dif.			
c	-0.14003	4	Viscosity			Infrared	620.	1
t_k |230 to	227.	4	centistokes			Solubility in +			
t_x |390 °C	520.	5	η °C			Acetone	∞	
A' | 0 to	7.23639	4				Carbon tet.	∞	
B' | 85 °C	1765.99	4				Benzene	∞	
C'	219.	5				Ether	∞	
A'* 15 to	1.87118	5				n-Heptane	∞	
B'* 85 °C	1666.99	5	B^v | to			Ethanol	∞	
			A^v | °C			Water		
Ac |270 to	7.53557	4	(B^v)| to			Water in		
Bc | t_c °C	2341.	4	(A^v)| °C					
Cc	291.	4	c_p liq. °K					
Cryos. A°								
consts. B°			c_p vap. °K					
t_e °C	211.22	4	c_v vap.					

$T_R = 0.75 T_c$

+ grams/100 grams solvent

REFERENCES: 1-Dow 2-API 3-Lit. 4-Calc. from det. data 5-Calc. by formula

SOURCE: 3[1]

PURIFICATION: 3[1]

LITERATURE REFERENCES: 3 Timmermans; 3[1] Young; 3[2] JACS 59, 2726 (1937)

D. R. Stull; 3[3] NBS Circ. 514; 3[4] Thesis, Bruxelles (1937) H. Bodson; 3[5] Lange

TABLE II. STYRENES   159

No. 1

NAME	Styrene	STRUCTURAL FORMULA
	Vinylbenzene	$CH{=}CH_2$

| Mole % Pur. 99.98 | Ref. 1 | Molecular Formula C_8H_8 | Molecular Weight 104.144 |

		Ref.			Ref.					Ref.
F.P. °C	-30.628	2	dt/dP			f	to			
F.P. 100%			°C/mm			g	— — °K			
			25°C	2.7360	5	h				
B.P. °C			BP	0.0496	4					
760 mm	145.2	2	t_e	0.0360	5	f'	to			
100	82.38	4	30 mm	0.6929	4	g'	— — °K			
30	54.7	4	ΔHm cal/g			h'				
10	33.6	5				m	300 to	-0.0543	4	
1	-1.6	5	ΔHv cal/g			n	600 °K	0.0013	4	
			25°C	102.40	5	o		-0.0$_6$65	4	
Pressure			30 mm	98.70	5					
mm 25°C	6.056	5	BP	84.69	5	m'	700 to	0.0902	4	
t_e	1147.	5	t_e	82.31	5	n'	1000 °K	0.0388	4	
Density			t_e (d, e)	82.17	5	o'		-0.0$_6$32	4	
g/ml 20°C	0.90600	2	$\Delta Hv/T_e$	19.72	5	Surface tension				
d_4^t 25	0.90122	2	d 55 to	107.16	5	dynes/cm. 20°C		32.3	1	
30	0.89644	4	e 60 °C	0.1548	5	γ	30	30.98	5	
a	0.92511	4	d' 20 to	105.51	5		40	29.67	5	
b	-0.0$_3$95	4	e' 55 °C	0.1246	5	Parachor [P]				
Ref. Index			d_c g/ml				20°C	274.0	4	
n_D 20°C	1.54682	2	v_c ml/g				30			
25	1.54395	2	t_c °C	363.7	5		40			
30	1.54093	4	P_c mm	28912.	5		Sugd.	274.1	5	
"C"	0.7896	4	PV/RT			Exp. L.1.%/wt.		4.	3'	
MR (Obs.)	36.444	2	25°C	1.0000	5	u.		19.	3'	
MR (Calc.)	36.346	5	30 mm	1.0000	5	Dispersion		265.	2	
(nD-d/2)	1.09382	2	BP	0.9603	5	Flash Point °C		32.	3'	
Dielectric	2.43	3	t_e	0.9486	5	Fire Point				
A 55 to	6.92409	4	t_c			M. Spec.		Yes	1	
B 205 °C	1420.0	4	ΔHc kcal/m	1018.83	2	Ultra V.		Yes	1	
C	206.	4	ΔHf	35.22	2	X-Ray Dif.				
A* 55 to	1.28861	5	ΔFf	51.10	2	Infrared		824.	1	
B* 180 °C	1330.7	5	Viscosity			Solubility in +				
K			centistokes			Acetone		∞		
c			η °C			Carbon tet.		∞		
t_k to						Benzene		∞		
t_x °C						Ether		∞		
A' 10 to	7.26725	5				n-Heptane		∞		
B' 55 °C	1604.6	5				Ethanol		∞		
C'	222.	5	B^v to			Water				
			A^v °C			Water in				
A'* 15 to	1.63073	5	(B^v) to							
B'* 55 °C	1509.4	5	(A^v) °C							
Ac 205 to	7.33218	5								
Bc t_c °C	1774.8	5	c_p liq. °K							
Cc	254.	5								
Cryos. A°			c_p vap300°K	0.28182	2					
consts. B°			400	0.36795	2					
t_e °C	161.45	5	c_v vap.							

$T_R = 0.75\ T_C$ + grams/100 grams solvent

REFERENCES: 1-Dow 2-API 3-Lit. 4-Calc. from det. data 5-Calc. by formula

SOURCE: Dow, API

PURIFICATION: Thermal cracking ethylbenzene and fractionation

LITERATURE REFERENCES: 3 NBS Circ. 514; 3' Nat. Fire Prot. Assoc. 325

No. 2

NAME	α-Methylstyrene	STRUCTURAL FORMULA
	Isopropenylbenzene	(CH_3) $C=CH_2$

Mole % Pur.	Ref.	Molecular Formula C_9H_{10}	Molecular Weight 118.170

		Ref.			Ref.				Ref.
F.P. °C	-23.21	2	dt/dP			f	to		
F.P. 100%			°C/mm			g	°K		
B.P. °C			25°C	6.187	5	h			
760 mm	165.38	2	BP	0.0520	4				
100	99.59	4	t_e	0.0364	5	f'	to		
30	70.60	4	30 mm	0.7256	4	g'	°K		
10	48.5	5				h'			
1	11.6	5	ΔHm cal/g			m	300 to	-0.0166	4
			ΔHv cal/g			n	600 °K	0.0012	4
Pressure			25°C	96.69	5	o		-0.0$_6$51	4
mm 25°C	2.500	5	30 mm	91.31	5				
t_e	1201.	5	BP	78.0	5	m'	700 to	0.1037	4
Density			t_e	75.49	5	n'	1000 °K	0.0$_3$87	4
g/ml 20°C	0.9106	2	t_e (d, e)	75.33	5	o'		-0.0$_6$30	4
d_4^t 25	0.9062	2	ΔHv/T_e	19.49	5	Surface tension			
30	0.9018	4				dynes/cm. 20°C		33.88	5
a	0.9282	4	d 70 to	101.22	5	$\jmath$	30	32.59	5
b	-0.0$_3$88	4	e 185 °C	0.1404	5		40	31.33	5
Ref. Index			d' 25 to	99.64	5	Parachor [P]			
n_D 20°C	1.5386	2	e' 70 °C	0.1181	5		20°C		
25	1.5358	2	d_c g/ml				30		
30	1.5321	4	v_c ml/g				40		
"C"	0.7744	5	t_c °C	381.7	5		Sugd.	313.1	5
MR (Obs.)	40.63	2	P_c mm	25547.	5	Exp. L.1.%/wt.			
MR (Calc.)	40.964	5	PV/RT			u.			
(nD-d/2)	1.0833	2	25°C	1.0000	5	Dispersion		265.	2
Dielectric	20° 2.2	3	30 mm	1.0000	5	Flash Point °C			
A 70 to	6.92366	4	BP	0.9569	5	Fire Point			
B 220 °C	1486.88	4	t_e	0.9434	5	M Spec.			
C	202.4	4	t_c			Ultra V.			
			ΔHc kcal/m	1162.46	2	X-Ray Dif.			
A* 70 to	1.32891	5	ΔHf	27.00	2	Infrared			
B* 195 °C	1395.14	5	ΔFf	49.84	2	Solubility in +			
K			Viscosity			Acetone		∞	
c			centistokes			Carbon tet.		∞	
t_k to			η °C			Benzene		∞	
t_x °C						Ether		∞	
A' 15 to	7.26679	5				n-Heptane		∞	
B' 70 °C	1680.13	5				Ethanol		∞	
C'	219.6	5	B^V to			Water			
A'* 20 to	1.67660	5	A^V °C			Water in			
B'* 70 °C	1583.9	5	(B^V) to						
Ac 220 to	7.3284	5	(A^V) °C						
Bc t_c °C	1847.	5	c_p liq. °K						
Cc	250.	5	c_p vap.300°K	0.29534	2				
Cryos. A°			400	0.37912	2				
consts. B°			c_v vap.						
t_e °C	184.40	5							

$T_R = 0.75 T_c$

+ grams/100 grams solvent

REFERENCES: 1-Dow 2-API 3-Lit. 4-Calc. from det. data 5-Calc. by formula

SOURCE:	API
PURIFICATION:	API

LITERATURE REFERENCES: 3 ASTM 109

TABLE II. STYRENES

No. 3

NAME	β-Methylstyrene	STRUCTURAL FORMULA
	Propenylbenzene	$CH = CH-CH_3$

Mole % Pur.	Ref.	Molecular Formula C_9H_{10}	Molecular Weight 118.170	

		Ref.				Ref.				Ref.
F.P. °C	-52.25	2	dt/dP °C/mm				f	to °K		
F.P. 100%			25°C	7.565	5		g			
B.P. °C			BP	0.0524	4		h			
760 mm	170.	2	t_e	0.0368	5		f'	to °K		
100	104.	4	30 mm	0.7320	4		g'			
30	74.	4	ΔHm cal/g				h'			
10	52.	5	ΔHv cal/g				m	300 to	-0.0254	4
1	15.	5	25°C	98.54	5		n	600 °K	0.0012	4
Pressure			30 mm	92.52	5		o		-0.0$_6$55	4
mm 25°C	2.006	5	BP	77.93	5					
t_e	1195.	5	t_e	75.30	5		m'	700 to	0.0832	4
Density			t_e (d, e)	75.04	5		n'	1000 °K	0.0$_3$93	4
g/ml 20°C	0.911	2	$\Delta Hv/T_e$	19.25	5		o'		-0.0$_6$34	4
d_4^t 25	0.907	2	d 75 to	103.86	5		Surface tension			
30	0.903	4	e 185 °C	0.1526	5		dynes/cm. 20°C		33.94	5
a	0.927	4	d' 25 to	101.58	5		ɣ	30	32.77	5
b	-0.0$_3$8	4	e' 75 °C	0.1219	5			40	31.62	5
Ref. Index			d_c g/ml				Parachor [P]			
n_D 20°C	1.549	2	v_c ml/g					20°C		
25	1.546	4	t_c °C	389.5	5			30		
30	1.544	4	P_c mm	25871.	5			40		
"C"	0.7881	4	PV/RT					Sugd.	313.1	5
MR (Obs.)	41.3	2	25°C	1.0000	5		Exp. L.l.%/wt.			
MR (Calc.)	40.964	5	30 mm	1.0000	5		u.			
(nD-d/2)	1.094	2	BP	0.9444	5		Dispersion		265.	2
Dielectric	20° 2.7	3	t_e	0.9295	5		Flash Point °C			
A 75 to	6.92339	4	t_c				Fire Point			
B 225 °C	1499.80	4	ΔHc kcal/m	1164.46	2		M. Spec.			
C	201.0	4	ΔHf	29.00	2		Ultra V.			
A* 75 to	1.34680	5	ΔFf	51.84	2		X-Ray Dif.			
B* 200 °C	1413.57	5	Viscosity				Infrared			
K			centistokes				Solubility in +			
c			η °C				Acetone		∞	
t_k to							Carbon tet.		∞	
t_x °C							Benzene		∞	
A' 25 to	7.26651	5					Ether		∞	
B' 75 °C	1694.73	5					n-Heptane		∞	
C'	218.3	5	B^v to				Ethanol		∞	
A'* 25 to	1.67510	5	A^v °C				Water			
B'* 75 °C	1598.7	5	(B^v) to				Water in			
Ac 225 to	7.3273	5	(A^v) °C							
Bc t_c °C	1862.6	5	c_p liq. °K							
Cc	250.	5								
Cryos. A°			c_p vap 300°K	0.29703	2					
consts. B°			400	0.38250	2					
t_e °C	188.97	5	c_v vap.							

$T_R = 0.75 T_c$ + grams/100 grams solvent

REFERENCES: 1-Dow 2-API 3-Lit. 4-Calc. from det. data 5-Calc. by formula

SOURCE: API

PURIFICATION: API

LITERATURE REFERENCES: 3 NBS Circ. 514

No. 4

NAME	o-Methylstyrene					STRUCTURAL FORMULA
	o-Methylvinylbenzene					$CH=CH_2$ / CH_3

| Mole % Pur. | Ref. | Molecular Formula | C_9H_{10} | Molecular Weight 118.170 | | |

		Ref.			Ref.				Ref.
F.P. °C			dt/dP			f		to	
F.P. 100%	-68.57	3	°C/mm			g		°K	
B.P. °C			25°C	8.320	5	h			
760 mm	169.8	3	BP	0.05099	4				
100	105.	5	t_e	0.0357	5	f'		to	
30	76.	5	30 mm	0.7267	4	g'		°K	
10	54.	5				h'			
1	16.	5	ΔHm cal/g						
Pressure			**ΔHv cal/g**			m		300 to	-0.0166	4
mm 25°C	1.806	5	25°C	99.51	5	n		600 °K	0.0012	4
t_e	1194.	5	30 mm	93.99	5	o			-0.0$_6$51	4
Density			BP	80.05	5				
g/ml 20°C	0.9036	1	t_e	77.52	5	m'		700 to	0.1037	4
d_4^t 25	0.8990	4	t_e (d,e)	77.33	5	n'		1000 °K	0.0$_3$87	4
30	0.8944	4	ΔHv/T_e	19.86	5	o'			-0.0$_6$30	4
a	0.9194	4	d 75 to	105.25	5	Surface tension		
b	-0.0$_3$92	4	e 190 °C	0.1484	5	dynes/cm. 20°C	32.85	5
Ref. Index			d' 25 to	102.22	5	Ɣ 30	31.54	5
n_D 20°C	1.54654	4	e' 75 °C	0.1086	5	40	30.26	5
25	1.54374	3	d_c g/ml	0.3099	5			
30	1.54094	4	v_c ml/g	3.229	5	Parachor [P]		
"C"	0.7913	4	t_c °C	384.4	5	20°C		
MR (Obs.)	41.44	4	P_c mm	27617.	5	30		
MR (Calc.)	40.964	5	**PV/RT**			40		
(nD-d/2)	1.0947	4	25°C	1.0000	5	Sugd.	313.1	5
Dielectric			30 mm	1.0000	5	Exp. L.1.%/wt.		
A 75 to	7.09235	4	BP	0.9442	5	u.		
B 220 °C	1582.7	4	t_e	0.9299	5	Dispersion	265.	2
C	206.	5	t_c	0.257	5	Flash Point °C		
A* 75 to	1.51271	5	ΔHc kcal/m	1163.76	2	Fire Point		
B* 200 °C	1494.1	5	ΔHf	28.30	2	M Spec.		
K			ΔFf	51.14	2	Ultra V.		
c						X-Ray Dif.		
t_k to			**Viscosity**			Infrared		
t_x °C			**centistokes**			Solubility in +		
A' 15 to	7.44611	5	η °C			Acetone	∞	
B' 75 °C	1788.4	5				Carbon tet.	∞	
C'	224.	5				Benzene	∞	
A'* 20 to	1.84630	5	B^v to			Ether	∞	
B'* 75 °C	1688.2	5	A^v °C			n-Heptane	∞	
Ac 220 to	7.5014	5	(B^v) to			Ethanol	∞	
Bc t_c °C	1950.	5	(A^v) °C			Water		
Cc	253.	5	c_p liq. °K			Water in		
Cryos. A°								
consts. B°			c_p vap.300°K	0.29534	2			
t_e °C	188.1	5	400	0.37911	2			
			c_v vap.					

$T_R = 0.75 T_c$

+ grams/100 grams solvent

REFERENCES: 1-Dow 2-API 3-Lit. 4-Calc. from det. data 5-Calc. by formula

SOURCE:	3
PURIFICATION:	3

LITERATURE REFERENCES: 3 J.A.C.S. **75**, 1593 (1953) Clements et al.

TABLE II. STYRENES

No. 5

NAME	m-Methylstyrene	STRUCTURAL FORMULA
	m-Methylvinylbenzene	$CH=CH_2$

Mole % Pur.	Ref.	Molecular Formula C_9H_{10}	Molecular Weight 118.170	

		Ref.				Ref.					Ref.
F.P. °C			dt/dP			f		to		
F.P. 100%	-86.34	3	°C/mm			g		°K		
			25°C	7.9334	5	h				
B.P. °C			BP	0.05245	4					
760 mm	171.6	3	t_e	0.0367	5	f'		to		
100	105.	4	30 mm	0.7387	5	g'		°K		
30	76.	4	ΔHm cal/g			h'				
10	53.	5				m	300 to	-0.0166	4
1	15.	5	ΔHv cal/g			n	600 °K	0.0012	4
Pressure			25°C	97.68	5	o		-0.0651	4
mm 25°C	1.9295	5	30 mm	92.29	5	m'	700 to	0.1037	4
t_e	1199.	5	BP	78.45	5	n'	1000 °K	0.0387	4
Density			t_e	75.90	5	o'		-0.0630	4
g/ml 20°C	0.9113	4	t_e (d, e)	75.70	5	Surface tension			
d_4^t 25	0.9067	3	ΔHv/T_e	19.33	5	dynes/cm. 20°C	33.99	5
30	0.9021	4	d 75 to	103.17	5	δ 30	32.64	5
a	0.9297	4	e 190 °C	0.1441	5	40	31.32	5
b	-0.0392	4	d' 25 to	100.35	5	Parachor [P]			
Ref. Index			e' 75 °C	0.1067	5	20°C			
n_D 20°C	1.54390	4	d_c g/ml	0.288	5	30			
25	1.54114	3	v_c ml/g	3.466	5	40			
30	1.53834	4	t_c °C	389.0	5	Sugd.	313.1	5
"C"	0.7813	5	P_c mm	25910.	5	Exp. L.1.%/wt.			
MR (Obs.)	40.962	4	PV/RT			u.			
MR (Calc.)	40.964	5	25°C	1.0000	5	Dispersion	265.	2
(nD-d/2)	1.0882	4	30 mm	1.0000	5	Flash Point °C			
Dielectric			BP	0.9441	5	Fire Point			
A 75 to	6.99468	4	t_e	0.9293	5	M. Spec.			
B 225 °C	1553.4	4	t_c	0.257	5	Ultra V.			
C	206.	5	ΔHc kcal/m	1163.06	2	X-Ray Dif.			
A* 75 to	1.41260	5	ΔHf	27.60	2	Infrared			
B* 200 °C	1464.1	5	ΔFf	50.02	2	Solubility in +			
K			Viscosity			Acetone	∞	
c			centistokes			Carbon tet.	∞	
t_k to			η °C			Benzene	∞	
t_x °C						Ether	∞	
A' 15 to	7.34229	5				n-Heptane	∞	
B' 75 °C	1755.3	5				Ethanol	∞	
C'	224.	5	B^v to			Water		
A'* 20 to	1.74274	5	A^v °C			Water in		
B'* 75 °C	1655.1	5	(B^v) to					
Ac 225 to	7.4053	5	(A^v) °C					
Bc t_c °C	1926.	5	c_p liq. °K					
Cc	255.	5						
Cryos. A°			c_p vap.300°K	0.29534	2			
consts. B°			400	0.37911	2			
t_e °C	190.7	5	c_v vap.					
$T_R = 0.75\,T_c$						+ grams/100 grams solvent		

REFERENCES: 1-Dow 2-API 3-Lit. 4-Calc. from det. data 5-Calc. by formula

SOURCE:	3
PURIFICATION:	3

LITERATURE REFERENCES: 3 J.A.C.S. 75, 1593 (1953) Clements et al.

No. 6

NAME	p-Methylstyrene	STRUCTURAL FORMULA

p-Methylvinylbenzene

Mole % Pur.	Ref.	Molecular Formula C_9H_{10}	Molecular Weight 118.170

		Ref.			Ref.				Ref.
F.P. °C			dt/dP			f	to		
F.P. 100%	-34.15	3	°C/mm			g	°K		
B.P. °C			25°C	8.407	5	h			
760 mm	172.78	3	BP	0.05247	4				
100	106.1	5	t_e	0.0358	5	f'	to		
30	76.6	5	30 mm	0.7400	5	g'	°K		
10	54.1	5	ΔHm cal/g			h'			
1	16.	5	ΔHv cal/g			m	300 to	-0.0166	4
Pressure			25°C	98.20	5	n	600 °K	0.0012	4
mm 25°C	1.8112	5	30 mm	92.69	5	o		-0.0$_6$51	4
t_e	1238.	5	BP	80.73	5				
Density			t_e	78.21	5	m'	700 to	0.1037	4
g/ml 20°C	0.9106	4	t_e (d,e)	78.18	5	n'	1000 °K	0.0$_3$87	4
d_4^t 25	0.9060	3	ΔHv/T_e	19.81	5	o'		-0.0$_6$30	4
30	0.9014	4	d 75 to	102.23	5	Surface tension			
a	0.9290	4	e 195 °C	0.1244	5	dynes/cm. 20°C		33.88	5
b	-0.0$_3$92	4	d' 25 to	100.87	5	γ 30		32.53	5
Ref. Index			e' 75 °C	0.1067	5	40		31.22	5
n_D 20°C	1.54496	2	d_c g/ml	0.294	5	Parachor [P]			
25	1.54202	3	v_c ml/g	3.398	5	20°C			
30	1.53914	4	t_c °C	392.5	5	30			
"C"	0.7831	4	P_c mm	26569.	5	40			
MR (Obs.)	41.05	4	PV/RT			Sugd.		313.1	5
MR (Calc.)	40.964	5	25°C	1.0000	5	Exp. L.1.%/wt.			
(nD-d/2)	1.0897	4	30 mm	1.0000	5	u.			
Dielectric			BP	0.9667	5	Dispersion		265.	2
			t_e	0.9538	5	Flash Point °C			
A 75 to	7.00589	4	t_c	0.257	5	Fire Point			
B 225 °C	1562.5	4	ΔHc kcal/m	1162.86	2	M Spec.			
C	206.	5	ΔHf	27.40	2	Ultra V.			
A* 75 to	1.38211	5	ΔFf	50.24	2	X-Ray Dif.			
B* 205 °C	1461.5	5	Viscosity			Infrared			
K			centistokes			Solubility in +			
c			η °C			Acetone		∞	
t_k to						Carbon tet.		∞	
t_x °C						Benzene		∞	
A' 10 to	7.35420	5				Ether		∞	
B' 75 °C	1765.6	5	B^v to			n-Heptane		∞	
C'	223.8	5	A^v °C			Ethanol		∞	
A'* 15 to	1.75376	5	(B^v) to			Water			
B'* 75 °C	1665.2	5	(A^v) °C			Water in			
Ac 225 to	7.4170	5	c_p liq. °K						
Bc t_c °C	1938.0	5							
Cc	255.	5	c_p vap.300 °K	0.29534	2				
Cryos. A°			400	0.37911	2				
consts. B°			c_v vap.						
t_e °C	193.29	5							

$T_R = 0.75 T_c$ + grams/100 grams solvent

REFERENCES: 1-Dow 2-API 3-Lit. 4-Calc. from det. data 5-Calc. by formula

SOURCE: 3

PURIFICATION: 3

LITERATURE REFERENCES: 3 J.A.C.S. 75, 1593 (1953) Clements et al.

TABLE II. STYRENES

NAME	m- and p-Vinyltoluene (Commercial Product)	STRUCTURAL FORMULA
	m- and p-Methylstyrene	$CH=CH_2$ $CH=CH_2$

| Mole % Pur. 99.75 | Ref. 1 | Molecular Formula C_9H_{10} | Molecular Weight 118.170 | |

		Ref.			Ref.				Ref.
F.P. °C			dt/dP			f	to		
F.P. 100%			°C/mm			g	___ °K		
B.P. °C			25°C	8.955	5	h			
760 mm	167.7	4	BP	0.0491	5				
100	104.7	4	t_e	0.0340	5	f'	to		
30	76.5	4	30 mm	0.7118	4	g'	___ °K		
10	54.7	5	ΔHm cal/g			h'			
1	18.	5	ΔHv cal/g			m	300 to	-0.0166	4
Pressure			25°C	101.84	5	n	600 °K	0.0012	4
mm 25°C	1.6396	5	30 mm	96.28	5	o		-0.0_651	4
t_e	1206.		BP	83.47	5	m'	700 to	0.1037	4
Density			t_e	81.01	5	n'	1000 °K	0.0_387	4
g/ml 20°C	0.89768	1	t_e (d, e)	80.93	5	o'		-0.0_630	4
d_4^t 25	0.89353	1	ΔHv/T_e	20.86	5	Surface tension			
30	0.88938	4	d 75 to	107.02	5	dynes/cm. 20°C		31.53	1
a	0.91428	4	e 185 °C	0.1405	5	ɤ 30		30.44	1
b	-0.0_383	4	d' 25 to	104.55	5	40		29.38	1
Ref. Index			e' 75 °C	0.1080	5	Parachor [P]			
n_D 20°C	1.54213	1	d_c g/ml	0.30	5	20°C		311.9	4
25	1.53949	1	v_c ml/g	3.33	5	30		312.1	4
30	1.53415	1	t_c °C	382.	5	40		312.3	4
"C"	0.7905	4	P_c mm	31557.	5	Sugd.		313.1	5
MR (Obs.)	39.149	4	PV/RT			Exp. L.1.%/wt.	≠ 1.9vol.		1
MR (Calc.)	40.964	5	25°C	1.0000	5	u.			
(nD-d/2)	1.09329	4	30 mm	1.0000	5	Dispersion			
Dielectric	2.56	1	BP	0.9570	5	Flash Point °C		60.	1
A 75 to	7.2421	4	t_e	0.9441	5	Fire Point		68.	1
B 220 °C	1634.2	4	t_c			M. Spec.			
C	207.	5	ΔHc kcal/m	1151.18	1	Ultra V.			
A* 75 to	1.6413	5	ΔHf	15.72	1	X-Ray Dif.			
B* 195 °C	1539.3	5	ΔFf			Infrared			
K			Viscosity			Solubility in +			
c			centistokes			Acetone	∞		
t_k to			η 20 °C	0.9277	1	Carbon tet.	∞		
t_x °C			40	0.7263	1	Benzene	∞		
A' 10 to	7.6053	5	60	0.5922	1	Ether	∞		
B' 75 °C	1846.6	5	80	0.4970	1	n-Heptane	∞		
C'	225.	5	B^v 30 to	455.60	4	Ethanol	∞		
A'* 15 to	2.0035	5	A^v 90 °C	$\overline{2}.40647$	4	Water	0.0089		1
B'* 75 °C	1745.4	5	(B^v) to			Water in	0.047		1
Ac 220 to	7.6513	5	(A^v) °C						
Bc t_c °C	2001.0	5	c_p liq. 20°C	0.410	1				
Cc	252.3	5	40	0.428	4				
Cryos. A°			c_p vap.300°K	0.2953	2				
consts. B°			400	0.3791	2				
t_e °C	185.75	5	c_v vap.						

T_R = 0.75 T_C ≠ 70°C   + grams/100 grams solvent

REFERENCES: 1-Dow 2-API 3-Lit. 4-Calc. from det. data 5-Calc. by formula

SOURCE: Dow

PURIFICATION: Distillation

LITERATURE REFERENCES:

No. 8

NAME	m-Ethylstyrene					STRUCTURAL FORMULA
	m-Ethylvinylbenzene					$CH=CH_2$

Mole % Pur.		Ref.	Molecular Formula	$C_{10}H_{12}$	Molecular Weight 132.196		

C_2H_5

		Ref.			Ref.			Ref.
F.P. °C	-101.3	1	dt/dP			f	to	
F.P. 100%			°C/mm			g	°K	
B.P. °C			25°C	20.46	5	h		
760 mm	190.12	4	BP	0.0533	4			
100	122.3	4	t_e	0.0357	5	f'	to	
30	92.18	4	30 mm	0.7552	4	g'	°K	
10	69.1	5	ΔHm cal/g			h'		
1	30.5	5	ΔHv cal/g			m	to	
Pressure			25°C	96.42	5	n	°K	
mm 25°C	0.6776	5	30 mm	88.57	5	o		
t_e	1266.	5	BP	75.54	5			
Density			t_e	72.81	5	m'	to	
g/ml 20°C	0.89449	1	t_e (d, e)	72.63	5	n'	°K	
d_4^t 25	0.89045	1	ΔHv/T_e	19.84	5	o'		
30	0.88641	4	d 90 to	100.84	5	Surface tension		
a	0.91065	4	e 210 °C	0.1331	5	dynes/cm. 20°C	32.22	5
b	-0.0381	4	d' 25 to	99.34	5	γ 30	31.07	5
Ref. Index			e' 90 °C	0.1168	5	40	29.95	5
n_D 20°C	1.53512	1	d_c g/ml	0.286	5	Parachor [P]		
25	1.53250	1	v_c ml/g	3.50	5	20°C		
30	1.52992	4	t_c °C	403.2	5	30		
"C"	0.7837	4	P_c mm	24200.	5	40 Sugd.	352.1	5
MR (Obs.)	46.02	4	PV/RT			Exp. L.1.%/wt.		
MR (Calc.)	45.582	5	25°C	1.0000	5	u.		
(nD-d/2)	1.08788	4	30 mm	1.0000	5	Dispersion		
Dielectric			BP	0.9535	5	Flash Point °C		
A 90 to	7.03928	4	t_e	0.9381	5	Fire Point		
B 235 °C	1614.0	4	t_c	0.26	5			
C	198.	4	ΔHc kcal/m			M Spec.		
A* 90 to	1.47626	5	ΔHf			Ultra V.		
B* 220 °C	1519.2	5	ΔFf			X-Ray Dif.		
K			Viscosity			Infrared		
c			centistokes			Solubility in +		
t_k to			η °C			Acetone	∞	
t_x °C						Carbon tet.	∞	
A' 15 to	7.38970	5				Benzene	∞	
B' 90 °C	1823.8	5				Ether	∞	
C'	216.	5	B^v to			n-Heptane	∞	
A'* 20 to	1.8364	5	A^v °C			Ethanol	∞	
B'* 90 °C	1726.0	5	(B^v) to			Water		
Ac 235 to	7.4392	5	(A^v) °C			Water in		
Bc t_c °C	1978.1	5	c_p liq. °K					
Cc	244.	5	c_p vap. °K					
Cryos. A° consts. B°								
t_e °C	211.99	5	c_v vap.					

$T_R = 0.75 T_c$ 　　　　　　　　+ grams/100 grams solvent

REFERENCES: 1-Dow 2-API 3-Lit. 4-Calc. from det. data 5-Calc. by formula
SOURCE: Dow
PURIFICATION: Distillation
LITERATURE REFERENCES:

TABLE II. STYRENES   167

No. 9

NAME	p-Ethylstyrene	STRUCTURAL FORMULA
	p-Ethylvinylbenzene	CH= CH₂

| Mole
% Pur.99.70 | Ref.
1 | Molecular
Formula $C_{10}H_{12}$ | Molecular
Weight 132.196 | |

Structural formula: $CH=CH_2$ benzene ring with C_2H_5

		Ref.			Ref.					Ref.
F.P. °C	-49.73	1	dt/dP			f		to		
F.P. 100%			°C/mm			g		°K		
B.P. °C			25°C	18.58	5	h				
760 mm	192.78	4	BP	0.0556	4					
100	122.56	4	t_e	0.0371	5	f'		to		
30	91.64	4	30 mm	0.7731	4	g'		°K		
10	68.11	5				h'				
1	28.85	5	ΔHm cal/g							
Pressure			ΔHv cal/g			m		to		
mm 25°C	0.7665	5	25°C	93.87	5	n		°K		
t_e	1275.	5	30 mm	86.27	5	o				
Density			BP	73.33	5	m'		to		
g/ml 20°C	0.89249	1	t_e	70.56	5	n'		°K		
d_4^t 25	0.88845	1	t_e (d, e)	70.37	5	o'				
30	0.88441	4	ΔHv/T_e	19.07	5	Surface tension				
a	0.90865	4	d 90 to	98.00	5	dynes/cm. 20°C		31.93	5
b	-0.0₃81	4	e 215 °C	0.1280	5	ɣ 30		30.79	5
Ref. Index			d' 25 to	96.72	5	40		29.68	5
n_D 20°C	1.53763	1	e' 90 °C	0.1140	5	Parachor [P]				
25	1.53484	1	d_c g/ml	0.290	5	20°C				
30	1.53231	4	v_c ml/g	3.45	5	30				
"C"	0.7888	4	t_c °C	408.0	5	40				
MR (Obs.)	46.032	4	P_c mm	21761.	5	Sugd.	352.1	5
MR (Calc.)	45.582	5	PV/RT			Exp. L.1.%/wt.			
(nD-d/2)	1.09138	5	25°C	1.0000	5	u.			
Dielectric	3.350	1	30 mm	1.0000	5	Dispersion			
A 90 to	6.90071	4	BP	0.9531	5	Flash Point °C	65.	5
B 240 °C	1570.9	4	t_e	0.9370	5	Fire Point			
C	198.	4	t_c	0.25	5	M. Spec.			
A* 90 to	1.33502	5	ΔHc kcal/m			Ultra V.			
B* 225 °C	1475.3	5	ΔHf			X-Ray Dif.			
K			ΔFf			Infrared	562.	1
c			Viscosity			Solubility in +			
t_k to			centistokes			Acetone	∞	
t_x °C			η °C			Carbon tet.	∞	
A' 15 to	7.24240	5				Benzene	∞	
B' 90 °C	1775.1	5				Ether	∞	
C'	216.	5	B^v to			n-Heptane	∞	
A'* 20 to	1.68950	5	A^v °C			Ethanol	∞	
B'* 90 °C	1677.4	5	(B^v) to			Water		
Ac 240 to	7.3025	5	(A^v) °C			Water in		
Bc t_c °C	1940.5	5	c_p liq. °K					
Cc	247.	5						
Cryos. A°			c_p vap. °K					
consts. B°								
t_e °C	215.92	5	c_v vap.					

T_R = 0.75 T_c + grams/100 grams solvent

REFERENCES: 1-Dow 2-API 3-Lit. 4-Calc. from det. data 5-Calc. by formula

SOURCE: Dow

PURIFICATION: Distillation

LITERATURE REFERENCES:

No. 10

NAME	p-Isopropylstyrene	STRUCTURAL FORMULA
	p-Isopropylvinylbenzene	$CH=CH_2$

Mole % Pur. 99.13	Ref. 1	Molecular Formula $C_{11}H_{14}$	Molecular Weight 146.222	$CH(CH_3)_2$

		Ref.			Ref.				Ref.
F.P. °C	-44.66	1	dt/dP			f		to	
F.P. 100%			°C/mm			g	°K		
			25°C	42.27	5	h			
B.P. °C			BP	0.0541	4				
760 mm	204.15	4	t_e	0.0354	5	f'		to	
100	135.20	4	30 mm	0.7713	4	g'	°K		
30	104.48	4	ΔHm cal/g			h'			
10	80.9	5							
1	41.4	5	ΔHv cal/g			m		to	
			25°C	92.77	5	n	°K		
Pressure			30 mm	83.78	5	o			
mm 25°C	0.3081	5	BP	71.19	5				
t_e	1300.	5	t_e	68.42	5	m'		to	
Density			t_e (d,e)	68.24	5	n'	°K		
g/ml 20°C	0.88497	1	$ΔHv/T_e$	19.98	5	o'			
d_4^t 25	0.88101	1							
30	0.87705	4	d | 105 to	96.99	5	Surface tension			
a	0.90081	4	e | 230 °C	0.1264	5	dynes/cm. 20°C	31.39		5
b	-0.0379	4	d' | 25 to	95.60	5	γ 30	30.28		5
Ref. Index			e' | 105 °C	0.1131	5	40	29.20		5
n_D 20°C	1.52891	1							
25	1.52650	1	d_c g/ml	0.288	5	Parachor [P]			
30	1.52388	4	v_c ml/g	3.48	5	20°C			
"C"	0.7835	4	t_c °C	409.2	5	30			
MR (Obs.)	50.952	5	P_c mm	21962.	5	40			
MR (Calc.)	50.200	5	PV/RT			Sugd.	391.1		5
(nD-d/2)	1.08642	4	25°C	1.0000	5	Exp. L.1.%/wt.			
Dielectric			30 mm	1.0000	5	u.			
			BP	0.9499	5	Dispersion			
A |105 to	7.09845	4	t_e	0.9333	5	Flash Point °C			
B |245 °C	1683.5	4	t_c			Fire Point			
C	195.0	4	ΔHc kcal/m			M Spec.			
A* |105 to	1.5737	5	ΔHf			Ultra V.			
B* |240 °C	1588.4	5	ΔFf			X-Ray Dif.			
K			Viscosity			Infrared			
c			centistokes			Solubility in +			
t_k | to			η °C			Acetone	∞		
t_x | °C						Carbon tet.	∞		
A' | 20 to	7.45259	5				Benzene	∞		
B' |105 °C	1902.3	5				Ether	∞		
C'	213.9	5	B^v | to			n-Heptane	∞		
A'* 25 to	1.93717	5	A^v | °C			Ethanol	∞		
B'* 105 °C	1804.1	5	(B^v) | to			Water			
Ac |245 to	7.5338	5	(A^v) | °C			Water in			
Bc | t_c °C	2088.8	5	c_p liq. °K						
Cc	245.	5							
Cryos. A°			c_p vap. °K						
consts. B°									
t_e °C	227.52	5	c_v vap.						

$T_R = 0.76 T_c$	+ grams/100 grams solvent

REFERENCES: 1-Dow 2-API 3-Lit. 4-Calc. from det. data 5-Calc. by formula

SOURCE:	Dow
PURIFICATION:	Distillation

LITERATURE REFERENCES:

TABLE II. STYRENES

NAME	p-Isopropyl-α-methylstyrene	STRUCTURAL FORMULA

Structural formula: $CH_3-C=CH_2$ on benzene ring, $CH_3-CH-CH_3$

| Mole % Pur. | 99.27 | Ref. 1 | Molecular Formula | $C_{12}H_{16}$ | Molecular Weight 160.248 | |

		Ref.				Ref.						Ref.
F.P. °C	-30.63	1	dt/dP				f		to			
F.P. 100%			°C/mm				g		°K			
			25°C	110.78	5		h					
B.P. °C			BP	0.0544	5							
760 mm	220.82	4	t_e	0.0346	5		f'		to			
100	151.13	4	30 mm	0.7873	4		g'		°K			
30	119.85	4	ΔHm cal/g				h'					
10	95.8	5	ΔHv cal/g				m		to			
1	55.1	5	25°C	91.38	5		n		°K			
Pressure			30 mm	81.11	5		o					
mm 25°C	0.1089	5	BP	69.10	5							
t_e	1345.	5	t_e	66.29	5		m'		to			
Density			t_e (d, e)	66.12	5		n'		°K			
g/ml 20°C	0.89363	1	$\Delta Hv/T_e$	20.46	5		o'					
d_4^t 25	0.88974	1					Surface tension					
30	0.88585	4	d 120 to	95.37	5		dynes/cm. 20°C			32.85	5
a	0.90919	4	e 245 °C	0.1190	5		γ		30	31.72	5
b	-0.0378	4	d' 25 to	94.09	5				40	30.62	5
Ref. Index			e' 120 °C	0.1082	5							
n_D 20°C	1.52381	1					Parachor [P]					
25	1.52155	1	d_c g/ml						20°C			
30	1.51887	4	v_c ml/g						30			
"C"	0.7689	4	t_c °C	422.3	5				40			
MR (Obs.)	54.849	5	P_c mm	21589.	5				Sugd.	429.3	5
MR (Calc.)	54.818	5	PV/RT				Exp. L.1.%/wt.					
(nD-d/2)	1.07700	5	25°C	1.0000	5				u.			
Dielectric			30 mm	1.0000	5		Dispersion					
A 120 to	7.22972	4	BP	0.9489	5		Flash Point °C					
B 260 °C	1799.7	4	t_e	0.9315	5		Fire Point					
C	193.0	4	t_c				M. Spec.					
A* 120 to	1.73186	5	ΔHc kcal/m				Ultra V.					
B* 255 °C	1701.7	5	ΔHf				X-Ray Dif.					
K			ΔFf				Infrared					
c			Viscosity				Solubility in +					
t_k to			centistokes				Acetone			∞		
t_x °C			η °C				Carbon tet.			∞		
							Benzene			∞		
A' 20 to	7.59213	5					Ether			∞		
B' 120 °C	2033.6	5					n-Heptane			∞		
C'	212.7	5	B^v to				Ethanol			∞		
A'* 25 to	2.10754	5	A^v °C				Water					
B'* 120 °C	1933.8	5	(B^v) to				Water in					
Ac 260 to	7.7033	5	(A^v) °C									
Bc t_c °C	2256.6	5										
Cc	247.5	5	c_p liq. °K									
Cryos. A°												
consts. B°			c_p vap. °K									
t_e °C	245.85	5	c_v vap.									
T_R = 0.77 T_c							+ grams/100 grams solvent					

REFERENCES: 1-Dow 2-API 3-Lit. 4-Calc. from det. data 5-Calc. by formula

SOURCE: Dow

PURIFICATION: Distillation

LITERATURE REFERENCES:

No. 12

NAME	o-Chlorostyrene	STRUCTURAL FORMULA
	o-Chlorovinylbenzene	CH=CH$_2$, Cl (on benzene ring)

Mole % Pur. 100.0	Ref. 1	Molecular Formula C$_8$H$_7$Cl	Molecular Weight 138.593

		Ref.				Ref.				Ref.
F.P. °C	-63.15	1	dt/dP °C/mm			f		to °K		
F.P. 100%			25°C	15.145	5	g				
B.P. °C			BP	0.0554	4	h				
760 mm	188.66	4	t$_e$	0.0373	5	f'		to °K		
100	118.68	4	30 mm	0.7681	4	g'				
30	87.95	4	ΔHm cal/g			h'				
10	64.6	5	ΔHv cal/g			m		to °K		
1	25.6	5	25°C	88.01	5	n				
Pressure			30 mm	81.16	5	o				
mm 25°C	0.9566	5	BP	69.0	5	m'		to °K		
t$_e$	1265.	5	t$_e$	66.45	5	n'				
Density			t$_e$ (d, e)	66.25	5	o'				
g/ml 20°C	1.10001	1	ΔHv/T$_e$	19.00	5	Surface tension				
d$_4^t$ 25	1.09532	1	d	90 to	91.78	5	dynes/cm. 20°C	37.27	5
30	1.09063	4	e	210 °C	0.1207	5	γ 30	36.01	5
a	1.11877	4	d'	25 to	90.73	5	40	34.79	5
b	-0.0394	4	e'	90 °C	0.1088	5	Parachor [P]		
Ref. Index			d$_c$ g/ml	0.368	5	20°C		
n$_D$ 20°C	1.56487	1	v$_c$ ml/g	2.72	5	30		
25	1.56234	1	t$_c$ °C	423.6	5	40		
30	1.55974	4	P$_c$ mm	26089.	5	Sugd. 311.3		5
"C"	0.6704	4	PV/RT			Exp. L. 1.%/wt.		
MR (Obs.)	40.985	4	25°C	1.0000	5	u.		
MR (Calc.)	41.213	5	30 mm	1.0000	5	Dispersion		
(nD-d/2)	1.01487	4	BP	0.9544	5	Flash Point °C		
Dielectric			t$_e$	0.9385	5	Fire Point		
A 90 to	6.86644	4	t$_c$	0.247	5	M Spec.		
B 250 °C	1541.1	4	ΔHc kcal/m			Ultra V.	Yes	
C	198.	4	ΔHf			X-Ray Dif.		
A* 90 to	1.32347	5	ΔFf			Infrared		
B* 220 °C	1446.1	5	Viscosity			Solubility in +		
C			centistokes			Acetone	∞	
c			η °C			Carbon tet.	∞	
t$_k$ to °C						Benzene	∞	
t$_x$						Ether	∞	
A' 15 to	7.20597	5				n-Heptane	∞	
B' 90 °C	1741.4	5	B^v to °C			Ethanol	∞	
C'	216.	5	A^v			Water		
A'* 20 to	1.6767	5	(B^v) to			Water in		
B'* 90 °C	1644.6	5	(A^v) °C					
Ac 250 to	7.2722	5	c$_p$ liq. °K					
Bc t$_c$ °C	1925.6	5	c$_p$ vap. °K					
Cc	251.	5	c$_v$ vap.					
Cryos. A°								
consts. B°								
t$_e$ °C	211.41	5						
T$_R$ = 0.75 T$_c$						+ grams/100 grams solvent		

REFERENCES: 1-Dow 2-API 3-Lit. 4-Calc. from det. data 5-Calc. by formula

SOURCE: Dow

PURIFICATION: Distillation

LITERATURE REFERENCES:

TABLE II. STYRENES   171

No. 13

NAME	p-Chlorostyrene	STRUCTURAL FORMULA
	p-Chlorovinylbenzene	

Mole % Pur. 99.45	Ref. 1	Molecular Formula C_8H_7Cl	Molecular Weight 138.593	

$CH = CH_2$ ... Cl (structural formula of p-chlorostyrene)

		Ref.			Ref.			Ref.
F.P. °C	-15.90	1	dt/dP			f | to		
F.P. 100%			°C/mm			g | ___ °K		
B.P. °C			25°C	16.580	5	h |		
760 mm	192.00	4	BP	0.0563	4			
100	121.05	4	t_e	0.0376	5	f' | to		
30	89.96	4				g' | ___ °K		
10	66.3	5	30 mm	0.7770	4	h' |		
1	27.0	5	ΔHm cal/g			m | to		
Pressure			ΔHv cal/g			n | ___ °K		
mm 25°C	0.8725	5	25°C	88.14	5	o |		
t_e	1279.	5	30 mm	81.13	5			
Density			BP	69.10	5	m' | to		
g/ml 20°C	1.08682	1	t_e	66.53	5	n' | °K		
d_4^t 25	1.08214	1	t_e (d, e)	66.32	5	o' |		
30	1.07746	4	ΔHv/T_e	18.86	5	Surface tension		
a	1.10554	4	d | 90 to	91.73	5	dynes/cm. 20°C	35.51	5
b	-0.0₃94	4	e | 215 °C	0.1179	5	ɤ 30	34.30	5
Ref. Index			d' | 25 to	90.84	5	40	33.13	5
n_D 20°C	1.56601	1	e' | 90 °C	0.1079	5	Parachor [P]		
25	1.56343	1	d_c g/ml	0.353	5	20°C		
30	1.56082	4	v_c ml/g	2.83	5	30		
"C"	0.6797	4	t_c °C	427.4	5	40		
MR (Obs.)	40.985	4	P_c mm	25202.	5	Sugd.	311.3	5
MR (Calc.)	41.213	5	PV/RT			Exp. L.1.%/wt.		
(nD-d/2)	1.01487	4	25°C	1.0000	5	u.		
Dielectric			30 mm	1.0000	5	Dispersion		
A | 90 to	6.84248	4	BP	0.9560	5	Flash Point °C		
B |250 °C	1545.00	4	t_e	0.9403	5	Fire Point		
C	198.	4	t_c	0.245	5	M. Spec.		
A* | 90 to	1.29243	5	ΔHc kcal/m			Ultra V.	Yes	
B* | 225 °C	1448.02	5	ΔHf			X-Ray Dif.		
K			ΔFf			Infrared		
c			Viscosity			Solubility in +		
t_k | to			centistokes			Acetone	∞	
t_x | °C			η °C			Carbon tet.	∞	
A' | 25 to	7.18050	5				Benzene	∞	
B' | 90 °C	1745.8	5				Ether	∞	
C'	216.	5	B^v | to			n-Heptane	∞	
A'* 25 to	1.64955	5	A^v | °C			Ethanol	∞	
B'* 90 °C	1648.6	5	(B^v)| to			Water		
Ac | 250 to	7.24901	5	(A^v)| °C			Water in		
Bc | t_c °C	1932.8	5	c_p liq. °K					
Cc	251.	5	c_p vap. °K					
Cryos. A° consts. B°			c_v vap.					
t_e °C	215.58	5						

$T_R = 0.75 T_c$ + grams/100 grams solvent

REFERENCES:	1-Dow 2-API 3-Lit. 4-Calc. from det. data 5-Calc. by formula
SOURCE:	Dow
PURIFICATION:	Distillation
LITERATURE REFERENCES:	

No. 14

NAME	o-Bromostyrene	STRUCTURAL FORMULA
	o-Bromovinylbenzene	$CH=CH_2$, Br

Mole % Pur. 99.87	Ref. 1	Molecular Formula C_8H_7Br	Molecular Weight 183.052

		Ref.				Ref.				Ref.
F.P. °C	-52.75	1	dt/dP °C/mm				f	to		
F.P. 100%			25°C	38.989	5		g	°K		
B.P. °C			BP	0.0574	5		h			
760 mm	209.80	4	t_e	0.0374	5		f'	to		
100	137.19	4	30 mm	0.7999	4		g'	°K		
30	105.22	4	ΔHm cal/g				h'			
10	80.9	5	ΔHv cal/g				m	to		
1	40.2	5	25°C	71.78	5		n	°K		
Pressure			30 mm	64.78	5		o			
mm 25°C	0.3449	5	BP	54.93	5		m'	to		
t_e	1319.	5	t_e	52.70	5		n'	°K		
Density			t_e (d, e)	52.52	5		o'			
g/ml 20°C	1.41601	1	$\Delta Hv/T_e$	18.97	5		Surface tension			
d_4^t 25	1.41024	1	d | 105 to	74.69	5		dynes/cm. 20°C	39.95	5
30	1.40447	4	e | 230 °C	0.0942	5		30	38.66	5
a	1.43909	4	d' | 25 to	73.96	5		γ 40	37.41	5
b	-0.00115	4	e' | 105 °C	0.0872	5		Parachor [P]			
Ref. Index			d_c g/ml	0.459	5		20°C			
n_D 20°C	1.59268	1	v_c ml/g	2.18	5		30			
25	1.59014	1	t_c °C	453.0	5		40			
30	1.58755	4	P_c mm	26451.	5		Sugd.	325.0	5
"C"	0.5446	4	PV/RT				Exp. L.1.%/wt.			
MR (Obs.)	43.784	4	25°C	1.0000	5		u.			
MR (Calc.)	44.111	5	30 mm	1.0000	5		Dispersion			
(nD-d/2)	0.88468	5	BP	0.9502	5		Flash Point °C			
Dielectric			t_e	0.9322	5		Fire Point			
A |105 to	6.91038	4	t_c	0.25	5		M Spec.			
B |270 °C	1631.2	4	ΔHc kcal/m				Ultra V.			
C	195.	4	ΔHf				X-Ray Dif.			
A* |105 to	1.47612	5	ΔFf				Infrared			
B* |245 °C	1533.9	5	Viscosity				Solubility in +			
K			centistokes				Acetone	∞	
c			η °C				Carbon tet.	∞	
t_k | to							Benzene	∞	
t_x | °C							Ether	∞	
A' | 20 to	7.25268	5					n-Heptane	∞	
B' |105 °C	1843.2	5	B^v | to				Ethanol	∞	
C'	214.	5	A^v | °C				Water		
A'* 25 to	1.83421	5	(B^v) | to				Water in		
B'*105 °C	1744.9	5	(A^v) | °C						
Ac|270 to	7.3159	5	c_p liq. °K						
Bc| t_c °C	2031.5	5	c_p vap. °K						
Cc	249.	5	c_v vap.						
Cryos. A° consts. B°									
t_e °C	235.38	5							

$T_R = 0.75 T_c$

+ grams/100 grams solvent

REFERENCES: 1-Dow 2-API 3-Lit. 4-Calc. from det. data 5-Calc. by formula

SOURCE: Dow

PURIFICATION: Distillation

LITERATURE REFERENCES:

TABLE II. STYRENES

No. 15

NAME	p-Bromostyrene	STRUCTURAL FORMULA
	p-Bromovinylbenzene	CH=CH2 ... Br

Mole % Pur. 99.70	Ref. 1	Molecular Formula C_8H_7Br	Molecular Weight 183.052

		Ref.
F.P. °C	7.67	1
F.P. 100%		
B.P. °C		
760 mm	211.98	4
100	140.50	4
30	108.82	4
10	84.6	5
1	44.0	5
Pressure mm 25°C	0.2593	5
t_e	1324.	5
Density g/ml 20°C	1.39838	1
d_4^t 25	1.39263	1
30	1.38688	4
a	1.42138	4
b	-0.00115	4
Ref. Index n_D 20°C	1.59472	1
25	1.59212	1
30	1.58944	4
"C"	0.5532	4
MR (Obs.)	44.462	4
MR (Calc.)	44.111	5
(nD-d/2)	0.89553	4
Dielectric		
A 110 to	7.01490	4
B 270 °C	1682.5	4
C	195.	4
A* 110 to	1.57884	5
B* 250 °C	1584.8	5
K		
c		
t_k to		
t_x °C		
A' 20 to	7.36378	5
B' 110 °C	1901.2	5
C'	214.	5
A'* 25 to	1.94243	5
B'* 110 °C	1802.0	5
Ac 270 to	6.8754	5
Bc t_c °C	1554.8	5
Cc	177.	5
Cryos. A° consts. B°		
t_e °C	237.19	5

$T_R = 0.75 T_c$

		Ref.
dt/dP °C/mm		
25°C	50.385	5
BP	0.0563	5
t_e	0.0364	5
30 mm	0.7942	4
ΔHm cal/g		
ΔHv cal/g		
25°C	73.89	5
30 mm	67.34	5
BP	56.55	5
t_e	54.30	5
t_e (d, e)	53.91	5
$\Delta Hv/T_e$	19.47	5
d 110 to	78.72	5
e 235 °C	0.1046	5
d' 25 to	75.85	5
e' 110 °C	0.0782	5
d_c g/ml	0.45	5
v_c ml/g	2.22	5
t_c °C	453.4	5
P_c mm	25639.	5
PV/RT		
25°C	1.0000	5
30 mm	1.0000	5
BP	0.9500	5
t_e	0.9325	5
t_c	0.242	5
ΔHc kcal/m		
ΔHf		
ΔFf		
Viscosity centistokes η °C		
B^v to		
A^v °C		
(B^v) to		
(A^v) °C		
c_p liq. °K		
c_p vap. °K		
c_v vap.		

		Ref.
f to		
g °K		
h		
f' to		
g' °K		
h'		
m to		
n °K		
o		
m' to		
n' °K		
o'		
Surface tension dynes/cm. 20°C	38.00	5
γ 30	36.76	5
40	35.56	5
Parachor [P] 20°C		
30		
40		
Sugd.	325.0	5
Exp. L.1.%/wt. u.		
Dispersion		
Flash Point °C		
Fire Point		
M. Spec.		
Ultra V.		
X-Ray Dif.		
Infrared		
Solubility in +		
Acetone	∞	
Carbon tet.	∞	
Benzene	∞	
Ether	∞	
n-Heptane	∞	
Ethanol	∞	
Water		
Water in		

+ grams/100 grams solvent

REFERENCES: 1-Dow 2-API 3-Lit. 4-Calc. from det. data 5-Calc. by formula

SOURCE: Dow

PURIFICATION: Distillation

LITERATURE REFERENCES:

TABLE III.   THIAALKYL BENZENES

TABLE III. THIAALKYL BENZENES

No. 1

NAME	(1-Thiaethyl)-benzene	STRUCTURAL FORMULA
	Methyl phenyl sulfide	$S-CH_3$

Mole % Pur.		Ref.	Molecular Formula C_7H_8S		Molecular Weight 124.200		

		Ref.				Ref.					Ref.
F.P. °C			dt/dP				f		to		
F.P. 100%			°C/mm				g		°K		
B.P. °C			25°C	27.66	5		h				
760 mm	193.	2	BP	0.0517	5						
100	127.	5	t_e	0.0345	5		f'		to		
30	97.	5	30 mm	0.7509	5		g'		°K		
10	74.	5	ΔHm cal/g				h'				
1	35.	5	ΔHv cal/g				m		to		
Pressure			25°C	105.26	5		n		°K		
mm 25°C	0.4886	5	30 mm	97.26	5		o				
t_e	1264.	5	BP	83.58	5		m'		to		
Density			t_e	80.78	5		n'		°K		
g/ml 20°C	1.0579	2	t_e (d, e)	80.58	5		o'				
d_4^t 25	1.0535	2	ΔHv/T_e	20.59	5		Surface tension				
30	1.0491	4	d 97 to	111.03	5		dynes/cm. 20°C	41.01	5
a	1.0755	4	e 215 °C	0.1422	5		ɤ 30	39.66	5
b	-0.0388	4	d' 25 to	108.05	5		40	38.35	5
Ref. Index			e' 97 °C	0.1114	5		Parachor [P]		
n_D 20°C	1.5868	2	d_c g/ml				20°C		
25	1.5840	2	v_c ml/g				30		
30	1.5815	4	t_c °C				40		
"C"	0.7222	4	P_c mm				Sugd.	297.1	5
MR (Obs.)	39.445	2	PV/RT				Exp. L.l.%/wt.		
MR (Calc.)	39.425≠	5	25°C	1.0000	5		u.		
(nD-d/2)	1.0578	2	30 mm	1.0000	5		Dispersion	221.	2
Dielectric			BP	0.9480	5		Flash Point °C		
A 95 to	7.25779	5	t_e	0.9326	5		Fire Point		
B 230 °C	1733.3	5	t_c				M. Spec.		
C	203.	5	ΔHc kcal/m				Ultra V.		
A* 95 to	1.67133	5	ΔHf				X-Ray Dif.		
B* 225 °C	1638.13	5	ΔFf				Infrared		
K			Viscosity				Solubility in +		
c			centistokes				Acetone		
t_k to			η °C				Carbon tet.		
t_x °C							Benzene		
A' 15 to	7.62197	5					Ether		
B' 95 °C	1958.58	5					n-Heptane		
C'	222.	5	B^v to				Ethanol		
A'* 20 to	2.03077	5	A^v °C				Water		
B'* 95 °C	1855.89	5	(B^v) to				Water in		
Ac to			(A^v) °C						
Bc t_c °C			c_p liq. °K						
Cc									
Cryos. A°			c_p vap. °K						
consts. B°									
t_e °C	214.07	5	c_v vap.						

≠ C-S-C, S = 8.5   + grams/100 grams solvent

REFERENCES: 1-Dow 2-API 3-Lit. 4-Calc. from det. data 5-Calc. by formula

SOURCE: API

PURIFICATION: API

LITERATURE REFERENCES:

No. 2

NAME	(1-Thiapropyl)-benzene			STRUCTURAL FORMULA	
	Ethyl phenyl sulfide				

$S- C_2H_5$

| Mole % Pur. | Ref. | Molecular Formula $C_8H_{10}S$ | | Molecular Weight 138.226 | |

		Ref.			Ref.			Ref.
F.P. °C			dt/dP			f | | to		
F.P. 100%			°C/mm			g | | __°K_		
B.P. °C			25°C	52.22	5	h |		
760 mm	205.	2	BP	0.0524	5			
100	138.	5	t_e	0.03435	5	f' | | to		
30	107.	5	30 mm	0.7641	5	g' | | __°K_		
10	84.	5	ΔHm cal/g			h' |		
1	44.	5	ΔHv cal/g			m | | to		
Pressure			25°C	99.71	5	n | | __°K_		
mm 25°C	0.2455	5	30 mm	90.84	5	o |		
t_e	1288.8	5	BP	77.51	5			
Density			t_e	74.71	5	m' | | to		
g/ml 20°C	1.0211	2	t_e (d, e)	74.48	5	n' | | __°K_		
d_4^t 25	1.0166	2	ΔHv/T_e	20.64	5	o' |		
30	1.0121	4	d | 105 to	105.50	5	Surface tension		
a	1.0391	4	e | 225 °C	0.1366	5	dynes/cm. 20°C	38.00	5
b	-0.0390	4	d' | 25 to	102.40	5	30	36.68	5
Ref. Index			e' | 105 °C	0.1077	5	40	35.39	5
n_D 20°C	1.5670	2	d_c g/ml			Parachor [P]		
25	1.5644	2	v_c ml/g			20°C		
30	1.5618	4	t_c °C			30		
"C"	0.7247	4	P_c mm			40		
MR (Obs.)	45.15	2	PV/RT			Sugd.	336.1	5
MR (Calc.)	44.043≠	5	25°C	1.0000	5	Exp. L.1.%/wt.		
(nD-d/2)	1.0564	2	30 mm	1.0000	5	u.		
Dielectric			BP			Dispersion	200.	2
A |105 to	7.30081	5	t_e			Flash Point °C		
B |240 °C	1790.1	5	t_c			Fire Point		
C	200.	5	ΔHc kcal/m			M Spec.		
A* |105 to	1.76163	5	ΔHf			Ultra V.		
B* |235 °C	1696.53	5	ΔFf			X-Ray Dif.		
K			Viscosity			Infrared		
c			centistokes			Solubility in +		
t_k | __ to			η °C			Acetone		
t_x | °C						Carbon tet.		
A' | 25 to	7.66770	5				Benzene		
B' |105 °C	2022.76	5	B^v | to			Ether		
C'	219.	5	A^v | °C			n-Heptane		
A'* 25 to	2.11869	5	(B^v) | to			Ethanol		
B'*105 °C	1920.08	5	(A^v) | °C			Water		
Ac | to			c_p liq. °K			Water in		
Bc | t_c °C			c_p vap. °K					
Cc								
Cryos. A°								
consts. B°								
t_e °C	227.17	5	c_v vap.					

≠ C-S-C, S = 8.5

+ grams/100 grams solvent

REFERENCES: 1-Dow 2-API 3-Lit. 4-Calc. from det. data 5-Calc. by formula

SOURCE: API

PURIFICATION: API

LITERATURE REFERENCES:

TABLE III. THIAALKYL BENZENES   177

No. 3

NAME	4-Methyl-(1-thiaethyl)-benzene	STRUCTURAL FORMULA
	p-Methyl-(1-thiaethyl)-benzene	

Mole % Pur.	Ref.	Molecular Formula $C_8H_{10}S$	Molecular Weight 138.226	

		Ref.			Ref.				Ref.
F.P. °C			dt/dP			f $\mid$ to			
F.P. 100%			°C/mm			g $\mid$ ___ °K			
B.P. °C			25°C	102.74	5	h $\mid$			
760 mm	217.	2	BP	0.0528	5				
100	149.	5	t_e	0.0340	5	f' $\mid$ to			
30	118.	5	30 mm	0.7764	5	g' $\mid$ ___ °K			
10	94.	5	ΔHm cal/g			h' $\mid$			
1	54.	5	ΔHv cal/g			m $\mid$ to			
Pressure			25°C	105.06	5	n $\mid$ ___ °K			
mm 25°C	0.1184	5	30 mm	94.54	5	o $\mid$			
t_e	1318.4	5	BP	80.58	5				
Density			t_e	77.57	5	m' $\mid$ to			
g/ml 20°C	1.027	2	t_e (d, e)	77.28	5	n' $\mid$ ___ °K			
d_4^t 25	1.023	2	ΔHv/T_e	20.88	5	o' $\mid$			
30	1.019	4				Surface tension			
a	1.043	4	d $\mid$ 120 to	111.23	5	dynes/cm. 20°C	38.89	5
b	-0.0₃80	4	e $\mid$ 240 °C	0.1413	5	γ 30	37.69	5
Ref. Index			d' $\mid$ 25 to	107.88	5	40	36.52	5
n_D 20°C	1.5733	2	e' $\mid$ 120 °C	0.1129	5				
25	1.5707	2				Parachor [P]			
30	1.5681	4	d_c g/ml			20°C			
"C"	0.7280	4	v_c ml/g			30			
MR (Obs.)	44.369	2	t_c °C			40			
MR (Calc.)	44.043≠	5	P_c mm			Sugd.	336.1	5
(nD-d/2)	1.060	2	PV/RT			Exp. L.1.%/wt.			
Dielectric			25°C	1.0000	5	u.			
A $\mid$ 120 to	7.37224	5	30 mm	1.0000	5	Dispersion	215.	2
B $\mid$ 255 °C	1863.9	5	BP	0.9399	5	Flash Point °C			
C	198.	5	t_e	0.8640	5	Fire Point			
A* $\mid$ 120 to	1.82724	5	t_c			M. Spec.			
B* $\mid$ 250 °C	1769.65	5	ΔHc kcal/m			Ultra V.			
K			ΔHf			X-Ray Dif.			
c			ΔFf			Infrared			
t_k $\mid$ to			Viscosity			Solubility in +			
t_x $\mid$ °C			centistokes			Acetone			
A' $\mid$ 25 to	7.74363	5	η °C			Carbon tet.			
B' $\mid$ 120 °C	2106.15	5				Benzene			
C'	218.	5				Ether			
A'* 25 to	2.18922	5	B^v $\mid$ to			n-Heptane			
B'* 120 °C	2002.80	5	A^v $\mid$ °C			Ethanol			
Ac $\mid$ to			(B^v) $\mid$ to			Water			
Bc $\mid$ t_c °C			(A^v) $\mid$ °C			Water in			
Cc									
Cryos. A°			c_p liq. °K						
consts. B°			c_p vap. °K						
t_e °C	240.34	5	c_v vap.						

≠ C-S-C, S = 8.5   + grams/100 grams solvent

REFERENCES: 1-Dow 2-API 3-Lit.   4-Calc. from det. data   5-Calc. by formula

SOURCE:	API
PURIFICATION:	API

LITERATURE REFERENCES:

No. 4

NAME	(1-Thiabutyl)-benzene	STRUCTURAL FORMULA
	n-Propyl phenyl sulfide	

Mole % Pur.	Ref.	Molecular Formula $C_9H_{12}S$	Molecular Weight 152.252	S-C_3H_7

		Ref.			Ref.			Ref.
F.P. °C			dt/dP			f $\mid$ to		
F.P. 100%			°C/mm			g $\mid$ °K		
			25°C	123.26	5	h $\mid$		
B.P. °C			BP	0.0529	5			
760 mm	220.	2	t_e	0.0338	5	f' $\mid$ to		
100	152.	5	30 mm	0.7790	5	g' $\mid$ °K		
30	121.	5	ΔHm cal/g			h' $\mid$		
10	97.	5						
1	57.	5	ΔHv cal/g			m $\mid$ to		
Pressure			25°C	96.83	5	n $\mid$ °K		
mm 25°C	0.0972	5	30 mm	86.75	5	o $\mid$		
t_e	1326.6	5	BP	73.88	5			
Density			t_e	71.04	5	m' $\mid$ to		
g/ml 20°C	0.9995	2	t_e (d, e)	70.80	5	n' $\mid$ °K		
d_4^t 25	0.9952	2	ΔHv/T_e	20.92	5	o' $\mid$		
30	0.9909	4						
a	1.0167	4	d $\mid$ 120 to	102.47	5	Surface tension		
b	-0.0$_3$86	4	e $\mid$ 245 °C	0.1210	5	dynes/cm. 20°C	36.77	5
			d' $\mid$ 25 to	99.46	5	y 30	35.52	5
Ref. Index			e' $\mid$ 120 °C	0.1051	5	40	34.30	5
n_D 20°C	1.5571	2						
25	1.5551	2	d_c g/ml			Parachor [P]		
30	1.5531	4	v_c ml/g			20°C		
"C"	0.7279	4	t_c °C			30		
MR (Obs.)	49.044	2	P_c mm			40		
MR (Calc.)	48.661≠	5	PV/RT			Sugd.	375.1	5
(nD-d/2)	1.0574	2	25°C	1.0000	5	Exp. L.l.%/wt.		
Dielectric			30 mm	1.0000	5	u.		
A $\mid$ 120 to	7.38536	5	BP	0.9401	5	Dispersion	196.	2
B $\mid$ 260 °C	1878.4	5	t_e	0.9225	5	Flash Point °C		
C	197.	5	t_c			Fire Point		
A* $\mid$ 120 to	1.88039	5	ΔHc kcal/m			M Spec.		
B* $\mid$ 255 °C	1783.98	5	ΔHf			Ultra V.		
K			ΔFf			X-Ray Dif.		
c						Infrared		
t_k $\mid$ to			Viscosity			Solubility in +		
t_x $\mid$ °C			centistokes			Acetone		
A' $\mid$ 25 to	7.75758	5	η °C			Carbon tet.		
B' $\mid$ 120 °C	2122.53	5				Benzene		
C'	217.	5				Ether		
A'* 25 to	2.24414	5	B^v $\mid$ to			n-Heptane		
B'* 120 °C	2019.30	5	A^v $\mid$ °C			Ethanol		
Ac $\mid$ to			(B^v) $\mid$ to			Water		
Bc $\mid$ t_c °C			(A^v) $\mid$ °C			Water in		
Cc			c_p liq. °K					
Cryos. A°			c_p vap. °K					
consts. B°								
t_e °C	243.67	5	c_v vap.					

≠ C-S-C, S = 8.5

+ grams/100 grams solvent

REFERENCES: 1-Dow 2-API 3-Lit. 4-Calc. from det. data 5-Calc. by formula

SOURCE: API

PURIFICATION: API

LITERATURE REFERENCES:

TABLE III. THIAALKYL BENZENES

No. 5

NAME	(2-Methyl-1-thiapropyl)-benzene	STRUCTURAL FORMULA
	Isopropyl phenyl sulfide	

| Mole % Pur. | Ref. | Molecular Formula $C_9H_{12}S$ | Molecular Weight 152.252 | | | |

		Ref.			Ref.				Ref.
F. P. °C			dt/dP			f		to	
F. P. 100%			°C/mm			g		°K	
B. P. °C			25°C	63.52	5	h			
760 mm	208.	2	BP	0.0523	5				
100	141.	5	t_e	0.0341	5	f'		to	
30	110.	5	30 mm	0.7654	5	g'		°K	
10	87.	5	ΔHm cal/g			h'			
1	47.	5	ΔHv cal/g			m		to	
Pressure			25°C	92.19	5	n		°K	
mm 25°C	0.1982	5	30 mm	83.62	5	o			
t_e	1298.3	5	BP	71.35	5				
Density			t_e	68.73	5	m'		to	
g/ml 20°C	0.9852	2	t_e (d, e)	68.53	5	n'		°K	
d_4^t 25	0.9810	2	ΔHv/T_e	20.78	5	o'			
30	0.9768	4	d	110 to	97.48		Surface tension		
a	1.0020	4	e	230 °C	0.1256	5	dynes/cm. 20°C	34.71	5
b	-0.0₃84	4	d'	25 to	94.70	5	Ƴ 30	33.54	5
Ref. Index			e'	110 °C	0.1004	5	40	32.40	5
n_D 20°C	1.5464	2	d_c g/ml				Parachor [P]		
25	1.5446	2	v_c ml/g				20°C		
30	1.5428	4	t_c °C				30		
"C"	0.7256	4	P_c mm				40		
MR (Obs.)	48.964	2	PV/RT				Sugd.	375.1	5
MR (Calc.)	48.661≠	5	25°C	1.0000	5	Exp. L.1.%/wt.		
(nD-d/2)	1.0538	2	30 mm	1.0000	5	u.		
Dielectric			BP	0.9430	5	Dispersion	192.	2
A	110 to	7.32777	5	t_e	0.9265	5	Flash Point °C		
B	245 °C	1809.9	5	t_c			Fire Point		
C		199.	5	ΔHc kcal/m			M. Spec.		
			ΔHf			Ultra V.		
A*	110 to	1.82706	5	ΔFf			X-Ray Dif.	—	
B*	240 °C	1715.69	5				Infrared		
K			Viscosity			Solubility in +		
c			centistokes			Acetone		
t_k	to			η	°C		Carbon tet.		
t_x	°C						Benzene		
A'	25 to	7.69636	5				Ether		
B'	110 °C	2045.13	5				n-Heptane		
C'		218.	5	B^v	to		Ethanol		
A'*	25 to	2.18833	5	A^v	°C		Water		
B'*	110 °C	1942.58	5	(B^v)	to		Water in		
Ac	to			(A^v)	°C				
Bc	t_c °C			c_p liq.	°K				
Cc									
Cryos. A°			c_p vap.	°K					
consts. B°									
t_e °C	230.46	5	c_v vap.						

≠ C-S-C, S = 8.5   + grams/100 grams solvent

REFERENCES: 1-Dow 2-API 3-Lit. 4-Calc. from det. data 5-Calc. by formula

SOURCE:	API
PURIFICATION:	API

LITERATURE REFERENCES:

No. 6

NAME	3-Methyl-(1-thiapropyl)-benzene	STRUCTURAL FORMULA
	m-Methyl-(1-thiapropyl)-benzene	

Mole % Pur.	Ref.	Molecular Formula $C_9H_{12}S$	Molecular Weight 152.252

		Ref.			Ref.			Ref.
F.P. °C			dt/dP			f | to		
F.P. 100%			°C/mm			g | °K		
B.P. °C			25°C	117.63	5	h |		
760 mm	219.	2	BP	0.0528	5			
100	151.	5	t_e	0.0338	5	f' | to		
30	120.	5	30 mm	0.7773	5	g' | °K		
10	96.	5	ΔHm cal/g			h' |		
1	56.	5						
Pressure			ΔHv cal/g			m | to		
mm 25°C	0.1022	5	25°C	96.59	5	n | °K		
t_e	1327.3	5	30 mm	86.59	5	o |		
Density			BP	73.87	5			
g/ml 20°C	0.9987	2	t_e	71.06	5	m' | to		
d_4^t 25	0.9947	2	t_e (d, e)	70.83	5	n' | °K		
30	0.9907	4	ΔHv/T_e	20.98	5	o' |		
a	1.01470	4	d | 120 to	102.03	5	Surface tension		
b	-0.0₃80	4	e | 240 °C	0.1286	5	dynes/cm. 20°C	36.65	5
			d' | 25 to	99.22	5	30	35.49	5
Ref. Index			e' | 120 °C	0.1052	5	40	34.36	5
n_D 20°C	1.5590	2	d_c g/ml			Parachor [P]		
25	1.5570	2	v_c ml/g			20°C		
30	1.5550	4	t_c °C			30		
"C"	0.7312	4	P_c mm			40		
MR (Obs.)	49.22	2	PV/RT			Sugd.	375.1	5
MR (Calc.)	48.661 ≠	5	25°C	1.0000	5	Exp. L.1.%/wt.		
(nD-d/2)	1.0596	2	30 mm	1.0000	5	u.		
Dielectric			BP	0.9420	5	Dispersion		
A | 120 to	7.38306	5	t_e	0.9248	5	Flash Point °C		
B | 255 °C	1872.9	5	t_c			Fire Point		
C	197.	5	ΔHc kcal/m			M Spec.		
A* | 120 to	1.87513	5	ΔHf			Ultra V.		
B* | 250 °C	1777.50	5	ΔFf			X-Ray Dif.		
K			Viscosity			Infrared		
c			centistokes			Solubility in +		
t_k | to			η °C			Acetone		
t_x | °C						Carbon tet.		
A' | 25 to	7.75513	5				Benzene		
B' | 120 °C	2116.32	5	B^v | to			Ether		
C'	217.	5	A^v | °C			n-Heptane		
A'* 25 to	2.24240	5	(B^V) | to			Ethanol		
B'* 120 °C	2013.29	5	(A^V) | °C			Water		
Ac | to			c_p liq. °K			Water in		
Bc | t_c °C								
Cc			c_p vap. °K					
Cryos. A°								
consts. B°								
t_e °C	242.64	5	c_v vap.					

≠ C-S-C, S = 8.5

+ grams/100 grams solvent

REFERENCES: 1-Dow 2-API 3-Lit. 4-Calc. from det. data 5-Calc. by formula
SOURCE: API
PURIFICATION: API
LITERATURE REFERENCES:

TABLE III. THIAALKYL BENZENES

No. 7

NAME	4-Methyl-(1-thiapropyl)-benzene	STRUCTURAL FORMULA
	p-Methyl-(1-thiapropyl)-benzene	S–C_2H_5

Mole % Pur.	Ref.	Molecular Formula $C_9H_{12}S$	Molecular Weight 152.252		(structure: benzene ring with S-C_2H_5 top, CH_3 bottom)

		Ref.				Ref.					Ref.
F.P. °C			dt/dP				f	to			
F.P. 100%			°C/mm				g	°K			
B.P. °C			25°C	123.26	5		h				
760 mm	220.	2	BP	0.0529	5		f'	to			
100	152.	5	t_e	0.0338	5		g'	°K			
30	121.	5	30 mm	0.7790	5		h'				
10	97.;	5	ΔHm cal/g				m	to			
1	57.	5					n	°K			
Pressure			ΔHv cal/g				o				
mm 25°C	0.0972	5	25°C	96.83	5						
t_e	1329.8	5	30 mm	86.75	5		m'	to			
Density			BP	74.03	5		n'	°K			
g/ml 20°C	0.9996	2	t_e	71.19	5		o'				
d_4^t 25	0.9956	2	t_e (d, e)	70.98	5		Surface tension				
30	0.9916	4	ΔHv/T_e	20.97	5		dynes/cm. 20°C	36.78	5
a	1.0156	4	d 120 to	102.3	5		δ 30	35.62	5
b	-0.0380	4	e 245 °C	0.1284	5		40	34.48	5
Ref. Index			d' 25 to	99.46	5		Parachor [P]		
n_D 20°C	1.555	2	e' 120 °C	0.1051	5		20°C		
25	1.553	2	d_c g/ml				30		
30	1.551	4	v_c ml/g				40		
"C"	0.7253	4	t_c °C				Sugd.	375.1	5
MR (Obs.)	48.9	2	P_c mm				Exp. L.1.%/wt.		
MR (Calc.)	48.661≠	5	PV/RT				u.		
(nD-d/2)	1.055	2	25°C	1.0000	5		Dispersion		
Dielectric			30 mm	1.0000	5		Flash Point °C		
A 120 to	7.38535	5	BP	0.9420	5		Fire Point		
B 260 °C	1878.4	5	t_e	0.9245	5		M. Spec.		
C	197.	5	t_c				Ultra V.		
A* 120 to	1.87685	5	ΔHc kcal/m				X-Ray Dif.		
B* 255 °C	1782.86	5	ΔHf				Infrared		
K			ΔFf				Solubility in +		
c			Viscosity				Acetone		
t_k to			centistokes				Carbon tet.		
t_x °C			η °C				Benzene		
A' 25 to	7.75757	5					Ether		
B' 120 °C	2122.53	5					n-Heptane		
C'	217.	5	B_v to				Ethanol		
A'* 25 to	2.24413	5	A_v °C				Water		
B'* 120 °C	2019.30	5	(B^v) to				Water in		
Ac to			(A^v) °C						
Bc t_c °C			c_p liq. °K						
Cc									
Cryos. A°			c_p vap. °K						
consts. B°									
t_e °C	243.78	5	c_v vap.						

≠ C-S-C, S = 8.5   + grams/100 grams solvent

REFERENCES: 1-Dow 2-API 3-Lit. 4-Calc. from det. data 5-Calc. by formula

SOURCE: API

PURIFICATION: API

LITERATURE REFERENCES:

No. 8

NAME	2-Ethyl-(1-thiaethyl)-benzene	STRUCTURAL FORMULA
	o-Ethyl-(1-thiaethyl)-benzene	$S-CH_3$ C_2H_5

Mole % Pur.	Ref.	Molecular Formula $C_9H_{12}S$	Molecular Weight 152.252

Property	Value	Ref.	Property	Value	Ref.	Property	Value	Ref.
F.P. °C			dt/dP			f	to	
F.P. 100%			°C/mm			g	°K	
B.P. °C			25°C	192.95	5	h		
760 mm	228.	2	BP	0.0533	5			
100	159.	5	t_e	0.0336	5	f'	to	
30	128.	5	30 mm	0.7883	5	g'	°K	
10	104.	5	ΔHm cal/g			h'		
1	63.	5	ΔHv cal/g					
Pressure			25°C	99.87	5	m	to	
mm 25°C	0.0602	5	30 mm	88.82	5	n	°K	
t_e	1349.1	5	BP	75.75	5	o		
Density			t_e	72.79	5			
g/ml 20°C	1.025	2	t_e (d, e)	72.54	5	m'	to	
d_4^t 25	1.021	2	ΔHv/T_e	67.73	5	n'	°K	
30	1.017	4	d | 130 to	105.54	5	o'		
a	1.0410	4	e | 255 °C	0.1307	5	Surface tension		
b	-0.0₃80	4	d' | 25 to	102.55	5	dynes/cm. 20°C	40.67	5
Ref. Index			e' | 130 °C	0.1073	5	γ 30	39.41	5
n_D 20°C	1.5708	2	d_c g/ml			40	38.19	5
25	1.5688	2	v_c ml/g			Parachor [P]		
30	1.5668	4	t_c °C	452.61	5	20°C		
"C"	0.7264	4	P_c mm			30		
MR (Obs.)	48.8	2	PV/RT			40		
MR (Calc.)	48.661#	5	25°C	1.0000	5	Sugd.	375.1	5
(nD-d/2)	1.058	2	30 mm	1.0000	5	Exp. L.1.%/wt. u.		
Dielectric			BP	0.9402	5	Dispersion		
A |130 to	7.42660	5	t_e	0.9223	5	Flash Point °C		
B |270 °C	1927.4	5	t_c			Fire Point		
C	196.	5	ΔHc kcal/m			M Spec.		
A*|130 to	1.91448	5	ΔHf			Ultra V.		
B*|265 °C	1831.36	5	ΔFf			X-Ray Dif.		
K			Viscosity			Infrared		
c			centistokes			Solubility in +		
t_k | to			η °C			Acetone		
t_x | °C						Carbon tet.		
A' | 25 to	7.80142	5				Benzene		
B' |130 °C	2177.90	5	B^v | to			Ether		
C'	216.	5	A^v | °C			n-Heptane		
A'* 25 to	2.28373	5	(B^v) | to			Ethanol		
B'* 130 °C	2073.90	5	(A^v) | °C			Water		
Ac | to			c_p liq. °K			Water in		
Bc | t_c °C			c_p vap. °K					
Cc								
Cryos. A°			c_v vap.					
consts. B°								
t_e °C	252.59	5						

\# C-S-C, S = 8.5   + grams/100 grams solvent

REFERENCES: 1-Dow 2-API 3-Lit. 4-Calc. from det. data 5-Calc. by formula

SOURCE: API

PURIFICATION: API

LITERATURE REFERENCES:

TABLE IV. THIOPHENES

No. 1

NAME	Thiophene	STRUCTURAL FORMULA

Structural formula:

HC —— CH
‖   ‖
HC＼ₛ／CH

HC—CH / HC–S–CH (thiophene ring)

Mole % Pur. 99.989	Ref. 2	Molecular Formula C_4H_4S	Molecular Weight 84.138

		Ref.				Ref.				Ref.
F. P. °C	-38.21	2	dt/dP				f	to		
F. P. 100%	-38.252	2	°C/mm				g	°K		
B. P. °C			25°C	0.2655	5		h			
760 mm	84.16	2	BP	0.0428	2					
100	29.90	4	t_e	0.03533	5		f'	to		
30	5.94	4	30 mm	0.6002	4		g'	°K		
10	-12.3	4	ΔHm cal/g				h'			
1	-42.	5					m	to		
Pressure			ΔHv cal/g				n	°K		
mm 25°C	79.68	4	25°C	99.10	5		o			
t_e	970.8	5	30 mm	102.20	5					
Density			BP	89.40	2		m'	to		
g/ml 20°C	1.06485	2	t_e	87.49	5		n'	°K		
d_4^t 25	1.05887	2	t_e (d, e)	88.06	5		o'			
30	1.05309	2	$ΔHv/T_e$	20.14	5		Surface tension			
a	1.08877	4	d 5 to	103.17	5		dynes/cm. 20°C	33.89	5
b	-0.00118	4	e 90 °C	0.1636	5		8 30	32.37	5
Ref. Index			d' to				40	30.89	5
n_D 20°C	1.52890	2	e' °C				Parachor [P]		
25	1.52572	2	d_c g/ml	0.337	3		20°C		
30	1.52257	2	v_c ml/g	2.97	3		30		
"C"	0.6512	4	t_c °C	297.	3		40		
MR (Obs.)	24.365	2	P_c mm	37164.	3		S = 48.5 Sugd.	190.7	5
MR (Calc.)	24.738	5	PV/RT				Exp. L.1.%/wt.		
(nD-d/2)	0.99648	2	25°C	0.9985	5		u.		
Dielectric			30 mm	1.0000	5		Dispersion	162.7	2
A 5 to	6.95926	2	BP	0.9612	4		Flash Point °C		
B 155 °C	1246.038	2	t_e	0.9545	5		Fire Point		
C	221.354	2	t_c	0.2612	4		M. Spec.		
A* 5 to	1.29199	5	ΔHc kcal/m				Ultra V.		
B* 110 °C	1166.16	5	ΔHf				X-Ray Dif.		
K			ΔFf				Infrared		
c			Viscosity				Solubility in +		
t_k to			centistokes				Acetone	∞	
t_x °C			η °C				Carbon tet.	∞	
A' to							Benzene	∞	
B' °C							Ether	∞	
C'							n-Heptane	∞	
A'* to			B^v to				Ethanol	∞	
B'* °C			A^v °C				Water		
			(B^v) to				Water in		
Ac 155 to	7.13243	4	(A^v) °C						
Bc t_c °C	1378.58	4	c_p liq. 288 °K	0.3470	2				
Cc	241.	4	308	0.3569	2				
Cryos. A° consts. B°	0.0114	3'	c_p vap. °K						
t_e °C	92.34	5	c_v vap.						

$T_R = 0.75\, T_c$

+ grams/100 grams solvent

REFERENCES: 1-Dow   2-API   3-Lit.   4-Calc. from det. data   5-Calc. by formula

SOURCE: API

PURIFICATION: API

LITERATURE REFERENCES: 3 Ind. Eng. Chem. <u>44</u>, 1430 (1952) White et al.

No. 2

NAME	2-Methylthiophene	STRUCTURAL FORMULA

Structural formula:

$$HC \overline{\quad\quad} CH$$
$$HC \diagdown_{S} \diagup CCH_3$$

Mole % Pur.	Ref.	Molecular Formula C_5H_6S	Molecular Weight 98.164

		Ref.			Ref.					Ref.
F.P. °C	-63.38	2	dt/dP			f		to		
F.P. 100%			°C/mm			g		°K		
B.P. °C			25°C	0.7533	5	h				
760 mm	112.56	3,2	BP	0.0460	2					
100	54.26	4	t_e	0.0354	5	f'		to		
30	28.55	5	30 mm	0.6437	5	g'		°K		
10	9.20	5	ΔHm cal/g			h'				
1	-23.3	5	ΔHv cal/g			m		to		
Pressure			25°C	95.83	5	n		°K		
mm 25°C	24.89	5	30 mm	95.46	5	o				
t_e	1061.	5	BP	83.00	5					
Density			t_e	81.38	5	m'		to		
g/ml 20°C	1.0193	2	t_e (d, e)	81.20	5	n'		°K		
d_4^t 25	1.0139	2	ΔHv/T_e	20.08	5	o'				
30	1.0084	4				Surface tension				
a	1.0410	4	d 25 to	99.69	5	dynes/cm. 20°C	32.30	5		
b	-0.00108	4	e 125 °C	0.1483	5	γ 30	30.94	5		
Ref. Index			d' to			40	29.62	5		
n_D 20°C	1.5203	2	e' °C			Parachor [P]				
25	1.5174	2	d_c g/ml	0.351	5	20°C				
30	1.5144	4	v_c ml/g	2.846	5	30				
"C"	0.6699	4	t_c °C	333.0	5	40				
MR (Obs.)	29.29	2	P_c mm	35048.	5	S = 48.5 Sugd.	229.6	5		
MR (Calc.)	29.356	5	PV/RT			Exp. L.1.%/wt.				
(nD-d/2)	1.0106	2	25°C	1.0000	5	u.				
Dielectric			30 mm	1.0000	5	Dispersion	160.	2		
A 28 to	6.93897	3	BP	0.9580	5	Flash Point °C				
B 180 °C	1326.474	3	t_e	0.9585	5	Fire Point				
C	214.309	3	t_c	0.259	5	M Spec.				
A* 0 to	1.29767	5	ΔHc kcal/m			Ultra V.				
B* 28 °C	1239.4	5	ΔHf			X-Ray Dif.				
K			ΔFf			Infrared				
c			Viscosity			Solubility in +				
t_k to			centistokes			Acetone	∞			
t_x °C			η °C			Carbon tet.	∞			
A' 0 to	7.14504	5				Benzene	∞			
B' 28 °C	1428.6	5				Ether	∞			
C'	223.3	5	B^v to			n-Heptane	∞			
A'* to			A^v °C			Ethanol	∞			
B'* °C			(B^v) to			Water				
Ac 180 to	7.35668	5	(A^v) °C			Water in				
Bc t_c °C	1677.7	5	c_p liq. °K							
Cc	263.6	5								
Cryos. A°	0.025	3'	c_p vap. °K							
consts. B°										
t_e °C	124.66	5	c_v vap.							

$T_R = 0.75 T_C$ + grams/100 grams solvent

REFERENCES: 1-Dow   2-API   3-Lit.   4-Calc. from det. data   5-Calc. by formula
SOURCE: API
PURIFICATION: API
LITERATURE REFERENCES: 3 Ind. Eng. Chem. **44**, 1430 (1952), P. T. White, et al.

TABLE IV. THIOPHENES

NAME	3-Methylthiophene	STRUCTURAL FORMULA

Mole % Pur. 99.99	Ref. 3'	Molecular Formula C_5H_6S	Molecular Weight 98.164

		Ref.			Ref.				Ref.
F.P. °C	-68.97	3'	dt/dP °C/mm			f	to		
F.P. 100%			25°C	0.8426	5	g	°K		
			BP	0.0462	2	h			
B.P. °C			t_e	0.0355	5	f'	to		
760 mm	115.44	3	30 mm	0.6506	5	g'	°K		
100	56.75	4				h'			
30	30.79	5	ΔHm cal/g	25.65	3'				
10	10.96	5	ΔHv cal/g			m	to		
1	-22.2	5	25°C	96.42	5	n	°K		
Pressure			30 mm	95.85	5	o			
mm 25°C	22.15	5	BP	83.40	3²				
t_e	1063.	5	t_e	81.66	5	m'	to		
Density			t_e (d, e)	81.60	5	n'	°K		
g/ml 20°C	1.02183	2	ΔHv/T_e	20.00	5	o'			
d_4^t 25	1.01647	2	d 30 to	100.38	5	Surface tension			
30	1.01110	4	e 130 °C	0.1471	5	dynes/cm. 20°C	32.62	5
a	1.04326	4	d' 0 to	98.85	5	ɣ 30	31.27	5
b	-0.001067	4	e' 30 °C	0.0982	5	40	29.95	5
Ref. Index			d_c g/ml	0.357	5	Parachor [P]		
n_D 20°C	1.52042	2	v_c ml/g	2.799	5	20°C		
25	1.51758	2	t_c °C	337.6	5	30		
30	1.51467	4	P_c mm	35908.	5	40		
"C"	0.6684	4	PV/RT			S = 48.5 Sugd.	229.6	5
MR (Obs.)	29.225	2	25°C	1.0000	5	Exp. L.1.%/wt.		
MR (Calc.)	29.356	5	30 mm	1.0000	5	u.		
(nD-d/2)	1.0095	2	BP	0.9619	5	Dispersion	159.	2'
Dielectric			t_e	0.9529	5	Flash Point °C		
A 30 to	6.98611	3	t_c			Fire Point		
B 185 °C	1363.862	3	ΔHc kcal/m			M. Spec.		
C	216.784	3	ΔHf			Ultra V.		
A* 30 to	1.34753	5	ΔFf			X-Ray Dif.		
B* 140 °C	1276.5	5	Viscosity			Infrared		
K			centistokes			Solubility in +		
c			η 20 °C	0.676	2	Acetone		
t_k to			25	0.637	2	Carbon tet.		
t_x °C			30	0.599	2	Benzene		
A' 0 to	7.33318	5				Ether		
B' 30 °C	1541.1	5	B^v 10 to	303.20	4	n-Heptane		
C'	232.38	5	A^v 40 °C	2.79584	4	Ethanol		
A'* 10 to	1.67608	5	(B^v) to			Water		
B'* 30 °C	1443.4	5				Water in		
Ac 185 to	7.40824	5	(A^v) °C					
Bc t_c °C	1724.0	5	c_p liq. 293°K	0.3642	3'			
Cc	266.7	5						
Cryos. A°	0.0304	3²	c_p vap.125°K	0.3096	3'			
consts. B°			200	0.3477	3'			
t_e °C	127.66	5	c_v vap.					

$T_R = 0.75 T_c$ + grams/100 grams solvent

REFERENCES: 1-Dow 2-API 3-Lit. 4-Calc. from det. data 5-Calc. by formula

SOURCE: API

PURIFICATION: API

LITERATURE REFERENCES: 3 Ind. Eng. Chem. 44, 1430 (1952), P. T. White et al.;

3' J.A.C.S. 75, 5075 (1953), McCullough et al.

No. 4

NAME	2-Ethylthiophene	STRUCTURAL FORMULA

Structural formula:

$$HC\!\!-\!\!CH$$
$$HC\diagdown_S\diagup CC_2H_5$$

Mole % Pur.	Ref.	Molecular Formula C_6H_8S	Molecular Weight 112.190

		Ref.				Ref.				Ref.
F.P. °C			dt/dP				f	to		
F.P. 100%			°C/mm				g	°K		
			25°C	1.691	5		h			
B.P. °C			BP	0.04865	2					
760 mm	134.	2	t_e	0.0361	5		f'	to		
100	72.	4	30 mm	0.6832	5		g'	°K		
30	45.33	5					h'			
10	24.	5	ΔHm cal/g							
1	-10.	5	ΔHv cal/g				m	to		
Pressure			25°C	89.64	5		n	°K		
mm 25°C	10.39	5	30 mm	87.69	5		o			
t_e	1114.	5	BP	75.95	5					
Density			t_e	74.04	5		m'	to		
g/ml 20°C	0.9930	2	t_e (d,e)	74.00	5		n'	°K		
d_4^t 25	0.9880	2	ΔHv/T_e	19.68	5		o'			
30	0.9830	4					Surface tension			
a	1.0130	4	d 45 to	93.69	5		dynes/cm. 20°C	31.99	5	
b	-0.00100	4	e 150 °C	0.1324	5		γ 30	30.72	5	
Ref. Index			d' 20 to	92.04	5		40	29.49	5	
n_D 20°C	1.5122	2	e' 45 °C	0.0959	5					
25	1.5094	2	d_c g/ml				Parachor [P]			
30	1.5066	4	v_c ml/g				20°C			
"C"	0.6776	4	t_c °C	350.0	5		30			
MR (Obs.)	33.913	2	P_c mm	29781.	5		40			
MR (Calc.)	33.974#	5	PV/RT				Sugd.	268.7	5	
(nD-d/2)	1.0157	2	25°C	1.0000	5		Exp. L.1.%/wt.			
Dielectric			30 mm	1.0000	5		u.			
A 45 to	6.9563	5	BP	0.9600	5		Dispersion	154.	2	
B 195 °C	1414.2	5	t_e	0.9493	5		Flash Point °C			
C	213.0	5	t_c				Fire Point			
A* 45 to	1.3601	5	ΔHc kcal/m				M Spec.			
B* 160 °C	1324.29	5	ΔHf				Ultra V.			
K			ΔFf				X-Ray Dif.			
c							Infrared			
t_k to			Viscosity				Solubility in +			
t_x °C			centistokes				Acetone			
A' 15 to	7.30149	5	η °C				Carbon tet.			
B' 45 °C	1598.0	5					Benzene			
C'	229.	5	B^v to				Ether			
A'* 20 to	1.69543	5	A^v °C				n-Heptane			
B'* 45 °C	1499.7	5	(B^v) to				Ethanol			
Ac 195 to	7.37327	5	(A^v) °C				Water			
Bc t_c °C	1774.2	5					Water in			
Cc	261.9	5	c_p liq. °K							
Cryos. A°			c_p vap. °K							
consts. B°										
t_e °C	148.76	5	c_v vap.							

$T_R = 0.75\,T_c$ # C-S-C, S = 7.2   + grams/100 grams solvent

REFERENCES: 1-Dow 2-API 3-Lit. 4-Calc. from det. data 5-Calc. by formula
SOURCE: API
PURIFICATION: API
LITERATURE REFERENCES:

TABLE IV. THIOPHENES

NAME	3-Ethylthiophene	STRUCTURAL FORMULA

STRUCTURAL FORMULA

$$HC - CC_2H_5$$
$$HC_{\diagdown S\diagup}CH$$

Mole % Pur.	Ref.	Molecular Formula C_6H_8S	Molecular Weight 112.190

		Ref.			Ref.				Ref.
F.P. °C	-89.1	2	dt/dP			f	to		
F.P. 100%			°C/mm			g	°K		
			25°C	1.809	5	h			
B.P. °C			BP	0.0490	5				
760 mm	136.	2	t_e	0.0362	5	f'	to		
100	74.	4	30 mm	0.6865	5	g'	°K		
30	46.48	5	ΔHm cal/g			h'			
10	26.	5				m	to		
1	-9.	5	ΔHv cal/g			n	°K		
Pressure			25°C	89.92	5	o			
mm 25°C	9.679	5	30 mm	87.89	5				
t_e	1120.	5	BP	76.15	5	m'	to		
Density			t_e	74.19	5	n'	°K		
g/ml 20°C	0.9980	2	t_e (d, e)	74.18	5	o'			
d_4^t 25	0.9931	2	ΔHv/T_e	20.33	5				
30	0.9882	4				Surface tension			
a	1.0176	4	d 45 to	93.98	5	dynes/cm. 20°C	32.64	5
b	-0.0₃977	4	e 150 °C	0.1311	5	ɣ 30	31.34	5
			d' 20 to	92.28	5	40	30.14	5
Ref. Index			e' 45 °C	0.0945	5				
n_D 20°C	1.5146	2	d_c g/ml			Parachor [P]			
25	1.5120	2	v_c ml/g			20°C			
30	1.5092	4	t_c °C	354.	5	30			
"C"	0.6771	4	P_c mm	30020.	5	40			
						Sugd.	268.7	5
MR (Obs.)	33.88	2	PV/RT			Exp. L.1.%/wt.			
MR (Calc.)	33.974#	5	25°C	1.0000	5				
(nD-d/2)	1.0156	2	30 mm	1.0000	5	Dispersion			
Dielectric			BP	0.9600	5	Flash Point °C			
A 45 to	6.9530	5	t_e	0.9488	5	Fire Point			
B 200 °C	1422.0	5	t_c						
C	213.2	5	ΔHc kcal/m			M. Spec.			
			ΔHf			Ultra V.			
A* 45 to	1.3538	5	ΔFf			X-Ray Dif.			
B* 160 °C	1331.2	5				Infrared			
K			Viscosity						
c			centistokes			Solubility in +			
t_k to			η °C			Acetone			
t_x °C						Carbon tet.			
A' 15 to	7.2980	5				Benzene			
B' 45 °C	1606.8	5				Ether			
C'	229.0	5	B^v to			n-Heptane			
A'* 20 to	1.6903	5	A^v °C			Ethanol			
B'* 45 °C	1508.0	5	(B^v) to			Water			
Ac 200 to	7.3711	5	(A^v) °C			Water in			
Bc t_c °C	1786.2	5							
Cc	262.8	5	c_p liq. °K						
Cryos. A°			c_p vap. °K						
consts. B°									
t_e °C	151.07	5	c_v vap.						

$T_R = 0.75\ T_c$ # C-S-C, S = 7.2   + grams/100 grams solvent

REFERENCES: 1-Dow 2-API 3-Lit. 4-Calc. from det. data 5-Calc. by formula

SOURCE: API

PURIFICATION: API

LITERATURE REFERENCES:

No. 6

NAME	2,3-Dimethylthiophene	STRUCTURAL FORMULA

Structural formula:

$$HC-CCH_3$$
$$HC \quad CCH_3$$
$$\diagdown S \diagup$$

Mole % Pur.		Ref.	Molecular Formula C_6H_8S	Molecular Weight 112.190		

		Ref.			Ref.				Ref.
F.P. °C	-49.0	2	dt/dP			f	to		
F.P. 100%			°C/mm			g	°K		
B.P. °C			25°C	2.201	5	h			
760 mm	141.6	2	BP	0.04996	5				
100	78.4	5	t_e	0.0365	5	f'	to		
30	50.49	5	30 mm	0.6975	5	g'	°K		
10	29.3	5	ΔHm cal/g			h'			
1	-6.2	5							
Pressure			ΔHv cal/g			m	to		
mm 25°C	7.8498	5	25°C	91.16	5	n	°K		
t_e	1137.1	5	30 mm	88.69	5	o			
			BP	76.76	5				
Density			t_e	74.73	5	m'	to		
g/ml 20°C	1.0021	2	t_e (d,e)	74.67	5	n'	°K		
d_4^t 25	0.9970	2	ΔHv/T_e	19.46	5	o'			
30	0.9919	4							
a	1.0225	4	d 80 to	95.30	5	Surface tension			
b	-0.0₂102	4	e 160 °C	0.1309	5	dynes/cm. 20°C	33.18	5
			d' 25 to	93.59	5	30	31.85	5
Ref. Index			e' 80 °C	0.0970	5	40	30.56	5
n_D 20°C	1.5192	2							
25	1.5166	2	d_c g/ml			Parachor [P]			
30	1.5137	4	v_c ml/g			20°C			
"C"	0.6801	4	t_c °C	362.0	5	30			
MR (Obs.)	33.99	2	P_c mm	29100.	5	40			
MR (Calc.)	33.974#	5	PV/RT			Sugd.	268.7	5
(nD-d/2)	1.0182	2	25°C	1.0000	5				
Dielectric			30 mm	1.0000	5	Exp. L.l.%/wt.			
			BP	0.9602	5	u.			
A 80 to	6.9249	5	t_e	0.9487	5	Dispersion			
B 200 °C	1430.0	5	t_c			Flash Point °C			
C	212.	5				Fire Point			
A* 80 to	1.3204	5	ΔHc kcal/m			M Spec.			
B* 170 °C	1338.3	5	ΔHf			Ultra V.			
K			ΔFf			X-Ray Dif.			
c			Viscosity			Infrared			
t_k to			centistokes			Solubility in +			
t_x °C			η °C			Acetone			
A' 25 to	7.2681	5				Carbon tet.			
B' 80 °C	1615.9	5				Benzene			
C'	229.	5	B^V to			Ether			
A'* 25 to	1.6587	5	A^V °C			n-Heptane			
B'* 80 °C	1517.	5	(B^V) to			Ethanol			
Ac 200 to	7.3425	5	(A^V) °C			Water			
Bc t_c °C	1797.9	5				Water in			
Cc	262.	5	c_p liq. °K						
Cryos. A°			c_p vap. °K						
consts. B°									
t_e °C	157.59	5	c_v vap.						

$T_R = 0.75 T_c$ # C-S-C, S = 7.2

+ grams/100 grams solvent

REFERENCES: 1-Dow 2-API 3-Lit. 4-Calc. from det. data 5-Calc. by formula

SOURCE: API

PURIFICATION: API

LITERATURE REFERENCES:

TABLE IV. THIOPHENES

NAME	2,4-Dimethylthiophene	STRUCTURAL FORMULA

Structural formula:

$$H_3CC\text{---}CH$$
$$HC_{\diagdown S \diagup}CCH_3$$

Mole % Pur.	Ref.	Molecular Formula C_6H_8S	Molecular Weight 112.190	

		Ref.			Ref.				Ref.
F.P. °C			dt/dP °C/mm			f	to °K		
F.P. 100%			25°C BP	2.2627	5	g			
B.P. °C				0.0490	5	h			
760 mm	140.7	2	t_e	0.0365	5	f'	to °K		
100	78.5	5	30 mm	0.6900	5	g'			
30	50.96	5	ΔHm cal/g			h'			
10	29.9	5	ΔHv cal/g			m	to °K		
1	-5.3	5	25°C	92.46	5	n			
Pressure			30 mm	89.91	5	o			
mm 25°C	7.5284	5	BP	76.44	5	m'	to °K		
t_e	1108.2	5	t_e	74.41	5	n'			
Density			t_e (d, e)	74.24	5	o'			
g/ml 20°C	0.9956	2	ΔHv/T_e	19.48	5	Surface tension			
d_4^t 25	0.9905	2	d	50 to	97.56	5	dynes/cm. 20°C	32.33	5
30	0.9854	4	e	155 °C	0.1501	5	ɣ 30	31.02	5
a	1.0160	4	d'	25 to	94.91	5	40	29.76	5
b	-0.0₂102	4	e'	50 °C	0.0982	5	Parachor [P]		
Ref. Index			d_c g/ml			20°C		
n_D 20°C	1.5104	2	v_c ml/g			30		
25	1.5078	2	t_c °C	358.	5	40		
30	1.5048	4	P_c mm	30110.	5	Sugd.	268.7	5
"C"	0.6736	4	PV/RT			Exp. L.1.%/wt.		
MR (Obs.)	33.73	2	25°C	1.0000	5	u.		
MR (Calc.)	33.974#	5	30 mm	1.0000	5	Dispersion		
(nD-d/2)	1.0126	2	BP	0.9419	5	Flash Point °C		
Dielectric			t_e	0.9295	5	Fire Point		
A 50 to	6.9939	5	t_c			M. Spec.		
B 220 °C	1450.7	5	ΔHc kcal/m			Ultra V.		
C	212.0	5	ΔHf			X-Ray Dif.		
A* 50 to	1.42330	5	ΔFf			Infrared		
B* 165 °C	1367.90	5	Viscosity			Solubility in +		
K			centistokes			Acetone		
c			η °C			Carbon tet.		
t_k to						Benzene		
t_x °C						Ether		
A' 25 to	7.3415	5				n-Heptane		
B' 50 °C	1639.2	5	B^v to			Ethanol		
C'	229.	5	A^v °C			Water		
A'* 25 to	1.7316	5	(B^v) to			Water in		
B'* 50 °C	1540.3	5	(A^v) °C					
Ac 220 to	7.4100	5	c_p liq. °K					
Bc t_c °C	1814.	5						
Cc	261.	5	c_p vap. °K					
Cryos. A°								
consts. B°			c_v vap.					
t_e °C	155.33	5						

$T_R = 0.75 T_c$ # C-S-C, S = 7.2   + grams/100 grams solvent

REFERENCES: 1-Dow 2-API 3-Lit. 4-Calc. from det. data 5-Calc. by formula

SOURCE:	API
PURIFICATION:	API

LITERATURE REFERENCES:

NAME	2,5-Dimethylthiophene	STRUCTURAL FORMULA

Structural formula:
$$HC\text{---}CH$$
$$H_3CC \diagdown_S\diagup CCH_3$$

Mole % Pur.		Ref.	Molecular Formula C_6H_8S		Molecular Weight 112.190				

		Ref.				Ref.			Ref.
F.P. °C	-62.6	2	dt/dP				f | to		
F.P. 100%			°C/mm				g | °K		
B.P. °C			25°C	1.8690		5	h		
760 mm	136.7	2	BP	0.0490		5			
100	74.6	5	t_e	0.0361		5	f' | to		
30	47.14	5	30 mm	0.6872		5	g' | °K		
10	26.2	5	ΔHm cal/g				h'		
1	-8.8	5							
Pressure			ΔHv cal/g				m | to		
mm 25°C	9.3366	5	25°C	90.25		5	n | °K		
t_e	1121.8	5	30 mm	88.16		5	o |		
Density			BP	76.38		5			
g/ml 20°C	0.9850	2	t_e (d, e)	74.45		5	m' | to		
d_4^t 25	0.9799	2		74.39		5	n' | °K		
30	0.9748	4	$\Delta Hv/T_e$	19.65		5	o' |		
a	1.0054	4	d | 50 to	94.36		5	Surface tension		
b	-0.00102	4	e | 150 °C	0.1315		5	dynes/cm. 20°C	30.97	5
			d' | 25 to	92.62		5	30	29.71	5
Ref. Index			e' | 50 °C	0.0946		5	40	28.42	5
n_D 20°C	1.5129	2	d_c g/ml				Parachor [P]		
25	1.5104	2	v_c ml/g				20°C		
30	1.5072	4	t_c °C	352.		5	30		
"C"	0.6839	4	P_c mm	29180.		5	40		
MR (Obs.)	34.23	2	PV/RT				Sugd.	268.7	5
MR (Calc.)	33.974	5	25°C	1.0000		5	Exp. L.1.%/wt.		
(nD-d/2)	1.0204	2	30 mm	1.0000		5	u.		
Dielectric			BP	0.9597		5	Dispersion	162.	2
A | 50 to	6.9611	5	t_e	0.9487		5	Flash Point °C		
B |195 °C	1427.7	5	t_c				Fire Point		
C	213.2	5	ΔHc kcal/m				M Spec.		
A* | 50 to	1.3621	5	ΔHf				Ultra V.		
B* |160 °C	1337.0	5	ΔFf				X-Ray Dif.		
K							Infrared		
c			Viscosity				Solubility in +		
t_k | to			centistokes				Acetone		
t_x | °C			η °C				Carbon tet.		
A' | 25 to	7.3066	5					Benzene		
B' | 50 °C	1613.3	5					Ether		
C'	230.	5	B^v | to				n-Heptane		
A'* 25 to	1.6984	5	A^v | °C				Ethanol		
B'* 50 °C	1514.3	5	(B^v) | to				Water		
Ac |195 to	7.3785	5	(A^v) | °C				Water in		
Bc | t_c °C	1789.6	5	c_p liq. °K						
Cc	262.	5							
Cryos. A°			c_p vap. °K						
consts. B°									
t_e °C	151.83	5	c_v vap.						

$T_R = 0.75 T_c$	# C-S-C, S = 7.2	+ grams/100 grams solvent

REFERENCES: 1-Dow 2-API 3-Lit. 4-Calc. from det. data 5-Calc. by formula

SOURCE:	API
FURIFICATION:	API
LITERATURE REFERENCES:	

TABLE IV. THIOPHENES

NAME	3,4-Dimethylthiophene	STRUCTURAL FORMULA

$$H_3CC \underset{HC \diagdown_S \diagup CH}{\overset{\parallel \quad \parallel}{——CCH_3}}$$

Mole % Pur.	Ref.	Molecular Formula	C_6H_8S	Molecular Weight	112.190

		Ref.			Ref.						Ref.
F.P. °C			dt/dP			f		to			
F.P. 100%			°C/mm			g		°K			
			25°C	2.5399	5	h					
B.P. °C			BP	0.0502	5						
760 mm	145.	2	t_e	0.0371	5	f'		to			
100	81.	5	30 mm	0.7021	5	g'		°K			
30	53.38	5				h'					
10	32.	5	ΔHm cal/g								
1	-4.	5				m		to			
			ΔHv cal/g			n		°K			
Pressure			25°C	92.48	5	o					
mm 25°C	6.705	5	30 mm	89.69	5						
t_e	1117.5	5	BP	75.98	5	m'		to			
			t_e	73.88	5	n'		°K			
Density			t_e (d, e)	73.68	5	o'					
g/ml 20°C	1.008	2									
d_4^t 25	1.003	2	$\Delta Hv/T_e$	19.12	5	Surface tension					
30	0.998	4				dynes/cm. 20°C	33.97	5			
a	1.0280	4	d 55 to	97.68	5	8	30	32.72	5		
b	-0.0_3998	4	e 160 °C	0.1497	5		40	31.36	5		
			d' 25 to	94.94	5						
Ref. Index			e' 55 °C	0.0983	5	Parachor [P]					
n_D 20°C	1.5212	2					20°C				
25	1.5187	2	d_c g/ml				30				
30	1.5157	4	v_c ml/g				40				
			t_c °C	367.	5		Sugd.	268.7	5		
"C"	0.6785	4	P_c mm	29310.	5						
MR (Obs.)	33.9	2				Exp. L.1.%/wt.					
MR (Calc.)	33.974#	5	PV/RT			u.					
(nD-d/2)	1.017	2	25°C	1.0000	5	Dispersion	156.	2			
			30 mm	1.0000	5						
Dielectric			BP	0.9590	5	Flash Point °C					
A 55 to	6.9389	5	t_e	0.9265	5	Fire Point					
B 205 °C	1446.7	5	t_c								
C	211.5	5	ΔHc kcal/m			M. Spec.					
			ΔHf			Ultra V.					
A* 55 to	1.3675	5	ΔFf			X-Ray Dif.					
B* 170 °C	1363.9	5				Infrared					
K			Viscosity			Solubility in +					
c			centistokes			Acetone					
t_k to			η °C			Carbon tet.					
t_x °C						Benzene					
A' 25 to	7.2830	5				Ether					
B' 55 °C	1634.7	5				n-Heptane					
C'	228.	5	B^v to			Ethanol					
			A^v °C			Water					
A'* 25 to	1.67182	5	(B^v) to			Water in					
B'* 55 °C	1535.5	5	(A^v) °C								
Ac 205 to	7.3562	5									
Bc t_c °C	1817.0	5	c_p liq. °K								
Cc	262.	5									
Cryos. A°			c_p vap. °K								
consts. B°											
t_e °C	160.34	5	c_v vap.								

$T_R = 0.75\,T_c$	# C-S-C, S = 7.2	+ grams/100 grams solvent

REFERENCES: 1-Dow 2-API 3-Lit. 4-Calc. from det. data 5-Calc. by formula

SOURCE: API

PURIFICATION: API

LITERATURE REFERENCES:

No. 10

NAME	2-Propyltniophene	STRUCTURAL FORMULA

Structural formula:
$$HC\!-\!CH$$
$$\|\quad\ \ \|$$
$$HC\underset{S}{\diagdown}CC_3H_7$$

Mole % Pur.	Ref.	Molecular Formula $C_7H_{10}S$	Molecular Weight 126.216			

		Ref.			Ref.			Ref.
F.P. °C			dt/dP			f | to		
F.P. 100%			°C/mm			g | ⌐ ⌐ °K ⌐		
B.P. °C			25°C	4.2441	5	h |		
760 mm	158.5	2	BP	0.0520	5			
100	92.7	5	t_e	0.0368	5	f' | to		
30	63.72	5	30 mm	0.7254	5	g' | ⌐ ⌐ °K ⌐		
10	41.6	5	ΔHm cal/g			h' |		
1	4.8	5						
Pressure			ΔHv cal/g			m | to		
mm 25°C	3.849	5	25°C	85.69	5	n | ⌐ ⌐ °K ⌐		
t_e	1182.8	5	30 mm	82.12	5	o |		
Density			BP	70.79	5			
g/mil 20°C	0.9687	2	t_e	68.67	5	m' | to		
d_4^t 25	0.9639	2	t_e (d, e)	68.60	5	n' | ⌐ ⌐ °K ⌐		
30	0.9591	4	ΔHv/T_e	19.26	5	o' |		
a	0.9879	4	d | 65 to	89.74	5	Surface tension		
b	-0.0396	4	e | 175 °C	0.1195	5	dynes/cm. 20°C	31.22	5
			d' | 25 to	87.99	5	γ 30	30.00	5
Ref. Index			e' | 65 °C	0.0922	5	40	28.81	5
n_D 20°C	1.5049	2	d_c g/ml			Parachor [P]		
25	1.5023	2	v_c ml/g			20°C		
30	1.4995	4	t_c °C	371.	5	30		
"C"	0.6855	4	P_c mm	24502.	5	40		
MR (Obs.)	38.639	2	PV/RT			Sugd.	307.7	5
MR (Calc.)	38.292#	5	25°C	1.0000	5	Exp. L.1.%/wt.		
(nD-d/2)	1.0206	2	30 mm	1.0000	5	u.		
Dielectric			BP	0.9577	5	Dispersion	149.	2
A | 65 to	6.9194	5	t_e	0.9446	5	Flash Point °C		
B | 210 °C	1484.2	5	t_c			Fire Point		
C	209.	5	ΔHc kcal/m			M Spec.		
A* | 65 to	1.3536	5	ΔHf			Ultra V.		
B* | 185 °C	1390.2	5	ΔFf			X-Ray Dif.		
K						Infrared		
c			Viscosity			Solubility in +		
t_k | to			centistokes			Acetone		
t_x | °C			η °C			Carbon tet.		
A' | 25 to	7.2623	5				Benzene		
B' | 65 °C	1677.10	5				Ether		
C'	226.	5	B^v | to			n-Heptane		
A'* 25 to	1.6970	5	A^v | °C			Ethanol		
B'* 65 °C	1577.4	5	(B^v) | to			Water		
Ac | 210 to	7.3325	5	(A^v) | °C			Water in		
Bc | t_c °C	1850.4	5	c_p liq. °K					
Cc	258.	5						
Cryos. A°			c_p vap. °K					
consts. B°								
t_e °C	176.86	5	c_v vap.					

$T_R = 0.75 T_c$ # C-S-C, S = 7.2   + grams/100 grams solvent

REFERENCES: 1-Dow 2-API 3-Lit. 4-Calc. from det. data 5-Calc. by formula

SOURCE:	API
PURIFICATION:	API

LITERATURE REFERENCES:

TABLE IV. THIOPHENES

NAME	3-Propylthiophene	STRUCTURAL FORMULA

Mole % Pur.	Ref.	Molecular Formula $C_7H_{10}S$	Molecular Weight 126.216

		Ref.				Ref.					Ref.
F.P. °C			dt/dP			f		to		
F.P. 100%			°C/mm			g		°K		
			25°C	4.675	5	h				
B.P. °C			BP	0.05233	5					
760 mm	161.	2	t_e	0.03711	5	f'		to		
100	95.	5	30 mm	0.7296	5	g'		°K		
30	65.64	5	ΔHm cal/g			h'				
10	43.	5								
1	6.	5	ΔHv cal/g			m		to		
			25°C	86.38	5	n		°K		
Pressure			30 mm	82.59	5	o				
mm 25°C	3.4670	5	BP	70.71	5					
t_e	1151.03	5	t_e	68.53	5	m'		to		
			t_e (d, e)	68.42	5	n'		°K		
Density			ΔHv/T_e	19.11	5	o'				
g/ml 20°C	0.9716	2				Surface tension				
d_4^t 25	0.9669	2	d 65 to	90.76	5	dynes/cm. 20°C	31.60	5
30	0.9622	4	e 180 °C	0.1246	5	𝛾 30	30.39	5
a	0.9904	4	d' 25 to	88.72	5	40	29.22	5
b	-0.0₃94	4	e' 65 °C	0.0934	5			
Ref. Index						Parachor [P]		
n_D 20°C	1.5057	2	d_c g/ml			20°C		
25	1.5031	2	v_c ml/g			30		
30	1.5005	4	t_c °C	375.0	5	40		
"C"	0.6843	4	P_c mm	24530.	5	Sugd.	307.7	5
MR (Obs.)	38.58	2	PV/RT			Exp. L.l.%/wt.		
MR (Calc.)	38.292#	5	25°C	1.0000	5	u.		
(nD-d/2)	1.0199	2	30 mm	1.0000	5	Dispersion	148.	2
Dielectric			BP	0.9517	5	Flash Point °C		
A 65 to	6.9146	5	t_e	0.9379	5	Fire Point		
B 210 °C	1490.1	5	t_c			M. Spec.		
C	208.4	5	ΔHc kcal/m			Ultra V.		
A* 65 to	1.3572	5	ΔHf			X-Ray Dif.		
B* 190 °C	1398.7	5	ΔFf			Infrared		
K			Viscosity			Solubility in +		
c			centistokes			Acetone		
t_k to			η °C			Carbon tet.		
t_x °C						Benzene		
A' 25 to	7.2572	5				Ether		
B' 65 °C	1683.8	5				n-Heptane		
C'	226.	5	B^v to			Ethanol		
			A^v °C			Water		
A'* 25 to	1.6911	5	(B^v) to			Water in		
B'* 65 °C	1584.	5	(A^v) °C					
Ac 210 to	7.3274	5	c_p liq. °K					
Bc t_c °C	1858.3	5						
Cc	258.	5	c_p vap. °K					
Cryos. A° consts. B°			c_v vap.					
t_e °C	179.41	5						

$T_R = 0.75\,T_c$ # C-S-C, S = 7.2   + grams/100 grams solvent

REFERENCES: 1-Dow 2-API 3-Lit. 4-Calc. from det. data 5-Calc. by formula

SOURCE:	API
PURIFICATION:	API
LITERATURE REFERENCES:	

NAME	2-Isopropylthiophene	STRUCTURAL FORMULA

Structural formula:

$$HC\!-\!CH$$
$$HC\underset{S}{}CC_3H_7$$

Mole % Pur.	Ref.	Molecular Formula $C_7H_{10}S$	Molecular Weight 126.216

		Ref.				Ref.				Ref.
F.P. °C			dt/dP				f | | to		
F.P. 100%			°C/mm				g | | °K		
B.P. °C			25°C	3.432	5		h |		
760 mm	153.	2	BP	0.05130	5				
100	88.	5	t_e	0.0360	5		f' | | to		
30	59.46	5	30 mm	0.7161	5		g' | | °K		
10	38.	5	ΔHm cal/g				h' |		
1	1.	5	ΔHv cal/g				m | | to		
Pressure			25°C	84.21	5		n | | °K		
mm 25°C	4.844	5	30 mm	81.10	5		o |		
t_e	1191.0	5	BP	71.10	5		m' | | to		
Density			t_e	69.29	5		n' | | °K		
g/ml 20°C	0.9678	2	t_e (d, e)	69.21	5		o' |		
d_4^t 25	0.9633	2	$\Delta Hv/T_e$	19.70	5		Surface tension		
30	0.9588	4	d | 60 to	87.45	5		dynes/cm. 20°C	31.11	5
a	0.9858	4	e | 170 °C	0.1069	5		γ 30	29.97	5
b	-0.0₃90	4	d' | 25 to	86.4	5		40	28.85	5
Ref. Index			e' | 60 °C	0.09	5		Parachor [P]		
n_D 20°C	1.5038	2	d_c g/ml				20°C		
25	1.5013	2	v_c ml/g				30		
30	1.4988	4	t_c °C	364.	5		40		
"C"	0.6846	4	P_c mm	25000.	5		Sugd.	307.7	5
MR (Obs.)	38.61	2	PV/RT				Exp. L.1.%/wt.		
MR (Calc.)	38.292#	5	25°C	1.0000	5		u.		
(nD-d/2)	1.0199	2	30 mm	1.0000	5		Dispersion	150.	2
Dielectric			BP	0.9590	5		Flash Point °C		
A | 60 to	6.9243	5	t_e	0.9467	5		Fire Point		
B | 205 °C	1467.8	5	t_c				M Spec.		
C	210.	5	ΔHc kcal/m				Ultra V.		
A* | 60 to	1.3607	5	ΔHf				X-Ray Dif.		
B* | 180 °C	1374.0	5	ΔFf				Infrared		
K			Viscosity				Solubility in +		
c			centistokes				Acetone		
t_k | to			η °C				Carbon tet.		
t_x | °C							Benzene		
A' | 25 to	7.2675	5					Ether		
B' | 60 °C	1658.57	5					n-Heptane		
C'	227.	5	B^v | to				Ethanol		
A'* 25 to	1.70438	5	A^v | °C				Water		
B'* 60 °C	1559.10	5	(B^v) | to				Water in		
Ac | 205 to	7.3595	5	(A^v) | °C						
Bc | t_c °C	1851.	5	c_p liq. °K						
Cc	261.	5	c_p vap. °K						
Cryos. A°									
consts. B°									
t_e °C	170.6	5	c_v vap.						

$T_R = 0.75 T_c$ # C-S-C, S = 7.2   + grams/100 grams solvent

REFERENCES: 1-Dow 2-API 3-Lit. 4-Calc. from det. data 5-Calc. by formula

SOURCE:	API
PURIFICATION:	API

LITERATURE REFERENCES:

TABLE IV. THIOPHENES

NAME	3-Isopropylthiophene			STRUCTURAL FORMULA

$$HC \!-\!\! CC_3H_7$$
$$HC_{\diagdown S \diagup} CH$$

Mole % Pur.	Ref.	Molecular Formula $C_7H_{10}S$		Molecular Weight 126.216

		Ref.			Ref.			Ref.
F.P. °C			dt/dP			f | to		
F.P. 100%			°C/mm			g | ___ °K		
B.P. °C			25°C	3.9952	5	h |		
760 mm	157.	2	BP	0.05184	5			
100	91.	5	t_e	0.0366	5	f' | to		
30	62.51	5	30 mm	0.7230	5	g' | ___ °K		
10	41.	5				h' |		
1	4.	5	ΔHm cal/g					
			ΔHv cal/g			m | to		
Pressure			25°C	85.25	5	n | ___ °K		
mm 25°C	4.1105	5	30 mm	81.81	5	o |		
t_e	1169.0	5	BP	71.06	5			
Density			t_e	68.99	5	m' | to		
g/ml 20°C	0.9733	2	t_e (d, e)	68.95	5	n' | ___ °K		
d_4^t 25	0.9688	2	ΔHv/T_e	19.40	5	o' |		
30	0.9643	4				Surface tension		
a	0.9913	4	d | 65 to	88.92	5	dynes/cm. 20°C	31.82	5
b	-0.0$_3$90	4	e | 175 °C	0.1137	5	γ 30	30.66	5
Ref. Index			d' | 25 to	87.54	5	40	29.52	5
n_D 20°C	1.5052	2	e' | 65 °C	0.0918	5	Parachor ⊙		
25	1.5027	2	d_c g/ml			20°C		
30	1.5002	4	v_c ml/g			30		
"C"	0.6825	4	t_c °C	371.0	5	40		
			P_c mm	25050.	5	Sugd.	307.7	5
MR (Obs.)	38.48	2	PV/RT			Exp. L.1.%/wt.		
MR (Calc.)	38.292#	5	25°C	1.0000	5	u.		
(nD-d/2)	1.0186	2	30 mm	1.0000	5	Dispersion	145.	2
Dielectric			BP	0.9650	5	Flash Point °C		
A | 65 to	6.9174	5	t_e	0.9528	5	Fire Point		
B |210 °C	1478.2	5	t_c			M. Spec.		
C ___	209.2	5	ΔHc kcal/m			Ultra V.		
A* | 65 to	1.3401	5	ΔHf			X-Ray Dif.		
B* |185 °C	1381.1	5	ΔFf			Infrared		
K			Viscosity			Solubility in +		
c			centistokes			Acetone		
t_k | to			η °C			Carbon tet.		
t_x | °C						Benzene		
A' | 25 to	7.2601	5				Ether		
B' | 65 °C	1670.3	5				n-Heptane		
C' ___	226.	5	B^v | to			Ethanol		
A'* 25 to	1.6956	5	A^v | °C			Water		
B'* 65 °C	1570.7	5	(B^v)| to			Water in		
Ac|210 to	7.3310	5	(A^v)| °C					
Bc| t_c °C	1845.	5						
Cc ___	258.	5	c_p liq. °K					
Cryos. A°			c_p vap. °K					
consts. B°								
t_e °C	175.55	5	c_v vap.					

T_R = 0.75 T_c # C-S-C, S = 7.2   + grams/100 grams solvent

REFERENCES: 1-Dow 2-API 3-Lit. 4-Calc. from det. data 5-Calc. by formula

SOURCE: API

PURIFICATION: API

LITERATURE REFERENCES:

| NAME | 2-Ethyl-3-methylthiophene | | | | | | STRUCTURAL FORMULA |

STRUCTURAL FORMULA

$$\begin{array}{c} HC\!\!-\!\!CCH_3 \\ \| \quad \| \\ HC \diagdown_S \diagup CC_2H_5 \end{array}$$

| Mole % Pur. | Ref. | Molecular Formula | $C_7H_{10}S$ | Molecular Weight | 126.216 |

		Ref.				Ref.				Ref.
F.P. °C			dt/dP °C/mm				f	to °K		
F.P. 100%			25°C	4.7190	5		g			
B.P. °C			BP	0.05224	5		h			
760 mm	161.	2	t_e	0.3682	5		f'	to °K		
100	95.	5	30 mm	0.7286	5		g'			
30	65.79	5	ΔHm cal/g				h'			
10	44.	5	ΔHv cal/g				m	to °K		
1	7.	5	25°C	86.63	5		n			
Pressure			30 mm	82.77	5		o			
mm 25°C	3.4246	5	BP	71.31	5		m'	to °K		
t_e	1190.6	5	t_e	69.14	5		n'			
Density			t_e (d, e)	69.06	5		o'			
g/ml 20°C	0.9815	2	ΔHv/T_e	19.27	5		Surface tension			
d_4^t 25	0.9769	2	d $\,$ 45 to	90.69	5		dynes/cm. 20°C	32.91	5
30	0.9723	4	e 180 °C	0.1204	5		γ 30	31.69	5
a	0.9999	4	d' 25 to	88.996	5		40	30.50	5
b	-0.0₃92	4	e' 65 °C	0.0946	5		Parachor [P]		
Ref. Index			d_c g/ml				20°C		
n_D 20°C	1.5105	2	v_c ml/g				30		
25	1.5080	2	t_c °C	377.	5		40		
30	1.5053	2	P_c mm	25200.	5		Sugd.	307.7	5
"C"	0.6834	4	PV/RT				Exp. L.1.%/wt.		
MR (Obs.)	38.49	2	25°C	1.0000	5		u.		
MR (Calc.)	38.292#	5	30 mm	1.0000	5		Dispersion		
(nD-d/2)	1.0198	2	BP	0.9580	5		Flash Point °C		
Dielectric			t_e	0.9448	5		Fire Point		
A 65 to	6.9171	5	t_c				M Spec.		
B 210 °C	1489.4	5	ΔHc kcal/m				Ultra V.		
C	208.	5	ΔHf				X-Ray Dif.		
A* 65 to	1.3488	5	ΔFf				Infrared		
B* 190 °C	1395.1	5	Viscosity				Solubility in +		
K			centistokes				Acetone		
c			η °C				Carbon tet.		
t_k to							Benzene		
t_x °C			A' 25 to	7.2598	5		Ether		
A' 25 to	7.2598	5	B' 65 °C	1683.	5		n-Heptane		
B' 65 °C	1683.	5	C'	225.	5		Ethanol		
C'	225.	5	B^v to				Water		
A'* 25 to	1.6942	5	A^v °C				Water in		
B'* 65 °C	1583.6	5	(B^v) to						
Ac 210 to	7.3298	5	(A^v) °C						
Bc t_c °C	1858.7	5	c_p liq. °K						
Cc	257.	5	c_p vap. °K						
Cryos. A° consts. B°			c_v vap.						
t_e °C	179.73	5							

$T_R = 0.75\,T_c$ # C-S-C, S = 7.2 + grams/100 grams solvent

REFERENCES: 1-Dow 2-API 3-Lit. 4-Calc. from det. data 5-Calc. by formula

SOURCE: API

PURIFICATION: API

LITERATURE REFERENCES:

TABLE IV. THIOPHENES

No. 15

NAME	3-Ethyl-2-methylthiophene	STRUCTURAL FORMULA

Structural formula:

$$HC \text{———} CC_2H_5$$
$$HC \quad\quad CCH_3$$
$$\diagdown S \diagup$$

Mole % Pur.		Ref.	Molecular Formula	$C_7H_{10}S$	Molecular Weight 126.216		

		Ref.				Ref.			Ref.
F.P. °C			dt/dP				f	to	
F.P. 100%			°C/mm				g	°K	
B.P. °C			25°C	3.9952	5		h		
760 mm	157.	2	BP	0.05184	5				
100	91.	5	t_e	0.03696	5		f'	to	
30	62.51	5	30 mm	0.7230	5		g'	°K	
10	41.	5	ΔHm cal/g				h'		
1	4.	5	ΔHv cal/g				m	to	
Pressure			25°C	85.25	5		n	°K	
mm 25°C	4.1105	5	30 mm	81.81	5		o		
t_e	1172.78	5	BP	70.54	5				
Density			t_e	68.40	5		m'	to	
g/ml 20°C			t_e (d, e)	70.70	5		n'	°K	
d_4^t 25			$\Delta Hv/T_e$				o'		
30			d 60 to	89.26	5		Surface tension		
a			e 175 °C	0.1192	5		dynes/cm. 20°C		
b			d' 25 to	87.55	5		γ 30		
Ref. Index			e' 60 °C	0.09186	5		40		
n_D 20°C			d_c g/ml				Parachor [P]		
25			v_c ml/g				20°C		
30			t_c °C				30		
"C"			P_c mm				40		
MR (Obs.)			PV/RT				Sugd.	307.7	5
MR (Calc.)	38.292#	5	25°C	1.0000	5		Exp. L.l.%/wt.		
(nD-d/2)			30 mm	1.0000	5		u.		
Dielectric			BP	0.9538	5		Dispersion		
A 60 to	6.9174	5	t_e	0.9406	5		Flash Point °C		
B 190 °C	1478.2	5	t_c				Fire Point		
C	209.2	5	ΔHc kcal/m				M. Spec.		
A* 60 to	1.3598	5	ΔHf				Ultra V.		
B* 185 °C	1386.4	5	ΔFf				X-Ray Dif.		
K			Viscosity				Infrared		
c			centistokes				Solubility in +		
t_k to			η °C				Acetone		
t_x °C							Carbon tet.		
A' 25 to	7.2601	5					Benzene		
B' 60 °C	1670.3	5					Ether		
C'	226.3	5	B^v to				n-Heptane		
A'* 25 to	1.6956	5	A^v °C				Ethanol		
B'* 60 °C	1570.7	5	(B^v) to				Water		
Ac to			(A^v) °C				Water in		
$Bc_L t_c$ °C			c_p liq. °K						
Cc									
Cryos. A°			c_p vap. °K						
consts. B°									
t_e °C	174.93	5	c_v vap.						

\# C-S-C, S = 7.2

+ grams/100 grams solvent

REFERENCES: 1-Dow 2-API 3-Lit. 4-Calc. from det. data 5-Calc. by formula

SOURCE: API

PURIFICATION: API

LITERATURE REFERENCES:

No. 16

NAME	4-Ethyl-2-methylthiophene	STRUCTURAL FORMULA

H_5C_2C——C
‖   ‖
C CCH_3
S

Mole % Pur.		Ref.	Molecular Formula $C_7H_{10}S$		Molecular Weight 126.216	

		Ref.			Ref.				Ref.
F.P. °C	-59.	2	dt/dP °C/mm			f	| to		
F.P. 100%			25°C	5.0237	5	g | |__ °K			
B.F. °C			BP	0.05265	5	h |			
760 mm	163.	2	t_e	0.0369	5				
100	96.	5	30 mm	0.7334	5	f' | to			
30	67.10	5				g' | |__ °K			
10	45.	5	ΔHm cal/g			h' |			
1	8.	5							
Pressure			ΔHv cal/g			m | to			
mm 25°C	3.209	5	25°C	86.83	5	n | |__ °K			
t_e	1198.1	5	30 mm	82.87	5	o |			
Density			BP	71.48	5				
g/ml 20°C	0.9742	2	t_e	69.28	5	m' | to			
d_4^t 25	0.9696	2	t_e (d,e)	69.21	5	n' | |__ °K			
30	0.9650	4	ΔHv/T_e	19.20	5	o' |			
a	0.9926	4	d | 65 to	90.83	5	Surface tension			
b	-0.0₃92	4	e | 185 °C	0.1187	5	dynes/cm. 20°C	31.94	5	
Ref. Index			d' | 25 to	89.18	5	y 30	30.75	5	
n_D 20°C	1.5098	2	e' | 65 °C	0.0942	5	40	29.59	5	
25	1.5073	2	d_c g/ml			Parachor [P]			
30	1.5046	4	v_c ml/g			20°C			
"C"	0.6876	4	t_c °C	379.	5	30			
MR (Obs.)	38.74	2	P_c mm	24750.1	5	40			
MR (Calc.)	38.272#	5	PV/RT			Sugd.	307.7	5	
(nD-d/2)	1.0227	2	25°C	1.0000	5	Exp. L.1.%/wt.			
Dielectric			30 mm	1.0000	5	u.			
A | 65 to	6.9072	5	BP	0.9590	5	Dispersion			
B |210 °C	1493.8	5	t_e	0.9457	5	Flash Point °C			
C	208.	5	t_c			Fire Point			
A* | 65 to	1.3348	5	ΔHc kcal/m			M Spec.			
B* |195 °C	1398.4	5	ΔHf			Ultra V.			
K			ΔFf			X-Ray Dif.			
c			Viscosity			Infrared			
t_k | to			centistokes			Solubility in +			
t_x | °C			η °C			Acetone			
A' | 25 to	7.2493	5				Carbon tet.			
B' | 65 °C	1685.	5				Benzene			
C'	225.	5	B^v | to			Ether			
A'* 25 to	1.6826	5	A^v | °C			n-Heptane			
B'* 65 °C	1588.2	5	(B^v) | to			Ethanol			
Ac | 210 to	7.3203	5	(A^v) | °C			Water			
Bc | t_c °C	1864.9	5	c_p liq. °K			Water in			
Cc	258.	5							
Cryos. A°			c_p vap. °K						
consts. B°									
t_e °C	182.16	5	c_v vap.						

T_R = 0.75 T_c # C-S-C, S = 7.2   + grams/100 grams solvent

REFERENCES: 1-Dow   2-API   3-Lit.   4-Calc. from det. data   5-Calc. by formula

SOURCE:	API
PURIFICATION:	API
LITERATURE REFERENCES:	

TABLE IV. THIOPHENES

199

No. 17

NAME	5-Ethyl-2-methylthiophene	STRUCTURAL FORMULA

Structural formula:

$$HC \overline{\quad\quad} CH$$
$$H_5C_2C \diagdown_{S} \diagup CCH_3$$

Mole % Pur.		Ref.	Molecular Formula	$C_7H_{10}S$	Molecular Weight 126.216	

		Ref.			Ref.			Ref.
F.P. °C	-68.5	2	dt/dP			f	to	
F.P. 100%			°C/mm			g	°K	
B.P. °C			25°C	4.5061	5	h		
760 mm	160.1	2	BP	0.05224	5			
100	94.02	5	t_e	0.03685	5	f'	to	
30	64.92	5	30 mm	0.7282	5	g'	°K	
10	42.8	5	ΔHm cal/g			h'		
1	5.7	5	ΔHv cal/g			m	to	
Pressure			25°C	86.12	5	n	°K	
mm 25°C	3.6078	5	30 mm	82.39	5	o		
t_e	1189.6	5	BP	71.09	5			
Density			t_e	68.94	5	m'	to	
g/ml 20°C	0.9661	2	t_e (d, e)	68.87	5	n'	°K	
d_4^t 25	0.9618	2	ΔHv/T_e	19.25	5	o'		
30	0.9575	4	d 65 to	90.10	5	Surface tension		
a	0.9833	4	e 180 °C	0.1188	5	dynes/cm. 20°C	30.89	5
b	-0.0₃86	4	d' 25 to	88.45	5	δ 30	29.80	5
Ref. Index			e' 65 °C	0.09326	5	40	28.74	5
n_D 20°C	1.5073	2	d_c g/ml	0.3104	5	Parachor [P]		
25	1.5048	2	v_c ml/g	3.222	5	20°C		
30	1.5033	4	t_c °C	375.00	5	30		
"C"	0.6903	4	P_c mm	24840.1	5	40		
MR (Obs.)	38.90	2	PV/RT			Sugd.	307.7	5
MR (Calc.)	38.242#	5	25°C	1.0000	5	Exp. L.l. %/wt.		
(nD-d/2)	1.0242	2	30 mm	1.0000	5	u.		
Dielectric			BP	0.9590	5	Dispersion		
A 65 to	6.9128	5	t_e	0.9460	5	Flash Point °C		
B 210 °C	1486.2	5	t_c			Fire Point		
C	208.5	5	ΔHc kcal/m			M. Spec.		
A* 65 to	1.3432	5	ΔHf			Ultra V.		
B* 190 °C	1391.4	5	ΔFf			X-Ray Dif.		
K			Viscosity			Infrared		
c			centistokes			Solubility in +		
t_k to			η °C			Acetone		
t_x °C						Carbon tet.		
A' 25 to	7.2552	5				Benzene		
B' 65 °C	1679.4	5				Ether		
C'	225.7	5	B^v	to		n-Heptane		
A'* 25 to	1.6897	5	A^v °C			Ethanol		
B'* 65 °C	1579.8	5	(B^v)	to		Water		
Ac 210 to	7.3260	5	(A^v) °C			Water in		
Bc t_c °C	1854.8	5	c_p liq. °K					
Cc	258.	5						
Cryos. A° consts. B°			c_p vap. °K					
t_e °C	178.79	5	c_v vap.					

T_R = 0.75 T_c # C-S-C, S = 7.2   + grams/100 grams solvent

REFERENCES: 1-Dow 2-API 3-Lit. 4-Calc. from det. data 5-Calc. by formula
SOURCE: API
PURIFICATION: API
LITERATURE REFERENCES:

No. 18

NAME	2,3,4-Trimethylthiophene			STRUCTURAL FORMULA

$$H_3CC \text{———} CC_3H$$
$$\overset{\|}{HC} \underset{S}{} \overset{\|}{CCH_3}$$

Mole % Pur.	Ref.	Molecular Formula $C_7H_{10}S$	Molecular Weight 126.216

		Ref.				Ref.					Ref.
F.P. °C			dt/dP				f		to		
F.P. 100%			°C/mm				g		°K		
B.P. °C			25°C	7.2632	5		h				
760 mm	172.7	2	BP	0.054	5						
100	104.5	5	t_e	0.0373	5		f'		to		
30	74.45	5	30 mm	0.7506	5		g'		°K		
10	51.6	5					h'				
1	13.5	5	ΔHm cal/g								
Pressure			ΔHv cal/g				m		to		
mm 25°C	2.1577	5	25°C	89.33	5		n		°K		
t_e	1221.92	5	30 mm	84.50	5		o				
Density			BP	72.61	5						
g/ml 20°C	0.995	2	t_e	70.24	5		m'		to		
d_4^t 25	0.991	2	t_e (d, e)	70.12	5		n'		°K		
30	0.987	2	ΔHv/T_e	19.01	5		o'				
a	1.0101	4	d	75 to	93.52	5	Surface tension				
b	0.0380	4	e	195 °C	0.1211	5	dynes/cm. 20°C	34.76	5
			d'	25 to	91.78	5	y	30	33.65	5
Ref. Index			e'	75 °C	0.0977	5		40	32.57	5
n_D 20°C	1.5208	2	d_c g/ml				Parachor [P]			
25	1.5183	2	v_c ml/g					20°C		
30	1.5164	4	t_c °C	400.	5		30		
"C"	0.6869	4	P_c mm	25806.	5		40		
MR (Obs.)	38.6	2	PV/RT					Sugd.	307.7	5
MR (Calc.)	38.242#	5	25°C	1.0000	5		Exp. L.1.%/wt.		
(nD-d/2)	1.023	2	30 mm	1.0000	5		u.		
Dielectric			BP	0.9560	5		Dispersion		
A 75 to	6.8900	5	t_e	0.9415	5		Flash Point °C		
B 230 °C	1519.1	5	t_c				Fire Point		
C	206.2	5	ΔHc kcal/m				M Spec.		
A* 75 to	1.31375	5	ΔHf				Ultra V.		
B* 205 °C	1423.3	5	ΔFf				X-Ray Dif.		
K			Viscosity				Infrared		
c			centistokes				Solubility in		
t_k to			η °C				Acetone		
t_x °C							Carbon tet.		
A' 25 to	7.2310	5					Benzene		
B' 75 °C	1716.5	5					Ether		
C'	224.	5	B^v to				n-Heptane		
A'* 25 to	1.6607	5	A^v °C				Ethanol		
B'* 75 °C	1616.5	5	(B^v) to				Water		
Ac 230 to	7.3039	5	(A^v) °C				Water in		
Bc t_c °C	1903.0	5	c_p liq. °K						
Cc	258.	5							
Cryos. A°			c_p vap. °K						
consts. B°									
t_e °C	193.25	5	c_v vap.						

$T_R = 0.75 T_c$ # C-S-C, S = 7.2   + grams/100 grams solvent

REFERENCES: 1-Dow 2-API 3-Lit. 4-Calc. from det. data 5-Calc. by formula
SOURCE: API
PURIFICATION: API
LITERATURE REFERENCES:

TABLE IV THIOPHENES   201

No. 19

NAME	2,3,5-Trimethylthiophene	STRUCTURAL FORMULA

Mole % Pur.	Ref.	Molecular Formula $C_7H_{10}S$	Molecular Weight 126.216		

		Ref.			Ref.					Ref.
F.P. °C			dt/dP			f	to			
F.P. 100%			°C/mm			g	°K			
B.P. °C			25°C	5.6107	5	h				
760 mm	164.5	2	BP	0.05235	5					
100	98.2	5	t_e	0.03665	5	f'	to			
30	69.04	4	30 mm	0.7308	4	g'	°K			
10	46.8	5	ΔHm cal/g			h'				
1	9.6	5								
Pressure			ΔHv cal/g			m	to			
mm 25°C	2.8192	5	25°C	88.51	5	n	°K			
t_e	1200.6	5	30 mm	84.11	5	o				
Density			BP	72.31	5					
g/ml 20°C	0.9753	2	t_e	70.06	5	m'	to			
d_4^t 25	0.9708	2	t_e (d,e)	69.95	5	n'	°K			
30	0.9663	4	ΔHv/T_e	19.36	5	o'				
a	0.9933	4	d 70 to	92.64	5	Surface tension				
b	-0.0390	4	e 185 °C	0.1236	5	dynes/cm. 20°C	32.08	5		
Ref. Index			d' 25 to	91.01	5	ɣ 30	30.91	5		
n_D 20°C	1.5112	2	e' 70 °C	0.09994	5	40	29.77	5		
25	1.5088	2	d_c g/ml			Parachor [P]				
30	1.5061	4	v_c ml/g			20°C				
"C"	0.6886	4	t_c °C	382.	5	30				
MR (Obs.)	38.78	2	P_c mm	25450.	5	40				
MR (Calc.)	38.292#	5	PV/RT			Sugd.	307.7	5		
(nD-d/2)	1.0236	2	25°C	1.0000	5	Exp. L. 1.%/wt.				
Dielectric			30 mm	1.0000	5	u.				
A 70 to	6.9251	5	BP	0.9580	5	Dispersion				
B 210 °C	1498.4	5	t_e	0.9446	5	Flash Point °C				
C	206.	5	t_c			Fire Point				
A* 70 to	1.3546	5	ΔHc kcal/m			M. Spec.				
B* 195 °C	1404.2	5	ΔHf			Ultra V.				
K			ΔFf			X-Ray Dif.				
c			Viscosity			Infrared				
t_k to			centistokes			Solubility in +				
t_x °C			η °C			Acetone				
A' 25 to	7.2683	5				Carbon tet.				
B' 70 °C	1693.1	5				Benzene				
C'	223.3	5				Ether				
A'* 25 to	1.7029	5	B^v to			n-Heptane				
B'* 70 °C	1594.5	5	A^v °C			Ethanol				
Ac 210 to	7.3354	5	(B^v) to			Water				
Bc t_c °C	1866.6	5	(A^v) °C			Water in				
Cc	255.3	5	c_p liq. °K							
Cryos. A°										
consts. B°			c_p vap. °K							
t_e °C	183.63	5	c_v vap.							

$T_R = 0.75 T_c$	# C-S-C, S = 7.2	+ grams/100 grams solvent

REFERENCES: 1-Dow 2-API 3-Lit. 4-Calc. from det. data 5-Calc. by formula
SOURCE: API
PURIFICATION: API
LITERATURE REFERENCES:

TABLE V.   ALKYL NAPHTHALENES

TABLE V. ALKYL NAPHTHALENES

No. 1

NAME	Naphthalene		STRUCTURAL FORMULA

Mole % Pur. 99.4	Ref. 1	Molecular Formula $C_{10}H_8$	Molecular Weight 128.164

		Ref.			Ref.			Ref.
F.P. °C	80.21	1	dt/dP			f | to		
F.P. 100%	80.55	1	°C/mm			g | ___ °K		
			25°C	60.010	5	h |		
B.P. °C			BP	0.0584	2			
760 mm	217.955	2	t_e	0.0380	5	f' | to		
100	144.31	2				g' | ___ °K		
30	112.0	4	30 mm	0.8069	4	h' |		
10	87.5	5	ΔHm cal/g	33.67	1			
1	46.6	5	ΔHv cal/g			m | to		
Pressure			25°C	107.93	5	n | ___ °K		
mm 25°C	0.2129	5	30 mm	95.05	5	o |		
t_e	1326.	5	BP	78.66	5			
Density			t_e	74.89	5	m' | to		
g/ml 20°C	1.0253	5	t_e (d, e)	74.60	5	n' | ___ °K		
d_4^t 25	1.0116	5	ΔHv/T_e	18.55	5	o' |		
30	0.9979	5				Surface tension		
a	1.0801	5	d | 110 to	112.37	5	dynes/cm 121°C	29.3	36
b	-0.00274	5	e | 250 °C	0.1546	5	γ 30	35.23	5
Ref. Index			d' | 20 to	111.63	5	40	31.52	5
n_D 20°C			e' | 110 °C	0.1480	5			
25						Parachor [P]		
85	1.5898	2	d_c g/ml	0.314	31	121°C	314.1	4
"C"	0.7872	4	v_c ml/g	3.1847	4	30		
			t_c °C	469.00	32	40		
MR (Obs.)85°	44.34	2	P_c mm	29792.	33	Sugd.	312.9	5
MR (Calc.)	44.185	5	PV/RT			Exp. L.1.%/wt.		
(nD-d/2)85°	1.1022	2	25°C	1.0000	5	u.		
Dielectric	2.54	3	30 mm	1.0000	5	Dispersion 85°C	297.	2
A | 110 to	6.84577	2	BP	0.9400	5	Flash Point °C	87.78	37
B | 280 °C	1606.529	2	t_e	0.9208	5	Fire Point		
C	187.227	2	t_c	0.261	4	M. Spec.		
A* | 110 to	1.27158	5	ΔHc kcal/m	1230.7	34	Ultra V.		
B* | 260 °C	1516.4	5	ΔHf			X-Ray Dif.		
K			ΔFf			Infrared		
c			Viscosity			Solubility in +		
t_k | to			centistokes			Acetone	69.16	1
t_x | °C			η 80 °C	0.969	35	Carbon tet.	26.82	1
A' | 10 to	7.18400	5	121	0.4647	32	Benzene	65.71	1
B' | 110 °C	1815.3	5	205	0.401	35	Ether	57.12	1
C'	206.1	5	360	0.262	35	n-Heptane	19.82	1
A'* 10 to	1.61585	5	B^v | 80 to	1082.71	4	Ethanol	12.10	1
B'* 110 °C	1721.4	5	A^v | 220 °C	4.92089	4	Water	0.0040	1
Ac | 280 to	8.04266	5	(B^v)| to			Water in		
Bc | t_c °C	2930.8	5	(A^v)| °C					
Cc	352.3	5	c_p liq. °K					
Cryos. A° consts. B°	0.01740	1	c_p vap.25 °C	0.3130	4			
t_e °C F	244.24	5	c_v vap.					
T_R = 0.75 T_c						+ grams/100 grams solvent		

REFERENCES: 1-Dow 2-API 3-Lit. 4-Calc. from det. data 5-Calc. by formula

SOURCE: API

PURIFICATION: API

LITERATURE REFERENCES: 3 NBS Circ. 514; 3^1 Z. Physik. Chem. B49, 272 (1941)
E. Schroer; 3^2 Can. J. Res. 19, 73 (1941), Campbell and Campbell; 3^3 Ind. Eng. Chem.
34, 52 (1942), Meisner and Reading; 3^4 J. Chim. Phys. 28, 457 (1931), L. J. P. Keffler;
3^5 C.A. 44, 8721 (1950), Golik and Rarrkovich; 3^6 J. Phys. Chem. 38, 761 (1934), Lee
Ward; 3^7 Lange

No. 2

NAME	1-Methylnaphthalene		STRUCTURAL FORMULA

CH₃ structure:

Mole % Pur.	Ref.	Molecular Formula $C_{11}H_{10}$	Molecular Weight 142.190

		Ref.			Ref.			Ref.
F.P. °C	-30.57	2	dt/dP °C/mm			f	to °K	
F.P. 100%			25°C	183.3	5	g		
B.P. °C			BP	0.0604	2	h		
760 mm	244.642	2	t_e	0.0373	5	f'	to	
100	167.776	2				g'	°K	
30	133.6	4	30 mm	0.8577	4	h'		
10	107.4	5	ΔHm cal/g					
1	63.5	5				m	to °K	
Pressure			ΔHv cal/g			n		
mm 25°C	0.0671	5	25°C	100.96	5	o		
t_e	1400.8	5	30 mm	89.88	5			
			BP	76.45	5	m'	to	
Density			t_e	73.14	5	n'	°K	
g/ml 20°C	1.02015	2	t_e (d, e)	72.83	5	o'		
d_4^t 25	1.01630	2	ΔHv/T_e	18.98	5			
30	1.01245	4				Surface tension		
a	1.03555	4	d 90 to	106.04	5	dynes/cm. 20°C	40.68	5
b	-0.0₃77	4	e 270 °C	0.1210	5	γ 30	39.46	5
			d' 10 to	103.51	5	40	38.28	5
Ref. Index			e' 90 °C	0.1020	5			
n_D 20°C	1.6174	2	d_c g/ml	0.319	5	Parachor [P]		
25	1.6149	2	v_c ml/g	3.13	5	20°C		
30	1.6124	4	t_c °C	496.	5	30		
"C"	0.7852	4	P_c mm	26765.	5	40		
						Sugd.	352.0	5
MR (Obs.)	48.795	2	PV/RT			Exp. L.l.%/wt.		
MR (Calc.)	48.803	5	25°C	1.0000	5	u.		
(nD-d/2)	1.1073	2	30 mm	1.0000	5	Dispersion	295.	2
Dielectric	2.71	3	BP	0.9397	5	Flash Point °C		
A 130 to	7.06899	2	t_e	0.9191	5	Fire Point		
B 305 °C	1852.674	2	t_c	0.25	5	M Spec.		
C	197.716	2	ΔHc kcal/m			Ultra V.		
A* 130 to	1.50733	5	ΔHf			X-Ray Dif.		
B* 290 °C	1749.9	5	ΔFf			Infrared		
K			Viscosity			Solubility in +		
c			centistokes			Acetone		
t_k to			η °C			Carbon tet.		
t_x °C						Benzene		
A' 10 to	7.42128	5				Ether		
B' 130 °C	2093.5	5				n-Heptane		
C'	218.6	5	B^V to			Ethanol		
A'* 10 to	1.86734	5	A^V °C			Water		
B'* 130 °C	1986.9	5	(B^V) to			Water in		
Ac 305 to	7.48224	5	(A^V) °C					
Bc t_c °C	2290.2	5	c_p liq. °K					
Cc	253.8	5						
Cryos. A°			c_p vap. °K					
consts. B°								
t_e °C F	274.59	5	c_v vap.					

$T_R = 0.75 T_c$

REFERENCES: 1-Dow 2-API 3-Lit. 4-Calc. from det. data 5-Calc. by formula

SOURCE:	API
PURIFICATION:	API

LITERATURE REFERENCES: 3 NBS Circ. 514

TABLE V. ALKYL NAPHTHALENES 205

No. 3

NAME	2-Methylnaphthalene	STRUCTURAL FORMULA

Mole % Pur.	Ref.	Molecular Formula $C_{11}H_{10}$	Molecular Weight 142.190

		Ref.			Ref.			Ref.
F.P. °C	34.58	2	dt/dP °C/mm			f | to g | °K		
F.P. 100%			25°C	155.6	5	h |		
B.P. °C			BP	0.0600	2			
760 mm	241.052	2	t_e	0.0373	5	f' | to g' | °K		
100	164.684	2	30 mm	0.8521	4	h' |		
30	130.7	4	ΔHm cal/g	20.11	3[1]			
10	104.7	5				m | to n | °K		
1	61.1	5	ΔHv cal/g			o |		
Pressure			25°C	99.84	5			
mm 25°C	0.0800	5	30 mm	89.20	5	m' | to n' | °K		
t_e	1393.	5	BP	75.98	5	o' |		
Density			t_e	72.73	5			
g/ml 20°C	1.0058≠	4	t_e (d, e)	72.45	5	Surface tension		
d_4^t 25	1.0020≠	4	$\Delta Hv/T_e$	19.02	5	dynes/cm. 20°C	38.44	5
40	0.99045	3				ɤ 30	37.29	5
a	1.0210	4	d | 130 to	104.86	5	40	36.16	5
b	-0.0376	4	e | 270 °C	0.1198	5			
Ref. Index			d' | 20 to	102.36	5	Parachor [P]		
n_D 20°C			e' | 130 °C	0.1006	5	20°C		
25						30		
40	1.6019	2	d_c g/ml			40		
"C"	0.7823	4	v_c ml/g			Sugd.	352.0	5
MR (Obs.)	48.77≠	4	t_c °C	488.7	5			
MR (Calc.)	48.803	5	P_c mm	26274.	5	Exp. L. 1.% / wt.		
(nD-d/2)	1.1067≠	4	PV/RT			u.		
Dielectric	40° 2.57	5	25°C	1.0000	5	Dispersion 40°C	293.	2
A | 130 to	7.06850	2	30 mm	1.0000	5	Flash Point °C		
B | 300 °C	1840.268	2	BP	0.9410	5	Fire Point		
C	198.395	2	t_e	0.9207	5	M. Spec.		
A* | 130 to	1.50750	5	t_c			Ultra V.		
B* | 290 °C	1737.4	5	ΔHc kcal/m	1383.9	3[2]	X-Ray Dif.		
K			ΔHf			Infrared		
c			ΔFf			Solubility in +		
t_k | to			Viscosity			Acetone		
t_x | °C			centistokes			Carbon tet.		
A' | 15 to	7.42076	5	η °C			Benzene		
B' | 130 °C	2079.4	5				Ether		
C'	219.1	5	B^v | to			n-Heptane		
A'* 15 to	1.86810	5	A^v | °C			Ethanol		
B'* 130 °C	1973.0	5	(B^v)| to			Water		
Ac | 300 to	7.48161	5	(A^v)| °C			Water in		
Bc | t_e °C	2273.4	5	c_p liq. °K					
Cc	253.8	5	c_p vap. °K					
Cryos. A°								
consts. B°								
t_e °C F	270.51	5	c_v vap.					

$T_R = 0.75 T_c$ ≠ extrapolated + grams/100 grams solvent

REFERENCES: 1-Dow 2-API 3-Lit. 4-Calc. from det. data 5-Calc. by formula

SOURCE: API

PURIFICATION: API

LITERATURE REFERENCES: 3 J. Res. N.B.S. 24, 395 (1940) Mair and Streiff; 3' JACS 53, 3876 (1931) Huffman, Parks and Barmore; 3[2] JACS 61, 3543 (1939) Richardson and Parks

No. 4

NAME	1-Ethylnaphthalene					STRUCTURAL FORMULA		

C_2H_5

Mole % Pur.	Ref.	Molecular Formula $C_{12}H_{12}$		Molecular Weight 156.216				

		Ref.				Ref.			Ref.
F.P. °C	-13.88	2	dt/dP				f | to		
F.P. 100%			°C/mm				g | °K		
			25°C	487.72	5		h |		
B.P. °C			BP	0.0615	2				
760 mm	258.67	2	t_e	0.0375	5		f' | to		
100	180.68	2	30 mm	0.8627	4		g' | °K		
30	146.2	4	ΔHm cal/g				h' |		
10	120.0	5							
1	76.	5	ΔHv cal/g				m | to		
Pressure			25°C	103.15	5		n | °K		
mm 25°C	0.0225	5	30 mm	86.47	5		o |		
t_e	1435.2	5	BP	71.78	5				
Density			t_e	68.17	5		m' | to		
g/ml 20°C	1.00816	2	t_e (d, e)	67.61	5		n' | °K		
d_4^t 25	1.00446	2	ΔHv/T_e	18.89	5		o' |		
30	1.00076	4	d | 145 to	105.57	5		Surface tension		
a	1.02296	4	e | 290 °C	0.1306	5		dynes/cm. 20°C	40.54	5
b	-0.00074	4	d' | 15 to	106.59	5		γ 30	39.37	5
Ref. Index			e' | 145 °C	0.1376	5		40	38.21	5
n_D 20°C	1.6062	2	d_c g/ml	0.325	5		Parachor [P]		
25	1.6040	2	v_c ml/g	3.077	5		20°C		
30	1.6005	4	t_c °C	502.4	5		30		
"C"	0.7800	4	P_c mm	23234.	5		40		
MR (Obs.)	53.452	2	PV/RT				Sugd.	391.0	5
MR (Calc.)	53.421	5	25°C	1.0000	5		Exp. L.1.%/wt.		
(nD-d/2)	1.1021	2	30 mm	1.0000	5		u.		
Dielectric	2.58	5	BP	0.9370	5		Dispersion	285.	2
A | 145 to	6.9599	2	t_e	0.9150	5		Flash Point °C		
B | 310 °C	1791.4	2	t_c	0.248	5		Fire Point		
C	180.5	2	ΔHc kcal/m				M Spec.		
A* | 145 to	1.44271	5	ΔHf				Ultra V.		
B* | 300 °C	1695.6	5	ΔFf				X-Ray Dif.		
K			Viscosity				Infrared		
c			centistokes				Solubility in +		
t_k | to			η °C				Acetone		
t_x | °C							Carbon tet.		
A' | 0 to	7.30532	5					Benzene		
B' | 145 °C	2024.2	5					Ether		
C'	201.1	5	B^v | to				n-Heptane		
A'* 15 to	1.80518	5	A^v | °C				Ethanol		
B'* 145 °C	1928.3	5	(B^v) | to				Water		
Ac | 310 to	7.35228	5	(A^v) | °C				Water in		
Bc | t_c °C	2195.7	5							
Cc	232.9	5	c_p liq. °K						
Cryos. A°			c_p vap. °K						
consts. B°									
t_e °C F	290.54	5	c_v vap.						

$T_R = 0.75\, T_c$

+ grams/100 grams solvent

REFERENCES: 1-Dow 2-API 3-Lit. 4-Calc. from det. data 5-Calc. by formula

SOURCE: API

PURIFICATION: API

LITERATURE REFERENCES:

TABLE V. ALKYL NAPHTHALENES

No. 5

NAME	2-Ethylnaphthalene		STRUCTURAL FORMULA

Mole % Pur.		Ref.	Molecular Formula $C_{12}H_{12}$		Molecular Weight 156.216	

		Ref.			Ref.					Ref.
F.P. °C	-7.4	2	dt/dP				f	to		
F.P. 100%			°C/mm				g	°K		
			25°C	406.37	5		h			
B.P. °C			BP	0.0611	4					
760 mm	257.9	2	t_e	0.0370	5		f'	to		
100	180.1	2	30 mm	0.8691	4		g'	°K		
30	145.5	4	ΔHm cal/g				h'			
10	119.0	5								
1	74.	5	ΔHv cal/g				m	to		
			25°C	98.66	5		n	°K		
Pressure			30 mm	85.53	5		o			
mm 25°C	0.0282	5	BP	72.42	5					
t_e	1439.5	5	t_e	69.01	5		m'	to		
Density			t_e (d, e)	68.71	5		n'	°K		
g/ml 20°C	0.9922	2	ΔHv/T_e	19.15	5		o'			
d_4^t 25	0.9885	2					Surface tension			
30	0.9848	4	d 145 to.	102.50	5		dynes/cm. 20°C		38.04	5
a	1.0070	4	e 280 °C	0.1166	5		ɣ 30		36.91	5
b	-0.0₃74	4	d' 15 to	101.38	5		40		35.82	5
Ref. Index			e' 145 °C	0.1089	5		Parachor [P]			
n_D 20°C	1.5999	2	d_c g/ml				20°C			
25	1.5977	2	v_c ml/g				30			
30	1.5951	4	t_c °C	498.6	5		40			
"C"	0.7860	4	P_c mm	23788.	5		Sugd.		391.0	5
MR (Obs.)	53.85	2	PV/RT				Exp. L.1.%/wt.			
MR (Calc.)	53.421	5	25°C	1.0000	5		u.			
(nD-d/2)	1.1038	2	30 mm	1.0000	5		Dispersion		285.	2
Dielectric	2.260	5	BP	0.9411	5		Flash Point °C			
A 145 to	7.0819	2	t_e	0.9192	5		Fire Point			
B 305 °C	1886.	2	t_c							
C	191.0	2	ΔHc kcal/m				M. Spec.			
A* 145 to	1.55230	5	ΔHf				Ultra V.			
B* 300 °C	1782.9	5	ΔFf				X-Ray Dif.			
K			Viscosity				Infrared			
c			centistokes				Solubility in +			
t_k to			η °C				Acetone			
t_x °C							Carbon tet.			
A' 15 to	7.4350	5					Benzene			
B' 145 °C	2131.1	5					Ether			
C'	212.2	5	B_v to				n-Heptane			
A'* 15 to	1.92177	5	A_v °C				Ethanol			
B'* 145 °C	2027.3	5	(B^v) to				Water			
Ac 305 to	7.4859	5	(A^v) °C				Water in			
Bc t_c °C	2308.7	5	c_p liq. °K							
Cc	243.8	5								
Cryos. A°			c_p vap. °K							
consts. B°										
t_e °C F	289.67	5	c_v vap.							

$T_R = 0.75 T_c$ + grams/100 grams solvent

REFERENCES: 1-Dow 2-API 3-Lit.   4-Calc. from det. data 5-Calc. by formula

SOURCE:	API
PURIFICATION:	API
LITERATURE REFERENCES:	

No. 6

NAME	1,2-Dimethylnaphthalene				STRUCTURAL FORMULA

CH_3 CH_3

Mole % Pur.	Ref.	Molecular Formula $C_{12}H_{12}$	Molecular Weight 156.216

		Ref.				Ref.				Ref.
F.P. °C	-1.0	2	dt/dP				f	to		
F.P. 100%			°C/mm				g	°K		
B.P. °C			25°C	831.7	5		h			
760 mm	266.	2	BP	0.0611	5					
100	188.2	5	t_e	0.0364	5		f'	to		
30	153.7	5	30 mm	0.8666	5		g'	°K		
10	127.	5	ΔHm cal/g				h'			
1	83.	5								
			ΔHv cal/g				m	to		
Pressure			25°C	107.16	5		n	°K		
mm 25°C	0.0127	5	30 mm	89.16	5		o			
t_e	1469.	5	BP	74.89	5					
Density			t_e	71.14	5		m'	to		
g/ml 20°C	1.013	2	t_e (d, e)	70.71	5		n'	°K		
d_4^t 25	1.009	2	ΔHv/T_e	19.43	5		o'			
30	1.005	4	d 150 to	108.70	5		Surface tension			
a	1.029	4	e 290 °C	0.1271	5		dynes/cm. 20°C	41.33	5
b	-0.0₃8	4	d' 20 to	110.65	5		30	40.04	5
Ref. Index			e' 150 °C	0.1398	5		40	38.78	5
n_D 20°C	1.6164	2	d_c g/ml	0.330	5		Parachor [P]			
25	1.6142	2	v_c ml/g	3.03	5		20°C			
30	1.6111	2	t_c °C	511.	5		30			
"C"	0.7896	4	P_c mm	24536.	5		40			
MR (Obs.)	53.9	2	PV/RT				Sugd.	391.0	5
MR (Calc.)	53.421	5	25°C	1.0000	5		Exp. L.l.%/wt.			
(nD-d/2)	1.110	2	30 mm	1.0000	5		u.			
Dielectric	2.613	5	BP	0.9448	5		Dispersion	290.	2
A 150 to	7.0512	5	t_e	0.9232	5		Flash Point °C			
B 315 °C	1860.	5	t_c	0.24	5		Fire Point			
C	180.	5	ΔHc kcal/m				M Spec.			
A* 150 to	1.5148	5	ΔHf				Ultra V.			
B* 300 °C	1758.	5	ΔFf				X-Ray Dif.			
K			Viscosity				Infrared			
c			centistokes				Solubility in +			
t_k to			η °C				Acetone			
t_x °C							Carbon tet.			
A' 20 to	7.4024	5					Benzene			
B' 150 °C	2102.	5	B^v to				Ether			
C'	201.	5	A^v °C				n-Heptane			
A'* 20 to	1.8972	5	(B^v) to				Ethanol			
B'* 150 °C	2005.	5	(A^v) °C				Water			
Ac 315 to	7.4435	5	c_p liq. °K				Water in			
Bc t_c °C	2269.	5								
Cc	232.	5	c_p vap. °K							
Cryos. A° consts. B°			c_v vap.							
t_e °C F	298.88	5								

T_R = 0.75 T_c + grams/100 grams solvent

REFERENCES: 1-Dow   2-API   3-Lit.   4-Calc. from det. data   5-Calc. by formula

SOURCE:	API
PURIFICATION:	API

LITERATURE REFERENCES:

TABLE V. ALKYL NAPHTHALENES

No. 7

NAME	1, 3-Dimethylnaphthalene	STRUCTURAL FORMULA

STRUCTURAL FORMULA: (naphthalene ring with CH_3 at 1 and 3 positions)

Mole % Pur.	Ref.	Molecular Formula $C_{12}H_{12}$	Molecular Weight 156.216

		Ref.			Ref.					Ref.
F.P. °C	-4.0	2	dt/dP			f	|	to		
F.P. 100%			°C/mm			g	|	°K		
B.P. °C			25°C	726.7	5	h	|			
760 mm	263.	2	BP	0.0608	5					
100	185.7	5	t_e	0.0364	5	f'	|	to		
30	151.4	5	30 mm	0.8612	5	g'	|	°K		
10	125.	5	ΔHm cal/g			h'	|			
1	81.	5	ΔHv cal/g			m	|	to		
Pressure			25°C	106.46	5	n	|	°K		
mm 25°C	0.0146	5	30 mm	88.74	5	o	|			
t_e	1463.	5	BP	74.50	5					
Density			t_e	70.88	5	m'	|	to		
g/ml 20°C	1.0063	2	t_e (d, e)	70.36	5	n'	|	°K		
d_4^t 25	1.0026	2	$\Delta Hv/T_e$	19.47	5	o'	|			
30	0.9989	4	d | 150 to	108.05	5	Surface tension				
a	1.0211	4	e | 295 °C	0.1276	5	dynes/cm. 20°C		40.25	5	
b	-0.0374	4	d' | 15 to	109.97	5	γ		30	39.07	5
Ref. Index			e' | 150 °C	0.1402	5			40	37.93	5
n_D 20°C	1.6090	2	d_c g/ml	0.330	5	Parachor [P]				
25	1.6068	2	v_c ml/g	3.03	5	20°C				
30	1.6042	4	t_c °C	508.	5	30				
"C"	0.7860	4	P_c mm	24833.	5	40				
MR (Obs.)	53.75	2	PV/RT					Sugd.	391.0	5
MR (Calc.)	53.421	5	25°C	1.0000	5	Exp. L.l.%/wt.				
(nD-d/2)	1.1058	2	30 mm	1.0000	5	u.				
Dielectric	2.589	4	BP	0.9451	5	Dispersion		290.	2	
A | 150 to	7.0469	5	t_e	0.9247	5	Flash Point °C				
B | 313 °C	1845.6	5	t_c	0.24	5	Fire Point				
C	180.	5	ΔHc kcal/m			M. Spec.				
A* | 150 to	1.51108	5	ΔHf			Ultra V.				
B* | 300 °C	1743.97	5	ΔFf			X-Ray Dif.				
K			Viscosity			Infrared				
c			centistokes			Solubility in +				
t_k | to			η °C			Acetone		∞		
t_x | °C						Carbon tet.		∞		
A' | 20 to	7.3978	5				Benzene		∞		
B' | 150 °C	2085.	5				Ether		∞		
C'	200.9	5	B^v | to			n-Heptane		∞		
A'* 20 to	1.8944	5	A^v | °C			Ethanol		∞		
B'* 150 °C	1989.	5	(B^v)| to			Water				
Ac | 313 to	7.4389	5	(A^v)| °C			Water in				
Bc | t_c °C	2252.	5	c_p liq. °K							
Cc	232.	5	c_p vap. °K							
Cryos. A° consts. B°			c_v vap.							
t_e °C F	295.47	5								

T_R = 0.75 T_c + grams/100 grams solvent

REFERENCES: 1-Dow   2-API   3-Lit.   4-Calc. from det. data   5-Calc. by formula

SOURCE: API

PURIFICATION: API

LITERATURE REFERENCES:

No. 8

| NAME | 1,4-Dimethylnaphthalene | | | | | STRUCTURAL FORMULA |

		Ref.	Molecular Formula $C_{12}H_{12}$		Molecular Weight 156.216	

		Ref.				Ref.					Ref.
F.P. °C	7.66	2	dt/dP				f	to			
F.P. 100%			°C/mm				g	°K			
B.P. °C			25°C	907.1		5	ʌ¹				
760 mm	268.	2	BP	0.0614		5					
100	189.9	5	t_e	0.0365		5	f'	to			
30	155.2	5	30 mm	0.8703		5	g'	°K			
10	129.	5	ΔHm cal/g				h'				
1	84.	5									
Pressure			ΔHv cal/g				m	to			
mm 25°C	0.0116	5	25°C	107.58		5	n	°K			
t_e	1473.	5	30 mm	89.42		5	o				
Density			BP	74.94		5					
g/ml 20°C	1.0166	2	t_e	71.30		5	m'	to			
d_4^t 25	1.0129	2	t_e (d,e)	70.68		5	n'	°K			
30	1.0092	4	ΔHv/T_e	19.39		5	o'				
a	1.0314	4	d 155 to	109.34		5	Surface tension				
b	-0.0₃74	4	e 300 °C	0.1284		5	dynes/cm. 20°C	41.92	5
Ref. Index			d' 20 to	111.07		5	ɣ 30	40.71	5
n_D 20°C	1.6127	2	e' 155 °C	0.1395		5	40	39.53	5
25	1.6105	2	d_c g/ml	0.333		5	Parachor [P]				
30	1.6079	4	v_c ml/g	3.003		5	20°C				
"C"	0.7824	4	t_c °C	517.		5	30				
MR (Obs.)	53.47	2	P_c mm	25219.		5	40				
MR (Calc.)	53.421	5	PV/RT				Sugd.	391.0	5
(nD-d/2)	1.1044	2	25°C	1.0000		5	Exp. L.1.%/wt.				
Dielectric	2.601	5	30 mm	1.0000		5	u.				
A 155 to	7.0527	5	BP	0.9422		5	Dispersion	290.	2
B 320 °C	1869.0	5	t_e	0.9221		5	Flash Point °C				
C	180.	5	t_c	0.24		5	Fire Point				
A* 155 to	1.5160	5	ΔHc kcal/m				M Spec.				
B* 310 °C	1767.	5	ΔHf				Ultra V.				
K			ΔFf				X-Ray Dif.				
c							Infrared				
t_k to			Viscosity				Solubility in +				
t_x °C			centistokes				Acetone	∞	
A' 20 to	7.4040	5	η °C				Carbon tet.	∞	
B' 155 °C	2112.	5					Benzene	∞	
C'	201.	5					Ether	∞	
A'* 20 to	1.8982	5	B^v to				n-Heptane	∞	
B'* 155 °C	2015.	5	A^v °C				Ethanol	∞	
Ac 320 to	7.4460	5	(B^v) to				Water		
Bc t_c °C	2283.	5	(A^v) °C				Water in		
Cc	233.	5	c_p liq. °K								
Cryos. A°			c_p vap. °K								
consts. B°											
t_e °C F	301.16	5	c_v vap.								

T_R = 0.75 T_c					+ grams/100 grams solvent

REFERENCES: 1-Dow 2-API 3-Lit. 4-Calc. from det. data 5-Calc. by formula

SOURCE: API

PURIFICATION: API

LITERATURE REFERENCES:

TABLE V. ALKYL NAPHTHALENES

No. 9

NAME	1,5-Dimethylnaphthalene	STRUCTURAL FORMULA

Structural formula: naphthalene with CH$_3$ (top) and CH$_3$ (bottom)

Mole % Pur.	Ref.	Molecular Formula $C_{12}H_{12}$	Molecular Weight 156.216

Property	Value	Ref.	Property	Value	Ref.	Property	Value	Ref.
F.P. °C	82.0	2	dt/dP			f | to		
F.P. 100%			°C/mm			g | °K		
			25°C	794.3	5	h		
B.P. °C			BP	0.06076	5			
760 mm	265.	2	t_e	0.0364	5	f' | to		
100	187.4	5	30 mm	0.8649	5	g' | °K		
30	152.9	5	ΔHm cal/g			h'		
10	126.5	5	ΔHv cal/g			m | to		
1	82.	5	25°C	106.91	5	n | °K		
Pressure			30 mm	89.02	5	o		
mm 25°C	146.2	5	BP	74.71	5			
t_e	1467.	5	t_e	71.02	5	m' | to		
Density			t_e (d,e)	70.53	5	n' | °K		
g/ml 20°C	1.003 ?	5	ΔHv/T_e	19.43	5	o'		
d_4^t 25	0.999 ?	5	d | 150 to	108.5	5	Surface tension		
30	0.995	5	e | 290 °C	0.1276	5	dynes/cm. 20°C	39.72	5
a	1.0190	5	d' | 15 to	110.4	5	γ 30	38.47	5
b	-0.0380	5	e' | 150 °C	0.1399	5	40	37.25	5
Ref. Index			d_c g/ml	0.330	5	Parachor [P]		
n_D 20°C			v_c ml/g	3.03	5	20°C		
25			t_c °C	508.1	5	30		
30			P_c mm	24142.	5	40		
"C"			PV/RT			Sugd.	391.0	5
MR (Obs.)			25°C	1.0000	5	Exp. L.1.%/wt.		
MR (Calc.)	53.421	5	30 mm	1.0000	5	u.		
(nD-d/2)			BP	0.9444	5	Dispersion		
Dielectric			t_e	0.9235	5	Flash Point °C		
A | 150 to	7.0493	5	t_c			Fire Point		
B | 313 °C	1855.	5	ΔHc kcal/m			M. Spec.		
C	180.	5	ΔHf			Ultra V.		
A* | 150 to	1.5133	5	ΔFf			X-Ray Dif.		
B* | 300 °C	1753.	5	Viscosity			Infrared		
K			centistokes			Solubility in +		
c			η °C			Acetone		
t_k | to						Carbon tet.		
t_x | °C						Benzene		
A' | 20 to	7.4003	5	B^v | to			Ether		
B' | 150 °C	2096.1	5	A^v | °C			n-Heptane		
C'	200.97	5	(B^v) | to			Ethanol		
A'* | 20 to	1.8958	5	(A^v) | °C			Water		
B'* | 150 °C	1999.2	5	c_p liq. °K			Water in		
Ac | 313 to	7.4411	5						
Bc | t_c °C	2261.2	5	c_p vap. °K					
Cc	231.3	5						
Cryos. A°			c_v vap.					
consts. B°								
t_e °C F	297.74	5						

T_R = 0.75 T_c

+ grams/100 grams solvent

REFERENCES: 1-Dow 2-API 3-Lit. 4-Calc. from det. data 5-Calc. by formula

SOURCE:	API
PURIFICATION:	API

LITERATURE REFERENCES:

No. 10

NAME	1,6-Dimethylnaphthalene	STRUCTURAL FORMULA

Mole % Pur.	Ref.	Molecular Formula $C_{12}H_{12}$	Molecular Weight 156.216		

		Ref.				Ref.				Ref.
F.P. °C	-14.	2	dt/dP			f		to		
F.P. 100%			°C/mm			g		°K		
B.P. °C			25°C	728.2	5	h				
760 mm	263.	2	BP	0.0607	5					
100	185.7	5	t_e	0.0363	5	f'		to		
30	151.4	5	30 mm	0.8611	5	g'		°K		
10	125.	5	ΔH̄m cal/g			h'				
1	81.	5								
Pressure			ΔHv cal/g			m		to		
mm 25°C	0.0146	5	25°C	106.49	5	n		°K		
t_e	1463.	5	30 mm	88.76	5	o				
			BP	74.62	5					
Density			t_e	70.89	5	m'		to		
g/ml 20°C	1.003	2	t_e (d, e)	70.51	5	n'		°K		
d_4^t 25	0.999	2	ΔHv/T_e	19.47	5	o'				
30	0.995	4				Surface tension				
a	1.019	4	d | 150 to	107.93	5	dynes/cm. 20°C	39.72	5		
b	-0.0₃8	4	e | 290 °C	0.1267	5	ɤ 30	38.47	5		
Ref. Index			d' | 20 to	109.99	5	40	37.25	5		
n_D 20°C	1.6073	2	e' | 150 °C	0.1403	5					
25	1.6051	2	d_c g/ml	0.330	5	Parachor [P]				
30	1.6021	4	v_c ml/g	3.025	5	20°C				
"C"	0.7865	4	t_c °C	505.	5	30				
MR (Obs.)	53.8	2	P_c mm	24170.	5	40				
MR (Calc.)	53.421	5	PV/RT			Sugd.	391.0	2		
(nD-d/2)	1.1058	2	25°C	1.0000	5	Exp. L.1.%/wt.				
Dielectric	2.583	5	30 mm	1.0000	5	u.				
A | 150 to	7.0478	5	BP	0.9465	5	Dispersion	290.	2		
B | 310 °C	1846.	5	t_e	0.9249	5	Flash Point °C				
C	180.	5	t_c	0.24	5	Fire Point				
A* | 150 to	1.5118	5	ΔHc kcal/m			M Spec.				
B* | 300 °C	1744.	5	ΔHf			Ultra V.				
K			ΔFf			X-Ray Dif.				
c			Viscosity			Infrared				
t_k | to			centistokes			Solubility in +				
t_x | °C			η °C			Acetone	∞			
A' | 20 to	7.3988	5				Carbon tet.	∞			
B' | 150 °C	2086.	5				Benzene	∞			
C'	201.	5	B^v | to			Ether	∞			
A'* 20 to	1.8953	5	A^v | °C			n-Heptane	∞			
B'* 150 °C	1989.	5	(B^v) | to			Ethanol	∞			
Ac | 310 to	7.4392	5	(A^v) | °C			Water				
Bc | t_c °C	2250.	5	c_p liq. °K			Water in				
Cc	231.	5								
Cryos. A°			c_p vap. °K							
consts. B°										
t_e °C F	295.47	5	c_v vap.							

T_R = 0.75 T_C	+ grams/100 grams solvent

REFERENCES: 1-Dow 2-API 3-Lit. 4-Calc. from det. data 5-Calc. by formula

SOURCE: API

PURIFICATION: API

LITERATURE REFERENCES:

TABLE V. ALKYL NAPHTHALENES   213

No. 11

NAME	1,7-Dimethylnaphthalene		STRUCTURAL FORMULA

Mole % Pur.	Ref.	Molecular Formula $C_{12}H_{12}$	Molecular Weight 156.216

		Ref.			Ref.				Ref.
F.P. °C	-13.⧧	2	dt/dP			f		to	
F.P. 100%			°C/mm			g		°K	
			25°C	728.2	5	h			
B.P. °C			BP	0.0608	5				
760 mm	263.	2	t_e	0.0363	5	f'		to	
100	185.7	5	30 mm	0.8611	5	g'		°K	
30	151.4	5	ΔHm cal/g			h'			
10	125.	5							
1	81.	5	ΔHv cal/g			m		to	
Pressure			25°C	106.49	5	n		°K	
mm 25°C	0.0146	5	30 mm	88.76	5	o			
t_e	1463.	5	BP	74.62	5				
Density			t_e	70.89	5	m'		to	
g/ml 20°C	1.003	2	t_e (d, e)	70.51	5	n'		°K	
d_4^t 25	0.999	2	ΔHv/T_e	19.47	5	o'			
30	0.995	4							
a	1.019	4	d ⌐150 to	107.93	5	Surface tension			
b	-0.0₃8	4	e │290 °C	0.1267	5	dynes/cm. 20°C	39.72		5
Ref. Index			d' ⌐20 to	109.99	5	ծ 30	38.47		5
n_D 20°C	1.607	2	e' │150 °C	0.1403	5	40	37.25		5
25	1.605	2	d_c g/ml	0.330	5	Parachor [P]			
30	1.602	4	v_c ml/g	3.025	5	20°C			
"C"	0.7865	4	t_c °C	505.	5	30			
MR (Obs.)	53.8	2	P_c mm	24170.	5	40			
MR (Calc.)	53.421	5	PV/RT			Sugd.	391.0		5
(nD-d/2)	1.105	2	25°C	1.0000	5	Exp. L.1.%/wt.			
Dielectric	2.58	5	30 mm	1.0000	5	u.			
A⌐150 to	7.0478	5	BP	0.9465	5	Dispersion	290.		2
B │310 °C	1846.	5	t_e	0.9249	5	Flash Point °C			
C	180.	5	t_c	0.24	5	Fire Point			
A*⌐150 to	1.5118	5	ΔHc kcal/m			M. Spec.			
B*│300 °C	1744.	5	ΔHf			Ultra V.			
K			ΔFf			X-Ray Dif.			
c			Viscosity			Infrared			
t_k ⌐ to			centistokes			Solubility in +			
t_x │ °C			η °C			Acetone	∞		
A'⌐20 to	7.3988	5				Carbon tet.	∞		
B'│150 °C	2086.	5				Benzene	∞		
C'	201.	5	B^v ⌐ to			Ether	∞		
A'*⌐20 to	1.8953	5	A^v │ °C			n-Heptane	∞		
B'*│150 °C	1989.	5	(B^v)│ to			Ethanol	∞		
Ac⌐310 to	7.4392	5	(A^v)│ °C			Water			
Bc┌t_c °C┐	2250.	5	c_p liq. °K			Water in			
Cc└ ─ ┘	231.	5							
Cryos. A°			c_p vap. °K						
consts. B°									
t_e °C F	295.47	5	c_v vap.						

$T_R = 0.75 T_c$ + grams/100 grams solvent

REFERENCES: 1-Dow   2-API   3-Lit.   4-Calc. from det. data   5-Calc. by formula

SOURCE:	API
PURIFICATION:	API

LITERATURE REFERENCES:

⧧ for metastable crystalline form, freezing point is -28. °C

No. 12

NAME	1,8-Dimethylnaphthalene	STRUCTURAL FORMULA H_3C CH_3

Mole % Pur.	Ref.	Molecular Formula $C_{12}H_{12}$	Molecular Weight 156.216

		Ref.				Ref.					Ref.
F.P. °C	65.	2	dt/dP				f	| to			
F.P. 100%			°C/mm				g	| °K			
B.P. °C			25°C	994.6	5		h				
760 mm	270.	2	BP	0.0616	5						
100	191.6	5	t_e	0.0366	5		f'	| to			
30	156.8	5	30 mm	0.8738	5		g'	| °K			
10	130.1	5	ΔHm cal/g				h'				
1	85.4	5	ΔHv cal/g				m	| to			
Pressure			25°C	108.06	5		n	| °K			
mm 25°C	0.0105	5	30 mm	89.71	5		o	|			
t_e	1478.	5	BP	75.34	5		m'	| to			
Density			t_e	71.47	5		n'	| °K			
g/ml 20°C	1.003 ?	5	t_e (d,e)	71.10	5		o'	|			
d_4^t 25	0.999 ?	5	ΔHv/T_e	19.36	5		Surface tension				
30	0.995 ?	5	d | 160 to	109.61	5		dynes/cm. 20°C	39.72	5
a	1.0190 ?	5	e | 300 °C	0.1269	5		γ 30	38.47	5
b	-0.0380 ?	5	d' | 15 to	111.55	5		40	37.25	5
Ref. Index			e' | 160 °C	0.1393	5		Parachor [P]		
n_D 20°C			d_c g/ml	0.30	5		20°C		
25			v_c ml/g	3.333	5		30		
30			t_c °C	515.	5		40		
"C"			P_c mm	24145.	5		Sugd.	391.0	5
MR (Obs.)			PV/RT				Exp. L.1.%/wt.		
MR (Calc.)	53.421	5	25°C	1.0000	5		u.		
(nD-d/2)			30 mm	1.0000	5		Dispersion		
Dielectric			BP	0.9439	5		Flash Point °C		
A |150 to	7.0564	5	t_e	0.9211	5		Fire Point		
B |320 °C	1879.	5	t_c	0.245	5		M Spec.		
C	180.	5	ΔHc kcal/m				Ultra V.		
A* |150 to	1.51925	5	ΔHf				X-Ray Dif.		
B* |310 °C	1777.1	5	ΔFf				Infrared		
K			Viscosity				Solubility in +		
c			centistokes				Acetone		
t_k | to			η °C				Carbon tet.		
t_x | °C							Benzene		
A' | 25 to	7.40789	5					Ether		
B' |150 °C	2123.2	5					n-Heptane		
C'	201.2	5	B^v | to				Ethanol		
A'* 25 to	1.90067	5	A^v | °C				Water		
B'*150 °C	2025.6	5	(B^v) | to				Water in		
Ac |320 to	7.45003	5	(A^v) | °C						
Bc |t_c °C	2291.6	5	c_p liq. °K						
Cc	232.0	5							
Cryos. A°			c_p vap. °K						
consts. B°									
t_e °C F	303.43	5	c_v vap.						

T_R = 0.75 T_c + grams/100 grams solvent

REFERENCES: 1-Dow 2-API 3-Lit.   4-Calc. from det. data   5-Calc. by formula
SOURCE: API
PURIFICATION: API
LITERATURE REFERENCES:

TABLE V. ALKYL NAPHTHALENES   215

No. 13

NAME	2,3-Dimethylnaphthalene	STRUCTURAL FORMULA

Mole % Pur.	Ref.	Molecular Formula	$C_{12}H_{12}$	Molecular Weight 156.216

		Ref.				Ref.					Ref.
F.P. °C	105.0	2	dt/dP				f		to		
F.P. 100%			°C/mm				g		°K		
			25°C	907.1	5		h				
B.P. °C			BP	0.0614	5						
760 mm	268.	2	t_e	0.0365	5		f'		to		
100	189.9	5	30 mm	0.8703	5		g'		°K		
30	155.2	5	ΔHm cal/g				h'				
10	128.7	5									
1	84.1	5	ΔHv cal/g				m		to		
			25°C	107.58	5		n		°K		
Pressure			30 mm	89.42	5		o				
mm 25°C	0.0116	5	BP	74.92	5						
t_e	1473.	5	t_e	71.28	5		m'		to		
			t_e (d, e)	70.66	5		n'		°K		
Density			$\Delta Hv/T_e$	19.39	5		o'				
g/ml 20°C	1.003	5									
d_4^t 25	0.999	5	d 155 to	109.36	5		Surface tension				
30	0.995	5	e 300 °C	0.1285	5		dynes/cm. 20°C	39.72		5
a	1.019	5	d' 15 to	111.07	5		ɤ 30	38.47		5
b	-0.0₃8	5	e' 155 °C	0.1395	5		40	37.25		5
Ref. Index			d_c g/ml	0.304	5		Parachor [P]			
n_D 20°C			v_c ml/g	3.29	5		20°C			
25			t_c °C	512.	5		30			
30			P_c mm	24129.	5		40			
"C"			PV/RT				Sugd.	391.0		5
MR (Obs.)			25°C	1.0000	5		Exp. L.1.%/wt.			
MR (Calc.)	53.421	5	30 mm	1.0000	5		u.			
(nD-d/2)			BP	0.9422	5		Dispersion			
Dielectric			t_e	0.9221	5		Flash Point °C			
A 155 to	7.0527	5	t_c	0.253	5		Fire Point			
B 315 °C	1869.	5	ΔHc kcal/m				M. Spec.			
C	180.		ΔHf				Ultra V.			
A* 155 to	1.51601	5	ΔFf				X-Ray Dif.			
B* 310 °C	1767.2	5					Infrared			
K			Viscosity				Solubility in +			
c			centistokes				Acetone			
t_k to			η °C				Carbon tet.			
t_x °C							Benzene			
A' 20 to	7.40396	5					Ether			
B' 155 °C	2111.9	5					n-Heptane			
C'	201.1	5	B^v to				Ethanol			
			A^v °C				Water			
A'* 20 to	1.89816	5	(B^v) to				Water in			
B'* 155 °C	2014.7	5	(A^v) °C							
Ac 315 to	7.44557	5	c_p liq. °K							
Bc t_c °C	2279.	5								
Cc	231.7	5	c_p vap. °K							
Cryos. A°										
consts. B°			c_v vap.							
t_e °C F	301.16	5								
$T_R = 0.75\,T_c$							+ grams/100 grams solvent			

REFERENCES: 1-Dow   2-API   3-Lit.   4-Calc. from det. data   5-Calc. by formula

SOURCE: API

PURIFICATION: API

LITERATURE REFERENCES:

No. 14

NAME	2,6-Dimethylnaphthalene			STRUCTURAL FORMULA

H_3C ... CH_3

Mole % Pur.		Ref.	Molecular Formula $C_{12}H_{12}$		Molecular Weight 156.216	

		Ref.				Ref.				Ref.
F.P. °C	112.0	2	dt/dP				f		to	
F.P. 100%			°C/mm				g		°K	
B.P. °C			25°C		0.0695	5	h			
760 mm	262.	2	BP		0.0606	5				
100	184.84	5	t_e		0.0363	5	f'		to	
30	150.6	5	30 mm		0.8594	5	g'		°K	
10	124.4	5	ΔHm cal/g				h'			
1	80.4	5	ΔHv cal/g							
Pressure			25°C		106.25	5	m		to	
mm 25°C	0.1531	5	30 mm		88.61	5	n		°K	
t_e	1461.	5	BP		74.51	5	o			
Density			t_e		70.80	5	m'		to	
g/ml 20°C	1.003	5	t_e (d,e)		70.42	5	n'		°K	
d_4^t 25	0.999	5	ΔHv/T_e		19.49	5	o'			
30	0.995	5	d ǀ 150 to		107.67	5	Surface tension			
a	1.019	5	e ǀ 300 °C		0.1266	5	dynes/cm. 20°C		39.72	5
b	-0.0₃8	5	d' ǀ 20 to		109.80	5	ɣ	30	38.47	5
Ref. Index			e' ǀ 150 °C		0.1404	5		40	37.25	5
n_D 20°C			d_c g/ml		0.308	5	Parachor [P]			
25			v_c ml/g		3.25	5	20°C			
30			t_c °C		504.	5	30			
"C"			P_c mm		24165.	5	40			
MR (Obs.)			PV/RT				Sugd.		391.0	5
MR (Calc.)	53.421	5	25°C		1.0000	5	Exp. L.1.%/wt.			
(nD-d/2)			30 mm		1.0000	5	u.			
Dielectric			BP		0.9469	5	Dispersion			
A ǀ 150 to	7.0460	5	t_e		0.9255	5	Flash Point °C			
B ǀ 310 °C	1841.	5	t_c		0.253	5	Fire Point			
C	180.	5	ΔHc kcal/m				M Spec.			
A* ǀ 150 to	1.5101	5	ΔHf				Ultra V.			
B* ǀ 310 °C	1739.3	5	ΔFf				X-Ray Dif.			
K			Viscosity				Infrared			
c			centistokes				Solubility in +			
t_k ǀ to			η °C				Acetone			
t_x ǀ °C							Carbon tet.			
A' ǀ 20 to	7.3968	5					Benzene			
B' ǀ 150 °C	2080.3	5					Ether			
C'	200.8	5	B^v ǀ to				n-Heptane			
A'* 20 to	1.8940	5	A^v ǀ °C				Ethanol			
B'* 150 °C	1983.8	5	(B^v) ǀ to				Water			
Ac ǀ 310 to	7.4372	5	(A^v) ǀ °C				Water in			
Bc ǀ t_c °C	2243.9	5	c_p liq. °K							
Cc	230.9	5								
Cryos. A°			c_p vap. °K							
consts. B°										
t_e °C F	294.33	5	c_v vap.							

$T_R = 0.75 T_c$ 　　　　　　　　　　　　　　 + grams/100 grams solvent

REFERENCES: 1-Dow 2-API 3-Lit. 4-Calc. from det. data 5-Calc. by formula
SOURCE:　　　API
PURIFICATION:　　　API
LITERATURE REFERENCES:

TABLE V. ALKYL NAPHTHALENES 217

No. 15

NAME	2,7-Dimethylnaphthalene	STRUCTURAL FORMULA

H_3C ⬡⬡ CH_3

Mole % Pur.	Ref.	Molecular Formula $C_{12}H_{12}$	Molecular Weight 156.216

		Ref.			Ref.				Ref.
F.P. °C	98.0	2	dt/dP			f	to		
F.P. 100%			°C/mm			g	°K		
B.P. °C			25°C	728.2	5	h			
760 mm	263.	2	BP	0.0607	5				
100	185.7	5	t_e	0.0363	5	f'	to		
30	151.4	5	30 mm	0.8611	5	g'	°K		
10	125.1	5	ΔHm cal/g			h'			
1	81.0	5	ΔHv cal/g			m	to		
Pressure			25°C	106.49	5	n	°K		
mm 25°C	0.0146	5	30 mm	88.76	5	o			
t_e	1463.	5	BP	74.62	5				
Density			t_e	70.89	5	m'	to		
g/ml 20°C	1.003	5	t_e (d, e)	70.51	5	n'	°K		
d_4^t 25	0.999	5	ΔHv/T_e	19.47	5	o'			
30	0.995	5	d 150 to	107.93	5	Surface tension			
a	1.019	5	e 300 °C	0.1267	5	dynes/cm. 20°C	39.72	5
b	-0.0$_3$8	5	d' 15 to	109.99	5	ɣ 30	38.47	5
Ref. Index			e' 150 °C	0.1403	5	40	37.25	5
n_D 20°C			d_c g/ml	0.308	5	Parachor [P]		
25			v_c ml/g	3.25	5	20°C		
30			t_c °C	505.	5	30		
"C"			P_c mm	24170.	5	40		
MR (Obs.)			PV/RT			Sugd.	391.0	5
MR (Calc.)	53.421	5	25°C	1.0000	5	Exp. L.1.%/wt.		
(nD-d/2)			30 mm	1.0000	5	u.		
Dielectric			BP	0.9465	5	Dispersion		
A 150 to	7.0478	5	t_e	0.9249	5	Flash Point °C		
B 310 °C	1846.	5	t_c	0.253	5	Fire Point		
C	180.	5	ΔHc kcal/m			M. Spec.		
A* 150 to	1.51179	5	ΔHf			Ultra V.		
B* 300 °C	1744.3	5	ΔFf			X-Ray Dif.		
K			Viscosity			Infrared		
c			centistokes			Solubility in +		
t_k to			η °C			Acetone		
t_x °C						Carbon tet.		
A' 25 to	7.39875	5				Benzene		
B' 150 °C	2085.9	5				Ether		
C'	200.9	5	B_v^v to			n-Heptane		
A'* 25 to	1.89535	5	A^v °C			Ethanol		
B'* 150 °C	1989.3	5	(B^v) to			Water		
Ac 310 to	7.43919	5	(A^v) °C			Water in		
Bc t_c °C	2250.0	5						
Cc	231.0	5	c_p liq. °K					
Cryos. A°								
consts. B°			c_p vap. °K					
t_e °C F	295.47	5	c_v vap.					
T_R = 0.75 T_c						+ grams/100 grams solvent		

REFERENCES: 1-Dow 2-API 3-Lit. 4-Calc. from det. data 5-Calc. by formula

SOURCE: API

PURIFICATION: API

LITERATURE REFERENCES:

No. 16

NAME	1-n-Propylnaphthalene	STRUCTURAL FORMULA

C_3H_7

Mole % Pur.	Ref.	Molecular Formula $C_{13}H_{14}$	Molecular Weight 170.242		

		Ref.			Ref.					Ref.
F.P. °C	-10,	2	dt/dP °C/mm			f	to			
F.P. 100%			25°C	1111.96	5	g	°K			
B.P. °C			BP	0.0619	5	h				
760 mm	272.5	2	t_e	0.0366	5					
100	193.7	5	30 mm	0.8784	5	f'	to			
30	158.7	5				g'	°K			
10	131.9	5	ΔHm cal/g			h'				
1	86.9	5	ΔHv cal/g			m	to			
Pressure			25°C	99.68	5	n	°K			
mm 25°C	0.0094	5	30 mm	82.63	5	o				
t_e	1483.	5	BP	69.36	5	m'	to			
Density			t_e	65.72	5	n'	°K			
g/ml 20°C	0.9918	2	t_e (d, e)	65.42	5	o'				
d_4^t 25	0.9882	2	$\Delta Hv/T_e$	19.31	5	Surface tension				
30	0.9846	4	d | 160 to	101.15	5	dynes/cm. 20°C	39.38	5		
a	1.0062	4	e | 310 °C	0.1166	5	γ 30	38.25	5		
b	-0.0372	4	d' | 25 to	102.86	5	40	37.14	5		
Ref. Index			e' | 160 °C	0.1275	5	Parachor [P]				
n_D 20°C	1.5952	2	d_c g/ml	0.30	5	20°C				
25	1.5930	2	v_c ml/g	3.33	5	30				
30	1.5904	2	t_c °C	508.		40				
"C"	0.7804	4	P_c mm	21914.	5	Sugd.	430.0	5		
MR (Obs.)	58.34	2	**PV/RT**			Exp. L.1.%/wt.				
MR (Calc.)	58.039	5	25°C	1.0000	5	u.				
(nD-d/2)	1.0993	2	30 mm	1.0000	5	Dispersion	265.	2		
Dielectric	2.545	5	BP	0.9432	5	Flash Point °C				
A | 155 to	7.0594	5	t_e	0.9196	5	Fire Point				
B | 335 °C	1890.8	5	t_c	0.255	5	M Spec.				
C	180.	5	ΔHc kcal/m			Ultra V.				
A* | 155 to	1.55935	5	ΔHf			X-Ray Dif.				
B* | 320 °C	1788.9	5	ΔFf			Infrared				
K			Viscosity			Solubility in +				
c			centistokes			Acetone				
t_k | to			η °C			Carbon tet.				
t_x | °C						Benzene				
A' | 20 to	7.41108	5				Ether				
B' | 155 °C	2136.5	5				n-Heptane				
C'	201.3	5	B^v | to			Ethanol				
			A^v | °C			Water				
A'* 20 to	1.93970	5	(B^v) | to			Water in				
B'* 155 °C	2038.6	5	(A^v) | °C							
Ac | 335 to	7.58084	5	c_p liq. °K							
Bc | t_c °C	2467.5	5								
Cc	253.5	5								
Cryos. A°			c_p vap. °K							
consts. B°										
t_e °C F	306.27	5	c_v vap.							

$T_R = 0.78 T_c$ + grams/100 grams solvent

REFERENCES: 1-Dow 2-API 3-Lit. 4-Calc. from det. data 5-Calc. by formula

SOURCE:	API
PURIFICATION:	API
LITERATURE REFERENCES:	

TABLE V. ALKYL NAPHTHALENES

No. 17

NAME	2-n-Propylnaphthalene					STRUCTURAL FORMULA

Structural formula: naphthalene ring with C_3H_7

| Mole % Pur. | | Ref. | Molecular Formula $C_{13}H_{14}$ | | Molecular Weight 170.242 | |

		Ref.				Ref.					Ref.
F.P. °C	-3.	2	dt/dP				f	to			
F.P. 100%			°C/mm				g	°K			
B.P. °C			25°C	1162.6	5		h				
760 mm	273.5	2	BP	0.0620	5						
100	194.6	5	t_e	0.0367	5		f'	to			
30	159.5	5	30 mm	0.8802	5		g'	°K			
10	132.6	5	ΔHm cal/g				h'				
1	87.6	5	ΔHv cal/g				m	to			
Pressure			25°C	99.88	5		n	°K			
mm 25°C	0.0089	5	30 mm	82.76	5		o				
t_e	1485.	5	BP	69.37	5		m'	to			
Density			t_e	65.77	5		n'	°K			
g/ml 20°C	0.9770	2	t_e (d, e)	65.38	5		o'				
d_4^t 25	0.9734	2	$\Delta Hv/T_e$	19.29	5		Surface tension				
30	0.9698	4	d 160 to	101.49	5		dynes/cm. 20°C		37.08	5	
a	0.9914	4	e 310 °C	0.1174	5		δ	30	36.00	5	
b	-0.0_372	4	d' 25 to	103.06	5			40	34.95	5	
Ref. Index			e' 160 °C	0.1273	5		Parachor [P]				
n_D 20°C	1.5872	2	d_c g/ml	0.302	5			20°C			
25	1.5850	2	v_c ml/g	3.31	5			30			
30	1.5825	4	t_c °C	506.9	5			40			
"C"	0.7825		P_c mm	21370.	5			Sugd.	430.0	5	
MR (Obs.)	58.58	2	PV/RT				Exp. L.1.%/wt.				
MR (Calc.)	58.039	5	25°C	1.0000	5		u.				
$(nD-d/2)$	1.0987	2	30 mm	1.0000	5		Dispersion	265.		2	
Dielectric	2.519	5	BP	0.9417	5		Flash Point °C				
A 160 to	7.0605	5	t_e	0.9190	5		Fire Point				
B 335 °C	1895.5	5	t_c	0.247	5		M. Spec.				
C	180.	5	ΔHc kcal/m				Ultra V.				
A* 160 to	1.56041	5	ΔHf				X-Ray Dif.				
B* 315 °C	1793.6	5	ΔFf				Infrared				
K			Viscosity				Solubility in +				
c			centistokes				Acetone				
t_k to			η °C				Carbon tet.				
t_x °C							Benzene				
A' 20 to	7.41227	5					Ether				
B' 160 °C	2141.9	5					n-Heptane				
C'	201.4	5	B^v to				Ethanol				
A'* 20 to	1.94025	5	A^v °C				Water				
B'* 160 °C	2043.7	5	(B^v) to				Water in				
Ac 335 to	7.58130	5	(A^v) °C								
Bc t_c °C	2470.1	5	c_p liq. °K								
Cc	252.9	5	c_p vap. °K								
Cryos. A°											
consts. B°											
t_e °C F	307.41	5	c_v vap.								

$T_R = 0.78 T_c$

+ grams/100 grams solvent

REFERENCES: 1-Dow 2-API 3-Lit. 4-Calc. from det. data 5-Calc. by formula

SOURCE: API

PURIFICATION: API

LITERATURE REFERENCES:

No. 18

NAME	1-n-Butylnaphthalene		STRUCTURAL FORMULA

STRUCTURAL FORMULA
C_4H_9

Mole % Pur.	Ref.	Molecular Formula $C_{14}H_{16}$	Molecular Weight 184.268

		Ref.			Ref.				Ref.
F.P. °C	-19.76	2	dt/dP °C/mm			f	to		
F.P. 100%			25°C	2370.9	5	g	°K		
B.P. °C			BP	0.0638	5	h			
760 mm	289.34	2	t_e	0.0371	5	f'	to		
100	208.0	5	30 mm	0.9087	5	g'	°K		
30	171.8	5	ΔHm cal/g			h'			
10	144.1	5	ΔHv cal/g			m	to		
1	97.5	5	25°C	95.32	5	n	°K		
Pressure			30 mm	78.33	5	o			
mm 25°C	0.0042	5	BP	65.37	5				
t_e	1516.	5	t_e	61.84	5	m'	to		
Density			t_e (d, e)	61.39	5	n'	°K		
g/ml 20°C	0.97673	2	ΔHv/T_e	19.03	5	o'			
d_4^t 25	0.97324	2	d 170 to	97.27	5	Surface tension			
30	0.96975	4	e 330 °C	0.1103	5	dynes/cm. 20°C	38.19	5
a	0.99069	4	d' 20 to	98.22	5	30	37.11	5
b	-0.0₃698	4	e' 170 °C	0.1158	5	40	36.06	5
Ref. Index			d_c g/ml	0.302	5	Parachor [P]			
n_D 20°C	1.5819	2	v_c ml/g	3.31	5	20°C			
25	1.5798	2	t_c °C	518.6	5	30			
30	1.5774	4	P_c mm	19440.	5	40			
"C"	0.7761	4				Sugd.	469.0	5
MR (Obs.)	62.953	2	PV/RT			Exp. L.1.%/wt.			
MR (Calc.)	62.657	2	25°C	1.0000	5	u.			
(nD-d/2)	1.0935	2	30 mm	1.0000	5	Dispersion	253.	2
Dielectric	2.502	5	BP	0.9346	5	Flash Point °C			
A 170 to	7.0814	5	t_e	0.9104	5	Fire Point			
B 345 °C	1971.5	5	t_c	0.240	5	M Spec.			
C	180.	5	ΔHc kcal/m			Ultra V.			
A* 170 to	1.61376	5	ΔHf			X-Ray Dif.			
B* 335 °C	1869.5	5	ΔFf			Infrared			
K			Viscosity			Solubility in +			
c			centistokes			Acetone			
t_k to			η °C			Carbon tet.			
t_x °C						Benzene			
A' 25 to	7.43447	5				Ether			
B' 170 °C	2227.7	5	B^v to			n-Heptane			
C'	202.2	5	A^v °C			Ethanol			
A'* 25 to	1.98763	5	(B^v) to			Water			
B'* 170 °C	2127.1	5	(A^v) °C			Water in			
Ac 345 to	7.60666	5	c_p liq. °K						
Bc t_c °C	2561.0	5							
Cc	253.3	5	c_p vap. °K						
Cryos. A° consts. B°			c_v vap.						
t_e °C F	325.43	5							

T_R = 0.78 T_c

+ grams/100 grams solvent

REFERENCES: 1-Dow   2-API   3-Lit.   4-Calc. from det. data   5-Calc. by formula

SOURCE: API

PURIFICATION: API

LITERATURE REFERENCES:

TABLE V. ALKYL NAPHTHALENES

NAME	2-n-Butylnaphthalene	STRUCTURAL FORMULA

Structural Formula: naphthalene ring with C_4H_9 substituent

Mole % Pur.	Ref.	Molecular Formula $C_{14}H_{16}$	Molecular Weight 184.268

		Ref.				Ref.					Ref.
F.P. °C	-5.	2	dt/dP				f	to			
F.P. 100%			°C/mm				g	°K			
B.P. °C			25°C	2673.0	5		h				
760 mm	292.	2	BP	0.0642	5						
100	210.2	5	t_e	0.0372	5		f'	to			
30	173.9	5	30 mm	0.9135	5		g'	°K			
10	146.0	5	ΔHm cal/g				h'				
1	99.2	5	ΔHv cal/g				m	to			
Pressure			25°C	95.83	5		n	°K			
mm 25°C	0.0037	5	30 mm	78.65	5		o				
t_e	1521.	5	BP	65.52	5						
Density			t_e	62.00	5		m'	to			
g/ml 20°C	0.9659	2	t_e (d, e)	61.47	5		n'	°K			
d_4^t 25	0.9624	2	ΔHv/T_e	18.99	5		o'				
30	0.9589	4	d 175 to	97.96	5		Surface tension				
a	0.9799	4	e 330 °C	0.1111	5		dynes/cm. 20°C		36.53	5
b	-0.0.79	4	d' 20 to	98.72	5		ठ	30	35.48	5
Ref. Index			e' 175 °C	0.1155	5			40	34.46	5
n_D 20°C	1.5776	2	d_c g/ml	3.01	5		Parachor [P]				
25	1.5755	2	v_c ml/g	3.31	5			20°C			
30	1.5731	4	t_c °C	520.2	5			30			
"C"	0.7794	4	P_c mm	19060.	5			40			
MR (Obs.)	63.27	2	PV/RT					Sugd.	469.0	5
MR (Calc.)	62.657	5	25°C	1.0000	5		Exp. L. 1.%/wt.				
(nD-d/2)	1.0946	2	30 mm	1.0000	5		u.				
Dielectric	2.489	5	BP	0.9325	5		Dispersion		253.	2
A 170 to	7.0848	5	t_e	0.9087	5		Flash Point °C				
B 345 °C	1984.3	5	t_c	0.235	5		Fire Point				
C	180.	5	ΔHc kcal/m				M. Spec.				
A* 170 to	1.61725	5	ΔHf				Ultra V.				
B* 330 °C	1882.5	5	ΔFf				X-Ray Dif.				
K			Viscosity				Infrared				
c			centistokes				Solubility in +				
t_k to			η °C				Acetone				
t_x °C							Carbon tet.				
A' 25 to	7.43808	5					Benzene				
B' 170 °C	2242.2	5					Ether				
C'	202.3	5	B^v to				n-Heptane				
A'* 25 to	1.98974	5	A^v °C				Ethanol				
B'*170 °C	2141.2	5	(B^v) to				Water				
Ac 345 to	7.60749	5	(A^v) °C				Water in				
Bc t_c °C	2571.9	5									
Cc	252.8	5	c_p liq. °K								
Cryos. A°											
consts. B°			c_p vap. °K								
t_e °C F	328.45	5	c_v vap.								

$T_R = 0.78 T_c$ + grams/100 grams solvent

REFERENCES: 1-Dow   2-API   3-Lit.   4-Calc. from det. data   5-Calc. by formula

SOURCE: API

PURIFICATION: API

LITERATURE REFERENCES:

NAME	1-n-Pentylnaphthalene		STRUCTURAL FORMULA C_5H_{11}

Mole % Pur.	Ref.	Molecular Formula $C_{15}H_{18}$	Molecular Weight 198.294

		Ref.				Ref.					Ref.
F.P. °C	-22.	2	dt/dP				f		to		
F.P. 100%			°C/mm				g		°K		
B.P. °C			25°C	8350.		5	h				
760 mm	307.	2	BP	0.0650		5					
100	224.1	5	t_e	0.0369		5	f'		to		
30	187.3	5	30 mm	0.9242		5	g'		°K		
10	159.1	5	ΔHm cal/g				h'				
1	112.	5	ΔHv cal/g				m		to		
Pressure			25°C	98.01		5	n		°K		
mm 25°C	0.0011	5	30 mm	76.66		5	o				
t_e	1565.	5	BP	63.34		5	m'		to		
Density			t_e	59.73		5	n'		°K		
g/ml 20°C	0.9656	2	t_e (d, e)	59.06		5	o'				
d_4^t 25	0.9622	2	$\Delta Hv/T_e$	19.14		5	Surface tension				
30	0.9588	4	d 185 to	97.50		5	dynes/cm. 20°C	37.45		5
a	0.9792	4	e 340 °C	0.1113		5	y	30	36.40	5
b	-0.0368	4	d' 25 to	101.30		5		40	35.38	5
Ref. Index			e' 185 °C	0.1316		5	Parachor [P]				
n_D 20°C	1.5725	2	d_c g/ml	0.296		5	20°C				
25	1.5704	2	v_c ml/g	3.38		5	30				
30	1.5681	4	t_c °C	531.0		5	40				
"C"	0.7732	5	P_c mm	17802.		5	Sugd.	508.0		5
MR (Obs.)	67.62	2	PV/RT				Exp. L.l.%/wt.				
MR (Calc.)	67.275	5	25°C	1.0000		5	u.				
(nD-d/2)	1.0897	2	30 mm	1.0000		5	Dispersion	243.		2
Dielectric	2.473	5	BP	0.9328		5	Flash Point °C				
A 185 to	7.0743	5	t_e	0.9094		5	Fire Point				
B 360 °C	2000.	5	t_c	0.230		5	M Spec.				
C	170.	5	ΔHc kcal/m				Ultra V.				
A* 185 to	1.6294	5	ΔHf				X-Ray Dif.				
B* 355 °C	1899.	5	ΔFf				Infrared				
K			Viscosity				Solubility in +				
c			centistokes				Acetone				
t_k to			η °C				Carbon tet.				
t_x °C							Benzene				
A' 20 to	7.4269	5					Ether				
B' 185 °C	2260.	5					n-Heptane				
C'	193.	5	B^v to				Ethanol				
A'* 25 to	2.0131	5	A^v °C				Water				
B'* 185 °C	2164.	5	(B^v) to				Water in				
Ac 360 to	7.6385	5	(A^v) °C								
Bc t_c °C	2645.	5	c_p liq. °K								
Cc	250.	5	c_p vap. °K								
Cryos. A° consts. B°											
t_e °C F	345.51	5	c_v vap.								

$T_R = 0.79 T_c$ · + grams/100 grams solvent

REFERENCES:	1-Dow 2-API 3-Lit. 4-Calc. from det. data 5-Calc. by formula
SOURCE:	API
PURIFICATION:	API
LITERATURE REFERENCES:	

TABLE V. ALKYL NAPHTHALENES

No. 21

NAME	2-n-Pentylnaphthalene	STRUCTURAL FORMULA
	2-n-Amylnaphthalene	C_5H_{11}

Mole % Pur.	Ref.	Molecular Formula $C_{15}H_{18}$	Molecular Weight 198.294

		Ref.			Ref.			Ref.
F.P. °C	-4.	2	dt/dP °C/mm			f | to		
F.P. 100%			25°C	9137.5	5	g | °K		
B.P. °C			BP	0.0656	5	h |		
760 mm	310.	2	t_e	0.0373	5	f' | to		
100	226.4	5	30 mm	0.9317	5	g' | °K		
30	189.3	5	ΔHm cal/g			h' |		
10	160.9	5	ΔHv cal/g			m | to		
1	113.2	5	25°C	98.19	5	n | °K		
Pressure			30 mm	76.69	5	o |		
mm 25°C	0.0_399	5	BP	63.25	5	m' | to		
t_e	1565.	5	t_e	59.41	5	n' | °K		
Density			t_e (d, e)	58.91	5	o' |		
g/ml 20°C	0.9561	2	ΔHv/T_e	18.94	5	Surface tension		
d_4^t 25	0.9527	4	d 190 to	97.79	5	dynes/cm. 20°C	35.99	5
30	0.9493	4	e 350 °C	0.1114	5	γ 30	34.98	5
a	0.9697	4	d' 25 to	101.46	5	40	33.99	5
b	-0.0_368	4	e' 190 °C	0.1308	5	Parachor [P]		
Ref. Index			d_c g/ml	0.296	5	20°C		
n_D 20°C	1.5694	2	v_c ml/g	3.38	5	30		
25	1.5673	2	t_c °C	533.2	5	40		
30	1.5650	4	P_c mm	17251.	5	Sugd.	508.0	5
"C"	0.7770	4	PV/RT			Exp. L.1.%/wt.		
MR (Obs.)	67.99	2	25°C	1.0000	5	u.		
MR (Calc.)	67.275		30 mm	1.0000	5	Dispersion	243.	2
(nD-d/2)	1.0914	2	BP	0.9310	5	Flash Point °C		
Dielectric	2.463	5	t_e	0.9041	5	Fire Point		
A 190 to	7.0600	5	t_c	0.230	5	M. Spec.		
B 370 °C	2005.9	5	ΔHc kcal/m			Ultra V.		
C	170.	5	ΔHf			X-Ray Dif.		
A* 190 to	1.6206	5	ΔFf			Infrared		
B* 360 °C	1906.5	5	Viscosity			Solubility in +		
K			centistokes			Acetone		
c			η °C			Carbon tet.		
t_k to						Benzene		
t_x °C						Ether		
A' 25 to	7.4117	5				n-Heptane		
B' 190 °C	2266.6	5	B^v | to			Ethanol		
C'	192.6	5	A^v | °C			Water		
A'* 25 to	1.9965	5	(B^v)| to			Water in		
B'* 190 °C	2170.2	5	(A^v)| °C					
Ac 370 to	7.6924	5						
Bc t_c °C	2750.	5	c_p liq. °K					
Cc	262.6	5	c_p vap. °K					
Cryos. A° consts. B°								
t_e °C F	348.92	5	c_v vap.					

$T_R = 0.80 T_c$ + grams/100 grams solvent

REFERENCES: 1-Dow 2-API 3-Lit. 4-Calc. from det. data 5-Calc. by formula

SOURCE: API

PURIFICATION: API

LITERATURE REFERENCES:

No. 22

NAME	1-n-Hexylnaphthalene	STRUCTURAL FORMULA

C_6H_{13}

Mole % Pur.	Ref.	Molecular Formula $C_{16}H_{20}$	Molecular Weight 212.320

		Ref.			Ref.				Ref.
F.P. °C	-18.	2	dt/dP °C/mm			f	to		
F.P. 100%			25°C	17328.	5	g	°K		
B.P. °C			BP	0.0666	5	h			
760 mm	322.	2		0.0372	5				
100	237.0	5	t_e			f'	to		
30	199.2	5	30 mm	0.9504	5	g'	°K		
10	170.2	5	ΔHm cal/g			h'			
1	121.4	5	ΔHv cal/g						
Pressure			25°C	94.37	5	m	to		
mm 25°C	0.0_351	5	30 mm	73.25	5	n	°K		
t_e	1593.	5	BP	60.43	5	o			
Density			t_e	56.66	5	m'	to		
g/ml 20°C	0.9566	2	t_e (d, e)	56.20	5	n'	°K		
d_4^t 25	0.9532	2	ΔHv/T_e	18.92	5	o'			
30	0.9498	4	d 200 to	94.03	5	Surface tension			
a	0.9702	4	e 365 °C	0.1043	5	dynes/cm. 20°C	36.89	5
b	-0.0_368	4	d' 25 to	97.40	5	γ 30	35.85	5
Ref. Index			e' 200 °C	0.1213	5	40	34.84	5
n_D 20°C	1.5647	2	d_c g/ml	0.292	5	Parachor [P]		
25	1.5626	2	v_c ml/g	3.42	5	20°C		
30	1.5604	4	t_c °C	539.3	5	30		
"C"	0.7706	4	P_c mm	15949.	5	40		
MR (Obs.)	72.26	2	PV/RT			Sugd.	547.0	5
MR (Calc.)	71.895	5	25°C	1.0000	5	Exp. L.1.%/wt.		
(nD-d/2)	1.0864	2	30 mm	1.0000	5	u.		
Dielectric	2.448	5	BP	0.9288	5	Dispersion	234.	2
A 200 to	7.1003	5	t_e	0.9006	5	Flash Point °C		
B 375 °C	2076.	5	t_c	0.228	5	Fire Point		
C	170.	5	ΔHc kcal/m			M Spec.		
A* 200 to	1.6850	5	ΔHf			Ultra V.		
B* 375 °C	1975.2	5	ΔFf			X-Ray Dif.		
K			Viscosity			Infrared		
c			centistokes			Solubility in +		
t_k to			η °C			Acetone		
t_x °C						Carbon tet.		
A' 25 to	7.4546	5				Benzene		
B' 200 °C	2345.8	5				Ether		
C'	193.3	5	B^v to			n-Heptane		
A'* 25 to	2.0620	5	A^v °C			Ethanol		
B'* 200 °C	2247.6	5	(B^v) to			Water		
Ac 375 to	7.7326	5	(A^v) °C			Water in		
Bc t_c °C	2825.	5	c_p liq. °K					
Cc	261.1	5	c_p vap. °K					
Cryos. A° consts. B°			c_v vap.					
t_e °C F	362.57	5						

$T_R = 0.80 T_C$

+ grams/100 grams solvent

REFERENCES: 1-Dow 2-API 3-Lit. 4-Calc. from det. data 5-Calc. by formula

SOURCE: API

PURIFICATION: API

LITERATURE REFERENCES:

TABLE V ALKYL NAPHTHALENES 225

No. 23

NAME	2-n-Hexylnaphthalene	STRUCTURAL FORMULA

C_6H_{13}

Mole % Pur.	Ref.	Molecular Formula $C_{16}H_{20}$	Molecular Weight 212.320

		Ref.			Ref.				Ref.
F.P. °C	-3.	2	dt/dP			f	to		
F.P. 100%			°C/mm			g	°K		
B.P. °C			25°C	19318.	5	h			
760 mm	324.	2	BP	0.0668	5				
100	238.8	5	t_e	0.0372	5	f'	to		
30	200.9	5	30 mm	0.9535	5	g'	°K		
10	171.7	5	ΔHm cal/g			h'			
1	122.8	5							
Pressure			ΔHv cal/g			m	to		
mm 25°C	0.0_345	5	25°C	94.82	5	n	°K		
t_e	1598.	5	30 mm	73.53	5	o			
Density			BP	60.64	5	m'	to		
g/ml 20°C	0.9479	2	t_e	56.87	5	n'	°K		
d_4^t 25	0.9445	2	t_e (d, e)	56.36	5	o'			
30	0.9411	4	ΔHv/T_e	18.93	5				
a	0.9615	4	d 200 to	94.55	5	Surface tension			
b	-0.0_368	4	e 365 °C	0.1047	5	dynes/cm. 20°C	35.57	5
			d' 25 to	97.85	5	γ 30	34.56	5
Ref. Index			e' 200 °C	0.1211	5	40	33.57	5
n_D 20°C	1.5620	2							
25	1.5599	2	d_c g/ml	0.292	5	Parachor [P]			
30	1.5577	4	v_c ml/g	3.42	5	20°C			
"C"	0.7742	4	t_c °C	540.2	5	30			
			P_c mm	15734.	5	40			
MR (Obs.)	72.64	2				Sugd.	547.0	5
MR (Calc.)	71.895	5	PV/RT						
(nD-d/2)	1.0880	2	25°C	1.0000	5	Exp. L.1.%/wt.			
Dielectric	2.440	5	30 mm	1.0000	5	u.			
			BP	0.9280	5	Dispersion	234.	2
A 200 to	7.1075	5	t_e	0.9002	5	Flash Point °C			
B 380 °C	2088.	5	t_c	0.228	5	Fire Point			
C	170.	5	ΔHc kcal/m			M. Spec.			
A* 200 to	1.69103	5	ΔHf			Ultra V.			
B* 370 °C	1986.86	5	ΔFf			X-Ray Dif.			
K						Infrared			
c			Viscosity			Solubility in +			
t_k to			centistokes			Acetone			
t_x °C			η °C			Carbon tet.			
A' 25 to	7.46221	5				Benzene			
B' 200 °C	2359.38	5				Ether			
C'	193.4	5	B^v to			n-Heptane			
A'* 25 to	2.06849	5	A^v °C			Ethanol			
B'* 200 °C	2261.	5	(B^v) to			Water			
Ac 380 to	7.7367	5	(A^v) °C			Water in			
Bc t_c °C	2834.	5							
Cc	260.3	5	c_p liq. °K						
Cryos. A°									
consts. B°			c_p vap. °K						
t_e °C F	364.85	5	c_v vap.						
T_R = 0.80 T_c						+ grams/100 grams solvent			

REFERENCES: 1-Dow 2-API 3-Lit. 4-Calc. from det. data 5-Calc. by formula

SOURCE:	API
PURIFICATION:	API
LITERATURE REFERENCES:	

No. 24

NAME	1-n-Heptylnaphthalene	STRUCTURAL FORMULA C_7H_{15}

Mole % Pur.		Ref.	Molecular Formula $C_{17}H_{22}$		Molecular Weight 226.346	

		Ref.				Ref.					Ref.
F.P. °C	-8.	2	dt/dP				f	|	to		
F.P. 100%			°C/mm				g	|	°K		
			25°C	46169.		5	h	|			
B.P. °C			BP	0.0681		5					
760 mm	340.	2	t_e	0.0372		5	f'	|	to		
100	253.0	5	30 mm	0.9779		5	g'	|	°K		
30	214.1	5	ΔHm cal/g				h'	|			
10	184.2	5	ΔHv cal/g				m	|	to		
1	133.9	5	25°C	92.33		5	n	|	°K		
Pressure			30 mm	71.06		5	o	|			
mm 25°C	0.0_318	5	BP	58.69		5					
t_e	1637.	5	t_e	54.93		5	m'	|	to		
Density			t_e (d, e)	54.46		5	n'	|	°K		
g/ml 20°C	0.9491	2	ΔHv/T_e	18.95		5	o'	|			
d_4^t 25	0.9458	2	d | 215 to	92.11		5	Surface tension				
30	0.9425	4	e | 385 °C	0.0983		5	dynes/cm. 20°C	36.45	5		
a	0.9623	4	d' | 25 to	95.14		5	γ	30	35.45	5	
b	-0.0_366	4	e' | 215 °C	0.1125		5		40	34.47	5	
Ref. Index			d_c g/ml	0.291		5	Parachor [P]				
n_D 20°C	1.5582	2	v_c ml/g	3.43		5	20°C				
25	1.5561	4	t_c °C	553.1		5	30				
30	1.5540	4	P_c mm	14865.		5	40				
"C"	0.7684	4	PV/RT				Sugd.	586.0	5		
MR (Obs.)	76.901	2	25°C	1.0000		5	Exp. L.1.%/wt.				
MR (Calc.)	76.513	5	30 mm	1.0000		5	u.				
(nD-d/2)	1.0836	2	BP	0.9256		5	Dispersion	226.	2		
Dielectric	2.428	5	t_e	0.8965		5	Flash Point °C				
A | 215 to	7.1631	5	t_c	0.224		5	Fire Point				
B | 405 °C	2184.	5	ΔHc kcal/m				M Spec.				
C	170.	5	ΔHf				Ultra V.				
A*| 215 to	1.7673	5	ΔFf				X-Ray Dif.				
B*| 395 °C	2081.1	5	Viscosity				Infrared				
K			centistokes				Solubility in +				
c			η °C				Acetone				
t_k | to							Carbon tet.				
t_x | °C							Benzene				
A' | 25 to	7.5213	5					Ether				
B' | 215 °C	2467.9	5					n-Heptane				
C'	194.2	5	B^v | to				Ethanol				
A'* 25 to	2.1461	5	A^v | °C				Water				
B'* 215 °C	2366.9	5	(B^v)| to				Water in				
Ac| 405 to	7.9748	5	(A^v)| °C								
Bc| t_c °C	3216.	5	c_p liq. °K								
Cc	292.6	5									
Cryos. A°			c_p vap. °K								
consts. B°											
t_e °C F	383.04	5	c_v vap.								

$T_R = 0.82 T_c$ + grams/100 grams solvent

REFERENCES: 1-Dow 2-API 3-Lit. 4-Calc. from det. data 5-Calc. by formula

SOURCE:	API
PURIFICATION:	API
LITERATURE REFERENCES:	

TABLE V. ALKYL NAPHTHALENES

No. 25

NAME	2-n-Heptylnaphthalene		STRUCTURAL FORMULA

C$_7$H$_{15}$

Mole % Pur.		Ref.	Molecular Formula C$_{17}$H$_{22}$	Molecular Weight 226.346		

		Ref.			Ref.			Ref.
F.P. °C	1.	2	dt/dP			f	to	
F.P. 100%			°C/mm			g	°K	
B.P. °C			25°C	48753.	5	h		
760 mm	341.	2	BP	0.0681	5			
100	253.9	5	t$_e$	0.0371	5	f'	to	
30	214.9	5	30 mm	0.9794	5	g'	°K	
10	185.0	5	ΔHm cal/g			h'		
1	134.6	5	ΔHv cal/g			m	to	
Pressure			25°C	92.54	5	n	°K	
mm 25°C	0.0$_3$17	5	30 mm	71.19	5	o		
t$_e$	1640.	5	BP	58.81	5			
Density			t$_e$	55.03	5	m'	to	
g/ml 20°C	0.9410	2	t$_e$ (d, e)	54.57	5	n'	°K	
d$_4^t$ 25	0.9377	2	ΔHv/T$_e$	18.95	5	o'		
30	0.9344	4				Surface tension		
a	0.9542	4	d 215 to	92.30	5	dynes/cm. 20°C	35.23	5
b	-0.0$_3$66	4	e 385 °C	0.0982	5	γ 30	34.25	5
Ref. Index			d' 25 to	95.35	5	40	33.29	5
n$_D$ 20°C	1.5556	2	e' 215 °C	0.1124	5			
25	1.5535	2	d$_c$ g/ml	0.291	5	Parachor [P]		
30	1.5514	4	v$_c$ ml/g	3.43	5	20°C		
"C"	0.7716	4	t$_c$ °C	552.8	5	30		
MR (Obs.)	77.27	2	P$_c$ mm	14649.	5	40		
MR (Calc.)	76.513	5	PV/RT			Sugd.	586.0	5
(nD-d/2)	1.0851	2	25°C	1.0000	5	Exp. L.1.%/wt.		
Dielectric	2.420	5	30 mm	1.0000	5	u.		
A 215 to	7.1665	5	BP	0.9257	5	Dispersion	226.	2
B 405 °C	2190.	5	t$_e$	0.8964	5	Flash Point °C		
C	170.	5	t$_c$	0.224	5	Fire Point		
A* 215 to	1.77003	5	ΔHc kcal/m			M. Spec.		
B* 395 °C	2087.	5	ΔHf			Ultra V.		
K			ΔFf			X-Ray Dif.		
c			Viscosity			Infrared		
t$_k$ to			centistokes			Solubility in $^+$		
t$_x$ °C			η °C			Acetone		
A' 25 to	7.5249	5				Carbon tet.		
B' 215 °C	2474.6	5				Benzene		
C'	194.3	5	B^v to			Ether		
A'* 25 to	2.1492	5	A^v °C			n-Heptane		
B'* 215 °C	2373.5	5	(B^v) to			Ethanol		
Ac 405 to	7.9712	5	(A^v) °C			Water		
Bc t$_c$ °C	3211.3	5				Water in		
Cc	291.1	5	c$_p$ liq. °K					
Cryos. A° consts. B°			c$_p$ vap. °K					
t$_e$ °C F	384.18	5	c$_v$ vap.					

T$_R$ = 0.82 T$_c$ $^+$ grams/100 grams solvent

REFERENCES: 1-Dow   2-API   3-Lit.   4-Calc. from det. data   5-Calc. by formula

SOURCE:	API
PURIFICATION:	API
LITERATURE REFERENCES:	

No. 26

NAME	1-n-Octylnaphthalene	STRUCTURAL FORMULA
		C_8H_{17}

Mole % Pur.	Ref.	Molecular Formula $C_{18}H_{24}$	Molecular Weight 240.372

		Ref.			Ref.			Ref.
F.P. °C	-2.	2	dt/dP °C/mm			f | to		
F.P. 100%			25°C	1.47×10^5	5	g | °K		
B.P. °C			BP	0.0690	5	h |		
760 mm	356.	2	t_e	0.0369	5	f' | to		
100	268.	4	30 mm	0.9952	5	g' | °K		
30	228.	4	ΔHm cal/g			h' |		
10	198.	5	ΔHv cal/g			m | to		
1	146.	5	25°C	93.22	5	n | °K		
Pressure mm 25°C	0.0_4535	5	30 mm	69.59	5	o |		
t_e	1681.	5	BP	57.37	5	m' | to		
Density g/ml 20°C	0.9427	2	t_e	53.52	5	n' | °K		
d_4^t 25	0.9394	2	t_e (d,e)	53.05	5	o' |		
30	0.9361	4	ΔHv/T_e	19.08	5	Surface tension		
a	0.9559	4	d | 230 to	91.38	5	dynes/cm. 20°C	36.10	5
b	-0.0_366	4	e | 400 °C	0.0955	5	γ 30	35.10	5
Ref. Index n_D 20°C	1.5526	2	d' | 25 to	96.13	5	40	34.12	5
25	1.5505	2	e' | 230 °C	0.1163	5	Parachor [P]		
30	1.5485	4	d_c g/ml			20°C		
"C"	0.7663	4	v_c ml/g			30		
MR (Obs.)	81.54	2	t_c °C	563.3	5	40		
MR (Calc.)	81.131	5	P_c mm	13752.	5	Sugd.	625.0	5
(nD-d/2)	1.0812	2	PV/RT			Exp. L.1.%/wt.		
Dielectric			25°C	1.0000	5	u.		
A |230 to	7.1956	5	30 mm	1.0000	5	Dispersion	219.	2
B |430 °C	2248.	5	BP	0.9258	5	Flash Point °C		
C	165.	5	t_e	0.8958	5	Fire Point		
A* |230 to	1.8164	5	t_c			M Spec.		
B* |410 °C	2144.	5	ΔHc kcal/m			Ultra V.		
K			ΔHf			X-Ray Dif.		
c			ΔFf			Infrared		
t_k | to			Viscosity			Solubility in +		
t_x | °C			centistokes			Acetone		
A' | 25 to	7.5558	5	η °C			Carbon tet.		
B' |230 °C	2540.	5				Benzene		
C'	190.	5				Ether		
A'* 25 to	2.2032	5	B^v | to			n-Heptane		
B'* 230 °C	2441.	5	A^v | °C			Ethanol		
Ac |430 to	8.28106	5	(B^v) | to			Water		
Bc | t_c °C	3725.7	5	(A^v) | °C			Water in		
Cc	336.0	5	c_p liq. °K					
Cryos. A°			c_p vap. °K					
consts. B°								
t_e °C F	401.24	5	c_v vap.					

$T_R = 0.84 T_c$

+ grams/100 grams solvent

REFERENCES: 1-Dow 2-API 3-Lit. 4-Calc. from det. data 5-Calc. by formula

SOURCE: API

PURIFICATION: API

LITERATURE REFERENCES:

TABLE V. ALKYL NAPHTHALENES   229

No. 27

NAME	2-n-Octylnaphthalene	STRUCTURAL FORMULA

C_8H_{17}

Mole % Pur.	Ref.	Molecular Formula $C_{18}H_{24}$	Molecular Weight 240.372

		Ref.			Ref.			Ref.
F.P. °C	12.	2	dt/dP			f | to		
F.P. 100%			°C/mm			g | °K		
B.P. °C			25°C	137028.	5	h |		
760 mm	357.	2	BP	0.0693	5			
100	267.3	5	t_e	0.0366	5	f' | to		
30	227.6	5	30 mm	0.9977	5	g' | °K		
10	197.2	5	ΔHm cal/g			h' |		
1	145.8	5	ΔHv cal/g			m | to		
Pressure			25°C	92.79	5	n | °K		
mm 25°C	0.0_458	5	30 mm	69.29	5	o |		
t_e	1705.	5	BP	56.73	5			
Density			t_e	53.90	5	m' | to		
g/ml 20°C	0.9350	2	t_e (d, e)	52.33	5	n' | °K		
d_4^t 25	0.9317	2	ΔHv/T_e	19.18	5	o' |		
30	0.9284	4	d | 230 to	91.37	4	Surface tension		
a	0.9482	4	e | 400 °C	0.0970	4	dynes/cm. 20°C	34.93	5
b	-0.0_366	4	d' | 25 to	95.69	4	γ 30	33.96	5
Ref. Index			e' | 230 °C	0.1160	4	40	33.00	5
n_D 20°C	1.5501	2	d_c g/ml	0.283	5	Parachor [P]		
25	1.5480	2	v_c ml/g	3.53	5	20°C		
30	1.5459	2	t_c °C	562.9	5	30		
"C"	0.7694	4	P_c mm	13516.	5	40		
MR (Obs.)	81.91	2	PV/RT			Sugd.	625.0	5
MR (Calc.)	81.131	5	25°C	1.0000	5	Exp. L.l.%/wt.		
(nD-d/2)	1.0826	2	30 mm	1.0000	5	u.		
Dielectric	2.403		BP	0.9172	5	Dispersion	219.	2
A | 230 to	7.1745	5	t_e	0.9073	5	Flash Point °C		
B | 410 °C	2237.	5	t_c	0.220	5	Fire Point		
C	·165.	5	ΔHc kcal/m			M. Spec.		
A* | 230 to	1.7759	5	ΔHf			Ultra V.		
B* | 410 °C	2125.2	5	ΔFf			X-Ray Dif.		
K			Viscosity			Infrared		
c			centistokes			Solubility in +		
t_k | to			η °C			Acetone		
t_x | °C						Carbon tet.		
A' | 25 to	7.5334	5				Benzene		
B' | 230 °C	2527.7	5				Ether		
C'	189.7	5	B^v | to			n-Heptane		
A'* 25 to	2.1811	5	A^v | °C			Ethanol		
B'* 230 °C	2428.2	5	(B^v)| to			Water		
Ac | 410 to	8.0941	5	(A^v)| °C			Water in		
$Bc \| t_c$ °C	3444.	5	c_p liq. °K					
Cc	306.1	5	c_p vap. °K					
Cryos. A°								
consts. B°			c_v vap.					
t_e °C F	402.38	5						

$T_R = 0.83\,T_c$ + grams/100 grams solvent

REFERENCES: 1-Dow 2-API 3-Lit. 4-Calc. from det. data 5-Calc. by formula

SOURCE:	API
PURIFICATION:	API

LITERATURE REFERENCES:

No. 28

NAME	1-n-Nonylnaphthalene					STRUCTURAL FORMULA		

C_9H_{19}

Mole % Pur.		Ref.	Molecular Formula	$C_{19}H_{26}$	Molecular Weight 254.398			

		Ref.				Ref.				Ref.
F.P. °C	8.	2	dt/dP °C/mm				f	| to	
F.P. 100%			25°C	337693.	5		g	| °K	
B.P. °C			BP	0.0706	5		h	|	
760 mm	372.	2	t_e	0.0371	5				
100	281.5	5	30 mm	1.0219	5		f'	| to	
30	240.9	5	ΔHm cal/g				g'	| °K	
10	209.7	5					h'	|	
1	157.	5	ΔHv cal/g						
Pressure			25°C	90.77	5		m	| to	
mm 25°C	0.0_423	5	30 mm	67.34	5		n	| °K	
t_e	1713.	5	BP	55.36	5		o	|	
Density			t_e	51.51	5				
g/ml 20°C	0.9371	2	t_e (d,e)	51.02	5		m'	| to	
d_4^t 25	0.9339	2	ΔHv/T_e	18.92	5		n'	| °K	
30	0.9307	4					o'	|	
a	0.9499	4	d | 240 to	89.36	5		Surface tension		
b	-0.0_364	4	e | 420 °C	0.0914	5		dynes/cm. 20°C	35.79	5
			d' | 25 to	93.48	5		ɣ 30	34.82	5
Ref. Index			e' | 240 °C	0.1085	5		40	33.87	5
n_D 20°C	1.5477	2	d_c g/ml	0.284	5		Parachor [P]		
25	1.5456	2	v_c ml/g	3.52	5		20°C		
30	1.5437	4	t_c °C	575.2	5		30		
"C"	0.7645	4	P_c mm	12682.	5		40 Sugd.	664.	5
MR (Obs.)	86.19	2	PV/RT				Exp. L.1.%/wt.		
MR (Calc.)	85.747	5	25°C	1.0000	5		u.		
(nD-d/2)	1.0792	2	30 mm	1.0000	5		Dispersion	212.	2
Dielectric	2.395	5	BP	0.9203	5		Flash Point °C		
A | 240 to	7.2272	5	t_e	0.8887	5		Fire Point		
B | 445 °C	2334.	5	t_c	0.215	5		M Spec.		
C	165.	5	ΔHc kcal/m				Ultra V.		
A* | 240 to	1.8708	5	ΔHf				X-Ray Dif.		
B* | 430 °C	2230.1	5	ΔFf				Infrared		
K			Viscosity				Solubility in +		
c			centistokes				Acetone		
t_k | to			η °C				Carbon tet.		
t_x | °C							Benzene		
A' | 25 to	7.5895	5					Ether		
B' | 240 °C	2637.4	5					n-Heptane		
C'	190.6	5	B^v | to				Ethanol		
			A^v | °C				Water		
A'* 25 to	2.2528	5	(B^v) | to				Water in		
B'* 240 °C	2535.	5	(A^v) | °C						
Ac | 445 to	8.3669	5							
Bc | t_c °C	3924.6	5	c_p liq. °K						
Cc	345.3	5							
Cryos. A°			c_p vap. °K						
consts. B°									
t_e °C F	419.44	5	c_v vap.						

$T_R = 0.84 T_c$ + grams/100 grams solvent

REFERENCES: 1-Dow 2-API 3-Lit. 4-Calc. from det. data 5-Calc. by formula

SOURCE: API

PURIFICATION: API

LITERATURE REFERENCES:

TABLE V. ALKYL NAPHTHALENES 231

No. 29

NAME	2-n-Nonylnaphthalene	STRUCTURAL FORMULA

Structural formula: naphthalene with C_9H_{19}

Mole % Pur.	Ref.	Molecular Formula $C_{19}H_{26}$	Molecular Weight 254.398

		Ref.			Ref.			Ref.
F.P. °C	12.	2	dt/dP			f	to	
F.P. 100%			°C/mm			g	___ °K	
B.P. °C			25°C	337693.	5	h		
760 mm	372.	2	BP	0.0706	5			
100	281.5	5	t_e	0.0371	5	f'	to	
30	240.9	5	30 mm	1.0219	5	g'	___ °K	
10	209.7	5	ΔHm cal/g			h'		
1	157.	5	ΔHv cal/g			m	to	
Pressure			25°C	90.77	5	n	___ °K	
mm 25°C	$0.0_4 23$	5	30 mm	67.34	5	o		
t_e	1713.	5	BP	55.36	5			
Density			t_e	51.50	5	m'	to	
g/ml 20°C	0.9298	2	t_e (d, e)	51.02	5	n'	___ °K	
d_4^t 25	0.9266	2	ΔHv/T_e	18.92	5	o'		
30	0.9234	4	d 240 to	89.37	5	Surface tension		
a	0.9426	4	e 420 °C	0.0914	5	dynes/cm. 20°C	34.69	5
b	$-0.0_3 64$	4	d' 25 to	93.48	5	γ 30	33.74	5
Ref. Index			e' 240 °C	0.1085	5	40	32.82	5
n_D 20°C	1.5454	2	d_c g/ml	0.284	5	Parachor [P]		
25	1.5433	2	v_c ml/g	3.52	5	20°C		
30	1.5424	4	t_c °C	573.6	5	30		
"C"	0.7688	4	P_c mm	12486.	5	40		
MR (Obs.)	86.56	2	PV/RT			Sugd.	664.	5
MR (Calc.)	85.747	5	25°C	1.0000	5	Exp. L.1.%/wt.		
(nD-d/2)	1.0805	2	30 mm	1.0000	5	u.		
Dielectric	2.388	5	BP	0.9203	5	Dispersion	212.	2
A 240 to	7.2272	5	t_e	0.8887	5	Flash Point °C		
B 440 °C	2334.	5	t_c	0.215	5	Fire Point		
C	165.	5	ΔHc kcal/m			M. Spec.		
A* 240 to	1.8708	5	ΔHf			Ultra V.		
B* 430 °C	2230.	5	ΔFf			X-Ray Dif.		
K			Viscosity			Infrared		
c			centistokes			Solubility in +		
t_k to			η °C			Acetone		
t_x °C						Carbon tet.		
A' 25 to	7.5895	5				Benzene		
B' 240 °C	2637.4	5	B^v to			Ether		
C'	190.6	5	A^v °C			n-Heptane		
A'* 25 to	2.2528	5	(B^v) to			Ethanol		
B'* 240 °C	2535.4	5	(A^v) °C			Water		
Ac 440 to	8.3581	5				Water in		
Bc t_c °C	3905.8	5	c_p liq. °K					
Cc	342.9	5	c_p vap. °K					
Cryos. A° consts. B°								
t_e °C F	419.44	5	c_v vap.					

$T_R = 0.84\, T_C$ + grams/100 grams solvent

REFERENCES: 1-Dow 2-API 3-Lit. 4-Calc. from det. data 5-Calc. by formula

SOURCE: API

PURIFICATION: API

LITERATURE REFERENCES:

No. 30

NAME	1-n-Decylnaphthalene	STRUCTURAL FORMULA $C_{10}H_{21}$

Mole % Pur.	Ref.	Molecular Formula $C_{20}H_{28}$	Molecular Weight 268.424

		Ref.				Ref.					Ref.
F.P. °C	15.	2	dt/dP °C/mm				f	to			
F.P. 100%			25°C	8.1×10^5	5		g	°K			
B.P. °C			BP	0.0717	5		h				
760 mm	387.	2	t_e	0.0370	5		f'	to			
100	295.	5	30 mm	1.0438	5		g'	°K			
30	253.	5	ΔHm cal/g				h'				
10	222.	5	ΔHv cal/g				m	to			
1	168.	5	25°C	88.87	5		n	°K			
Pressure			30 mm	65.58	5		o				
mm 25°C	0.0_5915	5	BP	54.00	5		m'	to			
t_e	1750.	5	t_e	50.14	5		n'	°K			
Density			t_e (d, e)	49.71	5		o'				
g/ml 20°C	0.9322	2	$ΔHv/T_e$	18.96	5		Surface tension				
d_4^t 25	0.9290	2	d | 255 to	87.58	5		dynes/cm. 20°C	35.53	5		
30	0.9258	4	e | 430 °C	0.0868	5		) 30	34.56	5		
a	0.9450	4	d' | 25 to	91.42	5		40	33.62	5		
b	-0.0_364	4	e' | 255 °C	0.1019	5		Parachor [P]				
Ref. Index			d_c g/ml	0.252	5		20°C				
n_D 20°C	1.5435	2	v_c ml/g	3.962	5		30				
25	1.5414	2	t_c °C	584.5	5		40				
30	1.5396	4	P_c mm	11737.	5		Sugd.	703.0	5		
"C"	0.7631	4	PV/RT				Exp. L.1.%/wt.				
MR (Obs.)	90.83	2	25°C	1.0000	5		u.				
MR (Calc.)	90.365	5	30 mm	1.0000	5		Dispersion	207.	2		
(nD-d/2)	1.0774	2	BP	0.9189	5		Flash Point °C				
Dielectric	2.382	5	t_e	0.8861	5		Fire Point				
A | 255 to	7.2812	5	t_c				M Spec.				
B | 450 °C	2429.	5	ΔHc kcal/m				Ultra V.				
C	165.	5	ΔHf				X-Ray Dif.				
A* | 255 to	1.9404	5	ΔFf				Infrared				
B* | 445 °C	2323.1	5	Viscosity				Solubility in +				
K			centistokes				Acetone				
c			η °C				Carbon tet.				
t_k | to							Benzene				
t_x | °C							Ether				
A' | 25 to	7.6469	5					n-Heptane				
B' | 255 °C	2745.	5					Ethanol				
C'	191.	5	B^v | to				Water				
A'* 25 to	2.3253	5	A^v | °C				Water in				
B'* 255 °C	2641.	5	(B^v) | to								
Ac | 450 to	8.4631	5	(A^v) | °C								
Bc | t_c °C	4108.	5	c_p liq. °K								
Cc	350.	5	c_p vap. °K								
Cryos. A° consts. B°											
t_e °C F	436.5	5	c_v vap.								

$T_R = 0.85 T_c$

+ grams/100 grams solvent

REFERENCES: 1-Dow   2-API   3-Lit.   4-Calc. from det. data   5-Calc. by formula

SOURCE:	API
PURIFICATION:	API
LITERATURE REFERENCES:	

TABLE V. ALKYL NAPHTHALENES

No. 31

NAME	2-n-Decylnaphthalene	STRUCTURAL FORMULA

$C_{10}H_{21}$

Mole % Pur.	Ref.	Molecular Formula	$C_{20}H_{28}$	Molecular Weight 268.424

		Ref.			Ref.				Ref.
F.P. °C	20.	2	dt/dP			f	to		
F.P. 100%			°C/mm			g	°K		
B.P. °C			25°C	809594.	5	h			
760 mm	387.	2	BP	0.0717	5				
100	294.9	5	t_e	0.0370	5	f'	to		
30	253.5	5	30 mm	1.0438	5	g'	°K		
10	221.6	5	ΔHm cal/g			h'			
1	168.	5	ΔHv cal/g			m	to		
Pressure			25°C	88.87	5	n	°K		
mm 25°C	0.0_592	5	30 mm	65.58	5	o			
t_e	1750.	5	BP	54.00	5				
Density			t_e	50.13	5	m'	to		
g/ml 20°C	0.9253	2	t_e (d, e)	49.70	5	n'	°K		
d_4^t 25	0.9221	2	ΔHv/T_e	18.96	5	o'			
30	0.9189	4	d 255 to	87.59	5	Surface tension			
a	0.9381	4	e 435 °C	0.0868	5	dynes/cm. 20°C	34.49	5	
b	-0.0_364	4	d' 25 to	91.42	5	γ 30	33.54	5	
Ref. Index			e' 255 °C	0.1019	5	40	32.62	5	
n_D 20°C	1.5413	2	d_c g/ml	0.282	5	Parachor [P]			
25	1.5392	2	v_c ml/g	3.55	5	20°C			
30	1.5374	4	t_c °C	582.9	5	30			
"C"	0.7658	4	P_c mm	11557.	5	40			
MR (Obs.)	91.20	2	PV/RT				Sugd.	703.0	5
MR (Calc.)	90.365	2	25°C	1.0000	5	Exp. L.1.%/wt.			
(nD-d/2)	1.0786	2	30 mm	1.0000	5	u.			
Dielectric	2.376	5	BP	0.9189	5	Dispersion	207.	2	
A 255 to	7.2812	5	t_e	0.8861	5	Flash Point °C			
B 450 °C	2429.	5	t_c	0.206	5	Fire Point			
C	165.	5	ΔHc kcal/m			M. Spec.			
A* 255 to	1.9404	5	ΔHf			Ultra V.			
B* 445 °C	2323.1	5	ΔFf			X-Ray Dif.			
K			Viscosity			Infrared			
c			centistokes			Solubility in +			
t_k to			η °C			Acetone			
t_x °C						Carbon tet.			
A' 25 to	7.6469	5				Benzene			
B' 255 °C	2744.7	5				Ether			
C'	191.4	5	B^v to			n-Heptane			
A'* 25 to	2.3253	5	A^v °C			Ethanol			
B'* 255 °C	2640.6	5	(B^v) to			Water			
Ac 450 to	8.4540	5	(A^v) °C			Water in			
Bc t_c °C	4088.2	5	c_p liq. °K						
Cc	348.1	5							
Cryos. A°			c_p vap. °K						
consts. B°									
t_e °C F	436.50	5	c_v vap.						

T_R = 0.85 T_c

+ grams/100 grams solvent

REFERENCES: 1-Dow 2-API 3-Lit. 4-Calc. from det. data 5-Calc. by formula

SOURCE: API

PURIFICATION: API

LITERATURE REFERENCES:

No. 32

NAME	1-n-Undecylnaphthalene	STRUCTURAL FORMULA

$C_{11}H_{23}$

Mole % Pur.	Ref.	Molecular Formula $C_{21}H_{30}$	Molecular Weight 282.450

		Ref.			Ref.				Ref.
F.P. °C	23.	2	dt/dP			f	to		
F.P. 100%			°C/mm			g	°K		
B.P. °C			25°C	1824546.	5	h			
760 mm	401.	2	BP	0.0727	5				
100	307.4	5	t_e	0.0369	5	f'	to		
30	265.2	5	30 mm	1.0645	5	g'	°K		
10	232.6	5	ΔHm cal/g			h'			
1	177.	5							
Pressure			ΔHv cal/g			m	to		
mm 25°C	0.0_54	5	25°C	86.92	5	n	°K		
t_e	1783.	5	30 mm	63.86	5	o			
Density			BP	52.59	5				
g/ml 20°C	0.9279*	2	t_e	48.77	5	m'	to		
d_4^t 25	0.9248	2	t_e (d, e)	48.32	5	n'	°K		
30	0.9217	4	ΔHv/T_e	18.98	5	o'			
a	0.9403	4	d | 265 to	85.89	5	**Surface tension**			
b	-0.0_362	4	e | 450 °C	0.0830	5	dynes/cm. 20°C	35.31	5
Ref. Index			d' | 25 to	89.32	5	ɣ 30	34.37	5
n_D 20°C	1.5399*	2	e' | 265 °C	0.0960	5	40	33.46	5
25	1.5379	2	d_c g/ml	0.280	5	**Parachor** [P]		
30	1.5359	4	v_c ml/g	3.57	5	20°C		
"C"	0.7616	4	t_c °C	594.4	5	30		
MR (Obs.)	95.49	2	P_c mm	11030.	5	40 Sugd.	742.0	5
MR (Calc.)	94.983	5	**PV/RT**			**Exp. L.1.%/wt.**		
(nD-d/2)	1.0760	2	25°C	1.0000	5	u.		
Dielectric	2.371	5	30 mm	1.0000	5	Dispersion	201.	2
			BP	0.9164	5	**Flash Point °C**		
A |265 to	7.3278	5	t_e	0.8832	5	**Fire Point**		
B |475 °C	2517.	5	t_c	0.206	5			
C	165.	5	ΔHc kcal/m			M Spec.		
			ΔHf			Ultra V.		
A* 265 to	2.0032	5	ΔFf			X-Ray Dif.		
B* |460 °C	2409.7	5				Infrared		
K			**Viscosity**			Solubility in +		
c			centistokes			Acetone		
t_k | to			η °C			Carbon tet.		
t_x | °C						Benzene		
A' 25 to	7.6964	5				Ether		
B' |265 °C	2844.1	5				n-Heptane		
C'	192.1	5	B^v | to			Ethanol		
A'* 25 to	2.3894	5	A^v | °C			Water		
B'* 265 °C	2738.1	5	(B^v)| to			Water in		
Ac |475 to	8.5591	5	(A^v)| °C					
Bc | t_c °C	4301.2	5	c_p liq. °K					
Cc	357.9	5						
Cryos. A°			c_p vap. °K					
consts. B°								
t_e °C F	452.42	5	c_v vap.					

$T_R = 0.85 T_c$ * for undercooled liquid   + grams/100 grams solvent

REFERENCES: 1-Dow   2-API   3-Lit.   4-Calc. from det. data   5-Calc. by formula

SOURCE: API

PURIFICATION: API

LITERATURE REFERENCES:

TABLE V. ALKYL NAPHTHALENES 235

No. 33

NAME	2-n-Undecylnaphthalene		STRUCTURAL FORMULA

$C_{11}H_{23}$

Mole % Pur.		Ref.	Molecular Formula $C_{21}H_{30}$	Molecular Weight 282.450

		Ref.			Ref.				Ref.
F.P. °C	20.	2	dt/dP			f	to		
F.P. 100%			°C/mm			g	°K		
B.P. °C			25°C	1824546.	5	h			
760 mm	401.	2	BP	0.0727	5				
100	307.4	5	t_e	0.0369	5	f'	to		
30	265.2	5	30 mm	1.0645	5	g'	°K		
10	232.6	5	ΔHm cal/g			h'			
1	177.	5							
Pressure			ΔHv cal/g			m	to		
mm 25°C	0.0_5394	5	25°C	86.92	5	n	°K		
t_e	1783.	5	30 mm	63.86	5	o			
Density			BP	52.58	5				
g/ml 20°C	0.9213	2	t_e	48.76	5	m'	to		
d_4^t 25	0.9182	2	t_e (d, e)	48.31	5	n'	°K		
30	0.9151	4	ΔHv/T_e	18.98	5	o'			
a	0.9337	4	d 265 to	85.89	5	Surface tension			
b	-0.0_362	4	e 450 °C	0.0831	5	dynes/cm. 20°C	34.31	5
Ref. Index			d' 25 to	89.32	5	ɣ 30	33.40	5
n_D 20°C	1.5376	2	e' 265 °C	0.0960	5	40	32.50	5
25	1.5356	2	d_c g/ml	0.280	5	Parachor [P]			
30	1.5336	4	v_c ml/g	3.57	5	20°C			
"C"	0.7641	4	t_c °C	592.9	5	30			
MR (Obs.)	95.83	2	P_c mm	10864.	5	40			
MR (Calc.)	94.983	5	PV/RT			Sugd.	742.0	5
(nD-d/2)	1.0770	2	25°C	1.0000	5	Exp. L.1.%/wt.			
Dielectric	2.364	5	30 mm	1.0000	5	u.			
A 265 to	7.3278	5	BP	0.9164	5	Dispersion	201.	2
B 460 °C	2517.	5	t_e	0.8832	5	Flash Point °C			
C	165.	5	t_c	0.206	5	Fire Point			
A* 265 to	2.0032	5	ΔHc kcal/m			M. Spec.			
B* 460 °C	2409.7	5	ΔHf			Ultra V.			
K			ΔFf			X-Ray Dif.			
c			Viscosity			Infrared			
t_k to			centistokes			Solubility in +			
t_x °C			η °C			Acetone			
A' 25 to	7.6964	5				Carbon tet.			
B' 265 °C	2844.1	5				Benzene			
C'	192.1	5	B^v to			Ether			
A'* 25 to	2.3894	5	A^v °C			n-Heptane			
B'* 265 °C	2738.1	5	(B^v) to			Ethanol			
Ac 460 to	8.5498	5	(A^v) °C			Water			
Bc t_c °C	4280.7	5				Water in			
Cc	355.5	5	c_p liq. °K						
Cryos. A°									
consts. B°			c_p vap. °K						
t_e °C F	452.42	5	c_v vap.						

$T_R = 0.85 T_c$ + grams/100 grams solvent

REFERENCES: 1-Dow 2-API 3-Lit. 4-Calc. from det. data 5-Calc. by formula
SOURCE: API
PURIFICATION: API
LITERATURE REFERENCES:

No. 34

NAME	1-n-Dodecylnaphthalene		STRUCTURAL FORMULA

STRUCTURAL FORMULA: $C_{12}H_{25}$

Mole % Pur.	Ref.	Molecular Formula $C_{22}H_{32}$	Molecular Weight 296.476

		Ref.			Ref.				Ref.
F.P. °C	27.	2	dt/dP			f	to		
F.P. 100%			°C/mm			g	°K		
B.P. °C			25°C	4200115.	5	h			
760 mm	415.	2	BP	0.0737	5				
100	320.0	5	t_e	0.0367	5	f'	to		
30	277.0	5	30 mm	1.0845	5	g'	°K		
10	243.8	5	ΔHm cal/g			h'			
1	187.	5	ΔHv cal/g			m	to		
Pressure			25°C	85.22	5	n	°K		
mm 25°C	$0.0_5 17$	5	30 mm	62.37	5	o			
t_e	1818.	5	BP	51.42	5	m'	to		
Density			t_e	47.60	5	n'	°K		
g/ml 20°C	0.9240*	2	t_e (d,e)	47.19	5	o'			
d_4^t 25	0.9209*	2	$\Delta Hv/T_e$	19.03	5	Surface tension			
30	0.9178	4	d 275 to	84.35	5	dynes/cm. 20°C	35.10	5
a	0.9364	4	e 470 °C	0.0793	5	γ 30	34.17	5
b	$-0.0_3 62$	4	d' 25 to	87.49	5	40	33.26	5
Ref. Index			e' 275 °C	0.0907	5	Parachor [P]		
n_D 20°C	1.5364*	2	d_c g/ml	0.278	5	20°C		
25	1.5344	2	v_c ml/g	3.6	5	30		
30	1.5325	4	t_c °C	602.7	5	40		
"C"	0.7603	4	P_c mm	10228.	5	Sugd.	781.	5
MR (Obs.)	100.11	2	PV/RT			Exp. L.l.%/wt.		
MR (Calc.)	99.601	5	25°C	1.0000	5	u.		
(nD-d/2)	1.0744	2	30 mm	1.0000	5	Dispersion	196.*	2
Dielectric	2.361	5	BP	0.9151	5	Flash Point °C		
A 275 to	7.3774	5	t_e	0.8811	5	Fire Point		
B 470 °C	2608.	5	t_c	0.20	5	M Spec.		
C	165.	5	ΔHc kcal/m			Ultra V.		
A* 275 to	2.0669	5	ΔHf			X-Ray Dif.		
B* 470 °C	2498.8	5	ΔFf			Infrared		
K			Viscosity			Solubility in +		
c			centistokes			Acetone		
t_k to			η °C			Carbon tet.		
t_x °C						Benzene		
A' 25 to	7.7491	5				Ether		
B' 275 °C	2947.0	5				n-Heptane		
C'	192.8	5	B^v to			Ethanol		
A'* 25 to	2.4557	5	A^v °C			Water		
B'* 275 °C	2838.9	5	(B^v) to			Water in		
Ac 470 to	8.6510	5	(A^v) °C					
Bc t_c °C	4482.7	5	c_p liq. °K					
Cc	363.1	5	c_p vap. °K					
Cryos. A°								
consts. B°								
t_e °C F	468.34	5	c_v vap.					

$T_R = 0.85 T_c$ * for undercooled liquid   + grams/100 grams solvent

REFERENCES: 1-Dow 2-API 3-Lit. 4-Calc. from det. data 5-Calc. by formula

SOURCE:	API
PURIFICATION:	API

LITERATURE REFERENCES:

TABLE V. ALKYL NAPHTHALENES 237

No. 35

NAME	2-n-Dodecylnaphthalene					STRUCTURAL FORMULA			

$C_{12}H_{25}$

Mole % Pur.		Ref.	Molecular Formula	$C_{22}H_{32}$	Molecular Weight 296.476				

		Ref.				Ref.			Ref.
F.P. °C	26.	2	dt/dP				f	to	
F.P. 100%			°C/mm				g	°K	
B.P. °C			25°C	3943913.	5		h		
760 mm	414.	2	BP	0.0737	5				
100	319.1	5	t_e	0.0368	5		f'	to	
30	276.2	5	30 mm	1.0832	5		g'	°K	
10	243.0	5	ΔHm cal/g				h'		
1	187.	5	ΔHv cal/g				m	to	
Pressure			25°C	85.03	5		n	°K	
mm 25°C	0.0_518	5	30 mm	62.25	5		o		
t_e	1815.5	5	BP	51.31	5		m'	to	
Density			t_e	47.48	5		n'	°K	
g/ml 20°C	0.9177	2	t_e (d, e)	47.09	5		o'		
d_4^t 25	0.9146	2	ΔHv/T_e	19.01	5		Surface tension		
30	0.9115	4	d 275 to	84.16	5		dynes/cm. 20°C	34.15	5
a	0.9301	4	e 465 °C	0.0793	5		𝛾 30	33.24	5
b	-0.0_362	4	d' 25 to	87.30	5		40	32.35	5
Ref. Index			e' 275 °C	0.0907	5				
n_D 20°C	1.5343	2	d_c g/ml	0.278	5		Parachor [P]		
25	1.5323	2	v_c ml/g	3.6	5		20°C		
30	1.5305	4	t_c °C	600.1	5		30		
"C"	0.7628	4	P_c mm	10061.	5		40		
MR (Obs.)	100.47	2					Sugd.	781.	5
MR (Calc.)	99.601	5	PV/RT				Exp. L.1.%/wt.		
(nD-d/2)	1.0754	2	25°C	1.0000	5		u.		
Dielectric	2.354	5	30 mm	1.0000	5		Dispersion	196.	2
A 275 to	7.3730	5	BP	0.9153	5		Flash Point °C		
B 470 °C	2601.	5	t_e	0.8809	5		Fire Point		
C	165.	5	t_c	0.20	5		M. Spec.		
A* 275 to	2.0635	5	ΔHc kcal/m				Ultra V.		
B* 470 °C	2492.2	5	ΔHf				X-Ray Dif.		
K			ΔFf				Infrared		
c			Viscosity				Solubility in +		
t_k to			centistokes				Acetone		
t_x °C			η °C				Carbon tet.		
A' 25 to	7.7444	5					Benzene		
B' 275 °C	2939.0	5					Ether		
C'	192.8	5	B^v to				n-Heptane		
A'* 25 to	2.4516	5	A^v °C				Ethanol		
B'* 275 °C	2831.1	5	(B^v) to				Water		
Ac 470 to	8.6301	5	(A^v) °C				Water in		
Bc t_c °C	4439.4	5	c_p liq. °K						
Cc	359.3	5							
Cryos. A°			c_p vap. °K						
consts. B°									
t_e °C F	467.20	5	c_v vap.						

$T_R = 0.85 T_C$ + grams/100 grams solvent

REFERENCES: 1-Dow 2-API 3-Lit. 4-Calc. from det. data 5-Calc. by formula

SOURCE: API

PURIFICATION: API

LITERATURE REFERENCES:

TABLE VI.   TETRAHYDRONAPHTHALENES

TABLE VI. TETRAHYDRONAPHTHALENES 239

No. 1

NAME	1, 2, 3, 4-Tetrahydronaphthalene	STRUCTURAL FORMULA

Mole % Pur.	Ref.	Molecular Formula $C_{10}H_{12}$	Molecular Weight 132.196

		Ref.			Ref.			Ref.
F.P. °C	-35.790	2	dt/dP			f $\quad$ to		
F.P. 100%			°C/mm			g $\quad$ °K		
			25°C	35.31	5	h		
B.P. °C			BP	0.0568	5			
760 mm	207.57	2	t_e	0.0369	5	f' $\quad$ to		
100	135.51	5	30 mm	0.7977	5	g' $\quad$ °K		
30	103.66	5	ΔHm cal/g			h'		
10	79.36	5						
1	38.70	5	ΔHv cal/g			m $\quad$ to		
			25°C	97.86	5	n $\quad$ °K		
Pressure			30 mm	89.21	5	o		
mm 25°C	0.3869	5	BP	76.45	5			
t_e	1320.0	5	t_e	73.55	5	m' $\quad$ to		
Density			t_e (d, e)	73.63	5	n' $\quad$ °K		
g/ml 20°C	0.9702	2	$\Delta Hv/T_e$	19.21	5	o'		
d_4^t 25	0.9662	2				Surface tension		
30	0.9622	4	d $\quad$ 105 to	101.93	5	dynes/cm 21.5°C	35.46	3
a	0.9862	4	e $\quad$ 240 °C	0.1228	5	γ $\quad$ 50	32.48	3
b	$-0.0_3 80$	4	d' $\quad$ 25 to	100.61	5	40	34.19	5
Ref. Index			e' $\quad$ 105 °C	0.110	5	Parachor [P]		
n_D 20°C	1.54135	2	d_c g/ml	0.309	5	21.5°C	332.9	4
25	1.53919	2	v_c ml/g	3.24	5	50	333.3	4
30	1.53703	4	t_c °C	446.	5	40		
"C"	0.7304	4	P_c mm	26364.	5	Sugd.	334.9	5
MR (Obs.)	42.84	2	PV/RT			Exp. L.1.%/wt.		
MR (Calc.)	42.58	5	25°C	1.0000	5	u.		
(nD-d/2)	1.05625	2	30 mm	1.0000	5	Dispersion	166.	2
Dielectric			BP	0.9540	5	Flash Point °C		
A $\quad$ 105 to	6.96965	4	t_e	0.9374	5	Fire Point		
B $\quad$ 265 °C	1662.4	4	t_c	0.252	5	M. Spec.		
C	199.	5	ΔHc kcal/m			Ultra V.		
A* $\quad$ 105 to	1.38581	5	ΔHf			X-Ray Dif.		
B* $\quad$ 245 °C	1561.3	5	ΔFf			Infrared		
K			Viscosity			Solubility in $^+$		
c			centistokes			Acetone		
t_k $\quad$ to			η $\quad$ °C			Carbon tet.		
t_x $\quad$ °C						Benzene		
A' $\quad$ 25 to	7.31568	5				Ether		
B' $\quad$ 105 °C	1878.46	5				n-Heptane		
C'	218.	5	B^v $\quad$ to			Ethanol		
A'* $\quad$ 25 to	1.75162	5	A^v $\quad$ °C			Water		
B'* 105 °C	1777.38	5	(B^v) $\quad$ to			Water in		
Ac $\quad$ 265 to	7.37894	5	(A^v) $\quad$ °C					
Bc $\quad t_c$ °C	2064.90	5	c_p liq. °K					
Cc	252.	5						
Cryos. A°			c_p vap. °K					
consts. B°								
t_e °C	232.9	5	c_v vap.					

T_R = 0.75 T_c

$^+$ grams/100 grams solvent

REFERENCES: 1-Dow 2-API 3-Lit. 4-Calc. from det. data 5-Calc. by formula

SOURCE: API

PURIFICATION: API

LITERATURE REFERENCES: 3 Phys. Chem. 101, 269 (1922) Herz and Schuftan

| NAME | 1-Methyl-1,2,3,4-Tetrahydronaphthalene | STRUCTURAL FORMULA |

Structural formula: HCH_3, H_2, H_2, H_2

| Mole % Pur. | Ref. | Molecular Formula $C_{11}H_{14}$ | Molecular Weight 146.222 |

		Ref.			Ref.			Ref.
F.P. °C			dt/dP			f	to	
F.P. 100%			°C/mm			g	°K	
B.P. °C			25°C	60.3	5	h		
760 mm	219.	2	BP	0.0578	5			
100	146.	5	t_e	0.0368	5	f'	to	
30	113.	5	30 mm	0.8139	5	g'	°K	
10	88.	5	ΔHm cal/g			h'		
1	47.	5	ΔHv cal/g			m	to	
Pressure			25°C	92.21	5	n	°K	
mm 25°C	0.2173	5	30 mm	83.08	5	o		
t_e	1349.88	5	BP	71.05	5			
Density			t_e	68.17	5	m'	to	
g/ml 20°C	0.9580	2	t_e (d,e)	68.00	5	n'	°K	
d_4^t 25	0.9543	2	ΔHv/T_e	19.2	5	o'		
30	0.9506	4				Surface tension		
a	0.9728	4	d ǀ 115 to	95.93	5	dynes/cm. 20°C	36.05	5
b	-0.0₃74	4	e ǀ 245 °C	0.1136	5	ɣ 30	34.95	5
Ref. Index			d' ǀ 25 to	94.8	5	40	33.87	5
n_D 20°C	1.5357	2	e' ǀ 115 °C	0.1036	5	Parachor [P]		
25	1.5336	2	d_c g/ml	0.302	5	20°C		
30	1.5312	4	v_c ml/g	3.31	5	30		
"C"	0.7325	2	t_c °C	446.	5	40		
MR (Obs.)	47.57	2	P_c mm	23063.	5	Sugd.	374.0	5
MR (Calc.)	47.197	5	PV/RT			Exp. L.1.%/wt.		
(nD-d/2)	1.0567	2	25°C	1.0000	5	u.		
Dielectric			30 mm	1.0000	5	Dispersion		
A ǀ 115 to	6.99355	5	BP	0.9525	5	Flash Point °C		
B ǀ 260 °C	1710.9	5	t_e	0.9347	5	Fire Point		
C	197.	5	t_c	0.250	5	M Spec.		
A* ǀ 115 to	1.44653	5	ΔHc kcal/m			Ultra V.		
B* ǀ 255 °C	1608.5	5	ΔHf			X-Ray Dif.		
K			ΔFf			Infrared		
c			Viscosity			Solubility in +		
t_k ǀ to			centistokes			Acetone		
t_x ǀ °C			η °C			Carbon tet.		
A' ǀ 25 to	7.34109	5				Benzene		
B' ǀ 115 °C	1933.3	5				Ether		
C'	217.	5	B^V ǀ to			n-Heptane		
A'* 25 to	1.81602	5	A^V ǀ °C			Ethanol		
B'* 115 °C	1831.7	5	(B^V) ǀ to			Water		
Ac ǀ 260 to	7.39905	5	(A^V) ǀ °C			Water in		
Bc ǀ t_c °C	2107.3	5	c_p liq. °K					
Cc	248.	5						
Cryos. A°			c_p vap. °K					
consts. B°								
t_e °C	245.87	5	c_v vap.					

$T_R = 0.75 T_c$

REFERENCES:	1-Dow	2-API	3-Lit.	4-Calc. from det. data	5-Calc. by formula
SOURCE:	API
PURIFICATION:	API
LITERATURE REFERENCES:

TABLE VI. TETRAHYDRONAPHTHALENES 241

No. 3

NAME	2-Methyl-1,2,3,4-Tetrahydronaphthalene	STRUCTURAL FORMULA

Mole % Pur.	Ref.	Molecular Formula $C_{11}H_{14}$	Molecular Weight 146.222

		Ref.			Ref.			Ref.
F.P. °C			dt/dP			f to		
F.P. 100%			°C/mm			g °K		
B.P. °C			25°C	55.873	5	h		
760 mm	218.	2	BP	0.0578	5			
100	145.	5	t_e	0.037	5	f' to		
30	112.	5	30 mm	0.8144	5	g' °K		
10	87.	5	ΔHm cal/g			h'		
1	46.	5	ΔHv cal/g			m to		
Pressure			25°C	91.34	5	n °K		
mm 25°C	0.2368	5	30 mm	82.56	5	o		
t_e	1347.47	5	BP	70.68	5			
Density			t_e	67.83	5	m' to		
g/ml 20°C	0.952	2	t_e (d, e)	67.67	5	n' °K		
d_4^t 25	0.948	2	$\Delta Hv/T_e$	19.15	5	o'		
d_4^t 30	0.944	4				Surface tension		
a	0.968	4	d 110 to	95.12	5	dynes/cm. 20°C	35.15	5
b	-0.0380	4	e 245 °C	0.1121	5	γ 30	33.99	5
Ref. Index			d' 25 to	93.86	5	40	32.85	5
n_D 20°C	1.531	2	e' 110 °C	0.1009	5	Parachor [P]		
25	1.529	2	d_c g/ml	0.292	5	20°C		
30	1.526	4	v_c ml/g	3.42	5	30		
"C"	0.7311	4	t_c °C	442.	5	40		
MR (Obs.)	47.5	2	P_c mm	22270.	5	Sugd.	374.0	5
MR (Calc.)	47.197	5	PV/RT			Exp. L.1.%/wt.		
(nD-d/2)	1.055	2	25°C	1.0000	5	u.		
Dielectric			30 mm	1.0000	5	Dispersion		
A 110 to	6.9885	5	BP	0.9526	5	Flash Point °C		
B 260 °C	1708.8	5	t_e	0.935	5	Fire Point		
C	198.	5	t_c	0.250	5	M. Spec.		
A* 110 to	1.44133	5	ΔHc kcal/m			Ultra V.		
B* 255 °C	1606.0	5	ΔHf			X-Ray Dif.		
K			ΔFf			Infrared		
c			Viscosity			Solubility in +		
t_k to			centistokes			Acetone		
t_x °C			η °C			Carbon tet.		
A' 25 to	7.33572	5				Benzene		
B' 110 °C	1930.9	5				Ether		
C'	216.	5	B^v to			n-Heptane		
A'* 25 to	1.81016	5	A^v °C			Ethanol		
B'* 110 °C	1828.7	5	(B^v) to			Water		
Ac 260 to	7.39465	5	(A^v) °C			Water in		
Bc t_c °C	2103.9	5	c_p liq. °K					
Cc	249.	5						
Cryos. A°			c_p vap. °K					
consts. B°								
t_e °C	244.81	5	c_v vap.					

T_R = 0.75 T_c

<small>+ grams/100 grams solvent</small>

REFERENCES: 1-Dow 2-API 3-Lit. 4-Calc. from det. data 5-Calc. by formula

SOURCE:	API
PURIFICATION:	API

LITERATURE REFERENCES:

No. 4

NAME	5-Methyl-1, 2, 3, 4-tetrahydronaphthalene	STRUCTURAL FORMULA

Mole % Pur.		Ref.	Molecular Formula $C_{11}H_{14}$	Molecular Weight 146.222	

		Ref.				Ref.				Ref.
F.P. °C	-22.90	2	dt/dP				f	to		
F.P. 100%			°C/mm				g	°K		
			25°C	129.63	5		h			
B.P. °C			BP	0.05894	5					
760 mm	234.35	2	t_e	0.0369	5		f'	to		
100	159.4	5	30 mm	0.8341	5		g'	°K		
30	126.14	5					h'			
10	100.71	5	ΔHm cal/g							
1	58.06	5					m	to		
			ΔHv cal/g				n	°K		
Pressure			25°C	97.78	5		o			
mm 25°C	0.0953	5	30 mm	86.62	5					
t_e	1379.9	5	BP	73.50	5		m'	to		
			t_e	70.32	5		n'	°K		
Density			t_e (d, e)	70.05	5		o'			
g/ml 20°C	0.9720	2	$\Delta Hv/T_e$	19.18	5					
d_4^t 25	0.9683	2					Surface tension			
30	0.9646	4	d | 125 to	101.90	5		dynes/cm. 20°C		38.20	5
a	0.9868	4	e | 265 °C	0.1212	5		y	30	37.05	5
b	-0.0_374	4	d' | 25 to	100.54	5			40	35.93	5
Ref. Index			e' | 125 °C	0.1104	5					
n_D 20°C	1.54395	2	d_c g/ml	0.293	5		Parachor [P]			
25	1.54190	2	v_c ml/g	3.41	5			20°C		
30	1.53985	4	t_c °C	470.	5			30		
"C"	0.7323	4	P_c mm	24250.	5			40		
MR (Obs.)	47.48	2	PV/RT					Sugd.	373.9	5
MR (Calc.)	47.20	5	25°C	1.0000	5		Exp. L. 1.%/wt.			
(nD-d/2)	1.05795	2	30 mm	1.0000	5		u.			
Dielectric			BP	0.9448	5		Dispersion	164.		2
A | 125 to	7.03372	5	t_e	0.9252	5		Flash Point °C			
B | 280 °C	1778.9	5	t_c	0.245	5		Fire Point			
C	194.	5	ΔHc kcal/m				M Spec.			
			ΔHf				Ultra V.			
A* | 125 to	1.48795	5	ΔFf				X-Ray Dif.			
B* | 275 °C	1678.2	5					Infrared			
K			Viscosity				Solubility in +			
c			centistokes				Acetone			
t_k | to			η °C				Carbon tet.			
t_x | °C							Benzene			
A' | 25 to	7.38379	5					Ether			
B' | 125 °C	2010.1	5	B^v | to				n-Heptane			
C'	214.	5	A^v | °C				Ethanol			
A'* 25 to	1.85270	9	(B^v) | to				Water			
B'* 125 °C	1908.06	5	(A^v) | °C				Water in			
Ac | 280 to	7.43838	5	c_p liq. °K							
Bc | t_c °C	2187.1	5								
Cc	246.	5	c_p vap. °K							
Cryos. A°										
consts. B°			c_v vap.							
t_e °C	262.85	5								

$T_R = 0.75 T_c$	+ grams/100 grams solvent
REFERENCES: 1-Dow 2-API 3-Lit. 4-Calc. from det. data 5-Calc. by formula	
SOURCE: API	
PURIFICATION: API	
LITERATURE REFERENCES:	

TABLE VI. TETRAHYDRONAPHTHALENES

No. 5

NAME	6-Methyl-1,2,3,4-Tetrahydronaphthalene	STRUCTURAL FORMULA

Mole % Pur.	Ref.	Molecular Formula $C_{11}H_{14}$	Molecular Weight 146.222

		Ref.				Ref.					Ref.
F.P. °C	-39.75	2	dt/dP				f		to		
F.P. 100%			°C/mm				g		°K		
			25°C	98.987	5		h				
B.P. °C			BP	0.0586	5						
760 mm	229.	2	t_e	0.0368	5		f'		to		
100	155.	5	30 mm	0.8272	5		g'		°K		
30	122.	5	ΔHm cal/g				h'				
10	96.	5									
1	54.	5	ΔHv cal/g				m		to		
			25°C	95.82	5		n		°K		
Pressure			30 mm	85.37	5		o				
mm 25°C	0.1274	5	BP	72.81	5						
t_e	1373.38	5	t_e	69.74	5		m'		to		
Density			t_e (d, e)	69.52	5		n'		°K		
g/ml 20°C	0.9537	2	ΔHv/T_e	19.23	5		o'				
d_4^t 25	0.9500	2					Surface tension				
30	0.9463	4	d | 120 to	99.6	5		dynes/cm. 20°C		35.41	5
			e | 255 °C	0.117	5		γ		30	34.32	5
a	0.9685	4	d' | 25 to	98.52	5				40	33.26	5
b	-0.0374	4	e' | 120 °C	0.1081	5						
Ref. Index			d_c g/ml	0.303	5		Parachor [P]				
n_D 20°C	1.53572	2	v_c ml/g	3.30	5		20°C				
25	1.53365	2	t_c °C	460.	5		30				
30	1.53122	4	P_c mm	23374.	5		40				
"C"	0.7358	4					Sugd.		374.0	5
MR (Obs.)	47.79	2	PV/RT				Exp. L.1.%/wt.				
MR (Calc.)	47.197	5	25°C	1.0000	5		u.				
(nD-d/2)	1.05887	2	30 mm	1.0000	5		Dispersion		166.	2
Dielectric			BP	0.9498	5		Flash Point °C				
A | 120 to	7.01848	5	t_e	0.9311	5		Fire Point				
B | 270 °C	1754.5	5	t_c	0.247	5						
C	195.	5	ΔHc kcal/m				M. Spec.				
A* | 120 to	1.46801	5	ΔHf				Ultra V.				
B* | 265 °C	1651.9	5	ΔFf				X-Ray Dif.				
K							Infrared				
c			Viscosity				Solubility in +				
t_k | to			centistokes				Acetone				
t_x | °C			η °C				Carbon tet.				
A' | 25 to	7.36759	5					Benzene				
B' | 120 °C	1982.5	5					Ether				
C'	215.	5					n-Heptane				
A'* 25 to	1.83858	5	B^v | to				Ethanol				
B'* 120 °C	1880.6	5	A^v | °C				Water				
			(B^v)| to				Water in				
Ac | 270 to	7.42299	5	(A^v)| °C								
Bc | t_c °C	2156.8	5									
Cc | —	246.	5	c_p liq. °K								
Cryos. A°											
consts. B°			c_p vap. °K								
t_e °C	257.13	5	c_v vap.								

T_R = 0.75 T_c

+ grams/100 grams solvent

REFERENCES: 1-Dow 2-API 3-Lit. 4-Calc. from det. data 5-Calc. by formula

SOURCE: API

PURIFICATION: API

LITERATURE REFERENCES:

No. 6

NAME	1-Ethyl-1,2,3,4-Tetrahydronaphthalene	STRUCTURAL FORMULA

STRUCTURAL FORMULA

HC_2H_5
H_2
H_2
H_2

Mole % Pur.	Ref.	Molecular Formula $C_{12}H_{16}$	Molecular Weight 160.248

		Ref.			Ref.			Ref.
F.P. °C			dt/dP			f | to		
F.P. 100%			°C/mm			g | __°K_		
			25°C	139.05	5	h		
B.P. °C			BP	0.0591	5			
760 mm	236.	2	t_e	0.0367	5	f' | to		
100	161.	5				g' | __°K_		
30	127.	5	30 mm	0.837	5	h' |		
10	102.	5	ΔHm cal/g					
1	59.	5						
			ΔHv cal/g			m | to		
Pressure			25°C	89.56	5	n | __°K_		
mm 25°C	0.08854	5	30 mm	79.26	5	o |		
t_e	1394.39	5	BP	67.63	5			
Density			t_e	64.69	5	m' | to		
g/ml 20°C	0.9535	2	t_e (d, e)	64.51	5	n' | __°K_		
d_4^t 25	0.9498	2	ΔHv/T_e	19.26	5	o' |		
30	0.9461	4				Surface tension		
a	0.7896	4	d | 125 to	92.92	5	dynes/cm. 20°C	36.47	5
b	-0.0374	4	e | 265 °C	0.1072	5	γ 30	35.35	5
			d' | 25 to	92.08	5	40	34.26	5
Ref. Index			e' | 125 °C	0.1006	5			
n_D 20°C	1.5321	2	d_c g/ml	0.303	5	Parachor [P]		
25	1.5300	2	v_c ml/g	3.30	5	20°C		
30	1.5278	4	t_c °C	458.	5	30		
"C"	0.7314	4	P_c mm	21103.	5	40		
MR (Obs.)	52.08	2	PV/RT			Sugd.	412.7	5
MR (Calc.)	51.815	5	25°C	1.0000	5	Exp. L. l.%/wt.		
(nD-d/2)	1.0553	2	30 mm	1.0000	5	u.		
Dielectric			BP	0.9501	5	Dispersion		
A | 125 to	7.03639	5	t_e	0.931	5	Flash Point °C		
B | 280 °C	1786.9	5	t_c	0.245	5	Fire Point		
C	194.	5	ΔHc kcal/m			M Spec.		
A* | 125 to	1.51917	5	ΔHf			Ultra V.		
B* | 275 °C	1682.6	5	ΔFf			X-Ray Dif.		
K						Infrared		
c			Viscosity					
t_k | __ to			centistokes			Solubility in +		
t_x | °C			η °C			Acetone		
A' | 25 to	7.38662	5				Carbon tet.		
B' | 125 °C	2019.1	5				Bᵤene		
C'	214.	5	B^v | to			Ether		
A'* 25 to	1.89434	5	A^v | °C			n-Heptane		
B'* 125 °C	1916.8	5	(B^V) | to			Ethanol		
Ac | 280 to	7.47391	5	(A^V) | °C			Water		
Bc | t_c °C	2229.9	5	c_p liq. °K			Water in		
Cc	250.	5						
Cryos. A°			c_p vap. °K					
consts. B°								
t_e °C	265.12	5	c_v vap.					

$T_R = 0.75 T_c$ + grams/100 grams solvent

REFERENCES: 1-Dow   2-API   3-Lit.   4-Calc. from det. data   5-Calc. by formula

SOURCE:	API
PURIFICATION:	API
LITERATURE REFERENCES:	

TABLE VI. TETRAHYDRONAPHTHALENES

No. 7

NAME	2-Ethyl-1, 2, 3, 4-Tetrahydronaphthalene	STRUCTURAL FORMULA

Mole % Pur.	Ref.	Molecular Formula $C_{12}H_{16}$	Molecular Weight 160.248

		Ref.			Ref.				Ref.
F.P. °C			dt/dP			f	to		
F.P. 100%			°C/mm			g	___ °K		
B.P. °C			25°C	133.0	5	h			
760 mm	235.	2	BP	0.059	5				
100	160.	5	t_e	0.0368	5	f'	to		
30	127.	5	30 mm	0.8353	5	g'	___ °K		
10	101.	5				h'			
1	58.	5	ΔHm cal/g						
Pressure			ΔHv cal/g			m	to		
mm 25°C	0.0928	5	25°C	89.34	5	n	___ °K		
t_e	1391.094	5	30 mm	79.11	5	o			
			BP	67.45	5				
Density			t_e	64.51	5	m'	to		
g/ml 20°C	0.938	2	t_e (d, e)	64.34	5	n'	___ °K		
d_4^t 25	0.934	2	ΔHv/T_e	19.25	5	o'			
30	0.930	4							
a	0.954	4	d 125 to	92.73	5	Surface tension			
b	-0.0380	4	e 265 °C	0.1076	5	dynes/cm. 20°C	34.15	5
Ref. Index			d' 25 to	91.85	5	𝛾 30	33.00	5
n_D 20°C	1.523	2	e' 125 °C	0.1007	5	40	31.88	5
25	1.521	2	d_c g/ml	0.291	5				
30	1.518	4	v_c ml/g	3.43	5	Parachor [P]			
"C"	0.7315	4	t_c °C	452.	5	20°C			
MR (Obs.)	52.2	2	P_c mm	20107.	5	30			
MR (Calc.)	51.815	5	PV/RT			40			
(nD-d/2)	1.054	2	25°C	1.0000	5	Sugd.	412.7	5
Dielectric			30 mm	1.0000	5	Exp. L. 1.%/wt.			
A 125 to	7.03372	5	BP	0.9499	5	u.			
B 300 °C	1781.6	5	t_e	0.9308	5	Dispersion			
C	194.	5	t_c	0.245	5	Flash Point °C			
A* 125 to	7.14946	5	ΔHc kcal/m			Fire Point			
B* 275 °C	1677.8	5	ΔHf			M. Spec.			
K			ΔFf			Ultra V.			
c						X-Ray Dif.			
t_k to			Viscosity			Infrared			
t_x °C			centistokes			Solubility in +			
A' 25 to	7.38379	5	η °C			Acetone			
B' 125 °C	2013.2	5				Carbon tet.			
C'	214.	5				Benzene			
A'* 25 to	1.89217	5				Ether			
B'* 125 °C	1911.03	5	B^v to			n-Heptane			
Ac 300 to	7.47328	5	A^v °C			Ethanol			
Bc t_c °C	2225.3	5	(B^v) to			Water			
Cc	250.	5	(A^v) °C			Water in			
Cryos. A°			c_p liq. °K						
consts. B°			c_p vap. °K						
t_e °C	263.95	5	c_v vap.						

T_R = 0.79 T_c + grams/100 grams solvent

REFERENCES: 1-Dow 2-API 3-Lit.   4-Calc. from det. data   5-Calc. by formula

SOURCE: API

PURIFICATION: API

LITERATURE REFERENCES:

No. 8

NAME	5-Ethyl-1,2,3,4-Tetrahydronaphthalene	STRUCTURAL FORMULA

Mole % Pur.	Ref.	Molecular Formula $C_{12}H_{16}$	Molecular Weight 160.248	H_5C_2

		Ref.			Ref.				Ref.
F.P. °C			dt/dP			f | | to		
F.P. 100%			°C/mm			g | |__ __°K_		
B.P. °C			25°C	189.15	5	h |		
760 mm	242.	2	BP	0.0596	5			
100	166.	5	t_e	0.0368	5	f' | | to		
30	133.	5	30 mm	0.8449	5	g' | |__ __°K_		
10	107.	5	ΔHm cal/g			h' |		
1	64.	5	ΔHv cal/g			m | | to		
Pressure			25°C	91.58	5	n | | °K		
mm 25°C	0.0637	5	30 mm	80.54	5	o |		
t_e	1404.61	5	BP	68.48	5	m' | | to		
Density			t_e	65.43	5	n' | |__ __°K_		
g/ml 20°C	0.973	2	t_e (d,e)	65.21	5	o' |		
d_4^t 25	0.969	2	ΔHv/T_e	19.24	5	Surface tension		
30	0.965	4	d | 135 to	95.14	5	dynes/cm. 20°C	39.54	5
a	0.989	4	e | 270 °C	0.1102	5	γ 30	38.26	5
b	-0.0380	4	d' | 25 to	94.15	5	40	37.01	5
Ref. Index			e' | 135 °C	0.1027	5	Parachor [P]		
n_D 20°C	1.540	2	d_c g/ml	0.307	5	20°C		
25	1.538	2	v_c ml/g	3.26	5	30		
30	1.535	2	t_c °C	467.	5	40		
"C"	0.7266	4	P_c mm	21549.	5	Sugd.	412.7	5
MR (Obs.)	51.7	2	PV/RT			Exp. L.l. %/wt.		
MR (Calc.)	51.815	5	25°C	1.0000	5	u.		
(nD-d/2)	1.054	2	30 mm	1.0000	5	Dispersion	163.	2
Dielectric			BP	0.9464	5	Flash Point °C		
A | 135 to	7.05506	5	t_e	0.9265	5	Fire Point		
B | 320 °C	1815.8	5	t_c	0.244	5	M Spec.		
C	193.	5	ΔHc kcal/m			Ultra V.		
A* | 135 to	1.53964	5	ΔHf			X-Ray Dif.		
B* | 280 °C	1712.6	5	ΔFf			Infrared		
K			Viscosity			Solubility in +		
c			centistokes			Acetone		
t_k | to			η °C			Carbon tet.		
t_x | °C						Benzene		
A' | 25 to	7.40647	5				Ether		
B' | 135 °C	2051.8	5				n-Heptane		
C'	214.	5	B^v | to			Ethanol		
A'* 25 to	1.91149	5	A^v | °C			Water		
B'* 135 °C	1949.2	5	(B^v) | to			Water in		
Ac | 320 to	7.50497	5	(A^v) | °C					
Bc | t_c °C	2274.0	5	c_p liq. °K					
Cc	250.	5	c_p vap. °K					
Cryos. A° consts. B°								
t_e °C	271.7	5	c_v vap.					

T_R = 0.80 T_c	+ grams/100 grams solvent

REFERENCES: 1-Dow   2-API   3-Lit.   4-Calc. from det. data   5-Calc. by formula

SOURCE: API

PURIFICATION: API

LITERATURE REFERENCES:

TABLE VI. TETRAHYDRONAPHTHALENES

NAME	6-Ethyl-1,2,3,4-Tetrahydronaphthalene	STRUCTURAL FORMULA

Mole % Pur.	Ref.	Molecular Formula $C_{12}H_{16}$	Molecular Weight 160.248

	Ref.			Ref.				Ref.
F.P. °C		dt/dP			f	to		
F.P. 100%		°C/mm			g	$°\underline{K}$		
B.P. °C		25°C	180.6	5	h			
760 mm	241.	2	BP	0.0595	5			
100	165.	5	t_e	0.0368	5	f'	to	
30	132.	5	30 mm	0.8432	5	g'	$°\underline{K}$	
10	106.	5	ΔHm cal/g			h'		
1	63.	5	ΔHv cal/g			m	to	
Pressure			25°C	91.34	5	n	$°\underline{K}$	
mm 25°C	0.0668	5	30 mm	80.37	5	o		
t_e	1402.3	5	BP	68.35	5	m'	to	
Density			t_e	65.32	5	n'	$°\underline{K}$	
g/ml 20°C	0.9568	2	t_e (d, e)	65.1	5	o'		
d_4^t 25	0.9531	2	ΔHv/T_e	19.25	5	Surface tension		
30	0.9493	4	d 130 to	94.86	5	dynes/cm. 20°C	36.98	5
a	0.9716	4	e 270 °C	0.1100	5	ɤ 30	35.84	5
b	-0.0₃74	4	d' 25 to	93.91	5	40	34.74	5
Ref. Index			e' 130 °C	0.1027	5	Parachor [P]		
n_D 20°C	1.5331	2	d_c g/ml	0.306	5	20°C		
25	1.5310	2	v_c ml/g	3.27	5	30		
30	1.5287	4	t_c °C	465.	5	40		
"C"	0.7301	4	P_c mm	21418.	5	Sugd.	412.7	5
MR (Obs.)	51.85	2	PV/RT			Exp. L.1.%/wt.		
MR (Calc.)	51.815	5	25°C	1.0000	5	u.		
(nD-d/2)	1.0547	2	30 mm	1.0000	5	Dispersion	165.	2
Dielectric			BP	0.9468	5	Flash Point °C		
A 130 to	7.05177	5	t_e	0.9271	5	Fire Point		
B 320 °C	1810.2	5	t_c	0.244	5	M. Spec.		
C	193.	5	ΔHc kcal/m			Ultra V.		
A* 130 to	1.53647	5	ΔHf			X-Ray Dif.		
B* 280 °C	1707.	5	ΔFf			Infrared		
K			Viscosity			Solubility in +		
c			centistokes			Acetone		
t_k to			η °C			Carbon tet.		
t_x °C						Benzene		
A' 25 to	7.40297	5				Ether		
B' 130 °C	2045.5	5				n-Heptane		
C'	213.	5	B_v^v to			Ethanol		
A'* 25 to	1.90862	5	A^v °C			Water		
B'* 130 °C	1943.	5	(B^v)| to			Water in		
Ac 320 to	7.50560	5	(A^v)| °C					
Bc t_c °C	2270.	5						
Cc	250.	5	c_p liq. °K					
Cryos. A°			c_p vap. °K					
consts. B°								
t_e °C	270.58	5	c_v vap.					

T_R = 0.80 T_C + grams/100 grams solvent

REFERENCES: 1-Dow 2-API 3-Lit. 4-Calc. from det. data 5-Calc. by formula

SOURCE: API

PURIFICATION: API

LITERATURE REFERENCES:

No. 10

NAME	1,1-Dimethyl-1,2,3,4-Tetrahydronaphthalene	STRUCTURAL FORMULA

$(CH_3)_2$

H_2

H_2

H_2

Mole % Pur.	Ref.	Molecular Formula $C_{12}H_{16}$	Molecular Weight 160.248

		Ref.			Ref.				Ref.
F.P. °C			dt/dP			f	to		
F.P. 100%			°C/mm			g	__ °K_		
B.P. °C			25°C	65.3072	5	h			
760 mm	221.	2	BP	0.0581	5				
100	147.	5	t_e	0.0367	5	f'	to		
30	115.	5	30 mm	0.8177	5	g'	__ °K_		
10	90.	5	ΔHm cal/g			h'			
1	48.	5	ΔHv cal/g						
Pressure			25°C	84.50	5	m	to		
mm 25°C	0.1998	5	30 mm	76.05	5	n	__ °K_		
t_e	1365.05	5	BP	65.39	5	o			
Density			t_e	62.72	5				
g/ml 20°C	0.950	2	t_e (d,e)	62.63	5	m'	to		
d_4^t 25	0.946	2	ΔHv/T_e	19.27	5	n'	__ °K_		
30	0.942	4				o'			
a	0.966	4	d	115 to	87.54	5	Surface tension		
b	-0.0380	4	e	250 °C	0.1002	5	dynes/cm. 20°C	35.94	5
			d'	25 to	86.86	5	γ 30	34.74	5
Ref. Index			e'	115 °C	0.0943	5	40	33.57	5
n_D 20°C	1.5292	2	d_c g/ml	0.297	5				
25	1.5271	2	v_c ml/g	3.37	5	Parachor [P]			
30	1.5243	4	t_c °C	435.	5	20°C			
"C"	0.7300	4	P_c mm	20018.	5	30			
MR (Obs.)	52.0	2	PV/RT			40			
MR (Calc.)	51.815	5	25°C	1.0000	5	Sugd. 412.7	5		
(nD-d/2)	1.0545	2	30 mm	1.0000	5	Exp. L.1.%/wt.			
Dielectric			BP	0.9577	5	u.			
A 115 to	6.99492	5	t_e	0.9404	5	Dispersion			
B 315 °C	1719.7	5	t_c	0.245	5	Flash Point °C			
C	197.	5	ΔHc kcal/m			Fire Point			
A* 115 to	1.47633	5	ΔHf			M Spec.			
B* 260 °C	1613.8	5	ΔFf			Ultra V.			
K			Viscosity			X-Ray Dif.			
c			centistokes			Infrared			
t_k to			η °C			Solubility in +			
t_x °C						Acetone			
A' 25 to	7.34254	5				Carbon tet.			
B' 115 °C	1943.2	5				Benzene			
C'	217.	5	B^v to			Ether			
A'* 25 to	1.85606	5	A^v °C			n-Heptane			
B'* 115 °C	1841.3	5	(B^V) to			Ethanol			
Ac 320 to	7.46083	5	(A^V) °C			Water			
Bc t_c °C	2180.	5	c_p liq. °K			Water in			
Cc	255.	5	c_p vap. °K						
Cryos. A°									
consts. B°			c_v vap.						
t_e °C	248.54	5							

$T_R = 0.80 T_c$ + grams/100 grams solvent

REFERENCES: 1-Dow 2-API 3-Lit. 4-Calc. from det. data 5-Calc. by formula

SOURCE:	API
PURIFICATION:	API
LITERATURE REFERENCES:	

TABLE VI. TETRAHYDRONAPHTHALENES

NAME	1, cis-2-Dimethyl-1, 2, 3, 4-Tetrahydronaphthalene	* STRUCTURAL FORMULA

STRUCTURAL FORMULA

HCH₃ / HCH₃ / H₂ / H₂

HCH_3
HCH_3
H_2
H_2

Mole % Pur.	Ref.	Molecular Formula $C_{12}H_{16}$	Molecular Weight 160.248

		Ref.			Ref.				Ref.
F.P. °C			dt/dP			f	to		
F.P. 100%			°C/mm			g	___ °K		
			25°C	127.2	5	h			
B.P. °C			BP	0.0593	5				
760 mm	235.	2	t_e	0.0373	5	f'	to		
100	160.	5	30 mm	0.8377	5	g'	___ °K		
30	126.	5	ΔHm cal/g			h'			
10	101.	5							
1	58.	5	ΔHv cal/g			m	to		
			25°C	88.45	5	n	___ °K		
Pressure			30 mm	78.7	5	o			
mm 25°C	0.0976	5	BP	67.55	5				
t_e	1403.8	5	t_e	64.65	5	m'	to		
Density			t_e (d, e)	64.52	5	n'	___ °K		
g/ml 20°C	0.9470	2	ΔHv/T_e	19.26	5	o'			
d_4^t 25	0.9433	2							
30	0.9396	4	d 125 to	91.62	5	Surface tension		
a	0.9618	4	e 265 °C	0.1024	5	dynes/cm. 20°C	35.48	5
b	-0.0₃74	4	d' 25 to	91.35	5	ɤ 30	34.39	5
Ref. Index			e' 125 °C	0.1003	5	40	33.32	5
n_D 20°C	1.5286	2	d_c g/ml	0.298	5	Parachor [P]		
25	1.5265	2	v_c ml/g	3.35	5	20°C		
30	1.5246	4	t_c °C	456.	5	30		
"C"	0.7318	4	P_c mm	20640.	5	40		
MR (Obs.)	52.16	2	PV/RT			Sugd.	412.7	5
MR (Calc.)	51.815	5	25°C	1.0000	5			
(nD-d/2)	1.0551	2	30 mm	1.0000	5	Exp. L.1.%/wt.		
Dielectric			BP	0.9566	5	u.		
			t_e	0.9382	5	Dispersion		
A 125 to	7.00994	5	t_c	0.244	5	Flash Point °C		
B 290 °C	1771.4	5	ΔHc kcal/m			Fire Point		
C	194.	5	ΔHf			M. Spec.		
A* 125 to	1.48194	5	ΔFf			Ultra V.		
B* 275 °C	1663.7	5				X-Ray Dif.		
K			Viscosity			Infrared		
c			centistokes			Solubility in +		
t_k to			η °C			Acetone		
t_x °C						Carbon tet.		
A' 25 to	7.35851	5				Benzene		
B' 125 °C	2001.6	5				Ether		
C'	214.	5	B^v to			n-Heptane		
A'* 25 to	1.86733	5	A^v °C			Ethanol		
B'* 125 °C	1899.6	5	(B^v) to			Water		
Ac 290 to	7.48207	5	(A^v) °C			Water in		
Bc t_c °C	2252.	5	c_p liq. °K					
Cc	255.	5						
Cryos. A°			c_p vap. °K					
consts. B°								
t_e °C	264.60	5	c_v vap.					

$T_R = 0.80\, T_C$

+ grams/100 grams solvent

REFERENCES: 1-Dow	2-API	3-Lit.	4-Calc. from det. data	5-Calc. by formula

SOURCE:	API
PURIFICATION:	API

LITERATURE REFERENCES:

* 1, trans-2-Dimethyl-1, 2, 3, 4-Tetrahydronaphthalene (same data)

No. 12

| NAME | 1, cis-3-Dimethyl-1, 2, 3, 4-Tetrahydronaphthalene | * STRUCTURAL FORMULA |

| Mole % Pur. | Ref. | Molecular Formula $C_{12}H_{16}$ | Molecular Weight 160.248 |

		Ref.				Ref.					Ref.
F.P. °C			dt/dP				f	to			
F.P. 100%			°C/mm				g	__°K_			
B.P. °C			25°C	118.34	5		h				
760 mm	234.	2	BP	0.0594	5						
100	159.	5	t_e	0.0368	5		f'	to			
30	125.	5	30 mm	0.8377	5		g'	__°K_			
10	100.	5	ΔHm cal/g				h'				
1	57.	5									
			ΔHv cal/g				m	to			
Pressure			25°C	88.11	5		n	__°K_			
mm 25°C	0.1058	5	30 mm	78.31	5		o				
t_e	1400.6	5	BP	67.26	5						
Density			t_e	64.38	5		m'	to			
g/ml 20°C	0.940	2	t_e (d, e)	64.27	5		n'	__°K_			
d_4^t 25	0.936	2	ΔHv/T_e	19.22	5		o'				
30	0.932	4	d $\|$ 125 to	91.01	5		Surface tension				
a	0.956	4	e $\|$ 265 °C	0.1015	5		dynes/cm. 20°C	34.45	5
b	-0.0380	4	d' $\|$ 25 to	90.56	5		ɤ 30	33.29	5
Ref. Index			e' $\|$ 125 °C	0.0979	5		40	32.16	5
n_D 20°C	1.525	2	d_c g/ml	0.29	5		Parachor [P]		
25	1.523	2	v_c ml/g	3.45	5		20°C		
30	1.520	4	t_c °C	451.	5		30		
"C"	0.7325	4	P_c mm	19905.	5		40		
MR (Obs.)	52.3	2	PV/RT				Sugd.	412.7	5
MR (Calc.)	51.815	5	25°C	1.0000	5		Exp. L.1.%/wt.		
(nD-d/2)	1.055	2	30 mm	1.0000	5		u.		
Dielectric			BP	0.9564	5		Dispersion		
			t_e	0.9380	5		Flash Point °C		
A $\|$ 125 to	7.00994	5	t_c	0.244	5		Fire Point		
B $\|$ 305 °C	1771.4	5	ΔHc kcal/m				M Spec.		
C	195.	5	ΔHf				Ultra V.		
A* $\|$ 125 to	1.48249	5	ΔFf				X-Ray Dif.		
B* $\|$ 275 °C	1663.5	5					Infrared		
K			Viscosity				Solubility in +		
c			centistokes				Acetone		
t_k $\|$ to			η °C				Carbon tet.		
t_x $\|$ °C							Benzene		
A' $\|$ 25 to	7.35851	5					Ether		
B' $\|$ 125 °C	2001.6	5					n-Heptane		
C'	215.	5	B^V $\|$ to				Ethanol		
A'* 25 to	1.86697	5	A^V $\|$ °C				Water		
B'* 125 °C	1899.1	5	(B^V) $\|$ to				Water in		
Ac $\|$ 305 to	7.48945	5	(A^V) °C						
Bc $\|$ t_c °C	2252.5	5	c_p liq. °K						
Cc	255.	5	c_p vap. °K						
Cryos. A° consts. B°			c_v vap.						
t_e °C	263.49	5							

$T_R = 0.80 T_c$ + grams/100 grams solvent

REFERENCES: 1-Dow 2-API 3-Lit. 4-Calc. from det. data 5-Calc. by formula

| SOURCE: | API |

| PURIFICATION: | API |

LITERATURE REFERENCES:

* 1, trans-3-Dimethyl-1, 2, 3, 4-Tetrahydronaphthalene (same data)

TABLE VI.   TETRAHYDRONAPHTHALENES   251

No. 13

NAME		1, cis-4-Dimethyl-1, 2, 3, 4-Tetrahydronaphthalene				* STRUCTURAL FORMULA		

HCH₃
H₂
H₂
HCH₃

Mole % Pur.	Ref.	Molecular Formula $C_{12}H_{16}$		Molecular Weight 160.248	

		Ref.			Ref.			Ref.
F.P. °C			dt/dP			f | to		
F.P. 100%			°C/mm			g | °K		
B.P. °C			25°C	118.34	5	h |		
760 mm	234.	2	BP	0.0594	5			
100	159.	5	t_e	0.0368	5	f' | to		
30	125.	5	30 mm	0.8377	5	g' | °K		
10	100.	5	ΔHm cal/g			h' |		
1	57.	5	ΔHv cal/g			m | to		
Pressure			25°C	88.11	5	n | °K		
mm 25°C	0.1058	5	30 mm	78.31	5	o |		
t_e	1400.65	5	BP	67.26	5			
Density			t_e	64.38	5	m' | to		
g/ml 20°C	0.940	2	t_e (d, e)	64.27	5	n' | °K		
d_4^t 25	0.936	2	ΔHv/T_e	19.22	5	o' |		
30	0.932	4				Surface tension		
a	0.956	4	d | 125 to	91.01	5	dynes/cm. 20°C	34.45	5
b	-0.0₃80	4	e | 265 °C	0.1015	5	30	33.29	5
Ref. Index			d' | 25 to	90.56	5	40	32.16	5
n_D 20°C	1.525	2	e' | 125 °C	0.0979	5			
25	1.523	2	d_c g/ml	0.29	5	Parachor [P]		
30	1.520	4	v_c ml/g	3.45	5	20°C		
"C"	0.7325	4	t_c °C	451.	5	30		
MR (Obs.)	52.3	2	P_c mm	19905.2	5	40		
MR (Calc.)	51.815	5	PV/RT			Sugd.	412.7	5
(nD-d/2)	1.055	2	25°C	1.0000	5	Exp. L. l.%/wt.		
Dielectric			30 mm	1.0000	5	u.		
A | 125 to	7.00994	5	BP	0.9564	5	Dispersion		
B | 305 °C	1771.4	5	t_e	0.9380	5	Flash Point °C		
C	195.	5	t_c	0.244	5	Fire Point		
A* | 125 to	1.48249	5	ΔHc kcal/m			M. Spec.		
B* | 275 °C	1663.5	5	ΔHf			Ultra V.		
K			ΔFf			X-Ray Dif.		
c			Viscosity			Infrared		
t_k | to			centistokes			Solubility in +		
t_x | °C			η °C			Acetone		
A' | 25 to	7.35851	5				Carbon tet.		
B' | 125 °C	2001.6	5				Benzene		
C'	215.	5	B^v | to			Ether		
A'* | 25 to	1.86697	5	A^v | °C			n-Heptane		
B'* 125 °C	1899.1	5	(B^v)| to			Ethanol		
Ac | 305 to	7.48945	5	(A^v)| °C			Water		
Bc | t_c °C	2252.5	5	c_p liq. °K			Water in		
Cc |	255.	5						
Cryos. A°			c_p vap. °K					
consts. B°								
t_e °C	263.49	5	c_v vap.					

T_R = 0.80 T_c + grams/100 grams solvent

REFERENCES: 1-Dow   2-API   3-Lit.   4-Calc. from det. data   5-Calc. by formula

SOURCE: API

PURIFICATION: API

LITERATURE REFERENCES:

* 1, trans-4-Dimethyl-1, 2, 3, 4-Tetrahydronaphthalene (same data)

NAME	2,2-Dimethyl-1,2,3,4-Tetrahydronaphthalene	STRUCTURAL FORMULA

Structural formula shown: H_2, $(CH_3)_2$, H_2, H_2

Mole % Pur.		Ref.	Molecular Formula $C_{12}H_{16}$		Molecular Weight 160.248	

		Ref.				Ref.				Ref.
F.P. °C			dt/dP				f	to		
F.P. 100%			°C/mm				g	°K		
B.P. °C			25°C	103.43		5	h			
760 mm	230.	2	BP	0.0586		5				
100	155.	5	t_e	0.0371		5	f'	to		
30	122.	5	30 mm	0.8287		5	g'	°K		
10	97.	5					h'			
1	55.	5	ΔHm cal/g							
Pressure			ΔHv cal/g				m	to		
mm 25°C	0.1216	5	25°C	87.66		5	n	°K		
t_e	1362.4	5	30 mm	78.06		5	o			
Density			BP	66.00		5	m'	to		
g/ml 20°C	0.935	2	t_e	63.13		5	n'	°K		
d_4^t 25	0.931	2	t_e (d, e)	62.89		5	o'			
30	0.927	4	ΔHv/T_e	19.05		5	Surface tension			
a	0.9510	4	d 120 to	91.79		5	dynes/cm. 20°C	33.72		5
b	-0.0₃80	4	e 260 °C	0.1121		5	γ 30	32.58		5
Ref. Index			d' 25 to	90.13		5	40	31.47		5
n_D 20°C	1.5200	2	e' 120 °C	0.0986		5	Parachor [P]			
25	1.5180	2	d_c g/ml	0.288		5	20°C			
30	1.5160	4	v_c ml/g	3.47		5	30			
"C"	0.7299		t_c °C	443.		5	40			
MR (Obs.)	52.1	2	P_c mm	19678.		5	Sugd.	412.7		5
MR (Calc.)	51.815	5	PV/RT				Exp. L.l.%/wt.			
(nD-d/2)	1.0525	2	25°C	1.0000		5	u.			
Dielectric			30 mm	1.0000		5	Dispersion			
A 120 to	7.02175	5	BP	0.9419		5	Flash Point °C			
B 300 °C	1759.9	5	t_e	0.9224		5	Fire Point			
C	195.	5	t_c	0.245		5	M Spec.			
A* 120 to	1.52426	5	ΔHc kcal/m				Ultra V.			
B* 270 °C	1661.5	5	ΔHf				X-Ray Dif.			
K			ΔFf				Infrared			
c			Viscosity				Solubility in +			
t_k to			centistokes				Acetone			
t_x °C			η °C				Carbon tet.			
A' 25 to	7.37106	5					Benzene			
B' 120 °C	1988.6	5					Ether			
C'	215.	5	B^v to				n-Heptane			
A'* 25 to	1.88123	5	A^v °C				Ethanol			
B'* 120 °C	1886.6	5	(B^v) to				Water			
Ac 300 to	7.47722	5	(A^v) °C				Water in			
Bc t_c °C	2206.	5	c_p liq. °K							
Cc	250.	5								
Cryos. A°			c_p vap. °K							
consts. B°										
t_e °C	257.72	5	c_v vap.							

$T_R = 0.80 T_c$ + grams/100 grams solvent

REFERENCES: 1-Dow   2-API   3-Lit.   4-Calc. from det. data   5-Calc. by formula

SOURCE:	API
PURIFICATION:	API
LITERATURE REFERENCES:	

TABLE VI. TETRAHYDRONAPHTHALENES   253

No. 15

NAME	2, cis-3-Dimethyl-1, 2, 3, 4-Tetrahydronaphthalene	* STRUCTURAL FORMULA

Mole % Pur.	Ref.	Molecular Formula $C_{12}H_{16}$	Molecular Weight 160.248

		Ref.			Ref.				Ref.
F.P. °C			dt/dP			f	to		
F.P. 100%			°C/mm			g	°K		
			25°C	113.09	5	h			
B.P. °C			BP	0.0588	5				
760 mm	232.	2	t_e	0.0372	5	f'	to		
100	157.	5	30 mm	0.8320	5	g'	°K		
30	124.	5	ΔHm cal/g			h'			
10	99.	5							
1	56.	5	ΔHv cal/g			m	to		
			25°C	88.13	5	n	°K		
Pressure			30 mm	78.39	5	o			
mm 25°C	0.11064	5	BP	62.20	5				
t_e	1365.3	5	t_e	63.30	5	m'	to		
			t_e (d, e)	63.05	5	n'	°K		
Density			ΔHv/T_e	19.03	5	o'			
g/ml 20°C	0.940	2							
d_4^t 25	0.936	2	d 125 to	92.38	5	Surface tension			
30	0.932	4	e 260 °C	0.1128	5	dynes/cm. 20°C	34.45	5
			d' 25 to	90.59	5	δ 30	33.29	5
a	0.9560	4	e' 125 °C	0.0984	5	40	32.16	5
b	-0.0380	4							
			d_c g/ml	0.291	5	Parachor [P]			
Ref. Index			v_c ml/g	3.44	5	20°C			
n_D 20°C	1.523	2	t_c °C	447.	5	30			
25	1.521	2	P_c mm	19872.	5	40			
30	1.518	4				Sugd.	412.7	5
"C"	0.7299	4	PV/RT						
MR (Obs.)	52.1	2	25°C	1.0000	5	Exp. L.1.%/wt.			
MR (Calc.)	51.815	5	30 mm	1.0000	5	u.			
(nD-d/2)	1.053	2	BP	0.9404	5	Dispersion			
Dielectric			t_e	0.9205	5	Flash Point °C			
A 125 to	7.02764	5	t_c	0.244	5	Fire Point			
B 300 °C	1770.7	5	ΔHc kcal/m			M. Spec.			
C	195.	5	ΔHf			Ultra V.			
A* 125 to	1.53111	5	ΔFf			X-Ray Dif.			
B* 270 °C	1672.6	5				Infrared			
K			Viscosity			Solubility in +			
c			centistokes			Acetone			
t_k to			η °C			Carbon tet.			
t_x °C						Benzene			
A' 25 to	7.37732	5				Ether			
B' 125 °C	2000.8	5				n-Heptane			
C'	215.	5	B^v to			Ethanol			
A'* 25 to	1.88684	5	A^v °C			Water			
B'* 125 °C	1898.6	5	(B^v) to			Water in			
Ac 300 to	7.47040	5	(A^v) °C						
Bc t_c °C	2211.	5	c_p liq. °K						
Cc	250.	5							
Cryos. A°			c_p vap. °K						
consts. B°									
t_e °C	259.91	5	c_v vap.						

$T_R = 0.80 T_c$ + grams/100 grams solvent

REFERENCES:	1-Dow 2-API 3-Lit. 4-Calc. from det. data 5-Calc. by formula
SOURCE:	API
PURIFICATION:	API
LITERATURE REFERENCES:	

* 2, trans-3-Dimethyl-1, 2, 3, 4-Tetrahydronaphthalene (same data)

No. 16

NAME	1,5-Dimethyl-1,2,3,4-Tetrahydronaphthalene	* STRUCTURAL FORMULA

Structural formula: HCH_3, H_2, H_2, H_3C, H_2

Mole % Pur.	Ref.	Molecular Formula $C_{12}H_{16}$	Molecular Weight 160.248

		Ref.			Ref.				Ref.
F.P. °C			dt/dP			f	to		
F.P. 100%			°C/mm			g	__ °K.		
B.P. °C			25°C	159.34	5	h			
760 mm	239.	2	BP	0.0594	5				
100	164.	5	t_e	0.0373	5	f'	to		
30	130.	5	30 mm	0.8419	5	g'	__ °K_		
10	104.	5	ΔHm cal/g			h'			
1	61.	5	ΔHv cal/g			m	to		
Pressure			25°C	90.28	5	n	__ °K		
mm 25°C	0.0767	5	30 mm	79.76	5	o			
t_e	1374.86	5	BP	67.00	5	m'	to		
Density			t_e	63.97	5	n'	__ °K_		
g/ml 20°C	0.941	2	t_e (d,e)	63.66	5	o'			
d_4^t 25	0.937	2	ΔHv/T_e	18.96	5	Surface tension			
30	0.933	4	d 130 to	94.94	5	dynes/cm. 20°C	34.59	5
a	0.957	4	e 270 °C	0.1169	5	y 30	33.43	5
b	-0.0₃80	4	d' 25 to	92.78	5	40	32.30	5
Ref. Index			e' 130 °C	0.1003	5	Parachor [P]		
n_D 20°C	1.526	2	d_c g/ml	0.291	5	20°C		
25	1.524	2	v_c ml/g	3.44	5	30		
30	1.521	4	t_c °C	456.	5	40		
"C"	-0.7331	4	P_c mm	20050.	5	Sugd. 412.7	5
MR (Obs.)	52.3	2	PV/RT			Exp. L.1.%/wt.		
MR (Calc.)	51.815	5	25°C	1.0000	5	u.		
(nD-d/2)	1.053	2	30 mm	1.0000	5	Dispersion		
Dielectric			BP	0.9348	5	Flash Point °C		
A 130 to	7.0457	5	t_e	0.9139	5	Fire Point		
B 310 °C	1803.4	5	t_c	0.243	5	M Spec.		
C	194.	5	ΔHc kcal/m			Ultra V.		
A* 130 to	1.55344	5	ΔHf			X-Ray Dif.		
B* 280 °C	1707.3	5	ΔFf			Infrared		
K			Viscosity			Solubility in +		
c			centistokes			Acetone		
t_k to			η °C			Carbon tet.		
t_x °C						Benzene		
A' 25 to	7.39652	5				Ether		
B' 130 °C	2037.8	5	B^V to			n-Heptane		
C'	214.	5	A^V °C			Ethanol		
A'* 25 to	1.9023	5	(B^V) to			Water		
B'* 130 °C	1934.9	5	(A^V) °C			Water in		
Ac 310 to	7.5032	5	c_p liq. °K					
Bc t_c °C	2260.	5						
Cc	250.	5	c_p vap. °K					
Cryos. A°								
consts. B°			c_v vap.					
t_e °C	267.53	5						

$T_R = 0.80 T_c$ + grams/100 grams solvent

REFERENCES: 1-Dow 2-API 3-Lit. 4-Calc. from det. data 5-Calc. by formula

SOURCE:	API
PURIFICATION:	API

LITERATURE REFERENCES:

* 1,6-Dimethyl-1,2,3,4-Tetrahydronaphthalene (same data);
  1,7-Dimethyl-1,2,3,4-Tetrahydronaphthalene (same data);
  1,8-Dimethyl-1,2,3,4-Tetrahydronaphthalene (same data).

TABLE VI. TETRAHYDRONAPHTHALENES

No. 17

NAME	2, 5-Dimethyl-1, 2, 3, 4-Tetrahydronaphthalene	STRUCTURAL FORMULA

Mole % Pur.	Ref.	Molecular Formula $C_{12}H_{16}$	Molecular Weight 160.248

		Ref.			Ref.			Ref.
F.P. °C			dt/dP			f | to		
F.P. 100%			°C/mm			g | _ _ _°K		
B.P. °C			25°C	139.05	5	h |		
760 mm	236.	2	BP	0.0591	5			
100	161.	5	t_e	0.0371	5	f' | to		
30	127.	5	30 mm	0.8370	5	g' | _ _ _°K		
10	102.	5	ΔHm cal/g			h' |		
1	59.	5						
			ΔHv cal/g			m | to		
Pressure			25°C	89.56	5	n | _ _ _°K		
mm 25°C	0.0885	5	30 mm	79.26	5	o |		
t_e	1378.4	5	BP	67.00	5			
Density			t_e	64.03	5	m' | to		
g/ml 20°C	0.946	2	t_e (d, e)	63.78	5	n' | _ _ _°K		
d_4^t 25	0.942	2	ΔHv/T_e	19.08	5	o' |		
30	0.938	4				Surface tension		
a	0.962	4	d | 125 to	93.66	5	dynes/cm. 20°C	35.33	5
b	-0.0380	4	e | 265 °C	0.113	5	δ 30	34.15	5
Ref. Index			d' | 25 to	92.08	5	40	33.00	5
n_D 20°C	1.526	2	e' | 125 °C	0.1006	5	Parachor [P]		
25	1.524	2	d_c g/ml	0.293	5	20°C		
30	1.522	4	v_c ml/g	3.41	5	30		
"C"	0.7292	4	t_c °C	454.	5	40		
			P_c mm	20330.	5	Sugd.	412.7	5
MR (Obs.)	52.0	2	PV/RT			Exp. L.1.%/wt.		
MR (Calc.)	51.815	5	25°C	1.0000	5	u.		
(nD-d/2)	1.053	2	30 mm	1.0000	5	Dispersion		
Dielectric			BP	0.9414	5	Flash Point °C		
A | 125 to	7.03639	5	t_e	0.9213	5	Fire Point		
B | 310 °C	1786.9	5	t_c	0.244	5	M. Spec.		
C	194.	5	ΔHc kcal/m			Ultra V.		
A* | 125 to	1.53495	5	ΔHf			X-Ray Dif.		
B* | 275 °C	1687.7	5	ΔFf			Infrared		
K			Viscosity			Solubility in +		
c			centistokes			Acetone		
t_k | to			η °C			Carbon tet.		
t_x | °C						Benzene		
A' | 25 to	7.38662	5				Ether		
B' | 125 °C	2019.1	5				n-Heptane		
C'	214.	5	B^v | to			Ethanol		
A'* 25 to	1.89434	5	A^v | °C			Water		
B'* 125 °C	1916.8	5	(B^v)| to			Water in		
Ac' 310 to	7.50565	5	(A^v)| °C					
Bc | t_c °C	2268.3	5	c_p liq. °K					
Cc	255.	5						
Cryos. A°			c_p vap. °K					
consts. B°								
t_e °C	264.53	5	c_v vap.					

$T_R = 0.80 T_C$ + grams/100 grams solvent

REFERENCES: 1-Dow 2-API 3-Lit. 4-Calc. from det. data 5-Calc. by formula
SOURCE: API
PURIFICATION: API
LITERATURE REFERENCES:

No. 18

NAME	2,6-Dimethyl-1,2,3,4-Tetrahydronaphthalene	STRUCTURAL FORMULA

Mole % Pur.	Ref.	Molecular Formula $C_{12}H_{16}$	Molecular Weight 160.248

		Ref.			Ref.			Ref.
F.P. °C			dt/dP			f	to	
F.P. 100%			°C/mm			g	°K	
			25°C	152.40	5	h		
B.P. °C			BP	0.0593	5			
760 mm	238.	2	t_e	0.0372	5	f'	to	
100	162.	5	30 mm	0.8402	5	g'	°K	
30	129.	5	ΔHm cal/g			h'		
10	103.	5						
1	60.	5	ΔHv cal/g			m	to	
Pressure			25°C	90.05	5	n	°K	
mm 25°C	0.0804	5	30 mm	79.60	5	o		
t_e	1375.8	5	BP	67.00	5			
Density			t_e	63.99	5	m'	to	
g/ml 20°C	0.941	2	t_e (d,e)	63.70	5	n'	°K	
d_4^t 25	0.937	2	ΔHv/T_e	19.01	5	o'		
30	0.933	4				Surface tension		
a	0.763	4	d 130 to	94.53	5	dynes/cm. 20°C	34.59	5
b	-0.0380	4	e 265 °C	0.1157	5	γ 30	33.43	5
Ref. Index			d' 25 to	92.56	5	40	32.30	5
n_D 20°C	1.526	2	e' 130 °C	0.1004	4			
25	1.524	2	d_c g/ml	0.290	5	Parachor [P]		
30	1.521	4	v_c ml/g	3.45	5	20°C		
"C"	0.7331	4	t_c °C	455.	5	30		
MR (Obs.)	52.4	2	P_c mm	20064.	5	40		
MR (Calc.)	51.815	5	PV/RT			Sugd.	412.7	5
(nD-d/2)	1.056	2	25°C	1.0000	5	Exp. L.1.%/wt.		
Dielectric			30 mm	1.0000	5	u.		
A 130 to	7.04307	5	BP	0.9369	5	Dispersion		
B 310 °C	1798.1	5	t_e	0.9162	5	Flash Point °C		
C	194.	5	t_c	0.244	5	Fire Point		
A* 130 to	1.54794	5	ΔHc kcal/m			M Spec.		
B* 275 °C	1701.0	5	ΔHf			Ultra V.		
K			ΔFf			X-Ray Dif.		
c			Viscosity			Infrared		
t_k to			centistokes			Solubility in +		
t_x °C			η °C			Acetone		
A' 25 to	7.39373	5				Carbon tet.		
B' 130 °C	2031.8	5				Benzene		
C'	214.	5	B^V to			Ether		
A'* 25 to	1.90013	5	A^V °C			n-Heptane		
B'* 130 °C	1929.1	5	$(\overline{B^V})$ to			Ethanol		
Ac 310 to	7.52365	5	$(\overline{A^V})$ °C			Water		
Bc t_c °C	2287.8	5	c_p liq. °K			Water in		
Cc	255.	5						
Cryos. A°			c_p vap. °K					
consts. B°								
t_e °C	266.52	5	c_v vap.					

$T_R = 0.80 T_c$ + grams/100 grams solvent

REFERENCES: 1-Dow 2-API 3-Lit. 4-Calc. from det. data 5-Calc. by formula
SOURCE: API
PURIFICATION: API
LITERATURE REFERENCES:

TABLE VI. TETRAHYDRONAPHTHALENES   257

No. 19

NAME	2,7-Dimethyl-1,2,3,4-Tetrahydronaphthalene	STRUCTURAL FORMULA

Mole % Pur.	Ref.	Molecular Formula $C_{12}H_{16}$	Molecular Weight 160.248

		Ref.			Ref.				Ref.
F.P. °C			dt/dP			f	to		
F.P. 100%			°C/mm			g	___ °K		
B.P. °C			25°C	145.6	5	h			
760 mm	237.	2	BP	0.0592	5				
100	162.	5	t_e	0.0372	5	f'	to		
30	128.	5	30 mm	0.8386	5	g'	___ °K		
10	103.	5	ΔHm cal/g			h'			
1	60.	5	ΔHv cal/g			m	to		
Pressure			25°C	89.81	5	n	___ °K		
mm 25°C	0.0843	5	30 mm	79.43	5	o			
t_e	1377.2	5	BP	67.00	5	m'	to		
Density			t_e	64.01	5	n'	___ °K		
g/ml 20°C	0.941	2	t_e (d,e)	63.74	5	o'			
d_4^t 25	0.937	2	ΔHv/T_e	19.04	5	Surface tension			
30	0.933	4	d	130 to	94.09	5	dynes/cm. 20°C	34.31	5
a	0.957	4	e	265 °C	0.1143	5	δ	30	33.43	5
b	-0.0₃80	4	d'	25 to	92.32	5		40	33.3	5
Ref. Index			e'	130 °C	0.1005	5				
n_D 20°C	1.526	2	d_c g/ml		0.291	5	Parachor [P]			
25	1.524	2	v_c ml/g		3.43	5	20°C			
30	1.522	4	t_c °C		454.	5	30			
"C"	0.7331	4	P_c mm		20070.	5	40			
MR (Obs.)	52.4	2	PV/RT				Sugd.	412.7	5
MR (Calc.)	51.815	5	25°C	1.0000	5	Exp. L.1.%/wt.			
(nD-d/2)	1.056	2	30 mm	1.0000	5	u.			
Dielectric			BP	0.9392	5	Dispersion			
A 130 to	7.03974	5	t_e	0.9188	5	Flash Point °C			
B 310 °C	1792.5	5	t_c	0.244	5	Fire Point			
C	194.	5	ΔHc kcal/m			M. Spec.			
A* 130 to	1.54142	5	ΔHf			Ultra V.			
B* 275 °C	1694.4	5	ΔFf			X-Ray Dif.			
K			Viscosity			Infrared			
c			centistokes			Solubility in +			
t_k to			η °C			Acetone			
t_x °C						Carbon tet.			
A' 25 to	7.3902	5				Benzene			
B' 130 °C	2025.5	5				Ether			
C'	214.	5	B^v to			n-Heptane			
A'* 25 to	1.89724	5	A_v °C			Ethanol			
B'* 130 °C	1923.	5	(B^v) to			Water			
Ac 310 to	7.51735	5	(A^v) °C			Water in			
Bc t_c °C	2279.3	5	c_p liq. °K						
Cc	255.	5							
Cryos. A° consts. B°			c_p vap. °K						
t_e °C	265.53	5	c_v vap.						

T_R = 0.80 T_c + grams/100 grams solvent

REFERENCES: 1-Dow   2-API   3-Lit.   4-Calc. from det. data   5-Calc. by formula

SOURCE: API

PURIFICATION: API

LITERATURE REFERENCES:

No. 20

NAME	2,8-Dimethyl-1,2,3,4-Tetrahydronaphthalene	STRUCTURAL FORMULA

Mole % Pur.	Ref.	Molecular Formula $C_{12}H_{16}$	Molecular Weight 160.248

		Ref.			Ref.			Ref.
F.P. °C			dt/dP			f | to		
F.P. 100%			°C/mm			g | °K		
B.P. °C			25°C	139.05	5	h |		
760 mm	236.	2	BP	0.0591	5			
100	161.	5	t_e	0.0371	5	f' | to		
30	127.	5	30 mm	0.8370	5	g' | °K		
10	102.	5	ΔHm cal/g			h' |		
1	59.	5	ΔHv cal/g			m | to		
Pressure			25°C	89.57	5	n | °K		
mm 25°C	0.0885	5	30 mm	79.26	5	o |		
t_e	1378.5	5	BP	67.00	5			
Density			t_e	64.03	5	m' | to		
g/ml 20°C	0.941	2	t_e (d,e)	63.78	5	n' | °K		
d_4^t 25	0.937	2	ΔHv/T_e	19.08	5	o' |		
30	0.933	4				Surface tension		
a	0.957	4	d | 125 to	93.66	5	dynes/cm. 20°C	34.59	5
b	-0.0₃80	4	e | 265 °C	0.1130	5	30	33.43	5
Ref. Index			d' | 25 to	92.08	5	40	32.30	5
n_D 20°C	1.526	2	e' | 125 °C	0.1006	5	Parachor [P]		
25	1.524	2	d_c g/ml	0.291	5	20°C		
30	1.521	4	v_c ml/g	3.43	5	30		
"C"	0.7331	4	t_c °C	453.	5	40		
MR (Obs.)	52.4	2	P_c mm	20079.	5	Sugd.	412.7	5
MR (Calc.)	51.815	5	PV/RT			Exp. L.l.%/wt.		
(nD-d/2)	1.056	2	25°C	1.0000	5	u.		
Dielectric			30 mm	1.0000	5	Dispersion		
A | 125 to	7.03639	5	BP	0.9414	5	Flash Point °C		
B | 310 °C	1786.9	5	t_e	0.9214	5	Fire Point		
C	194.	5	t_c	0.244	5	M Spec.		
A* | 125 to	1.53489	5	ΔHc kcal/m			Ultra V.		
B* | 275 °C	1687.7	5	ΔHf			X-Ray Dif.		
K			ΔFf			Infrared		
c			Viscosity			Solubility in +		
t_k | to			centistokes			Acetone		
t_x | °C			η °C			Carbon tet.		
A' | 25 to	7.38662	5				Benzene		
B' | 125 °C	2019.1	5				Ether		
C'	214.	5	B^v | to			n-Heptane		
A'* 25 to	1.89434	5	A^v | °C			Ethanol		
B'* 125 °C	1916.8	5	(B^v) | to			Water		
Ac | 310 to	7.51022	5	(A^v) | °C			Water in		
Bc | t_c °C	2270.9	5	c_p liq. °K					
Cc	255.	5						
Cryos. A°			c_p vap. °K					
consts. B°								
t_e °C	264.53	5	c_v vap.					

$T_R = 0.80 \, T_c$ + grams/100 grams solvent

REFERENCES: 1-Dow 2-API 3-Lit. 4-Calc. from det. data 5-Calc. by formula

SOURCE:	API

PURIFICATION:	API

LITERATURE REFERENCES:

TABLE VI. TETRAHYDRONAPHTHALENES

259

No. 21

NAME	5, 6-Dimethyl-1, 2, 3, 4-Tetrahydronaphthalene			STRUCTURAL FORMULA

Mole % Pur.	Ref.	Molecular Formula $C_{12}H_{16}$	Molecular Weight 160.248	

		Ref.				Ref.					Ref.
F.P. °C			dt/dP				f		to		
F.P. 100%			°C/mm				g		°K		
			25°C	320.5	5		h				
B.P. °C			BP	0.0603	5						
760 mm	252.	2	t_e	0.0370	5		f'		to		
100	175.	5					g'		°K		
30	141.	5	30 mm	0.8576	5		h'				
10	115.	5	ΔHm cal/g								
1	71.	5	ΔHv cal/g				m		to		
			25°C	95.14	5		n		°K		
Pressure			30 mm	82.72	5		o				
mm 25°C	0.03616	5	BP	69.50	5						
t_e	1411.6	5	t_e	66.24	5		m'		to		
Density			t_e (d, e)	65.89	5		n'		°K		
g/ml 20°C	0.975	2	ΔHv/T_e	19.11	5		o'				
d_4^t 25	0.971	2					Surface tension				
30	0.967	4	d 140 to	99.52	5		dynes/cm. 20°C		39.87	5
a	0.991	4	e 280 °C	0.1191	5		γ		30	38.58	5
b	-0.0380	4	d' 25 to	97.81	5				40	37.32	5
Ref. Index			e' 140 °C	0.1070	5						
n_D 20°C	1.552	2					Parachor [P]				
25	1.550	2	d_c g/ml	0.310	5		20°C				
30	1.547	4	v_c ml/g	3.23	5		30				
"C"	0.7402	4	t_c °C	480.			40				
MR (Obs.)	52.5	2	P_c mm	21855.	5		Sugd.		412.7	5
MR (Calc.)	51.815	5	PV/RT				Exp. L.1.%/wt.				
(nD-d/2)	1.064	2	25°C	1.0000	5		u.				
Dielectric			30 mm	1.0000	5		Dispersion				
A 140 to	7.08239	5	BP	0.9351	5		Flash Point °C				
B 330 °C	1861.3	5	t_e	0.9133	5		Fire Point				
C	191.	5	t_c	0.240	5						
A* 140 to	1.5799	5	ΔHc kcal/m				M. Spec.				
B* 290 °C	1763.3	5	ΔHf				Ultra V.				
K			ΔFf				X-Ray Dif.				
c							Infrared				
t_k to			Viscosity				Solubility in +				
°C			centistokes				Acetone				
t_x			η °C				Carbon tet.				
A' 25 to	7.4355	5					Benzene				
B' 140 °C	2103.2	5					Ether				
C'	211.9	5	B^v to				n-Heptane				
A'* 25 to	1.9367	5	A^v °C				Ethanol				
B'* 140 °C	2000.3	5	(B^v) to				Water				
Ac 330 to	7.54749	5	(A^v) °C				Water in				
Bc t_c °C	2341.8	5	c_p liq. °K								
Cc	250.	5									
Cryos. A°			c_p vap. °K								
consts. B°											
t_e °C	282.3	5	c_v vap.								

T_R = 0.80 T_c + grams/100 grams solvent

REFERENCES: 1-Dow 2-API 3-Lit. 4-Calc. from det. data 5-Calc. by formula

SOURCE:	API
PURIFICATION:	API
LITERATURE REFERENCES:	

No. 22

NAME	5,7-Dimethyl-1,2,3,4-Tetrahydronaphthalene			STRUCTURAL FORMULA

Mole % Pur.	Ref.	Molecular Formula $C_{12}H_{16}$	Molecular Weight 160.248

		Ref.			Ref.				Ref.
F.P. °C	-6.	2	dt/dP			f	to	°K	
F.P. 100%			°C/mm			g			
B.P. °C			25°C	337.5	5	h			
760 mm	253.1	2	BP	0.0604	5	f'	to	°K	
100	176.2	5	t_e	0.0370	5	g'			
30	142.0	5	30 mm	0.8594	5	h'			
10	115.7	5	ΔHm cal/g			m	to	°K	
1	71.7	5	ΔHv cal/g			n			
Pressure			25°C	95.41	5	o			
mm 25°C	0.0342	5	30 mm	82.90	5	m'	to	°K	
t_e	1414.0	5	BP	69.25	5	n'			
Density			t_e	66.33	5	o'			
g/ml 20°C	0.9583	2	t_e (d,e)	65.69	5	Surface tension			
d_4^t 25	0.9537	2	$\Delta Hv/T_e$	19.09	5	dynes/cm. 20°C	37.21	5	
30	0.9491	4	d 140 to	100.35	5	γ 30	35.80	5	
a	0.9767	4	e 285 °C	0.1229	5	40	34.43	5	
b	-0.0392	4	d' 25 to	98.08	5	Parachor [P]			
Ref. Index			e' 140 °C	0.1069	5	20°C			
n_D 20°C	1.5405	2	d_c g/ml	0.291	5	30			
25	1.5384	2	v_c ml/g	3.44	5	40			
30	1.5350	4	t_c °C	474.	5	Sugd.	412.7	5	
"C"	0.7384	4	P_c mm	20281.	5	Exp. L.1.%/wt.			
MR (Obs.)	52.51	2	PV/RT			u.			
MR (Calc.)	51.815	5	25°C	1.0000	5	Dispersion			
(nD-d/2)	1.0613	2	30 mm	1.0000	5	Flash Point °C			
Dielectric			BP	0.9348	5	Fire Point			
A 140 to	7.08594	5	t_e	0.9129	5	M Spec.			
B 325 °C	1867.5	5	t_c	0.240	5	Ultra V.			
C	191.	5	ΔHc kcal/m			X-Ray Dif.			
A* 140 to	1.5831	5	ΔHf			Infrared			
B* 295 °C	1769.4	5	ΔFf			Solubility in +			
K			Viscosity			Acetone			
c			centistokes			Carbon tet.			
t_k to			η °C			Benzene			
t_x °C						Ether			
A' 25 to	7.4393	5				n-Heptane			
B' 140 °C	2110.2	5	B^V to			Ethanol			
C'	212.0	5	A^V °C			Water			
A'* 25 to	1.9398	5	(B^V) to			Water in			
B'* 140 °C	2007.2	5	(A^V) °C						
Ac 325 to	7.55004	5	c_p liq. °K						
Bc t_c °C	2347.9	5	c_p vap. °K						
Cc	250.	5	c_v vap.						
Cryos. A°									
consts. B°									
t_e °C	283.5	5							
$T_R = 0.80 T_c$						+ grams/100 grams solvent			

REFERENCES: 1-Dow 2-API 3-Lit. 4-Calc. from det. data 5-Calc. by formula

SOURCE: API

PURIFICATION: API

LITERATURE REFERENCES:

TABLE VI.   TETRAHYDRONAPHTHALENES

No. 23

NAME	5,8-Dimethyl-1,2,3,4-Tetrahydronaphthalene	STRUCTURAL FORMULA

STRUCTURAL FORMULA

H₃C H₂

H₂

H₂

H₃C H₂

Mole % Pur.	Ref.	Molecular Formula $C_{12}H_{16}$	Molecular Weight 160.248

		Ref.			Ref.				Ref.
F.P. °C			dt/dP			f	to		
F.P. 100%			°C/mm			g	°K		
B.P. °C			25°C	352.2	5	h			
760 mm	254.	2	BP	0.0604	5	f'	to		
100	177.	5	t_e	0.0371	5	g'	°K		
30	143.	5	30 mm	0.8608	5	h'			
10	117.	5	ΔHm cal/g			m	to		
1	72.	5	ΔHv cal/g			n	°K		
Pressure			25°C	95.63	5	o			
mm 25°C	0.0327	5	30 mm	83.06	5	m'	to		
t_e	1415.4	5	BP	69.75	5	n'	°K		
Density			t_e	66.45	5	o'			
g/ml 20°C	0.967	2	t_e (d,e)	66.10	5	Surface tension			
d_4^t 25	0.963	2	ΔHv/T_e	19.09	5	dynes/cm. 20°C	38.58	5
30	0.959	4	d 145 to	100.1	5	ɣ 30	37.32	5
a	0.983	4	e 285 °C	0.1195	5	40	36.09	5
b	-0.0₃80	4	d' 25 to	98.3	5			
Ref. Index			e' 145 °C	0.1069	5	Parachor [P]		
n_D 20°C	1.547	2	d_c g/ml	0.306	5	20°C		
25	1.545	2	v_c ml/g	3.26	5	30		
30	1.542	4	t_c °C	482.	5	40		
"C"	0.73996	4	P_c mm	21618.	5	Sugd.	412.7	5
MR (Obs.)	52.5	2	PV/RT			Exp. L.1.%/wt.		
MR (Calc.)	51.815	5	25°C	1.0000	5	u.		
(nD-d/2)	1.063	2	30 mm	1.0000	5	Dispersion		
Dielectric			BP	0.9342	5	Flash Point °C		
A 145 to	7.08889	5	t_e	0.9122	5	Fire Point		
B 330 °C	1872.6	5	t_c	0.240	5	M. Spec.		
C	191.	5	ΔHc kcal/m			Ultra V.		
A* 145 to	1.5863	5	ΔHf			X-Ray Dif.		
B* 295 °C	1774.7	5	ΔFf			Infrared		
K			Viscosity			Solubility in +		
c			centistokes			Acetone		
t_k to			η °C			Carbon tet.		
t_x °C						Benzene		
A' 25 to	7.4424	5				Ether		
B' 145 °C	2116.0	5				n-Heptane		
C'	212.02	5	B^v to			Ethanol		
A'* 25 to	1.94237	5	A^v °C			Water		
B'* 145 °C	2012.8	5	(B^v) to			Water in		
Ac 330 to	7.54042	5	(A^v) °C					
Bc t_c °C	2346.5	5	c_p liq. °K					
Cc	250.	5						
Cryos. A°			c_p vap. °K					
consts. B°								
t_e °C	284.5	5	c_v vap.					

T_R = 0.80 T_c + grams/100 grams solvent

REFERENCES: 1-Dow 2-API 3-Lit. 4-Calc. from det. data 5-Calc. by formula

SOURCE: API

PURIFICATION: API

LITERATURE REFERENCES:

No. 24

NAME	6,7-Dimethyl-1,2,3,4-Tetrahydronaphthalene	STRUCTURAL FORMULA

Mole % Pur.	Ref.	Molecular Formula $C_{12}H_{16}$	Molecular Weight 160.248

		Ref.			Ref.			Ref.
F.P. °C	10.	2	dt/dP °C/mm			f | ____ to ____ °K		
F.P. 100%			25°C	320.55	5	g |		
B.P. °C			BP	0.0603	5	h |		
760 mm	252.	2	t_e	0.0369	5	f' | ____ to ____ °K		
100	175.	5	30 mm	0.8576	5	g' |		
30	141.	5	ΔHm cal/g			h' |		
10	115.	5	ΔHv cal/g			m | ____ to ____ °K		
1	71.	5	25°C	95.14	5	n |		
Pressure			30 mm	82.72	5	o |		
mm 25°C	0.0362	5	BP	69.70	5	m' | ____ to ____ °K		
t_e	1416.9	5	t_e	66.44	5	n' |		
Density			t_e (d, e)	66.12	5	o' |		
g/ml 20°C	0.954	2	$ΔHv/T_e$	19.16	5	Surface tension		
d_4^t 25	0.950	2	d | 140 to	99.27	5	dynes/cm. 20°C	36.54	5
30	0.946	4	e | 280 °C	0.1173	5	γ 30	35.33	5
a	0.970	4	d' | 25 to	97.81	5	40	34.15	5
b	-0.0380	4	e' | 140 °C	0.1070	5	Parachor [P]		
Ref. Index			d_c g/ml	0.302	5	20°C		
n_D 20°C	1.538	2	v_c ml/g	3.31	5	30		
25	1.536	2	t_c °C	477.	5	40		
30	1.534	4	P_c mm	21156.	5	Sugd.	412.7	5
"C"	0.7384	4	PV/RT			Exp. L.1.%/wt.		
MR (Obs.)	52.5	2	25°C	1.0000	5	u.		
MR (Calc.)	51.815	5	30 mm	1.0000	5	Dispersion		
(nD-d/2)	1.061	2	BP	0.9379	5	Flash Point °C		
Dielectric			t_e	0.9165	5	Fire Point		
A | 140 to	7.08239	5	t_c	0.240	5	M Spec.		
B | 325 °C	1861.3	5	ΔHc kcal/m			Ultra V.		
C	191.	5	ΔHf			X-Ray Dif.		
A* | 140 to	1.57467	5	ΔFf			Infrared		
B* | 290 °C	1761.6	5	Viscosity			Solubility in +		
K			centistokes			Acetone		
c			η °C			Carbon tet.		
t_k | ____ to						Benzene		
t_x | ____ °C						Ether		
A' | 25 to	7.43552	5				n-Heptane		
B' | 140 °C	2103.2	5	B^v | ____ to			Ethanol		
C'	212.	5	A^v | ____ °C			Water		
A'* 25 to	1.93669	5	$(B^{\overline{v}})$ | ____ to			Water in		
B'* 140 °C	2000.3	5	(A^v) | ____ °C					
Ac | 325 to	7.54194	5	c_p liq. °K					
Bc | t_c °C	2338.4	5						
Cc	250.	5	c_p vap. °K					
Cryos. A° consts. B°			c_v vap.					
t_e °C	282.49	5						

$T_R = 0.80 T_c$ + grams/100 grams solvent

REFERENCES: 1-Dow   2-API   3-Lit.   4-Calc. from det. data   5-Calc. by formula

SOURCE: API

PURIFICATION: API

LITERATURE REFERENCES:

TABLE VII. DECAHYDRONAPHTHALENES

263

No. 1

NAME	cis-Decahydronaphthalene		STRUCTURAL FORMULA

| Mole % Pur. | | Ref. | Molecular Formula $C_{10}H_{18}$ | Molecular Weight 138.164 | | | |

		Ref.			Ref.			Ref.
F.P. °C	-43.01	2	dt/dP			f | to		
F.P. 100%			°C/mm			g | °K		
			25°C	19.56	5	h |		
B.P. °C			BP	0.05613	5			
760 mm	195.65	2	t_e	0.03724	5	f' | to		
100	124.6	5	30 mm	0.7841	5	g' | °K		
30	93.26	5	ΔHm cal/g			h' |		
10	69.4	5						
1	29.5	5	ΔHv cal/g			m | to		
			25°C	88.72	5	n | °K		
Pressure			30 mm	82.06	5	o |		
mm 25°C	0.737	5	BP	70.41	5			
t_e	1287.0	5	t_e	67.82	5	m' | to		
			t_e (d, e)	67.70	5	n' | °K		
Density			ΔHv/T_e	19.02	5	o' |		
g/ml 20°C	0.8965	2						
d_4^t 25	0.8925	2	d | 100 to	92.67	5	Surface tension		
30	0.8885	4	e | 220 °C	0.1138	5	dynes/cm. 20°C	32.51	5
a	0.9125	4	d' | 20 to	91.16	5	30	31.36	5
b	-0.0380	4	e' | 100 °C	0.0976	5	40	30.25	5
Ref. Index								
n_D 20°C	1.4810	2	d_c g/ml	0.240	5	Parachor [P]		
25	1.4788	2	v_c ml/g	4.16	5	20°C		
30	1.4766	4	t_c °C	404.	5	30		
"C"	0.7077	4	P_c mm	18730.	5	40		
MR (Obs.)	43.858	2				Sugd.	368.0	5
MR (Calc.)	43.98	5	PV/RT					
(nD-d/2)	1.0328	2	25°C	1.0000	5	Exp. L.l.%/wt.		
Dielectric			30 mm	1.0000	5	u.		
			BP	0.9548	5	Dispersion		
A | 100 to	6.92860	5	t_e	0.9389	5	Flash Point °C		
B | 235 °C	1609.6	5	t_c	0.255	5	Fire Point		
C |	202.	5	ΔHc kcal/m			M. Spec.		
			ΔHf			Ultra V.		
A* | 100 to	1.37162	5	ΔFf			X-Ray Dif.		
B* | 230 °C	1509.6	5				Infrared		
K			Viscosity					
c			centistokes			Solubility in +		
t_k | to			η °C			Acetone		
t_x | °C						Carbon tet.		
A' | 25 to	7.2780	5				Benzene		
B' | 100 °C	1823.	5				Ether		
C' |	221.	5	B^v |			n-Heptane		
			A^v | to			Ethanol		
A'* 25 to	1.7383	5	(B^v)| °C			Water		
B'* 100 °C	1722.	5		to		Water in		
Ac | 235 to	7.16561	5	(A^v)| °C					
Bc | t_c °C	1921.	5						
Cc |	260.	5	c_p liq. °K					
Cryos. A°								
consts. B°			c_p vap. °K					
t_e °C	219.47	5	c_v vap.					

T_R = 0.75 T_c + grams/100 grams solvent

REFERENCES: 1-Dow 2-API 3-Lit. 4-Calc. from det. data 5-Calc. by formula

SOURCE: API

PURIFICATION: API

LITERATURE REFERENCES:

NAME	trans-Decahydronaphthalene	STRUCTURAL FORMULA

Mole % Pur.	Ref.	Molecular Formula	$C_{10}H_{18}$	Molecular Weight 138.164

		Ref.				Ref.				Ref.
F.P. °C	-30.4	2	dt/dP				f	to		
F.P. 100%			°C/mm				g	°K		
B.P. °C			25°C	13.53	5		h			
760 mm	187.25	2	BP	0.0554	5					
100	117.	5	t_e	0.03732	5		f'	to		
30	86.	5	30 mm	0.7717	5		g'	°K		
10	63.	5	ΔHm cal/g				h'			
1	24.	5								
			ΔHv cal/g				m	to		
Pressure			25°C	86.19	5		n	°K		
mm 25°C	1.0971	5	30 mm	80.30	5		o			
t_e	1263.2	5	BP	68.80	5					
Density			t_e	66.33	5		m'	to		
g/ml 20°C	0.8699	2	t_e (d, e)	66.22	5		n'	°K		
d_4^t 25	0.8659	2	$\Delta Hv/T_e$	18.97	5		o'			
30	0.8619	4	d	85 to	90.14	5	Surface tension			
a	0.8859	4	e	210 °C	0.1140	5	dynes/cm. 20°C	28.82	5
b	-0.0380	4	d'	25 to	88.59	5	30	27.77	5
Ref. Index			e'	85 °C	0.9597	5	40	26.75	5
n_D 20°C	1.4695	2	d_c g/ml	0.254	5	Parachor [P]			
25	1.4672	2	v_c ml/g	3.93	5	20°C			
30	1.4650	4	t_c °C	391.	5	30			
"C"	0.7130	5	P_c mm	19616.	5	40			
MR (Obs.)	44.30	2				Sugd.	368.0	5
MR (Calc.)	43.98	5	PV/RT			Exp. L.1.%/wt.			
(nD-d/2)	1.0345	2	25°C	1.0000	5	u.			
Dielectric			30 mm	1.0000	5	Dispersion			
A 85 to	6.90464	5	BP	0.9553	5	Flash Point °C			
B 225 °C	1570.3	5	t_e	0.9398	5	Fire Point			
C	203.	5	t_c	0.257	5				
A* 85 to	1.35573	5	ΔHc kcal/m			M Spec.			
B* 220 °C	1472.3	5	ΔHf			Ultra V.			
K			ΔFf			X-Ray Dif.			
c						Infrared			
t_k to			Viscosity			Solubility in +			
t_x °C			centistokes			Acetone			
A' 25 to	7.24657	5	η °C			Carbon tet.			
B' 85 °C	1774.4	5				Benzene			
C'	221.	5				Ether			
A'* 25 to	1.71053	5	B^v to			n-Heptane			
B'* 85 °C	1674.2	5	A^v °C			Ethanol			
Ac 225 to	7.31068	5	(B^v) to			Water			
Bc t_c °C	1937.4	5	(A^v) °C			Water in			
Cc	250.	5							
Cryos. A°			c_p liq. °K						
consts. B°			c_p vap. °K						
t_e °C	209.89	5	c_v vap.						

$T_R = 0.75 T_c$

+ grams/100 grams solvent

REFERENCES: 1-Dow 2-API 3-Lit. 4-Calc. from det. data 5-Calc. by formula

SOURCE:	API
PURIFICATION:	API
LITERATURE REFERENCES:	

TABLE VII. DECAHYDRONAPHTHALENES

265

No. 3

NAME	1-Methyl-(trans-Decahydronaphthalene)		STRUCTURAL FORMULA

| Mole % Pur. | Ref. | Molecular Formula $C_{11}H_{20}$ | Molecular Weight 152.270 | |

		Ref.				Ref.				Ref.
F.P. °C			dt/dP				f | to			
F.P. 100%			°C/mm				g | ___ °K			
B.P. °C			25°C	133.00	5		h |			
760 mm	235.	2	BP	0.0590	5					
100	160.	4	t_e	0.0369	5		f' | to			
30	126.6	4	30 mm	0.8353	5		g' | ___ °K			
10	101.	5	ΔHm cal/g				h' |			
1	58.	5								
Pressure			ΔHv cal/g				m | to			
mm 25°C	0.0928	5	25°C	94.02	5		n | ___ °K			
t_e	1384.2	5	30 mm	83.25	5		o |			
Density			BP	70.76	5					
g/ml 20°C			t_e	67.60	5		m' | to			
d_4^t 25			t_e (d, e)	67.86	5		n' | ___ °K			
30			ΔHv/T_e	19.17	5		o' |			
a			d | 125 to	97.83	5		Surface tension			
b			e | 265 °C	0.1152	5		dynes/cm. 20°C			
Ref. Index			d' | 25 to	96.67	5		γ 30			
n_D 20°C	1.4720	2	e' | 125 °C	0.1060	5		40			
25	1.4698	2	d_c g/ml				Parachor [P]			
30	1.4676	4	v_c ml/g				20°C			
"C"			t_c °C				30			
MR (Obs.)			P_c mm				40			
MR (Calc.)	48.598	5	PV/RT				Sugd.	407.0	5
(nD-d/2)			25°C	1.0000	5		Exp. L.1.%/wt.			
Dielectric			30 mm	1.0000	5		u.			
A | 127 to	7.03372	5	BP	0.9461	5		Dispersion			
B | 300°C	1781.6	5	t_e	0.9266	5		Flash Point °C			
C	194.	5	t_c				Fire Point			
A* | 127 to	1.50246	5	ΔHc kcal/m				M. Spec.			
B* | 275°C	1679.9	5	ΔHf				Ultra V.			
K			ΔFf				X-Ray Dif.			
c			Viscosity				Infrared			
t_k | to			centistokes				Solubility in +			
t_x | °C			η °C				Acetone			
A' | 20 to	7.38379	5					Carbon tet.			
B' | 127°C	2013.2	5					Benzene			
C'	214.	5	B^v | to				Ether			
A'* 20 to	1.86994	5	A^v | °C				n-Heptane			
B'* 127°C	1911.0	5	(B^v)| to				Ethanol			
Ac | to			(A^V)| °C				Water			
Bc | t_c °C							Water in			
Cc |			c_p liq. °K							
Cryos. A°										
consts. B°			c_p vap. °K							
t_e °C	263.7	5	c_v vap.							

+ grams/100 grams solvent

REFERENCES: 1-Dow 2-API 3-Lit. 4-Calc. from det. data 5-Calc. by formula

SOURCE: API

PURIFICATION: API

LITERATURE REFERENCES:

No. 4

NAME	9-Methyl-(cis-Decahydronaphthalene)	STRUCTURAL FORMULA

Mole % Pur.	Ref.	Molecular Formula $C_{11}H_{20}$	Molecular Weight 152.270

		Ref.				Ref.				Ref.
F.P. °C			dt/dP				f | to			
F.P. 100%			°C/mm				g | °K			
			25°C	49.10	5		h |			
B.P. °C			BP	0.0576	5					
760 mm	215.	2	t_e	0.0370	5		f' | to			
100	142.	5					g' | °K			
30	110.	5	30 mm	0.8093	5		h' |			
10	85.	5	ΔHm cal/g							
1	44.	5					m | to			
			ΔHv cal/g				n | °K			
Pressure			25°C	87.02	5		o |			
mm 25°C	0.27159	5	30 mm	78.79	5					
t_e	1336.1	5	BP	67.25	5		m' | to			
			t_e	64.52	5		n' | °K			
Density			t_e (d, e)	64.37	5		o' |			
g/ml 20°C	0.8910	2	ΔHv/T_e	19.10	5		Surface tension			
d_4^t 25	0.8870	2	d | 110 to	90.80	5		dynes/cm. 20°C	32.17	5
30	0.8830	4	e | 240 °C	0.1095	5		γ 30	31.03	5
a	0.9070	4	d' | 25 to	89.45	5		40	29.92	5
b	-0.0380	4	e' | 110 °C	0.0972	5					
Ref. Index			d_c g/ml	0.273	5		Parachor [P]			
n_D 20°C	1.4804	2	v_c ml/g	3.66	5		20°C			
25	1.4782	2	t_c °C	422.	5		30			
30	1.4755	4	P_c mm	19033.	5		40			
"C"	0.7108	4	PV/RT				Sugd.	407.0	5
MR (Obs.)	49.43	4	25°C	1.0000	5		Exp. L.1.%/wt.			
MR (Calc.)	48.598	5	30 mm	1.0000	5		u.			
(nD-d/2)	1.0349	4	BP	0.9511	5		Dispersion			
Dielectric			t_e	0.9335	5		Flash Point °C			
A | 110 to	6.98032	5	t_c	0.245	5		Fire Point			
B | 290 °C	1693.1	5	ΔHc kcal/m				M Spec.			
C	198.	5	ΔHf				Ultra V.			
A* | 110 to	1.45645	5	ΔFf				X-Ray Dif.			
B* | 250 °C	1592.0	5					Infrared			
K			Viscosity				Solubility in +			
c			centistokes				Acetone			
t_k | to			η °C				Carbon tet.			
t_x | °C							Benzene			
A' | 25 to	7.32702	5					Ether			
B' | 110 °C	1913.2	5					n-Heptane			
C'	217.	5	B^v | to				Ethanol			
A'* 25 to	1.82096	5	A^v | °C				Water			
B'* 110 °C	1811.5	5	(B^v) | to				Water in			
Ac | 290 to	7.45310	5	(A^v) | °C							
Bc | t_c °C	2148.5	5	c_p liq. °K							
Cc	255.	5								
Cryos. A°			c_p vap. °K							
consts. B°										
t_e °C	241.26	5	c_v vap.							

T_R = 0.80 T_c + grams/100 grams solvent

REFERENCES: 1-Dow   2-API   3-Lit.   4-Calc. from det. data   5-Calc. by formula

SOURCE: API

PURIFICATION: API

LITERATURE REFERENCES:

TABLE VII. DECAHYDRONAPHTHALENES

No. 5

NAME	9-Methyl-(trans-Decahydronaphthalene)	STRUCTURAL FORMULA

STRUCTURAL FORMULA

HCH_3 H_2
H_2 H H_2
H_2 H_2
H_2 H H_2

Mole % Pur.	Ref.	Molecular Formula $C_{11}H_{20}$	Molecular Weight 152.270

		Ref.			Ref.			Ref.
F.P. °C			dt/dP			f $\mid$ $\mid$ to		
F.P. 100%			°C/mm			g $\mid$ $\mid$ °K		
			25°C	30.28	5	h $\mid$		
B.P. °C			BP	0.0569	5			
760 mm	205.	2	t_e	0.0371	5	f' $\mid$ $\mid$ to		
100	133.	5	30 mm	0.7964	5	g' $\mid$ $\mid$ °K		
30	101.	5	ΔHm cal/g			h' $\mid$		
10	77.	5	ΔHv cal/g			m $\mid$ $\mid$ to		
1	36.	5	25°C	83.62	5	n $\mid$ $\mid$ °K		
Pressure			30 mm	76.54	5	o $\mid$		
mm 25°C	0.4583	5	BP	65.52	5			
t_e	1312.7	5	t_e	62.96	5	m' $\mid$ $\mid$ to		
Density			t_e (d, e)	62.86	5	n' $\mid$ $\mid$ °K		
g/ml 20°C	0.8620	2	ΔHv/T_e	19.05	5	o' $\mid$		
d_4^t 25	0.8580	2				Surface tension		
30	0.8540	4	d $\mid$ 100 to	87.27	5	dynes/cm. 20°C	28.18	5
a	0.8780	4	e $\mid$ 230 °C	0.1061	5	ɣ 30	27.15	5
b	-0.0₃80	4	d' $\mid$ 25 to	85.94	5	40	26.14	5
Ref. Index			e' $\mid$ 100 °C	0.0929	5	Parachor [P]		
n_D 20°C	1.4631	2	d_c g/ml	0.256	5	20°C		
25	1.4619	2	v_c ml/g	3.90	5	30		
30	1.4585	4	t_c °C	403.	5	40		
"C"	0.7102	4	P_c mm	17732.	5	Sugd.	407.0	5
MR (Obs.)	48.662	4	PV/RT			Exp. L.1.%/wt.		
MR (Calc.)	48.598	5	25°C	1.0000	5	u.		
(nD-d/2)	1.0321	4	30 mm	1.0000	5	Dispersion		
Dielectric			BP	0.9542	5	Flash Point °C		
A $\mid$ 100 to	6.95093	5	t_e	0.9375	5	Fire Point		
B $\mid$ 270 °C	1648.4	5	t_c	0.250	5	M. Spec.		
C	200.	5	ΔHc kcal/m			Ultra V.		
A* $\mid$ 100 to	1.43008	5	ΔHf			X-Ray Dif.		
B* $\mid$ 240 °C	1547.4	5	ΔFf			Infrared		
K			Viscosity			Solubility in +		
c			centistokes			Acetone		
t_k $\mid$ to			η °C			Carbon tet.		
t_x $\mid$ °C						Benzene		
A' $\mid$ 25 to	7.29578	5				Ether		
B' $\mid$ 100 °C	1862.6	5	B^v $\mid$ to			n-Heptane		
C'	219.	5	A^v $\mid$ °C			Ethanol		
A'* 25 to	1.79377	5	$(B^v)\mid$ to			Water		
B'* 100 °C	1761.3	5	$(A^v)\mid$ °C			Water in		
Ac^l 270 to	7.39336	5	c_p liq. °K					
Bc $\mid$ t_c °C	2053.4	5						
Cc	250.	5	c_p vap. °K					
Cryos. A°								
consts. B°			c_v vap.					
t_a °C	230.08	5						

$T_R = 0.80\, T_c$

+ grams/100 grams solvent

REFERENCES: 1-Dow 2-API 3-Lit. 4-Calc. from det. data 5-Calc. by formula
SOURCE: API
PURIFICATION: API
LITERATURE REFERENCES:

No. 6

NAME	9-Ethyl-(cis-Decahydronaphthalene)	STRUCTURAL FORMULA

Structural formula: HC_2H_5 ... H_2 ring structure

Mole % Pur.	Ref.	Molecular Formula $C_{12}H_{22}$	Molecular Weight 166.296

		Ref.			Ref.				Ref.
F.P. °C			dt/dP			f to			
F.P. 100%			°C/mm			g °K			
B.P. °C			25°C	118.21	5	h			
760 mm	233.	2	BP	0.0589	5				
100	158.	5	t_e	0.0368	5	f' to			
30	125.	5	30 mm	0.8337	5	g' °K			
10	99.	5	ΔHm cal/g			h'			
1	57.	5							
Pressure			ΔHv cal/g			m to			
mm 25°C	0.10558	5	25°C	85.14	5	n °K			
t_e	1387.4	5	30 mm	75.69	5	o			
			BP	64.64	5				
Density			t_e	61.85	5	m' to			
g/ml 20°C	0.8860	2	t_e (d,e)	61.70	5	n' °K			
d_4^t 25	0.8830	2	ΔHv/T_e	19.23	5	o'			
30	0.8800	4				Surface tension			
a	0.8980	4	d 125 to	88.43	5	dynes/cm. 20°C	31.88	5
b	-0.0360	4	e 260 °C	0.1021	5	𝛾 30	31.03	5
			d' 25 to	85.51	5	40	30.19	5
Ref. Index			e' 125 °C	0.0947	5				
n_D 20°C	1.480	2				Parachor [P]			
25	1.478	2	d_c g/ml	0.294	5	20°C			
30	1.476	4	v_c ml/g	3.40	5	30			
"C"	0.7147	4	t_c °C	442.	5	40			
MR (Obs.)	53.319	4	P_c mm	18781.	5	Sugd.	446.0	5
MR (Calc.)	53.216	5	PV/RT			Exp. L.l.%/wt.			
(nD-d/2)	1.037	4	25°C	1.0000	5	u.			
Dielectric			30 mm	1.0000	5	Dispersion			
			BP	0.9509	5				
A 125 to	7.03034	5	t_e	0.9321	5	Flash Point °C			
B 300 °C	1776.0	5	t_c	0.245	5	Fire Point			
C	195.	5	ΔHc kcal/m			M Spec.			
A* 125 to	1.52976	5	ΔHf			Ultra V.			
B* 270 °C	1671.5	5	ΔFf			X-Ray Dif.			
K			Viscosity			Infrared			
c			centistokes			Solubility in +			
t_k to			η °C			Acetone			
t_x °C						Carbon tet.			
A' 25 to	7.38019	5				Benzene			
B' 125 °C	2006.8	5				Ether			
C'	215.	5	B^v to			n-Heptane			
A'* 25 to	1.90514	5	A^v °C			Ethanol			
B'* 125 °C	1904.5	5	(B^v) to			Water			
Ac 300 to	7.49304	5	(A^v) °C			Water in			
Bc t_c °C	2227.8	5							
Cc	250.	5	c_p liq. °K						
Cryos. A°			c_p vap. °K						
consts. B°									
t_e °C	261.77	5	c_v vap.						

$T_R = 0.80 T_c$ + grams/100 grams solvent

REFERENCES: 1-Dow   2-API   3-Lit.   4-Calc. from det. data   5-Calc. by formula

SOURCE: API

PURIFICATION: API

LITERATURE REFERENCES:

TABLE VII. DECAHYDRONAPHTHALENES

No. 7

NAME	9-Ethyl-(trans-Decahydronaphthalene)		STRUCTURAL FORMULA

Structural formula:

HC_2H_5 H_2
H_2 H_2
H_2 H_2
H_2 H H_2

Mole % Pur.	Ref.	Molecular Formula	$C_{12}H_{22}$	Molecular Weight 166.296			

		Ref.			Ref.			Ref.
F.P. °C			dt/dP			f	to	
F.P. 100%			°C/mm			g	°K	
			25°C	80.25	5	h		
B.P. °C			BP	0.0583	5			
760 mm	225.	2	t_e	0.0367	5	f'	to	
100	150.94	5				g'	°K	
30	118.13	5	30 mm	0.8224	5	h'		
10	93.06	5	ΔHm cal/g					
1	51.07	5				m	to	
			ΔHv cal/g			n	°K	
Pressure			25°C	82.83	5	o		
mm 25°C	0.15986	5	30 mm	74.17	5			
t_e	1375.1	5	BP	63.65	5			
Density				60.96	5	m'	to	
g/ml 20°C	0.8610	2	t_e (d, e)	60.89	5	n'	°K	
d_4^t 25	0.8570	2	ΔHv/T_e	19.27	5	o'		
30	0.8530	4	d 120 to	85.80	5	Surface tension		
a	0.8770	4	e 255 °C	0.0985	5	dynes/cm. 20°C	28.43	5
b	-0.0₃80	4	d' 25 to	85.15	5	γ 30	27.39	5
Ref. Index			e' 120 °C	0.0929	5	40	26.38	5
n_D 20°C	1.466	2	d_c g/ml	0.256	5	Parachor [P]		
25	1.464	2	v_c ml/g	3.91	5	20°C		
30	1.462	4	t_c °C	420.	5	30		
"C"	0.7150	4	P_c mm	16475.	5	40		
						Sugd.	446.0	5
MR (Obs.)	53.492	4	PV/RT					
MR (Calc.)	53.216	5	25°C	1.0000	5	Exp. L.1.%/wt.		
(nD-d/2)	1.0355	4	30 mm	1.0000	5	u.		
Dielectric			BP	0.9568	5	Dispersion		
			t_e	0.9392	5	Flash Point °C		
A 120 to	7.00670	5	t_c	0.248	5	Fire Point		
B 280 °C	1737.0	5						
C	196.		ΔHc kcal/m			M. Spec.		
A* 120 to	1.50252	5	ΔHf			Ultra V.		
B* 265 °C	1630.9	5	ΔFf			X-Ray Dif.		
K						Infrared		
c			Viscosity			Solubility in +		
t_k to			centistokes			Acetone		
t_x °C			η °C			Carbon tet.		
						Benzene		
A' 25 to	7.35506	5				Ether		
B' 120 °C	1962.8	5				n-Heptane		
C'	215.8	5	B^v to			Ethanol		
A'* 25 to	1.88331	5	A^v °C			Water		
B'*120 °C	1860.8	5	(B^v) to			Water in		
Ac 280 to	7.50050	5	(A^v) °C					
Bc t_c °C	2216.5	5	c_p liq. °K					
Cc	255.	5						
Cryos. A°			c_p vap. °K					
consts. B°								
t_e °C	253.03	5	c_v vap.					

$T_R = 0.80 T_c$ + grams/100 grams solvent

REFERENCES: 1-Dow 2-API 3-Lit. 4-Calc. from det. data 5-Calc. by formula

SOURCE: API

PURIFICATION: API

LITERATURE REFERENCES:

No. 8

NAME	1,10-Dimethyl-(cis-Decahydronaphthalene)	STRUCTURAL FORMULA

STRUCTURAL FORMULA

CH_3 HCH_3

Mole % Pur.	Ref.	Molecular Formula $C_{12}H_{22}$	Molecular Weight 166.296

		Ref.			Ref.			Ref.
F.P. °C			dt/dP			f | to		
F.P. 100%			°C/mm			g | __ °K_		
B.P. °C			25°C	62.52	5	h |		
760 mm	220.	2	BP	0.05796	4			
100	146.42	5	t_e	0.0373	5	f' | to		
30	113.86	5	30 mm	0.8160	5	g' | __ °K_		
10	88.99	5	ΔHm cal/g			h' |		
1	47.36	5	ΔHv cal/g			m | to		
Pressure			25°C	81.22	5	n | __ °K_		
mm 25°C	0.20927	5	30 mm	73.13	5	o |		
t_e	1335.0	5	BP	62.46	5			
Density			t_e	59.22	5	m' | to		
g/ml 20°C	0.8896	2	t_e (d, e)	58.33	5	n' | __ °K_		
d_4^t 25	0.8856	2	ΔHv/T_e	18.95	5	o' |		
30	0.8816	4				Surface tension		
a	0.9056	4	d | 115 to	85.91	5	dynes/cm. 20°C	32.40	5
b	-0.0380	4	e | 245 °C	0.1122	5	𝛾 30	31.25	5
Ref. Index			d' | 25 to	83.49	5	40	30.13	5
n_D 20°C	1.4812	2	e' | 115 °C	0.0909	5	Parachor [P]		
25	1.4790	2	d_c g/ml	0.260	5	20°C		
30	1.4768	4	v_c ml/g	3.84	5	30		
"C"	0.7134	4	t_c °C	416.	5	40		
MR (Obs.)	53.217	4	P_c mm	16821.	5	Sugd.	446.0	5
MR (Calc.)	53.216	5	PV/RT			Exp. L.1.%/wt.		
(nD-d/2)	1.0364	4	25°C	1.0000	5	u.		
Dielectric			30 mm	1.0000	5	Dispersion		
A | 115 to	6.99208	5	BP	0.9525	5	Flash Point °C		
B | 280 °C	1714.4	5	t_e	0.9235	5	Fire Point		
C	197.	5	t_c	0.250	5	M Spec.		
A* | 115 to	1.5180	5	ΔHc kcal/m			Ultra V.		
B* | 255 °C	1617.3	5	ΔHf			X-Ray Dif.		
K			ΔFf			Infrared		
c			Viscosity			Solubility in +		
t_k | to			centistokes			Acetone		
t_x | °C			𝜂 °C			Carbon tet.		
A' | 25 to	7.33952	5				Benzene		
B' | 115 °C	1937.2	5				Ether		
C'	216.6	5	B^v | to			n-Heptane		
A'* 25 to	1.8697	5	A^v | °C			Ethanol		
B'* 115 °C	1835.5	5	(B^v) | to			Water		
Ac | 280 to	7.45224	5	(A^v) | °C			Water in		
Bc | t_c °C	2148.8	5						
Cc	250.	5	c_p liq. °K					
Cryos. A°								
consts. B°			c_p vap. °K					
t_e °C	246.4	5	c_v vap.					

$T_R = 0.80 T_c$ + grams/100 grams solvent

REFERENCES: 1-Dow   2-API   3-Lit.   4-Calc. from det. data   5-Calc. by formula

SOURCE: API

PURIFICATION: API

LITERATURE REFERENCES:

NAME	1,10-Dimethyl-(trans-Decahydronaphthalene)	STRUCTURAL FORMULA

Mole % Pur.	Ref.	Molecular Formula $C_{12}H_{22}$	Molecular Weight 166.296	

		Ref.			Ref.				Ref.
F.P. °C			dt/dP			f $\mid$ to			
F.P. 100%			°C/mm			g $\mid$ °K			
			25°C	43.75	5	h $\mid$			
B.P. °C			BP	0.0575	5				
760 mm	213.	2	t_e	0.0372	5	f' $\mid$ to			
100	140.	5	30 mm	0.8080	5	g' $\mid$ °K			
30	108.	5	ΔHm cal/g			h' $\mid$			
10	83.	5							
1	45.	5	ΔHv cal/g			m $\mid$ to			
			25°C	78.35	5	n $\mid$ °K			
Pressure			30 mm	71.56	5	o $\mid$			
mm 25°C	0.310	5	BP	61.14	5				
t_e	1327.0	5	t_e	58.48	5	m' $\mid$ to			
Density			t_e (d, e)	58.41	5	n' $\mid$ °K			
g/ml 20°C	0.8633	2	ΔHv/T_e	19.00	5	o' $\mid$			
d_4^t 25	0.8593	2							
30	0.8553	4	d $\mid$ 110 to	82.28	5	Surface tension			
			e $\mid$ 240 °C	0.9924	5	dynes/cm. 20°C	28.74	5
a	0.8799	4	d' $\mid$ 25 to	80.91	5	30	27.69	5
b	-0.0$_3$80	4	e' $\mid$ 110 °C	0.0868	5	40	26.66	5
Ref. Index									
n_D 20°C	1.4659	2	d_c g/ml	0.257	5	Parachor [P]			
25	1.4637	2	v_c ml/g	3.89	5	20°C			
30	1.4615	4	t_c °C	406.	5	30			
"C"	0.7131	4	P_c mm	16364.	5	40			
						Sugd.	446.0	5
MR (Obs.)	53.340	4	PV/RT						
MR (Calc.)	53.216	5	25°C	1.0000	5	Exp. L.1.%/wt.			
(nD-d/2)	1.04343	4	30 mm	1.0000	5	u.			
Dielectric			BP	0.9510	5	Dispersion			
			t_e	0.9314	5	Flash Point °C			
A $\mid$ 110 to	6.97377	5	t_c	0.25	5	Fire Point			
B $\mid$ 310 °C	1686.3	5							
C	199.	5	ΔHc kcal/m			M. Spec.			
A* $\mid$ 110 to	1.5010	5	ΔHf			Ultra V.			
B* $\mid$ 250 °C	1590.	5	ΔFf			X-Ray Dif.			
K						Infrared			
c			Viscosity			Solubility in $^+$			
t_k $\mid$ to			centistokes			Acetone			
t_x $\mid$ °C			η °C			Carbon tet.			
A' $\mid$ 25 to	7.3100	5				Benzene			
B' $\mid$ 110 °C	1901.5	5				Ether			
C'	218.	5				n-Heptane			
A'* 25 to	1.8219	5	B^v $\mid$ to			Ethanol			
B'* 110 °C	1793.	5	A^v $\mid$ °C			Water			
Ac $\mid$ 310 to	7.49780	5	$(B^v)\mid$ to			Water in			
Bc $\mid$ t_c °C	2187.1	5	$(A^v)\mid$ °C						
Cc	260.	5	c_p liq. °K						
Cryos. A°			c_p vap. °K						
consts. B°									
t_e °C	238.9	5	c_v vap.						

$T_R = 0.80 T_c$ $^+$ grams/100 grams solvent

REFERENCES: 1-Dow 2-API 3-Lit. 4-Calc. from det. data 5-Calc. by formula

SOURCE: API

PURIFICATION: API

LITERATURE REFERENCES:

TABLE VIII.   AROMATIC PHENOLS

TABLE VIII. AROMATIC PHENOLS

No. 1

NAME	Phenol		STRUCTURAL FORMULA

OH

(benzene ring with OH)

Mole % Pur. 99.96	Ref. 1	Molecular Formula C_6H_6O	Molecular Weight 94.108

		Ref.			Ref.				Ref.
F.P. °C	40.90	1	dt/dP			f | to			
F.P. 100%			°C/mm			g | ___ °K			
B.P. °C			25°C	24.83	5	h |			
760 mm	181.75	1	BP	0.04704	4				
100	120.7	1	t_e	0.03163	5	f' | to			
30	92.78	4	30 mm	0.7065	4	g' | ___ °K			
10	70.86	5				h' |			
1	33.6	5	ΔHm cal/g			m | to			
Pressure			ΔHv cal/g			n | ___ °K			
mm 25°C	0.5305	5	25°C	142.55	5	o |			
t_e	1240.	5	30 mm	133.44	5				
Density			BP	116.40	5	m' | to			
g/ml 41°C	1.05760	1	t_e	113.06	5	n' | ___ °K			
d_4^t 46	1.05331	1	t_e (d, e)	113.23	5	o' |			
51	1.0490		ΔHv/T_e	23.39	5	Surface tension			
a	1.0929	5	d 93 to	147.70	5	dynes/cm. 50°C	37.66	1
b	-0.0386	5	e | 200 °C	0.1722	5	४ 60	36.57	1
Ref. Index			d' | 20 to	145.91	5	70	35.51	1
n_D 41°C	1.54178	1	e' 93 °C	0.1344	5				
46	1.53937	1	d_c g/ml	0.401	5	Parachor [P]			
51	1.53718	4	v_c ml/g	2.494	5	50°C	222.0	4
"C"	0.6706	4	t_c °C	419.	3	60	222.2	4
MR (Obs.)	27.994	4	P_c mm	45980.	3	70	222.4	5
MR (Calc.)	27.832	5	PV/RT			0 = 15 Sugd.	222.1	5
(nD-d/2)	1.01298	4	25°C	1.0000	5	Exp. L.1.%/wt.			
Dielectric			30 mm	1.0000	5	u.			
A | 93 to	7.57893	1	BP	0.9550	5	Dispersion			
B | 240 °C	1817.0	1	t_e	0.9416	5	Flash Point °C			
C	205.	5	t_c	0.25	5	Fire Point			
A* | 93 to	1.87043	5	ΔHc kcal/m			M. Spec.			1
B* | 220 °C	1720.6	5	ΔHf			Ultra V.			1
K			ΔFf			X-Ray Dif.			1
c			Viscosity			Infrared			1
t_k | to			centistokes			Solubility in +			
t_x | °C			η 60 °C	2.5199	1	Acetone	∞		
A' | 20 to	7.86819	5	80	1.5968	1	Carbon tet.	∞		
B' | 93 °C	2011.4	5	100	1.0835	1	Benzene	∞		
C'	222.	5	120	0.8508	1	Ether	∞		
						n-Heptane			
A'* 20 to	2.1593	5	B^v 50 to	1166.0	4	Ethanol	∞		
B'* 93 °C	1909.4	5	A^v 90 °C	4.90200	4	Water	8.20	1
Ac | 240 to	7.9398	5	(B^v)| 95 to	770.4	4	Water in	37.14	1
Bc | t_c °C	2219.3	5	(A^v)|130 °C	3.97052	4				
Cc	257.6	5	c_p liq. °K						
Cryos. A°									
consts. B°			c_p vap. °K						
t_e °C	200.1	5	c_v vap.						

$T_R = 0.75 \, T_c$

+ grams/100 grams solvent

REFERENCES: 1-Dow 2-API 3-Lit. 4-Calc. from det. data 5-Calc. by formula

SOURCE: Dow

PURIFICATION: Distillation

LITERATURE REFERENCES: 3 ICT

No. 2

NAME	o-Cresol		STRUCTURAL FORMULA
	2-Methylphenol		OH CH₃

Mole % Pur.	99.90	Ref. 1	Molecular Formula C_7H_8O	Molecular Weight 108.134

		Ref.			Ref.				Ref.
F.P. °C	30.94	1	dt/dP			f	to		
F.P. 100%			°C/mm			g	°K		
B.P. °C			25°C	31.190	5	h			
760 mm	190.95	1	BP	0.04986	1				
100	126.54	1	t_e	0.03306	5	f'	to		
30	97.4	4	30 mm	0.7349	5	g'	°K		
10	74.9	5				h'			
1	36.8	5	ΔHm cal/g	31.37	4				
Pressure			ΔHv cal/g			m	to		
mm 25°C	0.4254	5	25°C	124.41	5	n	°K		
t_e	1267.7	5	30 mm	114.49	5	o			
Density			BP	99.12	5				
g/ml 41°C	1.02734	1	t_e	96.23	5	m'	to		
d_4^t 46	1.02298	1	t_e (d, e)	95.78	5	n'	°K		
51	1.01860	4	ΔHv/T_e	21.47	5	o'			
a	1.0630	4	d | 97 to	130.50	5	Surface tension			
b	-0.0₃87	4	e | 200 °C	0.1643	5	dynes/cm. 41°C	40.64	5	
Ref. Index			d' | 20 to	127.83	5	ɤ 46	39.30	5	
n_D 41°C	1.53610	1	e' | 97 °C	0.1370	5	51	37.99	5	
46	1.53362	1	d_c g/ml	0.374	5	Parachor [P]			
51	1.53124	4	v_c ml/g	2.67	5	20°C			
"C"			t_c °C	422.	3³	30			
MR (Obs.)	32.825	4	P_c mm	37544.	3³	40			
MR (Calc.)	32.450	5	PV/RT			Sugd.	261.1	5	
(nD-d/2)	1.02243	4	25°C	1.0000	5	Exp. L. 1.%/wt.			
Dielectric	11.5	3	30 mm	1.0000	5	u.			
A | 97 to	7.39476	4	BP	0.9519	5	Dispersion			
B | 250 °C	1777.8	4	t_e	0.9406	5	Flash Point °C	81.	3'	
C	203.	4	t_c	0.25	5	Fire Point			
A* | 97 to	1.7383	5	ΔHc kcal/m			M Spec.			
B* | 220 °C	1679.7	5	ΔHf			Ultra V.	Yes	1	
K			ΔFf			X-Ray Dif.			
c			Viscosity			Infrared	285.	1	
t_k | to			centistokes			Solubility in +			
t_x | °C			η 80 °C	1.47	3²	Acetone	∞		
A' | 10 to	7.7696	5	120	0.784	3²	Carbon tet.	∞		
B' | 97 °C	1984.7	5	160	0.515	3²	Benzene	∞		
C'	220.	5				Ether	∞		
A'* | 20 to	2.0803	5	B^v | 70 to	518.2	4	n-Heptane			
B'* | 97 °C	1883.3	5	A^v | 170 °C	2.69811	4	Ethanol	∞		
Ac | 250 to	7.7327	5	(B^v) | to			Water			
Bc | t_c °C	2098.	5	(A^v) | °C			Water in			
Cc	242.3	5	c_p liq. °K						
Cryos. A°									
consts. B°			c_p vap. °K						
t_e °C	211.24	5	c_v vap.						

$T_R = 0.75 T_c$ + grams/100 grams solvent

REFERENCES: 1-Dow 2-API 3-Lit. 4-Calc. from det. data 5-Calc. by formula

SOURCE: Dow

PURIFICATION: Distillation

LITERATURE REFERENCES: 3 NBS Circ. 325; 3' Nat. Fire Prot. Assn. 325;
3² Ind. Eng. Chem. 36, 595 (1944) Pardee and Wenrich; 3³ I.C.T.

TABLE VIII. AROMATIC PHENOLS

275

No. .3

NAME	m-Cresol					STRUCTURAL FORMULA
	m-Methylphenol					OH

Mole % Pur.	Ref.	Molecular Formula	C_7H_8O	Molecular Weight 108.134			CH₃

		Ref.				Ref.				Ref.
F.P. °C	11.5	3	dt/dP				f	to		
F.P. 100%			°C/mm				g	°K		
			25°C	64.196	5		h			
B.P. °C			BP	0.04954	5					
760 mm	202.2	3	t_e	0.03220	5		f'	to		
100	138.0	3	30 mm	0.7405	5		g'	°K		
30	108.7	4	ΔHm cal/g				h'			
10	86.0	5	ΔHv cal/g				m	to		
1	47.2	5	25°C	131.87	5		n	°K		
Pressure			30 mm	120.66	5		o			
mm 25°C	0.1930	5	BP	104.70	5					
t_e	1295.0	5	t_e	101.28	5		m'	to		
Density			t_e (d, e)	101.08	5		n'	°K		
g/ml 80°C	0.986	3	$\Delta Hv/T_e$	23.04	5		o'			
d_4^t 120	0.954	3	d 110 to	139.2	5		Surface tension			
160	0.921	3	e 230 °C	0.1707	5		dynes/cm. 20°C			
a	1.050	5	d' 25 to	135.22	5		8	30		
b	-0.0380	5	e' 110 °C	0.1339	5			40		
Ref. Index			d_c g/ml	0.357	5		Parachor [P]			
n_D 20°C	1.5438	3	v_c ml/g	2.80	5			20°C		
25			t_c °C	426.	5			30		
30			P_c mm	36000.	5			40		
"C"	0.6926	4	PV/RT					Sugd. 261.1	5	
MR (Obs.)	33.10‡	5	25°C	1.0000	5		Exp. L.1.%/wt.			
MR (Calc.)	32.450	5	30 mm	1.0000	5		u.			
(nD-d/2)	1.0249		BP	0.9520	5		Dispersion			
Dielectric			t_e	0.9374	5		Flash Point °C			
A 110 to	7.53185	4	t_c	0.25	5		Fire Point			
B 240 °C	1875.3	4	ΔHc kcal/m				M. Spec.			
C	201.	5	ΔHf				Ultra V.			
A* 110 to	1.8537	5	ΔFf				X-Ray Dif.			
B* 230 °C	1771.5	5					Infrared			
K			Viscosity				Solubility in +			
c			centistokes				Acetone	∞		
t_k to			η 80 °C	1.76	3		Carbon tet.	∞		
t_x °C			120	0.890	3		Benzene	∞		
A' 15 to	7.9424	5	160	0.570	3		Ether	∞		
B' 110 °C	2138.2	5					n-Heptane			
C'	220.	5	B^v 110 to	672.	4		Ethanol	∞		
A'* 20 to	2.2824	5	A^v 170 °C	2.2403	4		Water			
B'* 110 °C	2033.4	5	(B^v) to				Water in			
Ac 240 to	7.73634	5	(A^v) °C							
Bc t_c °C	2064.	5	c_p liq. °K							
Cc	223.3	5	c_p vap. °K							
Cryos. A°										
consts. B°			c_v vap.							
t_e °C	223.32	5								
‡ 80°C			$T_R = 0.75\ T_C$				+ grams/100 grams solvent			

REFERENCES:	1-Dow	2-API	3-Lit.	4-Calc. from det. data	5-Calc. by formula
SOURCE:	Lit.				
PURIFICATION:	Lit.				
LITERATURE REFERENCES:	3 Ind. Eng. Chem., 36, 596 (1944)				

No. 4

NAME	p-Cresol		STRUCTURAL FORMULA
	p-Methylphenol		OH

| Mole % Pur. 99.95 | Ref. 1 | Molecular Formula C_7H_8O | Molecular Weight 108.134 | | | CH₃ |

		Ref.			Ref.				Ref.
F.P. °C	34.78	1	dt/dP °C/mm			f | to			
F.P. 100%			25°C	62.82	5	g | °K			
B.P. °C			BP	0.04953	4	h |			
760 mm	201.92	1	t_e	0.03215	5	f' | to			
100	137.7	1	30 mm	0.7401	4	g' | °K			
30	108.4	4	ΔHm cal/g			h' |			
10	85.7	5							
1	46.9	5	ΔHv cal/g			m | to			
Pressure			25°C	131.68	5	n | °K			
mm 25°C	0.1976	5	30 mm	120.52	5	o |			
t_e	1297.	5	BP	104.85	5				
Density			t_e	101.38	5	m' | to			
g/ml 41°C	1.01788	1	t_e (d, e)	101.33	5	n' | °K			
d_4^t 46	1.01401	1	ΔHv/T_e	23.12	5	o' |			
51	1.01020	4				Surface tension			
a	1.0496	5	d | 108 to	138.68	5	dynes/cm. 20°C	38.88	5
b	-0.0₃77	5	e | 230 °C	0.1675	5	30	37.72	5
Ref. Index			d' | 25 to	134.66	5	40	36.60	5
n_D 41°C	1.53115	1	e' | 108 °C	0.1193	5			
46	1.57870	1	d_c g/ml	0.347	5	Parachor [P]		
51	1.52625	4	v_c ml/g	2.88	5	20°C		
"C"	0.6839	4	t_c °C	426.0	5	30		
MR (Obs.)	32.875	4	P_c mm	35000.	5	40		
MR (Calc.)	32.450	5	PV/RT			Sugd.	261.1	5
(nD-d/2)	1.02221	4	25°C	1.0000	5	Exp. L. 1.%/wt.		
Dielectric	9.9≠	3	30 mm	1.0000	5	u.		
A | 97 to	7.52871	4	BP	0.9519	5	Dispersion		
B | 250 °C	1872.4	4	t_e	0.9394	5	Flash Point °C		
C	201.	4	t_c	0.25	5	Fire Point		
A* | 97 to	1.8648	5	ΔHc kcal/m			M Spec.		
B* | 220 °C	1773.0	5	ΔHf			Ultra V.		1
K			ΔFf			X-Ray Dif.		
c			Viscosity			Infrared		1
t_k | to			centistokes			Solubility in +		
t_x | °C			η °C			Acetone	∞	
A' | 20 to	7.9375	5				Carbon tet.	∞	
B' | 97 °C	2134.5	5				Benzene	∞	
C'	222.	5	B^V | to			Ether	∞	
A'* 20 to	2.2788	5	A^V | °C			n-Heptane		
B'* 97 °C	2030.	5	$(B^{\overline{V}})$ | to			Ethanol	∞	
Ac | 250 to	7.8594	5	(A^V) | °C			Water		
Bc | t_c °C	2241.2	5	c_p liq. °K			Water in		
Cc	250.	5						
Cryos. A°			c_p vap. °K					
consts. B°								
t_e °C	223.02	5	c_v vap.					

T_R = 0.75 T_c	≠ 58°C	+ grams/100 grams solvent

REFERENCES: 1-Dow 2-API 3-Lit. 4-Calc. from det. data 5-Calc. by formula

SOURCE: Dow

PURIFICATION: Distillation

LITERATURE REFERENCES: 3 NBS Circ. 514

TABLE VIII. AROMATIC PHENOLS

NAME	2,3-Dimethylphenol			STRUCTURAL FORMULA
	2,3-Xylenol			

Structural formula: phenol ring with OH, CH$_3$, CH$_3$ (2,3 positions)

Mole % Pur.	Ref.	Molecular Formula $C_8H_{10}O$		Molecular Weight 122.160

		Ref.				Ref.					Ref.
F.P. °C	75.	3	dt/dP °C/mm				f to		g °K		
F.P. 100%			25°C	111.15	5		h				
B.P. °C			BP	0.0527	5		f' to		g' °K		
760 mm	218.	3	t_e	0.0336	5		h'				
100	150.	3	30 mm	0.7768	5						
30	119.2	5	ΔHm cal/g				m to		n °K		
10	95.4	5					o				
1	55.1	5	ΔHv cal/g								
Pressure			25°C	120.09	5		m' to		n' °K		
mm 25°C	0.1084	5	30 mm	107.49	5		o'				
t_e	1333.5	5	BP	92.77	5						
Density			t_e	89.64	5		Surface tension dynes/cm. 20°C				
g/ml 20°C			t_e (d,e)	89.22	5		γ 30				
d_4^t 25 30			ΔHv/T_e	21.26	5		40				
a			d 119 to	125.25	5		Parachor [P]				
b			e 230 °C	0.14898	5		20°C				
Ref. Index			d' 25 to	123.43	5		30				
n_D 20°C	1.5420	3	e' 119 °C	0.1337	5		40				
25			d_c g/ml				Sugd.	300.7	5		
30			v_c ml/g								
"C"			t_c °C				Exp. L. l. %/wt.				
MR (Obs.)			P_c mm				u.				
MR (Calc.)	37.068	5	PV/RT				Dispersion				
(nD-d/2)			25°C	1.0000	5						
Dielectric			30 mm	1.0000	5		Flash Point °C				
A 119 to	7.38850	4	BP	0.9473	5		Fire Point				
B 255 °C	1875.2	4	t_e	0.9306	5		M. Spec.				
C	.198.	5	t_c				Ultra V.				
A* 119 to	1.77518	5	ΔHc kcal/m				X-Ray Dif.				
B* 250 °C	1776.4	5	ΔHf				Infrared				
K			ΔFf				Solubility in +				
c			Viscosity centistokes				Acetone				
t_k to			η °C				Carbon tet.				
t_x °C							Benzene				
A' 20 to	7.72393	5					Ether				
B' 119 °C	2094.1	5					n-Heptane				
C'	216.	5	B^v to				Ethanol				
A'* 20 to	2.11725	5	A^v °C				Water				
B'* 119 °C	1991.8	5	(B^v) to				Water in				
Ac to			(A^v) °C								
Bc t_c °C			c_p liq. °K								
Cc											
Cryos. A°			c_p vap. °K								
consts. B°											
t_e °C	241.83	5	c_v vap.								

+ grams/100 grams solvent

REFERENCES: 1-Dow 2-API 3-Lit. 4-Calc. from det. data 5-Calc. by formula

SOURCE: Lit.

PURIFICATION: Lit.

LITERATURE REFERENCES: 3 Ind. Eng. Chem. 36, 596 (1944)

No. 6

NAME	2,4-Dimethylphenol	STRUCTURAL FORMULA

2,4-Xylenol

Mole % Pur.	Ref.	Molecular Formula $C_8H_{10}O$	Molecular Weight 122.160

		Ref.			Ref.				Ref.
F.P. °C	27.	3	dt/dP			f	to		
F.P. 100%			°C/mm			g	°K		
			25°C	75.47	5	h			
B.P. °C			BP	0.0520	5				
760 mm	210.0	3	t_e	0.0336	5	f'	to		
100	143.0	3	30 mm	0.7648	5	g'	°K		
30	112.7	5	ΔHm cal/g			h'			
10	89.3	5							
1	49.6	5	ΔHv cal/g			m	to		
			25°C	117.27	5	n	°K		
Pressure			30 mm	105.58	5	o			
mm 25°C	0.1634	5	BP	91.09	5				
t_e	1311.	5	t_e	87.49	5	m'	to		
Density			t_e (d, e)	87.70	5	n'	°K		
g/ml 20°C			$\Delta Hv/T_e$	22.12	5	o'			
d_4^t 25			d 115 to	122.35	5	Surface tension			
30			e 225 °C	0.1489	5	dynes/cm. 20°C			
a			d' 25 to	120.60	5	y 30			
b			e' 115 °C	0.1334	5	40			
Ref. Index			d_c g/ml			Parachor [P]			
n_D 20°C			v_c ml/g			20°C			
25			t_c °C			30			
30			P_c mm		Sugd.	40	Sugd.	300.1	5
"C"			PV/RT						
MR (Obs.)			25°C	1.0000	5	Exp. L.1.%/wt.			
MR (Calc.)	37.068	5	30 mm	1.0000	5	u.			
(nD-d/2)			BP	0.9475	5	Dispersion			
Dielectric			t_e	0.9314	5	Flash Point °C			
A 115 to	7.37688	4	t_c			Fire Point			
B 245 °C	1838.9	4	ΔHc kcal/m			M Spec.			
C	199.	5	ΔHf			Ultra V.			
A* 115 to	1.77045	5	ΔFf			X-Ray Dif.			
B* 240 °C	1741.7	5				Infrared			
K			Viscosity			Solubility in +			
c			centistokes			Acetone			
t_k to			η °C			Carbon tet.			
t_x °C						Benzene			
A' 25 to	7.69866	5				Ether			
B' 115 °C	2045.0	5				n-Heptane			
C'	216.	5.	B^v to			Ethanol			
A'* 25 to	2.09652	5	A^v °C			Water			
B'* 115 °C	1943.8	5	(B^v) to			Water in			
Ac . to			(A^v) °C						
Bc t_c °C			c_p liq. °K						
Cc									
Cryos. A°			c_p vap. °K						
consts. B°									
t_e °C	232.74	5	c_v vap.						

+ grams/100 grams solvent

REFERENCES: 1-Dow 2-API 3-Lit. 4-Calc. from det. data 5-Calc. by formula

SOURCE: Lit.

PURIFICATION: Lit.

LITERATURE REFERENCES: 3 Ind. Eng. Chem., 36, 596 (1944)

TABLE VIII. AROMATIC PHENOLS

NAME	2,5-Dimethylphenol	STRUCTURAL FORMULA
	2,5-Xylenol	

Mole % Pur.	Ref.	Molecular Formula $C_8H_{10}O$	Molecular Weight 122.160

		Ref.				Ref.						Ref.
F.P. °C	73.5	3	dt/dP				f		to			
F.P. 100%			°C/mm				g		°K			
			25°C	75.47	5		h					
B.P. °C			BP	0.05198	5							
760 mm	210.	3	t_e	0.03395	5		f'		to			
100	143.	3	30 mm	0.7648	5		g'		°K			
30	112.7	5	ΔHm cal/g				h'					
10	89.3	5	ΔHv cal/g				m		to			
1	49.6	5	25°C	117.27	5		n		°K			
Pressure			30 mm	105.58	5		o					
mm 25°C	0.16343	5	BP	91.09	5							
t_e	1292.90	5	t_e	88.10	5		m'		to			
Density			t_e (d, e)	87.80	5		n'		°K			
g/ml 80°C	0.9650	3	ΔHv/T_e	21.30			o'					
d_4^t 120	0.9320	3	d 115 to	122.35	5		Surface tension					
160	0.8990	3	e 235 °C	0.1489	5		dynes/cm. 20°C					
a	1.0310	4	d' 25 to	120.60	5		¥ 30					
b	-0.0₃825	4	e' 115 °C	0.1334	5		40					
Ref. Index			d_c g/ml				Parachor [P]					
n_D 20°C			v_c ml/g				20°C					
25			t_c °C				30					
30			P_c mm				40					
"C"			PV/RT				Sugd.	300.1			5	
MR (Obs.)			25°C	1.0000	5		Exp. L.1.%/wt.					
MR (Calc.)	37.068	5	30 mm	1.0000	5		u.					
(nD-d/2)			BP	0.9368	5		Dispersion					
Dielectric			t_e	0.9196	5		Flash Point °C					
A 115 to	7.37688	4	t_c				Fire Point					
B 250 °C	1838.9	4	ΔHc kcal/m				M. Spec.					
C	199.	5	ΔHf				Ultra V.					
A* 115 to	1.79110	5	ΔFf				X-Ray Dif.					
B* 245 °C	1748.1	5					Infrared					
K			Viscosity				Solubility in +					
c			centistokes				Acetone					
t_k to			η 80 °C	1.61	3		Carbon tet.					
t_x °C			120	0.825	3		Benzene					
A' 25 to	7.69866	5	160	0.528	3		Ether					
B' 115 °C	2044.96	5					n-Heptane					
C'	216.	5	B^v to				Ethanol					
A'* 25 to	2.09652	5	A^v °C				Water					
B'*115 °C	1943.8	5	(B^v) to				Water in					
Ac to			(A^v) °C									
Bc t_c °C			c_p liq. °K									
Cc												
Cryos. A°			c_p vap. °K									
consts. B°												
t_e °C	232.13	5	c_v vap.									

+ grams/100 grams solvent

REFERENCES: 1-Dow 2-API 3-Lit. 4-Calc. from det. data 5-Calc. by formula

SOURCE: Lit.

PURIFICATION: Lit.

LITERATURE REFERENCES: 3 Ind. Eng. Chem. 36, 596 (1944)

No. 8

NAME	2, 6-Dimethylphenol					STRUCTURAL FORMULA

2, 6-Xylenol

STRUCTURAL FORMULA

OH
CH₃〈 〉CH₃

Mole % Pur.	Ref.	Molecular Formula $C_8H_{10}O$		Molecular Weight 122.160		

		Ref.				Ref.				Ref.
F.P. °C	49.0	3	dt/dP				f	to		
F.P. 100%			°C/mm				g	°K		
B.P. °C			25°C	85.49	5		h			
760 mm	212.	3	BP	0.0519	5					
100	145.	3	t_e	0.0334	5		f'	to		
30	114.7	5	30 mm	0.7662	5		g'	°K		
10	91.2	5					h'			
1	51.4	5	ΔHm cal/g							
			ΔHv cal/g				m	to		
Pressure			25°C	118.19	5		n	°K		
mm 25°C	0.14316	5	30 mm	106.46	5		o			
t_e	1315.9	5	BP	91.90	5					
Density			t_e	88.39	5		m'	to		
g/ml 20°C			t_e (d, e)	88.48	5		n'	°K		
d_4^t 25			ΔHv/T_e	21.25	5		o'			
30										
a			d 115 to	123.60	5		Surface tension			
b			e 235 °C	0.1495	5		dynes/cm. 20°C			
			d' 25 to	121.46	5		y 30			
Ref. Index			e' 115 °C	0.1309	5		40			
n_D 20°C			d_c g/ml				Parachor [P]			
25			v_c ml/g				20°C			
30			t_c °C				30			
"C"			P_c mm				40			
MR (Obs.)			PV/RT				Sugd.	300.1	5
MR (Calc.)	37.068	5	25°C	1.0000	5		Exp. L.1.%/wt.			
(nD-d/2)			30 mm	1.0000	5		u.			
Dielectric			BP	0.9472	5		Dispersion			
A 115 to	7.40318	4	t_e	0.9309	5		Flash Point °C			
B 250 °C	1858.7	4	t_c				Fire Point			
C	199.	5	ΔHc kcal/m				M Spec.			
A* 115 to	1.7955	5	ΔHf				Ultra √.			
B* 245 °C	1761.1	5	ΔFf				X-Ray Dif.			
K			Viscosity				Infrared			
c			centistokes				Solubility in +			
t_k to			η °C				Acetone			
t_x °C							Carbon tet.			
A' 25 to	7.74327	5					Benzene			
B' 115 °C	2078.2	5					Ether			
C'	217.	5	B^v to				n-Heptane			
A'* 25 to	2.13909	5	A^v °C				Ethanol			
B'* 115 °C	1976.16	5	$(B^{\overline{v}})$ to				Water			
Ac to			$(A^{\overline{v}})$ °C				Water in			
Bc t_c °C			c_p liq. °K							
Cc										
Cryos. A°			c_p vap. °K							
consts. B°										
t_e °C	234.88	5	c_v vap.							

+
grams/100 grams solvent

REFERENCES: 1-Dow 2-API 3-Lit. 4-Calc. from det. data 5-Calc. by formula

SOURCE: Lit.

PURIFICATION: Lit.

LITERATURE REFERENCES: 3 Ind. Eng. Chem., 36, 596 (1944)

TABLE VIII. AROMATIC PHENOLS

No. 9

NAME	3,4-Dimethylphenol			STRUCTURAL FORMULA
	3,4-Xylenol			

| Mole % Pur. | Ref. | Molecular Formula $C_8H_{10}O$ | Molecular Weight 122.160 | STRUCTURAL FORMULA |

		Ref.			Ref.						Ref.
F.P. °C	62.5	3	dt/dP			f		to			
F.P. 100%			°C/mm			g		°K			
			25°C	283.78	5	h					
B.P. °C			BP	0.0499	5						
760 mm	225.	3	t_e	0.0316	5	f'		to			
100	160.0	3	30 mm	0.7580	5	g'		°K			
30	130.1	5	ΔHm cal/g			h'					
10	106.8	5				m		to			
1	67.0	5	ΔHv cal/g			n		°K			
			25°C	131.86	5	o					
Pressure			30 mm	116.35	5						
mm 25°C	0.0387	5	BP	100.90	5	m'		to			
t_e	1332.25	5	t_e	97.67	5	n'		°K			
Density			t_e (d,e)	97.25	5	o'					
g/ml 80°C	0.9830	3	$\Delta Hv/T_e$	22.92	5						
d_4^t 120	0.9520	3				Surface tension					
160	0.9210	3	d 130 to	137.57	5	dynes/cm. 80°C		34.00	5		
a	1.0450	4	e 240 °C	0.1628	5	∂ 120		29.90	5		
b	-0.0₃775	4	d' 25 to	135.54	5	160		26.03	5		
Ref. Index			e' 130 °C	0.1475	5						
n_D 20°C						Parachor [P]					
25			d_c g/ml			20°C					
30			v_c ml/g			30					
"C"			t_c °C			40					
			P_c mm			Sugd.	300.1		5		
MR (Obs.)			PV/RT								
MR (Calc.)	37.068	5	25°C	1.0000	5	Exp. L.1.%/wt.					
(nD-d/2)			30 mm	1.0000	5	u.					
Dielectric			BP	0.9368	5	Dispersion					
A 130 to	7.70494	4	t_e	0.9198	5	Flash Point °C					
B 265 °C	2030.9	4	t_c			Fire Point					
C	196.	5	ΔHc kcal/m			M. Spec.					
A* 130 to	2.10945	5	ΔHf			Ultra V.					
B* 260 °C	1939.0	5	ΔFf			X-Ray Dif.					
K			Viscosity			Infrared					
c			centistokes			Solubility in ±					
t_k to			η 80 °C	3.05	3	Acetone					
t_x °C			120	1.270	3	Carbon tet.					
A' 25 to	8.04870	5	160	0.737	3	Benzene					
B' 130 °C	2261.3	5				Ether					
C'	214.	5	B^v to			n-Heptane					
A'* 25 to	2.43692	5	A^v °C			Ethanol					
B'* 130 °C	2158.7	5	(B^v) to			Water					
Ac to			(A^v) °C			Water in					
Bc t_c °C			c_p liq. °K								
Cc											
Cryos. A°			c_p vap. °K								
consts. B°											
t_e °C	247.39	5	c_v vap.								

+ grams/100 grams solvent

REFERENCES: 1-Dow 2-API 3-Lit. 4-Calc. from det. data 5-Calc. by formula

SOURCE: Lit.

PURIFICATION: Lit.

LITERATURE REFERENCES: 3 Ind. Eng. Chem., 36, 596 (1944)

No. 10

NAME	3,5-Dimethylphenol					STRUCTURAL FORMULA		
	3,5-Xylenol					OH H_3C CH_3		

Mole % Pur.		Ref.	Molecular Formula $C_8H_{10}O$		Molecular Weight 122.160		

		Ref.				Ref.				Ref.
F.P. °C			dt/dP				f		to	
F.P. 100%			°C/mm				g		°K	
			25°C	206.40	5		h			
B.P. °C			BP	0.0495	5					
760 mm	219.5	3	t_e	0.0316	5		f'		to	
100	155.0	3					g'		°K	
30	125.4	5	30 mm	0.7514	5		h'			
10	102.3	5	ΔHm cal/g							
1	62.8	5					m		to	
Pressure			ΔHv cal/g				n		°K	
mm 25°C	0.0543	5	25°C	129.06	5		o			
t_e	1320.2	5	30 mm	114.63	5					
			BP	99.45	5		m'		to	
Density			t_e	96.32	5		n'		°K	
g/ml 80°C	0.9680	3	t_e (d,e)	95.92	5		o'			
d_4^t 120	0.9350	3	ΔHv/T_e	22.87	5		Surface tension			
160	0.9020	3	d | 125 to	134.85	5		dynes/cm. 80°C	31.98	5
a	1.0340	4	e | 240 °C	0.1613	5		γ 120	27.83	5
b	-0.0₃825	4	d' | 25 to	132.65	5		160	24.05	5
Ref. Index			e' | 125 °C	0.1437	5		Parachor [P]		
n_D 20°C							20°C		
25			d_c g/ml				30		
30			v_c ml/g				40		
"C"			t_c °C				Sugd. 300.1		5
MR (Obs.)			P_c mm				Exp. L.l.%/wt.		
MR (Calc.)	37.068	5	PV/RT				u.		
(nD-d/2)			25°C	1.0000	5		Dispersion		
Dielectric			30 mm	1.0000	5		Flash Point °C		
			BP	0.9390	5		Fire Point		
A | 125 to	7.68771	4	t_e	0.9222	5				
B | 255 °C	2002.1	4	t_c				M Spec.		
C	197.	5					Ultra V.		
A* | 125 to	2.09296	5	ΔHc kcal/m				X-Ray Dif.		
B* | 250 °C	1909.8	5	ΔHf				Infrared		
K			ΔFf				Solubility in +		
c			Viscosity				Acetone		
t_k | to			centistokes				Carbon tet.		
t_x | °C			η 80 °C	2.50	3		Benzene		
A' | 25 to	8.03449	5	120	1.075	3		Ether		
B' | 125 °C	2231.9	5	160	0.635	3		n-Heptane		
C'	215.	5	B^v | to				Ethanol		
A'* 25 to	2.42472	5	A^v | °C				Water		
B'* 125 °C	2129.3	5	$(B^{\overline{v}})$ | to				Water in		
Ac | to			(A^v) | °C						
Bc | t_c °C									
Cc			c_p liq. °K						
Cryos. A°			c_p vap. °K						
consts. B°									
t_e °C	241.38	5	c_v vap.						

+ grams/100 grams solvent

REFERENCES: 1-Dow 2-API 3-Lit. 4-Calc. from det. data 5-Calc. by formula

SOURCE: Lit.

PURIFICATION: Lit.

LITERATURE REFERENCES: ³ Ind. Eng. Chem., 36, 596 (1944)

TABLE VIII. AROMATIC PHENOLS

283

No. 11

NAME	o-Ethylphenol	STRUCTURAL FORMULA
	2-Ethylphenol	OH / C_2H_5

Mole % Pur.	Ref.	Molecular Formula $C_8H_{10}O$	Molecular Weight 122.160

		Ref.			Ref.		Ref.
F.P. °C			dt/dP			f | to	
F.P. 100%			°C/mm			g | __ °K	
B.P. °C			25°C	51.1706	5	h |	
760 mm	207.	3	BP	0.05343	5		
100	138.5	3	t_e	0.0347	5	f' | to	
30	107.7	5	30 mm	0.7740	5	g' | __ °K	
10	84.1	5				h' |	
1	44.2	5	ΔHm cal/g				
Pressure			ΔHv cal/g			m | to	
mm 25°C	0.2525	5	25°C	111.95	5	n | __ °K	
t_e	1306.5	5	30 mm	101.67	5	o |	
Density			BP	87.65	5		
g/ml 20°C			t_e	84.31	5	m' | to	
d_4^t 25			t_e (d, e)	84.36	5	n' | __ °K	
30			ΔHv/T_e	20.46	5	o' |	
a			d | 105 to	116.89	5	Surface tension	
b			e | 230 °C	0.1413	5	dynes/cm. 20°C	
Ref. Index			d' | 25 to	115.06	5	ɣ 30	
n_D 20°C			e' | 105 °C	0.1242	5	40	
25			d_c g/ml			Parachor [P]	
30			v_c ml/g			20°C	
"C"			t_c °C			30	
			P_c mm			40	
MR (Obs.)			PV/RT			Sugd.	300.1	5
MR (Calc.)	37.068	5	25°C	1.0000	5	Exp. L.1.%/wt.	
(nD-d/2)			30 mm	1.0000	5	u.	
Dielectric			BP	0.9489	5	Dispersion	
A | 105 to	7.23343	4	t_e	0.9327	5	Flash Point °C	
B | 245 °C	1771.5	4	t_c			Fire Point	
C	200.	5	ΔHc kcal/m			M. Spec.	
A*| 105 to	1.62547	5	ΔHf			Ultra V.	
B*| 240 °C	1673.3	5	ΔEf			X-Ray Dif.	
K			Viscosity			Infrared	
c			centistokes			Solubility in +	
t_k | to			η °C			Acetone	
t_x | °C						Carbon tet.	
A' | 25 to	7.57011	5				Benzene	
B' | 105 °C	1984.8	5				Ether	
C'	218.	5	B^v | to			n-Heptane	
A'* 25 to	1.96893	5	A^v | °C			Ethanol	
B'* 105 °C	1883.0	5	(B^v)| to			Water	
Ac| to			(A^v)| °C			Water in	
Bc| t_c °C							
Cc			c_p liq. °K				
Cryos. A°			c_p vap. °K				
consts. B°							
t_e °C	230.3	5	c_v vap.				

+ grams/100 grams solvent

REFERENCES: 1-Dow 2-API 3-Lit. 4-Calc. from det. data 5-Calc. by formula

SOURCE: Lit.

PURIFICATION: Lit.

LITERATURE REFERENCES: 3 Ind. Eng. Chem., 36, 596 (1944)

No. 12

NAME	m-Ethylphenol	STRUCTURAL FORMULA
	3-Ethylphenol	OH

Mole % Pur.	Ref.	Molecular Formula $C_8H_{10}O$	Molecular Weight 122.160	C_2H_5

		Ref.			Ref.			Ref.
F.P. °C	-4.0	3	dt/dP °C/mm			f | to		
F.P. 100%			25°C	176.35	5	g | °K		
B.P. °C			BP	0.0483	5	h |		
760 mm	214.	3	t_e	0.0308	5	f' | to		
100	151.0	3	30 mm	0.7366	5	g' | °K		
30	122.0	5	ΔHm cal/g			h' |		
10	99.3	5	ΔHv cal/g			m | to		
1	60.5	5	25°C	128.74	5	n | °K		
Pressure			30 mm	114.96	5	o |		
mm 25°C	0.0637	5	BP	99.67	5	m' | to		
t_e	1317.9	5	t_e	95.92	5	n' | °K		
Density			t_e (d, e)	96.14	5	o' |		
g/ml 20°C			$\Delta Hv/T_e$	23.04	5	Surface tension		
d_4^t 25			d | 120 to	135.23	5	dynes/cm. 20°C		
30			e | 235 °C	0.1662	5	ɣ 30		
a			d' | 25 to	132.30	5	40		
b			e' | 120 °C	0.1421	5	Parachor [P]		
Ref. Index			d_c g/ml			20°C		
n_D 20°C			v_c ml/g			30		
25			t_c °C			40		
30			P_c mm			Sugd.	300.1	5
"C"			PV/RT			Exp. L.1.%/wt.		
MR (Obs.)			25°C	1.0000	5	u.		
MR (Calc.)	37.068	5	30 mm	1.0000	5	Dispersion		
(nD-d/2)			BP	0.9470	5	Flash Point °C		
Dielectric			t_e	0.9316	5	Fire Point		
A | 120 to	7.74624	4	t_c			M Spec.		
B | 250 °C	1999.7	4	ΔHc kcal/m			Ultra V.		
C	197.	5	ΔHf			X-Ray Dif.		
A* | 120 to	2.14114	5	ΔFf			Infrared		
B* | 245 °C	1903.9	5	Viscosity			Solubility in +		
K			centistokes			Acetone		
c			η °C			Carbon tet.		
t_k | to						Benzene		
t_x | °C						Ether		
A' | 25 to	8.11966	5				n-Heptane		
B' | 120 °C	2245.0	5	B^v | to			Ethanol		
C'	216.	5	A^v | °C			Water		
A'* 25 to	2.5110	5	(B^v) | to			Water in		
B'* 120 °C	2142.3	5	(A^v) | °C					
Ac | to			c_p liq. °K					
Bc | t_c °C								
Cc			c_p vap. °K					
Cryos. A°								
consts. B°								
t_e °C	235.24	5	c_v vap.					

+ grams/100 grams solvent

REFERENCES: 1-Dow 2-API 3-Lit. 4-Calc. from det. data 5-Calc. by formula

SOURCE: Lit.

PURIFICATION: Lit.

LITERATURE REFERENCES: 3 Ind. Eng. Chem., 36, 596 (1944)

TABLE VIII. AROMATIC PHENOLS

NAME	p-Ethylphenol			STRUCTURAL FORMULA
	4-Ethylphenol			OH

| Mole % Pur. | Ref. | Molecular Formula $C_8H_{10}O$ | Molecular Weight 122.160 | C_2H_5 |

		Ref.			Ref.				Ref.
F.P. °C	47.0	3	dt/dP			f | to			
F.P. 100%			°C/mm			g | ___ °K			
B.P. °C			25°C	159.09	5	h |			
760 mm	219.	3	BP	0.0509	5				
100	153.0	3	t_e	0.0322	5	f' | to			
30	122.9	5	30 mm	0.7623	5	g' | ___ °K			
10	99.5	5	ΔHm cal/g			h' |			
1	59.7	5	ΔHv cal/g			m | to			
Pressure			25°C	125.36	5	n | ___ °K			
mm 25°C	0.07253	5	30 mm	111.59	5	o |			
t_e	1340.0	5	BP	96.50	5	m' | to			
Density			t_e (d,e)	92.99	5	n' | ___ °K			
g/ml 20°C			t_e (d,e)	92.86	5	o' |			
d_4^t 25			ΔHv/T_e	22.04	5	Surface tension			
30			d | 125 to	130.88	5	dynes/cm. 20°C			
a			e | 245 °C	0.1570	5	પ 30			
b			d' | 25 to	128.89	5	40			
Ref. Index			e' | 125 °C	0.1407	5	Parachor [P]			
n_D 20°C			d_c g/ml			20°C			
25	1.5239	3	v_c ml/g			30			
30			t_c °C			40			
"C"			P_c mm			Sugd.	300.1	5	
MR (Obs.)			PV/RT			Exp. L.1.%/wt.			
MR (Calc.)	37.068	5	25°C	1.0000	5	u.			
(nD-d/2)			30 mm	1.0000	5	Dispersion			
Dielectric			BP	0.9505	5	Flash Point °C			
A | 125 to	7.55177	4	t_e	0.9346	5	Fire Point			
B | 255 °C	1943.1	4	t_c			M. Spec.			
C	197.	5	ΔHc kcal/m			Ultra V.			
A* | 125 to	1.93471	5	ΔHf			X-Ray Dif.			
B* | 250 °C	1843.7	5	ΔFf			Infrared			
K			Viscosity			Solubility in +			
c			centistokes			Acetone			
t_k | to			η °C			Carbon tet.			
t_x | °C						Benzene			
A' | 25 to	7.89361	5				Ether			
B' | 125 °C	2167.9	5				n-Heptane			
C'	215.	5	B^v | to			Ethanol			
A'* 25 to	2.28558	5	A^v | °C			Water			
B'* 125 °C	2065.8	5	(B^v)| to			Water in			
Ac | to			(A^v)| °C						
Bc | t_c °C			c_p liq. °K						
Cc									
Cryos. A°			c_p vap. °K						
consts. B°									
t_e °C	242.15	5	c_v vap.						

+ grams/100 grams solvent

REFERENCES: 1-Dow 2-API 3-Lit. 4-Calc. from det. data 5-Calc. by formula
SOURCE: Lit.
PURIFICATION: Lit.
LITERATURE REFERENCES: 3 Ind. Eng. Chem., 36, 596 (1944)

No. 14

NAME	o-Propylphenol	STRUCTURAL FORMULA
	2-Propylphenol	OH / C_3H_7

Mole % Pur.	Ref.	Molecular Formula $C_9H_{12}O$	Molecular Weight 136.186

		Ref.				Ref.				Ref.
F.P. °C			dt/dP °C/mm				f | to			
F.P. 100%			25°C	320.22	5		g | °K			
			BP	0.04725	5		h			
B.P. °C			t_e	0.02964	5					
760 mm	220.	3	30 mm	0.7325	5		f' | to			
100	158.	5					g' | °K			
30	129.2	5	ΔHm cal/g				h'			
10	106.7	5	ΔHv cal/g							
1	67.8	5	25°C	121.46	5		m | to			
			30 mm	107.53	5		n | °K			
Pressure			BP	93.55	5		o			
mm 25°C	0.03336	5	t_e	90.41	5					
t_e	1338.8	5	t_e (d, e)	90.26	5		m' | to			
			ΔHv/T_e	23.93	5		n' | °K			
Density							o'			
g/ml 80°C	1.015	3	d | 130 to	127.42	5					
d_4^t 25			e | 240 °C	0.15396	5		Surface tension			
30			d' | 25 to	124.80	5		dynes/cm. 20°C			
			e' | 130 °C	0.1337	5		γ 30			
a							40			
b			d_c g/ml							
			v_c ml/g				Parachor [P]			
Ref. Index			t_c °C				20°C			
n_D 20°C			P_c mm				30			
25							40			
30			PV/RT				Sugd.	339.1	5	
"C"			25°C	1.0000	5					
			30 mm	1.0000	5		Exp. L. l. %/wt.			
MR (Obs.)			BP	0.9502	5		u.			
MR (Calc.)	41.686	5	t_e	0.9352	5		Dispersion			
$(n_D - d/2)$			t_c							
							Flash Point °C			
Dielectric			ΔHc kcal/m				Fire Point			
A | 130 to	7.92416	4	ΔHf							
B | 255 °C	2103.	4	ΔFf				M Spec.			
C	197.	5					Ultra V.			
			Viscosity				X-Ray Dif.			
A* | 130 to	2.35515	5	centistokes				Infrared			
B* | 250 °C	2004.1	5	η °C							
K							Solubility in +			
c							Acetone			
t_k | to							Carbon tet.			
t_x | °C							Benzene			
A' | 25 to	8.27990	5					Ether			
B' | 130 °C	2341.6	5	B^v | to				n-Heptane			
C'	215.	5	A^v | °C				Ethanol			
			(B^v) | to				Water			
A'* 25 to	2.71468	5	(A^v) | °C				Water in			
B'* 130 °C	2238.4	5								
Ac | to			c_p liq. °K							
Bc | t_c °C										
Cc			c_p vap. °K							
Cryos. A°										
consts. B°			c_v vap.							
t_e °C	241.38	5								

+ grams/100 grams solvent

REFERENCES: 1-Dow 2-API 3-Lit. 4-Calc. from det. data 5-Calc. by formula
SOURCE: Lit.
PURIFICATION: Lit.
LITERATURE REFERENCES: 3 Ind. Eng. Chem., 36, 596 (1944)

TABLE VIII. AROMATIC PHENOLS

No. 15

NAME	m-Propylphenol	STRUCTURAL FORMULA
	3-Propylphenol	

| Mole % Pur. | | Ref. | Molecular Formula $C_9H_{12}O$ | Molecular Weight 136.186 | |

		Ref.				Ref.			Ref.
F.P. °C	26.0	3	dt/dP			f	| to		
F.P. 100%			°C/mm			g	| __ °K		
			25°C	414.70	5	h	|		
B.P. °C			BP	0.04890	5				
760 mm	228.	3	t_e	0.30300	5	f'	| to		
100	163.9	3	30 mm	0.7522	5	g'	| __ °K		
30	134.4	5	ΔHm cal/g			h'	|		
10	111.2	5							
1	71.5	5	ΔHv cal/g			m	| to		
Pressure			25°C	122.17	5	n	| __ °K		
mm 25°C	0.02561	5	30 mm	107.42	5	o	|		
t_e	1362.42	5	BP	93.32	5				
Density			t_e	90.07	5	m'	| to		
g/ml 20°C			t_e (d, e)	89.88	5	n'	| __ °K		
d_4^t 25			ΔHv/T_e	23.41	5	o'	|		
30			d | 135 to	127.66	5	Surface tension			
a			e | 250 °C	0.1506	5	dynes/cm. 20°C			
b			d' | 25 to	125.55	5	ɤ 30			
Ref. Index			e' | 135 °C	0.1349	5	40			
n_D 20°C			d_c g/ml			Parachor [P]			
25			v_c ml/g			20°C			
30			t_c °C			30			
"C"			P_c mm			40			
MR (Obs.)			PV/RT			Sugd. 339.1		5	
MR (Calc.)	41.686	5	25°C	1.0000	5	Exp. L.1.%/wt.			
(nD-d/2)			30 mm	1.0000	5	u.			
Dielectric			BP	0.9500	5	Dispersion			
A | 135 to	7.83536	4	t_e	0.9344	5	Flash Point °C			
B | 265 °C	2100.7	4	t_c			Fire Point			
C	196.	5	ΔHc kcal/m			M. Spec.			
A* | 135 to	2.25857	5	ΔHf			Ultra V.			
B* | 260 °C	1999.7	5	ΔFf			X-Ray Dif.			
K			Viscosity			Infrared			
c			centistokes			Solubility in +			
t_k | to			η °C			Acetone			
t_x | °C						Carbon tet.			
A' | 25 to	8.18176	5				Benzene			
B' | 135 °C	2335.8	5				Ether			
C'	214.	5	B^v | to			n-Heptane			
A'* 25 to	2.61424	5	A^v | °C			Ethanol			
B'* 135 °C	2232.5	5	(B^v)| to			Water			
Ac | to			(A^v)| °C			Water in			
Bc | t_c °C									
Cc |			c_p liq. °K						
Cryos. A°			c_p vap. °K						
consts. B°									
t_e °C	250.86	5	c_v vap.						

+ grams/100 grams solvent

REFERENCES: 1-Dow 2-API 3-Lit. 4-Calc. from det. data 5-Calc. by formula

SOURCE: Lit.

PURIFICATION: Lit.

LITERATURE REFERENCES: 3 Ind. Eng. Chem., 36, 596 (1944)

No. 16

NAME	p-Propylphenol	STRUCTURAL FORMULA

Structural formula: OH on benzene ring, C_3H_7

Mole % Pur.		Ref.	Molecular Formula $C_9H_{12}O$	Molecular Weight 136.186		

		Ref.				Ref.					Ref.
F.P. °C	22.0	3	dt/dP °C/mm			f		to		
F.P. 100%			25°C	380.97	5	g		°K		
B.P. °C			BP	0.05118	5	h				
760 mm	232.6	3	t_e	0.03157	5	f'		to		
100	166.0	5	30 mm	0.7743	5	g'		°K		
30	135.4	5	ΔHm cal/g			h'				
10	111.67	5	ΔHv cal/g			m		to		
1	71.04	5	25°C	119.73	5	n		°K		
Pressure			30 mm	104.90	5	o				
mm 25°C	0.02845	5	BP	90.81	5	m'		to		
t_e	1377.07	5	t_e	87.48	5	n'		°K		
Density			t_e (d, e)	87.27	5	o'				
g/ml 80°C	1.009	3	$ΔHv/T_e$	22.47	5	Surface tension				
d_4^t 30			d 135 to	124.54	5	dynes/cm. 20°C				
25			e 260 °C	0.1450	5	y 30				
a			d' 20 to	123.09	5	40				
b			e' 135 °C	0.1343	5	Parachor [P]				
Ref. Index			d_c g/ml			20°C				
n_D 20°C			v_c ml/g			30				
25			t_c °C			40				
30			P_c mm			Sugd.	339.1	5		
"C"			PV/RT			Exp. L. l.%/wt.				
MR (Obs.)			25°C	1.0000	5	u.				
MR (Calc.)	41.686	5	30 mm	1.0000	5	Dispersion				
(nD-d/2)			BP	0.9500	5	Flash Point °C				
Dielectric			t_e	0.9335	5	Fire Point				
A 135 to	7.65517	5	t_c			M Spec.				
B 360 °C	2041.5	5	ΔHc kcal/m			Ultra V.				
C	195.	5	ΔHf			X-Ray Dif.				
A* 135 to	2.0737	5	ΔFf			Infrared				
B* 275 °C	1939.3	5	Viscosity			Solubility in +				
K			centistokes			Acetone				
c			η °C			Carbon tet.				
t_k to						Benzene				
t_x °C						Ether				
A' 20 to	7.9917	5	B^V to			n-Heptane				
B' 135 °C	2270.0	5	A^V °C			Ethanol				
C'	213.	5	(B^V) to			Water				
A'* 20 to	2.4247	5	(A^V) °C			Water in				
B'* 135 °C	2167.2	5	c_p liq. °K							
Ac to										
Bc t_c °C										
Cc										
Cryos. A°			c_p vap. °K							
consts. B°										
t_e °C	257.04	5	c_v vap.							

+ grams/100 grams solvent

REFERENCES: 1-Dow   2-API   3-Lit.   4-Calc. from det. data   5-Calc. by formula

SOURCE: Lit.

PURIFICATION: Lit.

LITERATURE REFERENCES: 3 Ind. Eng. Chem., 36, 596 (1944)

TABLE VIII. AROMATIC PHENOLS 289

No. 17

NAME	o-tert-Butylphenol		STRUCTURAL FORMULA
	2-tert-Butylphenol		OH $C(CH_3)_3$
Mole % Pur.	Ref.	Molecular Formula $C_{10}H_{14}O$	Molecular Weight 150.212

		Ref.			Ref.					Ref.
F.P. °C			dt/dP			f		to		
F.P. 100%			°C/mm			g		°K		
B.P. °C			25°C	136.54	5	h				
760 mm	221.	3	BP	0.05269	5					
100	153.	3	t_e	0.03327	5	f'		to		
30	122.2	5	30 mm	0.7782	5	g'		°K		
10	98.3	5	ΔHm cal/g			h'				
1	57.9	5	ΔHv cal/g			m		to		
Pressure			25°C	99.45	5	n		°K		
mm 25°C	0.08663	5	30 mm	88.58	5	o				
t_e	1347.3	5	BP	76.35	5	m'		to		
Density			t_e	73.53	5	n'		°K		
g/ml 20°C			t_e (d, e)	73 35	5	o'				
d_4^t 25			ΔHv/T_e	21.50	5					
30			d 125 to	103.69	5	Surface tension dynes/cm. 20°C				
a			e 245 °C	0.1237	5	γ 30				
b			d' 25 to	102.25	5	40				
Ref. Index			e' 125 °C	0.1119	5					
n_D 20°C			d_c g/ml			Parachor [P]				
25			v_c ml/g			20°C				
30			t_c °C			30				
"C"			P_c mm			40				
MR (Obs.)			PV/RT			Sugd.	378.1		5	
MR (Calc.)	46.304	5	25°C	1.0000	5	Exp. L.1.%/wt.				
(nD-d/2)			30 mm	1.0000	5	u.				
Dielectric			BP	0.9503	5	Dispersion				
A 125 to	7.41439	4	t_e	0.9340	5	Flash Point °C				
B 420°C	1895.0	4	t_c			Fire Point				
C	197.	5	ΔHc kcal/m			M. Spec.				
A* 125 to	1.88268	5	ΔHf			Ultra V.				
B* 255°C	1794.0	5	ΔFf			X-Ray Dif.				
K			Viscosity			Infrared				
c			centistokes			Solubility in +				
t_k to			η °C			Acetone				
t_x °C						Carbon tet.				
A' 25 to	7.74923	5				Benzene				
B' 125°C	2114.8	5	B^v to			Ether				
C'	215.	5	A^v °C			n-Heptane				
A'* 25 to	2.23152	5	(B^v) to			Ethanol				
B'* 125°C	2012.8	5	(A^v) °C			Water				
Ac to			c_p liq. °K			Water in				
Bc t_c °C										
Cc			c_p vap. °K							
Cryos. A°										
consts. B°			c_v vap.							
t_e °C	245.25	5								

+ grams/100 grams solvent

REFERENCES: 1-Dow 2-API 3-Lit. 4-Calc. from det. data 5-Calc. by formula

SOURCE: Lit.

PURIFICATION: Lit.

LITERATURE REFERENCES: 3 Ind. Eng. Chem., 36, 596 (1944)

No. 18

NAME	m-tert-Butylphenol		STRUCTURAL FORMULA

Mole % Pur.	Ref.	Molecular Formula $C_{10}H_{14}O$	Molecular Weight 150.212

		Ref.			Ref.			Ref.
F.P. °C	41.	2	dt/dP			f | to		
F.P. 100%			°C/mm			g | °K		
			25°C	528.09	5	h |		
B.P. °C			BP	0.0523	5			
760 mm	240.	3	t_e	0.0319	5	f' | to		
100	172.	3				g' | °K		
30	140.9	5	30 mm	0.7883	5	h' |		
10	116.7	5	ΔHm cal/g					
1	75.4	5				m | to		
Pressure			ΔHv cal/g			n | °K		
mm 25°C	0.0201	5	25°C	110.59	5	o |		
t_e	1398.7	5	30 mm	95.92	5			
Density			BP	82.88	5	m' | to		
g/ml 20°C			t_e	79.67	5	n' | °K		
d_4^t 25			t_e (d, e)	79.50	5	o' |		
30			ΔHv/T_e	22.21	5			
a			d | 140 to	114.45	5	Surface tension		
b			e | 270 °C	0.1315	5	dynes/cm. 20°C		
Ref. Index			d' | 20 to	113.75	5	y 30		
n_D 20°C			e' | 140 °C	0.1266	5	40		
25			d_c g/ml			Parachor [P]		
30			v_c ml/g			20°C		
"C"			t_c °C			30		
MR (Obs.)			P_c mm			40		
MR (Calc.)	46.304	5	PV/RT			Sugd. 378.1		5
(nD-d/2)			25°C	1.0000	5	Exp. L.1.%/wt.		
Dielectric			30 mm	1.0000	5	u.		
A | 140 to	7.60868	4	BP	0.9501	5	Dispersion		
B | 330 °C	2047.2	4	t_e	0.9329	5	Flash Point °C		
C	193.	5	t_c			Fire Point		
A* | 140 to	2.06375	5	ΔHc kcal/m			M Spec.		
B* | 275 °C	1943.8	5	ΔHf			Ultra V.		
K			ΔFf			X-Ray Dif.		
c			Viscosity			Infrared		
t_k | to			centistokes			Solubility in +		
t_x | °C			η °C			Acetone		
A' | 20 to	7.93924	5				Carbon tet.		
B' | 140 °C	2273.9	5				Benzene		
C'	211.	5	B^v | to			Ether		
A'* 20 to	2.41358	5	A^v | °C			n-Heptane		
B'* 140 °C	2171.7	5	(B^v) | to			Ethanol		
Ac | to			(A^v) | °C			Water		
Bc | t_c °C			c_p liq. °K			Water in		
Cc								
Cryos. A°			c_p vap. °K					
consts. B°								
t_e °C	265.71	5	c_v vap.					

+ grams/100 grams solvent

REFERENCES: 1-Dow 2-API 3-Lit. 4-Calc. from det. data 5-Calc. by formula

SOURCE: Lit.

PURIFICATION: Lit.

LITERATURE REFERENCES: 3 Ind. Eng. Chem., 36, 596 (1944)

TABLE VIII. AROMATIC PHENOLS   291

No. 19

NAME	p-tert-Butylphenol	STRUCTURAL FORMULA
	4-tert-Butylphenol	OH

Mole % Pur.		Ref.	Molecular Formula $C_{10}H_{14}O$		Molecular Weight 150.212		$C(CH_3)_3$

		Ref.			Ref.			Ref.
F.P. °C	100.	3	dt/dP			f | to		
F.P. 100%			°C/mm			g | _ _ _°K		
B.P. °C			25°C	396.83	5	h |		
760 mm	239.5	3	BP	0.05373	5			
100	170.	3	t_e	0.03297	5	f' | to		
30	138.4	5	30 mm	0.8000	5	g' | _ _ _°K		
10	113.9	5	ΔHm cal/g			h' |		
1	72.2	5						
			ΔHv cal/g			m | to		
Pressure			25°C	107.16	5	n | _ _ _°K		
mm 25°C	0.02766	5	30 mm	93.40	5	o |		
t_e	1393.17	5	BP	80.54	5			
Density			t_e	77.15	5	m' | to		
g/ml 80°C	0.908	3	t_e (d, e)	77.18	5	n' | _ _ _°K		
d_4^t 25			ΔHv/T_e	21.50	5	o' |		
30								
a			d | 140 to	111.01	5	Surface tension		
b			e | 265 °C	0.1272	5	dynes/cm. 20°C		
			d' | 25 to	110.20	5	ɤ 30		
Ref. Index			e' | 140 °C	0.1213	5	40		
n_D 20°C			d_c g/ml					
25			v_c ml/g			Parachor [P]		
30			t_c °C			20°C		
"C"			P_c mm			30		
						40		
MR (Obs.)			PV/RT			Sugd.	378.1	5
MR (Calc.)	46.304	5	25°C	1.0000	5	Exp. L.1.%/wt.		
(nD-d/2)			30 mm	1.0000	5	u.		
Dielectric			BP	0.9497	5	Dispersion		
A | 140 to	7.49264	4	t_e	0.9289	5	Flash Point °C		
B | 370°C	1999.8	4	t_c			Fire Point		
C	194.	5	ΔHc kcal/m			M. Spec.		
A* | 140 to	1.95278	5	ΔHf			Ultra V.		
B* | 275°C	1897.7	5	ΔFf			X-Ray Dif.		
K			Viscosity			Infrared		
c			centistokes			Solubility in +		
t_k | to			η °C			Acetone		
t_x | °C						Carbon tet.		
A' | 25 to	7.81835	5				Benzene		
B' | 140°C	2222.2	5				Ether		
C'	212.	5	B^v | to			n-Heptane		
A'* 25 to	2.29311	5	A^v | °C			Ethanol		
B'* 140°C	2119.7	5	(B^v)| to			Water		
Ac | to			(A^v)| °C			Water in		
Bc | t_c °C								
Cc			c_p liq. °K					
Cryos. A°			c_p vap. °K					
consts. B°								
t_e °C	265.87	5	c_v vap.					

+ grams/100 grams solvent

REFERENCES: 1-Dow 2-API 3-Lit. 4-Calc. from det. data 5-Calc. by formula

SOURCE: Lit.

PURIFICATION: Lit.

LITERATURE REFERENCES: 3 Ind. Eng. Chem., 36, 596 (1944)

No. 20

NAME	o-n-Butylphenol	STRUCTURAL FORMULA
	2-n-Butylphenol	

OH C_4H_9

Mole % Pur.	Ref.	Molecular Formula	$C_{10}H_{14}O$	Molecular Weight 150.212

		Ref.			Ref.					Ref.
F.P. °C	-20.	3	dt/dP			f	to			
F.P. 100%			°C/mm			g	°K			
			25°C	216.93	5	h				
B.P. °C			BP	0.05566	5					
760 mm	235.	3	t_e	0.03444	5	f'	to			
100	163.5	3	30 mm	0.8109	5	g'	°K			
30	131.3	5	ΔHm cal/g			h'				
10	106.5	5								
1	64.6	5	ΔHv cal/g			m	to			
			25°C	101.47	5	n	°K			
Pressure			30 mm	88.98	5	o				
mm 25°C	0.05344	5	BP	76.41	5					
t_e	1388.6	5	t_e	73.34	5	m'	to			
Density			t_e (d, e)	73.12	5	n'	°K			
g/ml 80°C	0.975	3	ΔHv/T_e	20.58	5	o'				
d_4^t 25 30			d 130 to	104.91	5	Surface tension				
a			e 260 °C	0.1213	5	dynes/cm. 20°C				
b			d' 25 to	104.41	5	ɣ 30				
			e' 130 °C	0.1175	5	40				
Ref. Index										
n_D 20°C	1.496	3	d_c g/ml			Parachor [P]				
25			v_c ml/g			20°C				
30			t_c °C			30				
"C"			P_c mm			40				
MR (Obs.)			PV/RT			Sugd.	378.1			5
MR (Calc.)	46.304	5	25°C	1.0000	5	Exp. L.1.%/wt.				
(nD-d/2)			30 mm	1.0000	5	u.				
Dielectric			BP	0.9500	5	Dispersion				
A 130 to	7.28486	4	t_e	0.9324	5	Flash Point °C				
B 460 °C	1889.3	4	t_c			Fire Point				
C	194.	5	ΔHc kcal/m			M Spec.				
A* 130 to	1.74142	5	ΔHf			Ultra V.				
B* 280 °C	1785.8	5	ΔFf			X-Ray Dif.				
K			Viscosity			Infrared				
c			centistokes			Solubility in +				
t_k to			η °C			Acetone				
t_x °C						Carbon tet.				
A' 25 to	7.60622	5				Benzene				
B' 130 °C	2104.2	5				Ether				
C'	212.	5	B^v to			n-Heptane				
A'* 25 to	2.08587	5	A^v °C			Ethanol				
B'* 130 °C	2002.8	5	(B^v) to			Water				
Ac to			(A^v) °C			Water in				
Bc t_c °C			c_p liq. °K							
Cc			c_p vap. °K							
Cryos. A°										
consts. B°			c_v vap.							
t_e °C	262.10	5								

+ grams/100 grams solvent

REFERENCES: 1-Dow 2-API 3-Lit. 4-Calc. from det. data 5-Calc. by formula
SOURCE: Lit.
PURIFICATION: Lit.
LITERATURE REFERENCES: 3 Ind. Eng. Chem., 36, 596 (1944)

TABLE VIII. AROMATIC PHENOLS   293

No. 21

NAME	m-n-Butylphenol	STRUCTURAL FORMULA
	3-n-Butylphenol	OH

Mole % Pur.	Ref.	Molecular Formula $C_{10}H_{14}O$	Molecular Weight 150.212	C_4H_9

			Ref.			Ref.			Ref.
F.P. °C				dt/dP			f | to		
F.P. 100%				°C/mm			g | °K		
B.P. °C				25°C	806.34	5	h |		
760 mm	248.	3		BP	0.0531	5			
100	179.	3		t_e	0.0320	5	f' | to		
30	147.4	5		30 mm	0.8003	5	g' | °K		
10	122.8	5		ΔHm cal/g			h' |		
1	80.9	5		ΔHv cal/g			m | to		
Pressure				25°C	113.34	5	n | °K		
mm 25°C	0.0129	5		30 mm	97.48	5	o |		
t_e	1418.2	5		BP	84.09	5	m' | to		
Density				t_e	80.76	5	n' | °K		
g/ml 80°C	0.9740	3		t_e (d, e)	80.54	5	o' |		
d_4^t 25 30				ΔHv/T_e	22.14	5	Surface tension dynes/cm. 20°C		
a				d | 145 to	117.1	5	γ 30		
b				e | 275 °C	0.1331	5	40		
Ref. Index				d' | 25 to	116.57	5			
n_D 20°C 25 30				e' | 145 °C	0.1295	5	Parachor [P] 20°C		
"C"				d_c g/ml			30		
MR (Obs.)				v_c ml/g			40		
MR (Calc.)	46.304	5		t_c °C			Sugd. 378.1		5
(nD-d/2)				P_c mm			Exp. L.1.%/wt.		
Dielectric				PV/RT			u.		
A | 145 to	7.61676	5		25°C	1.0000	5	Dispersion		
B | 290 °C	2083.8	5		30 mm	1.0000	5	Flash Point °C		
C	192.	5		BP	0.9480	5	Fire Point		
A* | 145 to	2.06862	5		t_e	0.9303	5	M. Spec.		
B* | 285 °C	1979.9	5		t_c			Ultra V.		
K				ΔHc kcal/m			X-Ray Dif.		
c				ΔHf			Infrared		
t_k | to				ΔFf			Solubility in +		
t_x | °C				Viscosity			Acetone		
A' | 25 to	7.94237	5		centistokes			Carbon tet.		
B' | 145 °C	2310.7	5		η °C			Benzene		
C'	210.	5					Ether		
A'* 25 to	2.41353	5					n-Heptane		
B'* 145 °C	2208.2	5		B^v | to			Ethanol		
Ac | to				A^v | °C			Water		
Bc | t_c °C				(B^v) | to			Water in		
Cc				(A^v) °C					
Cryos. A°				c_p liq. °K					
consts. B°				c_p vap. °K					
t_e °C	274.69	5		c_v vap.					

+ grams/100 grams solvent

REFERENCES: 1-Dow 2-API 3-Lit. 4-Calc. from det. data 5-Calc. by formula

SOURCE: Lit.

PURIFICATION: Lit.

LITERATURE REFERENCES: 3 Ind. Eng. Chem., 36, 596 (1944)

NAME	p-n-Butylphenol	STRUCTURAL FORMULA
	4-n-Butylphenol	

Mole % Pur.	Ref.	Molecular Formula $C_{10}H_{14}O$	Molecular Weight 150.212	

OH

C_4H_9

		Ref.			Ref.				Ref.
F.P. °C	22.	3	dt/dP			f	to		
F.P. 100%			°C/mm			g	°K		
B.P. °C			25°C	764.86	5	h			
760 mm	248.0	3	BP	0.05338	5				
100	179.0	3	t_e	0.03202	5	f'	to		
30	147.0	5	30 mm	0.8026	5	g'	°K		
10	122.4	5	ΔHm cal/g			h'			
1	80.4	5	ΔHv cal/g			m	to		
Pressure			25°C	112.74	5	n	°K		
mm 25°C	0.01364	5	30 mm	97.00	5	o			
t_e	1428.1	5	BP	84.09	5	m'	to		
Density			t_e	80.79	5	n'	°K		
g/ml 80°C	0.978	3	t_e (d, e)	80 62	5	o'			
d_4^t 25			ΔHv/T_e	22.13	5	Surface tension			
30			d 145 to	115.79	5	dynes/cm. 20°C			
a			e 275 °C	0.1278	5	y 30			
b			d' 25 to	115.97	5	40			
Ref. Index			e' 145 °C	0.1290	5	Parachor [P]			
n_D 20°C	1.5165	3	d_c g/ml			20°C			
25			v_c ml/g			30			
30			t_c °C			40			
"C"			P_c mm			Sugd.	378.1	5	
MR (Obs.)			PV/RT			Exp. L.1.%/wt.			
MR (Calc.)	46.304	5	25°C	1.0000	5	u.			
(nD-d/2)			30 mm	1.0000	5	Dispersion			
Dielectric			BP	0.9500	5	Flash Point °C			
A 145 to	7.5913	4	t_e	0.9360	5	Fire Point			
B 380 °C	2072.6	4	t_c			M Spec.			
C	192.	5	ΔHc kcal/m			Ultra V.			
A* 145 to	2.03285	5	ΔHf			X-Ray Dif.			
B* 285 °C	1965.2	5	ΔFf			Infrared			
K			Viscosity			Solubility in +			
c			centistokes			Acetone			
t_k to			η °C			Carbon tet.			
t_x °C						Benzene			
A' 25 to	7.91596	5				Ether			
B' 145 °C	2298.6	5				n-Heptane			
C'	210.	5				Ethanol			
A'* 25 to	2.38740	5	B^V to			Water			
B'* 145 °C	2196.1	5	A^V °C			Water in			
Ac to			(B^V) to						
Bc t_c °C			(A^V) °C						
Cc			c_p liq. °K						
Cryos. A°			c_p vap. °K						
consts. B°									
t_e °C	275.16	5	c_v vap.						

+ grams/100 grams solvent

REFERENCES: 1-Dow   2-API   3-Lit.   4-Calc. from det. data   5-Calc. by formula

SOURCE: Lit.

PURIFICATION: Lit.

LITERATURE REFERENCES: 3 Ind. Eng. Chem., 36, 596 (1944)

TABLE VIII. AROMATIC PHENOLS

No. 23

NAME	2-tert-Butyl-4-methylphenol	STRUCTURAL FORMULA

Structural formula: OH, C(CH$_3$)$_3$, CH$_3$ on benzene ring

Mole % Pur.		Ref.	Molecular Formula C$_{11}$H$_{16}$O	Molecular Weight 164.238	

		Ref.			Ref.			Ref.
F.P. °C	51.7	3	dt/dP			f	to	
F.P. 100%			°C/mm			g	°K	
B.P. °C			25°C	308.75	5	h		
760 mm	237.	3	BP	0.05422	5			
100	167.	3	t$_e$	0.03334	5	f'	to	
30	135.3	5	30 mm	0.8016	5	g'	°K	
10	110.7	5	ΔHm cal/g			h'		
1	69.1	5	ΔHv cal/g			m	to	
Pressure			25°C	96.05	5	n	°K	
mm 25°C	0.03628	5	30 mm	83.94	5	o		
t$_e$	1392.3	5	BP	72.28	5	m'	to	
Density			t$_e$	69.41	5	n'	°K	
g/ml 80°C	0.922	3	t$_e$ (d, e)	69.25	5	o'		
d$_4^t$ 120	0.892	3	ΔHv/T$_e$	21.24	5	Surface tension		
160	0.862	3	d 135 to	99.44	5	dynes/cm. 20°C		
a			e 265 °C	0.1146	5	ɣ 30		
b			d' 25 to	98.80	5	40		
Ref. Index			e' 140 °C	0.1098	5	Parachor [P]		
n$_D$ 20°C			d$_c$ g/ml			20°C		
25			v$_c$ ml/g			30		
30			t$_c$ °C			40		
"C"			P$_c$ mm			Sugd.	417.1	5
MR (Obs.)			PV/RT			Exp. L.1.%/wt.		
MR (Calc.)	50.922	5	25°C	1.0000	5	u.		
(nD-d/2)			30 mm	1.0000	5	Dispersion		
Dielectric			BP	0.9500	5	Flash Point °C		
A 135 to	7.42327	4	t$_e$	0.9325	5	Fire Point		
B 370°C	1957.8	4	t$_c$			M. Spec.		
C	194.	5	ΔHc kcal/m			Ultra V.		
A* 135 to	1.91788	5	ΔHf			X-Ray Dif.		
B* 275 °C	1854.1	5	ΔFf			Infrared		
K			Viscosity			Solubility in +		
c			centistokes			Acetone		
t$_k$ to			η 80 °C	2.55	3	Carbon tet.		
t$_x$ °C			120	1.170	3	Benzene		
A' 25 to	7.74834	5	160	0.713	3	Ether		
B' 140°C	2177.7	5				n-Heptane		
C'	212.	5	B^v 110 to	831.0	4	Ethanol		
A'* 25 to	2.26405	5	A^v 170 °C	3.9548	4	Water		
B'* 140 °C	2075.7	5	(B^v) to			Water in		
Ac to			(A^v) °C					
Bc t$_c$ °C			c$_p$ liq. °K					
Cc								
Cryos. A°			c$_p$ vap. °K					
consts. B°								
t$_e$ °C	263.48	5	c$_v$ vap.					

+ grams/100 grams solvent

REFERENCES: 1-Dow 2-API 3-Lit. 4-Calc. from det. data 5-Calc. by formula

SOURCE: Lit.

PURIFICATION: Lit.

LITERATURE REFERENCES: 3 Ind. Eng. Chem., 36, 596 (1944)

No. 24

NAME	2-sec-Butyl-4-methylphenol	STRUCTURAL FORMULA

Structural formula: OH, CH(CH$_3$)CH$_2$CH$_3$, CH$_3$ (phenol ring)

Mole % Pur.	Ref.	Molecular Formula $C_{11}H_{16}O$	Molecular Weight 164.238	

		Ref.			Ref.				Ref.
F.P. °C			dt/dP °C/mm			f	to		
F.P. 100%			25°C	420.7	5	g	°K		
B.P. °C			BP	0.0524	5	h			
760 mm	237.0	3	t_e	0.0321	5	f'	to		
100	169.0	5	30 mm	0.7869	5	g'	°K		
30	137.9	5	ΔHm cal/g			h'			
10	113.8	5	ΔHv cal/g			m	to		
1	72.6	5	25°C	99.34	5	n	°K		
Pressure			30 mm	86.62	5	o			
mm 25°C	0.0257	5	BP	74.82	5	m'	to		
t_e	1390.9	5	t_e	71.95	5	n'	°K		
Density			t_e (d, e)	71.79	5	o'			
g/ml 20°C			ΔHv/T_e	22.06	5	Surface tension			
d_4^t 25			d 140 to	103.03	5	dynes/cm. 20°C			
30			e 260 °C	0.1190	5	γ 30			
a			d' 25 to	102.15	5	40			
b			e' 140 °C	0.1127	5	Parachor [P]			
Ref. Index			d_c g/ml			20°C			
n_D 20°C			v_c ml/g			30			
25			t_c °C			40			
30			P_c mm			Sugd.	417.1	5	
"C"			PV/RT			Exp. L.1.%/wt.			
MR (Obs.)			25°C	1.0000	5	u.			
MR (Calc.)	50.922	5	30 mm	1.0000	5	Dispersion			
(nD-d/2)			BP	0.9500	5	Flash Point °C			
Dielectric			t_e	0.9333	5	Fire Point			
A 140 to	7.58277	4	t_c			M Spec.			
B 275 °C	2026.5	4	ΔHc kcal/m			Ultra V.			
C	194.	5	ΔHf			X-Ray Dif.			
A* 140 to	2.07791	5	ΔFf			Infrared			
B* 270 °C	1923.1	5	Viscosity			Solubility in +			
K			centistokes			Acetone			
c			η °C			Carbon tet.			
t_k to						Benzene			
t_x °C						Ether			
A' 25 to	7.91389	5				n-Heptane			
B' 140 °C	2252.3	5				Ethanol			
C'	212.	5	B^v to			Water			
A'* 25 to	2.42779	5	A^v °C			Water in			
B'* 140 °C	2149.8	5	(B^v) to						
Ac to			(A^v) °C						
Bc t_c °C									
Cc									
Cryos. A°			c_p liq °K						
consts. B°			c_p vap. °K						
t_e °C	262.47	5	c_v vap.						

+ grams/100 grams solvent

REFERENCES: 1-Dow   2-API   3-Lit.   4-Calc. from det. data   5-Calc. by formula

SOURCE: Lit.

PURIFICATION: Lit.

LITERATURE REFERENCES: 3 Ind. Eng. Chem., 36, 596 (1944)

TABLE VIII. AROMATIC PHENOLS

297

No. 25

NAME	p-tert-Hydroxybenzene	STRUCTURAL FORMULA
	4-tert-Amylphenol	

Mole % Pur.	Ref.	Molecular Formula $C_{11}H_{16}O$	Molecular Weight 164.238	OH / CH2 C(CH3)3

		Ref.			Ref.				Ref.
F.P. °C			dt/dP			f | | to			
F.P. 100%			°C/mm			g | | °K			
			25°C	2093.2	5	h |			
B.P. °C			BP	0.05374	5				
760 mm	262.5	3	t_e	0.0317	5	f' | | to			
100	192.5	5	30 mm	0.8155	5	g' | | °K			
30	160.3	5	ΔHm cal/g			h' |			
10	135.3	5				m | | to			
1	92.5	5	ΔHv cal/g			n | | °K			
			25°C	110.30	5	o |			
Pressure			30 mm	92.93	5				
mm 25°C	0.00466	5	BP	80.15	5	m' | | to			
t_e	1456.7	5	t_e	76.81	5	n' | | °K			
Density			t_e (d, e)	76.60	5	o' |			
g/ml 80°C	0.962	3	ΔHv/T_e	22.37	5				
d_4^t 25 30						Surface tension dynes/cm. 20°C			
a			d | 160 to	113.0	5	ɣ 30			
b			e | 290 °C	0.1251	5	40			
			d' | 25 to	113.50	5				
Ref. Index			e' | 160 °C	0.1284	5	Parachor [P]			
n_D 20°C 25 30			d_c g/ml v_c ml/g t_c °C			20°C 30 40			
"C"			P_c mm			Sugd.	417.5	5
MR (Obs.) MR (Calc.) (nD-d/2)	50.922	5	PV/RT 25°C	1.0000	5	Exp. L.1.%/wt. u.			
Dielectric			30 mm	1.0000	5	Dispersion			
			BP	0.9470	5				
A | 160 to	7.68125	5	t_e	0.9284	5	Flash Point °C Fire Point			
B | 305 °C	2167.4	5	t_c						
C	189.	5	ΔHc kcal/m			M. Spec. Ultra V.			
A* | 160 to	2.16322	5	ΔHf			X-Ray Dif.			
B* | 300 °C	2062.1	5	ΔFf			Infrared			
K			Viscosity			Solubility in +			
c			centistokes			Acetone			
t_k | to			η °C			Carbon tet.			
t_x | °C						Benzene			
A' | 25 to	7.9982	5				Ether			
B' | 160 °C	2396.5	5	B^v | to			n-Heptane			
C'	207.	5	A^v | °C			Ethanol			
A'* 25 to	2.50585	5	(B^v)| to			Water			
B'* 160 °C	2294.2	5	(A^v)| °C			Water in			
Ac | to									
Bc | t_c °C			c_p liq. °K						
Cc |									
Cryos. A° consts. B°			c_p vap. °K						
t_e °C	290.74	5	c_v vap.						

+ grams/100 grams solvent

REFERENCES: 1-Dow 2-API 3-Lit. 4-Calc. from det. data 5-Calc. by formula

SOURCE: Lit.

PURIFICATION: Lit.

LITERATURE REFERENCES: 3 Ind. Eng. Chem., 36, 596 (1944)

No. 26

NAME	4-n-Amylphenol					STRUCTURAL FORMULA

OH

Mole % Pur.	Ref.	Molecular Formula $C_{11}H_{16}O$		Molecular Weight 164.238		C_5H_{11}

		Ref.				Ref.				Ref.
F.P. °C	23.	3	dt/dP °C/mm				f	to °K		
F.P. 100%			25°C	983.04	5		g			
B.P. °C			BP	0.0531	5		h			
760 mm	250.5	3	t_e	0.0317	5		f'	to °K		
100	181.5	5	30 mm	0.8012	5		g'			
30	149.9	5	ΔHm cal/g				h'			
10	125.3	5	ΔHv cal/g				m	to °K		
1	83.29	5	25°C	105.28	5		n			
Pressure			30 mm	90.10	5		o			
mm 25°C	0.0104	5	BP	78.11	5		m'	to °K		
t_e	1434.9	5	t_e	75.01	5		n'			
Density			t_e (d, e)	74.87	5		o'			
g/ml 80°C	0.960	3	ΔHv/T_e	22.36	5		Surface tension			
d_4^t 30 25			d 150 to	107.96	5		dynes/cm. 20°C			
a			e 275 °C	0.1191	5		$\jmath$ 30			
b			d' 25 to	108.32	5		40			
Ref. Index			e' 150 °C	0.1216	5		Parachor [P]			
n_D 20°C	1.5272	3	d_c g/ml				20°C			
25			v_c ml/g				30			
30			t_c °C				40			
"C"			P_c mm				Sugd.	417.1	5
MR (Obs.)			PV/RT				Exp. L.1.%/wt.			
MR (Calc.)	50.922	5	25°C	1.0000	5		u.			
(nD-d/2)			30 mm	1.0000	5		Dispersion			
Dielectric			BP	0.9533	5		Flash Point °C			
A 150 to	7.63596	4	t_e	0.9362	5		Fire Point			
B 290 °C	2099.4	4	t_c				M Spec.			
C	191.	5	ΔHc kcal/m				Ultra V.			
A* 150 to	2.11460	5	ΔHf				X-Ray Dif.			
B* 285 °C	1991.9	5	ΔFf				Infrared			
K			Viscosity				Solubility in +			
c			centistokes				Acetone			
t_k to			η °C				Carbon tet.			
t_x °C							Benzene			
A' 25 to	7.96118	5					Ether			
B' 150 °C	2327.0	5	B^v to				n-Heptane			
C'	209.	5	A^v °C				Ethanol			
A'* 25 to	2.47102	5	(B^v) to				Water			
B'* 150 °C	2224.9	5	(A^v) °C				Water in			
Ac to			c_p liq. °K							
Bc t_c °C										
Cc			c_p vap. °K							
Cryos. A°										
consts. B°										
t_e °C	277.71	5	c_v vap.							

+ grams/100 grams solvent

REFERENCES: 1-Dow　2-API　3-Lit.　4-Calc. from det. data　5-Calc. by formula

SOURCE:　　　　　　Lit.

PURIFICATION:　　　　Lit.

LITERATURE REFERENCES:　3 Ind. Eng. Chem., 36, 596 (1944)

TABLE VIII. AROMATIC PHENOLS

NAME	4-tert-Amyl-2-methylphenol	STRUCTURAL FORMULA

OH
CH_3

Mole % Pur.	Ref.	Molecular Formula $C_{12}H_{18}O$	Molecular Weight 178.264	$CH_2C(CH_3)_3$

		Ref.				Ref.			Ref.
F.P. °C			dt/dP				f | to		
F.P. 100%			°C/mm				g | ___ °K		
B.P. °C			25°C	4860.2	5		h |		
760 mm	273.	3	BP	0.05356	5		f' | to		
100	203.	5	t_e	0.0309	5		g' | ___ °K		
30	170.7	5	30 mm	0.8205	5		h' |		
10	145.5	5	ΔHm cal/g				m | to		
1	102.2	5	ΔHv cal/g				n | ___ °K		
Pressure			25°C	107.45	5		o |		
mm 25°C	0.0019	5	30 mm	89.23	5		m' | to		
t_e	1492.4	5	BP	77.30	5		n' | ___ °K		
Density			t_e	74.04	5		o' |		
g/ml 20°C			t_e (d, e)	73.89	5		Surface tension		
d_4^t 30			ΔHv/T_e	22.94	5		dynes/cm. 20°C		
a			d | 170 to	109.15	5		ɣ 30		
b			e | 300 °C	0.1167	5		40		
Ref. Index			d' | 25 to	110.57	5		Parachor [P]		
n_D 20°C			e' | 170 °C	0.1250	5		20°C		
25			d_c g/ml				30		
30			v_c ml/g				40		
"C"			t_c °C				Sugd.	456.1	5
MR (Obs.)			P_c mm				Exp. L.1.%/wt.		
MR (Calc.)	55.540	5	PV/RT				u.		
(nD-d/2)			25°C	1.0000	5		Dispersion		
Dielectric			30 mm	1.0000	5		Flash Point °C		
A | 170 to	7.78820	4	BP	0.9506	5		Fire Point		
B | 380°C	2257.4	4	t_e	0.9322	5		M. Spec.		
C	187.	5	t_c				Ultra V.		
A* | 170 to	2.29102	5	ΔHc kcal/m				X-Ray Dif.		
B* | 315 °C	2147.9	5	ΔHf				Infrared		
K			ΔFf				Solubility in +		
c			Viscosity				Acetone		
t_k | to			centistokes				Carbon tet.		
t_x | °C			η °C				Benzene		
A' | 25 to	8.10579	5					Ether		
B' | 170 °C	2490.3	5					n-Heptane		
C'	205.	5	B^v | to				Ethanol		
A'* 25 to	2.64192	5	A^v | °C				Water		
B'* 170 °C	2387.8	5	(B^v)| to				Water in		
Ac | to			(A^v)| °C						
Bc | t_c °C			c_p liq. °K						
Cc									
Cryos. A°			c_p vap. °K						
consts. B°									
t_e °C	302.22	5	c_v vap.						

+ grams/100 grams solvent

REFERENCES: 1-Dow 2-API 3-Lit. 4-Calc. from det. data 5-Calc. by formula

SOURCE: Lit.

PURIFICATION: Lit.

LITERATURE REFERENCES: 3 Ind. Eng. Chem., 36, 596 (1944)

No. 28

NAME	4-tert-Amyl-3-methylphenol	STRUCTURAL FORMULA

OH

CH₃

CH₂ C(CH₃)₃

| Mole % Pur. | Ref. | Molecular Formula $C_{12}H_{18}O$ | Molecular Weight 178.264 | |

		Ref.			Ref.				Ref.
F.P. °C			dt/dP			f	to		
F.P. 100%			°C/mm			g	°K		
			25°C	4440.67	5	h			
B.P. °C			BP	0.05397	5				
760 mm	273.	3	t_e	0.0312	5	f'	to		
100	202.5	5				g'	°K		
30	170.1	5	30 mm	0.8240	5	h'			
10	144.7	5	ΔHm cal/g						
1	101.4	5				m	to		
			ΔHv cal/g			n	°K		
Pressure			25°C	106.64	5	o			
mm 25°C	0.00209	5	30 mm	88.61	5				
t_e	1487.8	5	BP	76.50	5	m'	to		
Density			t_e	73.23	5	n'	°K		
g/ml 20°C			t_e (d, e)	73.05	5	o'			
d_4^t 25			$ΔHv/T_e$	22.68	5	Surface tension			
30						dynes/cm. 20°C			
a			d 170 to	108.6	5	γ 30			
b			e 300 °C	0.1176	5	40			
Ref. Index			d' 25 to	109.7	5				
n_D 20°C			e' 170 °C	0.1243	5	Parachor [P]			
25			d_c g/ml			20°C			
30			v_c ml/g			30			
"C"			t_c °C			40			
			P_c mm			Sugd.	456.1	5
MR (Obs.)			PV/RT			Exp. L.1.%/wt.			
MR (Calc.)	55.540	5	25°C	1.0000	5	u.			
(nD-d/2)			30 mm	1.0000	5	Dispersion			
Dielectric			BP	0.9480	5	Flash Point °C			
A 170 to	7.75037	4	t_e	0.9292	5	Fire Point			
B 410 °C	2240.0	4	t_c			M Spec.			
C	187.	5	ΔHc kcal/m			Ultra V.			
A* 170 to	2.25809	5	ΔHf			X-Ray Dif.			
B* 310 °C	2132.3	5	ΔFf			Infrared			
K			Viscosity			Solubility in +			
c			centistokes			Acetone			
t_k to			η °C			Carbon tet.			
t_x °C						Benzene			
A' 25 to	8.06660	5				Ether			
B' 170 °C	2471.5	5				n-Heptane			
C'	205.	5	B^v to			Ethanol			
A'* 25 to	2.60314	5	A^v °C			Water			
B'* 170 °C	2369.2	5	$(B^{\overline{v}})$ to			Water in			
Ac to			$(A^{\overline{v}})$ °C						
Bc t_c °C			c_p liq. °K						
Cc									
Cryos. A°			c_p vap. °K						
consts. B°									
t_e °C	302.32	5	c_v vap.						

+ grams/100 grams solvent

REFERENCES: 1-Dow   2-API   3-Lit.   4-Calc. from det. data   5-Calc. by formula

SOURCE: Lit.

PURIFICATION: Lit.

LITERATURE REFERENCES: 3 Ind. Eng. Chem., 36, 596 (1944)

No. 29

NAME	2-tert-Amyl-4-methylphenol	STRUCTURAL FORMULA

Structural formula: OH, $CH_2C(CH_3)_3$ (benzene ring with CH_3)

Mole % Pur.	Ref.	Molecular Formula $C_{12}H_{18}O$	Molecular Weight 178.264

		Ref.			Ref.				Ref.
F.P. °C	27.	3	dt/dP			f	to		
F.P. 100%			°C/mm			g	°K		
			25°C	1139.07	5	h			
B.P. °C			BP	0.05302	5				
760 mm	252.	3	t_e	0.03167	5	f'	to		
100	183.	5				g'	°K		
30	151.3	5	30 mm	0.8022	5	h'			
10	126.7	5	ΔHm cal/g						
1	84.8	5				m	to		
			ΔHv cal/g			n	°K		
Pressure			25°C	98.87	5	o			
mm 25°C	0.00880	5	30 mm	83.49	5				
t_e	1432.76	5	BP	72.15	5	m'	to		
Density			t_e	69.23	5	n'	°K		
g/ml 20°C			t_e (d, e)	69.10	5	o'			
d_4^t 25 30			ΔHv/T_e	22.34	5	Surface tension			
			d 150 to	100.53	5	dynes/cm. 20°C			
a			e 280 °C	0.1126	5	γ 30			
b			d' 25 to	101.92	5	40			
Ref. Index			e' 150 °C	0.1218	5				
n_D 20°C			d_c g/ml			Parachor [P]			
25			v_c ml/g			20°C			
30			t_c °C			30			
"C"			P_c mm			40			
						Sugd.	456.1	5	
MR (Obs.)			PV/RT			Exp. L.l.%/wt.			
MR (Calc.)	55.540	5	25°C	1.0000	5	u.			
(nD-d/2)			30 mm	1.0000	5	Dispersion			
Dielectric			BP	0.9500	5	Flash Point °C			
A 150 to	7.65505	4	t_e	0.9324	5	Fire Point			
B 380 °C	2115.0	4	t_c						
C	191.	5	ΔHc kcal/m			M. Spec.			
A* 150 to	2.17451	5	ΔHf			Ultra V.			
B* 290 °C	2009.3	5	ΔFf			X-Ray Dif.			
K			Viscosity			Infrared			
c			centistokes			Solubility in +			
t_k to			η °C			Acetone			
t_x °C						Carbon tet.			
A' 25 to	7.90769	5				Benzene			
B' 150 °C	2291.5	5	B^v to			Ether			
C'	205.	5	A^v °C			n-Heptane			
A'* 25 to	2.45682	5	(B^v) to			Ethanol			
B'* 150 °C	2192.1	5	(A^v) °C			Water			
Ac to						Water in			
Bc t_c °C			c_p liq. °K						
Cc									
Cryos. A°			c_p vap. °K						
consts. B°									
t_e °C	279.12	5	c_v vap.						

+ grams/100 grams solvent

REFERENCES:	1-Dow 2-API 3-Lit. 4-Calc. from det. data 5-Calc. by formula
SOURCE:	Lit.
PURIFICATION:	Lit.
LITERATURE REFERENCES:	3 Ind. Eng. Chem., 36, 596 (1944)

No. 30

NAME	6-tert-Butyl-2,4-dimethylphenol				STRUCTURAL FORMULA

$$OH$$
$$(CH_3)_3C \bigcirc CH_3$$
$$CH_3$$

Mole % Pur.	Ref.	Molecular Formula $C_{12}H_{18}O$		Molecular Weight 178.264	

		Ref.			Ref.			Ref.
F.P. °C	22.3	3	dt/dP			f $\vert$ $\quad$ to		
F.P. 100%			°C/mm			g $\vert$ $\_\_$ °K $\_$		
B.P. °C			25°C	866.44	5	h $\vert$		
760 mm	249.	3	BP	0.0531	5			
100	180.	5	t_e	0.03199	5	f' $\vert$ $\quad$ to		
30	148.4	5	30 mm	0.80096	5	g' $\vert$ $\_\_$ °K $\_$		
10	123.8	5	ΔHm cal/g			h' $\vert$		
1	81.8	5						
Pressure			ΔHv cal/g			m $\vert$ $\quad$ to		
mm 25°C	0.01192	5	25°C	95.94	5	n $\vert$ $\_\_$ °K $\_$		
t_e	1418.2	5	30 mm	82.45	5	o $\vert$		
Density			BP	72.11	5			
g/ml 80°C	0.917	3	t_e	69.70	5	m' $\vert$ $\quad$ to		
d_4^t 120	0.888	3	t_e (d,e)	69.37	5	n' $\vert$ $\_\_$ °K $\_$		
160	0.859	3	ΔHv/T_e	22.64	5	o' $\vert$		
a	0.9458	4	d $\vert$ 150 to	97.70	5	Surface tension dynes/cm. 20°C		
b	-0.0372	4	e $\vert$ 275 °C	0.1028	5	y $\qquad$ 30		
Ref. Index			d' $\vert$ 25 to	98.67	5	$\qquad$ 40		
n_D 20°C			e' $\vert$ 150 °C	0.1093	5			
25			d_c g/ml			Parachor [P]		
30			v_c ml/g			20°C		
"C"			t_c °C			30		
MR (Obs.)			P_c mm			40		
MR (Calc.)			PV/RT			Sugd. 456.1	5	
(nD-d/2)			25°C	1.0000	5	Exp. L.1.%/wt.		
Dielectric			30 mm	1.0000	5	u.		
A $\vert$ 150 to	7.62910	4	BP	0.9467	5	Dispersion		
B $\vert$ 290 °C	2094.0	4	t_e	0.9286	5	Flash Point °C		
C	192.	5	t_c			Fire Point		
A* $\vert$ 150 to	2.15724	5	ΔHc kcal/m			M Spec.		
B* $\vert$ 285 °C	1990.8	5	ΔHf			Ultra V.		
K			ΔFf			X-Ray Dif.		
c			Viscosity			Infrared		
t_k $\vert$ $\quad$ to			centistokes			Solubility in +		
t_x $\vert$ $\quad$ °C			η 80 °C	2.10	3	Acetone		
A' $\vert$ 25 to	7.95443	5	120	1.060	3	Carbon tet.		
B' $\vert$ 150 °C	2321.3	5	160	0.670	3	Benzene		
C'	210.	5				Ether		
A'* 25 to	2.49929	5	B^v $\vert$ 120 to	848.5	4	n-Heptane		
B'* 150 °C	2218.7	5	A^v $\vert$ 170 °C	3.8674	4	Ethanol		
Ac $\vert$ $\quad$ to			$(B^v)\vert$ $\quad$ to			Water		
Bc $\vert$ t_c °C			$(A^v)\vert$ $\quad$ °C			Water in		
Cc			c_p liq. °K					
Cryos. A°								
consts. B°			c_p vap. °K					
t_e °C	275.68	5	c_v vap.					

+ grams/100 grams solvent

REFERENCES: 1-Dow 2-API 3-Lit. 4-Calc. from det. data 5-Calc. by formula

SOURCE: Lit.

PURIFICATION: Lit.

LITERATURE REFERENCES: 3 Ind. Eng. Chem., **36**, 596 (1944)

TABLE VIII. AROMATIC PHENOLS

NAME	4-tert-Butyl-2,5-dimethylphenol	STRUCTURAL FORMULA

Structural formula:
$$\text{OH, } CH_3, H_3C, C(CH_3)_3 \text{ (phenol ring)}$$

Mole % Pur.	Ref.	Molecular Formula $C_{12}H_{18}O$	Molecular Weight 178.264

		Ref.			Ref.			Ref.
F.P. °C	71.2	3	dt/dP			f | to		
F.P. 100%			°C/mm			g | °K		
B.P. °C			25°C	2123.	5	h |		
760 mm	264.	3	BP	0.05417	5			
100	193.5	5	t_e	0.03184	5	f' | to		
30	161.1	5	30 mm	0.8199	5	g' | °K		
10	136.0	5	ΔHm cal/g			h' |		
1	92.98	5	ΔHv cal/g			m | to		
Pressure			25°C	101.45	5	n | °K		
mm 25°C	0.00460	5	30 mm	85.50	5	o |		
t_e	1461.3	5	BP	73.65	5	m' | to		
Density			t_e	70.54	5	n' | °K		
g/ml 80°C	0.939	3	t_e (d, e)	70.35	5	o' |		
d_4^t 25· 30			ΔHv/T_e	22.22	5	Surface tension dynes/cm. 20°C		
a			d | 160 to	104.1	5	ɣ		
b			e | 290 °C	0.1152	5	30		
Ref. Index			d' | 25 to	104.4	5	40		
n_D 20°C	1.5311	3	e' | 160 °C	0.1174	5	Parachor [P]		
25			d_c g/ml			20°C		
30			v_c ml/g			30		
"C"			t_c °C			40		
			P_c mm			Sugd.	456.1	5
MR (Obs.)			PV/RT			Exp. L.l.%/wt.		
MR (Calc.)	55.540	5	25°C	1.0000	5	u.		
(nD-d/2)			30 mm	1.0000	5	Dispersion		
Dielectric			BP	0.9469	5	Flash Point °C		
A | 160 to	7.65967	5	t_e	0.9283	5	Fire Point		
B | 400 °C	2164.8	5	t_c			M. Spec.		
C	189.	5	ΔHc kcal/m			Ultra V.		
A* | 160 to	2.17552	5	ΔHf			X-Ray Dif.		
B* | 300 °C	2058.9	5	ΔFf			Infrared		
K			Viscosity			Solubility in +		
c			centistokes			Acetone		
t_k | to			η °C			Carbon tet.		
t_x | °C						Benzene		
A' | 25 to	7.97750	5				Ether		
B' | 160 °C	2393.1	5				n-Heptane		
C'	207.	5	B^v | to			Ethanol		
A'* 25 to	2.51749	5	A^v | °C			Water		
B'* 160 °C	2290.6	5	(B^v) | to			Water in		
Ac | to			(A^v) | °C					
Bc | t_c °C			c_p liq. °K					
Cc |								
Cryos. A°			c_p vap. °K					
consts. B°								
t_e °C	292.6	5	c_v vap.					

+ grams/100 grams solvent

REFERENCES: 1-Dow 2-API 3-Lit. 4-Calc. from det. data 5-Calc. by formula
SOURCE: Lit.
PURIFICATION: Lit.
LITERATURE REFERENCES: 3 Ind. Eng. Chem., 36, 596 (1944)

No. 32

| NAME | 4-tert-Butyl-2,6-dimethylphenol | STRUCTURAL FORMULA |

Structural formula: OH, CH3, H3C, C(CH3)3

| Mole % Pur. | Ref. | Molecular Formula $C_{12}H_{18}O$ | Molecular Weight 178.264 |

		Ref.				Ref.					Ref.
F.P. °C	82.4	3	dt/dP				f		to		
F.P. 100%			°C/mm				g		°K		
B.P. °C			25°C	536.9	5		h				
760 mm	248.	3	BP	0.05539	5						
100	176.5	5	t_e	0.03350	5		f'		to		
30	144.1	5	30 mm	0.8186	5		g'		°K		
10	119.0	5	ΔHm cal/g				h'				
1	76.49	5	ΔHv cal/g				m		to		
Pressure			25°C	91.63	5		n		°K		
mm 25°C	0.02015	5	30 mm	79.04	5		o				
t_e	1422.1	5	BP	67.94	5						
Density			t_e	65.10	5		m'		to		
g/ml 80°C	0.916	3	t_e (d,e)	64.94	5		n'		°K		
d_4^t 25 30			$\Delta Hv/T_e$	21.12	5		o'				
a			d | 145 to	94.42	5		Surface tension dynes/cm. 20°C				
b			e | 275 °C	0.1068	5		ɣ		30		
Ref. Index			d' | 25 to	94.28	5				40		
n_D 20°C 25 30			e' | 145 °C	0.1058	5						
			d_c g/ml				Parachor [P]		20°C		
"C"			v_c ml/g						30		
MR (Obs.)			t_c °C						40		
MR (Calc.)	55.540	5	P_c mm						Sugd.	456.1	5
(nD-d/2)			PV/RT				Exp. L.1.%/wt.				
Dielectric			25°C	1.0000	5		u.				
			30 mm	1.0000	5		Dispersion				
A | 145 to	7.42037	5	BP	0.9490	5		Flash Point °C				
B | 290 °C	1997.4	5	t_e	0.9306	5		Fire Point				
C	192.	5	t_c				M Spec.				
A* | 145 to	1.94338	5	ΔHc kcal/m				Ultra V.				
B* | 285 °C	1892.3	5	ΔHf				X-Ray Dif.				
K			ΔFf				Infrared				
c			Viscosity				Solubility in +				
t_k | to			centistokes				Acetone				
t_x | °C			η 80 °C	2.72	3		Carbon tet.				
A' | 25 to	7.73868	5	120	1.32	3		Benzene				
B' | 145 °C	2217.1	5	160	0.820	3		Ether				
C'	210.	5					n-Heptane				
A'* | 25 to	2.2864	5	B^v | 100 to	926.	4		Ethanol				
B'* 145 °C	2115.1	5	A^v | 170 °C	3.76552	4		Water				
Ac | to			(B^v) | to				Water in				
Bc | t_c °C			(A^v) | °C								
Cc			c_p liq. °K								
Cryos. A° consts. B°			c_p vap. °K								
t_e °C	276.1	5	c_v vap.								

+ grams/100 grams solvent

REFERENCES: 1-Dow 2-API 3-Lit. 4-Calc. from det. data 5-Calc. by formula

SOURCE: Lit.

PURIFICATION: Lit.

LITERATURE REFERENCES: 3 Ind. Eng. Chem., 36, 596 (1944)

TABLE VIII. AROMATIC PHENOLS

NAME	6-tert-Butyl-3,4-dimethylphenol	STRUCTURAL FORMULA

Structural formula: $(CH_3)_3C$ —benzene ring with OH, CH_3, CH_3

Mole % Pur.	Ref.	Molecular Formula $C_{12}H_{18}O$	Molecular Weight 178.264	

		Ref.				Ref.				Ref.
F.P. °C	46.0	3	dt/dP			f		to		
F.P. 100%			°C/mm			g		°K		
			25°C	1145.47	5	h				
B.P. °C			BP	0.05518	5					
760 mm	258.5	3	t_e	0.03278	5	f'		to		
100	187.0	3	30 mm	0.8244	5	g'		°K		
30	154.4	5	ΔHm cal/g			h'				
10	129.1	5								
1	86.1	5	ΔHv cal/g			m		to		
			25°C	96.38	5	n		°K		
Pressure			30 mm	82.42	5	o				
mm 25°C	0.00898	5	BP	70.90	5					
t_e	1449.04	5	t_e	67.88	5	m'		to		
Density			t_e (d, e)	67.71	5	n'		°K		
g/ml 80°C	0.920	3	ΔHv/T_e	21.59	5	o'				
d_4^t 120	0.892	3				Surface tension				
160	0.863	3	d 155 to	99.50	5	dynes/cm. 20°C				
a	0.976	4	e 285 °C	0.1107	5	ɣ		30		
b	-0.0370	4	d' 25 to	99.08	5			40		
Ref. Index			e' 155 °C	0.1079	5					
n_D 20°C	1.5222	3	d_c g/ml			Parachor [P]				
25			v_c ml/g					20°C		
30			t_c °C					30		
"C"	0.6852	4	P_c mm					40		
MR (Obs.)	56.53	4	PV/RT					Sugd.	456.1	5
MR (Calc.)	55.540	5	25°C	1.0000	5	Exp. L.1.%/wt.				
(nD-d/2)	1.041	4	30 mm	1.0000	5	u.				
Dielectric			BP	0.9480	5	Dispersion				
			t_e	0.9292	5	Flash Point °C				
A 155 to	7.52518	4	t_c			Fire Point				
B 300°C	2083.0	4	ΔHc kcal/m			M. Spec.				
C	190.	5	ΔHf			Ultra V.				
A* 155 to	2.04246	5	ΔFf			X-Ray Dif.				
B* 295°C	1977.0	5	Viscosity			Infrared				
K			centistokes			Solubility in +				
c			η 80°C	3.50	3	Acetone				
t_k to			120	1.37	3	Carbon tet.				
t_x °C			160	0.782	3	Benzene				
A' 25 to	7.87640	5				Ether				
B' 155°C	2331.9	5				n-Heptane				
C'	210.	5	B^v 110 to	1037.	4	Ethanol				
A'* 25 to	2.41745	5	A^v 170°C	3.4994	4	Water				
B'* 155°C	2228.4	5	(B^v) to			Water in				
Ac to			(A^v) °C							
Bc t_c °C			c_p liq. °K							
Cc										
Cryos. A°			c_p vap. °K							
consts. B°										
t_e °C	287.30	5	c_v vap.							

+ grams/100 grams solvent

REFERENCES: 1-Dow 2-API 3-Lit. 4-Calc. from det. data 5-Calc. by formula

SOURCE: Lit.

PURIFICATION: Lit.

LITERATURE REFERENCES: 3 Ind. Eng. Chem., 36, 596 (1944)

No. 34

NAME	4-tert-Butyl-2-ethylphenol				STRUCTURAL FORMULA

OH
C_2H_5
$C(CH_3)_3$

Mole % Pur.	Ref.	Molecular Formula $C_{12}H_{18}O$		Molecular Weight 178.264	

		Ref.				Ref.				Ref.
F.P. °C			dt/dP °C/mm			f		to		
F.P. 100%			25°C	1329.2	5	g		°K		
B.P. °C			BP	0.0538	5	h				
760 mm	257.	3	t_e	0.0320	5	f'		to		
100	187.	5	30 mm	0.8123	5	g'		°K		
30	154.9	5	ΔHm cal/g			h'				
10	130.0	5	ΔHv cal/g			m		to		
1	87.4	5	25°C	98.10	5	n		°K		
Pressure			30 mm	83.85	5	o				
mm 25°C	0.0076	5	BP	72.26	5	m'		to		
t_e	1443.5	5	t_e (d,e)	69.24	5	n'		°K		
Density				69.09	5	o'				
g/ml 20°C			$ΔHv/T_e$	22.12	5	Surface tension				
d_4^t 25			d | 155 to	101.45	5	dynes/cm. 20°C				
30			e | 285 °C	0.1136	5	y 30				
a			d' | 25 to	100.84	5	40				
b			e' | 155 °C	0.1096	5	Parachor [P]				
Ref. Index			d_c g/ml			20°C				
n_D 20°C			v_c ml/g			30				
25			t_c °C			40				
30			P_c mm			Sugd.	456.1	5		
"C"			PV/RT			Exp. L. l. %/wt.				
MR (Obs.)			25°C	1.0000	5	u.				
MR (Calc.)	55.540	5	30 mm	1.0000	5	Dispersion				
(nD-d/2)			BP	0.9480	5	Flash Point °C				
Dielectric			t_e	0.9297	5	Fire Point				
A | 155 to	7.62460	5	t_c			M Spec.				
B | 350 °C	2120.5	5	ΔHc kcal/m			Ultra V.				
C	190.	5	ΔHf			X-Ray Dif.				
A* | 155 to	2.14398	5	ΔFf			Infrared				
B* | 295 °C	2015.2	5	Viscosity			Solubility in +				
K			centistokes			Acetone				
c			η °C			Carbon tet.				
t_k | to						Benzene				
t_x | °C						Ether				
A' | 25 to	7.98104	5				n-Heptane				
B' | 155 °C	2373.5	5				Ethanol				
C'	210.	5	B^V | to			Water				
A'* 25 to	2.52158	5	A^V | °C			Water in				
B'* 155 °C	2269.9	5	(B^V) | to							
Ac | to			(A^V) | °C							
Bc | t_c °C			c_p liq. °K							
Cc										
Cryos. A°			c_p vap. °K							
consts. B°										
t_e °C	284.90	5	c_v vap.							

+ grams/100 grams solvent

REFERENCES: 1-Dow 2-API 3-Lit. 4-Calc. from det. data 5-Calc. by formula

SOURCE: Lit.

PURIFICATION: Lit.

LITERATURE REFERENCES: 3 Ind. Eng. Chem., 36, 596 (1944)

TABLE VIII. AROMATIC PHENOLS

No. 35

NAME	2-tert-Butyl-4-ethylphenol		STRUCTURAL FORMULA

OH
C(CH₃)₃

Mole % Pur.	Ref.	Molecular Formula $C_{12}H_{18}O$	Molecular Weight 178.264	C_2H_5

		Ref.			Ref.				Ref.
F.P. °C			dt/dP			f	to		
F.P. 100%			°C/mm			g	°K		
			25°C	768.07	5	h			
B.P. °C			BP	0.0542	5				
760 mm	250.	3	t_e	0.0326	5	f'	to		
100	179.	5				g'	°K		
30	147.7	5	30 mm	0.8101	5	h'			
10	122.9	5	ΔHm cal/g						
1	80.6	5				m	to		
			ΔHv cal/g			n	°K		
Pressure			25°C	94.79	5	o			
mm 25°C	0.0136	5	30 mm	81.26	5				
t_e	1426.8	5	BP	69.96	5	m'	to		
			t_e	67.08	5	n'	°K		
Density			t_e (d, e)	66.91	5	o'			
g/ml 20°C			ΔHv/T_e	21.71	5				
d_4^t 25						Surface tension			
30			d 150 to	97.59	5	dynes/cm. 20°C			
a			e 280 °C	0.1105	5	8 30			
b			d' 25 to	97.54	5	40			
Ref. Index			e' 150 °C	0.1102	5				
n_D 20°C			d_c g/ml			Parachor [P]			
25			v_c ml/g			20°C			
30			t_c °C			30			
"C"			P_c mm			40 Sugd.	456.1	5
MR (Obs.)			PV/RT			Exp. L.1.%/wt.			
MR (Calc.)	55.540	5	25°C	1.0000	5	u.			
(nD-d/2)			30 mm	1.0000	5	Dispersion			
Dielectric			BP	0.9490	5	Flash Point °C			
A 150 to	7.52987	5	t_e	0.9311	5	Fire Point			
B 295 °C	2050.2	5	t_c						
C	191.	5	ΔHc kcal/m			M. Spec.			
A* 150 to	2.05210	5	ΔHf			Ultra V.			
B* 290 °C	1945.3	5	ΔFf			X-Ray Dif.			
K						Infrared			
c			Viscosity			Solubility in +			
t_k to			centistokes			Acetone			
t_x °C			η °C			Carbon tet.			
A' 25 to	7.85152	5				Benzene			
B' 150 °C	2273.9	5				Ether			
C'	209.	5	B^v to			n-Heptane			
A'* 25 to	2.39804	5	A^v °C			Ethanol			
B'* 150 °C	2172.1	5	(B^v) to			Water			
Ac to			(A^v) °C			Water in			
Bc t_c °C			c_p liq. °K						
Cc									
Cryos. A°			c_p vap. °K						
consts. B°									
t_e °C	277.56	5	c_v vap.						

+ grams/100 grams solvent

REFERENCES: 1-Dow 2-API 3-Lit. 4-Calc. from det. data 5-Calc. by formula

SOURCE: Lit.

PURIFICATION: Lit.

LITERATURE REFERENCES: 3 Ind. Eng. Chem., 36, 596 (1944)

No. 36

NAME	2,4-di-tert-Butylphenol	STRUCTURAL FORMULA

Structural formula: OH with C(CH₃)₃ groups

Mole % Pur.	Ref.	Molecular Formula $C_{14}H_{22}O$	Molecular Weight 206.316	

		Ref.			Ref.			Ref.
F.P. °C	56.5	3	dt/dP			f | to		
F.P. 100%			°C/mm			g | °K		
			25°C	1410.12	5	h |		
B.P. °C			BP	0.0560	5			
760 mm	263.5	3	t_e	0.03303	5	f' | to		
100	191.	5	30 mm	0.8344	5	g' | °K		
30	158.0	5	ΔHm cal/g			h' |		
10	132.4	5						
1	89.0	5	ΔHv cal/g			m | to		
Pressure			25°C	84.16	5	n | °K		
mm 25°C	0.00722	5	30 mm	71.54	5	o |		
t_e	1463.8	5	BP	61.46	5			
Density			t_e	58.74	5	m' | to		
g/ml 20°C			t_e (d,e)	58.62	5	n' | °K		
d_4^t 25 30			ΔHv/T_e	21.40	5	o' |		
a			d | 160 to	86.64	5	Surface tension		
b			e | 300 °C	0.09556	5	dynes/cm. 20°C		
Ref. Index			d' | 25 to	86.53	5	γ 30		
n_D 20°C			e' | 160 °C	0.09489	5	40		
25			d_c g/ml			Parachor [P]		
30			v_c ml/g			20°C		
"C"			t_c °C			30		
MR (Obs.)			P_c mm			40		
MR (Calc.)	60.158	5	PV/RT			Sugd.	534.1	5
(nD-d/2)			25°C	1.0000	5	Exp. L.1.%/wt.		
Dielectric			30 mm	1.0000	5	u.		
A | 160 to	7.49747	5	BP	0.9480	5	Dispersion		
B | 400 °C	2089.0	5	t_e	0.9288	5	Flash Point °C		
C	189.	5	t_c			Fire Point		
A* | 160 to	2.07361	5	ΔHc kcal/m			M Spec.		
B* | 320 °C	1981.8	5	ΔHf			Ultra V.		
K			ΔFf			X-Ray Dif.		
c						Infrared		
t_k | to			Viscosity			Solubility in +		
t_x | °C			centistokes			Acetone		
A' | 25 to	7.8450	5	η °C			Carbon tet.		
B' | 160 °C	2337.	5				Benzene		
C'	209.	5	B^V | to			Ether		
A'* 25 to	2.44774	5	A^V | °C			n-Heptane		
B'* 160 °C	2233.4	5	(B^V) | to			Ethanol		
Ac | to			(A^V) | °C			Water		
Bc | t_c °C						Water in		
Cc			c_p liq. °K					
Cryos. A°			c_p vap. °K					
consts. B°								
t_e °C	293.23	5	c_v vap.					

+ grams/100 grams solvent

REFERENCES: 1-Dow 2-API 3-Lit. 4-Calc. from det. data 5-Calc. by formula

SOURCE: Lit.

PURIFICATION: Lit.

LITERATURE REFERENCES: 3 Ind. Eng. Chem., 36, 596 (1944)

TABLE VIII. AROMATIC PHENOLS

No. 37

NAME	4-Diisobutylphenol		STRUCTURAL FORMULA

OH

Mole % Pur.	Ref.	Molecular Formula $C_{14}H_{22}O$	Molecular Weight 206.316	$C(CH_3)_2CH_2C(CH_3)_2CH_3$

		Ref.			Ref.				Ref.
F.P. °C	84.	3	dt/dP			f	to		
F.P. 100%			°C/mm			g	°K		
			25°C	5367.9	5	h			
B.P. °C			BP	0.0553	5				
760 mm	279.	3	t_e	0.0318	5	f'	to		
100	207.	5	30 mm	0.8388	5	g'	°K		
30	173.9	5	ΔHm cal/g			h'			
10	148.2	5							
1	104.1	5	ΔHv cal/g			m	to		
			25°C	92.69	5	n	°K		
Pressure			30 mm	76.52	5	o			
mm 25°C	0.0017	5	BP	65.79	5				
t_e	1501.02	5	t_e	62.82	5	m'	to		
			t_e (d, e)	62.68	5	n'	°K		
Density			ΔHv/T_e	22.24	5	o'			
g/ml 20°C									
d_4^t 25			d 175 to	94.27	5	Surface tension			
30			e 310 °C	0.1021	5	dynes/cm. 20°C			
a			d' 25 to	95.41	5	ɣ 30			
b			e' 175 °C	0.1086	5	40			
Ref. Index									
n_D 20°C			d_c g/ml			Parachor [P]			
25			v_c ml/g			20°C			
30			t_c °C			30			
"C"			P_c mm			40			
						Sugd.	534.1	5	
MR (Obs.)			PV/RT			Exp. L.l.%/wt.			
MR (Calc.)	60.158	5	25°C	1.0000	5	u.			
(nD-d/2)			30 mm	1.0000	5	Dispersion			
Dielectric			BP	0.9460	5	Flash Point °C			
A 175 to	7.68856	5	t_e	0.9259	5	Fire Point			
B 325 °C	2235.6	5	t_c						
C	·186.	5	ΔHc kcal/m			M. Spec.			
A* 175 to	2.25887	5	ΔHf			Ultra V.			
B* 325 °C	2128.0	5	ΔFf			X-Ray Dif.			
K						Infrared			
c			Viscosity			Solubility in +			
t_k to			centistokes			Acetone			
t_x °C			η °C			Carbon tet.			
A' 25 to	7.99920	5				Benzene			
B' 175 °C	2464.8	5				Ether			
C'	204.	5	B^v to			n-Heptane			
A'* 25 to	2.59789	5	A^v °C			Ethanol			
B'* 175 °C	2362.6	5	(B^v) to			Water			
Ac to			(A^v) °C			Water in			
Bc t_c °C									
Cc			c_p liq. °K						
Cryos. A°			c_p vap. °K						
consts. B°									
t_e °C	309.46	5	c_v vap.						

+ grams/100 grams solvent

REFERENCES: 1-Dow 2-API 3-Lit. 4-Calc. from det. data 5-Calc. by formula

SOURCE: Lit.

PURIFICATION: Lit.

LITERATURE REFERENCES: 3 Ind. Eng. Chem., 36, 596 (1944)

No. 38

NAME	2, 4, 6-Triallylphenol			STRUCTURAL FORMULA

Structural formula: OH on benzene ring with $H_2C=HCH_2C$ and $CH_2CH=CH_2$ and $CH_2CH=CH_2$ substituents

Mole % Pur.		Ref.	Molecular Formula $C_{15}H_{18}O$		Molecular Weight 214.294			

		Ref.				Ref.			Ref.
F.P. °C			dt/dP °C/mm				f	to °K	
F.P. 100%			25°C	15510.91	5		g		
B.P. °C			BP	0.0559	5		h		
760 mm	294.	3	t_e	0.0314	5		f'	to °K	
100	221.	5	30 mm	0.8540	5		g'		
30	187.4	5	ΔHm cal/g				h'		
10	161.1	5	ΔHv cal/g				m	to °K	
1	116.2	5	25°C	95.04	5		n		
Pressure			30 mm	76.78	5		o		
mm 25°C	0.0_356	5	BP	65.98	5				
t_e	1540.5	5	t_e	62.87	5		m'	to °K	
Density			t_e (d, e)	62.74	5		n'		
g/ml 20°C			$\Delta Hv/T_e$	22.48	5		o'		
d_4^t 25			d	185 to	95.74	5	Surface tension		
30			e	325 °C	0.1012	5	dynes/cm. 20°C		
a			d'	25 to	97.86	5	y 30		
b			e'	185 °C	0.1125	5	40		
Ref. Index			d_c g/ml				Parachor [P]		
n_D 20°C			v_c ml/g				20°C		
25			t_c °C				30		
30			P_c mm				40		
"C"			PV/RT				Sugd.	534.1	5
MR (Obs.)			25°C	1.0000	5	Exp. L.1.%/wt.		
MR (Calc.)	64.776	5	30 mm	1.0000	5	u.		
(nD-d/2)			BP	0.9450	5	Dispersion		
Dielectric			t_e	0.9240	5	Flash Point °C		
A 185 to	7.75543	5	t_c			Fire Point		
B 400 °C	2352.0	5	ΔHc kcal/m			M Spec.		
C	183.	5	ΔHf			Ultra V.		
A* 185 to	2.33371	5	ΔFf			X-Ray Dif.		
B* 335 °C	2216.1	5	Viscosity			Infrared		
K			centistokes			Solubility in +		
c			η °C			Acetone		
t_k to						Carbon tet.		
t_x °C						Benzene		
A' 25 to	8.06057	5				Ether		
B' 185 °C	2556.7	5	B^v to			n-Heptane		
C'	201.	5	A^v °C			Ethanol		
A'* 25 to	2.67062	5	$(B^{\overline{v}})$ to			Water		
B'* 185 °C	2454.7	5	(A^v) °C			Water in		
Ac to								
Bc t_c °C			c_p liq. °K					
Cc			c_p vap. °K					
Cryos. A°								
consts. B°			c_v vap.					
t_e °C	326.05	5						

+ grams/100 grams solvent

REFERENCES: 1-Dow 2-API 3-Lit. 4-Calc. from det. data 5-Calc. by formula

SOURCE: Lit.

PURIFICATION: Lit.

LITERATURE REFERENCES: 3 Ind. Eng. Chem., 36, 596 (1944)

TABLE VIII. AROMATIC PHENOLS

No. 39

NAME	4,6-di-tert-Butyl-2-methylphenol	STRUCTURAL FORMULA

$$OH$$
$$(CH_3)_3C \bigodot CH_3$$
$$C(CH_3)_3$$

Mole % Pur.	Ref.	Molecular Formula	$C_{15}H_{24}O$	Molecular Weight 220.342		

		Ref.				Ref.				Ref.
F.P. °C	51.	3	dt/dP			f		to		
F.P. 100%			°C/mm			g		°K		
B.P. °C			25°C	2400.9	5	h				
760 mm	269.	3	BP	0.0555	5	f'		to		
100	197.	5	t_e	0.0324	5	g'		°K		
30	164.1	5	30 mm	0.8337	5	h'				
10	138.5	5	ΔHm cal/g			m		to		
1	94.9	5	ΔHv cal/g			n		°K		
Pressure			25°C	82.30	5	o				
mm 25°C	0.0041	5	30 mm	68.95	5	m'		to		
t_e	1473.4	5	BP	59.17	5	n'		°K		
Density			t_e	56.50	5	o'				
g/ml 80°C	0.891	3	t_e (d,e)	56.40	5	Surface tension				
d_4^t 120	0.862	3	ΔHv/T_e	21.77	5	dynes/cm. 20°C				
160	0.833	3	d 165 to	84.24	5	γ 30				
a	0.939	4	e 300 °C	0.0932	5	40				
b	-0.0360	4	d' 25 to	84.70	5	Parachor [P]				
Ref. Index			e' 165 °C	0.0960	5	20°C				
n_D 20°C			d_c g/ml			30				
25			v_c ml/g			40				
30			t_c °C			Sugd.	534.1	5
"C"			P_c mm							
MR (Obs.)			PV/RT			Exp. L.1.%/wt.				
MR (Calc.)	64.776	5	25°C	1.0000	5	u.				
(nD-d/2)			30 mm	1.0000	5	Dispersion				
Dielectric			BP	0.9460	5	Flash Point °C				
A 165 to	7.59070	5	t_e	0.9260	5	Fire Point				
B 350 °C	2152.4	5	t_c			M. Spec.				
C	188.	5	ΔHc kcal/m			Ultra V.				
A* 165 to	2.19636	5	ΔHf			X-Ray Dif.				
B* 310 °C	2046.2	5	ΔFf			Infrared				
K			Viscosity			Solubility in +				
c			centistokes			Acetone				
t_k to			η °C			Carbon tet.				
t_x °C						Benzene				
A' 25 to	7.90327	5				Ether				
B' 165 °C	2378.1	5				n-Heptane				
C'	206.	5	B^v to			Ethanol				
A'* 25 to	2.53457	5	A^v °C			Water				
B'* 165 °C	2275.9	5	(B^v) to			Water in				
Ac to			(A^v) °C							
Bc t_c °C			c_p liq. °K							
Cc										
Cryos. A°			c_p vap. °K							
consts. B°										
t_e °C	298.71	5	c_v vap.							

+ grams/100 grams solvent

REFERENCES: 1-Dow 2-API 3-Lit. 4-Calc. from det. data 5-Calc. by formula

SOURCE: Lit.

PURIFICATION: Lit.

LITERATURE REFERENCES: 3 Ind. Eng. Chem., 36, 596 (1944)

No. 40

NAME	4,6-di-tert-Butyl-3-methylphenol	STRUCTURAL FORMULA

$(CH_3)_3C$ — phenol ring with OH, CH_3, $C(CH_3)_3$

Mole % Pur.	Ref.	Molecular Formula $C_{15}H_{24}O$	Molecular Weight 220.342	

		Ref.			Ref.				Ref.
F.P. °C	62.1	3	dt/dP			f	to		
F.P. 100%			°C/mm			g	°K		
			25°C	8488.1	5	h			
B.P. °C			BP	0.0543	5				
760 mm	282.	3	t_e	0.0311	5	f'	to		
100	211.	5				g'	°K		
30	178.2	5	30 mm	0.8325	5	h'			
10	152.6	5	ΔHm cal/g						
1	108.8	5				m	to		
			ΔHv cal/g			n	°K		
Pressure			25°C	89.77	5	o			
mm 25°C	0.0011	5	30 mm	73.59	5				
t_e	1506.2	5	BP	63.28	5	m'	to		
Density			t_e	60.40	5	n'	°K		
g/ml 80°C	0.912	3	t_e (d,e)	60.30	5	o'			
d_4^t 120	0.882	3	ΔHv/T_e	22.74	5	Surface tension			
160	0.853	3				dynes/cm. 20°C			
a	0.972	4	d | 180 to	91.29	5	ɣ 30			
b	-0.0₃75	4	e | 315 °C	0.0993	5	40			
Ref. Index			d' | 25 to	92.41	5				
n_D 20°C			e' | 180 °C	0.1056	5	Parachor [P]			
25			d_c g/ml			20°C			
30			v_c ml/g			30			
"C"			t_c °C			40			
			P_c mm			Sugd.	534.1	5	
MR (Obs.)			PV/RT			Exp. L.1.%/wt.			
MR (Calc.)	64.776	5	25°C	1.0000	5	u.			
(nD-d/2)			30 mm	1.0000	5	Dispersion			
Dielectric			BP	0.9451	5	Flash Point °C			
A | 180 to	7.79349	5	t_e	0.9250	5	Fire Point			
B | 325 °C	2294.2	5	t_c						
C	185.	5	ΔHc kcal/m			M Spec.			
A* | 180 to	2.39293	5	ΔHf			Ultra V.			
B* | 320 °C	2187.4	5	ΔFf			X-Ray Dif.			
K						Infrared			
c			Viscosity			Solubility in +			
t_k | to			centistokes			Acetone			
t_x | °C			η °C			Carbon tet.			
A' | 25 to	8.10651	5				Benzene			
B' | 180 °C	2527.2	5				Ether			
C'	203.	5	B^v | to			n-Heptane			
A'* 25 to	2.73216	5	A^v | °C			Ethanol			
B'* 180 °C	2425.1	5	(B^v) | to			Water			
Ac | to			(A^v) | °C			Water in			
Bc | t_c °C			c_p liq. °K						
Cc			c_p vap. °K						
Cryos. A°			c_v vap.						
consts. B°									
t_e °C	312.05	5							

+   grams/100 grams solvent

REFERENCES: 1-Dow   2-API   3-Lit.   4-Calc. from det. data   5-Calc. by formula

SOURCE: Lit.

PURIFICATION: Lit.

LITERATURE REFERENCES: 3 Ind. Eng. Chem., 36, 596 (1944)

TABLE VIII. AROMATIC PHENOLS 313

No. 41

NAME	2,6-di-tert-Butyl-4-methylphenol		STRUCTURAL FORMULA

Structural formula:

$$OH$$
$$(CH_3)_3C \bigodot C(CH_3)_3$$
$$CH_3$$

Mole % Pur.		Ref.	Molecular Formula	$C_{15}H_{24}O$	Molecular Weight 220.342	

		Ref.				Ref.				Ref.
F.P. °C	70.	3	dt/dP °C/mm				f	to		
F.P. 100%			25°C	2091.7	5		g	°K		
B.P. °C			BP	0.0546	5		h			
760 mm	265.	3	t_e	0.0321	5		f'	to		
100	194.	5	30 mm	0.8243	5		g'	°K		
30	161.5	5	ΔHm cal/g				h'			
10	136.2	5	ΔHv cal/g				m	to		
1	92.98	5	25°C	81.80	5		n	°K		
Pressure			30 mm	68.90	5		o			
mm 25°C	0.0047	5	BP	59.21	5		m'	to		
t_e	1462.0	5	t_e	56.60	5		n'	°K		
Density			t_e (d, e)	56.51	5		o'			
g/ml 80°C	0.899	3	ΔHv/T_e	21.99	5		Surface tension			
d_4^t 120	0.870	3					dynes/cm. 20°C			
160	0.841	3	d 160 to	84.02	5		δ 30			
a	0.959	4	e 295 °C	0.0936	5		40			
b	-0.0375	4	d' 25 to	84.17	5					
Ref. Index			e' 160 °C	0.0945	5		Parachor [P]			
n_D 20°C			d_c g/ml				20°C			
25			v_c ml/g				30			
30			t_c °C				40			
"C"			P_c mm				Sugd.	534.1	5	
MR (Obs.)			PV/RT				Exp. L.1.%/wt.			
MR (Calc.)	64.776	5	25°C	1.0000	5		u.			
(nD-d/2)			30 mm	1.0000	5		Dispersion			
Dielectric			BP	0.9460	5		Flash Point °C			
A 160 to	7.63222	5	t_e	0.9266	5		Fire Point			
B 350 °C	2157.1	5	t_c				M. Spec.			
C	189.	5	ΔHc kcal/m				Ultra V.			
A* 160 to	2.24064	5	ΔHf				X-Ray Dif.			
B* 305 °C	2051.4	5	ΔFf				Infrared			
K			Viscosity				Solubility in +			
c			centistokes				Acetone			
t_k to			η 80 °C	3.47	3		Carbon tet.			
t_x °C			120	1.540	3		Benzene			
A' 25 to	7.94836	5	160	0.920	3		Ether			
B' 160 °C	2384.4	5					n-Heptane			
C'	207.	5	B^v to				Ethanol			
			A^v °C				Water			
A'* 25 to	2.58018	5	(B^v) to				Water in			
B'* 160 °C	2281.9	5	(A^v) °C							
Ac to			c_p liq. °K							
Bc t_c °C										
Cc			c_p vap. °K							
Cryos. A°										
consts. B°										
t_e °C	293.87	5	c_v vap.							

+ grams/100 grams solvent

REFERENCES:	1-Dow 2-API 3-Lit. 4-Calc. from det. data 5-Calc. by formula
SOURCE:	Lit.
PURIFICATION:	Lit.
LITERATURE REFERENCES:	3 Ind. Eng. Chem., 36, 596 (1944)

No. 42

NAME	4-Diisobutyl-2-methylphenol	STRUCTURAL FORMULA

OH

Mole % Pur.	Ref.	Molecular Formula $C_{15}H_{24}O$	Molecular Weight 220.342

$C(CH_3)_2 CH_2 C(CH_3)_3$

		Ref.			Ref.			Ref.
F.P. °C	49.5	3	dt/dP			f | | to		
F.P. 100%			°C/mm			g | |__ °K		
B.P. °C			25°C	6973.82	5	h |		
760 mm	275.	5	BP	0.05262	5			
100	206.	5	t_e	0.03068	5	f' | | to		
30	174.0	5	30 mm	0.8139	5	g' | |__ °K		
10	148.9	5	ΔHm cal/g			h' |		
1	105.9	5						
Pressure			ΔHv cal/g			m | | to		
mm 25°C	0.00129	5	25°C	89.18	5	n | |__ °K		
t_e	1465.4	5	30 mm	73.86	5	o |		
Density			BP	63.01	5	m' | | to		
g/ml 20°C			t_e	60.17	5	n' | |__ °K		
d_4^t 25			t_e (d,e)	60.02	5	o' |		
30			ΔHv/T_e	23.02	5			
a			d | 174 to	92.56	5	Surface tension		
b			e | 305 °C	0.1074	5	dynes/cm. 20°C		
			d' | 20 to	91.75	5	30		
Ref. Index			e' | 174 °C	0.1028	5	40		
n_D 20°C			d_c g/ml			Parachor [P]		
25			v_c ml/g			20°C		
30			t_c °C			30		
"C"			P_c mm			40		
MR (Obs.)			PV/RT			Sugd.	578.1	5
MR (Calc.)			25°C	1.0000	5	Exp. L.1.%/wt.		
(nD-d/2)			30 mm	1.0000	5	u.		
Dielectric			BP	0.9350	5	Dispersion		
A | 174 to	7.89769	5	t_e	0.9144	5	Flash Point °C		
B |_410 °C	2317.8	5	t_c			Fire Point		
C	187.	5	ΔHc kcal/m			M Spec.		
A* | 174 to	2.52399	5	ΔHf			Ultra V.		
B* |_315 °C	2219.8	5	ΔFf			X-Ray Dif.		
K			Viscosity			Infrared		
c			centistokes			Solubility in +		
t_k | __ to			η °C			Acetone		
t_x | °C						Carbon tet.		
A' | 20 to	8.21783	5				Benzene		
B' |_174 °C	2554.7	5				Ether		
C'	205.	5	B^v | to			n-Heptane		
A'* 20 to	2.84385	5	A^v | °C			Ethanol		
B'* 174 °C	2451.7	5	(B^v) | to			Water		
Ac | to			(A^v) | °C			Water in		
Bc |_ t_c °C			c_p liq. °K					
Cc								
Cryos. A°			c_p vap. °K					
consts. B°								
t_e °C	302.84	5	c_v vap.					

+ grams/100 grams solvent

REFERENCES: 1-Dow   2-API   3-Lit.   4-Calc. from det. data   5-Calc. by formula

SOURCE: Lit.

PURIFICATION: Lit.

LITERATURE REFERENCES: 3 Ind. and Eng. Chem. 36, no. 7, 596-597 (1944)

TABLE VIII. AROMATIC PHENOLS

No. 43

NAME	4-Diisobutyl-3-methylphenol	STRUCTURAL FORMULA

Mole % Pur.	Ref.	Molecular Formula $C_{15}H_{24}O$	Molecular Weight 220.342	OH CH₃ $C(CH_3)_2 CH_2 C(CH_3)_3$

Column 1

Property	Value	Ref.
F.P. °C	49.8	3
F.P. 100%		
B.P. °C		
760 mm	275.	3
100	206.	5
30	174.0	5
10	148.9	5
1	105.9	5
Pressure mm 25°C	0.00129	5
t_e	1484.7	5
Density g/ml 80°C	0.904	3
d_4^t 120	0.876	3
160	0.847	3
a		
b		
Ref. Index n_D 20°C		
25		
30		
"C"		
MR (Obs.)		
MR (Calc.) (nD-d/2)	64.776	5
Dielectric		
A 175 to 315 °C	7.89759	5
B	2317.8	5
C	187.	5
A* 175 to 310 °C	2.50338	5
B*	2212.4	5
K		
c		
t_k to °C		
t_x		
A' 25 to 175 °C	8.21772	5
B'	2554.7	5
C'	205.	5
A'* 25 to 175 °C	2.84374	5
B'*	2451.7	5
Ac to		
Bc t_c °C		
Cc		
Cryos. A°		
consts. B°		
t_e °C	303.44	5

Column 2

Property	Value	Ref.
dt/dP °C/mm		
25°C	6975.3	5
BP	0.05263	5
t_e	0.03036	5
30 mm	0.8140	5
ΔHm cal/g		
ΔHv cal/g		
25°C	89.18	5
30 mm	73.86	5
BP	63.68	5
t_e	60.88	5
t_e (d, e)	60.81	5
ΔHv/T_e	23.26	5
d 175 to 300 °C	91.40	5
e	0.1008	5
d' 25 to 175 °C	91.75	5
e'	0.1028	5
d_c g/ml		
v_c ml/g		
t_c °C		
P_c mm		
PV/RT		
25°C	1.0000	5
30 mm	1.0000	5
BP	0.9450	5
t_e	0.9254	5
t_c		
ΔHc kcal/m		
ΔHf		
ΔFf		
Viscosity centistokes η		
80°C	5.00	3
120	1.970	3
160	1.125	3
B^v 110 to	1036.	4
A^v 170 °C	3.6597	4
(B^v) to		
(A^v) °C		
c_p liq. °K		
c_p vap. °K		
c_v vap.		

Column 3

Property	Value	Ref.
f, g, h to °K		
f', g', h' to °K		
m, n, o to °K		
m', n', o' to °K		
Surface tension dynes/cm. 20°C γ		
30		
40		
Parachor [P] 20°C		
30		
40		
Sugd.	534.1	5
Exp. L.1.%/wt. u.		
Dispersion		
Flash Point °C		
Fire Point		
M. Spec.		
Ultra V.		
X-Ray Dif.		
Infrared		
Solubility in +		
Acetone		
Carbon tet.		
Benzene		
Ether		
n-Heptane		
Ethanol		
Water		
Water in		

+ grams/100 grams solvent

REFERENCES: 1-Dow 2-API 3-Lit. 4-Calc. from det. data 5-Calc. by formula

SOURCE: Lit.

PURIFICATION: Lit.

LITERATURE REFERENCES: 3 Ind. Eng. Chem., **36**, 596 (1944)

No. 44

NAME	2-Diisobutyl-4-methylphenol	STRUCTURAL FORMULA

$$OH$$
$$C(CH_3)_2CH_2C(CH_3)_2CH_3$$
$$CH_3$$

Mole % Pur.	Ref.	Molecular Formula $C_{15}H_{24}O$	Molecular Weight 220.342	

		Ref.			Ref.			Ref.
F.P. °C	46.2	3	dt/dP			f	to	
F.P. 100%			°C/mm			g	°K	
B.P. °C			25°C	2884.7	5	h		
760 mm	269.	3	BP	0.05453	5			
100	198.0	5	t_e	0.03188	5	f'	to	
30	165.4	5	30 mm	0.8262	5	g'	°K	
10	140.0	5				h'		
1	96.70	5	ΔH_m cal/g					
			ΔH_v cal/g			m	to	
Pressure			25°C	83.64	5	n	°K	
mm 25°C	0.00332	5	30 mm	70.00	5	o		
t_e	1470.8	5	BP	60.11	5			
Density			t_e	57.43	5	m'	to	
g/ml 80°C	0.904	3	t_e (d,e)	57.33	5	n'	°K	
d_4^t 120	0.876	3	$\Delta H_v/T_e$	22.14	5	o'		
160	0.847	3				Surface tension		
a			d 165 to	85.78	5	dynes/cm. 20°C		
b			e 300 °C	0.0954	5	γ	30	
Ref. Index			d' 25 to	86.07	5		40	
n_D 20°C			e' 165 °C	0.0972	5			
25			d_c g/ml			Parachor [P]		
30			v_c ml/g			20°C		
"C"			t_c °C			30		
			P_c mm			40		
MR (Obs.)			PV/RT			Sugd.	534.1	5
MR (Calc.)	64.776	5	25°C	1.0000	5	Exp. L.1.%/wt.		
(nD-d/2)			30 mm	1.0000	5	Dispersion	u.	
Dielectric			BP	0.9451	5			
A 165 to	7.66944	5	t_e	0.9253	5	Flash Point °C		
B 400 °C	2188.4	5	t_c			Fire Point		
C	188.	5	ΔH_c kcal/m			M Spec.		
A* 165 to	2.2774	5	ΔH_f			Ultra V.		
B* 310 °C	2083.0	5	ΔF_f			X-Ray Dif.		
K						Infrared		
c			Viscosity			Solubility in +		
t_k to			centistokes			Acetone		
t_x °C			η 80 °C	5.70	3	Carbon tet.		
A' 25 to	7.9848	5	120	2.130	3	Benzene		
B' 165 °C	2417.0	5	160	1.158	3	Ether		
C'	206.	5				n-Heptane		
A'* 25 to	2.6153	5	B^v 110 to	1127.	4	Ethanol		
B'* 165 °C	2314.6	5	A^v 170 °C	3.4622	4	Water		
Ac to			(B^v) to			Water in		
Bc t_c °C			(A^v) °C					
Cc			c_p liq. °K					
Cryos. A°			c_p vap. °K					
consts. B°								
t_e °C	298.11	5	c_v vap.					

          + grams/100 grams solvent

REFERENCES: 1-Dow 2-API 3-Lit. 4-Calc. from det. data 5-Calc. by formula

SOURCE: Lit.

PURIFICATION: Lit.

LITERATURE REFERENCES: 3 Ind. Eng. Chem., 36, 596 (1944)

TABLE VIII. AROMATIC PHENOLS

No. 45

NAME	4, 6-di-tert-Butyl-2, 3-dimethylphenol	STRUCTURAL FORMULA

STRUCTURAL FORMULA

OH
$(CH_3)_3C$ — CH_3
CH_3
$C(CH_3)_3$

Mole % Pur.		Ref.	Molecular Formula $C_{16}H_{26}O$		Molecular Weight 234.368	

		Ref.				Ref.				Ref.
F.P. °C	85.5	3	dt/dP				f	to		
F.P. 100%			°C/mm				g	$- - - °\underline{K}$		
B.P. °C			25°C	9972.56		5	h			
760 mm	284.	3	BP	0.05428		5	f'	to		
100	213.	5	t_e	0.0309		5	g'	$- - - °\underline{K}$		
30	180.2	5	30 mm	0.8337		5	h'			
10	154.5	5	ΔHm cal/g				m	to		
1	110.6	5					n	$- - - °\underline{K}$		
			ΔHv cal/g				o			
Pressure			25°C	85.15		5				
mm 25°C	0.0_389	5	30 mm	69.69		5	m'	to		
t_e	1510.3	5	BP	59.88		5	n'	$- - - °\underline{K}$		
Density			t_e	57.16		5	o'			
g/ml 20°C			t_e (d, e)	57.03		5	Surface tension			
d_4^t 25 30			ΔHv/T_e	22.81		5	dynes/cm. 20°C			
a			d 180 to	86.71		5	ɣ 30			
b			e 315 °C	0.0945		5	40			
Ref. Index			d' 25 to	87.64		5	Parachor [P]			
n_D 20°C 25 30			e' 180 °C	0.0996		5	20°C 30			
			d_c g/ml				40			
"C"			v_c ml/g				Sugd.	612.1		5
MR (Obs.)			t_c °C				Exp. L. 1.%/wt.			
MR (Calc.)			P_c mm				u.			
(nD-d/2)			PV/RT				Dispersion			
Dielectric			25°C	1.0000		5	Flash Point °C			
A 180 to	7.81831	5	30 mm	1.0000		5	Fire Point			
B 330 °C	2315.7	5	BP	0.9440		5	M. Spec.			
C	185.	5	t_e	0.9242		5	Ultra V.			
A* 180 to	2.44548	5	t_c				X-Ray Dif.			
B* 325 °C	2209.3	5	ΔHc kcal/m				Infrared			
K			ΔHf				Solubility in +			
c			ΔFf				Acetone			
t_k to			Viscosity				Carbon tet.			
t_x °C			centistokes				Benzene			
A' 25 to	8.13087	5	η °C				Ether			
B' 180 °C	2549.6	5					n-Heptane			
C'	203.	5	B^v to				Ethanol			
A'* 25 to	2.78205	5	A^v °C				Water			
B'* 180 °C	2447.2	5	(B^v) to				Water in			
Ac to			(A^v) °C							
Bc t_c °C										
Cc			c_p liq. °K							
Cryos. A°			c_p vap. °K							
consts. B°										
t_e °C	314.15	5	c_v vap.							

+ grams/100 grams solvent

REFERENCES: 1-Dow 2-API 3-Lit. 4-Calc. from det. data 5-Calc. by formula

SOURCE: Lit.

PURIFICATION: Lit.

LITERATURE REFERENCES: 3 Ind. Eng. Chem., 36, 596 (1944)

No. 46

NAME	4,6-di-tert-Butyl-2-ethylphenol	STRUCTURAL FORMULA

Structural formula: OH, $(CH_3)_3 C$ — ring — C_2H_5, $C(CH_3)_3$

Mole % Pur.	Ref.	Molecular Formula $C_{16}H_{26}O$	Molecular Weight 234.368	

		Ref.			Ref.			Ref.
F.P. °C	30.	3	dt/dP °C/mm			f	to °K	
F.P. 100%			25°C	3858.05	5	g		
B.P. °C			BP	0.05533	5	h		
760 mm	275.	3	t_e	0.03204	5	f'	to °K	
100	203.0	5	30 mm	0.8369	5	g'		
30	170.0	5	ΔHm cal/g			h'		
10	144.3	5	ΔHv cal/g			m	to °K	
1	100.4	5	25°C	79.82	5	n		
Pressure			30 mm	66.33	5	o		
mm 25°C	0.00245	5	BP	56.92	5	m'	to °K	
t_e	1489.4	5	t_e	54.35	5	n'		
Density			t_e (d, e)	54.22	5	o'		
g/ml 20°C			ΔHv/T_e	22.02	5	Surface tension		
d_4^t 25			d 170 to	81.55	5	dynes/cm. 20°C		
30			e 310 °C	0.0895	5	y 30		
a			d' 20 to	82.14	5	40		
b			e' 170 °C	0.0931	5	Parachor [P]		
Ref. Index			d_c g/ml			20°C		
n_D 20°C			v_c ml/g			30		
25			t_c °C			40		
30			P_c mm			Sugd.	612.1	5
"C"			PV/RT			Exp. L.1.%/wt.		
MR (Obs.)			25°C	1.0000	5	u.		
MR (Calc.)			30 mm	1.0000	5	Dispersion		
(nD-d/2)			BP	0.9451	5	Flash Point °C		
Dielectric			t_e	0.9256	5	Fire Point		
A 170 to	7.65186	4	t_c			M Spec.		
B 420 °C	2204.2	4	ΔHc kcal/m			Ultra V.		
C	187.	5	ΔHf			X-Ray Dif.		
A* 170 to	2.28152	5	ΔFf			Infrared		
B* 320 °C	2097.6	5	Viscosity			Solubility in +		
K			centistokes			Acetone		
c			η °C			Carbon tet.		
t_k to						Benzene		
t_x °C						Ether		
A' 20 to	7.96322	5				n-Heptane		
B' 170 °C	2432.1	5	B^V to			Ethanol		
C'	205.	5	A^V °C			Water		
A'* 25 to	2.61865	5	(B^V) to			Water in		
B'* 170 °C	2329.7	5	(A^V) °C					
Ac to			c_p liq. °K					
Bc t_c °C								
Cc								
Cryos. A°			c_p vap. °K					
consts. B°								
t_e °C	305.14	5	c_v vap.					

+ grams/100 grams solvent

REFERENCES: 1-Dow 2-API 3-Lit. 4-Calc. from det. data 5-Calc. by formula

SOURCE: Lit.

PURIFICATION: Lit.

LITERATURE REFERENCES: 3 Ind. Eng. Chem., 36, 596 (1944)

TABLE VIII. AROMATIC PHENOLS

No. 47

NAME	4,6-di-tert-Butyl-3-ethylphenol		STRUCTURAL FORMULA

STRUCTURAL FORMULA:

$(CH_3)_3C$ — OH — C_2H_5 — $C(CH_3)_3$

Mole % Pur.	Ref.	Molecular Formula $C_{16}H_{26}O$	Molecular Weight 234.368

		Ref.				Ref.				Ref.
F.P. °C	80.5	3	dt/dP				f	to		
F.P. 100%			°C/mm				g	°K		
			25°C	15347.82	5		h			
B.P. °C			BP	0.05420	5					
760 mm	289.	3	t_e	0.03063	5		f'	to		
100	218.	3	30 mm	0.8361	5		g'	°K		
30	185.1	5	ΔHm cal/g				h'			
10	159.4	5								
1	115.2	5	ΔHv cal/g				m	to		
Pressure			25°C	87.41	5		n	°K		
mm 25°C	0.0356	5	30 mm	71.00	5		o			
t_e	1524.	5	BP	61.05	5					
Density			t_e	58.26	5		m'	to		
g/ml 20°C			t_e (d, e)	58.13	5		n'	°K		
d_4^t $\begin{matrix}25\\30\end{matrix}$			ΔHv/T_e	23.04	5		o'			
a			d 185 to	88.73	5	Surface tension				
b			e 325 °C	0.09579	5	dynes/cm. 20°C				
Ref. Index			d' 20 to	89.98	5	Ɣ 30				
n_D 20°C			e' 185 °C	0.1025	5	40				
25			d_c g/ml			Parachor [P]				
30			v_c ml/g			20°C				
"C"			t_c °C			30				
MR (Obs.)			P_c mm			40				
MR (Calc.)	65.304	5	PV/RT			Sugd.	612.1	5		
(nD-d/2)			25°C	1.0000	5	Exp. L.l.%/wt.				
Dielectric			30 mm	1.0000	5	u.				
A 185 to	7.86793	4	BP	0.9440	5	Dispersion				
B 450 °C	2358.9	4	t_e	0.9241	5	Flash Point °C				
C	184.	5	t_c			Fire Point				
A* 185 to	2.49180	5	ΔHc kcal/m			M. Spec.				
B* 330 °C	2251.9	5	ΔHf			Ultra V.				
K			ΔFf			X-Ray Dif.				
c			Viscosity			Infrared				
t_k to			centistokes			Solubility in +				
t_x °C			η °C			Acetone				
A' 20 to	8.17959	5				Carbon tet.				
B' 185 °C	2594.6	5				Benzene				
C'	202.	5	B^v to			Ether				
			A^v °C			n-Heptane				
A'* 20 to	2.82882	5	(B^v) to			Ethanol				
B'* 185 °C	2492.5	5	(A^v) °C			Water				
Ac^l to						Water in				
Bc t_c °C			c_p liq. °K							
Cc										
Cryos. A°			c_p vap. °K							
consts. B°										
t_e °C	319.50	5	c_v vap.							

+ grams/100 grams solvent

REFERENCES:	1-Dow	2-API	3-Lit.	4-Calc. from det. data	5-Calc. by formula

SOURCE: Lit.

PURIFICATION: Lit.

LITERATURE REFERENCES: 3 Ind. Eng. Chem., 36, 596 (1944)

No. 48

NAME	2,6-di-tert-Butyl-4-ethylphenol	STRUCTURAL FORMULA

STRUCTURAL FORMULA

$(CH_3)_3C$ — OH — $C(CH_3)_3$

C_2H_5

Mole % Pur.		Ref.	Molecular Formula	$C_{16}H_{26}O$	Molecular Weight	234.368	

		Ref.				Ref.					Ref.
F.P. °C	44.0	3	dt/dP				f		to		
F.P. 100%			°C/mm				g		°K		
			25°C	2501.8	5		h				
B.P. °C			BP	0.05632	5						
760 mm	272.	3	t_e	0.03286	5		f'		to		
100	199.0	5	30 mm	0.8424	5		g'		°K		
30	165.7	5	ΔHm cal/g				h'				
10	139.9	5									
1	95.9	5	ΔHv cal/g				m		to		
Pressure			25°C	77.00	5		n		°K		
mm 25°C	0.00391	5	30 mm	64.63	5		o				
t_e	1481.2	5	BP	55.30	5						
Density			t_e	52.75	5		m'		to		
g/ml 20°C			t_e (d,e)	52.63	5		n'		°K		
d_4^t 30			ΔHv/T_e	21.48	5		o'				
a			d | 165 to	79.18	5		Surface tension dynes/cm. 20°C				
b			e | 300 °C	0.0878	5		30				
			d' | 25 to	79.19	5		40				
Ref. Index			e' | 165 °C	0.0879	5						
n_D 20°C			d_c g/ml				Parachor [P]				
25			v_c ml/g				20°C				
30			t_c °C				30				
"C"			P_c mm				40				
							Sugd.	612.1		5
MR (Obs.)			PV/RT				Exp. L.1.%/wt.				
MR (Calc.)			25°C	1.0000	5		u.				
(nD-d/2)			30 mm	1.0000	5		Dispersion				
Dielectric			BP	0.9450	5		Flash Point °C				
A | 165 to	7.53824	5	t_e	0.9248	5		Fire Point				
B | 400 °C	2137.8	5	t_c				M Spec.				
C	187.	5	ΔHc kcal/m				Ultra V.				
A* | 165 to	2.17079	5	ΔHf				X-Ray Dif.				
B* | 320 °C	2032.0	5	ΔFf				Infrared				
K			Viscosity				Solubility in +				
c			centistokes				Acetone				
t_k | to			η °C				Carbon tet.				
t_x | °C							Benzene				
A' | 25 to	7.88193	5					Ether				
B' | 165 °C	2387.1	5	B^v | to				n-Heptane				
C'	207.	5	A^v | °C				Ethanol				
A'* 25 to	2.53776	5	(B^v) | to				Water				
B'* 165 °C	2284.0	5	(A^v) | °C				Water in				
Ac | to			c_p liq. °K								
Bc | t_c °C											
Cc			c_p vap. °K								
Cryos. A°											
consts. B°			c_v vap.								
t_e °C	302.46	5									

+ grams/100 grams solvent

REFERENCES: 1-Dow 2-API 3-Lit. 4-Calc. from det. data 5-Calc. by formula

SOURCE: Lit.

PURIFICATION: Lit.

LITERATURE REFERENCES: 3 Ind. Eng. Chem., 36, 596 (1944)

TABLE VIII. AROMATIC PHENOLS

321

No. 49

NAME	2, 6-di-tert-Amyl-4-methylphenol	STRUCTURAL FORMULA

$(CH_3)_3CH_2C$ —⬡— $CH_2C(CH_3)_3$ with OH (top) and CH_3 (bottom)

Mole % Pur.	Ref.	Molecular Formula $C_{17}H_{28}O$	Molecular Weight 248.394	

		Ref.			Ref.			Ref.
F.P. °C			dt/dP			f	to	
F.P. 100%			°C/mm			g	°K	
			25°C	6170.7	5	h		
B.P. °C			BP	0.05611	5			
760 mm	283.	3	t_e	0.03215	5	f'	to	
100	210.	3	30 mm	0.8483	5	g'	°K	
30	176.5	5	ΔHm cal/g			h'		
10	150.5	5						
1	106.0	5	ΔHv cal/g			m	to	
			25°C	77.46	5	n	°K	
Pressure			30 mm	63.58	5	o		
mm 25°C	0.00149	5	BP	54.43	5			
t_e	1509.4	5	t_e	51.87	5	m'	to	
Density			t_e (d, e)	51.75	5	n'	°K	
g/ml 80°C	0.931	3	ΔHv/T_e	21.93	5	o'		
d_4^t 25 30			d 175 to	78.75	5	Surface tension dynes/cm. 20°C		
a			e 315 °C	0.08595	5	ɣ 30		
b			d' 25 to	79.75	5	40		
Ref. Index			e' 175 °C	0.09157	5			
n_D 20°C	1.4950	3	d_c g/ml			Parachor [P]		
25			v_c ml/g			20°C		
30			t_c °C			30		
"C"			P_c mm			40		
MR (Obs.)			PV/RT			Sugd.	651.1	5
MR (Calc.)	68.872	5	25°C	1.0000	5	Exp. L.1.%/wt.		
(nD-d/2)			30 mm	1.0000	5	u.		
Dielectric			BP	0.9440	5	Dispersion		
A 175 to	7.64684	4	t_e	0.9236	5	Flash Point °C		
B 420 °C	2230.5	4	t_c			Fire Point		
C	185.	5	ΔHc kcal/m			M. Spec.		
A* 175 to	2.29872	5	ΔHf			Ultra V.		
B* 325 °C	2123.7	5	ΔFf			X-Ray Dif.		
K			Viscosity			Infrared		
c			centistokes			Solubility in +		
t_k to			η °C			Acetone		
t_x °C						Carbon tet.		
A' 25 to	7.95403	5				Benzene		
B' 175 °C	2458.1	5				Ether		
C'	203.	5	B^v to			n-Heptane		
A'* 25 to	2.63281	5	A^v °C			Ethanol		
B'* 175 °C	2356.2	5	(B^v) to			Water		
Ac to			(A^v) °C			Water in		
Bc t_c °C								
Cc			c_p liq. °K					
Cryos. A°			c_p vap. °K					
consts. B°								
t_e °C	314.21	5	c_v vap.					

+ grams/100 grams solvent

REFERENCES: 1-Dow 2-API 3-Lit. 4-Calc. from det. data 5-Calc. by formula

SOURCE: Lit.

PURIFICATION: Lit.

LITERATURE REFERENCES: 3 Ind. Eng. Chem., 36, 596 (1944)

No. 50

NAME	2,4,6-tri-tert-Butylphenol	STRUCTURAL FORMULA

Structural formula: OH, $(CH_3)_3C$ — [ring] — $C(CH_3)_3$, $C(CH_3)_3$

Mole % Pur.	Ref.	Molecular Formula $C_{18}H_{30}O$	Molecular Weight 262.420	

		Ref.			Ref.					Ref.
F.P. °C	131.	3	dt/dP			f	to			
F.P. 100%			°C/mm			g	°K			
B.P. °C			25°C	4965.56	5	h				
760 mm	278.	3	BP	0.05529	5					
100	206.	5	t_e	0.03225	5	f'	to			
30	172.9	5	30 mm	0.8382	5	g'	°K			
10	147.2	5	ΔHm cal/g			h'				
1	103.2	5	ΔHv cal/g			m	to			
Pressure			25°C	72.55	5	n	°K			
mm 25°C	0.00187	5	30 mm	59.94	5	o				
t_e	1474.96	5	BP	50.78	5					
Density			t_e	48.37	5	m'	to			
g/ml 20°C			t_e (d,e)	48.20	5	n'	°K			
d_4^t 25 30			ΔHv/T_e	21.85	5	o'				
a			d	170 to	75.01	5	Surface tension dynes/cm. 20°C			
b			e	310 °C	0.0872	5	γ 30			
Ref. Index			d'	25 to	74.68	5	40			
n_D 20°C 25 30			e'	170 °C	0.0853	5	Parachor [P] 20°C 30 40			
"C"			d_c g/ml v_c ml/g t_c °C				Sugd.	690.1	5
MR (Obs.)			P_c mm							
MR (Calc.) (nD-d/2)			PV/RT			Exp. L.l.%/wt.			
Dielectric			25°C	1.0000	5	u.			
			30 mm	1.0000	5	Dispersion			
A 170 to	7.67633	4	BP	0.9450	5	Flash Point °C			
B 420 °C	2225.1	4	t_e	0.9127	5	Fire Point			
C	186.	5	t_c			M Spec.			
A* 170 to	2.37639	5	ΔHc kcal/m			Ultra V.			
B* 320 °C	2126.6	5	ΔHf			X-Ray Dif.			
K			ΔFf			Infrared			
c			Viscosity centistokes			Solubility in +			
t_k to			η °C			Acetone			
t_x °C						Carbon tet.			
A' 25 to	7.98721	5				Benzene			
B' 170 °C	2453.9	5				Ether			
C'	204.	5	B^v to			n-Heptane			
A'* 25 to	2.6910	5	A^v °C			Ethanol			
B'* 170 °C	2351.8	5	(B^v) to			Water			
Ac to			(A^v) °C			Water in			
Bc t_c °C			c_p liq. °K						
Cc			c_p vap. °K						
Cryos. A° consts. B°			c_v vap.						
t_e °C	307.64	5							

+ grams/100 grams solvent

REFERENCES: 1-Dow 2-API 3-Lit. 4-Calc. from det. data 5-Calc. by formula

SOURCE: Lit.

PURIFICATION: Lit.

LITERATURE REFERENCES: 3 Ind. Eng. Chem., 36, 596 (1944)

TABLE VIII. AROMATIC PHENOLS 323

No. 51

NAME	p-tert-Octylphenol	STRUCTURAL FORMULA
	p-(1,1,3,3-Tetramethylbutyl)phenol	OH

| Mole % Pur. 99.76 | Ref. 1 | Molecular Formula $C_{14}H_{22}O$ | Molecular Weight 206.316 | $C(CH_3)_2CH_2C(CH_3)_3$ |

		Ref.				Ref.					Ref.
F.P. °C	85.02	1	dt/dP				f	to			
F.P. 100%			°C/mm				g	°K			
B.P. °C			25°C	4201.5	5		h				
760 mm	290.45	1	BP	0.6079	5						
100	212.20	1	t_e	0.0347	5		f'	to			
30	176.87	4	30 mm	0.8910	5		g'	°K			
10	149.62	4	ΔHm cal/g				h'				
1	103.55	4	ΔHv cal/g				m	to			
Pressure			25°C	89.26	5		n	°K			
mm 25°C	0.00228	5	30 mm	72.99	5		o				
t_e	1532.4	5	BP	62.13	5						
Density			t_e	59.02	5		m'	to			
g/ml 20°C			t_e (d,e)	58.80	5		n'	°K			
d_4^t 25 30			ΔHv/T_e	20.35	5		o'				
a			d 175 to	89.91	5		Surface tension				
b			e 325 °C	0.9564	5		dynes/cm. 20°C				
			d' 25 to	91.94	5		δ 30				
Ref. Index			e' 175 °C	0.1071	5		40				
n_D 20°C 25 30			d_c g/ml v_c ml/g t_c °C				Parachor [P] 20°C 30				
"C"			P_c mm				40				
MR (Obs.)			PV/RT				Sugd.	458.4	5		
MR (Calc.)			25°C	1.0000	5		Exp. L.1.%/wt.				
(nD-d/2)			30 mm	1.0000	5		u.				
Dielectric			BP	0.9430	5		Dispersion				
A 175 to	7.34058	1	t_e	0.9204	5		Flash Point °C				
B 440 °C	2115.9	1	t_c				Fire Point				
C	184.	1	ΔHc kcal/m				M. Spec.				
A* 175 to	1.90520	5	ΔHf				Ultra V.				
B* 335 °C	2007.1	5	ΔFf				X-Ray Dif.				
K			Viscosity				Infrared				
c			centistokes				Solubility in +				
t_k to			η °C				Acetone				
t_x °C							Carbon tet.				
A' 25 to	7.63305	5					Benzene				
B' 175 °C	2332.3	5	B^v to				Ether				
C'	202.	5	A^v °C				n-Heptane				
A'* 25 to	2.23218	5	(B^v) to				Ethanol				
B'* 175 °C	2231.1	5	(A^v) °C				Water				
Ac to							Water in				
Bc t_c °C Cc			c_p liq. °K								
Cryos. A° consts. B°			c_p vap. °K								
t_e °C	325.23	5	c_v vap.								

+ grams/100 grams solvent

REFERENCES:	1-Dow	2-API	3-Lit.	4-Calc. from det. data	5-Calc. by formula

SOURCE: Dow

PURIFICATION: Distillation

LITERATURE REFERENCES:

No. 52

NAME	o-Chlorophenol	STRUCTURAL FORMULA

Mole % Pur. 99.82	Ref. 1	Molecular Formula C_6H_5ClO	Molecular Weight 128.557

		Ref.				Ref.				Ref.
F.P. °C	9.00	1	dt/dP °C/mm				f	to		
F.P. 100%			25°C	9.6406	5		g	°K		
B.P. °C			BP	0.0522	5		h			
760 mm	174.90	1	t_e	0.03583	5		f'	to		
100	108.50	4	30 mm	0.7400	5		g'	°K		
30	79.0	4	ΔHm cal/g	25.102	4		h'			
10	56.4	5	ΔHv cal/g				m	to		
1	18.5	5	25°C	91.56	5		n	°K		
Pressure			30 mm	86.37	5		o			
mm 25°C	1.5573	5	BP	74.46	5					
t_e	1225.5	5	t_e	72.09	5		m'	to		
Density			t_e (d, e)	71.98	5		n'	°K		
g/ml 20°C	1.2634	1	ΔHv/T_e	19.80	5		o'			
d_4^t 25	1.2577	1	d	80 to 96.19	5	Surface tension				
30	1.2518	4	e	195 °C 0.1243	5	dynes/cm. 20°C	41.22	1		
a			d'	25 to 93.96	5	y	30	39.89	1	
b			e'	80 °C 0.0960	5		40	38.58	1	
Ref. Index			d_c g/ml			Parachor [P]				
n_D 20°C	1.55939	1	v_c ml/g			20°C	257.8	4		
25	1.55676	1	t_c °C			30	258.1	4		
30	1.54437	1	P_c mm			40	258.3	4		
"C"	0.5783	4	PV/RT			Sugd.	259.3	5		
MR (Obs.)	32.87	4	25°C	1.0000	5	Exp. L.1.%/wt.				
MR (Calc.)	32.699	5	30 mm	1.0000	5	u.				
(nD-d/2)	0.92766	5	BP	0.9551	5	Dispersion				
Dielectric	5.997	1	t_e	0.9411	5	Flash Point °C				
A 80 to	7.05272	5	t_c			Fire Point				
B 300 °C	1589.1	5	ΔHc kcal/m			M Spec.				
C	206.	5	ΔHf			Ultra V.				
A* 80 to	1.48398	5	ΔFf			X-Ray Dif.				
B* 205 °C	1493.3	5	Viscosity			Infrared				
K			centistokes			Solubility in +				
c			η 20 °C	3.0696	1	Acetone				
t_k to			40	1.7818	1	Carbon tet.				
t_x °C			60	1.1882	1	Benzene				
A' 20 to	7.42442	5	80	0.8709	1	Ether				
B' 80 °C	1808.0	5				n-Heptane				
C'	225.	5	B^v 30 to	860.15	4	Ethanol				
A'* 20 to	1.85717	5	A^v 90 °C	3.50455	4	Water	2.25	1		
B'* 80 °C	1706.3	5	(B^v) to			Water in				
Ac to			(A^v) °C							
Bc t_c °C			c_p liq. °K							
Cc										
Cryos. A°	0.0206	1	c_p vap. °K							
consts. B°										
t_e °C	194.84	5	c_v vap.							

+ grams/100 grams solvent

REFERENCES: 1-Dow   2-API   3-Lit.   4-Calc. from det. data   5-Calc. by formula

SOURCE: Dow

PURIFICATION: Distillation

LITERATURE REFERENCES:

TABLE IX. THIOPHENOLS

NAME	Benzenethiol	STRUCTURAL FORMULA
	Thiophenol	SH

Mole % Pur.	Ref.	Molecular Formula C_6H_6S	Molecular Weight 110.174

		Ref.			Ref.			Ref.
F.P. °C	-14.8	2	dt/dP			f to		
F.P. 100%			°C/mm			g °K		
			25°C	5.4681	5	h		
B.P. °C			BP	0.0550	5			
760 mm	168.7	2	t_e	0.0384	5	f' to		
100	99.5	5				g' °K		
30	69.33	5	30 mm	0.7538	5	h'		
10	46.4	5	ΔHm cal/g					
1	8.4	5				m to		
			ΔHv cal/g			n °K		
Pressure			25°C	98.38	5	o		
mm 25°C	2.9814	5	30 mm	93.58	5			
t_e	1209.93	5	BP	80.20	5	m' to		
Density			t_e	77.61	5	n' °K		
g/ml 20°C	1.0766	2	t_e (d, e)	77.44	5	o'		
d_4^t 25	1.0724	2	ΔHv/T_e	18.49	5	Surface tension		
30	1.0682	4				dynes/cm. 20°C	40.46	5
a	1.0934	4	d 70 to	102.92	5	γ 30	39.21	5
b	-0.0384	4	e 190 °C	0.1347	5	40	37.99	5
Ref. Index			d' 25 to	101.08	5			
n_D 20°C	1.5893	2	e' 70 °C	0.1082	5	Parachor [P]		
25	1.5864	2	d_c g/ml			20°C		
30	1.5844	4	v_c ml/g			30		
"C"	0.7125	4	t_c °C			40		
MR (Obs.)	34.50	2	P_c mm			Sugd.	258.1	5
MR (Calc.)	34.807≠	5	PV/RT			Exp. L.l.%/wt.		
(nD-d/2)	1.0510	2	25°C	1.0000	5	u.		
Dielectric			30 mm	1.0000	5	Dispersion	216.	2
A 70 to	6.78419	5	BP	0.9550	5	Flash Point °C		
B 205 °C	1466.5	5	t_e	0.9405	5	Fire Point		
C	207.	5	t_c			M. Spec.		
A* 70 to	1.15400	5	ΔHc kcal/m			Ultra V.		
B* 200 °C	1371.81	5	ΔHf			X-Ray Dif.		
K			ΔFf			Infrared		
c			Viscosity			Solubility in +		
t_k to			centistokes			Acetone		
t_x °C			η °C			Carbon tet.		
A' 25 to	7.11854	5				Benzene		
B' 70 °C	1657.1	5				Ether		
C'	224.	5				n-Heptane		
A'* 25 to	1.49236	5	B^v to			Ethanol		
B'* 70 °C	1557.6	5	A^v °C			Water		
			(B^v) to			Water in		
Ac to			(A^v) °C					
Bc t_c °C								
Cc			c_p liq. °K					
Cryos. A°			c_p vap. °K					
consts. B°								
t_e °C	189.20	5	c_v vap.					

≠ S = 8.5   + grams/100 grams solvent

REFERENCES: 1-Dow 2-API 3-Lit. 4-Calc. from det. data 5-Calc. by formula

SOURCE: API

PURIFICATION: API

LITERATURE REFERENCES:

No. 2

NAME	2-Methylbenzenethiol				STRUCTURAL FORMULA
	o-Methylthiophenol				SH
					C_6H_4 CH$_3$

Mole % Pur.	Ref.	Molecular Formula C_7H_8S		Molecular Weight 124.200	

		Ref.			Ref.			Ref.
F.P. °C	15.	2	dt/dP			f	to	
F.P. 100%			°C/mm			g	°K	
B.P. °C			25°C	16.98	5	h		
760 mm	194.2	2	BP	0.0568	5			
100	122.5	5	t_e	0.0379	5	f'	to	
30	91.02	5	30 mm	0.7870	5	g'	°K	
10	67.1	5	ΔHm cal/g			h'		
1	27.2	5	ΔHv cal/g			m	to	
Pressure			25°C	97.03	5	n	°K	
mm 25°C	0.8634	5	30 mm	89.89	5	o		
t_e	1278.6	5	BP	76.80	5			
Density			t_e	73.98	5	m'	to	
g/ml 20°C	1.041	2	t_e (d, e)	73.78	5	n'	°K	
d_4^t 25	1.037	2	ΔHv/T_e	18.71	5	o'		
30	1.033	4	d 90 to	100.14	5	Surface tension		
a	1.0570	4	e 220 °C	0.1269	5	dynes/cm. 20°C	38.45	5
b	-0.0380	4	d' 25 to	99.73	5	γ 30	37.28	5
Ref. Index			e' 90 °C	0.1081	5	40	36.14	5
n_D 20°C	1.570	2	d_c g/ml			Parachor [P]		
25	1.568	2	v_c ml/g			20°C		
30	1.565	4	t_c °C			30		
"C"	0.7143	4	P_c mm			40		
MR (Obs.)	39.1	2	PV/RT			Sugd.	297.1	5
MR (Calc.)	39.425≠	5	25°C	1.0000	5	Exp. L.1.%/wt.		
(nD-d/2)	1.050	2	30 mm	1.0000	5	u.		
Dielectric			BP	0.9520	5	Dispersion		
A 90 to	6.86693	5	t_e	0.9356	5	Flash Point °C		
B 235 °C	1579.3	5	t_c			Fire Point		
C	202.	5	ΔHc kcal/m			M Spec.		
A* 90 to	1.27077	5	ΔHf			Ultra V.		
B* 230 °C	1481.43	5	ΔFf			X-Ray Dif.		
K			Viscosity			Infrared		
c			centistokes			Solubility in +		
t_k to			η °C			Acetone		
t_x °C						Carbon tet.		
A' 25 to	7.20649	5				Benzene		
B' 90 °C	1784.6	5				Ether		
C'	220.	5	B^v to			n-Heptane		
A'* 25 to	1.62142	5	A^v °C			Ethanol		
B'* 90 °C	1684.0	5	(B^v) to			Water		
Ac to			(A^v) °C			Water in		
Bc t_c °C								
Cc			c_p liq. °K					
Cryos. A°								
consts. B°			c_p vap. °K					
t_e °C	218.01	5	c_v vap.					

≠ S = 8.5   + grams/100 grams solvent

REFERENCES:	1-Dow 2-API 3-Lit. 4-Calc. from det. data 5-Calc. by formula
SOURCE:	API
PURIFICATION:	API
LITERATURE REFERENCES:	

TABLE IX. THIOPHENOLS   327

No. 3

NAME	3-Methylbenzenethiol			STRUCTURAL FORMULA
	m-Methylthiophenol			SH

Mole % Pur.	Ref.	Molecular Formula C_7H_8S		Molecular Weight 124.200	

		Ref.			Ref.						Ref.
F.P. °C			dt/dP			f		to			
F.P. 100%			°C/mm			g		°K			
B.P. °C			25°C	17.64	5	h					
760 mm	195.1	2	BP	0.05688	5						
100	123.3	5	t_e	0.03802	5	f'		to			
30	91.75	5	30 mm	0.7885	5	g'		°K			
10	67.8	5	ΔHm cal/g			h'					
1	27.8	5	ΔHv cal/g			m		to			
Pressure			25°C	97.30	5	n		°K			
mm 25°C	0.8290	5	30 mm	90.09	5	o					
t_e	1277.38	5	BP	76.80	5	m'		to			
Density			t_e	73.97	5	n'		°K			
g/ml 20°C	1.044	2	t_e (d, e)	73.74	5	o'					
d_4^t 25	1.040	2	ΔHv/T_e	18.67	5	Surface tension					
30	1.036	4	d 90 to	101.88	5	dynes/cm. 20°C			38.90	5
a	1.060	4	e 220 °C	0.1285	5	ठ		30	37.72	5
b	-0.0380	4	d' 25 to	99.997	5			40	36.57	5
Ref. Index			e' 90 °C	0.1080	5	Parachor [P]					
n_D 20°C	1.572	2	d_c g/ml					20°C			
25	1.569	2	v_c ml/g					30			
30	1.567	4	t_c °C					40			
"C"	0.7146	4	P_c mm					Sugd.	297.1	5
MR (Obs.)	39.2	2	PV/RT			Exp. L.l.%/wt.					
MR (Calc.)	39.425≠	5	25°C	1.0000	5	u.					
(nD-d/2)	1.050	2	30 mm	1.0000	5	Dispersion					
Dielectric			BP	0.9498	5	Flash Point °C					
A 90 to	6.87023	5	t_e	0.9330	5	Fire Point					
B 235 °C	1584.2	5	t_c			M. Spec.					
C	202.	5	ΔHc kcal/m			Ultra V.					
A* 90 to	1.27717	5	ΔHf			X-Ray Dif.					
B* 230 °C	1487.25	5	ΔFf			Infrared					
K			Viscosity			Solubility in +					
c			centistokes			Acetone					
t_k to			η °C			Carbon tet.					
t_x °C						Benzene					
A' 25 to	7.21000	5				Ether					
B' 90 °C	1790.10	5				n-Heptane					
C'	221.	5	B^v to			Ethanol					
A'* 25 to	1.62433	5	A^v °C			Water					
B'* 90 °C	1689.3	5	(B^v) to			Water in					
Ac to			(A^v) °C								
Bc t_c °C			c_p liq. °K								
Cc											
Cryos. A°			c_p vap. °K								
consts. B°											
t_e °C	218.89	5	c_v vap.								

≠ S = 8.5   + grams/100 grams solvent

REFERENCES: 1-Dow   2-API   3-Lit.   4-Calc. from det. data   5-Calc. by formula
SOURCE: API
PURIFICATION: API
LITERATURE REFERENCES:

No. 4

NAME	4-Methylbenzenethiol		STRUCTURAL FORMULA
	p-Methylthiophenol		SH

| Mole % Pur. | Ref. | Molecular Formula C_7H_8S | Molecular Weight 124.200 | CH_3 |

		Ref.			Ref.			Ref.
F.P. °C	44.	2	dt/dP			f	to	
F.P. 100%			°C/mm			g	°K	
B.P. °C			25°C	17.50	5	h		
760 mm	194.9	2	BP	0.05686	5			
100	123.1	5	t_e	0.03814	5	f'	to	
30	91.59	5	30 mm	0.7881	5	g'	°K	
10	67.6	5	ΔHm cal/g			h'		
1	27.6	5	ΔHv cal/g			m	to	
Pressure			25°C	97.24	5	n	°K	
mm 25°C	0.836	5	30 mm	90.05	5	o		
t_e	1271.5	5	BP	76.50	5	m'	to	
Density			t_e	73.65	5	n'	°K	
g/ml 20°C			t_e (d, e)	73.78	5	o'		
d_4^t 25 30			ΔHv/T_e	18.60	5	Surface tension dynes/cm. 20°C		
a			d | 90 to	101.79	5	γ 30		
b			e | 220 °C	0.1282	5	40		
Ref. Index			d' | 25 to	99.94	5	Parachor [P]		
n_D 20°C 25 30			e' | 90 °C	0.1081	5	20°C 30 40		
"C"			d_c g/ml v_c ml/g t_c °C					
MR (Obs.)			P_c mm				Sugd.	297.1	5
MR (Calc.) (nD-d/2)	39.425≠	5	PV/RT			Exp. L.1.%/wt.		
Dielectric			25°C	1.0000	5	u.		
			30 mm	1.0000	5	Dispersion		
A | 90 to	6.86972	5	BP	0.9466	5	Flash Point °C		
B | 235 °C	1583.2	5	t_e	0.9296	5	Fire Point		
C	202.	5	t_c			M Spec.		
A* | 90 to	1.28237	5	ΔHc kcal/m			Ultra V.		
B* | 230 °C	1487.9	5	ΔHf			X-Ray Dif.		
K			ΔFf			Infrared		
c			Viscosity			Solubility in +		
t_k | to			centistokes			Acetone		
t_x | °C			η °C			Carbon tet.		
A' | 25 to	7.20945	5				Benzene		
B' | 90 °C	1789.0	5				Ether		
C'	221.	5	B^v | to			n-Heptane		
A'* 25 to	1.62391	5	A^v | °C			Ethanol		
B'* 90 °C	1688.2	5	(B^v) | to			Water		
Ac | to			(A^v) | °C			Water in		
Bc | t_c °C			c_p liq. °K					
Cc								
Cryos. A° consts. B°			c_p vap. °K					
t_e °C	218.46	5	c_v vap.					

≠ S = 8.5   + grams/100 grams solvent

REFERENCES: 1-Dow 2-API 3-Lit. 4-Calc. from det. data 5-Calc. by formula

SOURCE: API

PURIFICATION: API

LITERATURE REFERENCES:

No. 5

NAME	2-Ethylbenzenethiol			STRUCTURAL FORMULA
	o-Ethylthiophenol			

SH

C_2H_5

Mole % Pur.	Ref.	Molecular Formula $C_8H_{10}S$	Molecular Weight 138.226

		Ref.			Ref.				Ref.
F.P. °C			dt/dP			f $\vert$ to			
F.P. 100%			°C/mm			g $\vert$ __ _°K			
			25°C	34.90	5	h $\vert$			
B.P. °C			BP	0.05799	5				
760 mm	210.	2	t_e	0.0385	5	f' $\vert$ to			
100	137.	5				g' $\vert$ __ _°K			
30	104.28	5	30 mm	0.8092	5	h' $\vert$			
10	80.	5	ΔHm cal/g						
1	39.	5				m $\vert$ to			
			ΔHv cal/g			n $\vert$ __ _°K			
Pressure			25°C	92.42	5	o $\vert$			
mm 25°C	0.3963	5	30 mm	84.39	5				
t_e	1287.78	5	BP	70.6	5	m' $\vert$ to			
Density			t_e	67.74	5	n' $\vert$ __ _°K			
g/ml 20°C	1.0349	2	t_e (d, e)	67.39	5	o' $\vert$			
d_4^t 25	1.0309	2	ΔHv/T_e	18.44	5				
30	1.0269	4				Surface tension			
a	1.0509	4	d $\vert$ 105 to	97.99	5	dyneε/cm. 20°C	40.10	5	
b	-0.0₃80	4	e $\vert$ 235 °C	0.1304	5	ɤ 30	38.87	5	
Ref. Index			d' $\vert$ 25 to	94.95	5	40	37.67	5	
n_D 20°C	1.5700	2	e' $\vert$ 105 °C	0.1012	5				
25	1.5680	2				Parachor [P]			
30	1.5653	4	d_c g/ml			20°C			
"C"	0.7185	4	v_c ml/g			30			
			t_c °C			40			
MR (Obs.)	43.82	2	P_c mm			Sugd.	336.1	5	
MR (Calc.)	44.043≠	5	PV/RT			Exp. L.1.%/wt.			
(nD-d/2)	1.0525	2	25°C	1.0000	5	u.			
Dielectric			30 mm	1.0000	5	Dispersion			
A $\vert$ 105 to	6.92105	5	BP	0.9309	5	Flash Point °C			
B $\vert$ 250 °C	1656.5	5	t_e	0.9114	5	Fire Point			
C	200.	5	t_c			M. Spec.			
			ΔHc kcal/m			Ultra V.			
A* $\vert$ 105 to	1.39456	5	ΔHf			X-Ray Dif.			
B* $\vert$ 245 °C	1566.6	5	ΔFf			Infrared			
K			Viscosity			Solubility in +			
c			centistokes			Acetone			
t_k $\vert$ to			η °C			Carbon tet.			
t_x $\vert$ °C						Benzene			
A' $\vert$ 25 to	7.26402	5				Ether			
B' $\vert$ 105 °C	1871.79	5				n-Heptane			
C'	219.	5	B^v $\vert$ to			Ethanol			
			A^v $\vert$ °C			Water			
A'* 25 to	1.71747	5	$(B^v)\vert$ to			Water in			
B'* 105 °C	1769.80	5	$(A^v)\vert$ °C						
Ac $\vert$ to									
Bc $\vert$ t_c °C			c_p liq. °K						
Cc									
Cryos. A°			c_p vap. °K						
consts. B°									
t_e °C	234.64	5	c_v vap.						

≠ S = 8.5   + grams/100 grams solvent

REFERENCES: 1-Dow 2-API 3-Lit. 4-Calc. from det. data 5-Calc. by formula

SOURCE: API

PURIFICATION: API

LITERATURE REFERENCES:

No. 6

NAME	3-Ethylbenzenethiol					STRUCTURAL FORMULA			
	m-Ethylthiophenol					SH			
Mole % Pur.	Ref.	Molecular Formula $C_8H_{10}S$		Molecular Weight 138.226		C_2H_5			

		Ref.				Ref.			Ref.
F.P. °C			dt/dP				f | to		
F.P. 100%			°C/mm				g | °K		
B.P. °C			25°C	37.38	5		h		
760 mm	211.	2	BP	0.05795	5				
100	138.	5	t_e	0.03854	5		f' | to		
30	105.33	5	30 mm	0.8089	5		g' | °K		
10	81.	5	ΔHm cal/g				h' |		
1	40.	5	ΔHv cal/g				m | to		
Pressure			25°C	93.24	5		n | °K		
mm 25°C	0.3668	5	30 mm	84.89	5		o |		
t_e	1283.01	5	BP	70.6	5				
Density			t_e	67.70	5		m' | to		
g/ml 20°C	1.038	2	t_e (d, e)	67.30	5		n' | °K		
d_4^t 25	1.034	2	ΔHv/T_e	18.40	5		o' |		
30	1.030	4	d | 105 to	99.13	5		Surface tension		
a	1.0540	4	e | 235 °C	0.1352	5		dynes/cm. 20°C	40.58	5
b	-0.0₃80	4	d' | 25 to	95.84	5		γ 30	39.34	5
Ref. Index			e' | 105 °C	0.1039	5		40	38.13	5
n_D 20°C	1.572	2	d_c g/ml				Parachor [P]		
25	1.569	2	v_c ml/g				20°C		
30	1.567	4	t_c °C				30		
"C"	0.7187	4	P_c mm				40		
MR (Obs.)	43.8	2	PV/RT				Sugd.	336.1	5
MR (Calc.)	44.085≠	5	25°C	1.0000	5		Exp. L.1.%/wt.		
(nD-d/2)	1.053	2	30 mm	1.0000	5		u.		
Dielectric			BP	0.9264	5		Dispersion		
A | 105 to	6.92379	5	t_e	0.9066	5		Flash Point °C		
B | 250 °C	1657.6	5	t_c				Fire Point		
C	199.	5	ΔHc kcal/m				M Spec.		
A* | 105 to	1.40506	5	ΔHf				Ultra V.		
B* | 245 °C	1570.5	5	ΔFf				X-Ray Dif.		
K			Viscosity				Infrared		
c			centistokes				Solubility in †		
t_k | to			η °C				Acetone		
t_x | °C							Carbon tet.		
A' | 25 to	7.26693	5					Benzene		
B' | 105 °C	1873.04	5					Ether		
C'	218.	5	B^v | to				n-Heptane		
A'* 25 to	1.72091	5	A^v | °C				Ethanol		
B'* 105 °C	1771.6	5	(B^v) | to				Water		
Ac | to			(A^v) | °C				Water in		
Bc | t_c °C			c_p liq. °K						
Cc									
Cryos. A°			c_p vap. °K						
consts. B°									
t_e °C	235.43	5	c_v vap.						

≠ S = 8.5   † grams/100 grams solvent

REFERENCES: 1-Dow   2-API   3-Lit.   4-Calc. from det. data   5-Calc. by formula

SOURCE: API

PURIFICATION: API

LITERATURE REFERENCES:

TABLE IX. THIOPHENOLS

No. 7

NAME	4-Ethylbenzenethiol					STRUCTURAL FORMULA		
	p-Ethylthiophenol					SH		
Mole % Pur.	Ref.	Molecular Formula $C_8H_{10}S$		Molecular Weight 138.226		C_2H_5		
			Ref.		Ref.			Ref.
F.P. °C				dt/dP			f		to	
F.P. 100%				°C/mm			g		°K	
				25°C	37.38	5	h		
B.P. °C				BP	0.05795	5			
760 mm	211.	2		t_e	0.03854	5	f'		to	
100	138.	5		30 mm	0.8089	5	g'		°K	
30	105.33	5		ΔHm cal/g			h'		
10	81.	5							
1	40.	5		ΔHv cal/g			m		to	
Pressure				25°C	93.24	5	n		°K	
mm 25°C	0.3668	5		30 mm	84.89	5	o		
t_e	1283.01	5		BP	70.6	5			
Density				t_e	67.70	5	m'		to	
g/ml 20°C	1.038	2		t_e (d, e)	67.39	5	n'		°K	
d_4^t 25	1.034	2		ΔHv/T_e	18.40	5	o'		
30	1.030	4		d 105 to	99.13	5	Surface tension		
a	1.0540	4		e 235 °C	0.1352	5	dynes/cm. 20°C	40.58	5
b	-0.0380	4		d' 25 to	95.84	5	δ 30	39.34	5
Ref. Index				e' 105 °C	0.1039	5	40	38.13	5
n_D 20°C	1.572	2		d_c g/ml			Parachor [P]		
25	1.569	2		v_c ml/g			20°C		
30	1.567	4		t_c °C			30		
"C"	0.7187	4		P_c mm			40		
							Sugd.	336.1	5
MR (Obs.)	43.8	2		PV/RT			Exp. L.1.%/wt.		
MR (Calc.)	44.085≠	5		25°C	1.0000	5	u.		
(nD-d/2)	1.053	2		30 mm	1.0000	5	Dispersion		
Dielectric				BP	0.9264	5	Flash Point °C		
A 105 to	6.92379	5		t_e	0.9066	5	Fire Point		
B 250 °C	1657.6	5		t_c			M. Spec.		
C	199.	5		ΔHc kcal/m			Ultra V.		
A* 105 to	1.40506	5		ΔHf			X-Ray Dif.		
B* 245 °C	1570.47	5		ΔFf			Infrared		
K				Viscosity			Solubility in +		
c				centistokes			Acetone		
t_k to				η °C			Carbon tet.		
t_x °C							Benzene		
A' 25 to	7.26693	5					Ether		
B' 105 °C	1873.04	5					n-Heptane		
C'	218.	5		B^v to			Ethanol		
A'* 25 to	1.72091	5		A^v °C			Water		
B'* 105 °C	1771.59	5		(B^v) to			Water in		
Ac to				(A^v) °C					
Bc t_c °C				c_p liq. °K					
Cc									
Cryos. A°				c_p vap. °K					
consts. B°									
t_e °C	235.43	5		c_v vap.					
≠ S = 8.5							+ grams/100 grams solvent		

REFERENCES: 1-Dow 2-API 3-Lit. 4-Calc. from det. data 5-Calc. by formula

SOURCE: API

PURIFICATION: API

LITERATURE REFERENCES:

No. 8

NAME	2,4-Dimethylbenzenethiol	STRUCTURAL FORMULA
	2,4-Dimethylthiophenol	

SH
CH₃

CH₃

| Mole % Pur. | Ref. | Molecular Formula $C_8H_{10}S$ | Molecular Weight 138.226 |

		Ref.				Ref.				Ref.
F.P. °C			dt/dP				f	to		
F.P. 100%			°C/mm				g	°K		
B.P. °C			25°C	32.01	5		h			
760 mm	208.	2	BP	0.05781	5					
100	135.	5	t_e	0.03834	5		f'	to		
30	102.27	5	30 mm	0.8059	5		g'	°K		
10	78.	5	ΔHm cal/g				h'			
1	37.	5								
Pressure			ΔHv cal/g				m	to		
mm 25°C	0.4347	5	25°C	91.88	5		n	°K		
t_e	1288.13	5	30 mm	84.00	5		o			
Density			BP	70.8	5					
g/ml 20°C			t_e	67.68	5		m'	to		
d_4^t 25			t_e (d,e)	67.72	5		n'	°K		
30			ΔHv/T_e	18.50	5		o'			
a			d 100 to	96.87	5		Surface tension			
b			e 235 °C	0.1254	5		dynes/cm. 20°C			
Ref. Index			d' 25 to	94.42	5		y 30			
n_D 20°C			e' 100 °C	0.1014	5		40			
25			d_c g/ml				Parachor [P]			
30			v_c ml/g				20°C			
"C"			t_c °C				30			
MR (Obs.)			P_c mm				40			
MR (Calc.)	44.085≠	5	PV/RT				Sugd.	336.1		5
(nD-d/2)			25°C	1.0000	5		Exp. L.I. %/wt.			
Dielectric			30 mm	1.0000	5		u.			
A 100 to	6.91390	5	BP	0.9344	5		Dispersion			
B 250 °C	1645.5	5	t_e	0.9154	5		Flash Point °C			
C	200.	5	t_c				Fire Point			
A* 100 to	1.38306	5	ΔHc kcal/m				M Spec.			
B* 245 °C	1554.3	5	ΔHf				Ultra V.			
K			ΔFf				X-Ray Dif.			
c			Viscosity				Infrared			
t_k to			centistokes				Solubility in +			
t_x °C			η °C				Acetone			
A' 25 to	7.25642	5					Carbon tet.			
B' 100 °C	1859.4	5					Benzene			
C'	219.	5					Ether			
A'* 25 to	1.71116	5	B^V to				n-Heptane			
B'* 100 °C	1757.7	5	A^V °C				Ethanol			
Ac to			(B^V) to				Water			
Bc t_c °C			(A^V) °C				Water in			
Cc			c_p liq. °K							
Cryos. A°			c_p vap. °K							
consts. B°										
t_e °C	232.58	5	c_v vap.							

≠ S = 8.5

+ grams/100 grams solvent

REFERENCES: 1-Dow   2-API   3-Lit.   4-Calc. from det. data   5-Calc. by formula

SOURCE: API

PURIFICATION: API

LITERATURE REFERENCES:

TABLE IX. THIOPHENOLS

No. 9

NAME	2,5-Dimethylbenzenethiol	STRUCTURAL FORMULA
	2,5-Dimethylthiophenol	SH, CH₃, H₃C

Mole % Pur.	Ref.	Molecular Formula $C_8H_{10}S$	Molecular Weight 138.226

		Ref.				Ref.			Ref.
F.P. °C			dt/dP				f ⎱ to		
F.P. 100%			°C/mm				g ⎰ °K		
B.P. °C			25°C	28.14	5		h		
760 mm	205.	2	BP	0.05753	5		f' ⎱ to		
100	132.	5	t_e	0.03803	5		g' ⎰ °K		
30	100.24	5	30 mm	0.8010	5		h'		
10	76.	5	ΔHm cal/g				m ⎱ to		
1	35.	5	ΔHv cal/g				n ⎰ °K		
Pressure			25°C	91.08	5		o		
mm 25°C	0.4988	5	30 mm	83.43	5		m' ⎱ to		
t_e	1294.15	5	BP	70.9	5		n' ⎰ °K		
Density			t_e	67.84	5		o'		
g/ml 20°C			t_e (d, e)	67.95	5		Surface tension		
d_4^t 25			$\Delta Hv/T_e$	18.65	5		dynes/cm. 20°C		
30			d ⎸ 100 to	95.43	5		30		
a			e ⎸ 230 °C	0.1196	5		40		
b			d' ⎸ 25 to	93.63	5				
Ref. Index			e' ⎸ 100 °C	0.1017	5		Parachor [P]		
n_D 20°C							20°C		
25			d_c g/ml				30		
30			v_c ml/g				40		
"C"			t_c °C				Sugd.	336.1	5
MR (Obs.)			P_c mm				Exp. L.1.%/wt.		
MR (Calc.)	44.085‡	5	PV/RT				u.		
(nD-d/2)			25°C	1.0000	5		Dispersion		
Dielectric			30 mm	1.0000	5		Flash Point °C		
A ⎸ 100 to	6.90353	5	BP	0.9430	5		Fire Point		
B ⎸ 245 °C	1629.2	5	t_e	0.9249	5		M. Spec.		
C	-200.	5	t_c				Ultra V.		
A* ⎸ 100 to	1.36040	5	ΔHc kcal/m				X-Ray Dif.		
B* ⎸ 240 °C	1534.2	5	ΔHf				Infrared		
K			ΔFf				Solubility in +		
c			Viscosity				Acetone		
t_k ⎡ to			centistokes				Carbon tet.		
t_x ⎣ °C			η °C				Benzene		
A' ⎸ 25 to	7.24539	5					Ether		
B' ⎸ 100 °C	1840.9	5					n-Heptane		
C'	219.	5	B^v ⎸ to				Ethanol		
A'* 25 to	1.70209	5	A^v ⎸ °C				Water		
B'* 100 °C	1739.8	5	(B^v) ⎸ to				Water in		
Ac ⎸ to			(A^v) ⎸ °C						
Bc ⎣ t_c °C			c_p liq. °K						
Cc									
Cryos. A°			c_p vap. °K						
consts. B°									
t_e °C	229.69	5	c_v vap.						

‡ S = 8.5

+ grams/100 grams solvent

REFERENCES: 1-Dow 2-API 3-Lit. 4-Calc. from det. data 5-Calc. by formula

SOURCE: API

PURIFICATION: API

LITERATURE REFERENCES:

TABLE X.   AROMATIC AMINES

TABLE X. AROMATIC AMINES

NAME	Aniline	STRUCTURAL FORMULA

STRUCTURAL FORMULA
NH_2

Mole % Pur. 99.86	Ref. 1	Molecular Formula C_6H_7N	Molecular Weight 93.116

		Ref.			Ref.				Ref.
F.P. °C	-6.30	1	dt/dP			f	to		
F.P. 100%	99.86	1	°C/mm			g	°K		
B.P. °C			25°C	20.29	5	h			
760 mm	184.13	4	BP	0.05022	4				
100	119.60	4	t_e	0.0340	5	f'	to		
30	90.62	5	30 mm	0.7298	5	g'	°K		
10	68.29	5	ΔHm cal/g			h'			
1	30.55	5				m	to		
Pressure			ΔHv cal/g			n	°K		
mm 25°C	0.67142	5	25°C	139.32	5	o			
t_e	1244.8	5	30 mm	129.02	5				
Density			BP	110.80	5	m'	to		
g/ml 20°C	1.02173	1	t_e	107.16	5	n'	°K		
d_4^t 25	1.01750	1	t_e (d, e)	106.93	5	o'			
30	1.01327	4	$\Delta Hv/T_e$	20.91	5	Surface tension			
a	1.03865	4	d 90 to	146.67	5	dynes/cm. 20°C	45.50	5
b	-0.03846	4	e 205 °C	0.1948	5	δ 30	44.02	5
Ref. Index			d' 20 to	143.24	5	40	42.56	5
n_D 20°C	1.58628	1	e' 90 °C	0.1570	5	Parachor [P]		
25	1.58364	1	d_c g/ml	0.314	5	20°C		
50	1.57068	5	v_c ml/g	3.187	5	30		
"C"	0.7634	4	t_c °C	426.	3	40		
MR (Obs.)	30.562	4	P_c mm	39820.	3	Sugd.	236.70	5
MR (Calc.)	30.617	5	PV/RT			Exp. L.1.%/wt.		
(nD-d/2)	1.07459	4	25°C	1.0000	5	u.		
Dielectric			30 mm	1.0000	5	Dispersion		
A 90 to	7.24179	4	BP	0.9524	5	Flash Point °C		
B 250 °C	1675.3	4	t_e	0.9374	5	Fire Point		
C	200.	4	t_c	0.26	5	M. Spec.		
A* 90 to	1.53517	5	ΔHc kcal/m			Ultra V.	Yes	1
B* 230 °C	1582.3	5	ΔHf			X-Ray Dif.		
K			ΔFf			Infrared	Yes	1
c			Viscosity			Solubility in +		
t_k to			centistokes			Acetone	∞	
t_x °C			η °C			Carbon tet.	∞	
A' 15 to	7.63851	5				Benzene	∞	
B' 90 °C	1913.8	5				Ether	∞	
C'	220.	5	B^v to			n-Heptane	∞	
A'* 20 to	1.92924	5	A^v °C			Ethanol	∞	
B'* 90 °C	1813.6	5	(B^v) to			Water	3.65	1
Ac 250 to	7.75568	4	(A^v) °C			Water in	5.28	1
Bc t_c °C	2140.4	4	c_p liq. °K					
Cc	258.8	4						
Cryos. A°			c_p vap. °K					
consts. B°								
t_e °C	204.00	5	c_v vap.					

+ grams/100 grams solvent

REFERENCES: 1-Dow 2-API 3-Lit. 4-Calc. from det. data 5-Calc. by formula

SOURCE: Dow

PURIFICATION: Distillation

LITERATURE REFERENCES: 3 ICT

No. 2

NAME	o-Toluidine	STRUCTURAL FORMULA
		NH$_2$ CH$_3$ (benzene ring)

Mole % Pur. 99.8	Ref. 1	Molecular Formula C$_7$H$_9$N	Molecular Weight 107.150

Column 1

		Ref.
F.P. °C	-23.68	1
F.P. 100%	-14.73	1
B.P. °C		
760 mm	200.23	4
100	133.41	4
30	103.33	4
10	80.14	5
1	40.95	5
Pressure mm 25°C	0.31703	5
t_e	1287.0	5
Density g/ml 20°C	0.99843	1
d_4^t 25	0.99430	1
d_4 30	0.99017	4
a	1.01495	4
b	-0.0$_3$83	4
Ref. Index		
n_D 20°C	1.57246	1
25	1.56987	1
30	1.56731	4
"C"	0.7477	4
MR (Obs.)	35.279	4
MR (Calc.)	35.235	4
(nD-d/2)	1.07325	4
Dielectric		
A ∣103 to	7.28896	4
B ∣320 °C	1768.7	4
C	201.	5
A* ∣103 to	1.63008	5
B* ∣235 °C	1671.9	5
K		
c		
t_k ∣ to		
t_x ∣ °C		
A' ∣ 20 to	7.63271	5
B' ∣103 °C	1984.1	5
C'	219.	5
A'* 20 to	1.97647	5
B'* 103 °C	1882.4	5
Ac ∣ to		
Bc ∣ t_c °C		
Cc		
Cryos. A°	0.01492	1
consts. B°		
t_e °C	222.2	5

Column 2

		Ref.
dt/dP °C/mm		
25°C	41.11	5
BP	0.05201	5
t_e	0.03417	5
30 mm	0.7580	5
ΔHm cal/g	16.81	4
ΔHv cal/g		
25°C	126.55	5
30 mm	115.62	5
BP	99.47	5
t_e	96.08	5
t_e (d, e)	95.82	5
ΔHv/T$_e$	21.74	5
d ∣ 100 to	132.86	5
e ∣ 225 °C	0.1667	5
d' ∣ 25 to	130.04	5
e' ∣ 100 °C	0.1395	5
d_c g/ml		
v_c ml/g		
t_c °C		
P_c mm		
PV/RT		
25°C	1.0000	5
30 mm	1.0000	5
BP	0.9500	5
t_e	0.9337	5
t_c		
ΔHc kcal/m		
ΔHf		
ΔFf		
Viscosity centistokes		
η 20 °C	4.4335	1
40	2.5028	1
60	1.6420	1
80	1.1751	1
B^v ∣ 40 to	908.	4
A^v ∣ 90 °C	2.50092	4
(B^v)∣ to		
(A^v)∣ °C		
c_p liq. °K		
c_p vap. °K		
c_v vap.		

Column 3

		Ref.
f ∣ to		
g ∣ °K		
h		
f' ∣ to		
g' ∣ °K		
h'		
m ∣ to		
n ∣ °K		
o		
m' ∣ to		
n' ∣ °K		
o'		
Surface tension dynes/cm. 20°C	43.55	5
γ 30	42.13	5
40	40.71	5
Parachor [P]		
20°C		
30		
40		
Sugd.	275.7	5
Exp. L.1.%/wt.		
u.		
Dispersion		
Flash Point °C		
Fire Point		
M Spec.		
Ultra V.		
X-Ray Dif.		
Infrared		1
Solubility in +		
Acetone		
Carbon tet.	∞	
Benzene		
Ether	∞	
n-Heptane		
Ethanol	∞	
Water		
Water in		

+ grams/100 grams solvent

REFERENCES: 1-Dow   2-API   3-Lit.   4-Calc. from det. data   5-Calc. by formula

SOURCE: Dow SSR 135 - 415

PURIFICATION: Distillation

LITERATURE REFERENCES:

TABLE X. AROMATIC AMINES

No. 3

NAME	m-Toluidine	STRUCTURAL FORMULA
	m-Amino methylbenzene	

NH_2 / CH_3 benzene ring

Mole % Pur. 99.78	Ref. 1	Molecular Formula C_7H_9N	Molecular Weight 107.150

		Ref.			Ref.			Ref.
F.P. °C	-30.40	1	dt/dP			f | to		
F.P. 100%			°C/mm			g | °K		
			25°C	46.95	5	h |		
B.P. °C			BP	0.05246	5			
760 mm	203.35	4	t_e	0.03425	5	f' | to		
100	135.98	5	30 mm	0.7633	5	g' | °K		
30	105.67	5	ΔHm cal/g	15.79	4	h' |		
10	82.33	5						
1	42.89	5	ΔHv cal/g			m | to		
			25°C	127.77	5	n | °K		
Pressure			30 mm	116.25	5	o |		
mm 25°C	0.2749	5	BP	100.03	5			
t_e	1297.72	5	t_e	96.59	5	m' | to		
			t_e (d,e)	96.29	5	n' | °K		
Density			ΔHv/T_e	20.74	5	o' |		
g/ml 20°C	0.98890	1						
d_4^t 25	0.98485	1	d | 100 to	133.80	5	Surface tension		
30	0.98080	4	e | 215 °C	0.1661	5	dynes/cm. 20°C	37.90	1
a	1.00510	4	d' | 25 to	131.34	5	δ 30	37.04	1
b	-0.03810	4	e' | 100 °C	0.1428	5	40	36.09	1
Ref. Index								
n_D 20°C	1.56811	1	d_c g/ml			Parachor [P]		
25	1.56570	1	v_c ml/g			20°C	268.8	4
50	1.55361	1	t_c °C			30	269.5	4
"C"	0.7497	4	P_c mm			40	270.0	4
						Sugd.	275.7	5
MR (Obs.)	35.453	4	PV/RT					
MR (Calc.)	35.235	5	25°C	1.0000	5	Exp. L.1.%/wt.		
(nD-d/2)	1.06866	4	30 mm	1.0000	5	u.		
			BP	0.9500	5	Dispersion		
Dielectric	7.888	1	t_e	0.9346	5			
A | 105 to	7.27435	4	t_c			Flash Point °C		
B | 320 °C	1772.06	4				Fire Point		
C	200.	4	ΔHc kcal/m					
A* | 105 to	1.61099	5	ΔHf			M. Spec.		
B* | 240 °C	1674.3	5	ΔFf			Ultra V.		
K						X-Ray Dif.		
c			Viscosity			Infrared		
t_k | to			centistokes					
t_x | °C			η 20°C	3.9060	1	Solubility in +		
			40	2.2142	1	Acetone	∞	
A' | 20 to	7.61573	5	60	1.4838	1	Carbon tet.	∞	
B' | 105 °C	1986.9	5	80	1.0798	1	Benzene	∞	
C'	218.	5				Ether	∞	
			B^v | 40 to	862.5	4	n-Heptane	∞	
A'* 20 to	1.95909	5	A^v | 90°C	3.5914	4	Ethanol	∞	
B'* 105 °C	1885.5	5	(B^v)| to			Water		
			(A^v)| °C			Water in		
Ac | to								
Bc | t_c °C			c_p liq. °K					
Cc								
Cryos. A°	0.01456	1	c_p vap. °K					
consts. B°								
t_e °C	225.86	5	c_v vap.					

+ grams/100 grams solvent

REFERENCES: 1-Dow 2-API 3-Lit. 4-Calc. from det. data 5-Calc. by formula

SOURCE: Dow

PURIFICATION: Distillation

LITERATURE REFERENCES:

No. 4

NAME	p-Toluidine	STRUCTURAL FORMULA
	p-Amino methylbenzene	

Mole % Pur.	Ref.	Molecular Formula C_7H_9N	Molecular Weight 107.150

Structural formula: NH_2 on benzene ring, CH_3 para position.

		Ref.			Ref.				Ref.
F.P. °C	43.7	3[2]	dt/dP °C/mm			f	to °K		
F.P. 100%			25°C	39.24	5	g			
B.P. °C			BP	0.05250	4	h			
760 mm	200.55	3'	t_e	0.03459	5	f'	to °K		
100	133.2	4	30 mm	0.7620	5	g'			
30	102.9	5	ΔHm cal/g			h'			
10	79.63	5	ΔHv cal/g			m	to °K		
1	40.27	5	25°C	125.34	5	n			
Pressure mm 25°C	0.3353	5	30 mm	114.78	5	o			
t_e	1283.7	5	BP	98.74	5	m'	to °K		
Density g/ml 50°C	0.9619	3	t_e	95.01	5	n'			
d_4^t 70	0.9444	3	t_e (d, e)	95.11	5	o'			
90	0.9276	3	ΔHv/T_e	20.53	5	Surface tension dynes/cm. 50°C	34.88	3
a	1.0156	4	d | 103 to	131.69	5	70	32.80	3
b	-0.0₃875	4	e | 230 °C	0.1643	5	90	30.89	3
Ref. Index			d' | 20 to	128.73	5			
n_D 25°C	1.56357	4	e' | 103 °C	0.1355	5	Parachor [P]		
45	1.55397	3	d_c g/ml			50°C	270.8	4
50	1.55348	4	v_c ml/g			70	271.3	4
"C"	0.7423	4	t_c °C			90	272.4	4
MR (Obs.)	35.20‡	4	P_c mm			Sugd.	275.7	5
MR (Calc.)	35.235	5	PV/RT			Exp. L.1.%/wt.		
(nD-d/2)	1.06587	4	25°C	1.0000	5	u.		
Dielectric			30 mm	1.0000	5	Dispersion		
A | 103 to	7.25137	5	BP	0.9465	5	Flash Point °C		
B | 330 °C	1755.0	5	t_e	0.9305	5	Fire Point		
C	201.	5	t_c			M Spec.		
A* | 103 to	1.5971	5	ΔHc kcal/m			Ultra V.		
B* | 240 °C	1659.6	5	ΔHf			X-Ray Dif.		
K			ΔFf			Infrared		
c			Viscosity centistokes			Solubility in +		
t_k | to			η °C			Acetone		
t_x | °C						Carbon tet.		
A' | 20 to	7.61234	5				Benzene		
B' | 103 °C	1981.3	5				Ether		
C'	220.	5	B^v | to			n-Heptane		
A'* | 20 to	1.9551	5	A^v | °C			Ethanol		
B'* | 103 °C	1878.9	5	(B^v) | to			Water		
Ac | to			(A^v) | °C			Water in		
Bc | t_c °C								
Cc			c_p liq. °K					
Cryos. A° consts. B°			c_p vap. °K					
t_e °C	222.6	5	c_v vap.					

‡ 45°C   + grams/100 grams solvent

REFERENCES: 1-Dow 2-API 3-Lit. 4-Calc. from det. data 5-Calc. by formula

SOURCE: Lit.

PURIFICATION: Lit.

LITERATURE REFERENCES: 3 J.A.C.S. 54, 2398 (1932) Buehler et al; 3' J. Chim. Phys. 34, 707 (1937) Timmerman and Hermaut-Roland; 3[2] J. Chem. Soc. (London) 107, 276 (1915) Cauwood and Turner

TABLE X. AROMATIC AMINES

NAME	p-Ethyl aniline					STRUCTURAL FORMULA		
	p-Amino ethylbenzene					NH_2		

| Mole % Pur. 99.63 | Ref. 1 | Molecular Formula $C_8H_{11}N$ | | Molecular Weight 121.176 | | C_2H_5 | | |

		Ref.				Ref.				Ref.
F.P. °C	-5.08	1	dt/dP				f	to		
F.P. 100%	-4.87	4	°C/mm				g	°K		
			25°C	85.39	5		h			
B.P. °C			BP	0.05442	5					
760 mm	217.82	1	t_e	0.03466	5		f'	to		
100	147.78	5					g'	°K		
30	116.44	5	30 mm	0.7892	5		h'			
10	92.31	5	ΔHm cal/g	21.0	4		m	to		
1	51.61	5	ΔHv cal/g				n	°K		
Pressure			25°C	117.19	5		o			
mm 25°C	0.1457	5	30 mm	105.16	5					
t_e	1340.3	5	BP	90.01	5		m'	to		
Density			t_e	87.09	5		n'	°K		
g/ml 20°C	0.96787	1	t_e (d, e)	86.33	5		o'			
d_4^t 25	0.96388	1	ΔHv/T_e	20.47	5		Surface tension			
30	0.95987	4	d 148 to	122.5	5		dynes/cm. 20°C	35.10	1
a	0.98383	4	e 230 °C	0.1494	5		γ 30	34.14	1
b	-0.0₃80	4	d' 20 to	120.5	5		40		
Ref. Index			e' 148 °C	0.1317	5				
n_D 20°C	1.55535	1	d_c g/ml				Parachor [P]		
25	1.55291	1	v_c ml/g				20°C	304.7	4
35	1.54825	1	t_c °C				30	305.1	4
"C"	0.7498	4	P_c mm				40		
MR (Obs.)	40.197	4	PV/RT				Sugd.	314.7	5
MR (Calc.)	39.853	5	25°C	1.0000	5		Exp. L. l. %/wt.		
(nD-d/2)	1.07142	4	30 mm	1.0000	5		u.		
Dielectric	4.840	1	BP	0.9452	5		Dispersion		
A 148 to	7.24490	4	t_e	0.9343	5		Flash Point °C		
B 340 °C	1813.6	4	t_c				Fire Point		
C	198.	5	ΔHc kcal/m				M. Spec.		
A* 148 to	1.6206	5	ΔHf				Ultra V.		
B* 255 °C	1712.3	5	ΔFf				X-Ray Dif.		
K			Viscosity				Infrared		
c			centistokes				Solubility in +		
t_k to			η 20 °C	3.849	1		Acetone		
t_x °C			40	2.3149	1		Carbon tet.		
A' 20 to	7.57508	5	60	1.5733	1		Benzene		
B' 148 °C	2027.2	5					Ether		
C'	216.	5	B^v 35 to	875.3	4		n-Heptane		
			A^v 70 °C	3.56984	4		Ethanol		
A'* 20 to	1.96742	5	(B^v) to				Water		
B'* 148 °C	1925.6	5	(A^v) °C				Water in		
Ac to									
Bc t_c °C			c_p liq. °K						
Cc									
Cryos. A°	0.01783	1	c_p vap. °K						
consts. B°									
t_e °C	242.4	5	c_v vap.						

+ grams/100 grams solvent

REFERENCES: 1-Dow 2-API 3-Lit. 4-Calc. from det. data 5-Calc. by formula

SOURCE: Dow

PURIFICATION: Distillation

LITERATURE REFERENCES:

No. 6

NAME	n-Butylaniline	STRUCTURAL FORMULA
	n-Butyl aminobenzene	$NH(C_4H_9)$

Mole % Pur. 99.82	Ref. 1	Molecular Formula $C_{10}H_{15}N$	Molecular Weight 149.138

		Ref.			Ref.			Ref.
F.P. °C	-14.40	1	dt/dP °C/mm			f | to		
F.P. 100%			25°C	322.92	5	g | °K		
B.P. °C			BP	0.0563	5	h |		
760 mm	241.59	1	t_e	0.03446	5	f' | to		
100	169.26	5	30 mm	0.8207	5	g' | °K		
30	136.69	5	ΔHm cal/g			h' |		
10	111.65	5	ΔHv cal/g			m | to		
1	69.59	5	25°C	107.44	5	n | °K		
Pressure			30 mm	90.92	5	o |		
mm 25°C	0.03415	5	BP	78.08	5			
t_e	1407.01	5	t_e	74.87	5	m' | to		
Density			t_e (d, e)	74.65	5	n' | °K		
g/ml 20°C	0.93226	1	$ΔHv/T_e$	20.57	5	o' |		
d_4^t 25	0.92835	1				Surface tension		
30	0.92444	4	d | 140 to	107.66	5	dynes/cm. 20°C	33.85	1
a	0.94790	4	e | 270 °C	0.1224	5	30	32.88	1
b	-0.0₃78	4	d' | 25 to	111.14	5	40	31.98	1
Ref. Index			e' | 140 °C	0.1479	5			
n_D 20°C	1.53412	1	d_c g/ml			Parachor [P]		
25	1.53167	1	v_c ml/g			20°C	385.9	4
30	1.52935	4	t_c °C			30	386.3	4
"C"	0.7507	4	P_c mm			40	386.9	4
MR (Obs.)	49.736	4	PV/RT			Sugd.	385.6	5
MR (Calc.)	49.089	5	25°C	1.0000	5	Exp. L.1.%/wt.		
(nD-d/2)	1.0780	4	30 mm	1.0000	5	u.		
Dielectric			BP	0.9500	5	Dispersion		
A | 140 to	7.29253	4	t_e	0.9316	5	Flash Point °C		
B | 370 °C	1917.28	4	t_c			Fire Point		
C	193.	4	ΔHc kcal/m			M Spec.		
A* | 140 to	1.74100	5	ΔHf			Ultra V.		
B* | 280 °C	1812.6	5	ΔFf			X-Ray Dif.		
K			Viscosity			Infrared		
c			centistokes			Solubility in +		
t_k | to			η 20 °C	3.4579	1	Acetone	∞	
t_x | °C			40	2.1212	1	Carbon tet.	∞	
A' | 25 to	7.43364	5	60	1.4674	1	Benzene	∞	
B' | 140 °C	2011.5	5	80	1.1127	1	Ether	∞	
C'	201.	5	B^V | 30 to	774.92	4	n-Heptane	∞	
A'* | 25 to	1.92009	5	A^V | 90 °C	3.85239	4	Ethanol	∞	
B'* 140 °C	1917.1	5	(B^V) | to			Water		
Ac | to			(A^V) | °C			Water in		
Bc | t_c °C			c_p liq. °K					
Cc								
Cryos. A°	0.03234	1	c_p vap. °K					
consts. B°								
t_e °C	269.64	5	c_v vap.					

+ grams/100 grams solvent

REFERENCES: 1-Dow   2-API   3-Lit.   4-Calc. from det. data   5-Calc. by formula

SOURCE: Dow

PURIFICATION: Distillation

LITERATURE REFERENCES:

TABLE X. AROMATIC AMINES 341

No. 7

NAME	4-Amino-1,3-dimethylbenzene	STRUCTURAL FORMULA
	4-Amino-m-xylene	CH₃, CH₃, NH₂

Mole % Pur.	Ref.	Molecular Formula $C_8H_{11}N$	Molecular Weight 121.176	(structure)

		Ref.			Ref.				Ref.
F.P. °C	16.	3	dt/dP			f	to		
F.P. 100%			°C/mm			g	°K		
			25°C	80.52	5	h			
B.P. °C			BP	0.05330	5				
760 mm	214.0	3'	t_e	0.03422	5	f'	to		
100	145.5	5	30 mm	0.07776	5	g'	°K		
30	114.6	5	ΔHm cal/g			h'			
10	90.9	5	ΔHv cal/g			m	to		
1	50.7	5	25°C	117.67	5	n	°K		
			30 mm	105.75	5	o			
Pressure			BP	90.82	5				
mm 25°C	0.1539	5	t_e	87.48	5	m'	to		
t_e	1324.7	5	t_e (d, e)	87.24	5	n'	°K		
Density			ΔHv/T_e	20.74	5	o'			
g/ml 25°C	0.9723	3				Surface tension			
d_4^t 50	0.9520	3	d 115 to	122.97	5	dynes/cm. 25°C	36.75	3
70	0.9355	3	e 240 °C	0.1503	5	δ 50	34.46	3
a	0.9918	4	d' 20 to	120.99	5	70	32.38	3
b	-0.0₃78	4	e' 115 °C	0.1330	5	Parachor [P]		
Ref. Index			d_c g/ml			25°C	307.2	4
n_D 25°C	1.55689	4	v_c ml/g			50	308.2	4
45	1.54729	3	t_c °C			70	308.8	4
50	1.54489	4	P_c mm			Sugd.	314.7	5
"C"	0.7483	4	PV/RT			Exp. L.1.%/wt.		
MR (Obs.)	40.185‡	4	25°C	1.0000	5	u.		
MR (Calc.)	39.853	5	30 mm	1.0000	5	Dispersion		
(nD-d/2)	1.06899	4	BP	0.9485	5			
Dielectric			t_e	0.9317	5	Flash Point °C		
A 115 to	7.2977	5	t_c			Fire Point		
B 340 °C	1819.8	5	ΔHc kcal/m			M. Spec.		
C	198.	5	ΔHf			Ultra V.		
A* 115 to	1.68241	5	ΔFf			X-Ray Dif.		
B* 250 °C	1721.3	5				Infrared		
K			Viscosity			Solubility in +		
c			centistokes			Acetone		
t_k to			η °C			Carbon tet.		
t_x °C						Benzene		
A' 20 to	7.63281	5				Ether		
B' 115 °C	2035.4	5				n-Heptane		
C'	216.	5	B^v to			Ethanol		
A'* 20 to	2.02577	5	A^v °C			Water		
B'* 115 °C	1933.9	5	(B^v) to			Water in		
Ac to			(A^v) °C					
Bc t_c °C			c_p liq. °K					
Cc								
Cryos. A°			c_p vap. °K					
consts. B°								
t_e °C	237.82	5	c_v vap.					

‡ 45°C + grams/100 grams solvent

REFERENCES: 1-Dow 2-API 3-Lit. 4-Calc. from det. data 5-Calc. by formula

SOURCE: Lit.

PURIFICATION: Lit.

LITERATURE REFERENCES: 3 J.A.C.S. 54, 2398 (1932); 3' Ber. 35, 3749, Junghahn

No. 8

NAME	o-Chloroaniline	STRUCTURAL FORMULA
	o-Amino chlorobenzene	NH$_2$ Cl (benzene ring)

Mole % Pur. 99.86	Ref. 1	Molecular Formula C$_6$H$_6$ClN	Molecular Weight 127.570

Column 1

		Ref.
F.P. °C	-1.94	1
F.P. 100%		
B.P. °C		
760 mm	208.84	1
100	139.48	4
30	108.43	4
10	84.55	4
1	44.3	5
Pressure		
mm 25°C	0.2533	5
t_e	1311.	5
Density		
g/ml 20°C	1.21266	1
d_4^t 25	1.20787	1
30	1.20308	4
a	1.23182	4
b	$-0.0_3 96$	4
Ref. Index		
n_D 20°C	1.58894	1
25	1.58644	1
30	1.57441	1
"C"	0.6322	4
MR (Obs.)	35.45	4
MR (Calc.)	35.484	5
(nD-d/2)	0.98261	4
Dielectric		
A ⌐110 to	7.19240	4
B ⌐330 °C	1762.74	4
C	200.0	5
A* ⌐110 to	1.60261	5
B* ⌐240 °C	1664.35	5
K		
c		
t_k ⌐ to		
t_x ⌐ °C		
A' ⌐25 to	7.55246	5
B' ⌐110 °C	1991.84	5
C'	219.4	5
A'* 25 to	1.96779	5
B'* 110 °C	1888.93	5
Ac ⌐ to		
Bc ⌐t_c °C		
Cc		
Cryos. A°	0.01785	1
consts. B°		
t_e °C	232.59	5

Column 2

		Ref.
dt/dP °C/mm		
25°C	51.44	5
BP	0.0542	5
t_e	0.0352	5
30 mm	0.7812	5
ΔHm cal/g		
ΔHv cal/g		
25°C	106.33	5
30 mm	96.80	5
BP	83.06	5
t_e	80.06	5
t_e (d, e)	79.81	5
ΔHv/T_e	20.19	5
d ⌐110 to	111.63	5
e ⌐230 °C	0.1368	5
d' ⌐25 to	109.19	5
e' ⌐110 °C	0.1143	5
d_c g/ml		
v_c ml/g		
t_c °C		
P_c mm		
PV/RT		
25°C	1.0000	5
30 mm	1.0000	5
BP	0.9482	5
t_e	0.9316	5
t_c		
ΔHc kcal/m		
ΔHf		
ΔFf		
Viscosity centistokes		
η 20 °C	2.9157	1
40	1.8458	1
60	1.3057	1
80	1.0250	1
B^V ⌐40 to	706.49	4
A^V ⌐90 °C	2.01047	4
(B^V) ⌐ to		
(A^V) ⌐ °C		
c_p liq. °K		
c_p vap. °K		
c_v vap.		

Column 3

		Ref.
f ⌐ to °K		
g		
h		
f' ⌐ to °K		
g'		
h'		
m ⌐ to °K		
n		
o		
m' ⌐ to °K		
n'		
o'		
Surface tension dynes/cm. 20°C	43.66	1
γ 30	42.54	1
40	41.35	1
Parachor [P]		
20°C	270.5	4
30	270.8	4
40	271.1	4
Sugd.	273.9	5
Exp. L.1.%/wt.		
u.		
Dispersion		
Flash Point °C		
Fire Point		
M Spec.		
Ultra V.		
X-Ray Dif.		
Infrared		
Solubility in +		
Acetone		
Carbon tet.	∞	
Benzene	∞	
Ether		
n-Heptane		
Ethanol		
Water	0.876	1
Water in		

+ grams/100 grams solvent

REFERENCES: 1-Dow 2-API 3-Lit. 4-Calc. from det. data 5-Calc. by formula

SOURCE: Dow

PURIFICATION: Distillation, absorption

LITERATURE REFERENCES:

TABLE X. AROMATIC AMINES

343

No. 9

NAME	m-Chloroaniline	STRUCTURAL FORMULA
	m-Amino chlorobenzene	NH_2 / Cl

Mole % Pur. 99.79	Ref. 1	Molecular Formula C_6H_6ClN	Molecular Weight 127.573

		Ref.			Ref.			Ref.
F.P. °C	-10.29	1	dt/dP			f | to °K		
F.P. 100%			°C/mm			g |		
			25°C	144.58	5	h |		
B.P. °C			BP	0.0560	5			
760 mm	229.92	1	t_e	0.0356	5	f' | to °K		
100	158.16	1				g' |		
30	125.95	4	30 mm	0.8109	5	h' |		
10	101.15	4	ΔHm cal/g	19.02	4	m | to °K		
1	59.3	5	ΔHv cal/g			n |		
Pressure			25°C	114.36	5	o |		
mm 25°C	0.0838	5	30 mm	102.01	5			
t_e	1344.	5	BP	86.21	5	m' | to °K		
Density			t_e	82.74	5	n' |		
g/ml 20°C	1.21606	1	t_e (d, e)	82.30	5	o' |		
d_4^t 25	1.21147	1	ΔHv/T_e	19.96	5	Surface tension		
30	1.20688	4	d | 125 to	121.15	5	dynes/cm. 20°C	45.68	1
a	1.23442	4	e | 250 °C	0.1520	5	ɣ 30	44.52	1
b	-0.0₃92	4	d' | 20 to	117.41	5	40	43.42	1
Ref. Index			e' | 125 °C	0.1223	5	Parachor [P]		
n_D 20°C	1.59414	1	d_c g/ml			20°C	272.7	4
25	1.59190	1	v_c ml/g			30	273.0	4
30	1.58028	1	t_c °C			40	273.4	4
"C"	0.6355	4	P_c mm			Sugd.	273.9	5
MR (Obs.)	35.50	4	PV/RT			Exp. L. l. %/wt.		
MR (Calc.)	35.484	5	25°C	1.0000	5	u.		
(nD-d/2)	0.98611	4	30 mm	1.0000	5	Dispersion		
Dielectric			BP	0.9330	5	Flash Point °C		
A | 125 to	7.23603	4	t_e	0.9135	5	Fire Point		
B | 350 °C	1857.75	4	t_c			M. Spec.		
C	196.64	4	ΔHc kcal/m			Ultra V.		
A* | 125 to	1.65667	5	ΔHf			X-Ray Dif.		
B* | 265 °C	1764.50	5	ΔFf			Infrared		
K			Viscosity			Solubility in +		
c			centistokes			Acetone		
t_k | to			η 20 °C	3.3538	1	Carbon tet.	∞	
t_x | °C			40	2.0285	1	Benzene	∞	
A' | 25 to	7.59884	5	60	1.3939	1	Ether		
B' | 125 °C	2099.20	5	80	1.0387	1	n-Heptane		
C'	216.96	5	B^v | 40 to	803.91	4	Ethanol		
A'* 25 to	7.0050	5	A^v | 90°C	3.74043	4	Water		
B'* 125 °C	1995.12	5	(B^v) | to			Water in		
Ac | to			(A^v) | °C					
Bc | t_c °C			c_p liq. °K					
Cc								
Cryos. A°	0.01769	1	c_p vap. °K					
consts. B°								
t_e °C	255.63	5	c_v vap.					

+ grams/100 grams solvent

REFERENCES: 1-Dow 2-API 3-Lit. 4-Calc. from det. data 5-Calc. by formula

SOURCE: Dow

PURIFICATION: Distillation, chromotographed

LITERATURE REFERENCES:

No. 10

NAME	m-Aminobenzotrifluoride					STRUCTURAL FORMULA

Mole % Pur. | Ref. | Molecular Formula $C_7H_6F_3N$ | Molecular Weight 161.118

Structural formula: NH_2 ... CF_3 (benzene ring)

		Ref.				Ref.					Ref.
F.P. °C	5.65	3	dt/dP				f	|	to		
F.P. 100%			°C/mm				g	|	°K		
			25°C	28.86	5		h	|			
B.P. °C			BP	0.0513	5						
760 mm	191.13	3	t_e	0.0346	5		f'	|	to		
100	125.59	4	30 mm	0.7370	4		g'	|	°K		
30	96.28	4	ΔHm cal/g				h'	|			
10	73.76	4	ΔHv cal/g				m	|	to		
1	35.8	5	25°C	83.95	5		n	|	°K		
Pressure			30 mm	76.15	5		o	|			
mm 25°C	0.4527	5	BP	64.24	5						
t_e	1247.	5	t_e	61.97	5		m'	|	to		
Density			t_e (d, e)	61.69	5		n'	|	°K		
g/ml 20°C			$ΔHv/T_e$	20.60	5		o'	|			
d_4^t 25			d | 95 to	88.23	5		Surface tension				
30			e | 210 °C	0.1255	5		dynes/cm. 20°C				
a			d' | 25 to	86.69	5		y		30		
b			e' | 95 °C	0.1095	5				40		
Ref. Index			d_c g/ml				Parachor [P]				
n_D 20°C	1.4788	3	v_c ml/g						20°C		
25	1.4769	3	t_c °C						30		
30	1.4750	3	P_c mm						40		
"C"			PV/RT						Sugd.	301.5	5
MR (Obs.)			25°C	1.0000	5		Exp. L.l.%/wt.				
MR (Calc.)	34.785	5	30 mm	1.0000	5		u.				
(nD-d/2)			BP	0.9410	5		Dispersion				
Dielectric			t_e	0.9230	5		Flash Point °C				
A | 95 to	7.17030	3	t_c				Fire Point				
B | 370 °C	1650.21	3	ΔHc kcal/m				M Spec.				
C	193.58	3	ΔHf				Ultra V.				
A* | 95 to	1.71965	5	ΔFf				X-Ray Dif.				
B* | 230 °C	1564.62	5					Infrared				
K			Viscosity				Solubility in +				
c			centistokes				Acetone				
t_k | to			η °C				Carbon tet.				
t_x | °C							Benzene				
A' | 25 to	7.52897	5					Ether				
B' | 95 °C	1864.69	5					n-Heptane				
C'	211.84	5	B^v | to				Ethanol				
			A^v | °C				Water				
A'* 25 to	2.06433	5	(B^v) | to				Water in				
B'* 95 °C	1769.39	5	(A^v) | °C								
Ac | to			c_p liq. °K								
Bc | t_c °C											
Cc			c_p vap. °K								
Cryos. A°											
consts. B°			c_v vap.								
t_e °C	211.44	5									

+ grams/100 grams solvent

REFERENCES: 1-Dow   2-API   3-Lit.   4-Calc. from det. data   5-Calc. by formula

SOURCE: Lit.

PURIFICATION: Lit.

LITERATURE REFERENCES: 3 J.A.C.S. 75, 1997 (1953) Kardon and Saylor

TABLE XI. NITROBENZENES   345

No. 1

NAME	Nitrobenzene	STRUCTURAL FORMULA
		NO₂

Mole % Pur.	Ref.	Molecular Formula $C_6H_5No_2$	Molecular Weight 123.108

		Ref.			Ref.					Ref.
F.P. °C	5.7	3[7]	dt/dP			f		to		
F.P. 100%			°C/mm			g		°K		
B.P. °C			25°C	47.17	5	h				
760 mm	210.85	3[8]	BP	0.05573	5					
100	139.83	5	t_e	0.03615	5	f'		to		
30	108.2	5	30 mm	0.7934	5	g'		°K		
10	83.9	5	ΔHm cal/g	22.50	3[6]	h'				
1	43.1	5	ΔHv cal/g			m		to		
Pressure			25°C	107.14	5	n		°K		
mm 25°C	0.284	5	30 mm	98.65	5	o				
t_e	1317.0	5	BP	84.30	5					
Density			t_e	80.85	5	m'		to		
g/ml 20°C	1.2032	3	t_e (d, e)	80.64	5	n'		°K		
d_4^t 25	1.1982	5	ΔHv/T_e	19.75	5	o'				
30	1.1936	3[2]				Surface tension				
a	1.2232	4	d | 108 to	113.78	5	dynes/cm. 20°C		43.33	5
b	-0.00100	4	e | 235 °C	0.1398	5	ɣ		30	41.96	5
			d' | 20 to	109.69	5			40	40.52	5
Ref. Index			e' | 108 °C	0.1019	5					
n_D 20°C	1.55230	3[3]	d_c g/ml			Parachor [P]				
25	1.55006	3[4]	v_c ml/g			20°C				
30	1.54782	4	t_c °C	482.8	3[9]	30				
"C"	0.6001	4	P_c mm			40				
MR (Obs.)	32.708	4	PV/RT					Sugd.	262.5	5
MR (Calc.)	32.507	5	25°C	1.0000	5	Exp. L. 1.%/wt.				
(nD-d/2)	0.95070	4	30 mm	1.0000	5	u.				
Dielectric	34.89	3[5]	BP	0.9475	5	Dispersion				
A |108 to	7.08283	5		0.9305	5	Flash Point °C				
B |300 °C	1722.2	5	t_e			Fire Point				
C	199.	5	t_c			M. Spec.				
A* |108 to	1.47568	5	ΔHc kcal/m			Ultra V.				
B* |250 °C	1623.4	5	ΔHf			X-Ray Dif.				
K			ΔFf			Infrared				
c			Viscosity			Solubility in +				
t_k | to			centistokes			Acetone				
t_x | °C			η °C			Carbon tet.				
A' | 15 to	7.55755	5				Benzene	∞			
B' |108 °C	2026.	5				Ether	∞			
C'	225.	5	B^v | to			n-Heptane				
A'* 20 to	1.95137	5	A_v | °C			Ethanol				
B'*108 °C	1919.3	5	(B^v)| to			Water				
Ac | to			(A^v)| °C			Water in				
Bc | t_c °C			c_p liq. °K							
Cc										
Cryos. A°			c_p vap. °K							
consts. B°										
t_e °C	235.54	5	c_v vap.							

+ grams/100 grams solvent

REFERENCES: 1-Dow 2-API 3-Lit. 4-Calc. from det. data 5-Calc. by formula

SOURCE:

PURIFICATION:

LITERATURE REFERENCES: 3 Z. Anorg. Chem. 199, 91 (1931); 3[1] J. Chem. Soc. (London) 768 (1933) Sugden; 3[2] J. Chem. Soc. (London) 65, 1025 (1896) R. Perkins; 3[3] Thesis Freiburg (1919) E. Dummer; 3[4] J. Chem. Soc. (London) 127, 1049 (1925); 3[5] J. Chem. Soc. 570 (1930); 3[6] Z. Physik Chem. 72, 225 (1910); 3[7] J. Gen. Chem. (U.S.S.R.) 17, 665 (1947); Udovenko and Ayrapetova; 3[8] C. Zentral II 442 (1910) Z. El. Ch. 34, 112 Stachorski; 3[9] ICT.

No. 2

NAME	o-Ethylnitrobenzene	STRUCTURAL FORMULA

NO_2, C_2H_5

Mole % Pur. 99.95	Ref. 1	Molecular Formula $C_8H_9No_2$	Molecular Weight 151.160

		Ref.			Ref.				Ref.
F.P. °C	-12.26	1	dt/dP °C/mm			f g h	to °K		
F.P. 100%			25°C	144.64	5				
B.P. °C			BP	0.05723	5				
760 mm	232.52	4	t_e	0.03587	5	f' g' h'	to °K		
100	159.4	4	30 mm	0.8211	5				
30	126.73	4	ΔHm cal/g	23.23	1				
10	101.6	5	ΔHv cal/g			m n o	to °K		
1	59.4	5	25°C	96.22	5				
Pressure			30 mm	85.36	5				
mm 25°C	0.084	5	BP	72.73	5	m' n' o'	to °K		
t_e	1373.	5	t_e	69.74	5				
Density			t_e (d, e)	69.46	5				
g/ml 20°C	1.12066	1	ΔHv/T_e	19.77	5	Surface tension			
d_4^t 25	1.11602	1	d | 125 to	100.49	5	dynes/cm. 20°C	38.93	1
30	1.11138	1	e | 260 °C	0.1194	5	γ 30	37.80	1
a	1.13922	4	d' | 25 to	98.89	5	40	36.76	1
b	-0.0₃928	4	e' | 125 °C	0.1067	5	Parachor [P]		
Ref. Index			d_c g/ml			20°C	336.9	4
n_D 20°C	1.53557	1	v_c ml/g			30	336.5	4
25	1.53332	1	t_c °C			40	338.1	4
30	1.52179	1	P_c mm			Sugd.	340.5 ‡	5
"C"	0.6260	4	PV/RT			Exp. L.l.%/wt.		
MR (Obs.)	42.030	4	25°C	1.0000	5	u.		
MR (Calc.)	41.743	5	30 mm	1.0000	5	Dispersion		
(nD-d/2)	0.97524	4	BP	0.9450	5	Flash Point °C		
Dielectric	21.9 ‡		t_e	0.9257	5	Fire Point		
A | 125 to	7.14960	4	t_c			M Spec.		
B |290 °C	1825.0	4	ΔHc kcal/m			Ultra V.		
C	195.	5	ΔHf			X-Ray Dif.		
A* | 130 to	1.61974	5	ΔFf			Infrared		
B* |270 °C	1724.5	5	Viscosity			Solubility in +		
K			centistokes			Acetone	∞	
c			η 20 °C	2.2063	1	Carbon tet.	∞	
t_k | to			40	1.5363	1	Benzene	∞	
t_x | °C			60	1.1638	1	Ether	∞	
A' | 15 to	7.50205	5	80	0.9173	1	n-Heptane	∞	
B' |125 °C	2058.9	5	B^v | 30 to	619.91	4	Ethanol	∞	
C'	215.0	5	A^v | 90 °C	2.20719	4	Water		
A'* | 20 to	2.17972	5	(B^v) | to			Water in	0.159	1
B'* 125 °C	1955.4	5	(A^v) | °C					
Ac | to			c_p liq. °K					
Bc | t_c °C								
Cc			c_p vap. °K					
Cryos. A°	0.02581	1						
consts. B°								
t_e °C	259.91	5	c_v vap.					

T_R = 0.75 T_c ≠ 0.2°C   ‡ using O_2 as 60   + grams/100 grams solvent

REFERENCES: 1-Dow 2-API 3-Lit. 4-Calc. from det. data 5-Calc. by formula

SOURCE: Dow

PURIFICATION: Distillation

LITERATURE REFERENCES:

TABLE XII. AROMATIC ALCOHOLS (PHENYL ETHYL ALCOHOLS)

No. 1

NAME	Benzyl alcohol	STRUCTURAL FORMULA

$C H_2 OH$

Mole % Pur. 99.93	Ref. 1	Molecular Formula C_7H_8O	Molecular Weight 108.134

		Ref.			Ref.				Ref.
F.P. °C	-15.19	1	dt/dP °C/mm			f | to °K			
F.P. 100%			25°C	81.9213	5	g |			
B.P. °C			BP	0.04924	4	h |			
760 mm	205.1	1	t_e	0.03185	5	f' | to °K			
100	141.15	4	30 mm	0.7397	5	g' |			
30	111.9	4	ΔHm cal/g			h' |			
10	89.23	5							
1	50.51	5	ΔHv cal/g			m | to °K			
Pressure			25°C	135.75	5	n |			
mm 25°C	0.1469	5	30 mm	122.84	5	o |			
t_e	1300.7	5	BP	106.39	5				
Density			t_e	102.99	5	m' | to °K			
g/ml 20°C	1.04535	1	t_e (d, e)	102.66	5	n' |			
d_4^t 25	1.04156	1	ΔHv/T_e	22.30	5	o' |			
30	1.03777	4	d | 112 to	142.59	5	Surface tension			
a	1.06051	4	e | 225 °C	0.1765	5	dynes/cm. 20°C	42.76	4
b	-0.0₃758	4	d' | 20 to	139.47	5	8 30	41.27	4
Ref. Index			e' | 112 °C	0.1486	5	40	40.07	4
n_D 20°C	1.54035	1	d_c g/ml			Parachor [P]			
25	1.53837	1	v_c ml/g			20°C			
30	1.53639	4	t_c °C			30			
"C"	0.67673	4	P_c mm			40			
MR (Obs.)	32.474	4	PV/RT			0 = 18 Sugd.	264.1	5
MR (Calc.)	32.450	5	25°C	1.0000	5	Exp. L.1.%/wt.			
(nD-d/2)	1.01768	4	30 mm	1.0000	5	u.			
Dielectric			BP	0.9500	5	Dispersion			
A | 112 to	7.58200	1	t_e	0.9361	5	Flash Point °C			
B | 330°C	1904.3	1	t_c			Fire Point			
C	200.	1	ΔHc kcal/m			M. Spec.			
A* | 112 to	1.92156	5	ΔHf			Ultra V.			
B* | 240 °C	1806.4	5	ΔFf			X-Ray Dif.			
K			Viscosity			Infrared			
c			centistokes			Solubility in +			
t_k | to			η °C			Acetone			
t_x | °C						Carbon tet.			
A' | 20 to	7.93428	5				Benzene			
B' | 112 °C	2130.42	5				Ether			
C'	218.	5	B^v | to			n-Heptane			
A'* 20 to	2.27748	5	A^v | °C			Ethanol			
B'* 112 °C	2028.06	5	(B^v)| to			Water			
Ac | to			(A^v)| °C			Water in			
Bc | t_c °C			c_p liq. °K						
Cc									
Cryos. A°			c_p vap. °K						
consts. B°									
t_e °C	226.22	5	c_v vap.						

+ grams/100 grams solvent

REFERENCES:	1-Dow 2-API 3-Lit. 4-Calc. from det. data 5-Calc. by formula
SOURCE:	Dow
PURIFICATION:	Distillation
LITERATURE REFERENCES:	

No. 2

NAME	α-Phenyl ethyl alcohol		STRUCTURAL FORMULA
	α-Methylbenzyl alcohol		CH(OH)CH₃

Mole % Pur. ?	Ref. 1	Molecular Formula $C_8H_{10}O$	Molecular Weight 122.160

		Ref.				Ref.				Ref.
F.P. °C	Glassy	1	dt/dP				f | | to			
F.P. 100%			°C/mm				g | |__ °K			
B.P. °C			25°C	70.673	5		h |			
760 mm	203.4	1	BP	0.04944	4					
100	139.26	4	t_e	0.03211	5		f' | | to			
30	109.98	4	30 mm	0.7408	5		g' | |__ °K			
10	87.25	5	ΔHm cal/g				h' |			
1	48.52	5	ΔHv cal/g				m | | to			
Pressure			25°C	118.32	5		n | |__ °K			
mm 25°C	0.1730	5	30 mm	107.47	5		o |			
t_e	1295.6	5	BP	93.07	5					
Density			t_e	90.04	5		m' | | to			
g/ml 20°C	1.01353	1	t_e (d,e)	89.82	5		n' | |__ °K			
d_4^t 25	1.00949	1	ΔHv/T_e	22.10	5		o' |			
30	1.00545	4					Surface tension			
a	1.02969	4	d | 110 to	124.43	5		dynes/cm. 20°C	39.99	4
b	-0.0₃808	4	e | 220 °C	0.1542	5		30	38.73	4
Ref. Index			d' | 20 to	121.51	5		40	37.50	4
n_D 20°C	1.52752	1	e' | 110 °C	0.1277	5					
25	1.52527	1	d_c g/ml				Parachor [P]			
30	1.52302	4	v_c ml/g				20°C			
"C"	0.68244	4	t_c °C				30			
MR (Obs.)	37.085	4	P_c mm				40			
MR (Calc.)	37.068		PV/RT				0 ≈ 15 Sugd.	303.1	5
(nD-d/2)	1.02076	4	25°C	1.0000	5		Exp. L. 1.%/wt.			
Dielectric			30 mm	1.0000	5		u.			
A | 110 to	7.55432	1	BP	0.9500	5		Dispersion			
B |_330 °C	1889.9	1	t_e	0.9357	5		Flash Point °C			
C	201.	1	t_c				Fire Point			
A* | 110 to	1.94823	5	ΔHc kcal/m				M Spec.			
B* |_245 °C	1792.03	5	ΔHf				Ultra V.			
K			ΔFf				X-Ray Dif.			
c			Viscosity				Infrared			
t_k | to			centistokes				Solubility in +			
t_x | °C			η 20 °C	10.9568	1		Acetone			
A' | 20 to	7.90607	5	40	4.7356	1		Carbon tet.			
B' |_110 °C	2115.01	5	60	2.5905	1		Benzene			
C'	219.	5	80	1.6233	1		Ether			
			B^v | 30 to	1286.0	4		n-Heptane			
A'* | 20 to	2.30202	5	A^v | 90 °C	4.56939	4		Ethanol			
B'* | 110 °C	2012.15	5	(B^v) | to				Water			
Ac | to			(A^v) | °C				Water in			
Bc |_t_c_°C			c_p liq. °K							
Cc										
Cryos. A°			c_p vap. °K							
consts. B°										
t_e °C	224.48	5	c_v vap.							

+ grams/100 grams solvent

REFERENCES: 1-Dow   2-API   3-Lit.   4-Calc. from det. data   5-Calc. by formula

SOURCE: Dow

PURIFICATION: Distillation

LITERATURE REFERENCES:

TABLE XII. AROMATIC ALCOHOLS (PHENYL ETHYL ALCOHOLS)

No. 3

NAME	β-Phenyl ethyl alcohol		STRUCTURAL FORMULA
	Phenethyl alcohol		$CH_2\,CH_2\,OH$

Mole % Pur. ?	Ref. 1	Molecular Formula $C_8H_{10}O$	Molecular Weight 122.160

		Ref.			Ref.				Ref.
F.P. °C	Glassy	1	dt/dP			f | to			
F.P. 100%			°C/mm			g | °K			
B.P. °C			25°C	133.0844	5	h |			
760 mm	218.2	1	BP	0.05171	4				
100	151.33	4	t_e	0.03332	5	f' | to			
30	120.93	4	30 mm	0.7681	5	g' | °K			
10	97.39	5				h' |			
1	57.38	5	ΔHm cal/g						
Pressure			ΔHv cal/g			m | to			
mm 25°C	0.08837	5	25°C	122.99	5	n | °K			
t_e	1311.5	5	30 mm	109.66	5	o |			
Density			BP	93.08	5	m' | to			
g/ml 20°C	1.02023	1	t_e	89.62	5	n' | °K			
d_4^t 25	1.01642	1	t_e (d, e)	89.23	5	o' |			
30	1.01261	4	$\Delta Hv/T_e$	21.30	5	Surface tension			
a	1.03547	4	d | 121 to	130.28	5	dynes/cm. 20°C	41.06	4
b	-0.0_3762	4	e | 230 °C	0.1705	5	४ 30	39.95	4
Ref. Index			d' | 20 to	126.46	5	40	38.67	4
n_D 20°C	1.53252	1	e' | 121 °C	0.1389	5	Parachor [P]		
25	1.53052	1	d_c g/ml			20°C		
30	1.52852	4	v_c ml/g			30		
"C"	0.68402	4	t_c °C			40		
MR (Obs.)	37.133	4	P_c mm			Sugd.	303.1	5
MR (Calc.)	37.068	5	PV/RT			Exp. L.1.%/wt.		
(nD-d/2)	1.02241	4	25°C	1.0000	5	u.		
Dielectric			30 mm	1.0000	5	Dispersion		
A | 121 to	7.46926	1	BP	0.9347	5	Flash Point °C		
B | 340 °C	1905.1	1	t_e	0.9171	5	Fire Point		
C	197.	1	t_c			M. Spec.		
A* | 121 to	1.88168	5	ΔHc kcal/m			Ultra V.		
B* | 260 °C	1814.82	5	ΔHf			X-Ray Dif.		
K			ΔFf			Infrared		
c			Viscosity			Solubility in +		
t_k | to			centistokes			Acetone		
t_x | °C			η °C			Carbon tet.		
A' | 20 to	7.80851	5				Benzene		
B' | 121 °C	2126.92	5				Ether		
C'	215.	5				n-Heptane		
A'* 20 to	2.20184	5	B^V | to			Ethanol		
B'* 121 °C	2025.12	5	A^V | °C			Water		
Ac | to			(B^V) | to			Water in		
Bc | t_c °C			(A^V) | °C					
Cc								
Cryos. A°			c_p liq. °K					
consts. B°			c_p vap. °K					
t_e °C	240.81	5	c_v vap.					

+ grams/100 grams solvent

REFERENCES: 1-Dow 2-API 3-Lit. 4-Calc. from det. data 5-Calc. by formula
SOURCE: Dow
PURIFICATION: Distillation
LITERATURE REFERENCES:

No. 4

NAME	o-Ethyl-β-phenyl ethyl alcohol	STRUCTURAL FORMULA
	o-Ethylphenethyl alcohol	C_2H_5 CH_2CH_2OH

Mole % Pur. ?	Ref. 1	Molecular Formula $C_{10}H_{14}O$	Molecular Weight 150.212

		Ref.			Ref.			Ref.
F.P. °C	Glassy	1	dt/dP °C/mm			f to °K		
F.P. 100%			25°C	732.622	5	g		
B.P. °C			BP	0.05424	4	h		
760 mm	249.7	1	t_e	0.03291	5	f' to °K		
100	179.38	4	30 mm	0.8110	5	g'		
30	147.32	4	ΔHm cal/g			h'		
10	122.45	5	ΔHv cal/g			m to °K		
1	80.13	5	25°C	111.78	5	n		
Pressure			30 mm	96.15	5	o		
mm 25°C	0.01436	5	BP	82.15	5	m' to °K		
t_e	1410.6	5	t_e	78.79	5	n'		
Density			t_e (d, e)	78.45	5	o'		
g/ml 20°C	0.99720	1	ΔHv/T_e	21.52	5	Surface tension		
d_4^t 25	0.99365	1	d 147 to 116.30		5	dynes/cm. 20°C	40.97	4
30	0.99010	4	e 270 °C 0.1368		5	30	39.82	4
a	1.0114	4	d' 20 to 114.98		5	40	38.68	4
b	-0.0₃710	4	e' 147 °C 0.1278		5	Parachor [P]		
Ref. Index			d_c g/ml			20°C		
n_D 20°C	1.53045	1	v_c ml/g			30		
25	1.52859	1	t_c °C			40		
30	1.52673	4	P_c mm			Sugd. 381.1		5
"C"	0.6973	4	PV/RT			Exp. L.1.%/wt.		
MR (Obs.)	46.547	4	25°C	1.0000	5	u.		
MR (Calc.)	46.304	5	30 mm	1.0000	5	Dispersion		
(nD-d/2)	1.03185	4	BP	0.9404	5	Flash Point °C		
Dielectric			t_e	0.9219	5	Fire Point		
A 147 to	7.53399	1	t_c			M Spec.		
B 380 °C	2055.2	1	ΔHc kcal/m			Ultra V.		
C	192.	1	ΔHf			X-Ray Dif.		
A* 147 to	1.99777	5	ΔFf			Infrared		
B* 290 °C	1955.36	5	Viscosity			Solubility in +		
K			centistokes			Acetone		
c			η °C			Carbon tet.		
t_k to						Benzene		
t_x °C						Ether		
A' 20 to	7.85529	5				n-Heptane		
B' 147 °C	2279.03	5	B^V to			Ethanol		
C'	210.	5	A^V °C			Water		
A'* 20 to	2.32651	5	(B^V) to			Water in		
B'* 147 °C	2176.55	5	(A^V) °C					
Ac to			c_p liq. °K					
Bc t_c °C								
Cc			c_p vap. °K					
Cryos. A°								
consts. B°			c_v vap.					
t_e °C	276.73	5						

+ grams/100 grams solvent

REFERENCES: 1-Dow   2-API   3-Lit.   4-Calc. from det. data   5-Calc. by formula
SOURCE: Dow
PURIFICATION: Distillation
LITERATURE REFERENCES:

TABLE XII. AROMATIC ALCOHOLS (PHENYL ETHYL ALCOHOLS)

No. 5

NAME	p-Ethyl-β-phenyl ethyl alcohol	STRUCTURAL FORMULA
	p-Ethylphenethyl alcohol	C_2H_5

Mole % Pur. 99.17	Ref. 1	Molecular Formula $C_{10}H_{14}O$	Molecular Weight 150.212	CH_2CH_2OH

		Ref.			Ref.				Ref.
F.P. °C	7.87	1	dt/dP			f	to		
F.P. 100%			°C/mm			g	°K		
			25°C	695.204	5	h			
B.P. °C			BP	0.05476	4				
760 mm	250.0	1	t_e	0.03326	5	f'	to		
100	179.14	4	30 mm	0.8146	5	g'	°K		
30	146.91	4	ΔHm cal/g			h'			
10	121.95	5	ΔHv cal/g			m	to		
1	79.53	5	25°C	111.37	5	n	°K		
Pressure			30 mm	95.55	5	o			
mm 25°C	0.01519	5	BP	81.46	5	m'	to		
t_e	1411.5	5	t_e	78.04	5	n'	°K		
Density			t_e (d, e)	77.72	5	o'			
g/ml 20°C	0.98066	1	$\Delta Hv/T_e$	21.29	5	Surface tension			
d_4^t 25	0.97708	1	d 147 to	115.62	5	dynes/cm. 20°C	38.32	4
30	0.97350	4	e 275 °C	0.1366	5	ɤ 30	37.56	4
a	0.99498	4	d' 20 to	114.61	5	40	36.06	4
b	-0.0₃716	4	e' 147 °C	0.1298	5	Parachor [P]		
Ref. Index			d_c g/ml			20°C		
n_D 20°C	1.52293	1	v_c ml/g			30		
25	1.52107	1	t_c °C			40		
30	1.51921	4	P_c mm			Sugd.	381.1	5
"C"	0.69959	4	PV/RT			Exp. L.1.%/wt.		
MR (Obs.)	46.786	4	25°C	1.0000	5	u.		
MR (Calc.)	46.304	5	30 mm	1.0000	5	Dispersion		
(nD-d/2)	1.03260	4	BP	0.9400	5	Flash Point °C		
Dielectric			t_e	0.9215	5	Fire Point		
A 147 to	7.48252	1	t_c			M. Spec.		
B 380 °C	2029.3	1	ΔHc kcal/m			Ultra V.		
C	191.	1	ΔHf			X-Ray Dif.		
A* 147 to	1.94673	5	ΔFf			Infrared		
B* 290 °C	1929.88	5	Viscosity			Solubility in +		
K			centistokes			Acetone		
c			η °C			Carbon tet.		
t_k to						Benzene		
t_x °C						Ether		
A' 20 to	7.80242	5				n-Heptane		
B' 147 °C	2251.25	5	B^v to			Ethanol		
C'	209.	5	A^v °C			Water		
A'* 20 to	2.27512	5	(B^v) to			Water in		
B'* 147 °C	2149.56	5	(A^v) °C					
Ac to			c_p liq. °K					
Bc t_c °C								
Cc			c_p vap. °K					
Cryos. A°								
consts. B°			c_v vap.					
t_e °C	277.35	5						

+ grams/100 grams solvent

REFERENCES: 1-Dow 2-API 3-Lit. 4-Calc. from det. data 5-Calc. by formula

SOURCE: Dow

PURIFICATION: Distillation

LITERATURE REFERENCES:

No. 6

NAME	p-Chloro-β-phenyl ethyl alcohol	STRUCTURAL FORMULA
	p-Chlorophenethyl alcohol	Cl — (benzene ring) — CH2 CH2 OH

Mole % Pur. ?	Ref. 1	Molecular Formula C_8H_9ClO	Molecular Weight 156.609	

		Ref.				Ref.				Ref.
F.P. °C			dt/dP				f	to		
F.P. 100%			°C/mm				g	°K		
			25°C	954.659	5		h			
B.P. °C			BP	0.05654	4					
760 mm	259.16	1	t_e	0.03391	5		f'	to		
100	186.17	4	30 mm	0.8356	5		g'	°K		
30	153.07	4					h'			
10	127.49	5	ΔHm cal/g							
1	84.10	5	ΔHv cal/g				m	to		
			25°C	108.09	5		n	°K		
Pressure			30 mm	91.97	5		o			
mm 25°C	0.01093	5	BP	78.36	5					
t_e	1436.96	5	t_e (d, e)	74.97	5		m'	to		
Density				74.62	5		n'	°K		
g/ml 20°C	1.18036	1	$ΔHv/T_e$	20.91	5		o'			
d_4^t 25	1.17630	1					Surface tension			
30	1.17224	4	d	153 to	111.61	5	dynes/cm. 20°C		43.28	4
a	1.19660	4	e	285 °C	0.1283	5	γ 30		42.08	4
b	-0.0$_3$812	4	d'	20 to	111.23	5	40		40.94	4
Ref. Index			e'	153 °C	0.1258	5				
n_D 20°C	1.54865	1	d_c g/ml				Parachor [P]			
25	1.54670	1	v_c ml/g				20°C			
30	1.54475	1	t_c °C				30			
"C"	0.59411	4	P_c mm				40			
MR (Obs.)	42.181	4	PV/RT				Sugd.	340.3		5
MR (Calc.)	41.935	5	25°C	1.0000	5		Exp. L.l.%/wt.			
(nD-d/2)	0.95847	4	30 mm	1 0000	5		u.			
Dielectric			BP	0.9400	5		Dispersion			
A 153 to	7.42043	1	t_e	0.9198	5		Flash Point °C			
B 400 °C	2039.0	1	t_c				Fire Point			
C	190.	1	ΔHc kcal/m				M Spec.			
			ΔHf				Ultra V.			
A* 153 to	1.89572	5	ΔFf				X-Ray Dif.			
B* 300 °C	1937.82	5					Infrared			
K			Viscosity							
c			centistokes				Solubility in +			
t_k to			η °C				Acetone			
t_x °C							Carbon tet.			
A' 20 to	7.73226	5					Benzene			
B' 153 °C	2258.57	5	B^v to				Ether			
C'	208.	1	A^v °C				n-Heptane			
A'* 20 to	2.22051	5	(B^V) to				Ethanol			
B'* 153 °C	2156.76	5	(A^V) °C				Water			
Ac to			c_p liq. °K				Water in			
Bc t_c °C			c_p vap. °K							
Cc										
Cryos. A°			c_v vap.							
consts. B°										
t_e °C	288.30	5								

+ grams/100 grams solvent

REFERENCES: 1-Dow 2-API 3-Lit. 4-Calc. from det. data 5-Calc. by formula

SOURCE: Dow

PURIFICATION: Distillation

LITERATURE REFERENCES:

TABLE XIII. AROMATIC KETONES

No. 1

NAME	Acetophenone	STRUCTURAL FORMULA
	Methyl phenyl ketone	COCH$_3$

Mole % Pur.	Ref.	Molecular Formula C$_8$H$_8$O	Molecular Weight 124.176

		Ref.			Ref.		Ref.
F.P. °C	19.655	3	dt/dP			f | to	
F.P. 100%			°C/mm			g | °K	
			25°C	36.06	5	h |	
B.P. °C			BP	0.05385	4		
760 mm	202.0	3	t$_e$	0.03534	5	f' | to	
100	133.2	3	30 mm	0.7733	5	g' | °K	
30	102.4	5	ΔHm cal/g			h' |	
10	78.8	5					
1	39.0	5	ΔHv cal/g			m | to	
Pressure			25°C	106.23	5	n | °K	
mm 25°C	0.3715	5	30 mm	97.33	5	o |	
t$_e$	1294.2	5	BP	83.54	5		
Density			t$_e$	80.56	5	m' | to	
g/ml 20°C	1.02810	3	t$_e$ (d, e)	80.35	5	n' | °K	
d$_4^t$ 25	1.02382	3	ΔHv/T$_e$	20.08	5	o' |	
30	1.01947	3	d | 102 to	111.5	5	Surface tension	
a	1.04522	5	e | 225 °C	0.1384	5	dynes/cm. 15°C	40.09	3
b	-0.03856	5	d' | 20 to	109.11	5	ɤ 30	39.15	3
Ref. Index			e' | 102 °C	0.1150	5	40	38.21	3
n$_D$ 15°C	1.53075	3	d$_c$ g/ml			Parachor [P]	
25	1.53423	3	v$_c$ ml/g			20°C	
30	1.53380	4	t$_c$ °C			30	
"C"	0.6837	4	P$_c$ mm			40	
MR (Obs.)	37.715	4	PV/RT			O = 18 Sugd.	268.9	5
MR (Calc.)	37.554	5	25°C	1.0000	5	Exp. L.1.%/wt.	
(nD-d/2)	1.02232	4	30 mm	1.0000	5	u.	
Dielectric			BP	0.9498	5	Dispersion	
A | 102 to	7.15738	4	t$_e$	0.9336	5	Flash Point °C	
B | 330 °C	1723.46	4	t$_c$			Fire Point	
C	201.	4	ΔHc kcal/m			M. Spec.	
A* | 102 to	1.55909	5	ΔHf			Ultra V.	
B* | 245 °C	1625.6	5	ΔFf			X-Ray Dif.	
K			Viscosity			Infrared	
c			centistokes			Solubility in $^+$	
t$_k$ | to			η °C			Acetone	
t$_x$ | °C						Carbon tet.	
A' | 15 to	7.51308	4				Benzene	
B' | 102 °C	1946.1	4				Ether	
C'	220.	5				n-Heptane	
A'* 20 to	1.92025	5	B^v | to			Ethanol	
B'* 102 °C	1843.8	5	A^v | °C			Water	
			(B^v)| to			Water in	
Ac | to			(A^v)| °C				
Bc | t$_c$ °C							
Cc |			c$_p$ liq. °K				
Cryos. A°							
consts. B°			c$_p$ vap. °K				
t$_e$ °C	225.03	5	c$_v$ vap.				

$^+$ grams/100 grams solvent

REFERENCES: 1-Dow 2-API 3-Lit. 4-Calc. from det. data 5-Calc. by formula
SOURCE: Lit.
PURIFICATION: Lit.
LITERATURE REFERENCES: 3 Timmermans

No. 2

NAME	Benzophenone	STRUCTURAL FORMULA
	Diphenylketone	

Mole % Pur. 99.86	Ref. 1	Molecular Formula $C_{13}H_{10}O$	Molecular Weight 182.210

		Ref.				Ref.					Ref.
F.P. °C	47.93	1	dt/dP				f		to		
F.P. 100%			°C/mm				g		°K		
			50°C	11785.2	5		h				
B.P. °C			BP	0.06306	5						
760 mm	305.47	1	t_e	0.03622	5		f'		to		
100	224.45	4					g'		°K		
30	187.98	5	30 mm	0.9190	5		h'				
10	159.92	5	ΔHm cal/g	22.2875	4		m		to		
1	112.73	5	ΔHv cal/g				n		°K		
			25°C	107.43	5		o				
Pressure			30°C	84.13	5						
mm 50°C	0.00932	5	BP	70.02	5		m'		to		
t_e	1525.4	5	t_e	65.91	5		n'		°K		
Density			t_e (d, e)	65.72	5		o'				
g/ml 50°C	1.0846	3	ΔHv/T_e	19.54	5		Surface tension				
d_4^t 55	1.0805	3	d | 190 to	106.71	5		dynes/cm. 20°C				
60	1.0765	3	e | 345 °C	0.1201	5		γ		30		
a			d' | 25 to	111.00	5				40		
b			e' | 190 °C	0.1430	5						
Ref. Index			d_c g/ml				Parachor [P]				
n_D 20°C			v_c ml/g						20°C		
25			t_c °C						30		
30			P_c mm						40		
"C"			PV/RT						Sugd.	415.8	5
MR (Obs.)			25°C	1.0000	5		Exp. L.1.%/wt.				
MR (Calc.)	55.043	5	30 mm	1.0000	5		u.				
(nD-d/2)			BP	0.9188	5		Dispersion				
Dielectric 55° 10.98		1	t_e	0.8922	5		Flash Point °C				
A | 190 to	7.28937	1	t_c				Fire Point				
B | 600 °C	2144.6	1	ΔHc kcal/m	1556.	3		M Spec.				
C	181.	1	ΔHf				Ultra V.				
A* | 190 to	1.83504	5	ΔFf				X-Ray Dif.				
B* | 355 °C	2050.1	5					Infrared				
K			Viscosity				Solubility in +				
c			centistokes				Acetone				
t_k | to			η 60 °C	3.7982	1		Carbon tet.				
t_x | °C			80	2.4187	1		Benzene				
A' | 25 to	7.57278	5	100	1.7016	1		Ether				
B' | 190 °C	2358.9	5	120	1.2899	1		n-Heptane				
C'	199.	5	B^V | 70 to	947.93	4		Ethanol				
A'* | 25 to	2.26811	5	A^V | 130 °C	3.69974	4		Water 60°C	0.0076	1		
B'* | 190 °C	2317.7	5	(B^V) | to				Water in 60°C	0.793	1		
Ac | to			(A^V) | °C								
Bc | t_c °C			c_p liq. °K								
Cc											
Cryos. A°	0.01983	1	c_p vap. °K								
consts. B°											
t_e °C	341.31	5	c_v vap.								
							+ grams/100 grams solvent				

REFERENCES: 1-Dow   2-API   3-Lit.   4-Calc. from det. data   5-Calc. by formula

SOURCE: Dow

PURIFICATION: Distillation

LITERATURE REFERENCES: 3 J. Chem. Soc. 69, 1025 (1896) H. Perkin

No. 3

NAME	p-Chloroacetophenone		STRUCTURAL FORMULA

STRUCTURAL FORMULA: $CH_3C=O$ (on benzene ring with Cl)

Mole % Pur. 98.45	Ref. 1	Molecular Formula C_8H_7ClO	Molecular Weight 154.593

		Ref.			Ref.				Ref.
F.P. °C	18.40	1	dt/dP			f | to			
F.P. 100%			°C/mm			g | °K			
			25°C	193.85	5	h |			
B.P. °C			BP	0.05735	5				
760 mm	237.2	1	t_e	0.03568	5	f' | to			
100	163.88	4	30 mm	0.8255	5	g' | °K			
30	131.05	4	ΔHm cal/g			h' |			
10	105.84	5	ΔHv cal/g			m | to			
1	63.42	5	25°C	96.70	5	n | °K			
Pressure			30 mm	84.82	5	o |			
mm 25°C	0.06097	5	BP	72.29	5				
t_e	1384.6	5	t_e	69.20	5	m' | to			
Density			t_e (d, e)	69.00	5	n' | °K			
g/ml 20°C	1.19224	1	ΔHv/T_e	19.88	5	o' |			
d_4^t 25	1.18752	1	d | 131 to	100.30	5	Surface tension			
30	1.18280	4	e | 265 °C	0.1181	5	dynes/cm. 20°C	29.43	5
a	1.21072	1	d' | 25 to	99.51	5	γ 30	28.50	5
b	-0.03924	1	e' | 131 °C	0.1120	5	40	27.64	5
Ref. Index			d_c g/ml			Parachor [P]			
n_D 20°C	1.55498	1	v_c ml/g			20°C			
25	1.55283	1	t_c °C			30			
30	1.55022	4	P_c mm			40			
"C"	0.60835	1	PV/RT			Sugd.	302.0	5
MR (Obs.)	41.617	4	25°C	1.0000	5	Exp. L. 1.%/wt.			
MR (Calc.)	40.421	5	30 mm	1.0000	5	u.			
(nD-d/2)	0.95886	4	BP	0.9447	5	Dispersion			
Dielectric			t_e	0.9246	5	Flash Point °C			
A | 131 to	7.17747	1	t_c			Fire Point			
B | 350 °C	1852.9	1	ΔHc kcal/m			M. Spec.			
C	194.	1	ΔHf			Ultra V.			
A* | 131 to	1.65578	5	ΔFf			X-Ray Dif.			
B* | 275 °C	1752.4	5				Infrared			
K			Viscosity			Solubility in +			
c			centistokes			Acetone			
t_k | to			η °C			Carbon tet.			
t_x | °C						Benzene			
A' | 25 to	7.49315	5				Ether			
B' | 131 °C	2063.8	5				n-Heptane			
C'	212.	5	B^v | to			Ethanol			
A'* 25 to	1.98545	5	A^v | °C			Water			
B'* 131 °C	1962.5	5	(B^v)| to			Water in			
Ac | to			(A^v)| °C						
Bc | t_c °C			c_p liq. °K						
Cc									
Cryos. A°			c_p vap. °K						
consts. B°									
t_e °C	265.08	5	c_v vap.						

+ grams/100 grams solvent

REFERENCES: 1-Dow 2-API 3-Lit. 4-Calc. from det. data 5-Calc. by formula
SOURCE: Dow
PURIFICATION: Distillation
LITERATURE REFERENCES:

No. 4

NAME	Propiophenone	STRUCTURAL FORMULA
	Ethyl phenyl ketone	COC_2H_5

Mole % Pur. 99.57	Ref. 1	Molecular Formula $C_9H_{10}O$	Molecular Weight 134.170		

		Ref.			Ref.			Ref.
F.P. °C	18.61	1	dt/dP			f | to		
F.P. 100%			°C/mm			g | °K		
B.P. °C			25°C	80.74	5	h |		
760 mm	217.48	1	BP	0.05479	4			
100	147.30	5	t_e	0.03496	5	f' | to		
30	115.83	5	30 mm	0.79187	5	g' | °K		
10	91.63	5				h' |		
1	50.85	5	ΔHm cal/g					
			ΔHv cal/g			m | to		
Pressure			25°C	105.1	5	n | °K		
mm 25°C	0.15519	5	30 mm	94.36	5	o |		
t_e	1338.4	5	BP	81.01	5			
Density			t_e	77.93	5	m' | to		
g/ml 20°C	1.00962	1	t_e (d, e)	77.73	5	n' | °K		
d_4^t 25	1.00531	1	ΔHv/T_e	20.28	5	o' |		
30	1.0001	4				Surface tension		
a	1.02686	1	d | 115 to	109.56	5	dynes/cm. 30°C	36.42	1
b	-0.0_3862	1	e | 242 °C	0.1313	5	γ 40	35.21	1
			d' | 25 to	108.06	5	50	34.16	1
Ref. Index			e' | 115 °C	0.1183	5			
n_D 20°C	1.52684	1	d_c g/ml			Parachor [P]		
25	1.52450	1	v_c ml/g			30°C	330.9	4
30	1.52197	4	t_c °C			40	329.3	4
"C"	0.6842	1	P_c mm			50	329.8	4
MR (Obs.)	40.845	4	PV/RT			Sugd.	331.1	5
MR (Calc.)	40.172	5	25°C	1.0000	5	Exp. L.1.%/wt.		
(nD-d/2)	1.02203	4	30 mm	1.0000	5	u.		
Dielectric			BP	0.9500	5	Dispersion		
A | 115 to	7.21435	4	t_e	0.9329	5	Flash Point °C		
B | 350 °C	1800.5	4	t_c			Fire Point		
C	198.	5	ΔHc kcal/m			M Spec.		
A* | 115 to	1.63632	5	ΔHf			Ultra V.		
B* | 252 °C	1699.8	5	ΔFf			X-Ray Dif.		
K			Viscosity			Infrared		
c			centistokes			Solubility in +		
t_k | to			η °C			Acetone		
t_x | °C						Carbon tet.		
A' | 25 to	7.54342	5				Benzene		
B' | 115 °C	2012.9	5				Ether		
C'	216.	5	B^v | to			n-Heptane		
A'* | 25 to	1.97979	5	A^v | °C			Ethanol		
B'* 115 °C	1911.3	5	(B^v) | to			Water	0.0075	1
Ac | to			(A^v) | °C			Water in		
Bc | t_c °C			c_p liq. °K					
Cc								
Cryos. A°			c_p vap. °K					
consts. B°								
t_e °C	242.5	5	c_v vap.					

+ grams/100 grams solvent

REFERENCES: 1-Dow 2-API 3-Lit. 4-Calc. from det. data 5-Calc. by formula

SOURCE: Dow, Lit.

PURIFICATION: Distillation, Lit.

LITERATURE REFERENCES: 3 Jr. Chem. Soc. (London) 1948, p. 607, A. I. Vogel

TABLE XIV. AROMATIC ESTERS

No. 1

NAME	Methyl benzoate	STRUCTURAL FORMULA

CO_2CH_3

Mole % Pur. 99.80	Ref. 1	Molecular Formula $C_8H_8O_2$	Molecular Weight 136.144

		Ref.			Ref.				Ref.
F.P. °C	-12.38	1	dt/dP			f	to		
F.P. 100%			°C/mm			g	_ _ °K		
			25°C	33.56	5	h			
B.P. °C			BP	0.05371	4				
760 mm	199.35	1	t_e	0.0353	5	f'	to		
100	130.9	4	30 mm	0.7642	4	g'	_ _ °K		
30	100.46	4	ΔHm cal/g	17.09	4	h'			
10	77.1	4							
1	38.0	5	ΔHv cal/g			m	to		
			25°C	98.03	5	n	_ _ °K		
Pressure			30 mm	88.89	5	o			
mm 25°C	0.3944	5	BP	75.81	5				
t_e	1295.	5	t_e	73.15	5	m'	to		
Density			t_e (d, e)	72.77	5	n'	_ _ °K		
g/ml 20°C	1.08854	1	$\Delta Hv/T_e$	20.10	5	o'			
d_4^t 25	1.08377	1				Surface tension			
30	1.07900	4	d 100 to	102.17	5	dynes/cm. 20°C	37.90	1
a	1.10762	4	e 210 °C	0.1322	5	δ 30	36.64	1
b	-0.03954	4	d' 25 to	101.06	5	40	35.48	1
Ref. Index			e' 100 °C	0.1211	5			
n_D 20°C	1.51679	1	d_c g/ml	0.37	5	Parachor [P]		
25	1.51457	1	v_c ml/g	2.71	5	20°C	310.3	4
50	1.50298	1	t_c °C	438.	5	30	310.4	4
"C"			P_c mm	30000.	5	40	310.7	4
MR (Obs.)	37.825	4	PV/RT			Sugd.	310.9	5
MR (Calc.)	31.424	5	25°C	1.0000	5	Exp. L. l.%/wt.		
(nD-d/2)	0.97252	5	30 mm	1.0000	5	u.		
Dielectric			BP	0.9520	5	Dispersion		
A 100 to	7.07832	1	t_e	0.9392	5	Flash Point °C		
B 260°C	1656.25	1	t_c	0.25	5	Fire Point		
C	195.23	1	ΔHc kcal/m			M. Spec.		
A* 100 to	1.51406	5	ΔHf			Ultra V.		
B* 230°C	1557.9	5	ΔFf			X-Ray Dif.		
K			Viscosity			Infrared		
c			centistokes			Solubility in +		
t_k to			η 20°C	1.8904	1	Acetone		
t_x °C			40	1.3172	1	Carbon tet.		
A' 25 to	7.4312	5	60	0.9891	1	Benzene		
B' 100°C	1871.5	5	80	0.7838	1	Ether		
C'	213.9	5				n-Heptane		
A'* 25 to	1.8877	5	B^v 30 to	623.2	4	Ethanol		
B'* 100°C	1774.0	5	A^v 90°C	2.12977	4	Water		
Ac 260 to	7.3186	5	(B^v) to			Water in		
Bc t_c °C	1866.	5	(A^v) °C					
Cc	218.7	5	c_p liq. °K					
Cryos. A°	-0.01722	1						
consts. B°			c_p vap. °K					
t_e °C	222.37	5	c_v vap.					

$T_R = 0.75 T_c$

+ grams/100 grams solvent

REFERENCES: 1-Dow 2-API 3-Lit. 4-Calc. from det. data 5-Calc. by formula

SOURCE: Dow

PURIFICATION: Distillation

LITERATURE REFERENCES:

TABLE XV.   CYCLOPENTANES

No. 1

NAME	Cyclopentane		STRUCTURAL FORMULA

$$H_2C \overset{CH_2}{\underset{\;}{\diagup}} CH_2$$
$$H_2C - CH_2$$

Mole % Pur. 99.98	Ref. 2	Molecular Formula C_5H_{10}		Molecular Weight 70.130				
			Ref.			Ref.		Ref.
F.P. °C	-93.879	2	dt/dP °C/mm			f	| to	
F.P. 100%			25°C	0.07998	4	g | |___°K		
B.P. °C			BP	0.04003	2	h |		
760 mm	49.262	2	t_e	0.0359	5	f' | to		
100	-1.3	2				g' | |___°K		
30	-23.55	4	30 mm	0.5561	4	h' |		
10	-40.4	4	ΔHm cal/g	2.075	2	m | 300 to	-0.1231	4
1	-68.	5	ΔHv cal/g			n | |_600_°K	0.0015	4
Pressure			25°C	97.22	2	o |	-0.0₆4ö	4
mm 25°C	317.5	4	30 mm	105.85	5	m' | 700 to	-0.0598	4
t_e	873.3	5	BP	93.03	2	n' | |1000_°K	0.0014	4
Density			t_e	92.26	5	o' |	-0.0₆50	4
g/ml 20°C	0.74538	2	t_e (d, e)	92.27	5	Surface tension		
d_4^t 25	0.74045	2	ΔHv/T_e	19.80	5	dynes/cm. 20°C	21.77	5
30	0.73549	4	d | -25 to	101.71	5	30	20.58	5
a	0.76527	4	e | 55 °C	0.1761	5	ɣ 40	19.42	5
b	-0.0₃944	4	d' | to					
Ref. Index			e' | °C			Parachor [P]		
n_D 20°C	1.40645	2	d_c g/ml	0.270	2	20°C		
25	1.40363	2	v_c ml/g	3.70	2	30		
30	1.40074	4	t_c °C	238.60	2	40		
"C"	0.7264	4	P_c mm	33858.	2	Sugd.	203.5	5
MR (Obs.)	23.133	2	PV/RT			Exp. L.1.%/wt.		
MR (Calc.)	23.090	2	25°C	0.9813	4	u.		
(nD-d/2)	1.03376	2	30 mm	1.0000	5	Dispersion	94.2	2
Dielectric 20°	1.965	3	BP	0.9643	4	Flash Point °C	-42.0	5
A | -25 to	6.88676	2	t_e	0.9606	5	Fire Point		
B |110 °C	1124.162	2	t_c	0.276	2	M. Spec.		
C	231.361	2	ΔHc kcal/m	740.79	2	Ultra V.		
A* | -25 to	1.17294	4	ΔHf	-25.30	2	X-Ray Dif.		
B* | 70 °C	1047.8	4	ΔFf	8.70	2	Infrared	1161.	1
K	20.	5	Viscosity			Solubility in +		
c	-0.09169	4	centistokes			Acetone	∞	
t_k | to	92.	4	η -10 °C	0.815	2	Carbon tet.	∞	
t_x | °C	290.	5	0	0.726	2	Benzene	∞	
A' | to			20	0.589	2	Ether	∞	
B' | °C			40	0.490	2	n-Heptane	∞	
C'			B^v -10 to	365.24	4	Ethanol	∞	
A'* to			A^v | 50 °C	2.52405	4	Water		
B'* °C			(B^v)| to			Water in		
Ac |110 to	7.41293	4	(A^v)| °C					
Bc | t_c °C	1512.9	4	c_p liq. °K					
Cc |___	286.1	4						
Cryos. A°	0.00228	2	c_p vap.300°K	0.28490	2			
consts. B°			400	0.40268	2			
t_e °C	53.56	5	c_v vap.					

T_R = 0.75 T_c + grams/100 grams solvent

REFERENCES: 1-Dow 2-API 3-Lit. 4-Calc. from det. data 5-Calc. by formula

SOURCE: API

PURIFICATION: API

LITERATURE REFERENCES: 3 NBS Circ. 514

No. 2

NAME	Methylcyclopentane					STRUCTURAL FORMULA

$$\begin{array}{c} HC\text{-}CH_3 \\ H_2C \quad CH_2 \\ H_2C - CH_2 \end{array}$$

Mole % Pur.	Ref.	Molecular Formula C_6H_{12}		Molecular Weight 84.156	

		Ref.				Ref.					Ref.
F.P. °C	-142.455	2	dt/dP				f		to		
F.P. 100%			°C/mm				g		°K		
B.P. °C			25°C	0.1678	4		h				
760 mm	71.812	2	BP	0.04274	2						
100	17.86	2	t_e	0.0366	5		f'		to		
30	-5.82	4	30 mm	0.59195	4		g'		°K		
10	-23.7	4	ΔHm cal/g	19.678	2		h'				
1	-53.2	5									
Pressure			ΔHv cal/g				m		300 to	-0.0879	4
mm 25°C	137.5	4	25°C	89.83	2		n		600 °K	0.0015	4
t_e	927.6	5	30 mm	95.06	5		o			-0.0$_6$49	4
Density			BP	82.18	2						
g/ml 20°C	0.74864	2	t_e	81.11	5		m'		700 to	-0.0078	4
d_4^t 25	0.74394	2	t_e (d,e)	81.08	5		n'		1000 °K	0.0013	4
30	0.73922	4	ΔHv/T_e	19.41	5		o'			-0.0$_6$47	4
a	0.76748	4	d -5 to	94.10	5		**Surface tension**				
b	-0.0$_3$92	4	e 75 °C	0.1659	5		dynes/cm. 20°C			21.60	5
Ref. Index			d' to				γ		30	20.50	5
n_D 20°C	1.40970	2	e' °C						40	19.43	5
25	1.40700	2	d_c g/ml	0.264	2		**Parachor [P]**				
30	1.40425	4	v_c ml/g	3.79	2				20°C		
"C"	0.7287	4	t_c °C	259.61	2				30		
MR (Obs.)	27.833	2	P_c mm	28394.	2				40		
MR (Calc.)	27.708	5	**PV/RT**						Sugd.	242.5	5
(nD-d/2)	1.03538	2	25°C	0.9881	4		**Exp. L.1.%/wt.**				
Dielectric	20° 1.985	3	30 mm	1.0000	5			u.			
A -5 to	6.86283	2	BP	0.9540	4		Dispersion			96.1	2
B 125 °C	1186.059	2	t_e	0.9482	5		**Flash Point °C**			-25.0	5
C	226.042	2	t_c	0.273	2		Fire Point				
A* -5 to	1.21951	4	ΔHc kcal/m	885.60	2		**M Spec.**				
B* 90 °C	1109.8	4	ΔHf	-33.07	2		Ultra V.				
K	20.	5	ΔFf	7.53	2		X-Ray Dif.				
c	-0.08702	4	**Viscosity**				Infrared			1162.	1
t_k to	97.	4	**centistokes**				**Solubility in**	+			
t_x °C	312.8	5	η 20 °C	0.677	2		Acetone			∞	
A' to			40	0.555	2		Carbon tet.			∞	
B' °C			60	0.464	2		Benzene			∞	
C'			70	0.428	2		Ether			∞	
			B^v -20 to	390.17	4		n-Heptane			∞	
A'* to			A^v 30 °C	2.49985	4		Ethanol			∞	
B'* °C			(B^v) 30 to	404.34	4		Water				
Ac 125 to	7.34080	4	(A^v) 80 °C	2.45329	4		Water in				
Bc t_c °C	1546.9	4	c_p liq. °K				**Viscosity**				
Cc	276.1	4					centistokes				
Cryos. A°	0.04878	2	c_p vap.300 °K	0.31442	2				-10°C	0.960	2
consts. B°	0.0046	2	400	0.42908	2				0	0.847	2
t_e °C	78.43	5	c_v vap.								

$T_R = 0.75 T_c$

+ grams/100 grams solvent

REFERENCES: 1-Dow 2-API 3-Lit. 4-Calc. from det. data 5-Calc. by formula

SOURCE: API

PURIFICATION: API

LITERATURE REFERENCES: 3 NBS Circ. 514

TABLE XV. CYCLOPENTANES

No. 3

NAME	Ethylcyclopentane	STRUCTURAL FORMULA

H₂C—C₂H₅ structure:
```
        H₂C - C₂H₅
      H2C      CH2
      H2C ---- CH2
```

Mole % Pur. 99.95	Ref. 2	Molecular Formula C_7H_{14}	Molecular Weight 98.182

		Ref.				Ref.					Ref.
F.P. °C	-138.446	2	dt/dP				f	to			
F.P. 100%			°C/mm				g	°K			
B.P. °C			25°C	0.5056	4		h				
760 mm	103.466	2	BP	0.04623	2						
100	45.045	2	t_e	0.0364	5		f'	to			
30	19.36	4	30 mm	0.6423	4		g'	°K			
10	-0.09	4	ΔHm cal/g				h'				
1	-32.	5					m	300 to	-0.2309	4
Pressure			ΔHv cal/g				n	600 °K	0.0023	4
mm 25°C	39.93	4	25°C	88.81	2		o		-0.0₅15	4
t_e	1034.	5	30 mm	89.90	5					
			BP	78.58	2		m'	700 to	0.0098	4
Density			t_e	77.06	5		n'	1000 °K	0.0013	4
g/ml 20°C	0.76647	2	t_e (d, e)	77.07	5		o'		-0.0₆45	4
d_4^t 25	0.76217	2	ΔHv/T_e	19.51	5					
30	0.75786	4					Surface tension			
a	0.78366	4	d 20 to	92.51	5		dynes/cm. 20°C	23.30	5
b	-0.0₃85	4	e 115 °C	0.1346	5		४ 30	22.26	5
			d' to				40	21.25	5
Ref. Index			e' °C							
n_D 20°C	1.41981	2	d_c g/ml	0.262	2		Parachor [P]		
25	1.41730	2	v_c ml/g	3.817	2		20°C		
30	1.41483	4	t_c °C	296.30	2		30		
"C"	0.7283	4	P_c mm	25483.	2		40		
							Sugd.	281.5	5
MR (Obs.)	32.403	2	PV/RT						
MR (Calc.)	32.326	5	25°C	0.9963	4		Exp. L.1.%/wt.		
(nD-d/2)	1.03657	2	30 mm	1.0000	5		u.		
Dielectric	2.016	5	BP	0.9661	4		Dispersion	95.4	2
A 20 to	6.88709	2	t_e	0.9580	5		Flash Point °C	-1.0	5
B 155 °C	1293.599	2	t_c	0.269	2		Fire Point		
C	220.675	2	ΔHc kcal/m	1032.57	2		M. Spec.		
A* 20 to	1.25274	2	ΔHf	-39.10	2		Ultra V.		
B* 125 °C	1210.926	4	ΔFf	8.91	2		X-Ray Dif.		
K			Viscosity				Infrared	Yes	2
c			centistokes				Solubility in +		
t_k to			η 20 °C	0.740	2		Acetone	∞	
t_x °C			40	0.608	2		Carbon tet.	∞	
A' to			60	0.513	2		Benzene	∞	
B' °C			70	0.474	2		Ether	∞	
C'							n-Heptane	∞	
A'* to			B^v -20 to	387.70	4		Ethanol	∞	
B'* °C			A^v 30 °C	2.54691	4		Water		
			(B^v) 30 to	387.39	4		Water in		
Ac 155	7.33306	4	(A^v) 80 °C	2.54701	4		Viscosity		
Bc t_c °C	1654.1	4	c_p liq. °K				centistokes		
Cc	268.9	4					-10°C	1.047	2
Cryos. A°	0.04553	2	c_p vap.300°K	0.32338	2		0	0.924	2
consts. B°			p 400	0.44703	2				
t_e °C	114.65	5	c_v vap.						

$T_R = 0.75 T_c$

+ grams/100 grams solvent

REFERENCES: 1-Dow 2-API 3-Lit. 4-Calc. from det. data 5-Calc. by formula

SOURCE: API

PURIFICATION: API

LITERATURE REFERENCES:

No. 4

NAME	1,1-Dimethylcyclopentane		STRUCTURAL FORMULA

Structural formula:
$H_3C-C-CH_3$
$H_2C \quad CH_2$
$H_2C — CH_2$

Mole % Pur. 99.97	Ref. 2	Molecular Formula	C_7H_{14}	Molecular Weight 98.182

		Ref.				Ref.					Ref.
F.P. °C	-69.795	2	dt/dP				f		to		
F.P. 100%			°C/mm				g		°K		
B.P. °C			25°C	0.2869	4		h				
760 mm	87.846	2	BP	0.04497	2		f'		to		
100	31.202	2	t_e	0.0369	5		g'		°K		
30	6.4148	4	30 mm	0.6191	4		h'				
10	-12.31	4	ΔHm cal/g								
1	-43.1	5	ΔHv cal/g				m	300 to	-0.0773	4
			25°C	82.29	2		n	600 °K	0.0015	4
Pressure			30 mm	85.21	5		o		-0.0₆47	4
mm 25°C	75.69	4	BP	73.73	2					
t_e	981.	5	t_e	72.48	5		m'	700 to	0.0221	4
Density			t_e (d,e)	72.47	5		n'	1000 °K	0.0013	4
g/ml 20°C	0.75448	2	ΔHv/T_e	19.23	5		o'		-0.0₆46	4
d_4^t 25	0.74991	2					Surface tension			
30	0.74533	4	d 0 to	86.11	5		dynes/cm. 20°C	21.86	5
a	0.77276	4	e 100 °C	0.1409	5		γ 30	20.80	5
b	-0.0₃90	4	d'				40	19.76	5
			e' °C							
Ref. Index			d_c g/ml	0.28	2		Parachor [P]			
n_D 20°C	1.41356	2	v_c ml/g	3.57	2		20°C			
25	1.41091	2	t_c °C	277.	2		30			
30	1.40823	4	P_c mm	26600.	2		40			
"C"	0.7295	4					Sugd.	281.5	5
MR (Obs.)	32.489	2	PV/RT				Exp. L.l.%/wt.			
MR (Calc.)	32.326	5	25°C	0.9935	4		u.			
(nD-d/2)	1.03632	2	30 mm	1.0000	5		Dispersion	97.2	2
Dielectric	1.998	5	BP	0.9599	4		Flash Point °C	-12.	5
A 0 to	6.81724	2	t_e	0.9527	5		Fire Point		
B 140 °C	1219.474	2	t_c	0.27	2		M Spec.	Yes	1
C	221.946	2	ΔHc kcal/m	1029.89	2		Ultra V.		
			ΔHf	-41.14	2		X-Ray Dif.		
A* 0 to	1.21309	4	ΔFf	7.96	2		Infrared	Yes	2
B* 110 °C	1138.47	4	Viscosity				Solubility in +		
K			centistokes				Acetone	∞	
c			η °C				Carbon tet.	∞	
t_k to							Benzene	∞	
t_x °C							Ether	∞	
A' to							n-Heptane	∞	
B' °C							Ethanol	∞	
C'			B^v to				Water		
A'* to			A^v °C				Water in		
B'* °C			(B^v) to						
Ac 140 to	7.61456	4	(A^v) °C						
Bc t_c °C	1863.9	4	c_p liq. °K						
Cc	307.3	4							
Cryos. A°	0.00314	2	c_p vap.300°K	0.32755	2				
consts. B°			400	0.44356	2				
t_e °C	96.81	5	c_v vap.						

$T_R = 0.75 T_c$

+ grams/100 grams solvent

REFERENCES: 1-Dow 2-API 3-Lit. 4-Calc. from det. data 5-Calc. by formula

SOURCE:	API
PURIFICATION:	API
LITERATURE REFERENCES:	

TABLE XV. CYCLOPENTANES

No. 5

NAME	cis-1,2-Dimethylcyclopentane	STRUCTURAL FORMULA

$$H_2C\overset{HC-CH_3}{\underset{H_2C-CH_2}{\diagdown\;CHCH_3}}$$

Mole % Pur. 99.99	Ref. 2	Molecular Formula C_7H_{14}	Molecular Weight 98.182

		Ref.			Ref.				Ref.
F.P. °C	-53.896	2	dt/dP			f	to		
F.P. 100%			°C/mm			g	°K		
			25°C	0.4355	4	h			
B.P. °C			BP	0.04603	2				
760 mm	99.532	2	t_e	0.0366	5	f'	to		
100	41.465	2	30 mm	0.6364	4	g'	°K		
30	16.00	4	ΔHm cal/g			h'			
10	-3.26	4							
1	-34.9	5	ΔHv cal/g			m	300 to	-0.0762	4
			25°C	87.07	2	n	600 °K	0.0015	4
Pressure			30 mm	88.66	5	o		-0.0_649	4
mm 25°C	47.242	4	BP	77.16	2				
t_e	1020.	5		75.70	5	m'	700 to	0.0234	4
			t_e (d, e)	75.69	5	n'	1000 °K	0.0013	4
Density			ΔHv/T_e	19.39	5	o'		-0.0_646	4
g/ml 20°C	0.77262	2				Surface tension			
d_4^t 25	0.76807	2	d 10 to	90.86	5	dynes/cm. 20°C		24.05	5
30	0.76351	4	e 110 °C	0.1377	5	ɣ	30	22.93	5
a	0.79080	4	d' to				40	21.83	5
b	-0.0_390	4	e' °C						
Ref. Index			d_c g/ml	0.27	2	Parachor [P]			
n_D 20°C	1.42217	2	v_c ml/g	3.70	2	20°C			
25	1.41963	2	t_c °C	292.	2	30			
30	1.41691	4	P_c mm	25840.	2	40			
"C"	0.7264	4				Sugd.		281.5	5
MR (Obs.)	32.304	2	PV/RT			Exp. L.1.%/wt.			
MR (Calc.)	32.326	2	25°C	0.9957	4	u.			
(nD-d/2)	1.03586	2	30 mm	1.0000	5	Dispersion		97.3	2
Dielectric	2.023	5	BP	0.9646	4	Flash Point °C		-4.0	5
A 10 to	6.85008	2	t_e	0.9566	5	Fire Point			
B 150 °C	1269.140	2	t_c	0.27	2				
C	220.209	2	ΔHc kcal/m	1031.98	2	M. Spec.		Yes	1
A* 10 to	1.22418	4	ΔHf	-39.52	2	Ultra V.			
B* 120 °C	1183.67	4	ΔFf	9.29	2	X-Ray Dif.			
K			Viscosity			Infrared		Yes	2
c			centistokes			Solubility in +			
t_k to			η °C			Acetone		∞	
t_x °C						Carbon tet.		∞	
A' to						Benzene		∞	
B' °C						Ether		∞	
C'						n-Heptane		∞	
			B^v to			Ethanol		∞	
A'* to			A^v °C			Water			
B'* °C			(B^v) to			Water in			
Ac 150 to	7.44124	4	(A^v) °C						
Bc t_c °C	1745.6	4	c_p liq. °K						
Cc	284.3	4							
Cryos. A°	0.00415	2	c_p vap.300°K	0.32939	2				
consts. B°			400	0.44479	2				
t_e °C	110.18	5	c_v vap.						

$T_R = 0.75 T_c$ + grams/100 grams solvent

REFERENCES: 1-Dow 2-API 3-Lit. 4-Calc. from det. data 5-Calc. by formula

SOURCE: API

PURIFICATION: API

LITERATURE REFERENCES:

No. 6

NAME	trans-1, 2-Dimethylcyclopentane		STRUCTURAL FORMULA

$$H_2C \begin{matrix} HC-CH_3 \\ CHCH_3 \end{matrix}$$
$$H_2C-CH_2$$

Mole % Pur. 99.97	Ref. 2	Molecular Formula C_7H_{14}	Molecular Weight 98.182

		Ref.				Ref.					Ref.
F.P. °C	-117.58	2	dt/dP				f		to		
F.P. 100%			°C/mm				g		°K		
B.P. °C			25°C	0.3321	4		h				
760 mm	91.869	2	BP	0.04521	2						
100	34.856	2	t_e	0.0367	5		f'		to		
30	9.86	2	30 mm	0.6245	4		g'		°K		
10	-9.0	2	ΔHm cal/g				h'				
1	-40.1	4					m		300 to	-0.0720	4
Pressure			ΔHv cal/g				n		600 °K	0.0015	4
mm 25°C	64.039	4	25°C	84.12	2		o			-0.0_648	4
t_e	994.	5	30 mm	86.55	5						
Density			BP	75.12	2		m'		700 to	0.0530	4
g/ml 20°C	0.75144	2	t_e	73.80	5		n'		1000 °K	0.0012	4
d_4^t 25	0.74686	2	t_e (d,e)	73.79	5		o'			-0.0_642	4
30	0.74227	4	ΔHv/T_e	19.34	5		Surface tension				
a	0.76975	4	d	10 to	87.93	5	dynes/cm. 20°C			21.51	5
b	-0.0_390	4	e	100 °C	0.1394	5	ɣ		30	20.47	5
Ref. Index			d'	to					40	19.44	5
n_D 20°C	1.41200	2	e'	°C			Parachor [P]				
25	1.40941	2	d_c g/ml		0.27	2			20°C		
30	1.40667	4	v_c ml/g		3.70	2			30		
"C"	0.7298		t_c °C		282.	2			40		
MR (Obs.)	32.511	2	P_c mm		25840.	2			Sugd.	281.5	5
MR (Calc.)	32.326	5	PV/RT				Exp. L.l.%/wt.				
(nD-d/2)	1.03628	2	25°C	0.9944	4		u.				
Dielectric	1.994	5	30 mm	1.0000	5		Dispersion			96.4	2
A	0 to	6.84422	2	BP	0.9616	4	Flash Point °C			-10.0	5
B	145 °C	1242.748	2	t_e	0.9541	5	Fire Point				
C		221.686	2	t_c	0.27	2	M Spec.			Yes	1
A*	0 to	1.23203	4	ΔHc kcal/m	1030.27	2	Ultra V.				
B*	110 °C	1159.99	4	ΔHf	-40.94	2	X-Ray Dif.				
K			ΔFf	7.70	2		Infrared			Yes	2
c			Viscosity				Solubility in	+			
t_k	to		centistokes				Acetone			∞	
t_x	°C		η	°C			Carbon tet.			∞	
A'	to						Benzene			∞	
B'	°C						Ether			∞	
C'							n-Heptane			∞	
A'*	to		B^v	to			Ethanol			∞	
B'*	°C		A^v	°C			Water				
Ac	145 to	7.36128	4	(B^v)	to		Water in				
Bc	t_c °C	1648.7	4	(A^v)	°C						
Cc		277.1	4	c_p liq. °K							
Cryos. A°	0.03202	2	c_p vap.300°K	0.33041	2						
consts. B°	0.003	2	400	0.44519	2						
t_e °C	101.38	5	c_v vap.								

T_R = 0.75 T_c	+ grams/100 grams solvent
REFERENCES: 1-Dow 2-API 3-Lit. 4-Calc. from det. data 5-Calc. by formula	
SOURCE:	API
PURIFICATION:	API
LITERATURE REFERENCES:	

TABLE XV. CYCLOPENTANES

NAME	cis-1,3-Dimethylcyclopentane	STRUCTURAL FORMULA

STRUCTURAL FORMULA

$$H_2C \overset{CHCH_3}{\underset{H_2C-CHCH_3}{\diagup \diagdown} CH_2}$$

Mole % Pur.	Ref.	Molecular Formula C_7H_{14}	Molecular Weight 98.182

		Ref.			Ref.					Ref.
F.P. °C	-133.975	2	dt/dP			f		to		
F.P. 100%			°C/mm			g		°K		
			25°C	0.3298	4	h				
B.P. °C			BP	0.04525	2					
760 mm	91.725	2	t_e	0.0367	5	f'		to		
100	34.679	2	30 mm	0.6246	4	g'		°K		
30	9.68	4	ΔHm cal/g			h'				
10	-9.2	4				m		300 to	-0.0720	4
1	-40.3	5	ΔHv cal/g			n		600 °K	0.0015	4
Pressure			25°C	84.01	2	o			-0.0₆48	4
mm 25°C	64.58	4	30 mm	86.44	5					
t_e	994.	5	BP	74.97	2	m'		700 to	0.0530	4
			t_e	73.65	5	n'		1000 °K	0.0012	4
Density			t_e (d, e)	73.64	5	o'			-0.0₆42	4
g/ml 20°C	0.74880	2	ΔHv/T_e	19.31	5	Surface tension				
d_4^t 25	0.74435	2				dynes/cm. 20°C			21.21	5
30	0.73989	4	d 10 to	87.79	5	ɤ		30	20.20	5
a	0.76659	4	e 101 °C	0.1398	5			40	19.22	5
b	-0.0₃88	4	d' to							
Ref. Index			e' °C			Parachor [P]				
n_D 20°C	1.41074	2	d_c g/ml	0.27	2			20°C		
25	1.40813	2	v_c ml/g	3.70	2			30		
30	1.40555	4	t_c °C	282.	2			40		
"C"	0.7303	4	P_c mm	25840.	2			Sugd.	281.5	5
MR (Obs.)	32.537	2	PV/RT			Exp. L.1.%/wt.				
MR (Calc.)	32.326	5	25°C	0.9948	4	u.				
(nD-d/2)	1.03634	2	30 mm	1.0000	5	Dispersion			96.1	2
Dielectric	1.990	5	BP	0.9613	4	Flash Point °C			-10.0	5
A 10 to	6.83817	2	t_e	0.9538	5	Fire Point				
B 145 °C	1240.023	2	t_c	0.27	2	M. Spec.			Yes	1
C	221.621	2	ΔHc kcal/m	1031.00	2	Ultra V.				
A* 10 to	1.22680	4	ΔHf	-40.19	2	X-Ray Dif.				
B* 110 °C	1157.47	4	ΔFf	8.45	2	Infrared				
K			Viscosity			Solubility in +				
c			centistokes			Acetone			∞	
t_k to			η °C			Carbon tet.			∞	
t_x °C						Benzene			∞	
A' to						Ether			∞	
B' °C						n-Heptane			∞	
C'			B^v to			Ethanol			∞	
A'* to			A^v °C			Water				
B'* °C			(B^v) to			Water in				
Ac 145 to	7.21251	4	(A^v) °C							
Bc t_c °C	1528.2	4	c_p liq. °K							
Cc	261.8	4								
Cryos. A°	0.04515	2	c_p vap300°K	0.33041	2					
consts. B°			400	0.44519	2					
t_e °C	101.22	5	c_v vap.							
T_R = 0.75 T_c						+ grams/100 grams solvent				

REFERENCES: 1-Dow 2-API 3-Lit. 4-Calc. from det. data 5-Calc. by formula

SOURCE: API

PURIFICATION: API

LITERATURE REFERENCES:

No. 8

NAME	trans-1,3-Dimethylcyclopentane	STRUCTURAL FORMULA

Structural formula:

$$\begin{array}{ccc} & \text{CHCH}_3 & \\ H_2C & & CH_2 \\ H_2C & - & CHCH_3 \end{array}$$

Mole % Pur. 99.65	Ref. 2	Molecular Formula C_7H_{14}	Molecular Weight 98.182

		Ref.				Ref.					Ref.
F.P. °C	-133.702	2	dt/dP °C/mm			f		to			
F.P. 100%			25°C	0.3187	4	g		°K			
B.P. °C			BP	0.04518	2	h					
760 mm	90.773	2	t_e	0.0368	5	f'		to			
100	33.818	2	30 mm	0.6235	4	g'		°K			
30	8.862	4	ΔHm cal/g			h'					
10	-10.0	4	ΔHv cal/g			m	300 to	-0.0720	4
1	-41.	5	25°C	83.52	2	n	600 °K	0.0015	4
Pressure			30 mm	86.08	5	o		-0.0_648	4
mm 25°C	67.19	4	BP	74.68	2	m'	700 to	0.0530	4
t_e	990.6	5	t_e	73.38	5	n'	1000 °K	0.0012	4
Density			t_e (d, e)	73.38	5	o'		-0.0_642	4
g/ml 20°C	0.74479	2	ΔHv/T_e	19.30	5	Surface tension			
d_4^t 25	0.74025	2	d 0 to	87.32	5	dynes/cm. 20°C	20.76	5
30	0.73570	2	e 100 °C	0.1392	5	γ 30	19.75	5
a	0.76295	4	d' to			40	18.76	5
b	-0.0_389	4	e' °C			Parachor [P]		
Ref. Index			d_c g/ml	0.28	2	20°C		
n_D 20°C	1.40894	2	v_c ml/g	3.57	2	30		
25	1.40633	2	t_c °C	282.	2	40		
30	1.40369	4	P_c mm	26600.	2	Sugd.	281.5	5
"C"	0.7312	4	PV/RT			Exp. L.1.%/wt.		
MR (Obs.)	32.587	2	25°C	0.9941	4	u.		
MR (Calc.)	32.326	5	30 mm	1.0000	5	Dispersion	97.3	2
(nD-d/2)	1.03654	2	BP	0.9611	4	Flash Point °C	-11.0	5
Dielectric	1.985	5	t_e	0.9537	5	Fire Point		
A 0 to	6.83715	2	t_c	0.27	2	M Spec.	Yes	1
B 145 °C	1237.456	2	ΔHc kcal/m	1030.47	2	Ultra V.		
C	222.005	2	ΔHf	-40.68	2	X-Ray Dif.		
A* 0 to	1.22690	4	ΔFf	7.93	2	Infrared	Yes	2
B* 110 °C	1155.03	4	Viscosity			Solubility in +		
K			centistokes			Acetone	∞	
c			η °C			Carbon tet.	∞	
t_k to						Benzene	∞	
t_x °C						Ether	∞	
A' to						n-Heptane	∞	
B'			B^V to			Ethanol	∞	
C'			A^V °C			Water		
A'* to			(B^V) to			Water in		
B'* °C			(A^V) °C					
Ac 145 to	7.48224	4	c_p liq. °K					
Bc t_c °C	1753.6	4	c_p vap.300°K	0.33041	2			
Cc	291.5	4	400	0.44519	2			
Cryos. A°	0.04575	2	c_v vap.					
consts. B°								
t_e °C	100.14	5						

$T_R = 0.75\,T_c$ + grams/100 grams solvent

REFERENCES: 1-Dow   2-API   3-Lit.   4-Calc. from det. data   5-Calc. by formula

SOURCE: API

PURIFICATION: API

LITERATURE REFERENCES:

TABLE XV. CYCLOPENTANES   367

No. 9

NAME	n-Propylcyclopentane	STRUCTURAL FORMULA

STRUCTURAL FORMULA:

$$H_2C \overset{CHC_3H_7}{\underset{CH_2}{}}$$
$$H_2C - CH_2$$

Mole % Pur. 99.997	Ref. 2	Molecular Formula C_8H_{16}	Molecular Weight 112.208

		Ref.			Ref.			Ref.
F.P. °C	-117.340	2	dt/dP			f | ⌐ to ⌐		
F.P. 100%			°C/mm			g | | °K		
			25°C	1.4496	5	h |		
B.P. °C			BP	0.04888	2			
760 mm	130.949	2	t_e	0.0367	5	f' | to		
100	69.143	2	30 mm	0.6805	4	g' | °K		
30	41.94	4	ΔHm cal/g			h' |		
10	21.23	5				m | 300 to	-0.1994	4
1	-13.3	5	ΔHv cal/g			n | 600 °K	0.0022	4
Pressure			25°C	87.75	5	o |	-0.0₅14	4
mm 25°C	12.379	5	30 mm	86.15	5			
t_e	1099.	5	BP	74.01	5	m' | 700 to	0.0290	4
Density			t_e	72.13	5	n' | 1000 °K	0.0013	4
g/ml 20°C	0.77633	2	t_e (d, e)	72.06	5	o' |	-0.0₆43	4
d_4^t 25	0.77229	2	ΔHv/T_e	19.34	5	Surface tension		
30	0.76825	4	d | 40 to	91.88	5	dynes/cm. 20°C	24.17	5
a	0.79248	4	e | 145 °C	0.1364	5	ɣ 30	23.17	5
b	-0.0₃805	4	d' | 20 to	90.12	5	40	22.20	5
Ref. Index			e' | 40 °C	0.0945	5	Parachor [P]		
n_D 20°C	1.42626	2	d_c g/ml	0.269	5	20°C		
25	1.42389	2	v_c ml/g	3.72	5	30		
30	1.42156	4	t_c °C	317.1	5	40		
"C"	0.7295	4	P_c mm	21023.	5	Sugd.	320.5	5
MR (Obs.)	37.052	2	PV/RT			Exp. L. l. %/wt.		
MR (Calc.)	36.944	5	25°C	1.0000	5	u.		
(nD-d/2)	1.03810	2	30 mm	1.0000	5	Dispersion	95.6	2
Dielectric	2.034	5	BP	0.9553	5	Flash Point °C	19.	5
A | 40 to	6.90392	2	t_e	0.9444	5	Fire Point		
B | 170 °C	1384.386	2	t_c	0.265	5	M. Spec.	Yes	1
C	213.159	2	ΔHc kcal/m	1179.40	2	Ultra V.		
A* | 40 to	1.31959	5	ΔHf	-45.21	2	X-Ray Dif.		
B* | 155 °C	1297.41	5	ΔFf	10.12	2	Infrared	Yes	2
K			Viscosity			Solubility in ⁺		
c			centistokes			Acetone	∞	
t_k ⌐ to			η -20 °C	1.53	2	Carbon tet.	∞	
t_x | °C			0	1.133	2	Benzene	∞	
A' | 20 to	7.24581	5	20	0.878	2	Ether	∞	
B' | 40 °C	1564.31	5	40	0.711	2	n-Heptane	∞	
C'	229.2	5	B^v | -30 to	447.66	4	Ethanol	∞	
A'* 25 to	1.64286	-5	A^v | 30 °C	Σ.41669	4	Water		
B'* 40 °C	1406.8	5	(B^v)| 30 to	375.76	4	Water in		
Ac | 170 to	7.3143	5	(A^v)| 90 °C	Σ.65214	4	Viscosity		
Bc | t_c °C	1716.3	5	c_p liq. °K			centistokes		
Cc	256.6	5				60°C	0.597	2
Cryos. A°			c_p vap.300°K	0.33188	2	80	0.52	2
consts. B°			400	0.45300	2			
t_e °C	145.23	5	c_v vap.					
T_R = 0.75 T_c						⁺ grams/100 grams solvent		

REFERENCES: 1-Dow 2-API 3-Lit. 4-Calc. from det. data 5-Calc. by formula

SOURCE: API

PURIFICATION: API

LITERATURE REFERENCES:

No. 10

NAME	Isopropylcyclopentane					STRUCTURAL FORMULA

STRUCTURAL FORMULA

H_2C—CH-$CH(CH_3)_2$ CH_2
H_2C—CH_2

Mole % Pur.	Ref.	Molecular Formula	C_8H_{16}	Molecular Weight 112.208	

		Ref.			Ref.				Ref.
F.P. °C	-111.375	2	dt/dP			f		to	
F.P. 100%			°C/mm			g		°K	
B.P. °C			25°C	1.1536	5	h			
760 mm	126.419	2	BP	0.04913	2				
100	64.338	2	t_e	0.0367	5	f'		to	
30	37.05	4	30 mm	0.6825	4	g'		°K	
10	16.3	5	ΔHm cal/g			h'			
1	-18.4	5				m		to	
Pressure			ΔHv cal/g			n		°K	
mm 25°C	16.206	4	25°C	84.22	5	o			
t_e	1105.	5	30 mm	83.25	5				
Density			BP	73.00	5	m'		to	
g/ml 20°C	0.77653	2	t_e	71.29	5	n'		°K	
d_4^t 25	0.77259	2	t_e (d, e)	71.33	5	o'			
30	0.76864	4	ΔHv/T_e	19.31	5	Surface tension			
a	0.79228	4	d | 40 to	87.50	5	dynes/cm. 20°C	24.19	5
b	-0.0₃784	4	e | 140 °C	0.1147	5	ɣ	30	23.22	5
Ref. Index			d' | 25 to	86.24	5		40	22.27	5
n_D 20°C	1.42582	2	e' | 40 °C	0.0805	5	Parachor [P]		
25	1.42350	2	d_c g/ml			20°C		
30	1.42124	4	v_c ml/g			30		
"C"	0.7286	4	t_c °C	312.1	5	40		
MR (Obs.)	37.011	2	P_c mm	20568.	5	Sugd.	320.5	5
MR (Calc.)	36.944	5	PV/RT			Exp. L.1.%/wt.		
(nD-d/2)	1.03756	2	25°C	1.0000	5	u.		
Dielectric	2.033	5	30 mm	1.0000	5	Dispersion	95.5	2
A | 40 to	6.88622	2	BP	0.9688	4	Flash Point °C		
B |165 °C	1379.415	2	t_e	0.9590	5	Fire Point		
C	217.969	2	t_c			M Spec.		
A* | 40 to	1.27908	5	ΔHc kcal/m			Ultra V.		
B* |150 °C	1284.92	5	ΔHf			X-Ray Dif.		
K			ΔFf			Infrared		
c			Viscosity			Solubility in +		
t_k | to			centistokes			Acetone	∞	
t_x | °C			η °C			Carbon tet.	∞	
A' | 10 to	7.22699	5				Benzene	∞	
B' | 40 °C	1558.70	5				Ether	∞	
C'	234.0	5				n-Heptane	∞	
A'* 15 to	1.62692	5	B^V | to			Ethanol	∞	
B'* 40 °C	1460.16	5	A^V | °C			Water		
Ac |165 to	7.30422	5	(B^V) | to			Water in		
Bc | t_c °C	1718.9	5	(A^V) | °C					
Cc	262.6	5	c_p liq. °K					
Cryos. A°			c_p vap. °K					
consts. B°								
t_e °C	140.99	5	c_v vap.					

T_R = 0.75 T_c + grams/100 grams solvent

REFERENCES:	1-Dow	2-API	3-Lit.	4-Calc. from det. data	5-Calc. by formula
SOURCE:	API				
PURIFICATION:	API				
LITERATURE REFERENCES:					

TABLE XV. CYCLOPENTANES

No. 11

NAME	1-Ethyl-1-methylcyclopentane	STRUCTURAL FORMULA

Structural formula (drawn):
$$H_2C \underset{H_2C \,-\, CH_2}{\overset{CH_2}{\underset{\displaystyle }{\overset{\displaystyle }{C}}}} \overset{CH_3}{\underset{C_2H_5}{<}}$$

Mole % Pur. 99.91	Ref. 2	Molecular Formula C_8H_{16}	Molecular Weight 112.208

		Ref.			Ref.				Ref.
F.P. °C	-143.800	2	dt/dP			f	to		
F.P. 100%			°C/mm			g	°K		
B.P. °C			25°C	0.9602	5	h			
760 mm	121.522	2	BP	0.04863	2				
100	60.116	2	t_e	0.0366	5	f'	to		
30	33.15	4	30 mm	0.6742	4	g'	°K		
10	12.63	5	ΔHm cal/g			h'			
1	-21.6	5	ΔHv cal/g			m	to		
Pressure			25°C	82.82	5	n	°K		
mm 25°C	19.80	5	30 mm	82.17	5	o			
t_e	1094.	5	BP	72.12	5	m'	to		
Density			t_e	70.48	5	n'	°K		
g/ml 20°C	0.78093	2	t_e (d, e)	70.53	5	o'			
d_4^t 25	0.77670	2	ΔHv/T_e	19.35	5	Surface tension			
30	0.77246	4	d 35 to	85.94	5	dynes/cm. 20°C	24.74	5
a	0.79784	4	e 135 °C	0.1137	5	ɣ 30	23.68	5
b	-0.0₃841	4	d' 15 to	84.82	5	40	22.65	5
Ref. Index			e' 35 °C	0.0800	5	Parachor [P]		
n_D 20°C	1.42718	2	d_c g/ml	0.269	5	20°C		
25	1.42476	2	v_c ml/g	3.717	5	30		
30	1.42239	4	t_c °C	304.7	5	40		
"C"	0.7266	4	P_c mm	20351.	5	Sugd.	320.5	5
MR (Obs.)	36.904	2	PV/RT			Exp. L.1.%/wt.		
MR (Calc.)	36.944	5	25°C	1.0000	5	u.		
(nD-d/2)	1.03672	2	30 mm	1.0000	5	Dispersion	95.8	2
Dielectric	2.037	5	BP	0.9710	4	Flash Point °C		
A 35 to	6.87148	2	t_e	0.9617	5	Fire Point		
B 160 °C	1355.287	2	t_c	0.228	5	M. Spec.		
C	218.092	2	ΔHc kcal/m			Ultra V.		
A* 35 to	1.26648	5	ΔHf			X-Ray Dif.		
B* 145 °C	1261.35	5	ΔFf			Infrared		
K			Viscosity			Solubility in +		
c			centistokes			Acetone	∞	
t_k to			η °C			Carbon tet.	∞	
t_x °C						Benzene	∞	
A' 15 to	7.21132	5				Ether	∞	
B' 35 °C	1531.43	5				n-Heptane	∞	
C'	233.92	5	B^v to			Ethanol	∞	
A'* 20 to	1.60819	5	A^v °C			Water		
B'* 35 °C	1432.08	5	(B^v) to			Water in		
Ac 160 to	7.2886	5	(A^v) °C					
Bc t_c °C	1689.3	5	c_p liq. °K					
Cc	262.1	5						
Cryos. A°	0.0444	2	c_p vap. °K					
consts. B°								
t_e °C	135.53	5	c_v vap.					

$T_R = 0.75 T_c$ + grams/100 grams solvent

REFERENCES: 1-Dow 2-API 3-Lit. 4-Calc. from det. data 5-Calc. by formula

SOURCE: API

PURIFICATION: API

LITERATURE REFERENCES:

No. 12

NAME	cis-1-Ethyl-2-methylcyclopentane		STRUCTURAL FORMULA
Mole % Pur. 99.97	Ref. 2	Molecular Formula C_8H_{16}	Molecular Weight 112.208

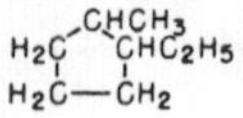

		Ref.
F.P. °C	-105.95	2
F.P. 100%		
B.P. °C 760 mm	128.050	2
100	66.116	2
30	38.86	4
10	18.10	5
1	-16.6	5
Pressure mm 25°C	14.70	4
t_e	1100.	5
Density g/ml 20°C	0.78522	2
d_4^t 25	0.78113	2
30	0.77704	4
a	0.80157	4
b	-0.0_3814	4
Ref. Index n_D 20°C	1.42933	2
25	1.42695	2
30	1.42459	4
"C"	0.7261	4
MR (Obs.)	36.864	2
MR (Calc.)	36.944	5
(nD-d/2)	1.03672	2
Dielectric	2.043	5
A 40 to	6.90561	2
B 170 °C	1388.307	2
C	216.888	2
A* 40 to	1.30956	5
B* 155 °C	1297.0	5
K		
c		
t_k to		
t_x °C		
A' 10 to	7.24761	5
B' 40 °C	1568.74	5
C'	233.0	5
A'* 15 to	1.64397	5
B'* 40 °C	1469.65	5
Ac 170 to	7.32203	5
Bc t_c °C	1727.1	5
Cc	261.3	5
Cryos. consts. A° B°		
t_e °C	142.39	5

		Ref.
dt/dP °C/mm 25°C	1.2539	5
BP	0.04897	2
t_e	0.0367	5
30 mm	0.6820	4
ΔHm cal/g		
ΔHv cal/g 25°C	85.45	5
30 mm	84.29	5
BP	73.31	5
t_e	71.55	5
t_e (d, e)	71.54	5
$\Delta Hv/T_e$	19.32	5
d 40 to	89.07	5
e 145 °C	0.1231	5
d' 20 to	87.54	5
e' 40 °C	0.0837	5
d_c g/ml	0.269	5
v_c ml/g	3.717	5
t_c °C	314.7	5
P_c mm	21054.	5
PV/RT 25°C	1.0000	5
30 mm	1.0000	5
BP	0.9619	4
t_e	0.9515	5
t_c	0.237	5
ΔHc kcal/m		
ΔHf		
ΔFf		
Viscosity centistokes η °C		
B^v to		
A^v °C		
(B^v) to		
(A^v) °C		
c_p liq. °K		
c_p vap. °K		
c_v vap.		

		Ref.
f g h to °K		
f' g' h' to °K		
m n o to °K		
m' n' o' to °K		
Surface tension dynes/cm. γ 20°C	25.29	5
30	24.25	5
40	23.23	5
Parachor [P] 20°C		
30		
40		
Sugd.	320.5	5
Exp. L.1.%/wt. u.		
Dispersion	94.6	2
Flash Point °C		
Fire Point		
M Spec.		
Ultra V.		
X-Ray Dif.		
Infrared		
Solubility in +		
Acetone	∞	
Carbon tet.	∞	
Benzene	∞	
Ether	∞	
n-Heptane	∞	
Ethanol	∞	
Water		
Water in		

$T_R = 0.75\ T_c$

+ grams/100 grams solvent

REFERENCES: 1-Dow 2-API 3-Lit. 4-Calc. from det. data 5-Calc. by formula

SOURCE: API

PURIFICATION: API

LITERATURE REFERENCES:

TABLE XV. CYCLOPENTANES

NAME	trans-1-Ethyl-2-methylcyclopentane	STRUCTURAL FORMULA

STRUCTURAL FORMULA:

$$\begin{array}{c} \text{CHCH}_3 \\ \text{H}_2\text{C}^{\diagup}\quad{}^{\diagdown}\text{CHC}_2\text{H}_5 \\ \text{H}_2\text{C}\!-\!\text{C H}_2 \end{array}$$

Mole % Pur.	Ref.	Molecular Formula C_8H_{16}	Molecular Weight 112.208

		Ref.			Ref.				Ref.
F.P. °C			dt/dP			f	to		
F.P. 100%			°C/mm			g	°K		
B.P. °C			25°C	0.9631	5	h			
760 mm	121.2	2	BP	0.0483	4				
100	60.1	2	t_e	0.0366	5	f'	to		
30	33.3	4	30 mm	0.6714	4	g'	°K		
10	12.8	5	ΔHm cal/g			h'			
1	-21.2	5	ΔHv cal/g			m	to		
Pressure			25°C	83.26	5	n	°K		
mm 25°C	19.63	5	30 mm	82.59	5	o			
t_e	1086.	5	BP	72.05	5	m'	to		
Density			t_e	70.41	5	n'	°K		
g/ml 20°C	0.7690	2	t_e (d, e)	70.42	5	o'			
d_4^t 25	0.7649	2	ΔHv/T_e	19.36	5	Surface tension			
30	0.7608	4	d 35 to	86.57	5	dynes/cm. 20°C	23.27	5
a	0.7854	4	e 135 °C	0.1198	5	ɣ 30	22.28	5
b	-0.0₃815	4	d' 15 to	85.31	5	40	21.32	5
Ref. Index			e' 35 °C	0.0818	5	Parachor [P]			
n_D 20°C	1.4219	2	d_c g/ml	0.263	5	20°C			
25	1.4195	2	v_c ml/g	3.802	5	30			
30	1.4171	4	t_c °C	302.4	5	40			
"C"	0.7293	4	P_c mm	20207.	5	Sugd.	320.5	5
MR (Obs.)	37.07	2	PV/RT			Exp. L.1.%/wt.			
MR (Calc.)	36.944	5	25°C	1.0000	5	u.			
(nD-d/2)	1.0374	2	30 mm	1.0000	5	Dispersion	95.	2
Dielectric	2.022	5	BP	0.9660	4	Flash Point °C			
A 35 to	6.8844	2	t_e	0.9565	5	Fire Point			
B 160 °C	1356.0	2	t_c	0.238	5	M. Spec.			
C	217.5	2	ΔHc kcal/m			Ultra V.			
A* 35 to	1.2889	5	ΔHf			X-Ray Dif.			
B* 145 °C	1264.7	5	ΔFf			Infrared			
K			Viscosity			Solubility in +			
c			centistokes			Acetone	∞		
t_k to			η °C			Carbon tet.	∞		
t_x °C						Benzene	∞		
A' 15 to	7.2251	5				Ether	∞		
B' 35 °C	1532.2	5				n-Heptane	∞		
C'	233.3	5	B^v to			Ethanol	∞		
A'* 20 to	1.6227	5	A^v °C			Water			
B'* 35 °C	1433.3	5	(B^v) to			Water in			
Ac 160 to	7.2999	5	(A^v) °C						
Bc t_c °C	1686.4	5	c_p liq. °K						
Cc	260.8	5							
Cryos. A°			c_p vap. °K						
consts. B°									
t_e °C	134.83	5	c_v vap.						

$T_R = 0.75\ T_c$ $\qquad$ + grams/100 grams solvent

REFERENCES: 1-Dow 2-API 3-Lit. 4-Calc. from det. data 5-Calc. by formula
SOURCE: API
PURIFICATION: API
LITERATURE REFERENCES:

No. 14

NAME	cis-1-Ethyl-3-methylcyclopentane		STRUCTURAL FORMULA

Structural formula:

$$H_2C \overset{CH-CH_3}{\underset{CHC_2H_5}{\overset{CH_2}{\big|}}}$$

Mole % Pur.	Ref.	Molecular Formula C_8H_{16}	Molecular Weight 112.208

		Ref.			Ref.			Ref.
F.P. °C			dt/dP			f $\mid$ to		
F.P. 100%			°C/mm			g $\mid$ °K		
B.P. °C			25°C	0.9734	5	h		
760 mm	121.4	2	BP	0.0483	4			
100	60.3	2	t_e	0.0366	5	f' $\mid$ to		
30	33.5	4	30 mm	0.6710	4	g' $\mid$ °K		
10	13.1	5	ΔHm cal/g			h'		
1	-21.	5						
Pressure			ΔHv cal/g			m $\mid$ to		
mm 25°C	19.38	4	25°C	83.47	5	n $\mid$ °K		
t_e	1085.	5	30 mm	82.76	5	o		
Density			BP	72.05	5			
g/ml 20°C	0.7724	2	t_e	70.39	5	m' $\mid$ to		
d_4^t 25	0.7681	2	t_e (d, e)	70.39	5	n' $\mid$ °K		
30	0.7638	4	ΔHv/T_e	19.35	5	o'		
a	0.7896	4	d $\mid$ 35 to	86.85	5	Surface tension		
b	-0.03855	4	e $\mid$ 135 °C	0.1219	5	dynes/cm. 20°C	23.68	5
			d' $\mid$ 15 to	85.54	5	ɣ 30	22.64	5
Ref. Index			e' $\mid$ 35 °C	0.0830	5	40	21.62	5
n_D 20°C	1.4203	2	d_c g/ml	0.265	5	Parachor [P]		
25	1.4179	2	v_c ml/g	3.773	5	20°C		
30	1.4151	4	t_c °C	302.5	5	30		
"C"	0.7231	4	P_c mm	20194.	5	40		
MR (Obs.)	36.79	2	PV/RT			Sugd.	320.5	5
MR (Calc.)	36.944	5	25°C	1.0000	5	Exp. L.1.%/wt.		
(nD-d/2)	1.0341	2	30 mm	1.0000	5	u.		
Dielectric	2.017	5	BP	0.9646	4	Dispersion	95.	2
A $\mid$ 35 to	6.8838	2	t_e	0.9550	5	Flash Point °C		
B $\mid$ 160 °C	1355.0	2	t_c	0.233	5	Fire Point		
C	217.1	2	ΔHc kcal/m			M Spec.		
A* $\mid$ 35 to	1.2909	5	ΔHf			Ultra V.		
B* $\mid$ 145 °C	1264.5	5	ΔFf			X-Ray Dif.		
K			Viscosity			Infrared		
c			centistokes			Solubility in +		
t_k $\mid$ to			η °C			Acetone	∞	
t_x $\mid$ °C						Carbon tet.	∞	
A' $\mid$ 10 to	7.2244	5				Benzene	∞	
B' $\mid$ 35 °C	1531.1	5				Ether	∞	
C'	232.9	5	B^v $\mid$ to			n-Heptane	∞	
A'* 15 to	1.6225	5	A^v $\mid$ °C			Ethanol	∞	
B'* 35 °C	1432.5	5	(B^V) $\mid$ to			Water		
Ac $\mid$ 160 to	7.2986	5	(A^V) $\mid$ °C			Water in		
Bc $\mid$ t_c °C	1684.5	5	c_p liq. °K					
Cc	260.3	5						
Cryos. A°			c_p vap. °K					
consts. B°								
t_e °C	134.98	5	c_v vap.					

$T_R = 0.75 T_c$

+ grams/100 grams solvent

REFERENCES: 1-Dow 2-API 3-Lit. 4-Calc. from det. data 5-Calc. by formula

SOURCE: API

PURIFICATION: API

LITERATURE REFERENCES:

TABLE XV. CYCLOPENTANES

No. 15

NAME	trans-1-Ethyl-3-methylcyclopentane		STRUCTURAL FORMULA

Structural formula:
$$H_2C \overset{CHCH_3}{\underset{CHCH_2C_2H_5}{\overset{CH_2}{|}}}$$
H_2C — CHC_2H_5

Mole % Pur.	Ref.	Molecular Formula	C_8H_{16}	Molecular Weight 112.208		

		Ref.				Ref.				Ref.
F.P. °C	-108.	2	dt/dP			f		to		
F.P. 100%			°C/mm			g		°K		
			25°C	0.9434	5	h				
B.P. °C			BP	0.0484	4					
760 mm	120.8	2	t_e	0.0366	5	f'		to		
100	59.7	2				g'		°K		
30	32.8	4	30 mm	0.6714	4	h'				
10	12.4	5	ΔHm cal/g							
1	-22.	5				m		to		
			ΔHv cal/g			n		°K		
Pressure			25°C	82.98	5	o				
mm 25°C	20.11	5	30 mm	82.34	5					
t_e	1088.	5	BP	72.00	5	m'		to		
Density			t_e	70.35	5	n'		°K		
g/ml 20°C	0.7619	2	t_e (d,e)	70.39	5	o'				
d_4^t 25	0.7577	2	ΔHv/T_e	19.36	5	Surface tension				
30	0.7535	2	d	35 to	86.19	5	dynes/cm. 20°C	22.42	5
a	0.7787	4	e	135 °C	0.1175	5	γ 30	21.44	5
b	-0.0₃835	4	d'	15 to	85.02	5	40	20.48	5
Ref. Index			e'	35 °C	0.0816	5			
n_D 20°C	1.4186	2	d_c g/ml	0.263	5	Parachor [P]		
25	1.4162	5	v_c ml/g	3.802	5	20°C		
30	1.4137	4	t_c °C	300.6	5	30		
"C"	0.7307	4	P_c mm	19781.	5	40		
MR (Obs.)	37.16	2	PV/RT			Sugd.	320.5	5
MR (Calc.)	36.944	5	25°C	1.0000	5	Exp. L.1.%/wt.		
(nD-d/2)	1.0376	2	30 mm	1.0000	5	u.		
Dielectric	2.012	5	BP	0.9686	4	Dispersion	95.	2
A 35 to	6.8743	2	t_e	0.9592	5	Flash Point °C		
B 155 °C	1351.0	2	t_c	0.231	5	Fire Point		
C	217.5	2	ΔHc kcal/m			M. Spec.		
A* 35 to	1.2749	5	ΔHf			Ultra V.		
B* 145 °C	1258.7	5	ΔFf			X-Ray Dif.		
K			Viscosity			Infrared		
c			centistokes			Solubility in +		
t_k to			η °C			Acetone	∞	
t_x °C						Carbon tet.	∞	
A' 10 to	7.21432	5				Benzene	∞	
B' 35 °C	1526.6	5				Ether	∞	
C'	233.3	5	B^v to			n-Heptane	∞	
A'* 15 to	1.61239	5	A^v °C			Ethanol	∞	
B'* 35 °C	1427.8	5	(B^v) to			Water		
Ac 155 to	7.2895	5	(A^v) °C			Water in		
Bc t_c °C	1680.0	5	c_p liq. °K					
Cc	260.6	5						
Cryos. A°			c_p vap. °K					
consts. B°								
t_e °C	134.54	5	c_v vap.					

$T_R = 0.75 T_c$ + grams/100 grams solvent

REFERENCES: 1-Dow 2-API 3-Lit. 4-Calc. from det. data 5-Calc. by formula

SOURCE: API

PURIFICATION: API

LITERATURE REFERENCES:

No. 16

| NAME | 1,1,2-Trimethylcyclopentane | STRUCTURAL FORMULA |

$$H_2C \overset{C-(CH_3)_2}{\underset{}{}} CHCH_3$$
$$H_2C-CH_2$$

| Mole % Pur. | Ref. | Molecular Formula | C_8H_{16} | Molecular Weight 112.208 |

		Ref.				Ref.				Ref.
F.P. °C	-21.64	2	dt/dP °C/mm				f	to		
F.P. 100%			25°C	0.7061	4		g	°K		
B.P. °C			BP	0.04818	2		h			
760 mm	113.729	2	t_e	0.0367	5		f'	to		
100	53.03	2	30 mm	0.6636	4		g'	°K		
30	26.46	4	ΔHm cal/g				h'			
10	6.38	4								
1	-26.6	5	ΔHv cal/g				m	to		
Pressure			25°C	80.03	5		n	°K		
mm 25°C	27.86	4	30 mm	79.88	5		o			
t_e	1078.	5	BP	70.34	5					
Density			t_e	68.82	5		m'	to		
g/ml 20°C	0.77252	2	t_e (d, e)	68.89	5		n'	°K		
d_4^t 25	0.76817	2	ΔHv/T_e	19.29	5		o'			
30	0.76380	4	d | 20 to	82.77	5		**Surface tension**			
a	0.78991	4	e | 130 °C	0.1093	5		dynes/cm. 20°C	23.69	5
b	-0.0₃86	4	d' | to				γ 30	22.63	5
Ref. Index			e' | °C				40	21.57	5
n_D 20°C	1.42298	2	d_c g/ml	0.265	5		**Parachor** [P]		
25	1.42051	2	v_c ml/g	3.773	5		20°C		
30	1.41792	2	t_c °C	292.18	5		30		
"C"	0.7278	4	P_c mm	19376.	5		40		
MR (Obs.)	36.986	2	**PV/RT**				Sugd.	320.5	5
MR (Calc.)	36.944	5	25°C	1.0000	5		**Exp. L.1.%/wt.**		
(nD-d/2)	1.03672	2	30 mm	1.0000	5		u.		
Dielectric	2.025	5	BP	0.9765	4		Dispersion	96.9	2
A | 20 to	6.82205	2	t_e	0.9680	5		**Flash Point °C**		
B |150 °C	1309.618	2	t_c	0.230	5		**Fire Point**		
C	218.557	2	ΔHc kcal/m				**M Spec.**		
A* | 20 to	1.21721	5	ΔHf				**Ultra V.**		
B* |140 °C	1215.70	5	ΔFf				**X-Ray Dif.**		
K			**Viscosity**				**Infrared**	Yes	2
c			centistokes				**Solubility in** +		
t_k | to			η °C				Acetone	∞	
t_x | °C							Carbon tet.	∞	
A' | to							Benzene	∞	
B' | °C							Ether	∞	
C'			B^v | to				n-Heptane	∞	
A'* to			A^v | °C				Ethanol	∞	
B'* °C			$(B^{\overline{v}})$ | to				Water		
Ac | 150 to	7.23621	5	(A^v) | °C				Water in		
Bc | t_c °C	1633.5	5	c_p liq. °K						
Cc	261.7	5							
Cryos. A°			c_p vap. °K						
consts. B°									
t_e °C	127.04	5	c_v vap.						

$T_R = 0.75\,T_c$ + grams/100 grams solvent

REFERENCES: 1-Dow 2-API 3-Lit. 4-Calc. from det. data 5-Calc. by formula

SOURCE: API

PURIFICATION: API

LITERATURE REFERENCES:

TABLE XV. CYCLOPENTANES 375

No. 17

NAME	1,1,3-Trimethylcyclopentane	STRUCTURAL FORMULA

$$H_2C \overset{C-(CH_3)_2}{\underset{CH_2}{|}}$$
$$H_2C-CHCH_3$$

Mole % Pur.		Ref.	Molecular Formula	C_8H_{16}	Molecular Weight	112.208

		Ref.			Ref.				Ref.
F.P. °C	-142.44	2	dt/dP			f	to		
F.P. 100%			°C/mm			g	°K		
B.P. °C			25°C	0.5137	4	h			
760 mm	104.893	2	BP	0.04724	2				
100	45.410	2	t_e	0.0365	5	f'	to		
30	19.39	4	30 mm	0.6496	4	g'	°K		
10	-0.26	4	ΔHm cal/g			h'			
1	-32.5	5	ΔHv cal/g			m	to		
Pressure			25°C	77.17	5	n	°K		
mm 25°C	39.73	4	30 mm	77.79	5	o			
t_e	1059.	5	BP	68.91	5				
Density			t_e	67.58	5	m'	to		
g/ml 20°C	0.74825	2	t_e (d, e)	67.62	5	n'	°K		
d_4^t 25	0.74392	2	ΔHv/T_e	19.42	5	o'			
30	0.73958	4	d 20 to	79.81	5	Surface tension			
a	0.76556	4	e 120 °C	0.1039	5	dynes/cm. 20°C	20.84	5
b	-0.0_3856	4	d' to			δ 30	19.88	5
Ref. Index			e' °C			40	18.95	5
n_D 20°C	1.41119	2	d_c g/ml	0.260	5	Parachor [P]		
25	1.40870	2	v_c ml/g	3.846	5	20°C		
30	1.40614	4	t_c °C	276.1	5	30		
"C"	0.7316	4	P_c mm	18455.	5	40		
MR (Obs.)	37.249	2	PV/RT			Sugd.	320.5	5
MR (Calc.)	36.944	5	25°C	0.9917	5	Exp. L.1.%/wt.		
(nD-d/2)	1.03707	2	30 mm	1.0000	5	u.		
Dielectric	1.991	5	BP	0.9826	5	Dispersion	98.6	2
A 20 to	6.80947	2	t_e	0.9751	5	Flash Point °C		
B 140 °C	1275.998	2	t_c	0.230	5	Fire Point		
C	219.899	2	ΔHc kcal/m			M. Spec.		
A* 20 to	1.2043	5	ΔHf			Ultra V.		
B* 130 °C	1181.7	5	ΔFf			X-Ray Dif.		
K			Viscosity			Infrared	Yes	2
c			centistokes			Solubility in +		
t_k to			η °C			Acetone	∞	
t_x °C						Carbon tet.	∞	
A' to						Benzene	∞	
B' °C						Ether	∞	
C'			B^v to			n-Heptane	∞	
A'* to			A^v °C			Ethanol	∞	
B'* °C			(B^v) to			Water		
Ac 140 to	7.22512	5	(A^v) °C			Water in		
Bc t_c °C	1591.6	5	c_p liq. °K					
Cc	261.8	5	c_p vap. °K					
Cryos. A° consts. B°			c_v vap.					
t_e °C	117.27	5						

$T_R = 0.75 T_c$

+ grams/100 grams solvent

REFERENCES: 1-Dow 2-API 3-Lit. 4-Calc. from det. data 5-Calc. by formula

SOURCE: API

PURIFICATION: API

LITERATURE REFERENCES:

No. 18

NAME	1, cis-2, cis-3-Trimethylcyclopentane		STRUCTURAL FORMULA

$$H_2C \underset{H_2C-CHCH_3}{\overset{CHCH_3}{\diagdown CHCH_3}}$$

Mole % Pur.		Ref.	Molecular Formula C_8H_{16}		Molecular Weight 112.208	

		Ref.				Ref.					Ref.
F.P. °C	-116.430	2	dt/dP °C/mm				f		to		
F.P. 100%			25°C		1.0064	5	g		°K		
B.P. °C			BP		0.0490	4	h				
760 mm	123.0	2	t_e		0.0367	5	f'		to		
100	61.2	2	30 mm		0.6769	4	g'		°K		
30	34.2	4	ΔHm cal/g				h'				
10	13.6	5	ΔHv cal/g								
1	-21.	5	25°C		83.14	5	m		to		
Pressure			30 mm		82.38	5	n		°K		
mm 25°C	18.82	5	BP		72.38	5	o				
t_e	1102.	5	t_e		70.71	5	m'		to		
Density			t_e (d, e)		70.76	5	n'		°K		
g/ml 20°C	0.7792	2	ΔHv/T_e		19.32	5	o'				
d_4^t 25	0.7751	2					Surface tension				
30	0.7710	4	d 35 to		86.23	5	dynes/cm. 20°C		24.53	5
a	0.7956	4	e 135 °C		0.1126	5	30		23.50	5
b	-0.0₃815	4	d' 15 to		85.21	5	40		22.50	5
Ref. Index			e' 35 °C		0.0828	5					
n_D 20°C	1.4262	2	d_c g/ml		0.265	5	Parachor [P]				
25	1.4238	2	v_c ml/g		3.773	5	20°C				
30	1.4214	4	t_c °C		307.4	5	30				
"C"	0.7267	4	P_c mm		20192.	5	40				
MR (Obs.)	36.91	2	PV/RT						Sugd.	320.5	5
MR (Calc.)	36.944	5	25°C		1.0000	5	Exp. L.1.%/wt.				
(nD-d/2)	1.0366	2	30 mm		1.0000	5	u.				
Dielectric	2.034	5	BP		0.9739	4	Dispersion		96.	2
A 35 to	6.8485	2	t_e		0.9647	5	Flash Point °C				
B 160 °C	1349.0	2	t_c		0.233	5	Fire Point				
C	217.0	2	ΔHc kcal/m				M Spec.				
A* 35 to	1.2378	5	ΔHf				Ultra V.				
B* 145 °C	1254.0	5	ΔFf				X-Ray Dif.				
K			Viscosity				Infrared				
c			centistokes				Solubility in +				
t_k to			η °C				Acetone		∞		
t_x °C							Carbon tet.		∞		
A' 10 to	7.1869	5					Benzene		∞		
B' 35 °C	1524.3	5					Ether		∞		
C'	232.8	5	B^v to				n-Heptane		∞		
A'* 15 to	1.5845	5	A^v °C				Ethanol		∞		
B'* 35 °C	1425.6	5	$(B^{\overline{v}})$ to				Water				
Ac 160 to	7.2644	5	$(A^{\overline{v}})$ °C				Water in				
Bc t_c °C	1682.9	5	c_p liq. °K								
Cc	261.3	5									
Cryos. A°			c_p vap. °K								
consts. B°											
t_e °C	137.42	5	c_v vap.								

T_R = 0.75 T_C			+ grams/100 grams solvent

REFERENCES: 1-Dow   2-API   3-Lit.   4-Calc. from det. data   5-Calc. by formula

SOURCE: API

PURIFICATION: API

LITERATURE REFERENCES:

TABLE XV. CYCLOPENTANES

377

No. 19

NAME	1, cis-2, trans-3-Trimethylcyclopentane	STRUCTURAL FORMULA

Structural formula:
$$H_2C \begin{array}{c} CHCH_3 \\ CHCH_3 \end{array}$$
$$H_2C-CHCH_3$$

Mole % Pur.	Ref.	Molecular Formula C_8H_{16}	Molecular Weight 112.208

		Ref.			Ref.			Ref.
F.P. °C	-112.	2	dt/dP			f	to	
F.P. 100%			°C/mm			g	°K	
			25°C	0.8224	5	h		
B.P. °C			BP	0.0483	4			
760 mm	117.5	2	t_e	0.0367	5	f'	to	
100	56.5	2	30 mm	0.6680	4	g'	°K	
30	29.8	4				h'		
10	9.5	5	ΔHm cal/g					
1	-24.	5				m	to	
			ΔHv cal/g			n	°K	
Pressure			25°C	81.53	5	o		
mm 25°C	23.48	4	30 mm	81.15	5			
t_e	1084.	5	BP	71.21	5	m'	to	
Density			t_e	69.62	5	n'	°K	
g/ml 20°C	0.7704	2	t_e (d, e)	69.67	5	o'		
d_4^t 25	0.7661	2	ΔHv/T_e	19.32	5	Surface tension		
30	0.7618	4	d 30 to	84.53	5	dynes/cm. 20°C	23.43	5
a	0.7876	4	e 130 °C	0.1133	5	30	22.40	5
b	-0.0385	4	d' 15 to	83.50	5	40	21.38	5
Ref. Index			e' 30 °C	0.0789	5			
n_D 20°C	1.4218	2	d_c g/ml	0.263	5	Parachor [P]		
25	1.4194	2	v_c ml/g	3.802	5	20°C		
30	1.4166	4	t_c °C	297.2	5	30		
"C"	0.7278	4	P_c mm	19664.	5	40		
MR (Obs.)	37.00	2				Sugd.	320.5	5
MR (Calc.)	36.944	5	PV/RT			Exp. L.1.%/wt.		
(nD-d/2)	1.0366	2	25°C	1.0000	5	u.		
Dielectric	2.022	5	30 mm	1.0000	5	Dispersion	96.	2
A 30 to	6.8480	2	BP	0.9726	5	Flash Point °C		
B 155 °C	1331.0	2	t_e	0.9635	5	Fire Point		
C	218.0	2	t_c			M. Spec.		
A* 30 to	1.2456	5	ΔHc kcal/m			Ultra V.		
B* 140 °C	1237.8	5	ΔHf			X-Ray Dif.		
K			ΔFf			Infrared		
c			Viscosity			Solubility in +		
t_k to			centistokes			Acetone	∞	
t_x °C			η °C			Carbon tet.	∞	
A' 10 to	7.1864	4				Benzene	∞	
B' 30 °C	1504.0	4				Ether	∞	
C'	233.6	4	B^v to			n-Heptane	∞	
A'* 15 to	1.5864	5	A^v °C			Ethanol	∞	
B'* 30 °C	1405.6	5	(B^v) to			Water		
Ac 155 to	7.2638	5	(A^v) °C			Water in		
Bc t_c °C	1658.8	5	c_p liq. °K					
Cc	261.4	5	c_p vap. °K					
Cryos. A° consts. B°								
t_e °C	131.1	5	c_v vap.					

$T_R = 0.75 T_c$

+ grams/100 grams solvent

REFERENCES: 1-Dow 2-API 3-Lit. 4-Calc. from det. data 5-Calc. by formula

SOURCE: API

PURIFICATION: API

LITERATURE REFERENCES:

No. 20

NAME	1, trans-2, cis-3-Trimethylcyclopentane	STRUCTURAL FORMULA

STRUCTURAL FORMULA:

$$H_2C \overset{CHCH_3}{\underset{CHCH_3}{\diagdown}}$$
$$H_2C—CHCH_3$$

Mole % Pur.	Ref.	Molecular Formula C_8H_{16}	Molecular Weight 112.208

		Ref.				Ref.				Ref.
F.P. °C	-112.705	2	dt/dP °C/mm				f | to			
F.P. 100%			25°C	0.6228	5		g | |__ °K			
			BP	0.0477	4		h |			
B.P. °C			t_e	0.0366	5		f' | to			
760 mm	110.2	2					g' | |__ °K			
100	50.0	2	30 mm	0.6581	4		h' |			
30	23.7	4	ΔHm cal/g							
10	3.8	5					m | to			
1	-29.	5	ΔHv cal/g				n | |__ °K			
			25°C	78.93	5		o |			
Pressure			30 mm	79.07	5					
mm 25°C	32.04	4	BP	69.87	5		m' | to			
t_e	1070.8	5	t_e	68.41	5		n' | |__ °K			
			t_e (d, e)	68.50	5		o' |			
Density			ΔHv/T_e	19.37	5					
g/ml 20°C	0.7535	2					Surface tension			
d_4^t 25	0.7492	2	d | 25 to	81.59	5		dynes/cm. 20°C	21.44	5
30	0.7449	4	e | 120 °C	0.1063	5		γ 30	20.47	5
a	0.7707	4	d' | to				40	19.52	5
b	-0.0₃852	4	e' | °C							
							Parachor [P]			
Ref. Index			d_c g/ml	0.260	5		20°C			
n_D 20°C	1.4138	2	v_c ml/g	3.846	5		30			
25	1.4114	2	t_c °C	284.4	5		40			
30	1.4088	4	P_c mm	18809.	5		Sugd. 320.5		5
"C"	0.7308	4	PV/RT							
MR (Obs.)	37.20	2	25°C	1.0000	5		Exp. L.1.%/wt.			
MR (Calc.)	36.944	5	30 mm	1.0000	5		u.			
(nD-d/2)	1.0370		BP	0.9792	5		Dispersion	96.	2
Dielectric	1.999	5	t_e	0.9711	5		Flash Point °C			
			t_c	0.230	5		Fire Point			
A | 25 to	6.8268	2								
B |145 °C	1301.0	2	ΔHc kcal/m				M Spec.			
C	219.5	2	ΔHf				Ultra V.			
			ΔFf				X-Ray Dif.			
A* | 25 to	1.2210	5					Infrared			
B* |135 °C	1206.6	5	Viscosity							
K			centistokes				Solubility in +			
c			η °C				Acetone	∞	
t_k | to							Carbon tet.	∞	
t_x | °C							Benzene	∞	
A' | to							Ether	∞	
B' | °C							n-Heptane	∞	
C' |__			B^v | to				Ethanol	∞	
			A^v | °C				Water		
A'* to			(B^v) | to				Water in		
B'* °C			(A^v) | °C						
Ac |145 to	7.2431	5							
Bc | t_c °C	1622.2	5	c_p liq. °K						
Cc |__	262.	5							
Cryos. A°			c_p vap. °K						
consts. B°									
t_e °C	123.13	5	c_v vap.						

$T_R = 0.75 T_c$

+ grams/100 grams solvent

REFERENCES: 1-Dow 2-API 3-Lit. 4-Calc. from det. data 5-Calc. by formula

SOURCE: API

PURIFICATION: API

LITERATURE REFERENCES:

TABLE XV. CYCLOPENTANES   379

No. 21

NAME	1, cis-2, cis-4-Trimethylcyclopentane		STRUCTURAL FORMULA

STRUCTURAL FORMULA:

$$H_2C \overset{CHCH_3}{\underset{}{}} CHCH_3$$
$$H_3CHC—CH_2$$

Mole % Pur.	Ref.	Molecular Formula C_8H_{16}	Molecular Weight 112.208

		Ref.			Ref.				Ref.
F.P. °C			dt/dP			f	to		
F.P. 100%			°C/mm			g	°K		
B.P. °C			25°C	0.8266	5	h			
760 mm	118.	2	BP	0.0486	4				
100	57.	2	t_e	0.0366	5	f'	to		
30	29.8	4	30 mm	0.6715	4	g'	°K		
10	9.4	5	ΔHm cal/g			h'			
1	-25.	5							
Pressure			ΔHv cal/g			m	to		
mm 25°C	23.49	5	25°C	81.10	5	n	°K		
t_e	1094.	5	30 mm	80.74	5	o			
			BP	71.47	5				
Density			t_e	69.87	5	m'	to		
g/ml 20°C	0.766	2	t_e (d, e)	69.99	5	n'	°K		
d^t_4 25	0.762	2	ΔHv/T_e	19.35	5	o'			
30	0.758	4				Surface tension			
a	0.782	4	d 30 to	83.87	5	dynes/cm. 20°C	22.90	5
b	-0.0$_3$79	4	e 130 °C	0.1051	5	30	21.95	5
			d' 10 to	83.00	5	40	21.02	5
Ref. Index			e' 30 °C	0.0760	5				
n_D 20°C	1.422	2	d_c g/ml			Parachor [P]			
25	1.420	2	v_c ml/g			20°C			
30	1.417	4	t_c °C	298.7	5	30			
"C"	0.7323	4	P_c mm	19618.	5	40			
MR (Obs.)	37.2	2				Sugd.	320.5	5
MR (Calc.)	36.944	5	PV/RT			Exp. L.1.%/wt.			
(nD-d/2)	1.039	2	25°C	1.0000	5	u.			
Dielectric	2.022	5	30 mm	1.0000	5	Dispersion	96.	2
			BP	0.9795	4	Flash Point °C			
A 30 to	6.842	2	t_e	0.9703	5	Fire Point			
B 155 °C	1335.	2	t_c						
C	219.	2	t_c			M. Spec.			
A* 30 to	1.227	5	ΔHc kcal/m			Ultra V.			
B* 140 °C	1238.	5	ΔHf			X-Ray Dif.			
K			ΔFf			Infrared			
c			Viscosity			Solubility in +			
t_k to			centistokes			Acetone	∞	
t_x °C			η °C			Carbon tet.	∞	
A' 10 to	7.180	5				Benzene	∞	
B' 30 °C	1509.	5				Ether	∞	
C'	235.	5	B^v to			n-Heptane	∞	
A'* 15 to	1.578	5	A^v °C			Ethanol	∞	
B'* 30 °C	1409.	5	(B^v) to			Water		
Ac 155 tc	7.260	5	(A^v) °C			Water in		
Bc t_c °C	1667.	5						
Cc	263.	5	c_p liq. °K					
Cryos. A°								
consts. B°			c_p vap. °K					
t_e °C	132.04	5	c_v vap.					

T_R = 0.75 T_c + grams/100 grams solvent

REFERENCES: 1-Dow 2-API 3-Lit. 4-Calc. from det. data 5-Calc. by formula

SOURCE:	API
PURIFICATION:	API
LITERATURE REFERENCES:	

No. 22

NAME	1, cis-2, trans-4-Trimethylcyclopentane	STRUCTURAL FORMULA

Structural formula:
$$H_2C\overset{CHCH_3}{\underset{H_3CHC-CH_2}{\diagup^{CHCH_3}}}$$

Mole % Pur.		Ref.	Molecular Formula	C_8H_{16}	Molecular Weight 112.208	

		Ref.				Ref.					Ref.
F.P. °C	-132.55	2	dt/dP °C/mm				f	to			
F.P. 100%			25°C	0.7969	5		g	°K			
B.P. °C			BP	0.04827	2		h				
760 mm	116.731	2	t_e	0.0366	5		f'	to			
100	55.824	2	30 mm	0.6678	4		g'	°K			
30	29.11	4					h'				
10	8.8	5	ΔHm cal/g				m	to			
1	-25.	5	ΔHv cal/g				n	°K			
Pressure			25°C	81.10	5		o				
mm 25°C	24.36	5	30 mm	80.79	5		m'	to			
t_e	1086.	5	BP	71.25	5		n'	°K			
Density			t_e	69.69	5		o'				
g/ml 20°C	0.76345	2	t_e (d, e)	69.77	5		Surface tension				
d_4^t 25	0.75920	2	ΔHv/T_e	19.38	5		dynes/cm. 20°C	22.60	5		
30	0.75494	4	d 30 to	83.95	5		ɣ 30	21.60	5		
a	0.78044	4	e 130 °C	0.1088	5		40	20.63	5		
b	-0.0384	4	d' 15 to	82.99	5		Parachor [P]				
Ref. Index			e' 30 °C	0.0757	5		20°C				
n_D 20°C	1.41855	2	d_c g/ml	0.262	5		30				
25	1.41612	2	v_c ml/g	3.817	5		40				
30	1.41363	4	t_c °C	295.4	5		Sugd.	320.5	5		
"C"	0.7291	4	P_c mm	19513.	5		Exp. L.l.%/wt.				
MR (Obs.)	37.082	2	PV/RT				u.				
MR (Calc.)	36.944	5	25°C	1.0000	5		Dispersion	95.7	2		
(nD-d/2)	1.03683	2	30 mm	1.0000	5		Flash Point °C				
Dielectric	2.012	5	BP	0.9759	4		Fire Point				
A 30 to	6.85448	2	t_e	0.9672	5		M Spec.				
B 155 °C	1333.894	2	t_c	0.233	5		Ultra V.				
C	218.952	2	ΔHc kcal/m				X-Ray Dif.				
A* 30 to	1.24624	5	ΔHf				Infrared	Yes	2		
B* 140 °C	1238.9	5	ΔFf				Solubility in +				
K			Viscosity				Acetone	∞			
c			centistokes				Carbon tet.	∞			
t_k to			η °C				Benzene	∞			
t_x °C							Ether	∞			
A' 10 to	7.19325	5					n-Heptane	∞			
B' 30 °C	1507.26	5	B^v to				Ethanol	∞			
C'	234.6	5	A^v °C				Water				
A'* 15 to	1.59246	5	(B^v) to				Water in				
B'* 30 °C	1408.3	5	(A^v) °C								
Ac 155 to	7.27153	5	c_p liq. °K								
Bc t_c °C	1662.38	5									
Cc	262.3	5	c_p vap. °K								
Cryos. A° consts. B°			c_v vap.								
t_e °C	130.36	5									

$T_R = 0.75 T_c$ + grams/100 grams solvent

REFERENCES: 1-Dow   2-API   3-Lit.   4-Calc. from det. data   5-Calc. by formula
SOURCE: API
PURIFICATION: API
LITERATURE REFERENCES:

TABLE XV. CYCLOPENTANES

NAME	1, trans-2, cis-4-Trimethylcyclopentane	STRUCTURAL FORMULA

Structural formula:
$$H_2C \overset{CHCH_3}{\underset{}{\diagdown}} CHCH_3$$
$$H_3CHC\!-\!CH_2$$

Mole % Pur.	Ref.	Molecular Formula C_8H_{16}	Molecular Weight 112.208	

	Ref.			Ref.				Ref.
F.P. °C	-130.78	2	dt/dP			f	to	
F.P. 100%			°C/mm			g	°K	
			25°C	0.6098	4	h		
B.P. °C			BP	0.04738	2			
760 mm	109.290	2	t_e	0.0363	5	f'	to	
100	49.519	2	30 mm	0.6551	4	g'	°K	
30	23.31	4	ΔHm cal/g			h'		
10	3.48	5						
1	-29.	5	ΔHv cal/g			m	to	
Pressure			25°C	79.05	4	n	°K	
mm 25°C	32.68	4	30 mm	79.23	5	o		
t_e	1070.	5	BP	70.16	5			
Density			t_e	68.72	5	m'	to	
g/ml 20°C	0.74727	2	t_e (d,e)	68.81	5	n'	°K	
d_4^t 25	0.74302	2	ΔHv/T_e	19.51	5	o'		
30	0.73876	4	d 25 to	81.68	5	Surface tension		
a	0.76426	4	e 120 °C	0.1054	5	dynes/cm. 20°C	20.74	5
b	-0.0₃842	4	d' to			ɤ 30	19.80	5
			e' °C			40	18.88	5
Ref. Index								
n_D 20°C	1.41060	2	d_c g/ml			Parachor [P]		
25	1.40812	2	v_c ml/g			20°C		
30	1.40565	4	t_c °C	282.2	5	30		
"C"	0.7315	4	P_c mm	18944.	5	40		
MR (Obs.)	37.251	2				Sugd.	320.5	5
MR (Calc.)	36.944	5	PV/RT			Exp. L.l.%/wt.		
(nD-d/2)	1.03696	2	25°C	1.0000	4	u.		
Dielectric	1.990	5	30 mm	1.0000	4	Dispersion	96.8	2
			BP	0.9805	4	Flash Point °C	3.0	5
A 25 to	6.84970	2	t_e	0.9726	5	Fire Point		
B 145 °C	1306.153	2	t_c					
C	219.808	2	ΔHc kcal/m			M. Spec.		
A* 25 to	1.24227	5	ΔHf			Ultra V.		
B* 130 °C	1211.22	5	ΔFf			X-Ray Dif.		
K			Viscosity			Infrared	Yes	2
c			centistokes			Solubility in +		
t_k to			η °C			Acetone	∞	
t_x °C						Carbon tet.	∞	
A' to						Benzene	∞	
B' °C						Ether	∞	
C'			B^v to			n-Heptane	∞	
A'* to			A^v °C			Ethanol	∞	
B'* °C			(B^v) to			Water		
						Water in		
Ac 145 to	7.2659	5	(A^v) °C					
Bc t_c °C	1626.0	5						
Cc	261.84	5	c_p liq. °K					
Cryos. A°			c_p vap. °K					
consts. B°								
t_e °C	122.08	5	c_v vap.					

$T_R = 0.75\,T_c$

+ grams/100 grams solvent

REFERENCES: 1-Dow 2-API 3-Lit. 4-Calc. from det. data 5-Calc. by formula

SOURCE:	API
PURIFICATION:	API
LITERATURE REFERENCES:	

No. 24

NAME	n-Butylcyclopentane	STRUCTURAL FORMULA

Structural formula:

$$H_2C\overset{\displaystyle CHC_4H_9}{\underset{\displaystyle CH_2}{\diagdown}}$$
$$H_2C - CH_2$$

Mole % Pur.	Ref.	Molecular Formula C_9H_{18}	Molecular Weight 126.234

		Ref.			Ref.			Ref.
F.P. °C	-107.985	2	dt/dP			f | | to		
F.P. 100%			°C/mm			g | |_ _ °K_		
B.P. °C			25°C	4.2217	5	h |		
760 mm	156.56	2	BP	0.0512	2			
100	91.8	2	t_e	0.0366	5	f' | | to		
30	63.3	4	30 mm	0.7137	4	g' | |_ _ °K_		
10	41.6	5	ΔHm cal/g			h' |		
1	5.3	5				m | 300 to	-0.1745	4
Pressure			ΔHv cal/g			n | 600°K	0.0021	4
mm 25°C	3.8013	5	25°C	87.23	5	o |	-0.0$_5$13(	4
t_e	1168.	5	30 mm	83.25	5			
Density			BP	70.75	5	m' | 700 to	0.0340	4
g/ml 20°C	0.7846	2	t_e	68.54	5	n' | 1000°K	0.0013	4
d_4^t 25	0.7808	2	t_e (d, e)	68.40	5	o' |	-0.0$_6$44	4
30	0.7770	4	ΔHv/T_e	19.35	5	**Surface tension**		
a	0.7998	4	d | 65 to	91.73	5	dynes/cm. 20°C	24.93	5
b	-0.0$_3$76	4	e | 175 °C	0.1340	5	γ 30	23.97	5
Ref. Index			d' | 15 to	89.82	5	40	23.04	5
n_D 20°C	1.4316	2	e' | 65 °C	0.1039	5	**Parachor [P]**		
25	1.4293	2	d_c g/ml	0.270	5	20°C		
30	1.4272	4	v_c ml/g	3.70	5	30		
"C"	0.7303	4	t_c °C	343.5	5	40		
MR (Obs.)	41.70	2	P_c mm	19349.	5	Sugd.	359.5	5
MR (Calc.)	41.562	5	**PV/RT**			**Exp. L.1.%/wt.**		
(nD-d/2)	1.0393	2	25°C	1.0000	5	u.		
Dielectric	2.049	5	30 mm	1.0000	5	Dispersion	96.	2
A | 65 to	6.9189	2	BP	0.9515	5	**Flash Point °C**		
B |190 °C	1460.0	2	t_e	0.9383	5	Fire Point		
C	205.0	2	t_c	0.235	5	**M Spec.**		
			ΔHc kcal/m	1326.42	2	Ultra V.		
A* | 65 to	1.3699	5	ΔHf	-51.22	2	X-Ray Dif.		
B* |185 °C	1371.9	5	ΔFf gas	14.69	2	Infrared		
K			**Viscosity**			**Solubility in** +		
c			centistokes			Acetone	∞	
t_k | to			η 20 °C	1.134	2	Carbon tet.	∞	
t_x | °C			40	0.889	2	Benzene	∞	
A' | 10 to	7.2617	5	60	0.724	2	Ether	∞	
B' | 65 °C	1649.8	5	80	0.61	2	n-Heptane	∞	
C'	221.9	5	B^v | -30 to	496.67	4	Ethanol	∞	
A'* 15 to	1.7021	5	A^v | 30 °C	2̄.36065	4	Water		
B'* 65 °C	1553.3	5	(B^v) | 30 to	452.36	4	Water in		
Ac |190 to	7.3197	5	(A^v) | 90 °C	2̄.50458	4	**Viscosity**		
Bc | t_c °C	1793.2	5	c_p liq. °K			centistokes		
Cc	247.7	5				-20°C	2.10	2
Cryos. A°			c_p vap.300°K	0.33858	2	0	1.508	2
consts. B°			400	0.45764	2			
t_e °C	174.06	5	c_v vap.					

$T_R = 0.75\,T_c$ + grams/100 grams solvent

REFERENCES: 1-Dow   2-API   3-Lit.   4-Calc. from det. data   5-Calc. by formula

SOURCE: API

PURIFICATION: API

LITERATURE REFERENCES:

TABLE XV. CYCLOPENTANES

No. 25

NAME	n-Pentylcyclopentane		STRUCTURAL FORMULA
	1-Cyclopentylpentane		$H_2C\overset{\displaystyle CHC_5H_{11}}{\underset{\displaystyle CH_2}{}}$ $H_2C—CH_2$
Mole % Pur.	Ref.	Molecular Formula $C_{10}H_{20}$	Molecular Weight 140.260

		Ref.			Ref.					Ref.
F.P. °C	-83.	2	dt/dP			f		to		
F.P. 100%			°C/mm			g		_ _ °K		
B.P. °C			25°C	12.120	5	h				
760 mm	180.	2	BP	0.0532	4					
100	113.	2	t_e	0.0364	5	f'		to		
30	83.	4	30 mm	0.7432	4	g'		_ _ °K		
10	60.	5	ΔHm cal/g			h'				
1	22.	5	ΔHv cal/g			m		300 to	-0.1550	4
Pressure			25°C	87.11	5	n		600 °K	0.0020	4
mm 25°C	1.1934	5	30 mm	80.58	5	o			-0.0$_5$12	4
t_e	1236.	5	BP	68.06	5					
Density			t_e	65.63	5	m'		700 to	0.0428	4
g/ml 20°C	0.7912	2	t_e (d, e)	65.39	5	n'		1000 °K	0.0013	4
d_4^t 25	0.7874	2	ΔHv/T_e	19.42	5	o'			-0.0$_6$43	4
30	0.7836	4	d | 85 to	91.26	5	Surface tension				
a	0.8064	4	e | 200 °C	0.1289	5	dynes/cm. 20°C			25.53	5
b	-0.0$_3$64	4	d' | 25 to	89.93	5	8			30	24.57	5
Ref. Index			e' | 85 °C	0.1128	5				40	23.62	5
n_D 20°C	1.4358	2	d_c g/ml			Parachor [P]				
25	1.4336	5	v_c ml/g			20°C				
30	1.4313	4	t_c °C	366.0	5	30				
"C"	0.7308	4	P_c mm	17703.	5	40				
MR (Obs.)	46.33	2	PV/RT						Sugd. 398.5	5
MR (Calc.)	46.180	5	25°C	1.0000	5	Exp. L.1.%/wt.				
(nD-d/2)	1.0402	2	30 mm	1.0000	5	u.				
Dielectric	2.062	5	BP	0.9515	4	Dispersion			96.	2
A | 85 to	6.929	2	t_e	0.9375	5	Flash Point °C				
B | 220 °C	1526.	2	t_c			Fire Point				
C	197.	2	ΔHc kcal/m	1473.34	2	M. Spec.				
A* | 85 to	1.405	5	ΔHf			Ultra V.				
B* | 210 °C	1435.	5	ΔFf			X-Ray Dif.				
K			Viscosity			Infrared				
c			centistokes			Solubility in +				
t_k | to			η -20°C	2.82	2	Acetone			∞	
t_x | °C			0	2.02	2	Carbon tet.			∞	
A' | 15 to	7.272	5	20	1.458	2	Benzene			∞	
B' | 85 °C	1724.	5	40	1.102	2	Ether			∞	
C'	215.	5				n-Heptane			∞	
			B^v | -30 to	531.71	4	Ethanol			∞	
A'* 20 to	1.755	5	A^v | 30 °C	$\overline{2}$.35028	4	Water				
B'* 85 °C	1630.	5	(B^v)| 30 to	511.21 :	'4	Water in				
Ac | 220 to	7.405	5	(A^v)| 90 °C	$\overline{2}$.40996	4	Viscosity				
Bc | t_c °C	1948.	5	c_p liq. °K			centiestokes				
Cc	251.	5				60°C			0.875	2
Cryos. A°			c_p vap.300°K	0.34386	2	80			0.72	2
consts. B°			P 400	0.46136	2					
t_e °C	200.71	5	c_v vap.							
T_R = 0.77 T_c						+ grams/100 grams solvent				

REFERENCES: 1-Dow 2-API 3-Lit. 4-Calc. from det. data 5-Calc. by formula

SOURCE:	API
PURIFICATION:	API

LITERATURE REFERENCES:

No. 26

NAME	n-Hexylcyclopentane				STRUCTURAL FORMULA
	1-Cyclopentylhexane				
Mole % Pur.	Ref.	Molecular Formula $C_{11}H_{22}$		Molecular Weight 154.286	

Structural formula:
$$H_2C \overset{\displaystyle CHC_6H_{13}}{\underset{\displaystyle H_2C - CH_2}{\quad CH_2}}$$

		Ref.			Ref.				Ref.
F.P. °C	-73.	2	dt/dP			f	to		
F.P. 100%			°C/mm			g	°K		
B.P. °C			25°C	36.80	5	h			
760 mm	203.	2	BP	0.05527	5				
100	133.	2	t_e	0.0367	5	f'	to		
30	102.	4	30 mm	0.7725	4	g'	°K		
10	79.	5	ΔHm cal/g			h'			
1	39.	5	ΔHv cal/g			m	300 to	-0.1387	4
Pressure			25°C	87.71	5	n	600 °K	0.0020	4
mm 25°C	0.3548	5	30 mm	78.32	5	o		$-0.0_5 12$	4
t_e	1286.	5	BP	65.18	5				
Density			t_e	62.36	5	m'	700 to	0.0494	4
g/ml 20°C	0.7965	2	t_e (d,e)	62.13	5	n'	1000 °K	0.0012	4
d_4^t 25	0.7927	2	ΔHv/T_e	19.26	5	o'		$-0.0_6 43$	4
30	0.7889	4				Surface tension			
a	0.8117	4	d 100 to	91.64	5	dynes/cm. 20°C		26.02	5
b	$-0.0_3 76$	4	e 225 °C	0.1303	5	𝛾 30		25.04	5
Ref. Index			d' 25 to	90.76	5	40		24.09	5
n_D 20°C	1.4392	2	e' 100 °C	0.1217	5	Parachor [P]			
25	1.4370	2	d_c g/ml			20°C			
30	1.4349	4	v_c ml/g			30			
"C"	0.7313	4	t_c °C	387.0	5	40			
MR (Obs.)	50.97	2	P_c mm	16025.	5	Sugd.		437.5	5
MR (Calc.)	50.798	5	PV/RT			Exp. L.1.%/wt.			
(nD-d/2)	1.0410	2	25°C	1.0000	5	u.			
Dielectric	2.071	5	30 mm	1.0000	5	Dispersion		96.	2
A 100 to	6.934	2	BP	0.9434	5	Flash Point °C			
B 240 °C	1589.	2	t_e	0.9249	5	Fire Point			
C	189.	2	t_c			M Spec.			
A* 100 to	1.4510	5	ΔHc kcal/m	1620.28	2	Ultra V.			
B* 235 °C	1501.	5	ΔHf			X-Ray Dif.			
K			ΔFf			Infrared			
c			Viscosity			Solubility in +			
t_k to			centistokes			Acetone		∞	
t_x °C			η -20 °C	3.77	2	Carbon tet.		∞	
A' 25 to	7.278	5	0	2.64	2	Benzene		∞	
B' 100 °C	1796.	5	20	1.87	2	Ether		∞	
C'	207.	5	40	1.378	2	n-Heptane		∞	
A'* 25 to	1.796	5	B^V -30 to	563.28	4	Ethanol		∞	
B'* 100 °C	1702.	5	A^V 30 °C	Σ.35169	4	Water			
Ac 240 to	7.444	5	(B^V) 30 to	552.35	4	Water in			
Bc t_c °C	2058.	5	(A^V) 90 °C	Σ.37568	4	Viscosity			
Cc	249.	5	c_p liq. °K			centistokes			
Cryos. A°						60°C		1.068	2
consts. B°			c_p vap.300°K	0.34825	2	80		0.87	2
t_e °C	226.4	5	400	0.46440	2				
			c_v vap.						

$T_R = 0.78\,T_c$ + grams/100 grams solvent

REFERENCES: 1-Dow   2-API   3-Lit.   4-Calc. from det. data   5-Calc. by formula

SOURCE: API

PURIFICATION: API

LITERATURE REFERENCES:

TABLE XV. CYCLOPENTANES

NAME	n-Heptylcyclopentane	STRUCTURAL FORMULA
	1-Cyclopentylheptane	

Structural formula: $H_2C{-}CHC_7H_{15}$ / $H_2C{-}CH_2$ (cyclopentane ring with C_7H_{15} substituent)

Mole % Pur. | Ref. | Molecular Formula $C_{12}H_{24}$ | Molecular Weight 168.312

		Ref.			Ref.				Ref.
F.P. °C	-53.	2	dt/dP			f		to	
F.P. 100%			°C/mm			g		°K	
B.P. °C			25°C	108.11	5	h			
760 mm	224.	2	BP	0.0571	5				
100	152.	2	t_e	0.0370	5	f'		to	
30	120.	4	30 mm	0.7993	4	g'		°K	
10	95.	5	ΔHm cal/g			h'			
1	55.	5	ΔHv cal/g			m	300 to	-0.1262	4
Pressure			25°C	88.18	5	n	600 °K	0.0019	4
mm 25°C	0.1101	5	30 mm	76.02	5	o		-0.0₅11	4
t_e	1329.	5	BP	62.39	5				
Density			t_e	59.35	5	m'	700 to	0.0593	4
з/ml 20°C	0.8010	2	t_e (d,e)	59.01	5	n'	1000 °K	0.0012	4
d_4^t 25	0.7973	2	ΔHv/T_e	19.10	5	o'		-0.0₆42	4
30	0.7936	4	d 120 to	91.68	5	Surface tension			
a	0.8158	4	e 250 °C	0.1308	5	dynes/cm. 20°C		26.44	5
b	-0.0₃74	4	d' 25 to	91.39	5	з 30		25.48	5
Ref. Index			e' 120 °C	0.1283	5	40		24.54	5
n_D 20°C	1.4421	2	d_c g/ml			Parachor [P]			
25	1.4400	2	v_c ml/g			20°C			
30	1.4376	4	t_c °C	405.8	5	30			
"C"	0.7317	4	P_c mm	14654.	5	40			
MR (Obs.)	55.61	2	PV/RT				Sugd.	476.5	5
MR (Calc.)	55.416	5	25°C	1.0000	5	Exp. L. l. %/wt.			
(nD-d/2)	1.0416	2	30 mm	1.0000	5	u.			
Dielectric	2.080	5	BP	0.9345	4	Dispersion		96.	2
A 120 to	6.942	2	t_e	0.9135	5	Flash Point °C			
B 270 °C	1649.	2	t_c			Fire Point			
C	182.	2	ΔHc kcal/m	1767.20	2	M. Spec.			
A* 120 to	1.497	5	ΔHf			Ultra V.			
B* 260 °C	1564.	5	ΔFf			X-Ray Dif.			
K			Viscosity			Infrared			
c			centistokes			Solubility in +			
t_k to			η -20 °C	4.94	2	Acetone		∞	
t_x °C			0	3.40	2	Carbon tet.		∞	
A' 20 to	7.286	5	20	2.35	2	Benzene		∞	
B' 120 °C	1863.	5	40	1.698	2	Ether		∞	
C'	201.	5	B^v -30 to	598.84	4	n-Heptane		∞	
A'* 25 to	1.838	5	A^v 30 °C	2̄.32863	4	Ethanol		∞	
B'* 120 °C	1772.	5	(B^v) 30 to	612.13	4	Water			
Ac 270 to	7.564	5	(A^v) 90 °C	2̄.27551	4	Water in			
Bc t_c °C	2259.	5	c_p liq. °K			Viscosity			
Cc	259.	5				centistokes			
Cryos. A°			c_p vap.300°K	0.35185	2	60°C		1.284	2
consts. B°			400	0.46699	2	80		1.02	2
t_e °C	249.9	5	c_v vap.						

$T_R = 0.80 T_c$

+ grams/100 grams solvent

REFERENCES: 1-Dow 2-API 3-Lit. 4-Calc. from det. data 5-Calc. by formula

SOURCE: API

PURIFICATION: API

LITERATURE REFERENCES:

NAME	n-Octylcyclopentane	STRUCTURAL FORMULA
	1-Cyclopentyloctane	

Structural Formula:

H_2C―CHC_8H_{17} / CH_2
H_2C―CH_2

Mole % Pur.	Ref.	Molecular Formula $C_{13}H_{26}$	Molecular Weight 182.338

		Ref.			Ref.					Ref.
F.P. °C	-44.	2	dt/dP			f		to		
F.P. 100%			°C/mm			g		°K		
			25°C	318.2	5	h				
B.P. °C			BP	0.0586	5					
760 mm	243.	2	t_e	0.0370	5	f'		to		
100	169.	2	30 mm	0.8215	4	g'		°K		
30	136.	4	ΔHm cal/g			h'				
10	111.	5				m		300 to	-0.1267	4
1	69.	5	ΔHv cal/g			n		600 °K	0.0019	4
Pressure			25°C	89.10	5	o			-0.0₅12	4
mm 25°C	0.0342	5	30 mm	74.03	5					
t_e	1373.	5	BP	60.16	5	m'		700 to	0.0638	4
Density			t_e	56.93	5	n'		1000 °K	0.0012	4
g/ml 20°C	0.8048	2	t_e (d, e)	56.51	5	o'			-0.0₆42	4
d_4^t 25	0.8011	2	ΔHv/T_e	19.07	5	Surface tension				
30	0.7974	4	d	135 to	91.65	5	dynes/cm. 20°C		26.80	5
a	0.8196	4	e	265 °C	0.1296	5	30		25.83	5
b	-0.0₃74	4	d'	25 to	92.50	5	40		24.88	5
Ref. Index			e'	135 °C	0.1358	5	Parachor [P]			
n_D 20°C	1.4446	2	d_c g/ml			20°C			
25	1.4425	2	v_c ml/g			30			
30	1.4403	4	t_c °C	421.3	5	40			
"C"	0.7322	4	P_c mm	13445.	5	Sugd. 515.5			5
MR (Obs.)	60.25	2	PV/RT			Exp. L.1.%/wt.			
MR (Calc.)	60.034	5	25°C	1.0000	5	u.			
(nD-d/2)	1.0422	2	30 mm	1.0000	5	Dispersion	97.		2
Dielectric	2.087	5	BP	0.9294	4	Flash Point °C			
A 135 to	6.957	2	t_e	0.9064	5	Fire Point			
B 295 °C	1704.	2	t_c			M Spec.			
C	175.	2	ΔHc kcal/m	1914.12	2	Ultra V.			
A* 135 to	1.543	5	ΔHf			X-Ray Dif.			
B* 280 °C	1620.	5	ΔFf			Infrared			
K			Viscosity			Solubility in +			
c			centistokes			Acetone		∞	
t_k to			η -20 °C	6.39	2	Carbon tet.		∞	
t_x °C			0	4.32	2	Benzene		∞	
A' 25 to	7.302	5	20	2.93	2	Ether		∞	
B' 135 °C	1925.	5	40	2.07	2	n-Heptane		∞	
C'	195.	5	B^v -30 to	628.48	4	Ethanol		∞	
A'* 25 to	1.884	5	A^v 30 °C	2.32334	4	Water			
B'* 135 °C	1836.	5	(B^v) 30 to	664.89	4	Water in			
Ac 295 to	7.740	5	(A^v) 90 °C	2.19308	4	Viscosity			
Bc t_c °C	2521.	5	c_p liq. °K			centistokes			
Cc	277.	5				60°C	1.528		2
Cryos. A°			c_p vap.300°K	0.35489	2	80	1.19		2
consts. B°			400	0.46913	2				
t_e °C	271.1	5	c_v vap.						

$T_R = 0.82 T_c$

+ grams/100 grams solvent

REFERENCES: 1-Dow 2-API 3-Lit. 4-Calc. from det. data 5-Calc. by formula
SOURCE: API
PURIFICATION: API
LITERATURE REFERENCES:

TABLE XV. CYCLOPENTANES 387

No. 29

NAME	n-Nonylcyclopentane	STRUCTURAL FORMULA
	1-Cyclopentylnonane	

Structural formula: CHC9H19 / H2C CH2 / H2C—CH2

Mole % Pur.	Ref.	Molecular Formula $C_{14}H_{28}$	Molecular Weight 196.364

		Ref.			Ref.				Ref.
F.P. °C	-29.	2	dt/dP			f		to	
Γ.P. 100%			°C/mm			g		___ °K	
B.P. °C			25°C	996.11	5	h			
760 mm	252.	2	BP	0.0601	5				
100	186.	2	t_e	0.0371	5	f'		to	
30	152.	4	30 mm	0.8439	4	g'		___ °K	
10	126.	5	ΔHm cal/g			h'			
1	83.	5	ΔHv cal/g			m		300 to	-0.1049	4
Pressure			25°C	90.54	5	n		600 °K	0.0018	4
mm 25°C	0.00998	5	30 mm	72.28	5	o			-0.0510	4
t_e	1411.	5	BP	57.97	5				
Density			t_e	54.61	5	m'		700 to	0.0647	4
g/ml 20°C	0.8081	2	t_e (d, e)	54.03	5	n'		1000 °K	0.0012	4
d_4^t 25	0.8045	2	ΔHv/T_e	18.97	5	o'			-0.0642	4
30	0.8009	4	d 150 to	92.07	5	Surface tension				
a	0.8225	4	e 285 °C	0.1301	5	dynes/cm. 20°C		27.12	5
b	-0.0372	4	d' 25 to	94.13	5	ɤ		30	26.16	5
Ref. Index			e' 150 °C	0.1437	5			40	25.23	5
n_D 20°C	1.4467	2	d_c g/ml			Parachor [P]			
25	1.4446	2	v_c ml/g					20°C	
30	1.4425	4	t_c °C	437.4	5			30	
"C"	0.7324	4	P_c mm	12418.	5			40	
MR (Obs.)	64.89	2	PV/RT					Sugd.	554.5	5
MR (Calc.)	64.652	5	25°C	1.0000	4	Exp. L.1.%/wt.			
(nD-d/2)	1.0427	2	30 mm	1.0000	5	u.			
Dielectric	2.093	5	BP	0.9210	4	Dispersion	97.	2
A 150 to	6.967	2	t_e	0.8968	5	Flash Point °C		
B 310 °C	1757.	2	t_c			Fire Point		
C	168.	2	ΔHc kcal/m	2061.05	2	M. Spec.		
A* 150 to	1.585	5	ΔHf			Ultra V.		
B* 300 °C	1677.	5	ΔFf			X-Ray Dif.		
K			Viscosity			Infrared		
c			centistokes			Solubility in +		
t_k to			η -20 °C	8.14	2	Acetone	∞	
t_x °C			0	5.41	2	Carbon tet.	∞	
A' 20 to	7.313	5	20	3.60	2	Benzene	∞	
B' 150 °C	1985.	5	40	2.49	2	Ether	∞	
C'	188.	5	B^v -30 to	657.60	4	n-Heptane	∞	
A'* 25 to	1.924	5	A^v 30 °C	$\bar{2}$.31346	4	Ethanol	∞	
B'* 150 °C	1897.	5	(B^v) 30 to	708.87	4	Water		
Ac to			(A^v) 90 °C	$\bar{2}$.13289	4	Water in		
Bc t_c °C			c_p liq. °K			Viscosity		
Cc						centistokes		
Cryos. A°			c_p vap.300°K	0.35755	2	60°C	1.80	2
consts. B°			400	0.47096	2	80	1.38	2
t_e °C	292.2	5	c_v vap.					

+ grams/100 grams solvent

REFERENCES: 1-Dow 2-API 3-Lit. 4-Calc. from det. data 5-Calc. by formula
SOURCE: API
PURIFICATION: API
LITERATURE REFERENCES:

No. 30

NAME	n-Decylcyclopentane	STRUCTURAL FORMULA

1-Cyclopentyldecane

H_2C–$\overset{CHC_{10}H_{21}}{}$–$CH_2$
H_2C—CH_2

Mole % Pur.	Ref.	Molecular Formula $C_{15}H_{30}$	Molecular Weight 210.390

		Ref.			Ref.				Ref.
F.P. °C	-22.13	2	dt/dP			f		to	
F.P. 100%			°C/mm			g		°K	
			25°C	3179.1	5	h			
B.P. °C			BP	0.0614	5				
760 mm	279.2	2	t_e	0.0372	5	f'		to	
100	201.3	2				g'		°K	
30	166.9	4	30 mm	0.8624	4	h'			
10	140.6	5	ΔHm cal/g						
1	96.6	5				m	300 to	-0.0965	4
Pressure			ΔHv cal/g			n	600 °K	0.0018	4
mm 25°C	0.00285	5	25°C	92.57	5	o		-0.0₆98	4
t_e	1446.	5	30 mm	70.70	5				
Density			BP	56.06	5	m'	700 to	0.0711	4
g/ml 20°C	0.81097	2	t_e	52.52	5	n'	1000 °K	0.0012	4
d_4^t 25	0.80739	2	t_e (d, e)	51.86	5	o'		-0.0₆41	4
30	0.80381	4	ΔHv/T_e	18.90	5	Surface tension			
a	0.82529	4	d	165 to	92.46	5	dynes/cm. 20°C	27.39	5
b	-0.0₃716	4	e	300 °C	0.1304	5	γ	30	26.44	5
Ref. Index			d'	25 to	96.43	5		40	25.51	5
n_D 20°C	1.44862	2	e'	165 °C	0.1541	5				
25	1.44659	2	d_c g/ml			Parachor [P]		
30	1.44438	4	v_c ml/g			20°C		
"C"	0.7327	4	t_c °C	450.6	5	30		
MR (Obs.)	69.534	2	P_c mm	11416.	5	40		
MR (Calc.)	69.276	5	PV/RT			Sugd. 593.5		5
(nD-d/2)	1.04314	2	25°C	1.0000	5	Exp. L.1.%/wt.		
Dielectric	2.098	5	30 mm	1.0000	5	u.		
A 165 to	6.971	2	BP	0.9153	4	Dispersion	96.9	2
B 330 °C	1798.	2	t_e	0.8889	5	Flash Point °C		
C	160.4	2	t_c			Fire Point		
A* 165 to	1.619	5	ΔHc kcal/m	2207.97	2	M Spec.		
B* 320 °C	1721.	5	ΔHf			Ultra V.		
K			ΔFf			X-Ray Dif.		
c			Viscosity			Infrared		
t_k to			centistokes			Solubility in +		
t_x °C			η 0 °C	6.69	2	Acetone	∞	
A' 20 to	7.317	5	20	4.37	2	Carbon tet.	∞	
B' 165 °C	2032.	5	40	2.96	2	Benzene	∞	
C'	181.	5	60	2.10	2	Ether	∞	
A'* 25 to	1.9563	5	B^v -10 to	757.56	4	n-Heptane	∞	
B'* 165 °C	1946.	5	A^v 50 °C	Σ.05252	4	Ethanol	∞	
Ac to			(B^v) 50 to	689.68	4	Water		
Bc t_c °C			(A^v) 110 °C	Σ.25236	4	Water in		
Cc			c_p liq. °K			Viscosity		
Cryos. A°			c_p vap.300°K	0.35981	2	centistokes		
consts. B°			400	0.47255	2	80°C	1.59	2
t_e °C	311.4	5	c_v vap.			100	1.26	2

+ grams/100 grams solvent

REFERENCES: 1-Dow 2-API 3-Lit. 4-Calc. from det. data 5-Calc. by formula
SOURCE: API
PURIFICATION: API
LITERATURE REFERENCES:

TABLE XV. CYCLOPENTANES

389

No. 31

NAME	n-Undecylcyclopentane		STRUCTURAL FORMULA		
	1-Cyclopentylundecane		$H_2C \overset{CHC_{11}H_{23}}{\underset{|}{\overset{|}{CH_2}}}$ $H_2C - CH_2$		
Mole % Pur.	Ref.	Molecular Formula $C_{16}H_{32}$	Molecular Weight 224.416		

		Ref.			Ref.				Ref.
F.P. °C	-10.	2	dt/dP			f ⌐ to		
F.P. 100%			°C/mm			g ⎮ _ _ _ °K		
B.P. °C			25°C	8312.7	5	h ⎮		
760 mm	296.	2	BP	0.0632	5			
100	216.	2	t_e	0.0373	5	f' ⌐ to		
30	180.	4	30 mm	0.8883	4	g' ⎮ _ _ _ °K		
10	153.	5	ΔHm cal/g			h' ⎮		
1	108.	5	ΔHv cal/g			m ⌐ 300 to	-0.0890	4
Pressure			25°C	91.95	5	n ⎮ 600 °K	0.0018	4
mm 25°C	0.00103	5	30 mm	68.33	5	o ⎮	-0.0_695	4
t_e	1498.	5	BP	54.28	5	m' ⌐ 700 to	0.0741	4
Density			t_e	50.73	5	n' ⎮ 1000 °K	0.0012	4
g/ml 20°C	0.8135	2	t_e (d, e)	50.02	5	o' ⎮	-0.0_641	4
d^t_4 25	0.8100	2	ΔHv/T_e	18.84	5	Surface tension		
30	0.8065	4	d ⌐ 180 to	90.23	5	dynes/cm. 20°C	27.63	5
a	0.8275	4	e ⎮ 325 °C	0.1215	5	ꝩ 30	26.70	5
b	-0.0_370	4	d' ⎮ 25 to	95.75	5	40	25.78	5
Ref. Index			e' ⎮ 180 °C	0.1521	5	Parachor [P]		
n_D 20°C	1.4503	2	d_c g/ml			20°C		
25	1.4482	2	v_c ml/g			30		
30	1.4459	4	t_c °C			40		
"C"	0.7336	4	P_c mm	10554.	5	Sugd.	632.5	5
MR (Obs.)	74.18	2	PV/RT			Exp. L.1.%/wt.		
MR (Calc.)	73.888	5	25°C	1.0000	5	u.		
(nD-d/2)	1.0435	2	30 mm	1.0000	5	Dispersion	97.	2
Dielectric	2.103	5	BP	0.9170	4	Flash Point °C		
A ⌐ 180 to	6.974	2	t_e	0.8908	5	Fire Point		
B ⎮ 350 °C	1854.	2	t_c			M. Spec.		
C	157.	2	ΔHc kcal/m	2354.89	2	Ultra V.		
A* 180 to	1.633	5	ΔHf			X-Ray Dif.		
B* 340 °C	1773.	5	ΔFf			Infrared		
K			Viscosity			Solubility in +		
c			centistokes			Acetone	∞	
t_k ⌐ to			η 0 °C	8.19	2	Carbon tet.	∞	
t_x ⎮ °C			20	5.25	2	Benzene	∞	
A' 25 to	7.320	5	40	3.49	2	Ether	∞	
B' 180 °C	2095.	5	60	2.44	2	n-Heptane	∞	
C'	178.	5	B^v -10 to	792.45	4	Ethanol	∞	
A'* 25 to	1.982	5	A^v 50 °C	$\overline{2}.01266$	4	Water		
B'* 180 °C	2010.	5	(B^v) 50 to	730.87	4	Water in		
Ac ⌐ to			(A^v) 110 °C	$\overline{2}.19391$	4	Viscosity		
Bc ⎮ t_c °C			c_p liq. °K			centistokes		
Cc ⎣						80°C	1.81	2
Cryos. A°			c_p vap.300°K	0.36183	2	100	1.42	2
consts. B°			400	0.47394	2			
t_e °C	331.1	5	c_v vap.					

+ grams/100 grams solvent

REFERENCES: 1-Dow 2-API 3-Lit. 4-Calc. from det. data 5-Calc. by formula
SOURCE: API
PURIFICATION: API
LITERATURE REFERENCES:

No. 32

NAME	n-Dodecylcyclopentane		STRUCTURAL FORMULA		
	1-Cyclopentyldodecane				

Structural formula: $H_2C{-}CH{-}CHC_{12}H_{25}$ / $H_2C{-}CH_2$ (cyclopentyl ring with CH_2 groups)

Mole % Pur.	Ref.	Molecular Formula $C_{17}H_{34}$		Molecular Weight 238.442	

		Ref.			Ref.			Ref.
F.P. °C	-5.	2	dt/dP			f	to	
F.P. 100%			°C/mm			g	__ °K__	
B.P. °C			25°C	26542.	5	h		
760 mm	312.	2	BP	0.0645	2			
100	230.	2	t_e	0.0373	5	f'	to	
30	194.	4	30 mm	0.9067	4	g'	__ °K__	
10	166.	5	ΔHm cal/g			h'		
1	120.	5	ΔHv cal/g			m	300 to	-0.0825	4
			25°C	93.70	5	n	__600 °K__	0.0018	4
Pressure			30 mm	66.87	5	o		-0.0₆93	4
mm 25°C	0.0₃298	5	BP	52.64	5				
t_e	1530.	5	t_e	48.97	5	m'	700 to	0.0766	4
Density			t_e (d, e)	48.19	5	n'	__1000 °K__	0.0012	4
g/ml 20°C	0.8158	2	$\Delta Hv/T_e$	18.77	5	o'		-0.0₆41	4
d_4^t 25	0.8123	2				Surface tension		
30	0.8088	4	d	195 to	90.25	5	dynes/cm. 20°C	27.86	5
a	0.8298	4	e	340 °C	0.1205	5	ɤ	30	26.92	5
b	-0.0₃70	4	d'	25 to	97.67	5		40	26.00	5
Ref. Index			e'	195 °C	0.1588	5	Parachor [P]	
n_D 20°C	1.4518	2	d_c g/ml				20°C	
25	1.4497	2	v_c ml/g				30	
30	1.4470	4	t_c °C	476.7	5		40	
"C"	0.7322	4	P_c mm	9718.	5		Sugd.	671.5	5
MR (Obs.)	78.82	2	PV/RT			Exp. L.1.%/wt.	
MR (Calc.)	78.506	5	25°C	1.0000	5	u.	
(nD-d/2)	1.0439	2	30 mm	1.0000	5	Dispersion	97.	2
Dielectric	2.108	5	BP	0.9116	5	Flash Point °C	
A 195 to	6.985	2	t_e	0.8837	5	Fire Point	
B 365 °C	1900.	2	t_c			M Spec.	
C	151.	2	ΔHc kcal/m	2501.82	2	Ultra V.	
A* 195 to	1.670	5	ΔHf			X-Ray Dif.	
B* 360 °C	1821.	5	ΔFf			Infrared	
K			Viscosity			Solubility in +	
c			centistokes			Acetone	∞	
t_k to			η 0 °C	9.92	2	Carbon tet.	∞	
t_x °C			20	6.25	2	Benzene	∞	
A' 20 to	7.332	5	40	4.08	2	Ether	∞	
B' 195 °C	2147.	5	60	2.80	2	n-Heptane	∞	
C'	173.	5	B^V -10 to	825.39	4	Ethanol	∞	
A'* 25 to	2.017	5	A^V 50 °C	$\bar{3}$.97532	4	Water	
B'* 195 °C	2063.	5	$(B^{\bar{V}})$ 50 to	764.01	4	Water in	
Ac to			(A^V) 110 °C	$\bar{2}$.15422	4	Viscosity	
Bc t_c °C						centistokes	
Cc			c_p liq. °K			80°C	2.05	2
Cryos. A°			c_p vap.300°K	0.36357	2	100	1.59	2
consts. B°			400	0.47517	2		
t_e °C	348.9	5	c_v vap.				

+ grams/100 grams solvent

REFERENCES: 1-Dow 2-API 3-Lit. 4-Calc. from det. data 5-Calc. by formula

SOURCE: API

PURIFICATION: API

LITERATURE REFERENCES:

No. 33

NAME	n-Tridecylcyclopentane	STRUCTURAL FORMULA
	1-Cyclopentyltridecane	

Structural formula: $CHC_{13}H_{27}$, H_2C CH_2, H_2C—CH_2

Mole % Pur.	Ref.	Molecular Formula $C_{18}H_{36}$		Molecular Weight 252.468

		Ref.			Ref.				Ref.
F.P. °C	5	2	dt/dP			f	to		
F.P. 100%			°C/mm			g	_ _ _°K		
B.P. °C			25°C	79840.	5	h			
760 mm	327.	2	BP	0.0657	5				
100	244.	2	t_e	0.0371	5	f'	to		
30	207.	4	30 mm	0.9255	4	g'	_ _ _°K		
10	178.	5	ΔHm cal/g			h'			
1	131.	5	ΔHv cal/g			m	300 to	-0.0767	4
Pressure			25°C	94.88	5	n	600 °K	0.0017	4
mm 25°C	0.0_4924	5	30 mm	65.27	5	o		-0.0_690	4
t_e	1581.	4	BP	51.59	5				
		5	t_e	47.80	5	m'	700 to	0.0789	4
Density			t_e (d, e)	47.09	5	n'	1000 °K	0.0012	4
g/ml 20°C	0.8178	2	ΔHv/T_e	18.86	5	o'		-0.0_641	4
d_4^t 25	0.8143	2	d	205 to	88.75	5	Surface tension			
30	0.8108	4	e	360 °C	0.1136	5	dynes/cm. 20°C	28.06	5
a	0.8318	4	d'	25 to	98.95	5	γ	30	27.11	5
b	-0.0_370	4	e'	205 °C	0.1630	5		40	26.18	5
Ref. Index			d_c g/ml			Parachor [P]			
n_D 20°C	1.4531	2	v_c ml/g			20°C		
25	1.4510	2	t_c °C	488.2	5	30		
30	1.4490	4	P_c mm	9025.	5	40		
"C"	0.7334	4	PV/RT			Sugd. 710.5	5
MR (Obs.)	83.46	2	25°C	1.0000	5	Exp. L.l.%/wt.		
MR (Calc.)	83.124	5	30 mm	1.0000	5	u.		
(nD-d/2)	1.0442	2	BP	0.9174	4	Dispersion	97.	2
Dielectric	2.111	5	t_e	0.8881	5	Flash Point °C		
A 205 to	6.993	2	t_c			Fire Point		
B 385 °C	1945.	2	ΔHc kcal/m	2648.74	2	M. Spec.		
C	146.	2	ΔHf			Ultra V.		
A* 205 to	1.684	5	ΔFf			X-Ray Dif.		
B* 375 °C	1862.	5	Viscosity			Infrared		
K			centistokes			Solubility in +		
c			η 20 °C	7.39	2	Acetone	∞	
t_k to			40	4.74	2	Carbon tet.	∞	
t_x °C			60	3.20	2	Benzene	∞	
A' 20 to	7.341	5	80	2.31	2	Ether	∞	
B' 205 °C	2198.	5				n-Heptane	∞	
C'	168.	5	B^v 10 to	887.77	4	Ethanol	∞	
			A^v 70 °C	3.84077	4	Water		
A'* 25 to	2.047	5	(B^v) 70 to	792.48	4	Water in		
B'* 205 °C	2115.	5						
Ac to			(A^v) 110 °C	2.12228	4	Viscosity		
Bc t_c °C			c_p liq. °K			centistokes		
Cc						100°C	1.77	2
Cryos. A°			c_p vap300°K	0.36512	2	110	1.55	2
consts. B°			400	0.47626	2			
t_e °C	366.6	5	c_v vap.					

+ grams/100 grams solvent

REFERENCES: 1-Dow 2-API 3-Lit. 4-Calc. from det. data 5-Calc. by formula

SOURCE: API

PURIFICATION: API

LITERATURE REFERENCES:

No. 34

NAME	n-Tetradecylcyclopentane	STRUCTURAL FORMULA
	1-Cyclopentyltetradecane	$H_2C\overset{CHC_{14}H_{29}}{\underset{CH_2}{}}$

Mole % Pur.	Ref.	Molecular Formula $C_{19}H_{38}$	Molecular Weight 266.494

		Ref.			Ref.				Ref.
F.P. °C	9.	2	dt/dP			f	to		
F.P. 100%			°C/mm			g	°K		
			25°C	244430.	5	h			
B.P. °C			BP	0.0668	5				
760 mm	341.	2	t_e	0.0371	5	f'	to		
100	256.	2	30 mm	0.9420	4	g'	°K		
30	219.	4	ΔHm cal/g			h'			
10	190.	5							
1	142.	5	ΔHv cal/g			m	300 to	-0.0713	4
			25°C	96.32	5	n	600 °K	0.0017	4
Pressure			30 mm	63.81	5	o		-0.0₆88	4
mm 25°C	0.0₄28	5	BP	50.24	5				
t_e	1614.	5	t_e	46.34	5	m'	700 to	0.0811	4
			t_e (d, e)	45.63	5	n'	1000 °K	0.0012	4
Density			ΔHv/T_e	18.83	5	o'		-0.0₆41	4
g/ml 20°C	0.8196	2							
d_4^t 25	0.8162	2	d 220 to	88.05	5	Surface tension			
30	0.8128	4	e 375 °C	0.1109	5	dynes/cm. 20°C	28.23	5
			d' 25 to	100.52	5	γ	30	27.31	5
a	0.8332	4	e' 220 °C	0.1679	5		40	26.40	5
b	-0.0₃68	4	d_c g/ml						
			v_c ml/g			Parachor [P]			
Ref. Index			t_c °C	499.2	5	20°C		
n_D 20°C	1.4543	2	P_c mm	8481.	5	30		
25	1.4522	4				40		
30	1.4503	4	PV/RT			Sugd.	749.5	5
"C"	0.7337	4	25°C	1.0000	5			
			30 mm	1.0000	5	Exp. L.1.%/wt.		
MR (Obs.)	88.10	2	BP	0.9158	4	u.		
MR (Calc.)	88.742	5	t_e	0.8845	5	Dispersion	97.	2
(nD-d/2)	1.0445	2	t_c					
			ΔHc kcal/m	2795.66	2	Flash Point °C		
Dielectric	2.115	5	ΔHf			Fire Point		
A 220 to	7.003	2	ΔFf			M Spec.		
B 400 °C	1987.	2				Ultra V.		
C	141.	2	Viscosity			X-Ray Dif.		
			centistokes			Infrared		
A* 220 to	1.713	5	η 20 °C	8.67	2			
B* 390 °C	1905.	5	40	5.47	2	Solubility in +		
K			60	3.63	2	Acetone	∞	
c			80	2.59	2	Carbon tet.	∞	
t_k to						Benzene	∞	
t_x °C			B^V 10 to	923.48	4	Ether	∞	
A' 20 to	7.351	5	A^V 70 °C	3.78836	4	n-Heptane	∞	
B' 220 °C	2245.	5				Ethanol	∞	
C'	164.	5	(B^V) 70 to	813.43	4	Water		
			(A^V) 120 °C	2.11027	4	Water in		
A'* 25 to	2.078	5						
B'* 220 °C	2164.	5	c_p liq. °K					
						Viscosity		
Ac to			c_p vap.300°K	0.36654	2	centistokes		
Bc t_c °C			400	0.47723	2	100°C	1.96	2
Cc			c_v vap.			110	1.71	2
Cryos. A°								
consts. B°								
t_e °C	382.6	5						

+ grams/100 grams solvent

REFERENCES: 1-Dow 2-API 3-Lit. 4-Calc. from det. data 5-Calc. by formula

SOURCE: API

PURIFICATION: API

LITERATURE REFERENCES:

TABLE XV. CYCLOPENTANES

No. 35

NAME	n-Pentadecylcyclopentane	STRUCTURAL FORMULA
	1-Cyclopentylpentadecane	$CHC_{15}H_{31}$ H_2C CH_2 $H_2C—CH_2$

Mole % Pur.	Ref.	Molecular Formula $C_{20}H_{40}$	Molecular Weight 280.520

		Ref.			Ref.				Ref.
F. P. °C	17.	2	dt/dP			f	to		
F. P. 100%			°C/mm			g	_ _ °K		
B. P. °C			25°C	794272.	5	h			
760 mm	355.	2	BP	0.0679	5				
100	269.	2	t_e	0.0371	5	f'	to		
30	231.	4	30 mm	0.9585	5	g'	_ _ °K		
10	201.	5	ΔHm cal/g			h'			
1	152.	5	ΔHv cal/g			m	300 to	-0.0667	4
Pressure			25°C	98.13	5	n	600 °K	0.0017	4
mm 25°C	0.0_581	5	30 mm	62.51	5	o		-0.0_686	4
t_e	1649.	5	BP	49.04	5				
Density			t_e	45.05	5	m'	700 to	0.0847	4
g/ml 20°C	0.8213	2	t_e (d, e)	44.33	5	n'	1000 °K	0.0012	4
d_4^t 25	0.8178	2	$ΔHv/T_e$	18.81	5	o'		-0.0_641	4
30	0.8143	4	d 230 to	87.46	5	Surface tension			
a	0.8353	4	e 390 °C	0.1082	5	dynes/cm. 20°C		28.40	5
b	-0.0_37	4	d' 25 to	102.46	5	𝛾	30	27.45	5
Ref. Index			e' 230 °C	0.1733	5		40	26.51	5
n_D 20°C	1.4554	2	d_c g/ml			Parachor [P]			
25	1.4533	5	v_c ml/g				20°C		
30	1.4513	4	t_c °C	507.2	5		30		
"C"	0.7339	4	P_c mm	7723.	5		40		
MR (Obs.)	92.74	2	PV/RT				Sugd.	788.5	5
MR (Calc.)	92.360	5	25°C	1.0000	5	Exp. L.1.%/wt.			
(nD-d/2)	1.0447	2	30 mm	1.0000	5	u.			
Dielectric	2.118	5	BP	0.9146	4	Dispersion		97.	2
A 230 to	7.013	2	t_e	0.8822	5	Flash Point °C			
B 410 °C	2029.	2	t_c			Fire Point			
C	136.	2	ΔHc kcal/m	2942.58	2	M. Spec.			
A* 230 to	1.739	5	ΔHf			Ultra V.			
B* 405 °C	1947.	5	ΔFf			X-Ray Dif.			
K			Viscosity			Infrared			
c			centistokes			Solubility in +			
t_k to			η 30 °C	7.88	2	Acetone		∞	
t_x °C			40	6.27	2	Carbon tet.		∞	
A' 25 to	7.362	5	60	4.09	2	Benzene		∞	
B' 230 °C	2293.	5	80	2.89	2	Ether		∞	
C'	159.	5	B^v 20 to	959.11	4	n-Heptane		∞	
A'* 25 to	2.109	5	A^v 70 °C	3.73324	4	Ethanol		∞	
B'* 230 °C	2213.	5	(B^v) 70 to	842.49	4	Water			
Ac to			(A^v) 120 °C	2.07561	4	Water in			
Bc t_c °C			c_p liq. °K			Viscosity			
Cc						centistokes			
Cryos. A°			c_p vap.300°K	0.36778	2		100°C	2.16	2
consts. B°			400	0.47811	2		110	1.88	2
t_e °C	398.53	5	c_v vap.						

+ grams/100 grams solvent

REFERENCES: 1-Dow 2-API 3-Lit. 4-Calc. from det. data 5-Calc. by formula

SOURCE: API

PURIFICATION: API

LITERATURE REFERENCES:

No. 36

NAME	n-Hexadecylcyclopentane	STRUCTURAL FORMULA
	1-Cyclopentylhexadecane	$H_2C \overset{CHC_{16}H_{33}}{\underset{}{\diagup}} CH_2$ $H_2C — CH_2$

Mole % Pur.	Ref.	Molecular Formula $C_{21}H_{42}$	Molecular Weight 294.546

		Ref.			Ref.				Ref.
F.P. °C	21.	2	dt/dP °C/mm			f	to °K		
F.P. 100%			25°C	2.3×10^6	5	g			
B.P. °C			BP	0.0690	5	h			
760 mm	368.	2	t_e	0.0370	5				
100	280.	2	30 mm	0.9750	5	f'	to °K		
30	241.	4	ΔHm cal/g			g'			
10	212.	2	ΔHv cal/g			h'			
1	162.	4	25°C	99.15	5	m	300 to	0.0625	4
Pressure			30 mm	61.08	5	n	600 °K	0.0017	4
mm 25°C	0.0_526	5	BP	47.89	5	o		-0.0_685	4
t_e	1687.	5	t_e	43.89	5	m'	700 to	0.0849	4
Density			t_e (d, e)	43.14	5	n'	1000 °K	0.0012	4
g/ml 20°C	0.8228	2	$\Delta Hv/T_e$	18.82	5	o'		-0.0_641	4
d_4^t 25	0.8194	2	d 240 to	86.21	5	Surface tension			
30	0.8160	4	e 410 °C	0.1041	5	dynes/cm. 20°C		28.55	5
a	0.8364	4	d' 25 to	103.55	5	ℽ 30		27.62	5
b	-0.0_368	4	e' 240 °C	0.1759	5	40		26.71	5
Ref. Index			d_c g/ml			Parachor [P]			
n_D 20°C	1.4564	2	v_c ml/g			20°C			
25	1.4543	2	t_c °C	517.5	5	30			
30	1.4524	4	P_c mm	7302.	5	40			
"C"	0.7340	4	PV/RT			Sugd.		827.5	5
MR (Obs.)	97.38‡	2	25°C	1.0000	5	Exp. L.1.%/wt.			
MR (Calc.)	96.978	5	30 mm	1.0000	5	u.			
(nD-d/2)	1.0450‡	2	BP	0.9151	5	Dispersion		97.	2
Dielectric	2.121	5	t_e	0.8828	5	Flash Point °C			
A 240 to	7.021	2	t_c			Fire Point			
B 430 °C	2070.	2	ΔHc kcal/m	3089.51	2	M Spec.			
C	132.	2	ΔHf			Ultra V.			
A* 240 to	1.758	2	ΔFf			X-Ray Dif.			
B* 420 °C	1986.	2	Viscosity			Infrared			
K			centistokes			Solubility in +			
c			η 30 °C	9.04	2	Acetone		∞	
t_k to			40	7.14	2	Carbon tet.		∞	
t_x °C			60	4.60	2	Benzene		∞	
A' 25 to	7.370	5	80	3.21	2	Ether		∞	
B' 240 °C	2339.	5	B^v 20 to	988.07	4	n-Heptane		∞	
C'	156.	5	A^v 70 °C	$\overline{3}.69736$	4	Ethanol		∞	
A'* 25 to	2.135	5	(B^v) 70 to	869.10	4	Water			
B'* 240 °C	2261.	5	(A^v) 120 °C	$\overline{2}.04496$	4	Water in			
Ac to			c_p liq. °K			Viscosity			
Bc t_c °C						centistokes			
Cc			c_p vap.300°K	0.36894	2	100°C		2.38	2
Cryos. A°			400	0.47891	2	110		2.06	2
consts. B°			c_v vap.						
t_e °C	413.62	5							

‡ for undercooled liquid   + grams/100 grams solvent

REFERENCES: 1-Dow 2-API 3-Lit. 4-Calc. from det. data 5-Calc. by formula

SOURCE:	API
PURIFICATION:	API
LITERATURE REFERENCES:	

TABLE XV. CYCLOPENTANES 395

No. 37

NAME	n-Heptadecylcyclopentane			STRUCTURAL FORMULA

1-Cyclopentylheptadecane

STRUCTURAL FORMULA

$$H_2C \overset{CHC_{17}H_{35}}{\underset{H_2C—CH_2}{CH_2}}$$

Mole % Pur.	Ref.	Molecular Formula $C_{22}H_{44}$	Molecular Weight 308.572	

		Ref.				Ref.					Ref.
F.P. °C	27.	2	dt/dP				f	to			
F.P. 100%			°C/mm				g	°K			
			25°C	$5.68x10^5$	5		h				
B.P. °C			BP	0.0699	5						
760 mm	380.	2	t_e	0.0363	5		f'	to			
100	290.	5	30 mm	1.0284	5		g'	°K			
30	249.	5	ΔHm cal/g				h'				
10	218.	5									
1	164.	5	ΔHv cal/g				m	to			
			25°C	75.17	5		n	°K			
Pressure			30 mm	56.95	5		o				
mm 25°C	0.0_4134	5	BP	46.89	5						
t_e	1724.	5	t_e	43.47	5		m'	to			
			t_e (d, e)	43.26	5		n'	°K			
Density			ΔHv/T_e	19.15	5		o'				
g/ml 20°C	$0.8241^{\neq}$	2									
d_4^t 25	$0.8207^{\neq}$	2	d 250 to	76.11	5		Surface tension			
30	0.8173	4	e 425 °C	0.0769	5		dynes/cm. 20°C	28.68	5
a	0.8377	4	d' 25 to	77.20	5		ỿ 30	27.74	5
b	-0.0_368	4	e' 250 °C	0.0813	5		40	26.83	5
Ref. Index			d_c g/ml				Parachor [P]		
n_D 20°C	$1.4572^{\neq}$	2	v_c ml/g				20°C		
25	$1.4552^{\neq}$	2	t_c °C	525.	5		30		
30	1.4532	4	P_c mm	7031.	5		40		
"C"	0.7341	4					Sugd.	866.5	5
MR (Obs.)	$102.02^{\neq}$	2	PV/RT						
MR (Calc.)	101.596	5	25°C	1.0000	5		Exp. L.1.%/wt.		
(nD-d/2)	$1.0452^{\neq}$	2	30 mm	1.0000	5		u.		
Dielectric	2.123	5	BP	0.9165	5		Dispersion	$97.^{\neq}$	2
			t_e	0.8846	5				
A 250 to	7.37712	5	t_c				Flash Point °C		
B 445 °C	2473.0	5					Fire Point		
C	170.	5	ΔHc kcal/m				M. Spec.		
A* 250 to	2.10488	5	ΔHf				Ultra V.		
B* 435 °C	2368.7	5	ΔFf				X-Ray Dif.		
K			Viscosity				Infrared		
c			centistokes				Solubility in +		
t_k to			η °C				Acetone	∞	
t_x °C							Carbon tet.	∞	
A' 25 to	7.7488	5					Benzene	∞	
B' 250 °C	2794.	5					Ether	∞	
C'	196.	5	B^v to				n-Heptane	∞	
			A^v °C				Ethanol	∞	
A'* 25 to	2.4848	5	(B^v) to				Water		
B'* 250 °C	2687.	5	(A^v) °C				Water in		
Ac to			c_p liq. °K						
Bc t_c °C									
Cc									
Cryos. A°			c_p vap. °K						
consts. B°									
t_e °C	427.	5	c_v vap.						

≠ for undercooled liquid

+ grams/100 grams solvent

REFERENCES: 1-Dow 2-API 3-Lit. 4-Calc. from det. data 5-Calc. by formula

SOURCE: API

PURIFICATION: API

LITERATURE REFERENCES:

No. 38

NAME	n-Octadecylcyclopentane		STRUCTURAL FORMULA
	1-Cyclopentyloctadecane		

H₂C—CHC₁₈H₃₇ CH₂ / H₂C—CH₂

Structural formula:
$$\begin{array}{c} \text{CHC}_{18}\text{H}_{37} \\ \text{H}_2\text{C} \quad\quad \text{CH}_2 \\ \text{H}_2\text{C}\text{---}\text{CH}_2 \end{array}$$

Mole % Pur.	Ref.	Molecular Formula $C_{23}H_{46}$		Molecular Weight 322.598					
			Ref.			Ref.			Ref.
F.P. °C	30.	2	dt/dP				f | | to		
F.P. 100%			°C/mm				g | |__ °K_		
B.P. °C			25°C	1.06×10^6	5		h |		
760 mm	391.	2	BP	0.07076	5				
100	300.	5	t_e	0.0362	5		f' | | to		
30	258.	5	30 mm	1.0448	5		g' | |__ °K_		
10	226.	5	ΔHm cal/g				h' |		
1	172.	5	ΔHv cal/g				m | | to		
Pressure			25°C	73.51	5		n | |__ °K_		
mm 25°C	0.0_5704	5	30 mm	55.51	5		o |		
t_e	1755.	5	BP	45.81	5				
Density			t_e	42.40	5		m' | | to		
g/ml 20°C	0.8254‡	2	t_e (d, e)	42.23	5		n' | |__ °K_		
d_4^t 25	0.8220‡	2	ΔHv/T_e	19.18	5		o' |		
30	0.8186	4	d | 260 to	74.40	5		Surface tension		
a	0.8390	4	e |_440_°C	0.0731	5		dynes/cm. 20°C	28.81	5
b	-0.0_368	4	d' | 25 to	75.44	5		۷ 30	27.87	5
Ref. Index			e' | 260 °C	0.0771	5		40	26.96	5
n_D 20°C	1.4581‡	2	d_c g/ml				Parachor [P]		
25	1.4560‡	2	v_c ml/g				20°C		
30	1.4541	4	t_c °C	531.	5		30		
"C"	0.7343	4	P_c mm	6541.	5		40		
MR (Obs.)	106.66‡	2	PV/RT				Sugd.	905.5	5
MR (Calc.)	106.214	5	25°C	1.0000	5		Exp. L.1.%/wt.		
(nD-d/2)	1.0454‡	2	30 mm	1.0000	5		u.		
Dielectric	2.126		BP	0.9169	5		Dispersion	97.‡	2
A | 260 to	7.41131	5	t_e	0.8846	5		Flash Point °C		
B |_460_°C	2541.6	5	t_c				Fire Point		
C	170.	5	ΔHc kcal/m				M Spec.		
A* | 260 to	2.14959	5	ΔHf				Ultra V.		
B* |_450_°C	2434.5	5	ΔFf				X-Ray Dif.		
K			Viscosity				Infrared		
c			centistokes				Solubility in +		
t_k | to			η °C				Acetone	∞	
t_x | °C							Carbon tet.	∞	
A' | 25 to	7.7852	5					Benzene	∞	
B' |_260_°C	2872.	5					Ether	∞	
C'	197.	5	B^v | to				n-Heptane	∞	
A'* 25 to	2.5346	5	A^v | °C				Ethanol	∞	
B'* 260 °C	2763.	5	(B^v) | to				Water		
Ac | to			(A^v) | °C				Water in		
Bc |_t_c_			c_p liq. °K						
Cc									
Cryos. A°			c_p vap. °K						
consts. B°									
t_e °C	440.	5	c_v vap.						

‡ for undercooled liquid

+ grams/100 grams solvent

REFERENCES: 1-Dow 2-API 3-Lit. 4-Calc. from det. data 5-Calc. by formula

SOURCE: API

PURIFICATION: API

LITERATURE REFERENCES:

TABLE XV. CYCLOPENTANES

No. 39

NAME	n-Nonadecylcyclopentane	STRUCTURAL FORMULA
	1-Cyclopentylnonadecane	$CHC_{19}H_{39}$

Mole % Pur.	Ref.	Molecular Formula $C_{24}H_{48}$	Molecular Weight 336.624

Structural formula:

$$H_2C \quad CH_2$$
$$H_2C—CH_2$$

		Ref.			Ref.					Ref.
F.P. °C	35.	2	dt/dP			f		to		
F.P. 100%			°C/mm			g		°K		
B.P. °C			25°C	2.00×10^6	5	h				
760 mm	402.	2	BP	0.07157	5					
100	310.	5	t_e	0.0345	5	f'		to		
30	268.	5	30 mm	1.0608	5	g'		°K		
10	235.	5	ΔHm cal/g			h'				
1	180.	5	ΔHv cal/g			m		to		
Pressure			25°C	72.03	5	n		°K		
mm 25°C	0.0_5364	5	30 mm	54.24	5	o				
t_e	1891.	5	BP	46.83	5	m'		to		
Density			t_e	43.57	5	n'		°K		
g/ml 20°C	$0.8266^{\neq}$	2	t_e (d, e)	43.84	5	o'				
d_4^t 25	$0.8232^{\neq}$	2	$\Delta Hv/T_e$	20.10	5	Surface tension				
30	0.8198	4	d | 270 to	68.97	5	dynes/cm. 20°C		28.93	5
a	0.8402	4	e | 450 °C	0.0551	5	γ	30	27.99	5
b	-0.0_368	4	d' | 25 to	73.86	5		40	27.08	5
Ref. Index			e' | 270 °C	0.0734	5	Parachor [P]				
n_D 20°C	$1.4588^{\neq}$	2	d_c g/ml			20°C				
25	$1.4568^{\neq}$	2	v_c ml/g			30				
30	1.4548	4	t_c °C	542.	5	40				
"C"	0.7343	4	P_c mm	6403.	5	Sugd.	944.5		5
MR (Obs.)	$111.30^{\neq}$	2	PV/RT			Exp. L.1.%/wt.				
MR (Calc.)	110.832	5	25°C	1.0000	5	u.				
(nD-d/2)	$1.0456^{\neq}$	2	30 mm	1.0000	5	Dispersion		$97.^{\neq}$	2
Dielectric	2.128	5	BP	0.9572	5	Flash Point °C				
A | 270 to	7.44786	5	t_e	0.9315	5	Fire Point				
B | 475 °C	2612.4	5	t_c			M. Spec.				
C	170.	5	ΔHc kcal/m			Ultra V.				
A* | 270 to	2.11794	5	ΔHf			X-Ray Dif.				
B* | 465 °C	2468.4	5	ΔFf			Infrared				
K			Viscosity			Solubility in +				
c			centistokes			Acetone		∞		
t_k | to			η °C			Carbon tet.		∞		
t_x | °C						Benzene		∞		
A' | 25 to	7.8240	5				Ether		∞		
B' | 270 °C	2952.	5				n-Heptane		∞		
C'	198.	5	B^v | to			Ethanol		∞		
A'* 25 to	2.5861	5	A^v | °C			Water				
B'* 270 °C	2842.	5	(B^v)| to			Water in				
Ac | to			(A^v)| °C							
Bc t_c °C			c_p liq. °K							
Cc										
Cryos. A°			c_p vap. °K							
consts. B°										
t_e °C	456.	5	c_v vap.							

$\neq$ for undercooled liquid   + grams/100 grams solvent

REFERENCES: 1-Dow 2-API 3-Lit. 4-Calc. from det. data 5-Calc. by formula

SOURCE:	API
PURIFICATION:	· API

LITERATURE REFERENCES:

No. 40

NAME	n-Eicosylcyclopentane	STRUCTURAL FORMULA
	1-Cyclopentyleicosane	$CHC_{20}H_{41}$ H_2C CH_2 H_2C—CH_2

Mole % Pur.	Ref.	Molecular Formula	$C_{25}H_{50}$	Molecular Weight 350.650	

		Ref.				Ref.				Ref.
F.P. °C	38.	2	dt/dP				f	to		
F.P. 100%			°C/mm				g	°K		
B.P. °C			25°C	5.24×10^6	5		h			
760 mm	413.	2	BP	0.07112	5					
100	321.	5	t_e	0.0343	5		f'	to		
30	279.	5	30 mm	1.0667	5		g'	°K		
10	246.	5	ΔHm cal/g				h'			
1	190.	5	ΔHv cal/g				m	to		
Pressure			25°C	71.84	5		n	°K		
mm 25°C	$0.0_5 134$	5	30 mm	53.92	5		o			
t_e	1876.	5	BP	45.89	5		m'	to		
Density			t_e	42.54	5		n'	°K		
g/ml 20°C	$0.8276^{\neq}$	2	t_e (d, e)	42.70	5		o'			
d_4^t 25	$0.8242^{\neq}$	2	$\Delta Hv/T_e$	20.17	5		Surface tension			
30	0.8208	4	d 280 to	70.56	5		dynes/cm. 20°C	29.03	5	
a	0.8412	4	e 455 °C	0.0597	5		30	28.09	5	
b	$-0.0_3 68$	4	d' 25 to	73.60	5		40	27.17	5	
Ref. Index			e' 280 °C	0.0707	5		Parachor [P]			
n_D 20°C	$1.4595^{\neq}$	2	d_c g/ml				20°C			
25	$1.4575^{\neq}$	2	v_c ml/g				30			
30	1.4554	2	t_c °C	545.	5		40			
"C"	0.7344	4	P_c mm	5959.	5		Sugd.	983.5	5	
MR (Obs.)	$115.94^{\neq}$	2	PV/RT				Exp. L. l. %/wt.			
MR (Calc.)	115.450	5	25°C	1.0000	5		u.			
(nD-d/2)	$1.0457^{\neq}$	2	30 mm	1.0000	5		Dispersion	$97.^{\neq}$	2	
Dielectric	2.130		BP	0.9406	5		Flash Point °C			
A 280 to	7.56514	5	t_e	0.9118	5		Fire Point			
B 485 °C	2731.0	5	t_c				M Spec.			
C	170.	5	ΔHc kcal/m				Ultra V.			
A* 280 to	2.27815	5	ΔHf				X-Ray Dif.			
B* 475 °C	2598.6	5	ΔFf				Infrared			
K			Viscosity				Solubility in +			
c			centistokes				Acetone	∞		
t_k to			η °C				Carbon tet.	∞		
t_x °C							Benzene	∞		
A' 25 to	7.9487	5					Ether	∞		
B' 280 °C	3086.	5					n-Heptane	∞		
C'	198.	5	B^v to				Ethanol	∞		
A'* 25 to	2.7216	5	A^v °C				Water			
B'* 280 °C	2974.	5	(B^v) to				Water in			
Ac to			(A^v) °C							
Bc t_c °C										
Cc			c_p liq. °K							
Cryos. A°			c_p vap. °K							
consts. B°										
t_e °C	466.	5	c_v vap.							

$\neq$ for undercooled liquid

+ grams/100 grams solvent

REFERENCES: 1-Dow 2-API 3-Lit. 4-Calc. from det. data 5-Calc. by formula
SOURCE: API
PURIFICATION: API
LITERATURE REFERENCES:

TABLE XV. CYCLOPENTANES

NAME	n-Heneicosylcyclopentane	STRUCTURAL FORMULA
	1-Cyclopentylheneicosane	$CHC_{21}H_{43}$ H_2C CH_2 H_2C-CH_2

Mole % Pur.	Ref.	Molecular Formula $C_{26}H_{52}$	Molecular Weight 364.676

		Ref.			Ref.			Ref.
F.P. °C	42.	2	dt/dP			f | to		
F.P. 100%			°C/mm			g | - - °K		
B.P. °C			25°C	6.9×10^6	5	h |		
760 mm	423.	2	BP	0.07306	5			
100	328.	5	t_e	0.0343	5	f' | to		
30	285.	5	30 mm	1.0907	5	g' | - - °K		
10	252.	5	ΔHm cal/g			h' |		
1	195.	5	ΔHv cal/g			m | to		
Pressure			25°C	69.31	5	n | °K		
mm 25°C	0.0_5101	5	30 mm	51.93	5	o |		
t_e	1950.		BP	44.94	5	m' | to		
Density			t_e	41.69	5	n' | °K		
g/ml 20°C	0.8286‡	2	t_e (d, e)	42.03	5	o' |		
d_4^t 25	0.8252‡	2	ΔHv/T_e	20.17	5	Surface tension		
30	0.8218	4	d | 285 to	66.40	5	dynes/cm. 20°C	29.13	5
a	0.8422	4	e | 470 °C	0.0507	5	γ 30	28.19	5
b	-0.0_368	4	d' | 25 to	70.98	5	40	27.27	5
Ref. Index			e' | 285 °C	0.0668	5	Parachor [P]		
n_D 20°C	1.4602‡	2	d_c g/ml			20°C		
25	1.4582‡	2	v_c ml/g			30		
30	1.4562	4	t_c °C	553.	5	40		
"C"	0.7345	4	P_c mm	5559.	5	Sugd.	1022.5	5
MR (Obs.)	120.58‡	2	PV/RT			Exp. L.l.%/wt.		
MR (Calc.)	120.068	5	25°C	1.0000	5	u.		
(nD-d/2)	1.0459‡	2	30 mm	1.0000	5	Dispersion	97.‡	2
Dielectric	2.132	5	BP	0.9563	5	Flash Point °C		
A | 285 to	7.51897	5	t_e	0.9301	5	Fire Point		
B | 500 °C	2750.4	5	t_c			M. Spec.		
C	170.	5	ΔHc kcal/m			Ultra V.		
A* | 285 to	2.21011	5	ΔHf			X-Ray Dif.		
B* | 490 °C	2600.7	5	ΔFf			Infrared		
K			Viscosity			Solubility in +		
c			centistokes			Acetone	∞	
t_k | to			η °C			Carbon tet.	∞	
t_x | °C						Benzene	∞	
A' | 25 to	7.8996	5				Ether	∞	
B' | 285 °C	3108.	5				n-Heptane	∞	
C'	199.	5	B^v | to			Ethanol	∞	
A'* 25 to	2.6854	5	A^v | °C			Water		
B'* 285 °C	2994.	5	(B^v)| to			Water in		
Ac | to			(A^v)| °C					
Bc t_c °C			c_p liq. °K					
Cc								
Cry's. A°			c_p vap. °K					
consts. B°								
t_e °C	480.	5	c_v vap.					

‡ for undercooled liquid | + grams/100 grams solvent

REFERENCES: 1-Dow 2-API 3-Lit. 4-Calc. from det. data 5-Calc. by formula

SOURCE: API

PURIFICATION: API

LITERATURE REFERENCES:

No. 42

NAME	n-Docosylcyclopentane	STRUCTURAL FORMULA
	1-Cyclopentyldocosane	CHC₂₂H₄₅ / H₂C CH₂ / H₂C—CH₂

Mole % Pur.	Ref.	Molecular Formula	$C_{27}H_{54}$	Molecular Weight 378.702	

		Ref.			Ref.				Ref.
F.P. °C	45.	2	dt/dP °C/mm			f	to	
F.P. 100%			25°C	1.26×10^7	5	g $\_\_$ °K		
B.P. °C			BP	0.07375	5	h		
760 mm	433.	2	t_e	0.0340	5	f'	to	
100	337.	4	30 mm	1.1048	5	g' $\_\_$ °K		
30	294.	5	ΔHm cal/g			h'		
10	260.	5	ΔHv cal/g			m	to	
1	202.	5	25°C	68.04	5	n $\_\_$ °K		
Pressure mm 25°C	0.0_6546	5	30 mm	50.88	5	o		
t_e.	1985.	5	BP	44.20	5	m'	to	
Density			t_e	40.96	5	n' $\_\_$ °K		
g/ml 20°C	0.8295‡	2	t_e (d, e)	41.37	5	o'		
d_4^t 25	0.8262‡	2	$\Delta Hv/T_e$	20.27	5	Surface tension		
30	0.8229	4	d 295 to	64.96	5	dynes/cm. 20°C	29.23	5
a	0.8427	4	e 475 °C	0.0479	5	𝛾 30	28.31	5
b	-0.0_366	4	d' 25 to	69.64	5	40	27.41	5
Ref. Index			e' 295 °C	0.0639	5	Parachor [P]		
n_D 20°C	1.4608‡	2	d_c g/ml			20°C		
25	1.4588‡	2	v_c ml/g			30		
30	1.4568	4	t_c °C	561.	5	40		
"C"	0.7346	4	P_c mm	5343.	5	Sugd.	1061.5	5
MR (Obs.)	125.22‡	2	PV/RT			Exp. L. l.%/wt.		
MR (Calc.)	124.686	5	25°C	1.0000	5	u.		
(nD-d/2)	1.0460‡	2	30 mm	1.0000	5	Dispersion	97.‡	2
Dielectric	2.134	5	BP	0.9584	5	Flash Point °C		
A 295 to	7.55306	5	t_e	0.9321	5	Fire Point		
B 510 °C	2817.4	5	t_c			M Spec.		
C	170.	5	ΔHc kcal/m			Ultra V.		
A* 295 to	2.24989	5	ΔHf			X-Ray Dif.		
B* 500 °C	2663.0	5	ΔFf			Infrared		
K			Viscosity			Solubility in +		
c			centistokes			Acetone	∞	
t_k to			η °C			Carbon tet.	∞	
t_x °C						Benzene	∞	
A' 25 to	7.9358	5				Ether	∞	
B' 295 °C	3184.	5				n-Heptane	∞	
C'	199.	5	B^v to			Ethanol	∞	
A'* 25 to	2.7329	5	A^v °C			Water		
B'* 295 °C	3069.	5	(B^v) to			Water in		
Ac to			(A^v) °C					
Bc t_c °C			c_p liq. °K					
Cc								
Cryos. A° consts. B°			c_p vap. °K					
t_e °C	492.	5	c_v vap.					

‡ for undercooled liquid + grams/100 grams solvent

REFERENCES: 1-Dow 2-API 3-Lit. 4-Calc. from det. data 5-Calc. by formula

SOURCE: API

PURIFICATION: API

LITERATURE REFERENCES:

TABLE XV. CYCLOPENTANES 401

No. 43

NAME	n-Tricosylcyclopentane	STRUCTURAL FORMULA
	1-Cyclopentyltricosane	$H_2C \quad CHC_{23}H_{47}$ CH_2 $H_2C—CH_2$

Mole % Pur.	Ref.	Molecular Formula $C_{28}H_{56}$	Molecular Weight 392.728

		Ref.				Ref.						Ref.
F.P. °C	49.	2	dt/dP				f		to			
F.P. 100%			°C/mm				g		°K			
			25°C	2.2x10^7	5		h					
B.P. °C			BP	0.0743	5							
760 mm	442.	2	t_e	0.0339	5		f'		to			
100	345.	5	30 mm	1.1168	5		g'		°K			
30	301.	5	ΔHm cal/g				h'					
10	267.	5										
1	208.	5	ΔHv cal/g				m		to			
			25°C	66.79	5		n		°K			
Pressure			30 mm	49.86	5		o					
mm 25°C	0.0$_6$31	5	BP	43.34	5							
t_e	2010.	5	t_e	40.09	5		m'		to			
			t_e (d, e)	40.54	5		n'		°K			
Density							o'					
g/ml 20°C	0.8304$^{\neq}$	2	ΔHv/T_e	20.30	5							
d_4^t 25	0.8270$^{\neq}$	2					Surface tension					
30	0.8236	4	d 300 to	63.85	5		dynes/cm. 20°C		29.32	5		
			e 500 °C	0.0464	5		ɤ		30	28.37	5	
a	0.8440	4	d' 25 to	68.32	5				40	27.44	5	
b	-0.0$_3$68	4	e' 300 °C	0.0612	5							
							Parachor [P]					
Ref. Index			d_c g/ml						20°C			
n_D 20°C	1.4614$^{\neq}$	2	v_c ml/g						30			
25	1.4593$^{\neq}$	2	t_c °C	563.	5				40			
30	1.4573	4	P_c mm	4535.	5				Sugd.	1100.5	5	
"C"	0.7347	4										
MR (Obs.)	129.86$^{\neq}$	2	PV/RT				Exp. L.1.%/wt.					
MR (Calc.)	129.304	5	25°C	1.0000	5		u.					
(nD-d/2)	1.0462$^{\neq}$	2	30 mm	1.0000	5		Dispersion		97.$^{\neq}$		2	
Dielectric	2.136	5	BP	0.9579	5		Flash Point °C					
A 300 to	7.58769	5	t_e	0.9315	5		Fire Point					
B 515 °C	2880.6	5	t_c									
C	170.	5	ΔHc kcal/m				M. Spec.					
			ΔHf				Ultra V.					
A* 300 to	2.29492	5	ΔFf				X-Ray Dif.					
B* 510 °C	2723.8	5					Infrared					
K			Viscosity				Solubility in $^+$					
c			centistokes				Acetone		∞			
t_k to			η °C				Carbon tet.		∞			
t_x °C							Benzene		∞			
A' 25 to	7.9727	5					Ether		∞			
B' 300 °C	3255.	5					n-Heptane		∞			
C'	200.	5	B^v to				Ethanol		∞			
			A^v °C				Water					
A'* 25 to	2.7809	5	(B^v) to				Water in					
B'* 300 °C	3139.	5	(A^v) °C									
Ac to												
Bc t_c °C			c_p liq. °K									
Cc			c_p vap. °K									
Cryos. A°												
consts. B°			c_v vap.									
t_e °C	502.	5										

$\neq$ for undercooled liquid $^+$ grams/100 grams solvent

REFERENCES: 1-Dow   2-API   3-Lit.   4-Calc. from det. data   5-Calc. by formula

SOURCE: API

PURIFICATION: API

LITERATURE REFERENCES:

No. 44

NAME	n-Tetracosylcyclopentane	STRUCTURAL FORMULA

| | 1-Cyclopentyltetracosane | |

Structural formula: H_2C $CHC_{24}H_{49}$ / CH_2 ; H_2C—CH_2

Mole % Pur.	Ref.	Molecular Formula $C_{29}H_{58}$	Molecular Weight 406.754

		Ref.			Ref.				Ref.
F.P. °C	51.	2	dt/dP °C/mm			f	to		
F.P. 100%			25°C	2.3×10^8	5	g	$\underline{\quad °K\quad}$		
B.P. °C			BP	0.07485	5	h			
760 mm	451.	2	t_e	0.0341	5	f'	to		
100	354.	5	30 mm	1.1075	5	g'	$\underline{\quad °K\quad}$		
30	310.	5				h'			
10	277.	5	ΔHm cal/g						
1	219.	5	ΔHv cal/g			m	to		
Pressure			25°C	77.64	5	n	$\underline{\quad °K\quad}$		
mm 25°C	0.0_624	5	30 mm	50.10	5	o			
t_e	2032.	5	BP	42.53	5	m'	to		
Density			t_e	38.93	5	n'	$\underline{\quad °K\quad}$		
g/ml 20°C	$0.8312^{\neq}$	2	t_e (d, e)	39.21	5	o'			
d_4^t 25	$0.8278^{\neq}$	2	ΔHv/T_e	20.15	5	Surface tension			
30	0.8244	4	d 310 to	66.81	5	dynes/cm. 20°C	29.40	5
a	0.8448	4	e 510 °C	0.0534	5	y 30	28.45	5
b	-0.0_368	4	d' 25 to	80.05	5	40	27.52	5
Ref. Index			e' 310 °C	0.0965	5	Parachor [P]		
n_D 20°C	$1.4619^{\neq}$	2	d_c g/ml			20°C		
25	$1.4599^{\neq}$	2	v_c ml/g			30		
30	1.4578	2	t_c °C			40		
"C"	0.7273	4	P_c mm	567.1	5	Sugd.	1139.5	5
MR (Obs.)	$134.50^{\neq}$	2		4194.	5	Exp. L. 1.%/wt.		
MR (Calc.)	133.922	5	PV/RT			u.		
(nD-d/2)	$1.0463^{\neq}$	2	25°C	1.0000	5	Dispersion	$97.^{\neq}$	2
Dielectric	2.137	5	30 mm	1.0000	5	Flash Point °C		
A 310 to	7.43095	5	BP	0.9570	5	Fire Point		
B 520 °C	2711.9	5	t_e	0.9291	5	M Spec.		
C	145.	5	t_c			Ultra V.		
A* 310 to	2.16291	5	ΔHc kcal/m			X-Ray Dif.		
B* 515 °C	2567.8	5	ΔHf			Infrared		
K			ΔFf					
c			Viscosity			Solubility in +		
t_k to			centistokes			Acetone	∞	
t_x °C			η °C			Carbon tet.	∞	
A' 25 to	7.8060	5				Benzene	∞	
B' 310 °C	3064.	5				Ether	∞	
C'	174.	5	B^v to			n-Heptane	∞	
A'* 25 to	2.6513	5	A^v °C			Ethanol	∞	
B'* 310 °C	2966.	5	(B^v) to			Water		
Ac to			(A^v) °C			Water in		
Bc t_c °C								
Cc			c_p liq. °K					
Cryos. A°			c_p vap. °K					
consts. B°								
t_e °C	513.	5	c_v vap.					

≠ for undercooled liquid   + grams/100 grams solvent

REFERENCES: 1-Dow 2-API 3-Lit. 4-Calc. from det. data 5-Calc. by formula

SOURCE:	API
PURIFICATION:	API
LITERATURE REFERENCES:	

TABLE XV CYCLOPENTANES 403

No. 45

NAME	n-Pentacosylcyclopentane	STRUCTURAL FORMULA
	1-Cyclopentylpentacosane	H_2C $CHC_{25}H_{51}$ CH_2
Mole % Pur.	Ref. Molecular Formula $C_{30}H_{60}$ Molecular Weight 420.780	H_2C—CH_2

		Ref.			Ref.				Ref.
F.P. °C	54.	2	dt/dP			f	to		
F.P. 100%			°C/mm			g	°K		
B.P. °C			25°C	$4.3x10^8$	5	h			
760 mm	460.	2	BP	0.07539	5				
100	363.	5	t_e	0.03395	5	f'	to		
30	318.	5	30 mm	1.1196	5	g'	°K		
10	284.	5	ΔHm cal/g			h'			
1	225.	5	ΔHv cal/g			m	to		
Pressure			25°C	76.41	5	n	°K		
mm 25°C	0.0_713	5	30 mm	49.18	5	o			
t_e	2058.	5	BP	41.83	5	m'	to		
Density			t_e	38.26	5	n'	°K		
g/ml 20°C	$0.8319^{\neq}$	2	t_e (d, e)	38.56	5	o'			
d_4^t 25	$0.8286^{\neq}$	2	ΔHv/T_e	20.22	5	Surface tension			
30	0.8253	4	d 320 to	65.67	5	dynes/cm. 20°C	29.47	5
a	0.8451	4	e 520 °C	0.0518	5	γ 30	28.55	5
b	-0.0_366	4	d' 25 to	78.73	5	40	27.64	5
Ref. Index			e' 320 °C	0.0929	5			
n_D 20°C	$1.4624^{\neq}$	2	d_c g/ml			Parachor [P]		
25	$1.4604^{\neq}$	2	v_c ml/g			20°C		
30	1.4584	4	t_c °C	574.	5	30		
"C"	0.7348	4	P_c mm	4047.	5	40		
MR (Obs.)	$139.14^{\neq}$	2	PV/RT			Sugd.	1178.5	5
MR (Calc.)	138.546	5	25°C	1.0000	5	Exp. L.1.%/wt.		
(nD-d/2)	$1.0464^{\neq}$	2	30 mm	1.0000	5	u.		
Dielectric	2.139	5	BP	0.9570	5	Dispersion	$98.^{\neq}$	2
A 320 to	7.46658	5	t_e	0.9289	5	Flash Point °C		
B 540 °C	2774.4	5	t_c			Fire Point		
C	145.	5	ΔHc kcal/m			M. Spec.		
A* 320 to	2.20707	5	ΔHf			Ultra V.		
B* 530 °C	2627.7	5	ΔFf			X-Ray Dif.		
K			Viscosity			Infrared		
c			centistokes			Solubility in +		
t_k to			η °C			Acetone	∞	
t_x °C						Carbon tet.	∞	
A' 25 to	7.8439	5				Benzene	∞	
B' 320 °C	3135.	5				Ether	∞	
C'	174.	5	B^v to			n-Heptane	∞	
A'* 25 to	2.6992	5	A^v °C			Ethanol	∞	
B'*320 °C	3035.	5	(B^v) to			Water		
Ac to			(A^v) °C			Water in		
Bc t_c °C			c_p liq. °K					
Cc								
Cryos. A°			c_p vap. °K					
consts. B°								
t_e °C	523.	5	c_v vap.					

≠ for undercooled liquid + grams/100 grams solvent

REFERENCES: 1-Dow 2-API 3-Lit. 4-Calc. from det. data 5-Calc. by formula

SOURCE: API

PURIFICATION: API

LITERATURE REFERENCES:

No. 46

NAME	n-Hexacosylcyclopentane		STRUCTURAL FORMULA		
	1-Cyclopentylhexacosane		H_2C $CHC_{26}H_{53}$ CH_2		
Mole % Pur.	Ref.	Molecular Formula $C_{31}H_{62}$	Molecular Weight 434.806	H_2C—CH_2	

		Ref.			Ref.				Ref.
F.P. °C	56.	2	dt/dP			f	to		
F.P. 100%			°C/mm			g	°K		
B.P. °C			25°C	$7.03x10^8$	5	h			
760 mm	468.	2	BP	0.07610	5				
100	370.	5	t_e	0.03384	5	f'	to		
30	325.	5	30 mm	1.1321	5	g'	°K		
10	290.	5	ΔHm cal/g			h'			
1	231.	5	ΔHv cal/g			m	to		
Pressure			25°C	74.89	5	n	°K		
mm 25°C	0.0_877	5	30 mm	48.11	5	o			
t_e	2089.	5	BP	41.07	5	m'	to		
Density			t_e	37.52	5	n'	°K		
g/ml 20°C	$0.8326^{\neq}$	2	t_e (d, e)	37.89	5	o'			
d_4^t 25	$0.8293^{\neq}$	2	$\Delta Hv/T_e$	20.24	5	Surface tension			
30	0.8260	4	d 325 to	64.08	5	dynes/cm. 20°C	29.54	5	
a	0.8458	4	e 530 °C	0.0492	5	y 30	28.62	5	
b	-0.0_366	4	d' 25 to	77.13	5	40	27.71	5	
Ref. Index			e' 325 °C	0.0893	5	Parachor [P]			
n_D 20°C	$1.4628^{\neq}$	2	d_c g/ml			20°C			
25	$1.4608^{\neq}$	2	v_c ml/g			30			
30	1.4588	4	t_c °C	578.	5	40			
"C"	0.7348	4	P_c mm	3797.	5	Sugd.	1217.5	5	
MR (Obs.)	$143.78^{\neq}$	2	PV/RT			Exp. L.1.%/wt.			
MR (Calc.)	143.158	5	25°C	1.0000	5	u.			
(nD-d/2)	$1.0465^{\neq}$	2	30 mm	1.0000	5	Dispersion	$98.^{\neq}$	2	
Dielectric	2.140	5	BP	0.9594	5	Flash Point °C			
A 325 to	7.48387	5	t_e	0.9315	5	Fire Point			
B 540 °C	2821.7	5	t_c			M Spec.			
C	145.	5	ΔHc kcal/m			Ultra V.			
A* 325 to	2.22858	5	ΔHf			X-Ray Dif.			
B* 540 °C	2670.4	5	ΔFf			Infrared			
K			Viscosity			Solubility in +			
c			centistokes			Acetone	∞		
t_k to			η °C			Carbon tet.	∞		
t_x °C						Benzene	∞		
A' 25 to	7.8623	5				Ether	∞		
B' 325 °C	3188.	5				n-Heptane	∞		
C'	175.	5	B^v to			Ethanol	∞		
A'* 25 to	2.7278	5	A^v °C			Water			
B'* 325 °C	3088.	5	(B^v) to			Water in			
Ac to			(A^v) °C						
Bc t_c °C			c_p liq. °K						
Cc									
Cryos. A°			c_p vap. °K						
consts. B°									
t_e °C	533.	5	c_v vap.						

$\neq$ for undercooled liquid   + grams/100 grams solvent

REFERENCES: 1-Dow 2-API 3-Lit. 4-Calc. from det. data 5-Calc. by formula

SOURCE: API

PURIFICATION: API

LITERATURE REFERENCES:

No. 47

NAME	n-Heptacosylcyclopentane	STRUCTURAL FORMULA
	1-Cyclopentylheptacosane	

Structural Formula:

$$\begin{array}{c} \text{CHC}_{27}\text{H}_{55} \\ \text{H}_2\text{C} \quad \text{CH}_2 \\ \text{H}_2\text{C}-\text{CH}_2 \end{array}$$

Mole % Pur.		Ref.	Molecular Formula $C_{32}H_{64}$		Molecular Weight 448.832	

		Ref.				Ref.					Ref.
F.P. °C	59.	2	dt/dP °C/mm				f	to °K			
F.P. 100%			25°C	1.3x10^9	5		g				
B.P. °C			BP	0.07631	5		h				
760 mm	476.	2	t_e	0.03367	5		f'	to °K			
100	377.	5	30 mm	1.1406	5		g'				
30	332.	5	ΔHm cal/g				h'				
10	297.	5	ΔHv cal/g				m	to °K			
1	237.	5	25°C	73.92	5		n				
Pressure			30 mm	47.39	5		o				
mm 25°C	0.0$_8$40	5	BP	40.39	5		m'	to °K			
t_e	2103.	5	t_e	36.81	5		n'				
Density			t_e (d, e)	37.22	5		o'				
g/ml 20°C	0.8333$^{\neq}$	2	ΔHv/T_e	20.29	5		Surface tension				
d_4^t 25	0.8299$^{\neq}$	2	d 330 to	63.53	5		dynes/cm. 20°C		29.62	5	
30	0.8265	4	e 530 °C	0.0486	5		γ 30		28.66	5	
a	0.8469	4	d' 25 to	76.07	5		40		27.73	5	
b	-0.0$_3$68	4	e' 330 °C	0.0864	5		Parachor [P]				
Ref. Index			d_c g/ml				20°C				
n_D 20°C	1.4633$^{\neq}$	2	v_c ml/g				30				
25	1.4612$^{\neq}$	2	t_c °C	578.	5		40				
30	1.4592	4	P_c mm	3434.	5		Sugd.		1256.5	5	
"C"	0.7349	4	PV/RT				Exp. L.l.%/wt.				
MR (Obs.)	148.42$^{\neq}$	2	25°C	1.0000	5		u.				
MR (Calc.)	147.776	5	30 mm	1.0000	5		Dispersion		98.$^{\neq}$	2	
(nD-d/2)	1.0466$^{\neq}$	2	BP	0.9565	5		Flash Point °C				
Dielectric	2.141	5	t_e	0.9283	5		Fire Point				
A 330 to	7.53111	5	t_c				M. Spec.				
B 550 °C	2887.8	5	ΔHc kcal/m				Ultra V.				
C	145.	5	ΔHf				X-Ray Dif.				
A* 330 to	2.28943	5	ΔFf				Infrared				
B* 540 °C	2736.6	5	Viscosity				Solubility in $^+$				
K			centistokes				Acetone		∞		
c			η °C				Carbon tet.		∞		
t_k to							Benzene		∞		
t_x °C							Ether		∞		
A' 25 to	7.9125	5					n-Heptane		∞		
B' 330 °C	3263.	5	B^v to				Ethanol		∞		
C'	175.	5	A^v °C				Water				
A'* 25 to	2.7876	5	(B^v) to				Water in				
B'* 330 °C	3162.	5	(A^v) °C								
Ac to			c_p liq. °K								
Bc t_c °C			c_p vap. °K								
Cc											
Cryos. A°			c_v vap.								
.consts. B°											
t_e °C	541.	5									

$\neq$ for undercooled liquid $^+$ grams/100 grams solvent

REFERENCES: 1-Dow 2-API 3-Lit. 4-Calc. from det. data 5-Calc. by formula

SOURCE: API

PURIFICATION: API

LITERATURE REFERENCES:

NAME	n-Octacosylcyclopentane	STRUCTURAL FORMULA

	1-Cyclopentyloctacosane	

$$\begin{array}{c} \text{CHC}_{28}\text{H}_{57} \\ \text{H}_2\text{C} \quad \text{CH}_2 \\ \text{H}_2\text{C}-\text{CH}_2 \end{array}$$

Mole % Pur.	Ref.	Molecular Formula	$C_{33}H_{66}$	Molecular Weight 462.858

		Ref.			Ref.			Ref.
F.P. °C	61.	2	dt/dP			f | to		
F.P. 100%			°C/mm			g | °K		
B.P. °C			25°C	2.2×10^9	5	h |		
760 mm	483.	2	BP	0.07669	5			
100	384.	5	t_e	0.03354	5	f' | to		
30	338.	5	30 mm	1.1497	5	g' | °K		
10	301.	5	ΔHm cal/g			h' |		
1	243.	5						
Pressure			ΔHv cal/g			m | to		
mm 25°C	0.0_824	5	25°C	72.66	5	n | °K		
t_e	2123.	5	30 mm	46.52	5	o |		
Density			BP	39.70	5			
g/ml 20°C	0.8339‡	2	t_e	36.15	5	m' | to		
d_4^t 25	0.8306‡	2	t_e (d, e)	36.59	5	n' | °K		
30	0.8273	4	ΔHv/T_e	20.35	5	o' |		
a	0.8471	4	d | 340 to	62.42	5	Surface tension		
b	-0.0$_3$66	4	e | 540 °C	0.0470	5	dynes/cm. 20°C	29.68	5
Ref. Index			d' | 25 to	74.75	5	ɣ 30	28.75	5
n_D 20°C	1.4637‡	2	e' | 340 °C	0.0835	5	40	27.84	5
25	1.4617‡	2	d_c g/ml			Parachor [P]		
30	1.4597	2	v_c ml/g			20°C		
"C"	0.7350	4	t_c °C	583.	5	30		
MR (Obs.)	153.06‡	2	P_c mm	3333.	5	40		
MR (Calc.)	152.394	5	PV/RT			Sugd.	1295.5	5
(nD-d/2)	1.0467‡	2	25°C	1.0000	5	Exp. L.1.%/wt.		
Dielectric	2.142	5	30 mm	1.0000	5	u.		
A | 340 to	7.56023	5	BP	0.9566	5	Dispersion	98.‡	2
B | 560 °C	2938.7	5	t_e	0.9280	5	Flash Point °C		
C	145.	5	t_c			Fire Point		
A* | 340 to	2.32753	5	ΔHc kcal/m			M Spec.		
B* | 550 °C	2785.6	5	ΔHf			Ultra V.		
K			ΔFf			X-Ray Dif.		
c			Viscosity			Infrared		
t_k | to			centistokes			Solubility in +		
t_x | °C			η °C			Acetone	∞	
A' | 25 to	7.9435	5				Carbon tet.	∞	
B' | 340 °C	3321.	5				Benzene	∞	
C'	175.	5	B^v | to			Ether	∞	
A'* 25 to	2.8282	5	A^v | °C			n-Heptane	∞	
B'* 340 °C	3218.	5	(B^v) | to			Ethanol	∞	
Ac | to			(A^v) | °C			Water		
Bc | t_c °C						Water in		
Cc			c_p liq. °K					
Cryos. A°			c_p vap. °K					
consts. B°								
t_e °C	549.	5	c_v vap.					

‡ for undercooled liquid   + grams/100 grams solvent

REFERENCES: 1-Dow   2-API   3-Lit.   4-Calc. from det. data   5-Calc. by formula

SOURCE: API

PURIFICATION: API

LITERATURE REFERENCES:

TABLE. XV. CYCLOPENTANES

407

No. 49

NAME	n-Nonacosylcyclopentane		STRUCTURAL FORMULA	
	1-Cyclopentylnonacosane			

Structural formula:
$$H_2C \overset{CHC_{29}H_{59}}{\underset{H_2C-CH_2}{\overset{|}{\underset{|}{CH_2}}}}$$

Mole % Pur.	Ref.	Molecular Formula $C_{34}H_{68}$	Molecular Weight 476.884

		Ref.			Ref.			Ref.
F.P. °C	63.	2	dt/dP			f $\vert$ $\quad$ to		
F.P. 100%			°C/mm			g $\vert$ $\quad$ °K		
B.P. °C			25°C	3.9×10^9	5	h $\vert$		
760 mm	491.	2	BP	0.07712	5			
100	391.	5	t_e	0.03340	5	f' $\vert$ $\quad$ to		
30	345.	5	30 mm	1.1599	5	g' $\vert$ $\quad$ °K		
10	309.	5	ΔHm cal/g			h' $\vert$		
1	249.	5	ΔHv cal/g			m $\vert$ $\quad$ to		
Pressure			25°C	71.61	5	n $\vert$ $\quad$ °K		
mm 25°C	0.0_813	5	30 mm	45.77	5	o $\vert$		
t_e	2146.	5	BP	39.10	5			
Density			t_e	35.55	5	m' $\vert$ $\quad$ to		
g/ml 20°C	$0.8345_4^{\neq}$	2	t_e (d, e)	36.03	5	n' $\vert$ $\quad$ °K		
d_4^t 25	$0.8312^{\neq}$	2	ΔHv/T_e	20.39	5	o' $\vert$		
30	0.8279	4	d $\vert$ 345 to	61.55	5	Surface tension		
a	0.8477	4	e $\vert$ 550 °C	0.0457	5	dynes/cm. 20°C	29.74	5
b	-0.0_366	4	d' $\vert$ 25 to	73.63	5	૪ 30	28.81	5
Ref. Index			e' $\vert$ 345 °C	0.0874	5	40	27.90	5
n_D 20°C	$1.4640^{\neq}$	2	d_c g/ml			Parachor [P]		
25	$1.4620^{\neq}$	2	v_c ml/g			20°C		
30	1.4600	4	t_c °C	586.	5	30		
"C"	0.7349	4	P_c mm	3123.	5	40		
MR (Obs.)	$157.71^{\neq}$	2	PV/RT			Sugd.	1334.5	5
MR (Calc.)	157.012	5	25°C	1.0000	5	Exp. L.1.%/wt.		
(nD-d/2)	$1.0468^{\neq}$	2	30 mm	1.0000	5	u.		
Dielectric	2.143	5	BP	0.9562	5	Dispersion	$98.^{\neq}$	2
A $\vert$ 345 to	7.59341	5	t_e	0.9276	5	Flash Point °C		
B $\vert$ 575 °C	2997.2	5	t_c			Fire Point		
C	145.	5	ΔHc kcal/m			M. Spec.		
A* 345 to	2.36899	5	ΔHf			Ultra V.		
B* 570 °C	2841.9	5	ΔFf			X-Ray Dif.		
K			Viscosity			Infrared		
c			centistokes			Solubility in +		
t_k $\vert$ to			η °C			Acetone	∞	
t_x $\vert$ °C						Carbon tet.	∞	
A' $\vert$ 25 to	7.9787	5				Benzene	∞	
B' $\vert$ 345 °C	3387.	5				Ether	∞	
C'	176.	5	B^v $\vert$ to			n-Heptane	∞	
A'* 25 to	2.8723	5	A^v $\vert$ °C			Ethanol	∞	
B'*345 °C	3283.	5	$(B^v)\vert$ to			Water		
Ac $\vert$ to			$(A^v)\vert$ °C			Water in		
Bc $\vert$ t_c °C			c_p liq. °K					
Cc								
Cryos. A°			c_p vap. °K					
consts. B°								
t_e °C	558.	5	c_v vap.					

≠ for undercooled liquid   + grams/100 grams solvent

REFERENCES: 1-Dow 2-API 3-Lit. 4-Calc. from det. data 5-Calc. by formula

SOURCE:	API
PURIFICATION:	API
LITERATURE REFERENCES:	

No. 50

NAME	n-Triacontylcyclopentane	STRUCTURAL FORMULA
	1-Cyclopentyltriacontane	$H_2C \overset{CHC_{30}H_{61}}{\underset{H_2C-CH_2}{\overset{CH_2}{|}}}$

Mole % Pur.	Ref.	Molecular Formula $C_{35}H_{70}$	Molecular Weight 490.910		

		Ref.				Ref.				Ref.
F.P. °C	65.	2	dt/dP				f	to		
F.P. 100%			°C/mm				g	°K		
			25°C	$6.6x10^9$	5		h			
B.P. °C			BP	0.07748	5					
760 mm	498.	2	t_e	0.03326	5		f'	to		
100	397.	5	30 mm	1.1686	5		g'	°K		
30	351.	5					h'			
10	315.	5	ΔHm cal/g							
1	254.	5	ΔHv cal/g				m	to		
Pressure			25°C	70.51	5		n	°K		
mm 25°C	0.0_978	5	30 mm	45.01	5		o			
t_e	2166.	5	BP	38.48	5					
Density			t_e	34.94	5		m'	to		
g/ml 20°C	0.8350≠	2	t_e (d, e)	35.45	5		n'	°K		
d_4^t 25	0.8317≠	2	ΔHv/T_e	20.43	5		o'			
30	0.8284	4	d ⏐ 350 to	60.61	5		Surface tension			
a	0.8482	4	e ⏐ 565 °C	0.0444	5		dynes/cm. 20°C	29.79	5
b	-0.0_366	4	d' ⏐ 25 to	72.46	5		γ 30	28.86	5
Ref. Index			e' ⏐ 350 °C	0.0782	5		40	27.95	5
n_D 20°C	1.4644≠	2	d_c g/ml				Parachor [P]			
25	1.4624≠	2	v_c ml/g				20°C			
30	1.4604	4	t_c °C	589.	5		30			
"C"	0.7350	4	P_c mm	2929.	5		40			
MR (Obs.)	162.35≠	2	PV/RT				Sugd.	1373.5	5
MR (Calc.)	161.630	5	25°C	1.0000	5		Exp. L.1.%/wt.			
(nD-d/2)	1.0469≠	2	30 mm	1.0000	5		u.			
Dielectric	2.144	5	BP	0.9561	5		Dispersion	98.≠	2
A ⏐350 to	7.62314	5	t_e	0.9273	5		Flash Point °C			
B ⏐580 °C	3049.3	5	t_c				Fire Point			
C	145.	5	ΔHc kcal/m				M Spec.			
A* ⏐350 to	2.40704	5	ΔHf				Ultra V.			
B* ⏐575 °C	2892.1	5	ΔFf				X-Ray Dif.			
K			Viscosity				Infrared			
c			centistokes				Solubility in +			
t_k ⏐ to			η °C				Acetone	∞	
t_x ⏐ °C							Carbon tet.	∞	
A' ⏐ 25 to	8.0103	5					Benzene	∞	
B' ⏐350 °C	3446.	5					Ether	∞	
C'	176.	5	B^v ⏐ to				n-Heptane	∞	
A'* 25 to	2.9130	5	A^v ⏐ °C				Ethanol	∞	
B'* 350 °C	3341.	5	(B^v) ⏐ to				Water		
Ac ⏐ to			(A^v) ⏐ °C				Water in		
Bc ⏐ t_c °C			c_p liq. °K						
Cc									
Cryos. A°			c_p vap. °K						
consts. B°									
t_e °C	566.	5	c_v vap.						

≠ for undercooled liquid   + grams/100 grams solvent

REFERENCES: 1-Dow   2-API   3-Lit.   4-Calc. from det. data   5-Calc. by formula

SOURCE: API

PURIFICATION: API

LITERATURE REFERENCES:

TABLE XV. CYCLOPENTANES

No. 51

NAME	n-Hentriacontylcyclopentane	STRUCTURAL FORMULA
	1-Cyclopentylhentriacontane	H_2C CHC$_{31}$H$_{63}$ / CH$_2$ H_2C——CH$_2$

Mole % Pur.	Ref.	Molecular Formula $C_{36}H_{72}$	Molecular Weight 504.936	

		Ref.			Ref.				Ref.
F.P. °C	67.	2	dt/dP			f $\vert$ to			
F.P. 100%			°C/mm			g $\vert$ __ °K			
B.P. °C			25°C	1.1×10^{10}	5	h $\vert$			
760 mm	505.	2	BP	0.0778	5				
100	404.	5	t_e	0.0331	5	f' $\vert$ to			
30	357.	5	30 mm	1.1770	5	g' $\vert$ __ °K			
10	321.	5	ΔHm cal/g			h' $\vert$			
1	259.	5	ΔHv cal/g			m $\vert$ to			
Pressure			25°C	69.50	5	n $\vert$ °K			
mm 25°C	0.0$_9$45	5	30 mm	44.31	5	o $\vert$			
t_e	2185.		BP	37.90	5				
Density			t_e	34.32	5	m' $\vert$ to			
g/ml 20°C	0.8356$^{\neq}$	2	t_e (d, e)	34.90	5	n' $\vert$ __ °K			
d_4^t 25	0.8322$^{\neq}$	2	ΔHv/T_e	20.45	5	o' $\vert$			
30	0.8288	4	d $\vert$ 355 to	59.81	5	Surface tension			
a	0.8492	4	e $\vert$ 565 °C	0.0434	5	dynes/cm. 20°C	29.85	5
b	-0.0$_3$68	4	d' $\vert$ 25 to	71.39	5	δ 30	28.89	5
Ref. Index			e' $\vert$ 355 °C	0.0758	5	40	27.96	5
n_D 20°C	1.4648$^{\neq}$	2	d_c g/ml			Parachor [P]			
25	1.4628$^{\neq}$	2	v_c ml/g			20°C			
30	1.4607	4	t_c °C	588.	5	30			
"C"	0.7351	4	P_c mm	2637.	5	40			
MR (Obs.)	166.99$^{\neq}$	2	PV/RT			Sugd.	1412.5	5
MR (Calc.)	166.248	5	25°C	1.0000	5	Exp. L.l.%/wt.			
(nD-d/2)	1.0470$^{\neq}$	2	30 mm	1.0000	5	u.			
Dielectric	2.146	5	BP	0.0956	5	Dispersion	98.$^{\neq}$	2
A $\vert$ 355 to	7.65505	5	t_e	0.0927	5	Flash Point °C			
B $\vert$ 580 °C	3103.3	5	t_c			Fire Point			
C	145.	5	ΔHc kcal/m			M. Spec.			
A* 355 to	2.44753	5	ΔHf			Ultra V.			
B* 570 °C	2944.5	5	ΔFf			X-Ray Dif.			
K			Viscosity			Infrared			
c			centistokes			Solubility in +			
t_k $\vert$ to			η °C			Acetone	∞	
t_x $\vert$ °C						Carbon tet.	∞	
A' $\vert$ 25 to	8.0443	5				Benzene	∞	
B' $\vert$ 355 °C	3507.	5				Ether	∞	
C'	177.	5	$B^v \vert$ to			n-Heptane	∞	
A'* 25 to	2.9556	5	$A^v \vert$ °C			Ethanol	∞	
B'* 355 °C	3401.	5	$(B^v) \vert$ to			Water		
Ac $\vert$ to			$(A^v) \vert$ °C			Water in		
Bc $\vert$ t_c °C			c_p liq. °K					
Cc								
Cryos. A°			c_p vap. °K					
consts. B°								
t_e °C	574.	5	c_v vap.					

$\neq$ for undercooled liquid   + grams/100 grams solvent

REFERENCES: 1-Dow   2-API   3-Lit.   4-Calc. from det. data   5-Calc. by formula

SOURCE: API

PURIFICATION: API

LITERATURE REFERENCES:

No. 52

NAME	n-Dotriacontylcyclopentane	STRUCTURAL FORMULA
	1-Cyclopentyldotriacontane	$H_2C{-}CHC_{32}H_{65}$ $H_2C{-}CH_2$

Mole % Pur.	Ref.	Molecular Formula $C_{37}H_{74}$	Molecular Weight 518.962

		Ref.				Ref.					Ref.
F.P. °C	69.	2	dt/dP				f	to			
F.P. 100%			°C/mm				g	°K			
B.P. °C			25°C	1.8×10^{10}	5		h				
760 mm	512.	2	BP	0.0782	5						
100	410.	5	t_e	0.0329	5		f'	to			
30	363.	5	30 mm	1.1861	5		g'	°K			
10	327.	5	ΔHm cal/g				h'				
1	265.	5									
Pressure			ΔHv cal/g				m	to			
mm 25°C	0.0_927	5	25°C	68.47	5		n	°K			
t_e	2215.	5	30 mm	43.61	5		o				
Density			BP	37.46	5						
g/ml 20°C	$0.8360^{\neq}$	2	t_e	33.93	5		m'	to			
d_4^t 25	$0.8327^{\neq}$	2	t_e (d, e)	34.55	5		n'	°K			
30	0.8294	4	ΔHv/T_e	20.58	5		o'				
a	0.8492	4	d │ 365 to	58.63	5		Surface tension				
b	-0.0_366	4	e │ 570 °C	0.0413	5		dynes/cm. 20°C		29.89	5	
Ref. Index			d' │ 25 to	70.30	5			30	28.96	5	
n_D 20°C	$1.4651^{\neq}$	2	e' │ 365 °C	0.0735	5			40	28.05	5	
25	$1.4631^{\neq}$	2	d_c g/ml				Parachor [P]				
30	1.4611	4	v_c ml/g					20°C			
"C"	0.7352	4	t_c °C	594.	5			30			
MR (Obs.)	$171.63^{\neq}$	2	P_c mm	2584.	5			40			
MR (Calc.)	170.866	5	PV/RT					Sugd.	1451.5	5	
(nD-d/2)	$1.0471^{\neq}$	2	25°C	1.0000	5		Exp. L.1.%/wt.				
Dielectric	2.146	5	30 mm	1.0000	5		u.				
A │ 365 to	7.68178	5	BP	0.9588	5		Dispersion		$98.^{\neq}$	2	
B │ 595 °C	3154.2	5	t_e	0.9306	5		Flash Point °C				
C	145.	5	t_c				Fire Point				
A* │ 365 to	2.47545	5	ΔHc kcal/m				M Spec.				
B* │ 590 °C	2990.1	5	ΔHf				Ultra V.				
K			ΔFf				X-Ray Dif.				
c							Infrared				
t_k │ to			Viscosity				Solubility in +				
t_x │ °C			centistokes				Acetone		∞		
A' │ 25 to	8.0727	5	η °C				Carbon tet.		∞		
B' │ 365 °C	3564.	5					Benzene		∞		
C'	177.	5					Ether		∞		
A'* 25 to	2.9924	5	B^v │ to				n-Heptane		∞		
B'* 365 °C	3458.	5	A^v │ °C				Ethanol		∞		
Ac │ to			(B^v) │ to				Water				
Bc │ t_c °C			(A^v) │ °C				Water in				
Cc											
Cryos. A°			c_p liq. °K								
consts. B°			c_p vap. °K								
t_e °C	582.	5	c_v vap.								

≠ for undercooled liquid   + grams/100 grams solvent

REFERENCES: 1-Dow 2-API 3-Lit. 4-Calc. from det. data 5-Calc. by formula

SOURCE:	API
PURIFICATION:	API
LITERATURE REFERENCES:	

TABLE XV. CYCLOPENTANES   411

No. 53

NAME	n-Tritriacontylcyclopentane	STRUCTURAL FORMULA
	1-Cyclopentyltritriacontane	$CHC_{33}H_{67}$ H_2C CH_2 H_2C-CH_2

Mole % Pur.	Ref.	Molecular Formula $C_{38}H_{76}$	Molecular Weight 532.988	

		Ref.			Ref.			Ref.
F.P. °C	70.	2	dt/dP			f	to	
F.P. 100%			°C/mm			g	°K	
B.P. °C			25°C	3.98×10^{10}	5	h		
760 mm	518.	2	BP	0.0784	5			
100	416.	5	t_e	0.0327	5	f'	to	
30	369.	5	30 mm	1.1926	5	g'	°K	
10	332.	5	ΔHm cal/g			h'		
1	269.	5	ΔHv cal/g			m	to	
Pressure			25°C	67.49	5	n	°K	
mm 25°C	0.0_916	5	30 mm	42.94	5	o		
t_e	2230.	5	BP	36.90	5			
Density			t_e	33.37	5	m'	to	
g/ml 20°C	$0.8365^{\neq}$	2	t_e (d, e)	34.02	5	n'	°K	
d_4^t 25	$0.8332^{\neq}$	2	ΔHv/T_e	20.63	5	o'		
30	0.8299	4	d 370 to	57.88	5	Surface tension		
a	0.8497	4	e 570 °C	0.0450	5	dynes/cm. 20°C	29.94	5
b	-0.0_366	4	d' 25 to	69.27	5	γ 30	29.01	5
Ref. Index			e' 370 °C	0.0714	5	40	28.10	5
n_D 20°C	$1.4654^{\neq}$	2	d_c g/ml			Parachor [P]		
25	$1.4634^{\neq}$	2	v_c ml/g			20°C		
30	1.4614	4	t_c °C	595.	5	30		
"C"	0.7351	4	P_c mm	2595.	5	40		
MR (Obs.)	$176.27^{\neq}$	2	PV/RT			Sugd.	1490.5	5
MR (Calc.)	175.484	5	25°C	1.0000	5	Exp. L.l.%/wt.		
(nD-d/2)	$1.0471^{\neq}$	2	30 mm	1.0000	5	u.		
Dielectric	2.147	5	BP	0.9582	5	Dispersion	$98.^{\neq}$	2
A 370 to	7.71327	5	t_e	0.9298	5	Flash Point °C		
B 600 °C	3203.9	5	t_c			Fire Point		
C	145.	5	ΔHc kcal/m			M. Spec.		
A* 370 to	2.51605	5	ΔHf			Ultra V.		
B* 590 °C	3038.7	5	ΔFf			X-Ray Dif.		
K			Viscosity			Infrared		
c			centistokes			Solubility in $^+$		
t_k to			η °C			Acetone	∞	
t_x °C						Carbon tet.	∞	
A' 25 to	8.1061	5				Benzene	∞	
B' 370 °C	3620.	5				Ether	∞	
C'	177.	5	B^v to			n-Heptane	∞	
A'* 25 to	3.0344	5	A^v °C			Ethanol	∞	
B'* 370 °C	3513.	5	(B^v) to			Water		
Ac to			(A^v) °C			Water in		
Bc t_c °C			c_p liq. °K					
Cc								
Cryos. A°			c_p vap. °K					
consts. B°								
t_e °C	589.	5	c_v vap.					

$\neq$ for undercooled liquid $^+$ grams/100 grams solvent

REFERENCES: 1-Dow 2-API 3-Lit. 4-Calc. from det. data 5-Calc. by formula

SOURCE: API

PURIFICATION: API

LITERATURE REFERENCES:

No. 54

NAME	n-Tetratriacontylcyclopentane	STRUCTURAL FORMULA

1-Cyclopentyltetratriacontane

$$H_2C \begin{array}{c} CHC_{34}H_{69} \\ CH_2 \end{array}$$
$$H_2C - CH_2$$

Mole % Pur.	Ref.	Molecular Formula	$C_{39}H_{78}$	Molecular Weight 547.014

		Ref.			Ref.				Ref.
F.P. °C	72.	2	dt/dP			f $\mid$ to			
F.P. 100%			°C/mm			g $\mid$ °K			
B.P. °C			25°C	4.95×10^{10}	5	h			
760 mm	525.	2	BP	0.0788	5				
100	422.	5	t_e	0.0327	5	f' $\mid$ to			
30	375.	5	30 mm	1.2016	5	g' $\mid$ °K			
10	338.	5	ΔHm cal/g			h' $\mid$			
1	274.	5				m $\mid$ to			
Pressure			ΔHv cal/g			n $\mid$ °K			
mm 25°C	$0.0_{10}98$	5	25°C	66.56	5	o $\mid$			
t_e	2247.	5	30 mm	42.32	5				
Density			BP	36.33	5	m' $\mid$ to			
g/ml 20°C	$0.8370^{\neq}$	2	t_e	32.74	5	n' $\mid$ °K			
d_4^t 25	$0.8336^{\neq}$	2	t_e (d, e)	33.46	5	o' $\mid$			
30	0.8302	4	ΔHv/T_e	20.59	5	Surface tension			
a	0.8506	4	d $\mid$ 375 to	57.26	5	dynes/cm. 20°C		30.00	5
b	$-0.0_3 68$	4	e $\mid$ 580 °C	0.0399	5	$\jmath$		30 29.04	5
Ref. Index			d' $\mid$ 25 to	68.29	5			40 28.10	5
n_D 20°C	$1.4657^{\neq}$	2	e' $\mid$ 375 °C	0.0693	5	Parachor [P]			
25	$1.4637^{\neq}$	2	d_c g/ml				20°C		
30	1.4616	4	v_c ml/g				30		
"C"	0.7351	4	t_c °C				40		
MR (Obs.)	$180.91^{\neq}$	2	P_c mm				Sugd. 1529.5		5
MR (Calc.)	180.102	5	PV/RT			Exp. L.l.%/wt.			
(nD-d/2)	$1.0472^{\neq}$	2	25°C	1.0000	5	u.			
Dielectric	2.148	5	30 mm	1.0000	5	Dispersion		$98.^{\neq}$	2
A $\mid$ 375 to	7.73950	5	BP	0.9569	5	Flash Point °C			
B $\mid$ 600 °C	3255.3	5	t_e	0.9281	5	Fire Point			
C	145.	5	t_c			M Spec.			
A* $\mid$ 375 to	2.55168	5	ΔHc kcal/m			Ultra V.			
B* $\mid$ 600 °C	3089.3	5	ΔHf			X-Ray Dif.			
K			ΔFf			Infrared			
c			Viscosity			Solubility in +			
t_k $\mid$ to			centistokes			Acetone		∞	
t_x $\mid$ °C			η °C			Carbon tet.		∞	
A' $\mid$ 250 to	8.1340	5				Benzene		∞	
B' $\mid$ 375 °C	3678.	5				Ether		∞	
C'	178.	5	B^v $\mid$ to			n-Heptane		∞	
A'* 25 to	3.0702	5	A^v $\mid$ °C			Ethanol		∞	
B'* 375 °C	3570.	5	(B^v) $\mid$ to			Water			
Ac $\mid$ to			(A^v) $\mid$ °C			Water in			
Bc $\mid$ t_c °C			c_p liq. °K						
Cc			c_p vap. °K						
Cryos. A°									
consts. B°			c_v vap.						
t_e °C	597.	5							

$\neq$ for undercooled liquid   + grams/100 grams solvent

REFERENCES: 1-Dow   2-API   3-Lit.   4-Calc. from det. data   5-Calc. by formula

SOURCE: API

PURIFICATION: API

LITERATURE REFERENCES:

TABLE XV. CYCLOPENTANES   413

NAME	n-Pentatriacontylcyclopentane	STRUCTURAL FORMULA
	1-Cyclopentylpentatriacontane	

Structural formula:

$$H_2C \overset{CHC_{35}H_{71}}{\underset{CH_2}{|}} \quad H_2C-CH_2$$

Mole % Pur.	Ref.	Molecular Formula $C_{40}H_{80}$	Molecular Weight 561.040

		Ref.			Ref.			Ref.
F.P. °C	74.	2	dt/dP			f $\vert$ to		
F.P. 100%			°C/mm			g $\vert$ __ °K		
B.P. °C			25°C	7.9×10^{10}	5	h $\vert$		
760 mm	531.	2	BP	0.07904	5			
100	428.	5	t_e	0.03256	5	f' $\vert$ to		
30	380.	5	30 mm	1.2085	5	g' $\vert$ __ °K		
10	343.	5	ΔHm cal/g			h' $\vert$		
1	279.	5	ΔHv cal/g			m $\vert$ to		
Pressure			25°C	65.64	5	n $\vert$ __ °K		
mm 25°C	$0.0_{10}61$	5	30 mm	41.71	5	o $\vert$		
t_e	2263.		BP	35.83	5			
Density			t_e	32.28	5	m' $\vert$ to		
g/ml 20°C	0.8374‡	2	t_e (d, e)	33.00	5	n' $\vert$ __ °K		
d_4^t 25	0.8341‡	2	ΔHv/T_e	20.66	5	o' $\vert$		
30	0.8308	4				Surface tension		
a	0.8506	4	d $\vert$ 380 to	56.51	5	dynes/cm. 20°C	30.04	5
b	-0.0_366	4	e $\vert$ 590 °C	0.03895	5	४ 30	29.10	5
Ref. Index			d' $\vert$ 25 to	67.33	5	40	28.19	5
n_D 20°C	1.4660‡	2	e' $\vert$ 380 °C	0.0674	5			
25	1.4640‡	2	d_c g/ml			Parachor [P]		
30	1.4620	4	v_c ml/g			20°C		
"C"	0.7352	4	t_c °C			30		
MR (Obs.)	185.55‡	2	P_c mm			40		
MR (Calc.)	184.720	5	PV/RT			Sugd.	1568.5	5
(nD-d/2)	1.0473‡	2	25°C	1.0000	5	Exp. L.1.%/wt.		
Dielectric	2.149	5	30 mm	1.0000	5	u.		
A $\vert$ 380 to	7.76813	5	BP	0.9566	5	Dispersion	98.‡	2
B $\vert$ 600 °C	3303.8	5	t_e	0.9277	5	Flash Point °C		
C	145.	5	t_c			Fire Point		
A* $\vert$ 380 to	2.58832	5	ΔHc kcal/m			M. Spec.		
B* $\vert$ 600 °C	3136.4	5	ΔHf			Ultra V.		
K			ΔFf			X-Ray Dif.		
c			Viscosity			Infrared		
t_k $\ulcorner$ to			centistokes			Solubility in +		
t_x $\vert$ °C			η °C			Acetone	∞	
A' $\vert$ 25 to	8.1645	5				Carbon tet.	∞	
B' $\vert$ 380 °C	3733.	5				Benzene	∞	
C'	178.	5				Ether	∞	
A'* 25 to	3.1086	5	B^v $\vert$ to			n-Heptane	∞	
B'* 380 °C	3624.	5	A^v $\vert$ °C			Ethanol	∞	
Ac $\vert$ to			$(B^v)\vert$ to			Water		
Bc $\llcorner$ t_c °C			$(A^v)\vert$ °C			Water in		
Cc			c_p liq. °K					
Cryos. A°								
consts. B°			c_p vap. °K					
t_e °C	604.	5	c_v vap.					

‡ for undercooled liquid   + grams/100 grams solvent

REFERENCES: 1-Dow   2-API   3-Lit.   4-Calc. from det. data   5-Calc. by formula

SOURCE: API

PURIFICATION: API

LITERATURE REFERENCES:

No. 56

NAME	n-Hexatriacontylcyclopentane	STRUCTURAL FORMULA

	1-Cyclopentylhexatriacontane	H_2C $\overset{CHC_{36}H_{73}}{\underset{H_2C-CH_2}{CH_2}}$

Mole % Pur.	Ref.	Molecular Formula $C_{41}H_{82}$	Molecular Weight 575.066

		Ref.				Ref.					Ref.
F.P. °C	75.	2	dt/dP				f | | to			
F.P. 100%			°C/mm				g | |__ °K_			
B.P. °C			25°C	1.3x10^11	5		h |			
760 mm	537.	2	BP	0.0793	5					
100	433.	5	t_e	0.0324	5		f' | | to			
30	385.	5	30 mm	1.2155	5		g' | |__ °K_			
10	348.	5	ΔHm cal/g				h' |			
1	284.	5	ΔHv cal/g				m | | to			
Pressure			25°C	64.76	5		n | |__ °K_			
mm 25°C	0.0_10^38	5	30 mm	41.12	5		o |			
t_e	2283.	5	BP	35.38	5		m' | | to			
Density			t_e	31.83	5		n' | |__ °K_			
g/ml 20°C	0.8378‡	2	t_e (d, e)	32.60	5		o' |			
d_4^t 25	0.8345‡	2	ΔHv/T_e	20.72	5		Surface tension			
30	0.8312	4					dynes/cm. 20°C	30.08	5
a	0.8510	4	d | 385 to	55.71	5		ɣ 30	29.14	5
b	-0.0_366	4	e | 600 °C	0.0379	5		40	28.23	5
Ref. Index			d' | 25 to	66.40	5		Parachor [P]		
n_D 20°C	1.4662‡	2	e' | 385 °C	0.0656	5		20°C		
25	1.4642‡	2	d_c g/ml				30		
30	1.4621	4	v_c ml/g				40		
"C"	0.7350	4	t_c °C				Sugd.	1607.5	5
MR (Obs.)	190.19‡	2	P_c mm				Exp. L.1.%/wt.		
MR (Calc.)	189.748	5	PV/RT				u.		
(nD-d/2)	1.0473‡	2	25°C	1.0000	5		Dispersion	98.‡	2
Dielectric	2.150	5	30 mm	1.0000	5		Flash Point °C		
A | 385 to	7.79534	5	BP	0.9574	5		Fire Point		
B | 610 °C	3351.7	5	t_e	0.9286	5		M Spec.		
C	145.	5	t_c				Ultra V.		
A* | 385 to	2.62093	5	ΔHc kcal/m				X-Ray Dif.		
B* | 610 °C	3181.7	5	ΔHf				Infrared		
K			ΔFf				Solubility in +		
c			Viscosity				Acetone	∞	
t_k | to			centistokes				Carbon tet.	∞	
t_x | °C			η °C				Benzene	∞	
A' | 25 to	8.1934	5					Ether	∞	
B' | 385 °C	3787.	5					n-Heptane	∞	
C'	179.	5	B^v | to				Ethanol	∞	
A'* 25 to	3.1453	5	A^v | °C				Water		
B'* 385 °C	3678.	5	(B^v) | to				Water in		
Ac | to			(A^v) | °C						
Bc | t_c °C			c_p liq. °K						
Cc									
Cryos. A°			c_p vap. °K						
consts. B°									
t_e °C	610.	5	c_v vap.						

≠ for undercooled liquid	+ grams/100 grams solvent

REFERENCES: 1-Dow 2-API 3-Lit. 4-Calc. from det. data 5-Calc. by formula
SOURCE: API
PURIFICATION: API
LITERATURE REFERENCES:

TABLE XVI. CYCLOPENTENES   415

No. 1

NAME	Cyclopentene	STRUCTURAL FORMULA

Mole % Pur.	Ref.	Molecular Formula C_5H_8	Molecular Weight 68.114

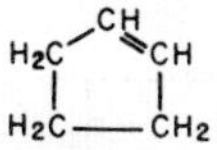

Structural formula:

$$H_2C{-}CH,\quad \overset{CH}{\underset{}{}},\quad H_2C{-}CH_2$$

H₂C—CH / CH (top) / H₂C——CH₂

Left column

Property	Value	Ref.
F.P. °C	-135.076	2
F.P. 100%		
B.P. °C		
760 mm	44.242	2
100	-5.465	4
30	-27.36	5
10	-43.97	5
1	-71.35	5
Pressure mm 25°C	380.22	5
t_e	855.03	5
Density g/ml 20°C	0.77199	2
d^t_4 25	0.76653	2
30	0.76104	4
a	0.79404	4
b	-0.00104	4
Ref. Index n_D 20°C	1.42246	2
25	1.41940	2
30	1.41612	4
"C"	0.7275	4
MR (Obs.)	22.443	2
MR (Calc.)	22.623	5
$(n_D\text{-}d/2)$	1.03646	2
Dielectric		
A -30 to	6.92066	4
B 105 °C	1121.818	4
C	233.446	5
A* -30 to	1.20562	5
B* 65 °C	1047.1	5
K		
c		
t_k to °C		
t_x		
A' to °C		
B'		
C'		
A'* to		
B'* °C		
Ac 105 to	7.35778	5
Bc t_c °C	1436.9	5
Cc	278.	5
Cryos. A° consts. B°		
t_e °C	47.80	5
$T_R = 0.75\,T_c$		

Middle column

Property	Value	Ref.
dt/dP °C/mm		
25°C	0.06801	5
BP	0.03928	2
t_e	0.03582	5
30 mm	0.5481	5
ΔHm cal/g	11.80	3
ΔHv cal/g		
25°C	97.98	5
30 mm	107.24	5
BP	94.25	5
t_e	93.60	5
t_e (d, e)	93.60	5
ΔHv/T_e	19.86	5
d -30 to	102.30	5
e 60 °C	0.1814	5
d' to		
e' °C		
d_c g/ml	0.277	5
v_c ml/g	3.613	5
t_c °C	231.	5
P_c mm	34112.	5
PV/RT		
25°C	0.9767	4
30 mm	1.0000	5
BP	0.9605	5
t_e	0.9574	5
t_c	0.267	5
ΔHc kcal/m		
ΔHf	1.16	2
ΔFf		
Viscosity centistokes		
η 30 °C	0.410	3
B^v to °C		
A^v		
(B^v) to		
(A^v) °C		
c_p liq. °K		
c_p vap 300°K	0.26544	2
400	0.36821	2
c_v vap.		

Right column

Property	Value	Ref.
f to °K		
g		
h		
f' to °K		
g'		
h'		
m 300 to	-0.08343	4
n 600 °K	0.00126	4
o	-0.0_6338	4
m' 700 to	-0.03077	4
n' 1000 °K	0.00122	4
o'	-0.0_6433	4
Surface tension dynes/cm. 20°C	22.65	3
δ 30	21.32	3
40		
Parachor [P] 20°C	192.81	4
30		
40		
Sugd.	192.5	5
Exp. L.l.%/wt. u.		
Dispersion	118.7	2
Flash Point °C		
Fire Point		
M. Spec.		2
Ultra V.		
X-Ray Dif.		
Infrared		1
Solubility in +		
Acetone		
Carbon tet.		
Benzene		
Ether		
n-Heptane		
Ethanol		
Water		
Water in		

+ grams/100 grams solvent

REFERENCES: 1-Dow 2-API 3-Lit. 4-Calc. from det. data 5-Calc. by formula

SOURCE: API

PURIFICATION: API

LITERATURE REFERENCES: 3. Timmermans

No. 2

NAME	1-Methylcyclopentene					STRUCTURAL FORMULA

Structural formula:

```
              C=CH3
        H2C      CH
        H2C ——— CH2
```

Mole % Pur.		Ref.	Molecular Formula C_6H_{10}		Molecular Weight 82.140	

		Ref.				Ref.					Ref.
F.P. °C	-127.	2	dt/dP °C/mm				f	| *to			
F.P. 100%			25°C	0.1924	5		g	| __ __ °K_			
B.P. °C			BP	0.04310	2		h				
760 mm	75.8	2	t_e	0.03642	5		f'	| to			
100	21.38	5					g'	| __ __ °K_			
30	-2.51	5	30 mm	0.5974	5		h'				
10	-20.60	5	ΔHm cal/g								
1	-50.36	5	ΔHv cal/g				m	| 300 to	-0.04019	4
Pressure			25°C	95.69	5		n	| 600 °K	0.00121	4
mm 25°C	117.6	5	30 mm	98.91	5		o		-0.0₆304	4
t_e	943.17	5	BP	85.80	5					
Density			t_e	84.61	5		m'	| 700 to	-0.03654	4
g/ml 20°C	0.7802	2	t_e (d,e)	84.59	5		n'	| 1000 °K	0.00130	4
d_4^t 25	0.7752	2	ΔHv/T_e	19.51	5		o'		-0.0₆487	4
30	0.7702	4	d | -5 to	98.49	5		Surface tension			
a	0.8003	4	e | 90 °C	0.1675	5		dynes/cm. 20°C	23.33	5
b	-0.0₃982	4	d' | to				γ 30	22.12	5
Ref. Index			e' | °C				40	20.95	5
n_D 20°C	1.4330	2	d_c g/ml	0.273	5		Parachor [P]		
25	1.4302	2	v_c ml/g	3.658	5		20°C		
30	1.4271	4	t_c °C	269.	5		30		
"C"	0.7367	4	P_c mm	29596.	5		40		
MR (Obs.)	27.36	2	PV/RT				Sugd.	231.5	5
MR (Calc.)	27.241	5	25°C	0.9921	4		Exp. L.1.%/wt.		
(nD-d/2)	1.0429	2	30 mm	1.0000	5		u.		
Dielectric			BP	0.9578	5		Dispersion	124.	2
A | -5 to	6.86884	4	t_e	0.9516	5		Flash Point °C		
B |130 °C	1199.6	4	t_c	0.263	5		Fire Point		
C	225.	5	ΔHc kcal/m				M Spec.		
A* | -5 to	1.2041	5	ΔHf				Ultra V.		
B* |105 °C	1121.3	5	ΔFf				X-Ray Dif.		
K			Viscosity				Infrared		
c			centistokes				Solubility in +		
t_k | to			η °C				Acetone		
t_x | °C							Carbon tet.		
A' | to							Benzene		
B' | °C							Ether		
C'			B^V | to				n-Heptane		
A'* | to			A^V | °C				Ethanol		
B'* °C			(B^V) | to				Water		
Ac |130 to	7:29519	5	(A^V) | °C				Water in		
Bc | t_c °C	1524.9	5	c_p liq. °K						
Cc	271.	5	c_p vap.300°K	0.29584	2				
Cryos. A°			400	0.39567	2				
consts. B°			c_v vap.						
t_e °C	83.04	5							

$T_R = 0.75 T_c$ + grams/100 grams solvent

REFERENCES: 1-Dow 2-API 3-Lit. 4-Calc. from det. data 5-Calc. by formula

SOURCE: API

PURIFICATION: API

LITERATURE REFERENCES:

TABLE XVI. CYCLOPENTENES

NAME	3-Methylcyclopentene			STRUCTURAL FORMULA

Structural formula:

H_2C—CH—CH
H_2C———$CHCH_3$ (ring)

| Mole % Pur. | Ref. | Molecular Formula C_6H_{10} | Molecular Weight 82.140 | |

		Ref.			Ref.					Ref.
F.P. °C			dt/dP			f		to		
F.P. 100%			°C/mm			g		°K		
B.P. °C			25°C	0.1339	5	h				
760 mm	65.0	2	BP	0.0418	2					
100	12.22	4	t_e	0.03622	5	f'		to		
30	-10.97	4	30 mm	0.5796	5	g'		°K		
10	-28.52	5	ΔHm cal/g			h'				
1	-57.40	5	ΔHv cal/g			m	300 to	-0.0608	4
Pressure			25°C	88.28	5	n	600 °K	0.0013	4
mm 25°C	176.7	5	30 mm	95.67	5	o		-0.0$_6$37	4
t_e	913.32	5	BP	83.17	5				
Density			t_e	82.20	5	m'	700 to	0.0098	4
g/ml 20°C	0.7622	2	t_e (d, e)	82.19	5	n'	1000 °K	0.0012	4
d_4^t 25	0.7572	2	ΔHv/T_e	19.62	5	o'		-0.0$_6$43	4
30	0.7522	4	d -10 to	93.87	5	**Surface tension**			
a	0.7822	4	e 80 °C	0.1646	5	dynes/cm. 20°C	21.22	5
b	-0.0$_3$97	4	d' to			ɣ	30	20.10	5
Ref. Index			e' °C				40	19.00	5
n_D 20°C	1.4207	2	d_c g/ml	0.268	5	**Parachor [P]**			
25	1.4179	2	v_c ml/g	3.735	5	20°C		
30	1.4148	4	t_c °C	250.	5	30		
"C"	0.7339	4	P_c mm	28713.	5	40		
MR (Obs.)	27.31	2	PV/RT			Sugd.	231.5	5
MR (Calc.)	27.24	4	25°C	0.9720	5	**Exp. L.1.%/wt.**		
(nD-d/2)	1.0396	2	30 mm	1.0000	5	u.		
Dielectric			BP	0.9590	5	Dispersion	119.	2
A -10 to	6.87259	4	t_e	0.9538	5	**Flash Point °C**		
B 119 °C	1165.6	4	t_c	0.27	5	Fire Point		
C	227.	5	ΔHc kcal/m			**M. Spec.**		
A* -10 to	1.21879	5	ΔHf			Ultra V.		
B* 80 °C	1089.0	5	ΔFf			X-Ray Dif.		
K			**Viscosity**			Infrared		
c			centistokes			**Solubility in** +		
t_k to			η °C			Acetone		
t_x °C						Carbon tet.		
A' to						Benzene		
B' °C						Ether		
C'			B^v to			n-Heptane		
A'* to			A^v °C			Ethanol		
B'* °C			(B^v) to			Water		
Ac 119 to	7.29924	5	(A^v) °C			Water in		
Bc t_c °C	1479.7	5	c_p liq. °K					
Cc	271.	5						
Cryos. A°			c_p vap. °K					
consts. B°								
t_e °C	70.96	5	c_v vap.					

$T_R = 0.75\ T_c$ + grams/100 grams solvent

REFERENCES: 1-Dow 2-API 3-Lit. 4-Calc. from det. data 5-Calc. by formula

SOURCE: API

PURIFICATION: API

LITERATURE REFERENCES:

No. 4

NAME	4-Methylcyclopentene				STRUCTURAL FORMULA
Mole % Pur.	Ref.	Molecular Formula C_6H_{10}		Molecular Weight 82.140	$(CH_3)-HC\!-\!\!-\!\!-CH_2$

		Ref.			Ref.				Ref.
F.P. °C			dt/dP			f | to			
F.P. 100%			°C/mm			g | °K			
B.P. °C			25°C	0.1886	5	h			
760 mm	75.2	2	BP	0.04300	2				
100	20.91	5	t_e	0.0364	5	f' | to			
30	-2.94	5	30 mm	0.5961	5	g' | °K			
10	-20.98	5	ΔHm cal/g			h' |			
1	-50.68	5				m | 300 to	-0.06816	4	
Pressure			ΔHv cal/g			n | 600 °K	0.00133	4	
mm 25°C	120.16	5	25°C	93.10	5	o |	-0.06426	4	
t_e	941.63	5	30 mm	98.82	5				
Density			BP	85.72	5	m' | 700 to	0.0427	4	
g/ml 20°C	0.7796	2	t_e	84.54	5	n' | 1000 °K	0.00111	4	
d_4^t 25	0.7747	2	t_e (d,e)	84.52	5	o' |	-0.06365	4	
30	0.7698	5	ΔHv/T_e	19.53	5	Surface tension			
a	0.7992	5	d | -2 to	98.32	5	dynes/cm. 20°C	23.25	5	
b	-0.03958	5	e | 100 °C	0.1676	5	ɣ 30	22.08	5	
Ref. Index			d' | to			40	20.93	5	
n_D 20°C	1.4306	2	e' | °C			Parachor [P]			
25	1.4278	2	d_c g/ml	0.276	5	20°C			
30	1.4249	4	v_c ml/g	3.627	5	30			
"C"	0.7334	5	t_c °C	268.	5	40			
MR (Obs.)	27.25	2	P_c mm	29679.	5	Sugd.	231.5	5	
MR (Calc.)	27.241	5	PV/RT			Exp. L.1.%/wt.			
(nD-d/2)	1.0408	2	25°C	0.9920	4	u.			
Dielectric			30 mm	1.0000	5	Dispersion			
A | -2 to	6.87015	5	BP	0.9579	5	Flash Point °C			
B | 130 °C	1197.6	4	t_e	0.9518	5	Fire Point			
C	225.	5	t_c	0.262	5	M Spec.			
A* | -2 to	1.20598	5	ΔHc kcal/m			Ultra V.			
B* | 100 °C	1119.4	5	ΔHf			X-Ray Dif.			
K			ΔFf			Infrared			
c			Viscosity			Solubility in +			
t_k | to			centistokes			Acetone			
t_x | °C			η °C			Carbon tet.			
A' | to						Benzene			
B' | °C						Ether			
C'			B^v | to			n-Heptane			
			A^v | °C			Ethanol			
A'* | to			(B^v) | to			Water			
B'* | °C			(A^v) | °C			Water in			
Ac | 130 to	7.29635	5	c_p liq. °K						
Bc | t_c °C	1522.2	5							
Cc	271.	5	c_p vap.300°K	0.29340	2				
Cryos. A°			400	0.39688	2				
consts. B°			c_v vap.						
t_e °C	82.37	5							

$T_R = 0.75\,T_c$ + grams/100 grams solvent

REFERENCES: 1-Dow 2-API 3-Lit. 4-Calc. from det. data 5-Calc. by formula

SOURCE: API

PURIFICATION: API

LITERATURE REFERENCES:

TABLE XVI. CYCLOPENTENES

419

NAME	1-Ethylcyclopentene	STRUCTURAL FORMULA

Structural formula:

$$H_2C \overset{C(C_2H_5)}{\underset{\underset{CH_2}{|}}{\overset{|}{C}}} \overset{CH}{\underset{CH_2}{|}}$$

Mole % Pur.	Ref.	Molecular Formula C_7H_{12}	Molecular Weight 96.166		

		Ref.			Ref.			Ref.
F.P. °C	-118.4	2	dt/dP			f | to		
F.P. 100%			°C/mm			g | °K		
			25°C	0.5569	5	h |		
B.P. °C			BP	0.0467	2			
760 mm	106.3	2	t_e	0.03698	5	f' | to		
100	47.36	5	30 mm	0.6466	5	g' | °K		
30	21.49	5	ΔHm cal/g			h' |		
10	1.91	5						
1	-30.28	5	ΔHv cal/g			m | to		
Pressure			25°C	91.96	5	n | °K		
mm 25°C	35.86	5	30 mm	92.51	5	o |		
t_e	1026.0	5	BP	79.58	5			
Density			t_e	77.96	5	m' | to		
g/ml 20°C	0.7982	2	t_e (d,e)	77.90	5	n' | °K		
d_4^t 25	0.7936	2	ΔHv/T_e	19.20	5	o' |		
30	0.7889	4				Surface tension		
a	0.8167	4	d 20 to	95.78	5	dynes/cm. 20°C	25.39	5
b	-0.0₃92	4	e | 130 °C	0.1524	5	γ 30	24.22	5
Ref. Index			d' | to			40	23.08	5
n_D 20°C	1.4410	2	e' | °C			Parachor [P]		
25	1.4384	2	d_c g/ml	0.264	5	20°C		
30	1.4355	4	v_c ml/g	3.784	5	30		
"C"	0.7325	4	t_c °C	303.	5	40		
MR (Obs.)	31.82	2	P_c mm	25668.	5	Sugd.	270.5	5
MR (Calc.)	31.859	5	PV/RT			Exp. L.l.%/wt.		
(nD-d/2)	1.0419	2	25°C	0.9995	4	u.		
Dielectric			30 mm	1.0000	5	Dispersion	119.	2
A | 20 to	6.86113	4	BP	0.9534	5	Flash Point °C		
B | 160 °C	1294.8	4	t_e	0.9443	5	Fire Point		
C	219.	5	t_c	0.260	5	M. Spec.		
A* | 20 to	1.23806	5	ΔHc kcal/m			Ultra V.		
B* | 135 °C	1212.6	5	ΔHf			X-Ray Dif.		
K			ΔFf			Infrared		
c			Viscosity			Solubility in ⁺		
t_k | to			centistokes			Acetone		
t_x | °C			η °C			Carbon tet.		
A' | to						Benzene		
B' | °C						Ether		
C'			B^v | to			n-Heptane		
A'* to			A^v | °C			Ethanol		
B'* °C			(B^v) | to			Water		
Ac | 160 to	7.28115	5	(A^v) | °C			Water in		
Bc | t_c °C	1631.7	5	c_p liq. °K					
Cc |	265.	5						
Cryos. A°			c_p vap. °K					
consts. B°								
t_e °C	117.31	5	c_v vap.					

$T_R = 0.75 T_c$

⁺ grams/100 grams solvent

REFERENCES: 1-Dow 2-API 3-Lit. 4-Calc. from det. data 5-Calc. by formula

SOURCE:	API
PURIFICATION:	API
LITERATURE REFERENCES:	

No. 6

NAME	3-Ethylcyclopentene	STRUCTURAL FORMULA

STRUCTURAL FORMULA:

$$H_2C \underset{H_2C - CHC_2H_5}{\overset{CH}{\underset{}{}} \overset{}{CH}}$$

Mole % Pur.	Ref.	Molecular Formula C_7H_{12}	Molecular Weight 96.166	

		Ref.			Ref.			Ref.
F.P. °C			dt/dP			f ⌐ to		
F.P. 100%			°C/mm			g ¦ °K		
			25°C	0.4152	5	h ¦		
B.P. °C			BP	0.0458	2			
760 mm	98.1	2	t_e	0.03683	5	f' ⌐ to		
100	40.33	5				g' ¦ °K		
30	14.99	5	30 mm	0.63319	5	h' ¦		
10	-4.18	5	ΔHm cal/g					
1	-35.68	5				m ⌐ to		
			ΔHv cal/g			n ¦ °K		
Pressure			25°C	88.99	5	o ¦		
mm 25°C	49.73	5	30 mm	90.35	5			
t_e	1005.7	5	BP	77.89	5	m' ⌐ to		
			t_e	76.42	5	n' ¦ °K		
Density			t_e (d, e)	76.38	5	o' ¦		
g/ml 20°C	0.7830	2	ΔHv/T_e	19.27	5	Surface tension		
d_4^t 25	0.7784	2	d ⌐ 10 to	92.60	5	dynes/cm. 20°C	23.51	5
30	0.7738	4	e ¦ 120 °C	0.1499	5	⌡ 30	22.40	5
a	0.8014	4	d' ¦ to			40	21.33	5
b	-0.0₃91	4	e' ¦ °C			Parachor [P]		
Ref. Index			d_c g/ml	0.262	5	20°C		
n_D 20°C	1.4319	2	v_c ml/g	3.821	5	30		
25	1.4293	2	t_c °C	288.	5	40		
30	1.4265	4	P_c mm	24859.	5	Sugd.	270.5	5
"C"	0.7323	4	PV/RT			Exp. L.1.%/wt.		
MR (Obs.)	31.85	2	25°C	1.0000	4	u.		
MR (Calc.)	31.859	5	30 mm	1.0000	5	Dispersion		
(nD-d/2)	1.0404	2	BP	0.9561	5	Flash Point °C		
Dielectric			t_e	0.9479	5	Fire Point		
A ⌐ 10 to	6.84968	4	t_c	0.261	5	M Spec.		
B ¦150 °C	1262.5	4	ΔHc kcal/m			Ultra V.		
C	220.	5	ΔHf			X-Ray Dif.		
A* ⌐ 10 to	1.23151	5	ΔFf			Infrared		
B* ¦130 °C	1181.1	5	Viscosity			Solubility in +		
K			centistokes			Acetone		
c			η °C			Carbon tet.		
t_k ⌐ to						Benzene		
t_x ¦ °C						Ether		
A' ⌐ to						n-Heptane		
B' ¦ °C			B^v ⌐ to			Ethanol		
C'			A^v ¦ °C			Water		
A'* to			(B^v) ¦ to			Water in		
B'* °C			(A^v) ¦ °C					
Ac ¦150 to	7.26899	5	c_p liq. °K					
Bc ¦ t_c °C	1589.9	5						
Cc	265.	5	c_p vap. °K					
Cryos. A°			c_v vap.					
consts. B°								
t_e °C	108.16	5						

$T_R = 0.75 T_c$ + grams/100 grams solvent

REFERENCES: 1-Dow 2-API 3-Lit. 4-Calc. from det. data 5-Calc. by formula

SOURCE: API

PURIFICATION: API

LITERATURE REFERENCES:

TABLE XVI. CYCLOPENTENES

No. 7

NAME	4-Ethylcyclopentene	STRUCTURAL FORMULA

Structural formula: $H_2C{-}CH{=}CH$ / $(C_2H_5)HC{-}CH_2$

Mole % Pur.	Ref.	Molecular Formula	C_7H_{12}	Molecular Weight 96.166		

		Ref.			Ref.				Ref.
F.P. °C			dt/dP			f		to	
F.P. 100%			°C/mm			g		°K	
			25°C	0.5431	5	h			
B.P. °C			BP	0.04700	2				
760 mm	106.	2	t_e	0.03725	5	f'		to	
100	46.76	5				g'		°K	
30	20.81	5	30 mm	0.6483	5	h'			
10	1.19	5	ΔHm cal/g						
1	-31.04	5	ΔHv cal/g			m		to	
Pressure			25°C	91.16	5	n		°K	
mm 25°C	37.07	5	30 mm	91.84	5	o			
t_e	1025.4	5	BP	78.95	5				
Density			t_e	77.34	5	m'		to	
g/ml 20°C	0.798	2	t_e (d, e)	77.28	5	n'		°K	
d_4^t 25	0.793	2	ΔHv/T_e	19.06	5	o'			
30	0.788	4				Surface tension			
a	0.8176	4	d 15 to	94.99	5	dynes/cm. 20°C	25.37	5
b	-0.0397	4	e 125 °C	0.1514	5	δ 30	24.13	5
Ref. Index			d' to			40	22.93	5
n_D 20°C	1.440	2	e' °C					
25	1.437	2	d_c g/ml	0.256	5	Parachor [P]		
30	1.434	4	v_c ml/g	3.898	5	20°C		
"C"	0.7312	4	t_c °C	302.	5	30		
MR (Obs.)	31.8	2	P_c mm	24877.	5	40		
MR (Calc.)	31.859	5	PV/RT			Sugd.	270.5	5
(nD-d/2)	1.041	2	25°C	0.9988	4	Exp. L.1.%/wt.		
Dielectric			30 mm	1.0000	5	u.		
			BP	0.9535	5	Dispersion		
A 15 to	6.83219	4	t_e	0.9443	5	Flash Point °C		
B 160 °C	1284.2	4	t_c	0.260	5	Fire Point		
C	219.	5	ΔHc kcal/m			M. Spec.		
A* 15 to	1.20935	5	ΔHf			Ultra V.		
B* 130 °C	1202.0	5	ΔFf			X-Ray Dif.		
K			Viscosity			Infrared		
c			centistokes			Solubility in +		
t_k to			η °C			Acetone		
t_x °C						Carbon tet.		
A' to						Benzene		
B' °C						Ether		
C'			B^v to			n-Heptane		
A'* to			A^v °C			Ethanol		
B'* °C			(B^v) to			Water		
Ac 160 to	7.25226	5	(A^v) °C			Water in		
Bc t_c °C	1620.5	5	c_p liq. °K					
Cc	266.	5						
. Cryos. A°			c_p vap. °K					
consts. B°								
t_e °C	117.06	5	c_v vap.					

$T_R = 0.75 T_c$

+ grams/100 grams solvent

REFERENCES: 1-Dow 2-API 3-Lit. 4-Calc. from det. data 5-Calc. by formula
SOURCE: API
PURIFICATION: API
LITERATURE REFERENCES:

No. 8

NAME	1,2-Dimethylcyclopentene	STRUCTURAL FORMULA

H_2C $C.CH_3$ CCH_3
H_2C——CH_2

Mole % Pur.	Ref.	Molecular Formula	C_7H_{12}	Molecular Weight	96.166	

		Ref.				Ref.					Ref.
F.P. °C	-90.4	2	dt/dP °C/mm				f	to		
F.P. 100%			25°C	0.5457	5		g	°K		
B.P. °C			BP	0.0467	2		h			
760 mm	105.8	2	t_e	0.03699	5		f'	to		
100	46.87	4	30 mm	0.6461	5		g'	°K		
30	21.02	4	ΔHm cal/g				h'			
10	1.46	5					m	300 to	-0.0167	4
1	-30.70	5	ΔHv cal/g				n	600 °K	0.0012	4
Pressure			25°C	91.59	5		o		-0.0$_6$31	4
mm 25°C	36.71	5	30 mm	92.29	5		m'	700 to	0.0260	4
t_e	1025.8	5	BP	79.45	5		n'	1000 °K	0.0012	4
Density			t_e	77.84	5		o'		-0.0$_6$42	4
g/ml 20°C	0.7976	2	t_e (d,e)	77.78	5		Surface tension			
d_4^t 25	0.7928	2	ΔHv/T_e	19.19	5		dynes/cm. 20°C		25.32	5
30	0.7878	4	d 21 to	95.47	5		ɣ 30		24.09	5
a	0.8171	4	e 125 °C	0.1514	5		40		22.90	5
b	-0.0$_3$97	4	d' to				Parachor [P]			
Ref. Index			e' °C				20°C			
n_D 20°C	1.4448	2	d_c g/ml	0.262	5		30			
25	1.4420	2	v_c ml/g	3.815	5		40			
30	1.4392	4	t_c °C	301.	5		Sugd.		270.5	5
"C"	0.7391	4	P_c mm	25374.	5		Exp. L.1.%/wt.			
MR (Obs.)	32.08	2	PV/RT				u.			
MR (Calc.)	31.859	4	25°C	0.9992	5		Dispersion		125.8	2
(nD-d/2)	1.0460	2	30 mm	1.0000	5		Flash Point °C			
Dielectric			BP	0.9544	5		Fire Point			
A 21 to	6.85494	4	t_e	0.9454	5		M Spec.			
B 158 °C	1290.8	4	t_c	0.260	5		Ultra V.			
C	219.	5	ΔHc kcal/m				X-Ray Dif.			
A* 21 to	1.23077	5	ΔHf				Infrared			
B* 126 °C	1208.3	5	ΔFf							
K			Viscosity				Solubility in +			
c			centistokes				Acetone			
t_k to			η °C				Carbon tet.			
t_x °C							Benzene			
A' to							Ether			
B' °C							n-Heptane			
C'			B^v to				Ethanol			
A'* to			A^v °C				Water			
B'* °C			(B^v) to				Water in			
Ac 158 to	7.27475	5	(A^v) °C							
Bc t_c °C	1626.6	5	c_p liq. °K							
Cc	265.	5								
Cryos. A° consts. B°			c_p vap. °K							
t_e °C	116.81	5	c_v vap.							

$T_R = 0.75 T_c$	+ grams/100 grams solvent

REFERENCES:	1-Dow	2-API	3-Lit.	4-Calc. from det. data	5-Calc. by formula
SOURCE:	API				
PURIFICATION:	API				
LITERATURE REFERENCES:					

TABLE XVI. CYCLOPENTENES

NAME	1,3-Dimethylcyclopentene	STRUCTURAL FORMULA

Structural formula:

$$H_2C \overset{C-CCH_3}{\underset{CH}{}}$$
$$H_2C - CHCH_3$$

Mole % Pur.	Ref.	Molecular Formula C_7H_{12}	Molecular Weight 96.166	

		Ref.				Ref.					Ref.
F.P. °C			dt/dP				f	to			
F.P. 100%			°C/mm				g	___ °K			
			25°C	0.3360	5		h				
B.P. °C			BP	0.045	2						
760 mm	92.	2	t_e	0.03665	5		f'	to			
100	35.19	4	30 mm	0.6236	5		g'	___ °K			
30	10.24	4	ΔHm cal/g				h'				
10	-8.64	5					m	300 to	-0.0406	4
1	-39.71	5	ΔHv cal/g				n	600 °K	0.0013	4
Pressure			25°C	86.54	5		o		-0.0₆42	4
mm 25°C	62.99	5	30 mm	88.73	5					
t_e	989.21	5	BP	76.75	5		m'	700 to	0.0291	4
Density			t_e	75.41	5		n'	1000 °K	0.0012	4
g/ml 20°C	0.766	2	t_e (d,e)	75.39	5		o'		-0.0₆42	4
d_4^t 25	0.761	2	ΔHv/T_e	19.37	5		Surface tension			
30	0.756	4	d	10 to	90.23	5	dynes/cm. 20°C	21.52	5
a	0.7861	4	e	110 °C	0.1466	5	δ	30	20.40	5
b	-0.0399	4	d'	to				40	19.31	5
Ref. Index			e'	°C			Parachor [P]			
n_D 20°C	1.428	2						20°C		
25	1.425	2	d_c g/ml	0.253	5			30		
30	1.423	4	v_c ml/g	3.949	5			40		
"C"	0.7422	4	t_c °C	276.	5			Sugd.	270.5	5
MR (Obs.)	32.3	2	P_c mm	24077.	5					
MR (Calc.)	31.859	4	PV/RT				Exp. L.1.%/wt.			
(nD-d/2)	1.045	2	25°C	0.9972	5		u.			
Dielectric			30 mm	1.0000	5		Dispersion			
A 10 to	6.86807	4	BP	0.9571	5		Flash Point °C			
B 137 °C	1252.0	4	t_e	0.9494	5		Fire Point			
C	222.	5	t_c	0.267	5		M. Spec.			
A* 10 to	1.25419	5	ΔHc kcal/m				Ultra V.			
B* 111 °C	1170.8	5	ΔHf				X-Ray Dif.			
K			ΔFf				Infrared			
c			Viscosity				Solubility in +			
t_k to			centistokes				Acetone			
t_x °C			η °C				Carbon tet.			
A' to							Benzene			
B' °C							Ether			
C'			B^v to				n-Heptane			
			A^v °C				Ethanol			
A'* to			(B^v) to				Water			
B'* °C							Water in			
Ac 137 to	7.28841	5	(A^v) °C							
Bc t_c °C	1573.3	5	c_p liq. °K							
Cc	266.	5								
Cryos. A°			c_p vap. °K							
consts. B°										
t_e °C	101.28	5	c_v vap.							

$T_R = 0.75\,T_c$

+ grams/100 grams solvent

REFERENCES: 1-Dow 2-API 3-Lit. 4-Calc. from det. data 5-Calc. by formula

SOURCE:	API
PURIFICATION:	API

LITERATURE REFERENCES:

No. 10

NAME	1,4-Dimethylcyclopentene	STRUCTURAL FORMULA

H_2C—CCH_3—CH ; CH_3HC——CH_2

Mole % Pur.	Ref.	Molecular Formula	C_7H_{12}	Molecular Weight	96.166

		Ref.				Ref.					Ref.
F.P. °C			dt/dP				f		to		
F.P. 100%			°C/mm				g		°K		
B.P. °C			25°C	0.3407	5		h				
760 mm	93.2	2	BP	0.046	2		f'		to		
100	35.35	5	t_e	0.03751	5		g'		°K		
30	10.09	5	30 mm	0.6304	5		h'				
10	-8.97	5	ΔHm cal/g				m	300 to	-0.0$_3$121	4	
1	-40.22	5	ΔHv cal/g				n	600 °K	0.00126	4	
Pressure			25°C	86.45	5		o		-0.0$_6$364	4	
mm 25°C	62.90	5	30 mm	87.69	5		m'	700 to	0.02807	4	
t_e	989.12	5	BP	75.33	5		n'	1000 °K	0.00118	4	
Density			t_e	73.96	5		o'		-0.0$_6$416	4	
g/ml 20°C	0.779	2	t_e (d, e)	73.92	5		Surface tension				
d^t 25	0.774	2	$\Delta Hv/T_e$	18.92	5		dynes/cm. 20°C	23.02	5		
d_4 30	0.769	2	d 0 to	89.19	5		γ 30	21.84	5		
a	0.7990	4	e 120 °C	0.1488	5		40	20.70	5		
b	-0.0$_3$99	4	d' to				Parachor [P]				
Ref. Index			e' °C				20°C				
n_D 20°C	1.4283	2	d_c g/ml	0.246	5		30				
25	1.4255	2	v_c ml/g	4.058	5		40				
30	1.4225	4	t_c °C	280.	5		Sugd.	270.5	5		
"C"	0.7303	4	P_c mm	23075.	5		Exp. L.1.%/wt.				
MR (Obs.)	31.8	2	PV/RT				u.				
MR (Calc.)	31.859	5	25°C	0.9963	4		Dispersion				
(nD-d/2)	1.0388	2	30 mm	1.0000	5		Flash Point °C				
Dielectric			BP	0.9538	5		Fire Point				
A 0 to	6.78405	4	t_e	0.9458	5		M Spec.				
B 140 °C	1226.4	4	t_c	0.261	5		Ultra V.				
C	221.	5	ΔHc kcal/m				X-Ray Dif.				
A* 0 to	1.17518	5	ΔHf				Infrared				
B* 140 °C	1146.7	5	ΔFf				Solubility in +				
K			Viscosity				Acetone				
c			centistokes				Carbon tet.				
t_k to			η °C				Benzene				
t_x °C							Ether				
A' to							n-Heptane				
B' °C			B^v to				Ethanol				
C'			A^v °C				Water				
A'* to			(B^v) to				Water in				
B'* °C			(A^v) °C								
Ac 140 to	7.20417	5	c_p liq. °K								
Bc t_c °C	1549.7	5									
Cc	266.	5	c_p vap.300 °K	0.31508	2						
Cryos. A°			400	0.41595	2						
consts. B°			c_v vap.								
t_e °C	102.69	5									
$T_R = 0.75 T_c$							+ grams/100 grams solvent				

REFERENCES: 1-Dow 2-API 3-Lit. 4-Calc. from det. data 5-Calc. by formula

SOURCE: API

PURIFICATION: API

LITERATURE REFERENCES:

NAME	1,5-Dimethylcyclopentene	STRUCTURAL FORMULA

$$(CH_3)HC \overset{\displaystyle C(CH_3)}{\underset{\displaystyle }{}} CH$$

$$H_2C \text{------} CH_2$$

Mole % Pur.	Ref.	Molecular Formula C_7H_{12}	Molecular Weight 96.166

		Ref.			Ref.				Ref.
F.P. °C	-118.	2	dt/dP			f	to		
F.P. 100%			°C/mm			g	°K		
			25°C	0.4814	5	h			
B.P. °C			BP	0.046	2				
760 mm	102.	2	t_e	0.03675	5	f'	to		
100	43.89	5				g'	°K		
30	18.36	5	30 mm	0.6386	5				
10	-0.98	5	ΔHm cal/g			h'			
1	-32.81	5	ΔHv cal/g			m	300 to	-0.04057	4
			25°C	90.71	5	n	600 °K	0.00131	4
Pressure			30 mm	91.69	5	o		-0.0₆416	4
mm 25°C	42.04	5	BP	78.96	5				
t_e	1013.58	5	t_e	77.43	5	m'	700 to	-0.0₄	4
Density			t_e (d, e)	77.38	5	n'	1000 °K	0.00126	4
g/ml 20°C	0.780	2	ΔHv/T_e	19.31	5	o'		-0.0₆468	4
d_4^t 25	0.775	2							
30	0.770	4	d 0 to	94.49	5	Surface tension			
a	0.8003	4	e 120 °C	0.1522	5	dynes/cm. 20°C		23.15	5
b	-0.00101	4	d' to			8 30		21.96	5
			e' °C			40		20.80	5
Ref. Index			d_c g/ml	0.263	5				
n_D 20°C	1.4331	2	v_c ml/g	3.796	5	Parachor [P]			
25	1.4304	2	t_c °C	292.	5	20°C			
30	1.4271	4	P_c mm	24909.	5	30			
"C"	0.7369	4				40			
MR (Obs.)	32.1	2	PV/RT				Sugd.	270.5	5
MR (Calc.)	31.859	5	25°C	0.9990	4	Exp. L.1.%/wt.			
(nD-d/2)	1.043	2	30 mm	1.0000	5	u.			
Dielectric			BP	0.9534	5	Dispersion		120.8	2
			t_e	0.9448	5	Flash Point °C			
A 0 to	6.88081	4	t_c	0.258	5	Fire Point			
B 150 °C	1288.0	4	ΔHc kcal/m			M. Spec.			
C	220.	5	ΔHf			Ultra V.			
A* 0 to	1.26224	5	ΔFf			X-Ray Dif.			
B* 130 °C	1206.5	5				Infrared			
K			Viscosity			Solubility in +			
c			centistokes			Acetone			
t_k to			η °C			Carbon tet.			
t_x °C						Benzene			
A' to						Ether			
B' °C						n-Heptane			
C'			B^v to			Ethanol			
			A^v °C			Water			
A'* to			(B^v) to			Water in			
B'* °C									
Ac 150 to	7.30037	5	(A^v) °C						
Bc t_c °C	1618.1	5	c_p liq. °K						
Cc	265.	5							
Cryos. A°			c_p vap.300°K	0.31508	2				
consts. B°			400	0.41699	2				
t_e °C	112.39	5	c_v vap.						

T_R = 0.75 T_c + grams/100 grams solvent

REFERENCES:	1-Dow 2-API 3-Lit. 4-Calc. from det. data 5-Calc. by formula
SOURCE:	API
PURIFICATION:	API
LITERATURE REFERENCES:	

No. 12

NAME	3, 3-Dimethylcyclopentene	STRUCTURAL FORMULA

Mole % Pur.		Ref.	Molecular Formula C_7H_{12}		Molecular Weight 96.166	

		Ref.			Ref.					Ref.
F.P. °C			dt/dP			f		to		
F.P. 100%			°C/mm			g		°K		
B.P. °C			25°C	0.2884	5	h				
760 mm	88.	2	BP	0.045	2					
100	31.32	5	t_e	0.03711	5	f'		to		
30	6.51	5	30 mm	0.6195	5	g'		°K		
10	-12.23	5	ΔHm cal/g			h'				
1	-43.00	5	ΔHv cal/g			m		300 to	-0.04785	4
Pressure			25°C	85.68	5	n		600 °K	0.00128	4
mm 25°C	75.30	5	30 mm	87.00	5	o			-0.0₆312	4
t_e	974.25	5	BP	74.84	5	m'		700 to	-0.03225	4
Density			t_e	73.58	5	n'		11000 °K	0.00136	4
g/ml 20°C	0.771	2	t_e (d, e)	73.54	5	o'			-0.0₆52	4
d_4^t 25	0.766	2	ΔHv/T_e	19.13	5	Surface tension				
30	0.761	4	d 5 to	87.97	5	dynes/cm. 20°C			22.08	5
a	0.7910	4	e 110 °C	0.1492	5	γ		30	20.94	5
b	-0.0₃99	4	d' to					40	19.82	5
Ref. Index			e' °C			Parachor [P]				
n_D 20°C	1.423	2	d_c g/ml	0.255	5			20°C		
25	1.420	2	v_c ml/g	3.924	5			30		
30	1.417	4	t_c °C	270.	5			40		
"C"	0.7292	4	P_c mm	23342.	5			Sugd.	270.5	5
MR (Obs.)	31.8	2	PV/RT			Exp. L. 1.%/wt.				
MR (Calc.)	31.859	5	25°C	0.9905	4	u.				
(nD-d/2)	1.038	2	30 mm	1.0000	5	Dispersion				
Dielectric			BP	0.9540	5	Flash Point °C				
A 5 to	6.81726	4	t_e	0.9466	5	Fire Point				
B 130 °C	1220.3	4	t_c	0.260	5	M Spec.				
C	222.	5	ΔHc kcal/m			Ultra V.				
A* 5 to	1.21398	5	ΔHf			X-Ray Dif.				
B* 120 °C	1141.5	5	ΔFf			Infrared				
K			Viscosity			Solubility in +				
c			centistokes			Acetone				
t_k to			η °C			Carbon tet.				
t_x °C						Benzene				
A' to						Ether				
B' °C						n-Heptane				
C'			B^v to			Ethanol				
			A^v °C			Water				
A'* to			(B^v) to			Water in				
B'* °C										
Ac 130 to	7.23721	5	(A^v) °C							
Bc t_c °C	1538.1	5	c_p liq. °K							
Cc	266.	5								
Cryos. A°			c_p vap.300°K	0.30780	2					
consts. B°			400	0.41387	2					
t_e °C	96.73	5	c_v vap.							
$T_R = 0.75 T_c$						+ grams/100 grams solvent				

REFERENCES: 1-Dow 2-API 3-Lit. 4-Calc. from det. data 5-Calc. by formula

SOURCE:	API
PURIFICATION:	API
LITERATURE REFERENCES:	

TABLE XVI. CYCLOPENTENES 427

No. 13

NAME	4,4-Dimethylcyclopentene	STRUCTURAL FORMULA

Structural formula:
$$H_2C \overset{CH}{\underset{\;}{\diagup}} CH$$
$$(CH_3)_2C \longrightarrow CH_2$$

Mole % Pur.	Ref.	Molecular Formula C_7H_{12}	Molecular Weight 96.166

		Ref.				Ref.				Ref.
F.P. °C			dt/dP				f $\vert$ $\quad$ to			
F.P. 100%			°C/mm				g $\vert$ $\lfloor$ _ _ °K			
			25°C	0.2884	5		h $\vert$			
B.P. °C			BP	0.0450	2					
760 mm	88.	2	t_e	0.03691	5		f' $\vert$ $\quad$ to			
100	31.32	5	30 mm	0.6195	5		g' $\vert$ $\lfloor$ _ _ °K			
30	6.51	5	ΔHm cal/g				h' $\vert$			
10	-12.23	5								
1	-43.00	5	ΔHv cal/g				m $\vert$ $\quad$ to			
			25°C	91.24	5		n $\vert$ $\lfloor$ _ _ °K			
Pressure			30 mm	87.00	5		o $\vert$			
mm 25°C	75.30	5	BP	75.30	5					
t_e	981.12	5	t_e	74.03	5		m' $\vert$ $\quad$ to			
Density			t_e (d, e)	74.01	5		n' $\vert$ $\lfloor$ _ _ °K			
g/ml 20°C	0.771	2	ΔHv/T_e	19.23	5		o' $\vert$			
d_4^t 25	0.766	2								
30	0.761	4	d $\vert$ 5 to	87.93	5		Surface tension			
a	0.7911	4	e $\vert$ 110 °C	0.1435	5		dynes/cm. 20°C	22.08	5
b	-0.0399	4	d' $\vert$ $\quad$ to				ɣ $\qquad$ 30	20.93	5
			e' $\vert$ $\quad$ °C				$\qquad$ 40	19.81	5
Ref. Index										
n_D 20°C	1.423	2	d_c g/ml	0.251	5		Parachor [P]			
25	1.420	2	v_c ml/g	3.991	5		20°C			
30	1.417	4	t_c °C	271.	5		30			
"C"	0.7292	4	P_c mm	23432.	5		40			
MR (Obs.)	31.8	2					Sugd.	270.5	5
MR (Calc.)	31.859	5	PV/RT				Exp. L.1.%/wt.			
(nD-d/2)	1.038	2	25°C	0.9968	4		u.			
Dielectric			30 mm	1.0000	5		Dispersion			
			BP	0.9600	5					
A $\vert$ 5 to	6.81726	4	t_e	0.9526	5		Flash Point °C			
B $\vert$ 130 °C	1220.3	4	t_c	0.265	5		Fire Point			
C	222.	5					M. Spec.			
A* $\vert$ 5 to	1.20391	5	ΔHc kcal/m				Ultra V.			
B* $\vert$ 110 °C	1139.2	5	ΔHf				X-Ray Dif.			
K			ΔFf				Infrared			
c			Viscosity				Solubility in +			
t_k $\vert$ $\quad$ to			centistokes				Acetone			
t_x $\vert$ $\quad$ °C			η $\qquad$ °C				Carbon tet.			
A' $\vert$ $\quad$ to							Benzene			
B' $\vert$ _ _ °C							Ether			
C'			B^v $\vert$ $\quad$ to				n-Heptane			
A'* $\quad$ to			A^v $\vert$ $\quad$ °C				Ethanol			
B'* $\quad$ °C			(B^v) $\vert$ _ _ to				Water			
Ac $\vert$ 130 to	7.23729	5	(A^v) $\vert$ °C				Water in			
Bc $\vert$ t_c °C	1538.4	5	c_p liq. °K							
Cc	266.	5								
Cryos. A°			c_p vap. °K							
consts. B°										
t_e °C	96.99	5	c_v vap.							

$T_R = 0.75\,T_c$

+ grams/100 grams solvent

REFERENCES: 1-Dow 2-API 3-Lit. 4-Calc. from det. data 5-Calc. by formula
SOURCE: $\qquad$ API
PURIFICATION: $\qquad$ API
LITERATURE REFERENCES:

TABLE XVII.   THIACYCLOPENTANES   No.

TABLE XVII. THIACYCLOPENTANES   429

No. 1

NAME	Thiacyclopentane	STRUCTURAL FORMULA
	Tetrahydrothiophene	

Mole % Pur.	Ref.	Molecular Formula C_4H_8S	Molecular Weight 88.170	

Structural formula:

$$H_2C \overset{S}{\underset{\underset{CH_2}{|}}{\overbrace{}}} CH_2 \quad H_2C - CH_2$$

		Ref.			Ref.				Ref.
F.P. °C	-96.16	2	dt/dP			f	to		
F.P. 100%			°C/mm			g	_ _ °K		
B.P. °C			25°C	1.02067	5	h			
760 mm	121.117	2	BP	0.04732	2				
100	61.152	5	t_e	0.03619	5	f'	to		
30	34.681	5	30 mm	0.6629	5	g'	_ _ °K		
10	14.477	5	ΔHm cal/g			h'			
1	-19.353	5	ΔHv cal/g			m	to		
Pressure			25°C	108.45	5	n	_ _ °K		
mm 25°C	18.10	5	30 mm	107.43	5	o			
t_e	1070.6	5	BP	92.78	5				
Density			t_e	90.72	5	m'	to		
g/ml 20°C	0.99869	2	t_e (d, e)	90.61	5	n'	_ _ °K		
d_4^t 25	0.99379	2	ΔHv/T_e	19.65	5	o'			
30	0.98885	4	d 35 to	113.30	5	Surface tension			
a	1.01836	4	e 140 °C	0.1695	5	dynes/cm. 20°C	33.68	5
b	-0.0398	4	d' 10 to	111.10	5	ɣ 30	32.37	5
Ref. Index			e' 35 °C	0.1049	5	40	31.10	5
n_D 20°C	1.50483	2	d_c g/ml	0.333	5	Parachor [P]		
25	1.50217	2	v_c ml/g	3.00	5	20°C		
30	1.49921	4	t_c °C	358.	5	30		
"C"	0.6638	4	P_c mm	38746.	5	40		
MR (Obs.)	26.179	2	PV/RT			Sugd. 212.7		5
MR (Calc.)	26.178	5	25°C	1.0000	5	Exp. L. 1.%/wt.		
(nD-d/2)	1.00548	2	30 mm	1.0000	5	u.		
Dielectric			BP	0.9550	5	Dispersion	113.7	2
A 35 to	6.9518	4	t_e	0.9452	5	Flash Point °C		
B 200 °C	1372.4	4	t_c	0.26	5	Fire Point		
C	216.	5	ΔHc kcal/m			M. Spec.		
A* 35 to	1.27236	5	ΔHf			Ultra V.		
B* 150 °C	1286.8	5	ΔFf			X-Ray Dif.		
K			Viscosity			Infrared		
c			centistokes			Solubility in +		
t_k to			η °C			Acetone		
t_x °C						Carbon tet.		
A' 10 to	7.34491	5				Benzene		
B' 35 °C	1576.6	5				Ether		
C'	234.	5				n-Heptane		
A'* 10 to	1.63884	5	B^v to			Ethanol		
B'* 35 °C	1477.7	5	A^v °C			Water		
Ac 200 to	7.37677	5	(B^v) to			Water in		
Bc t_c °C	1748.6	5	(A^v) °C					
Cc	270.	5	c_p liq. °K					
Cryos. A°								
consts. B°			c_p vap. °K					
t_e °C	133.91	5	c_v vap.					

$T_R = 0.75\ T_c$ + grams/100 grams solvent

REFERENCES: 1-Dow 2-API 3-Lit. 4-Calc. from det. data 5-Calc. by formula

SOURCE: API

PURIFICATION: API

LITERATURE REFERENCES:

No. 2

NAME	2-Methylthiacyclopentane	STRUCTURAL FORMULA

Tetrahydro-2-methylthiophene

Mole % Pur. 99.75	Ref. 3	Molecular Formula	$C_5H_{10}S$	Molecular Weight 102.196

		Ref.				Ref.				Ref.
F.P. °C	-100.71	2	dt/dP				f | to			
F.P. 100%			°C/mm				g | °K			
			25°C	1.5897	5		h |			
B.P. °C			BP	0.04895	4					
760 mm	133.23	2	t_e	0.03658	5		f' | to			
100	71.200	2					g' | °K			
30	43.82	5	30 mm	0.6856	5		h' |			
10	22.93	5	ΔHm cal/g							
1	-12.02	5					m | to			
			ΔHv cal/g				n | °K			
Pressure			25°C	96.77	5		o |			
mm 25°C	11.24	5	30 mm	95.01	5					
t_e	1103.1	5	BP	81.99	5		m' | to			
			t_e	79.98	5		n' | °K			
Density			t_e (d, e)	79.89	5		o' |			
g/ml 20°C	0.9552	2	ΔHv/T_e	19.42	5		**Surface tension**			
d_4^t 25	0.9512	2					dynes/cm. 20°C	30.63	5	
30	0.9472	4	d | 45 to	101.40	5		γ 30	29.61	5	
			e | 150 °C	0.1457	5		40	28.61	5	
a	0.9712	4	d' | 15 to	99.10	5					
b	-0.0380	4	e' | 45 °C	0.0935	5		**Parachor [P]**			
							20°C			
Ref. Index			d_c g/ml	0.33727	5		30			
n_D 20°C	1.4909	2	v_c ml/g	2.9649	5		40			
25	1.4884	2	t_c °C	362.	5		Sugd.	251.7	5	
30	1.4860	4	P_c mm	33467.	5					
"C"	0.6770	4	**PV/RT**				**Exp. L.l.%/wt.**			
MR (Obs.)	30.98	2	25°C	1.0000	5		u.			
MR (Calc.)	30.981	5	30 mm	1.0000	5		Dispersion	114.	2	
(nD-d/2)	1.0133	2	BP	0.9533	5		**Flash Point °C**			
Dielectric			t_e	0.9420	5		Fire Point			
A | 45 to	6.94997	3	t_c	0.256	5		**M Spec.**			
B | 200 °C	1418.506	3	ΔHc kcal/m				Ultra V.			
C	215.368	3	ΔHf				X-Ray Dif.			
A* | 45 to	1.32384	5	ΔFf				Infrared			
B* | 160 °C	1330.5	5	**Viscosity**				**Solubility in +**			
K			centistokes				Acetone			
c			η °C				Carbon tet.			
t_k | to							Benzene			
t_x | °C							Ether			
A' | 15 to	7.32227	5					n-Heptane			
B' | 45 °C	1618.1	5					Ethanol			
C'	233.	5	B^v | to				Water			
			A^v | °C				Water in			
A'* | 15 to	1.67142	5	(B^v)| to							
B'* | 45 °C	1517.2	5	(A^v)| °C							
Ac | 200 to	7.37365	5	c_p liq. °K							
Bc | t_c °C	1795.7	5								
Cc	268.	5	c_p vap. °K							
Cryos. A°										
consts. B°			c_v vap.							
t_e °C	147.67	5								

$T_R = 0.75 T_c$ +   grams/100 grams solvent

REFERENCES: 1-Dow   2-API   3-Lit.   4-Calc. from det. data   5-Calc. by formula

SOURCE: Lit.

PURIFICATION: Lit.

LITERATURE REFERENCES: 3 Ind. Eng. Chem. **44**, 1430 (1952), P. T. White et al.

TABLE XVII. THIACYCLOPENTANES 431

No. 3

NAME	3-Methylthiacyclopentane	STRUCTURAL FORMULA
	Tetrahydro-3-methylthiophene	H_2C — S — CH_2
Mole % Pur. 99.7	Ref. 3 Molecular Formula $C_5H_{10}S$ Molecular Weight 102.196	H_2C —— $CHCH_3$

		Ref.			Ref.				Ref.
F.P. °C	-81.16	2	dt/dP			f	to		
F.P. 100%			°C/mm			g	°K		
			25°C	1.9622	5	h			
B.P. °C			BP	0.04961	4				
760 mm	138.67	2	t_e	0.03654	5	f'	to		
100	75.90	5	30 mm	0.6954	5	g'	°K		
30	48.14	5	ΔHm cal/g			h'			
10	26.95	5	ΔHv cal/g			m	to		
1	-8.56	5	25°C	98.35	5	n	°K		
Pressure			30 mm	96.24	5	o			
mm 25°C	8.9596	5	BP	83.31	5				
t_e	1118.8	5	t_e	81.22	5	m'	to		
Density			t_e (d, e)	81.14	5	n'	°K		
g/ml 20°C	0.9634	2	ΔHv/T_e	19.44	5	o'			
d_4^t 25	0.9585	2	d 50 to	103.10	5	Surface tension			
30	0.9536	4	e 155 °C	0.1429	5	dynes/cm. 20°C	31.69	5
a	0.9830	4	d' 15 to	100.60	5	30	30.42	5
b	-0.0₃98	4	e' 50 °C	0.0909	5	40	29.18	5
Ref. Index			d_c g/ml	0.341	5	Parachor [P]			
n_D 20°C	1.4924	2	v_c ml/g	2.927	5	20°C			
25	1.4902	2	t_c °C	359.	5	30			
30	1.4871	4	P_c mm	33472.	5	40			
"C"	0.6732	4				Sugd.	251.7	5
MR (Obs.)	30.80	2	PV/RT			Exp. L. 1.%/wt.			
MR (Calc.)	30.797	5	25°C	1.0000	5	u.			
(nD-d/2)	1.0107	2	30 mm	1.0000	5	Dispersion	112.	2
Dielectric			BP	0.9532	5	Flash Point °C			
A 50 to	6.97939	3	t_e	0.9417	5	Fire Point			
B 200 °C	1454.378	3	t_c	0.254	5	M. Spec.			
C	216.179	3	ΔHc kcal/m			Ultra V.			
A* 50 to	1.34598	5	ΔHf			X-Ray Dif.			
B* 165 °C	1364.3	5	ΔFf			Infrared			
K			Viscosity			Solubility in +			
c			centistokes			Acetone	∞	
t_k to			η °C			Carbon tet.	∞	
t_x °C						Benzene	∞	
A' 15 to	7.35036	5				Ether	∞	
B' 50 °C	1657.1	5				n-Heptane	∞	
C'	234.	5	B^v to			Ethanol	∞	
A'* 15 to	1.69464	5	A^v °C			Water		
B'* 50 °C	1554.6	5	(B^v) to			Water in		
Ac 200 to	7.40495	5	(A^v) °C					
Bc t_c °C	1838.5	5	c_p liq. °K					
Cc	269.	5	c_p vap. °K					
Cryos. A° consts. B°			c_v vap.					
t_e °C	153.83	5						
T_R = 0.75 T_c						+ grams/100 grams solvent		

REFERENCES: 1-Dow 2-API 3-Lit. 4-Calc. from det. data 5-Calc. by formula

SOURCE: Lit.

PURIFICATION: Lit.

LITERATURE REFERENCES: 3 Ind. Eng. Chem. 44, 1430, (1952) P. T. White et al.

No. 4

NAME	2-Ethylthiacyclopentane		STRUCTURAL FORMULA

Structural formula: H_2C–S–$CH(C_2H_5)$; H_2C—CH_2 (thiacyclopentane ring)

Mole % Pur.	Ref.	Molecular Formula $C_6H_{12}S$	Molecular Weight 116.222

		Ref.				Ref.				Ref.
F.P. °C			dt/dP				f | to			
F.P. 100%			°C/mm				g | _ _°K_			
			25°C	4.02546	5		h |			
B.P. °C			BP	0.05176	4					
760 mm	157.	2	t_e	0.03699	5		f' | to			
100	91.	5					g' | _ _°K_			
30	63.	5	30 mm	0.7223	5		h' |			
10	41.	5	ΔHm cal/g							
1	4.	5	ΔHv cal/g				m | to			
Pressure			25°C	92.69	5		n | _ _°K_			
mm 25°C	4.07475	5	30 mm	89.00	5		o |			
t_e	1169.1	5	BP	76.20	5					
Density			t_e	73.92	5		m' | to			
g/ml 20°C	0.944	2	t_e (d, e)	73.79	5		n' | _ _°K_			
d_4^t 25	0.939	2	ΔHv/T_e	19.18	5		o' |			
30	0.934	4	d | 60 to	97.49	5		Surface tension			
a	0.964	4	e | 180 °C	0.1356	5		dynes/cm. 20°C	31.08	5
b	-0.0$_3$1	4	d' | 20 to	95.14	5		30	29.78	5
Ref. Index			e' | 60 °C	0.0981	5		40	28.52	5
n_D 20°C	1.490	2	d_c g/ml	0.3166	5		Parachor [P]		
25	1.487	2	v_c ml/g	3.1586	5		20°C		
30	1.484	4	t_c °C	379.	5		30		
"C"	0.6838	4	P_c mm	27149.	5		40		
MR (Obs.)	35.6	2	PV/RT				Sugd.	290.7	5
MR (Calc.)	35.595	5	25°C	1.0000	5		Exp. L.1.%/wt.		
(nD-d/2)	1.018	2	30 mm	1.0000	5		u.		
Dielectric			BP	0.9513	5		Dispersion		
			t_e	0.9380	5		Flash Point °C		
A | 60 to	6.92152	4	t_c	0.251	5		Fire Point		
B | 215 °C	1478.9	4	ΔHc kcal/m				M Spec.		
C	209.	5	ΔHf				Ultra V.		
A* | 60 to	1.33267	5	ΔFf				X-Ray Dif.		
B* | 185 °C	1388.4	5	Viscosity				Infrared		
K			centistokes				Solubility in +		
c			η °C				Acetone		
t_k | to							Carbon tet.		
t_x | °C							Benzene		
A' | 25 to	7.28229	5					Ether		
B' | 60 °C	1681.4	5	B^v | to				n-Heptane		
C'	227.	5	A^v | °C				Ethanol		
A'* 25 to	1.68091	5	(B^v) | to				Water		
B'* 60 °C	1581.3	5	(A^v) | °C				Water in		
Ac | 215 to	7.33644	5	c_p liq. °K						
Bc | t_c °C	1852.2	5							
Cc	260.	5	c_p vap. °K						
Cryos. A°									
consts. B°			c_v vap.						
t_e °C	174.76	5							

$T_R = 0.75 T_c$

+ grams/100 grams solvent

REFERENCES: 1-Dow 2-API 3-Lit. 4-Calc. from det. data 5-Calc. by formula
SOURCE: API
PURIFICATION: API
LITERATURE REFERENCES:

TABLE XVII. THIACYCLOPENTANES

433

No. 5

NAME	3-Ethylthiacyclopentane	STRUCTURAL FORMULA
	3-Ethyltetrahydrothiophene	

Mole % Pur.	Ref.	Molecular Formula $C_6H_{12}S$	Molecular Weight 116.222	

H_2C—S—CH_2 / H_2C——CHC_2H_5

		Ref.			Ref.			Ref.
F.P. °C			dt/dP			f $\mid$ to		
F.P. 100%			°C/mm			g $\mid$ °K		
B.P. °C			25°C	5.4821	5	h $\mid$		
760 mm	165.	2	BP	0.05277	4			
100	98.22	5	t_e	0.03714	5	f' $\mid$ to		
30	68.80	5	30 mm	0.7362	5	g' $\mid$ °K		
10	46.39	5	ΔHm cal/g			h' $\mid$		
1	8.94	5						
Pressure			ΔHv cal/g			m $\mid$ to		
mm 25°C	2.92058	5	25°C	94.96	5	n $\mid$ °K		
t_e	1192.4	5	30 mm	90.55	5	o $\mid$		
			BP	77.56	5			
Density			t_e	75.14	5	m' $\mid$ to		
g/ml 20°C	0.950	2	t_e (d, e)	75.00	5	n' $\mid$ °K		
d_4^t 25	0.945	2				o' $\mid$		
30	0.940	4	ΔHv/T_e	19.10	5			
a	0.96999	4	d $\mid$ 70 to	99.84	5	Surface tension		
b	-0.03999	4	e $\mid$ 185 °C	0.1350	5	dynes/cm. 20°C	31.88	5
			d' $\mid$ 25 to	97.48	5	γ 30	30.56	5
Ref. Index			e' $\mid$ 70 °C	0.1007	5	40	29.27	5
n_D 20°C	1.491	2	d_c g/ml	0.306	5	Parachor [P]		
25	1.489	2	v_c ml/g	3.264	5	20°C		
30	1.487	4	t_c °C	392.	5	30		
"C"	0.6821	4	P_c mm	27341.	5	40		
MR (Obs.)	35.4	2				Sugd.	290.7	5
MR (Calc.)	35.409	4	PV/RT			Exp. L.1.%/wt.		
(nD-d/2)	1.016	2	25°C	1.0000	5	u.		
Dielectric			30 mm	1.0000	5	Dispersion		
A $\mid$ 70 to	6.91995	4	BP	0.9514	5	Flash Point °C		
B $\mid$ 230 °C	1506.6	4	t_e	0.9375	5	Fire Point		
C	208.	5	t_c	0.250	5	M. Spec.		
A* $\mid$ 70 to	1.32274	5	ΔHc kcal/m			Ultra V.		
B* $\mid$ 195 °C	1414.3	5	ΔHf			X-Ray Dif.		
K			ΔFf			Infrared		
c			Viscosity			Solubility in +		
t_k $\mid$ to			centistokes			Acetone		
t_x $\mid$ °C			η °C			Carbon tet.		
A' $\mid$ 25 to	7.27389	5				Benzene		
B' $\mid$ 70 °C	1708.9	5				Ether		
C'	226.	5	B^v $\mid$ to			n-Heptane		
A'* $\mid$ 25 to	1.66916	5	A^v $\mid$ °C			Ethanol		
B'* $\mid$ 70 °C	1608.4	5	$(B^v)\mid$ to			Water		
Ac $\mid$ 230 to	7.33538	5	$(A^v)\mid$ °C			Water in		
Bc $\mid$ t_c °C	1888.2	5	c_p liq. °K					
Cc	260.	5						
Cryos. A°			c_p vap. °K					
consts. B°								
t_e °C	183.98	5	c_v vap.					

$T_R = 0.75\ T_c$

+ grams/100 grams solvent

REFERENCES: 1-Dow 2-API 3-Lit. 4-Calc. from det. data 5-Calc. by formula

SOURCE:	API
PURIFICATION:	API
LITERATURE REFERENCES:	

No. 6

NAME	2, cis-5-Dimethylthiacyclopentane	STRUCTURAL FORMULA

$$CH_3 \ HC \overset{S}{\diagup \diagdown} CHCH_3$$
$$H_2C\text{——}CH_2$$

Mole % Pur. 99.3	Ref. 3	Molecular Formula $C_6H_{12}S$	Molecular Weight 116.222

		Ref.				Ref.				Ref.
F.P. °C	-89.4	2	dt/dP °C/mm				f	to		
F.P. 100%			25°C	2.2744	5		g	°K		
B.P. °C			BP	0.05005	4		h			
760 mm	142.28	2	t_e	0.03670	5		f'	to		
100	78.99	5	30 mm	0.6969	5		g'	°K		
30	51.14	5	ΔHm cal/g				h'			
10	29.92	5					m	to		
1	-5.53	5	ΔHv cal/g				n	°K		
Pressure			25°C	88.53	5		o			
mm 25°C	7.5508	5	30 mm	86.04	5					
t_e	1131.4	5	BP	73.77	5		m'	to		
Density			t_e	71.74	5		n'	°K		
g/ml 20°C	0.9222	2	t_e (d, e)	71.64	5		o'			
d_4^t 25	0.9177	2	$\Delta Hv/T_e$	19.33	5		Surface tension			
d_4^t 30	0.9132	4	d ⎸ 50 to	92.92	5		dynes/cm. 20°C	28.30	5
a	0.9402	4	e ⎸ 160 °C	0.1346	5		ɣ	30	27.21	5
b	-0.0₃90	4	d' ⎸ 20 to	90.91	5			40	26.15	5
Ref. Index			e' ⎸ 50 °C	0.0953	5		Parachor [P]			
n_D 20°C	1.4799	2	d_c g/ml	0.3107	5		20°C			
25	1.4774	2	v_c ml/g	3.2189	5		30			
30	1.4749	4	t_c °C	355.	5		40			
"C"	0.6864	4	P_c mm	26598.	5		Sugd.	290.7	5
MR (Obs.)	35.80	2	PV/RT				Exp. L.1.%/wt.			
MR (Calc.)	35.793	4	25°C	1.0000	5		u.			
(nD-d/2)	1.0188	2	30 mm	1.0000	5		Dispersion	114.	2
Dielectric			BP	0.9549	5		Flash Point °C			
A ⎸ 50 to	6.90415	3	t_e	0.9429	5		Fire Point			
B ⎸ 200 °C	1417.766	3	t_c	0.254	5		M Spec.			
C	210.102	3	ΔHc kcal/m				Ultra V.			
A* ⎸ 50 to	1.32534	5	ΔHf				X-Ray Dif.			
B* ⎸ 170 °C	1329.4	5	ΔFf				Infrared			
K			Viscosity				Solubility in +			
c			centistokes				Acetone	∞		
t_k ⎸ to			η °C				Carbon tet.	∞		
t_x ⎸ °C							Benzene	∞		
A' ⎸ 20 to	7.27596	5					Ether	∞		
B' ⎸ 50 °C	1618.7	5					n-Heptane	∞		
C'	228.	5	B^v ⎸ to				Ethanol	∞		
A'* 20 to	1.68214	5	A^v ⎸ °C				Water			
B'* 50 °C	1520.1	5	(B^v) ⎸ to				Water in			
Ac ⎸ 200 to	7.31720	5	(A^v) ⎸ °C							
Bc ⎸ t_c °C	1774.9	5	c_p liq. °K							
Cc	259.	5								
Cryos. A° consts. B°			c_p vap. °K							
t_e °C	158.10	5	c_v vap.							

$T_R = 0.75 \ T_c$　　　　　　　　　　　　　　　　+ grams/100 grams solvent

REFERENCES: 1-Dow　2-API　3-Lit.　4-Calc. from det. data　5-Calc. by formula

SOURCE:　　　　　　Lit.

PURIFICATION:　　　Lit.

LITERATURE REFERENCES:　3 Ind. Eng. Chem. 44, 1430 (1952), P. T. White et al.

TABLE XVII. THIACYCLOPENTANES

NAME	2, trans-5-Dimethylthiacyclopentane	STRUCTURAL FORMULA
	trans-Tetrahydro-2, 5-dimethylthiophene	$H_3CHC \overset{S}{\diagdown} CHCH_3$
Mole % Pur.	Ref. Molecular Formula $C_6H_{12}S$ Molecular Weight 116.222	$H_2C—CH_2$

		Ref.				Ref.					Ref.
F.P. °C	-76.35	2	dt/dP				f	to			
F.P. 100%			°C/mm				g	°K			
			25°C	2.1717	5		h				
B.P. °C			BP	0.05025	4						
760 mm	142.0	2	t_e	0.03683	5		f'	to			
100	78.32	5	30 mm	0.7028	5		g'	°K			
30	50.25	4	ΔHm cal/g				h'				
10	28.84	5	ΔHv cal/g				m	to			
1	-6.97	5	25°C	86.92	5		n	°K			
Pressure			30 mm	84.84	5		o				
mm 25°C	8.0545	5	BP	73.30	5						
t_e	1130.8	5	t_e	71.45	5		m'	to			
Density			t_e (d, e)	71.31	5		n'	°K			
g/ml 20°C	0.9188	2	ΔHv/T_e	19.27	5		o'				
d_4^t 25	0.9142	2	d 50 to	91.17	5		Surface tension			
30	0.9096	4	e 170 °C	0.1258	5		dynes/cm. 20°C	27.89	5
a	0.9372	4	d' 25 to	88.97	5		ɤ 30	26.79	5
b	-0.0₃92	4	e' 50 °C	0.0820	5		40	25.71	5
Ref. Index			d_c g/ml	0.309	5		Parachor [P]		
n_D 20°C	1.4776	2	v_c ml/g	3.232	5		20°C		
25	1.4752	2	t_c °C	354.	5		30		
30	1.4725	4	P_c mm	26445.	5		40		
"C"	0.6859	4					Sugd.	290.7	5
MR (Obs.)	35.78	2	PV/RT				Exp. L.1.%/wt.		
MR (Calc.)	35.678	5	25°C	1.0000	5		u.		
(nD-d/2)	1.0182	2	30 mm	1.0000	5		Dispersion	114.	2
Dielectric			BP	0.9537	5		Flash Point °C		
A 50 to	6.94097	4	t_e	0.9430	5		Fire Point		
B 197 °C	1449.3	4	t_c	0.254	5		M. Spec.		
C	215.	4	ΔHc kcal/m				Ultra V.		
A* 50 to	1.35769	5	ΔHf				X-Ray Dif.		
B* 168 °C	1358.1	5	ΔFf				Infrared		
K			Viscosity				Solubility in +		
c			centistokes				Acetone		
t_k to			η °C				Carbon tet.		
t_x °C							Benzene		
A' 25 to	7.31175	5					Ether		
B' 50 °C	1652.7	5					n-Heptane		
C'	233.	5	B^v to				Ethanol		
A'* 25 to	1.71163	5	A^v °C				Water		
B'* 50 °C	1550.5	5	(B^v) to				Water in		
Ac 197 to	7.36133	5	(A^v) °C						
Bc t_c °C	1816.4	5	c_p liq. °K						
Cc	264.	5							
Cryos. A° consts. B°			c_p vap. °K						
t_e °C	157.80	5	c_v vap.						
T_R = 0.75 T_c							+ grams/100 grams solvent		

REFERENCES: 1-Dow 2-API 3-Lit. 4-Calc. from det. data 5-Calc. by formula

SOURCE: API

PURIFICATION: API

LITERATURE REFERENCES:

TABLE XVIII. THIACYCLOPROPANES

No.

TABLE XVIII. THIACYCLOPROPANES

No. 1

NAME	Thiacyclopropane	STRUCTURAL FORMULA
	(Ethylene sulfide)	H_2C——CH_2
		S

Mole % Pur.	Ref.	Molecular Formula C_2H_4S	Molecular Weight 60.118

Column 1

	Value	Ref.
F.P. °C	-109.	2
F.P. 100%		
B.P. °C		
760 mm	54.93	2
100	4.8	4
30	-17.39	5
10	-34.25	5
1	-62.12	5
Pressure		
mm 25°C	249.36	5
t_e	884.77	5
Density		
g/ml 20°C	1.013	2
d_4^t 25	1.007	2
30	1.001	4
a	1.0371	4
b	-0.0_2117	4
Ref. Index		
n_D 20°C	1.490	2
25	1.487	2
30	1.484	4
"C"	0.6373	4
MR (Obs.)	17.2	2
MR (Calc.)	16.926	5
(nD-d/2)	0.984	2
Dielectric		
A ⌐-17 to	6.98816	4
B ⌊147 °C⌋	1166.2	4
C	229.	5
A* -17 to	1.20992	5
B* ⌊69 °C⌋	1091.2	5
K		
c		
t_k ⌐ to⌐		
t_x ⌊ °C⌋		
A' ⌐ to		
B' ⌊ °C⌋		
C'		
A'* to		
B'* °C		
Ac⌐147 to	7.42828	5
Bc⌊t_c °C⌋	1520.8	5
Cc	282.	5
Cryos. A°		
consts. B°		
t_e °C	59.57	5

$T_R = 0.75 T_c$

Column 2

	Value	Ref.
dt/dP		
°C/mm		
25°C	0.09635	5
BP	0.0395	2
t_e	0.0350	5
30 mm	0.5559	5
ΔHm cal/g		
ΔHv cal/g		
25°C	120.81	5
30 mm	129.71	5
BP	113.50	5
t_e	112.48	5
t_e (d,e)	112.46	5
ΔHv/T_e	20.32	5
d ⌐-17 to	125.81	5
e ⌊ 59 °C	0.2242	5
d' ⌐ to		
e' ⌊ °C		
d_c g/ml	0.373	5
v_c ml/g	2.684	5
t_c °C	287.	5
P_c mm	57381.	5
PV/RT		
25°C	0.9875	5
30 mm	1.0000	5
BP	0.9597	5
t_e	0.9556	5
t_c	0.265	5
ΔHc kcal/m		
ΔHf		
ΔFf		
Viscosity		
centistokes		
η °C		
B^v ⌐ to		
A^v ⌊ °C		
(B^v) to		
(A^v) °C		
c_p liq. °K		
c_p vap. °K		
c_v vap.		

Column 3

		Value	Ref.
f	to		
g	°K		
h			
f'	to		
g'	°K		
h'			
m	to		
n	°K		
o			
m'	to		
n'	°K		
o'			
Surface tension			
dynes/cm. 20°C		33.53	5
γ 30		31.92	5
40		30.34	5
Parachor [P]			
20°C			
30			
40			
Sugd.		142.9	5
Exp. L.1.%/wt.			
u.			
Dispersion		128.	2
Flash Point °C			
Fire Point			
M. Spec.			
Ultra V.			
X-Ray Dif.			
Infrared			
Solubility in +			
Acetone			
Carbon tet.			
Benzene			
Ether			
n-Heptane			
Ethanol			
Water			
Water in			

+ grams/100 grams solvent

REFERENCES:	1-Dow 2-API 3-Lit. 4-Calc. from det. data 5-Calc. by formula
SOURCE:	API
PURIFICATION:	API
LITERATURE REFERENCES:	

No. 2

NAME	2-Methylthiacyclopropane	STRUCTURAL FORMULA
	2-Methylthiirane	H_2C————CH CH_3

Mole % Pur.	Ref.	Molecular Formula C_3H_6S	Molecular Weight 74.144

		Ref.			Ref.			Ref.
F.P. °C	-91.	2	dt/dP			f $\vert$ to		
F.P. 100%			°C/mm			g $\vert$ $\vert$__ °K		
B.P. °C			25°C	0.1909	5	h $\vert$		
760 mm	74.4	2	BP	0.041	2			
100	22.2	4	t_e	0.03463	5	f' $\vert$ to		
30	-0.96	4	30 mm	0.5816	5	g' $\vert$ $\vert$__ °K		
10	-18.62	5	ΔHm cal/g			h' $\vert$		
1	-47.88	5						
Pressure			ΔHv cal/g			m $\vert$ to		
mm 25°C	113.84	5	25°C	108.81	5	n $\vert$ $\vert$__ °K		
t_e	941.2	5	30 mm	113.84	5	o $\vert$		
Density			BP	99.48	5			
g/ml 20°C	0.944	2	t_e	98.21	5	m' $\vert$ to		
d_4^t 25	0.939	2	t_e (d, e)	98.18	5	n' $\vert$ $\vert$__ °K		
30	0.934	4	ΔHv/T_e	20.55	5	o' $\vert$		
a	0.9640	4	d $\vert$ -1 to	113.66	5	Surface tension		
b	-0.0₃979	4	e $\vert$ 90 °C	0.1906	5	dynes/cm. 20°C	28.72	5
			d' $\vert$ to			ɤ 30	27.50	5
Ref. Index			e' $\vert$ °C			40	26.30	5
n_D 20°C	1.475	2	d_c g/ml			Parachor [P]		
25	1.472	2	v_c ml/g			20°C		
30	1.469	4	t_c °C			30		
"C"	0.6642	4	P_c mm			40		
MR (Obs.)	22.1	2	PV/RT			Sugd.	181.9	5
MR (Calc.)	21.544	5	25°C	0.9657	5	Exp. L.1.%/wt.		
(nD-d/2)	1.003	2	30 mm	1.0000	5	u.		
Dielectric			BP	0.9602	5	Dispersion	126.	2
A $\vert$ -1 to	7.05348	4	t_e	0.9545	5	Flash Point °C		
B $\vert$ 150 °C	1249.3	4	t_c			Fire Point		
C	225.	5	ΔHc kcal/m			M Spec.		
A* $\vert$ -1 to	1.34217	5	ΔHf			Ultra V.		
B* $\vert$ 91 °C	1170.5	5	ΔFf			X-Ray Dif.		
K			Viscosity			Infrared		
c			centistokes			Solubility in +		
t_k $\vert$ to			η °C			Acetone		
t_x $\vert$ °C						Carbon tet.		
A' $\vert$ to						Benzene		
B' $\vert$ __ °C						Ether		
C'			B^v $\vert$ to			n-Heptane		
A'* $\vert$ to			A^v $\vert$ °C			Ethanol		
B'* °C			(B^v) $\vert$ to			Water		
Ac $\vert$ to			(A^v) $\vert$ °C			Water in		
Bc $\vert$ t_c °C								
Cc			c_p liq. °K					
Cryos. A°			c_p vap. °K					
consts. B°								
t_e °C	81.22	5	c_v vap.					

+ grams/100 grams solvent

REFERENCES: 1-Dow 2-API 3-Lit. 4-Calc. from det. data 5-Calc. by formula

SOURCE: API

PURIFICATION: API

LITERATURE REFERENCES:

TABLE XVIII. THIACYCLOPROPANES

No. 3

NAME	2-Ethylthiacyclopropane	STRUCTURAL FORMULA
	2-Ethylthiirane	H_2C————CH C_2H_5

Mole % Pur.	Ref.	Molecular Formula C_4H_8S	Molecular Weight 88.170

		Ref.				Ref.			Ref.
F.P. °C			dt/dP °C/mm			f		to °K	
F.P. 100%			25°C	0.6367	5	g			
B.P. °C			BP	0.04304	5	h			
760 mm	105.	2	t_e	0.03406	5	f'		to °K	
100	50.23	5	30 mm	0.6102	5	g'			
30	25.90	5	ΔHm cal/g			h'			
10	7.27	5	ΔHv cal/g			m		to °K	
1	-24.06	5	25°C	110.24	5	n			
Pressure			30 mm	110.14	5	o			
mm 25°C	28.55	5	BP	93.80	5	m'		to °K	
t_e	1022.6	5	t_e	91.89	5	n'			
Density			t_e (d, e)	91.73	5	o'			
g/ml 20°C	0.927	2	ΔHv/T_e	20.87	5	Surface tension			
d_4^t 25	0.922	2	d 25 to	115.49	5	dynes/cm. 20°C	29.08		5
30	0.917	4	e 115 °C	0.2066	5	γ 30	27.84		5
a	0.947	4	d' to			40	26.63		5
b	-0.0₃994	4	e' °C			Parachor [P]			
Ref. Index			d_c g/ml	0.385	5	20°C			
n_D 20°C	1.472	2	v_c ml/g	2.598	5	30			
25	1.470	2	t_c °C	327.	5	40			
30	1.467	4	P_c mm	43307.	5	Sugd.	220.9		5
"C"	0.6724	4	PV/RT			Exp. L.1.%/wt.			
MR (Obs.)	26.6	2	25°C	1.0000	5	u.			
MR (Calc.)	26.162	5	30 mm	1.0000	5	Dispersion			
(nD-d/2)	1.009	2	BP	0.9552	5	Flash Point °C			
Dielectric			t_e	0.9468	5	Fire Point			
A 25 to	7.04959	5	t_c	0.265	5	M. Spec.			
B 177 °C	1309.0	5	ΔHc kcal/m			Ultra V.			
C	209.	5	ΔHf			X-Ray Dif.			
A* 25 to	1.39875	5	ΔFf			Infrared			
B* 125 °C	1232.6	5	Viscosity			Solubility in +			
K			centistokes			Acetone			
c			η °C			Carbon tet.			
t_k to						Benzene			
t_x °C						Ether			
A' 5 to	7.47659	5				n-Heptane			
B' 25 °C	1517.3	5				Ethanol			
C'	227.	5	B^v to			Water			
A'* 5 to	1.72303	5	A^v °C			Water in			
B'* 25 °C	1404.3	5	(B^v) to						
Ac 177 to	7.45689	5	(A^v) °C						
Bc t_c °C	1642.2	5	c_p liq. °K						
Cc	255.	5							
Cryos. A°			c_p vap. °K						
consts. B°									
t_e °C	115.02	5	c_v vap.						

$T_R = 0.75 T_c$ + grams/100 grams solvent

REFERENCES: 1-Dow   2-API   3-Lit.   4-Calc. from det. data   5-Calc. by formula

SOURCE: API

PURIFICATION: API

LITERATURE REFERENCES:

No. 4

NAME	2,2-Dimethylthiacyclopropane	STRUCTURAL FORMULA
	2,2-Dimethylthiirane	

Mole % Pur.	Ref.	Molecular Formula C_4H_8S	Molecular Weight 88.170

Structural formula:

$$H_2C \underline{\quad\quad} C(CH_3)_2$$
(with S bridging above)

		Ref.			Ref.			Ref.
F.P. °C			dt/dP			f $\quad$ to		
F.P. 100%			°C/mm			g $\quad\quad$ °K		
B.P. °C			25°C	0.2948	5	h		
760 mm	86.	2	BP	0.04182	5	f' $\quad$ to		
100	32.79	4	t_e	0.03458	5	g' $\quad\quad$ °K		
30	9.15	4	30 mm	0.5928	5	h'		
10	-8.8	5	ΔHm cal/g			m $\quad$ to		
1	-36.7	5	ΔHv cal/g			n $\quad\quad$ °K		
Pressure			25°C	98.05	5	o		
mm 25°C	69.01	5	30 mm	101.03	5			
t_e	966.97	5	BP	87.26	5	m' $\quad$ to		
Density			t_e	85.59	5	n' $\quad\quad$ °K		
g/ml 20°C			t_e (d, e)	85.85	5	o'		
d_4^t $\quad$ 25			$\Delta Hv/T_e$	20.56	5			
$\quad$ 30			d $\quad$ 0 $\quad$ to	102.67	5	Surface tension		
a			e $\quad$ 90 $\quad$ °C	0.1792	5	dynes/cm. 20°C		
b			d' $\quad$ to			γ $\quad\quad$ 30		
Ref. Index			e' $\quad$ °C			40		
n_D $\quad$ 20°C	1.464	2	d_c g/ml			Parachor [P]		
$\quad$ 25	1.462	2	v_c ml/g			20°C		
$\quad$ 30			t_c °C			30		
"C"			P_c mm			40		
MR (Obs.)			PV/RT			Sugd. 220.9	5	
MR (Calc.)	26.162	5	25°C	0.9957	5	Exp. L.l.%/wt.		
(nD-d/2)			30 mm	1.0000	5	u.		
Dielectric			BP	0.9537	5	Dispersion		
A $\quad$ 0 to	7.04835	5	t_e	0.9469	5	Flash Point °C		
B $\quad$ 200 °C	1271.1	5	t_c			Fire Point		
C	219.	5	ΔHc kcal/m			M Spec.		
A* $\quad$ 0 to	1.41469	5	ΔHf			Ultra V.		
B* $\quad$ 110 °C	1195.1	5	ΔFf			X-Ray Dif.		
K			Viscosity			Infrared		
c			centistokes			Solubility in $\quad$ +		
t_k $\quad$ to			η $\quad\quad$ °C			Acetone		
t_x $\quad$ °C						Carbon tet.		
A' $\quad$ to						Benzene		
B' $\quad$ °C						Ether		
C'			B^v $\quad$ to			n-Heptane		
A'* $\quad$ to			A^v $\quad$ °C			Ethanol		
B'* $\quad$ °C			(B^v) $\quad$ to			Water		
Ac $\quad$ to			(A^v) $\quad$ °C			Water in		
Bc $\quad$ t_c °C			c_p liq. °K					
Cc								
Cryos. A°			c_p vap. °K					
consts. B°								
t_e °C	93.85	5	c_v vap.					

+ grams/100 grams solvent

REFERENCES: 1-Dow   2-API   3-Lit.   4-Calc. from det. data   5-Calc. by formula

SOURCE: API

PURIFICATION: API

LITERATURE REFERENCES:

TABLE XIX. CYCLOHEXANES

No. 1

NAME	Cyclohexane	STRUCTURAL FORMULA

Mole % Pur. 99.997	Ref. 2	Molecular Formula C_6H_{12}	Molecular Weight 84.156

		Ref.			Ref.				Ref.
F.P. °C	6.554	2	dt/dP			f		to	
F.P. 100%			°C/mm			g		°K	
			25°C	0.2272	4	h			
B.P. °C			BP	0.04376	4				
760 mm	80.738	2	t_e	0.0363	5	f'		to	
100	25.543	2	30 mm	0.6047	4	g'		°K	
30	1.3	4				h'			
10	-17.0	4	ΔHm cal/g	7.569	2	m		300 to	-0.1031	4
1	-47.0	5	ΔHv cal/g			n		600 °K	0.0015	4
Pressure			25°C	93.81	2	o			-0.0635	4
mm 25°C	97.582	4	30 mm	98.12	5	m'		700 to	-0.0853	4
t_e	964.9	5	BP	85.4	2	n'		1000 °K	0.0016	4
Density			t_e	84.10	5	o'			-0.0658	4
g/ml 20°C	0.77855	2	t_e (d, e)	84.09	5	Surface tension		
d_4^t 25	0.77389	2	ΔHv/T_e	19.55	5	dynes/cm. 20°C	24.30	5
30	0.76922	4				δ	30	23.13	5
a	0.79720	4	d 0 to	98.33	5		40	21.99	5
b	-0.0391	4	e 90 °C	0.1602	5	Parachor [P]		
Ref. Index			d' to			20°C		
n_D 20°C	1.42623	2	e' °C			30		
25	1.42354	2	d_c g/ml	0.2718	3	40		
30	1.42084	4	v_c ml/g	3.6792	3	Sugd. 240.1	5
"C"	0.7273	4	t_c °C	281.0	3	Exp. L.1. %/wt.	
MR (Obs.)	27.709	2	P_c mm	30835.	3	u.	
MR (Calc.)	27.708	5	PV/RT			Dispersion	96.1	2
(nD-d/2)	1.03696	2	25°C	0.9917	4	Flash Point °C	-17.2	3'
Dielectric	2.023	3²	30 mm	1.0000	5	Fire Point	
A -20 to	6.84498	2	BP	0.9643	4	M. Spec.	Yes	1
B 142°C	1203.526	2	t_e	0.9578	5	Ultra V.	
C	222.863	2	t_c	0.2767	4	X-Ray Dif.	
A* -20 to	1.17513	4	ΔHc kcal/m	881.67	2	Infrared	Yes	1
B* 100°C	1122.50	4	ΔHf	-37.34	2	Solubility in +	
K			ΔFf	6.37	2	Acetone	∞
c			Viscosity			Carbon tet.	∞
t_k to			centistokes			Benzene	∞
t_x °C			η 20 °C	1.258	2	Ether	∞
A' to			40	0.926	2	n-Heptane	∞
B' °C			60	0.714	2	Ethanol	∞
C'			80	0.569	2	Water	
A'* to			B^v 0 to	618.24	4	Water in	
B'* °C			A^v 45 °C	3.99246	4		
Ac 142 to	7.32217	4	(B^v) 45 to	579.52	4		
Bc t_c °C	1577.42	4	(A^v) 90 °C	2.11433	4		
Cc	275.8	4	c_p liq. °K				
Cryos. A°	0.00411	2	c_p vap.300°K	0.30396	2		
consts. B°	0.0372	2	400	0.42564	2		
t_e °C	88.89	5	c_v vap.				

$T_R = 0.75\,T_c$

+ grams/100 grams solvent

REFERENCES: 1-Dow 2-API 3-Lit. 4-Calc. from det. data 5-Calc. by formula

SOURCE: API

PURIFICATION: API

LITERATURE REFERENCES: 3 Young; 3' NFPA 325; 3² NBS Circ. 514

No. 2

NAME	Methylcyclohexane	STRUCTURAL FORMULA

Structural formula:
$$CHCH_3$$
$$H_2C \quad CH_2$$
$$H_2C \quad CH_2$$
$$C$$
$$H_2$$

Mole % Pur. 99.80	Ref. 2	Molecular Formula C_7H_{14}	Molecular Weight 98.182

		Ref.			Ref.				Ref.
F.P. °C	-126.593	2	dt/dP °C/mm			f	to		
F.P. 100%			25°C	0.4479	4	g	°K		
B.P. °C			BP	0.04671	2	h			
760 mm	100.934	2	t_e	0.0368	5	f'	to		
100	42.072	2	30 mm	0.6438	4	g'	°K		
30	16.30	4				h'			
10	-3.18	5	ΔHm cal/g	16.43	2				
1	-35.2	5	ΔHv cal/g			m	300 to	-0.0905	4
Pressure			25°C	86.07	2	n	600 °K	0.0015	4
mm 25°C	46.33	4	30 mm	87.82	5	o		-0.0650	4
t_e	1034.	5	BP	77.2	2				
Density			t_e	75.74	5	m'	700 to	-0.0284	4
g/ml 20°C	0.76939	2	t_e (d, e)	75.78	5	n'	1000 °K	0.0015	4
d_4^t 25	0.76506	2	ΔHv/T_e	19.29	5	o'		-0.0654	4
30	0.76072	2	d 15 to	89.87	5	Surface tension			
a	0.78670	4	e 115 °C	0.1255	5	dynes/cm. 20°C		23.81	1
b	-0.03856	4	d' to			γ 30		22.78	1
Ref. Index			e' °C			40		21.76	1
n_D 20°C	1.42312	2	d_c g/ml	0.285	3	Parachor [P]			
25	1.42058	2	v_c ml/g	3.509	3	20°C		282.0	4
30	1.41803	4	t_c °C	299.13	3	30		282.1	4
"C"	0.7309	4	P_c mm	26083.	3	40		282.2	4
MR (Obs.)	32.503	2	PV/RT			Sugd.		279.1	5
MR (Calc.)	32.326	5	25°C	0.9927	4	Exp. L.1.%/wt.			
(nD-d/2)	1.03843	2	30 mm	1.0000	5	u.			
Dielectric	2.02	3'	BP	0.9719	4	Dispersion		97.8	2
A 10 to	6.82689	2	t_e	0.9641	5	Flash Point °C		-1.0	5
B 155 °C	1272.864	2	t_c	0.252	4	Fire Point			
C	221.630	2	ΔHc kcal/m	1025.95	2	M Spec.		Yes	1
A* 15 to	1.18499	5	ΔHf	-45.45	2	Ultra V.			
B* 130 °C	1183.08	5	ΔFf	4.86	2	X-Ray Dif.			
K			Viscosity			Infrared		Yes	1
c			centistokes			Solubility in +			
t_k to °C			η 20 °C	0.954	2	Acetone		∞	
t_x			40	0.750	2	Carbon tet.		∞	
A' to			60	0.608	2	Benzene		∞	
B' °C			80	0.50	2	Ether		∞	
C'			B^v -30 to	489.49	4	n-Heptane		∞	
A'* to			A^v 30 °C	Σ.30973	4	Ethanol		∞	
B'* °C			(B^v) 30 to	479.97	4	Water			
Ac 155 to	7.3213	4	(A^v) 85 °C	Σ.34257	4	Water in			
Bc t_c °C	1673.1	4	c_p liq. °K						
Cc	277.	4							
Cryos. A°	0.03779	2	c_p vap.300°K	0.33112	2				
consts. B°	0.0032	2	400	0.45171	2				
t_e °C	112.24	5	c_v vap.						

$T_R = 0.75 T_c$

+ grams/100 grams solvent

REFERENCES: 1-Dow 2-API 3-Lit. 4-Calc. from det. data 5-Calc. by formula

SOURCE: API

PURIFICATION: API

LITERATURE REFERENCES: 3 Young; 3' NBS Cir. 514

TABLE XIX. CYCLOHEXANES 443

No. 3

NAME	Ethylcyclohexane	STRUCTURAL FORMULA

Structural formula:
$$\begin{array}{c} \text{CHC}_2\text{H}_5 \\ \text{H}_2\text{C} \qquad \text{CH}_2 \\ \text{H}_2\text{C} \qquad \text{CH}_2 \\ \text{C} \\ \text{H}_2 \end{array}$$

Mole % Pur. 99.9	Ref. 2	Molecular Formula C_8H_{16}	Molecular Weight 112.208

		Ref.				Ref.					Ref.
F.P. °C	-111.323	2	dt/dP °C/mm			f		to			
F.P. 100%			25°C BP	1.4219	5	g		°K			
B.P. °C				0.04969	2	h					
760 mm	131.783	2	t_e	0.0368	5	f'		to			
100	69.044	2	30 mm	0.6888	4	g'		°K			
30	41.49	4				h'					
10	20.5	5	ΔHm cal/g	17.735	2						
1	-14.4	5	ΔHv cal/g			m	300 to	-0.0792	4		
Pressure			25°C	86.32	5	n	600 °K	0.0016	4		
mm 25°C	12.83	5	30 mm	84.87	5	o		-0.0$_6$52	4		
t_e	1117.	5	BP	73.9	2	m'	700 to	-0.0168	4		
Density			t_e	72.05	5	n'	1000 °K	0.0015	4		
g/ml 20°C	0.78792	2	t_e (d, e)	72.06	5	o'		-0.0$_6$53	4		
d_4^t 25	0.78390	2	ΔHv/T_e	19.24	5	Surface tension					
30	0.77988	4	d 40 to	89.91	5	dynes/cm. 20°C		24.89	5		
a	0.80399	4	e 145 °C	0.1215	5	ɤ	30	23.88	5		
b	-0.0$_3$8	4	d' 10 to	88.52	5		40	22.90	5		
Ref. Index			e' 40 °C	0.088	5	Parachor [P]					
n_D 20°C	1.43304	2	d_c g/ml	0.287	5	20°C					
25	1.43073	2	v_c ml/g	3.484	5	30					
30	1.42836	4	t_c °C	321.3	5	40					
"C"	0.7295	4	P_c mm	20883.	5	Sugd.		318.1	5		
MR (Obs.)	37.015	2	PV/RT			Exp. L.1.%/wt.					
MR (Calc.)	36.944	5	25°C	1.0000	5	u.					
(nD-d/2)	1.03908	2	30 mm	1.0000	5	Dispersion		97.4	2		
Dielectric	2.054	5	BP	0.9656	4	Flash Point °C		22.0	5		
A 40 to	6.87041	2	t_e	0.9552	5	Fire Point					
B 170°C	1384.036	2	t_c	0.244	5	M. Spec.					
C	215.128	2	ΔHc kcal/m	1173.74	2	Ultra V.					
A* 40 to	1.26509	4	ΔHf	-50.72	2	X-Ray Dif.					
B* 155°C	1291.0	4	ΔFf	6.96	2	Infrared					
K			Viscosity centistokes			Solubility in +					
c			η 20 °C	1.069	2	Acetone		∞			
t_k to			40	0.843	2	Carbon tet.		∞			
t_x °C			60	0.692	2	Benzene		∞			
A' 10 to	7.21019	5	80	0.59	2	Ether		∞			
B' 40°C	1563.9	5				n-Heptane		∞			
C'	231.3	5	B^v -30 to	500.88	4	Ethanol		∞			
A'* 10 to	1.6049	5	A^v 30 °C	Σ.32067	4	Water					
B'* 40°C	1465.0	5	(B^v) 30 to	428.32	4	Water in					
Ac 170 to	7.2853	5	(A^v) 90 °C	Σ.55816	4						
Bc t_c °C	1724.55	5	c_p liq. °K								
Cc	260.2	5									
Cryos. A°	0.03827	2	c_p vap.300°K	0.34071	2						
consts. B°	0.00308	2	P 400	0.45986	2						
t_e °C	146.94	5	c_v vap.								

$T_R = 0.75 T_c$

+ grams/100 grams solvent

REFERENCES: 1-Dow 2-API 3-Lit. 4-Calc. from det. data 5-Calc. by formula

SOURCE: API

PURIFICATION: API

LITERATURE REFERENCES:

No. 4

NAME	1,1-Dimethylcyclohexane				STRUCTURAL FORMULA

Structural formula:

$$H_2C \underset{\substack{H_2C \diagdown \diagup CH_2 \\ C \\ H_2}}{\overset{C(CH_3)_2}{\diagup \diagdown}} CH_2$$

Mole % Pur. 99.93	Ref. 2	Molecular Formula C_8H_{16}		Molecular Weight 112.208			

		Ref.							Ref.
F.P. °C	-33.495	2	dt/dP			f		to	
F.P. 100%			°C/mm			g		°K	
B.P. °C			25°C	0.8561	5	h			
760 mm	119.543	2	BP	0.04920	2				
100	57.622	2	t_e	0.0374	5	f'		to	
30	30.55	4	30 mm	0.6758	4	g'		°K	
10	10.0	5	ΔHm cal/g	1.322	2	h'			
1	-24.0	5							
Pressure			ΔHv cal/g			m		300 to	-0.0775	4
mm 25°C	22.68	5	25°C	81.11	5	n		600 °K	0.0015	4
t_e	1081.	5	30 mm	80.59	5	o			-0.0$_6$40	4
Density			BP	70.2	2				
g/ml 20°C	0.78094	2	t_e	68.58	5	m'		700 to	0.0136	4
d_4^t 25	0.77677	2	t_e (d,e)	68.60	5	n'		1000 °K	0.0014	4
30	0.77259	4	$ΔHv/T_e$	18.93	5	o'			-0.0$_6$53	4
a	0.79761	4	d | 30 to	84.16	5	Surface tension			
b	-0.0$_3$83	4	e | 135 °C	0.1168	5	dynes/cm. 20°C	24.01	5
Ref. Index			d' | 15 to	83.47	5	γ 30	22.99	5
n_D 20°C	1.42900	2	e' | 30 °C	0.0941	5	40	22.00	5
25	1.42662	2	d_c g/ml	0.237	5	Parachor [P]		
30	1.42413	4	v_c ml/g	4.22	5	20°C		
"C"	0.7297	4	t_c °C	302.0	5	30		
MR (Obs.)	37.042	2	P_c mm	19310.	5	40		
MR (Calc.)	36.944	5	PV/RT			Sugd.	318.1	5
(nD-d/2)	1.03853	2	25°C	1.0000	5	Exp. L.1.%/wt.		
Dielectric	2.042	5	30 mm	1.0000	5	u.		
A | 30 to	6.80225	2	BP	0.9658	4	Dispersion	98.4	2
B | 160 °C	1323.861	2	t_e	0.9561	5	Flash Point °C	13.0	5
C	218.053	2	t_c	0.255	5	Fire Point		
A* | 30 to	1.20882	4	ΔHc kcal/m	1171.53	2	M Spec.		
B* | 145 °C	1232.87	4	ΔHf	-52.31	2	Ultra V.		
K			ΔFf	6.34	2	X-Ray Dif.		
c			Viscosity			Infrared	Yes	2
t_k | to			centistokes			Solubility in +		
t_x | °C			η °C			Acetone	∞	
A' | 0 to	7.00032	5				Carbon tet.	∞	
B' | 30 °C	1424.18	5				Benzene	∞	
C'	227.3	5	B^v | to			Ether	∞	
			A^v | °C			n-Heptane	∞	
A'* 15 to	1.40884	5	(B^v) | to			Ethanol	∞	
B'* 30 °C	1330.3	5	(A^v) | °C			Water		
Ac | 160 to	7.21947	5				Water in		
Bc | t_c °C	1656.4	5	c_p liq. °K					
Cc	262.7	5						
Cryos. A°	0.00424	2	c_p vap.300°K	0.33153	2			
consts. B°	0.00174	2	400	0.45184	2			
t_e °C	133.26	5	c_v vap.					

$T_R = 0.75 T_c$ + grams/100 grams solvent

REFERENCES: 1-Dow 2-API 3-Lit. 4-Calc. from det. data 5-Calc. by formula

SOURCE: API

PURIFICATION: API

LITERATURE REFERENCES:

TABLE XIX. CYCLOHEXANES

No. 5

NAME	1, cis-2-Dimethylcyclohexane					STRUCTURAL FORMULA		

Structural formula:

$$H_2C \begin{array}{c} CHCH_3 \\ CHCH_3 \\ CH_2 \end{array}$$
$$H_2C \quad C \quad H_2$$

Mole % Pur. 99.99	Ref. 2	Molecular Formula C_8H_{16}		Molecular Weight 112.208				

		Ref.			Ref.			Ref.
F.P. °C	-50.023	2	dt/dP			f |	to	
F.P. 100%			°C/mm			g |	°K	
			25°C	1.2820	5	h |		
B.P. °C			BP	0.04988	2			
760 mm	129.728	2	t_e	0.0371	5	f' |	to	
100	66.824	2	30 mm	0.6889	4	g' |	°K	
30	39.25	4				h' |		
10	18.3	5	ΔHm cal/g	3.5024	2			
1	-16.6	5				m |	300 to	-0.0757	4
			ΔHv cal/g			n |	600 °K	0.0015	4
Pressure			25°C	84.87	5	o |		-0.0₆44	4
mm 25°C	14.47	5	30 mm	83.65	5			
t_e	1111.	5	BP	72.9	2	m' |	700 to	0.0085	4
Density			t_e	71.10	5	n' |	1000 °K	0.0014	4
g/ml 20°C	0.79627	2	t_e (d, e)	71.11	5	o' |		-0.0₆49	4
d_4^t 25	0.79222	2	ΔHv/T_e	19.09	5	Surface tension		
30	0.78817	4				dynes/cm. 20°C	25.96	5
a	0.81246	4	d | 40 to	88.32	5	γ 30	24.91	5
b	-0.0₃806	4	e | 150 °C	0.1189	5	40	23.89	5
			d' | 15 to	87.00	5			
Ref. Index			e' | 40 °C	0.0852	5	Parachor [P]		
n_D 20°C	1.43596	2				20°C		
25	1.43358	2	d_c g/ml	0.273	5	30		
30	1.43128	4	v_c ml/g	3.670	5	40		
"C"	0.7265	4	t_c °C	319.7	5	Sugd.	318.1	5
MR (Obs.)	36.842	2	P_c mm	20630.	5			
MR (Calc.)	36.944	5	PV/RT			Exp. L.1.%/wt.		
(nD-d/2)	1.03783	2	25°C	1.0006	5	u.		
Dielectric	2.062	5	30 mm	1.0000	5	Dispersion	95.9	2
A | 40 to	6.84164	2	BP	0.9661	4	Flash Point °C	22.	5
B | 170 °C	1369.525	2	t_e	0.9557	5	Fire Point		
C	216.040	2	t_c	0.251	5	M. Spec.		
A* | 40 to	1.23717	4	ΔHc kcal/m	1173.64	2	Ultra V.		
B* | 155 °C	1276.40	4	ΔHf	-50.64	2	X-Ray Dif.		
K			ΔFf	7.50	2	Infrared	Yes	2
c			Viscosity			Solubility in +		
t_k | to			centistokes			Acetone	∞	
t_x | °C			η °C			Carbon tet.	∞	
A' | 15 to	7.17960	5				Benzene	∞	
B' | 40 °C	1547.5	5				Ether	∞	
C'	232.1	5	B^V | to			n-Heptane	∞	
A'* 15 to	1.57655	5	A^V | °C			Ethanol	∞	
B'* 40 °C	1448.9	5	(B^V) | to			Water		
Ac | 170 to	7.25816	5	(A^V) | °C			Water in		
Bc | t_c °C	1711.3	5	c_p liq. °K					
Cc |	261.7	5						
Cryos. A°	0.00397	2	c_p vap.300°K	0.33598	2			
consts. B°	0.00133	2	400	0.45540	2			
t_e °C	144.76	5	c_v vap.					

$T_R = 0.75 T_c$ + grams/100 grams solvent

REFERENCES: 1-Dow   2-API   3-Lit.   4-Calc. from det. data   5-Calc. by formula

SOURCE: API

PURIFICATION: API

LITERATURE REFERENCES:

NAME	1, trans-2-Dimethylcyclohexane	STRUCTURAL FORMULA

Structural formula:
H_2C—$CHCH_3$ / $CHCH_3$
H_2C—CH_2
H_2

Mole % Pur. 99.92	Ref. 2	Molecular Formula C_8H_{16}	Molecular Weight 112.208

		Ref.			Ref.				Ref.
F.P. °C	-88.194	2	dt/dP °C/mm			f	to °K		
F.P. 100%			25°C	0.990	5	g			
B.P. °C			BP	0.04951	2	h			
760 mm	123.419	2	t_e	0.0374	5	f'	to °K		
100	61.005	2	30 mm	0.6833	4	g'			
30	33.66	4	ΔHm cal/g	22.342	2	h'			
10	12.9	5	ΔHv cal/g			m	300 to	-0.0917	4
1	-22.0	5	25°C	81.96	5	n	600 °K	0.0016	4
Pressure			30 mm	75.93	5	o		-0.0658	4
mm 25°C	19.40	5	BP	71.1	2	m'	700 to	0.0185	4
t_e	1092.	5	t_e	69.45	5	n'	1000 °K	0.0014	4
Density			t_e (d, e)	69.48	5	o'		-0.0649	4
g/ml 20°C	0.77601	2	ΔHv/T_e	18.97	5	Surface tension			
d_4^t 25	0.77204	2	d 35 to	85.19	5	dynes/cm. 20°C	23.41	5	
30	0.76806	4	e 140 °C	0.1142	5	γ 30	22.46	5	
a	0.79188	4	d' 10 to	83.71	5	40	21.53	5	
b	-0.0378	4	e' 35 °C	0.070	5	Parachor [P]			
Ref. Index			d_c g/ml	0.242	5	20°C			
n_D 20°C	1.42695	2	v_c ml/g	4.13	5	30			
25	1.42470	2	t_c °C	307.5	5	40			
30	1.42229	4	P_c mm	19616.	5	Sugd.	318.1	5	
"C"	0.7309	4	PV/RT			Exp. L. 1.%/wt.			
MR (Obs.)	37.121	2	25°C	1.0000	5	u.			
MR (Calc.)	36.944	5	30 mm	1.0000	5	Dispersion	97.9	2	
(nD-d/2)	1.03895	2	BP	0.9652	4	Flash Point °C	17.	5	
Dielectric	2.036	5	t_e	0.9553	5	Fire Point			
A 35 to	6.83722	2	t_c	0.251	5	M Spec.			
B 160 °C	1356.100	2	ΔHc kcal/m	1171.77	2	Ultra V.			
C	219.342	2	ΔHf	-52.19	2	X-Ray Dif.			
A* 35 to	1.23855	4	ΔFf	6.06	2	Infrared	Yes	2	
B* 150 °C	1263.29	4	Viscosity			Solubility in +			
K			centistokes			Acetone	∞		
c			η °C			Carbon tet.	∞		
t_k to °C						Benzene	∞		
t_x						Ether	∞		
A' 0 to	7.17491	5				n-Heptane	∞		
B' 35 °C	1532.4	5	B^V to			Ethanol	∞		
C'	235.3	5	A^V °C			Water			
A'* 15 to	1.56941	5	(B^V) to			Water in			
B'* 35 °C	1431.86	5	(A^V) °C						
Ac 160 to	7.25729	5	c_p liq. °K						
Bc t_c °C	1695.7	5							
Cc	264.5	5							
Cryos. A°	0.03664	2	c_p vap.300°K	0.34133	2				
consts. B°	0.00336	2	c_p 400	0.46253	2				
t_e °C	137.62	5	c_v vap.						

$T_R = 0.75 T_C$ + grams/100 grams solvent

REFERENCES: 1-Dow 2-API 3-Lit. 4-Calc. from det. data 5-Calc. by formula

SOURCE:	API
PURIFICATION:	API
LITERATURE REFERENCES:	

TABLE XIX. CYCLOHEXANES 447

No. 7

NAME	1, cis-3-Dimethylcyclohexane	STRUCTURAL FORMULA

Structural formula:

H_2C $\overset{CHCH_3}{\underset{CH_2}{|}}$ CH_2
H_2C $\underset{CH_2}{|}$ $CHCH_3$

Mole % Pur. 99.91	Ref. 2	Molecular Formula C_8H_{16}	Molecular Weight 112.208

		Ref.			Ref.					Ref.
F.P. °C	-75.573	2	dt/dP			f		to		
F.P. 100%			°C/mm			g		°K		
			25°C	0.8928	5	h				
B.P. °C			BP	0.04880	2					
760 mm	120.088	2	t_e	0.0371	5	f'		to		
100	58.547	2	30 mm	0.6741	4	g'		°K		
30	31.57	4	ΔHm cal/g	23.047	2	h'				
10	11.1	5				m		300 to	-0.0660	4
1	-23.	5	ΔHv cal/g			n		600 °K	0.0015	4
			25°C	81.91	5	o			-0.0640	4
Pressure			30 mm	81.34	5					
mm 25°C	21.50	5	BP	70.90	2	m'		700 to	-0.0207	4
t_e	1082.	5	t_e	69.28	5	n'		1000 °K	0.0015	4
			t_e (d, e)	69.29	5	o'			-0.0653	4
Density			ΔHv/T_e	19.10	5	Surface tension				
g/ml 20°C	0.76603	2				dynes/cm. 20°C			22.23	5
d_4^t 25	0.76196	2	d 30 to	85.07	5	8		30	21.29	5
30	0.75788	4	e 135 °C	0.1180	5			40	20.38	5
a	0.78230	4	d' 15 to	83.83	5	Parachor [P]				
b	-0.0381	4	e' 30 °C	0.0787	5	20°C				
Ref. Index			d_c g/ml	0.239	5	30				
n_D 20°C	1.42294	2	v_c ml/g	4.188	5	40				
25	1.42063	2	t_c °C	301.	5	Sugd.			318.1	5
30	1.41822	4	P_c mm	19427.	5					
"C"	0.7339	4								
MR (Obs.)	37.296	2	PV/RT			Exp. L. 1.%/wt.				
MR (Calc.)	36.944	5	25°C	1.0000	5	u.				
(nD-d/2)	1.03993	2	30 mm	1.0000	5	Dispersion			99.1	2
Dielectric	2.025		BP	0.9651	4	Flash Point °C			15.	5
A 32 to	6.84293	2	t_e	0.9554	5	Fire Point				
B 60°C	1340.658	2	t_c	0.255	5	M. Spec.				
C	218.281	2	ΔHc kcal/m	1170.63	2	Ultra V.				
A* 32 to	1.24982	5	ΔHf	-53.30	2	X-Ray Dif.				
B* 145°C	1249.65	5	ΔFf	5.02	2	Infrared			Yes	2
K			Viscosity			Solubility in +				
c			centistokes			Acetone			∞	
t_k to			η °C			Carbon tet.			∞	
t_x °C						Benzene			∞	
A' 0 to	7.18098	5				Ether			∞	
B' 32°C	1514.9	5				n-Heptane			∞	
C'	234.0	5	B^v to			Ethanol			∞	
A'* 15 to	1.57896	5	A^v °C			Water				
B'* 32°C	1415.8	5	(B^v) to			Water in				
Ac 160 to	7.2598	5	(A^v) °C							
Bc t_c °C	1671.9	5								
Cc	262.1	5	c_p liq. °K							
Cryos. A°	0.03333	2	c_p vap.300°K	0.33777	2					
consts. B°	0.00345	2	400	0.45630	2					
t_e °C	133.70	5	c_v vap.							

$T_R = 0.75 T_c$ | + grams/100 grams solvent

REFERENCES: 1-Dow   2-API   3-Lit.   4-Calc. from det. data   5-Calc. by formula

SOURCE: API

PURIFICATION: API

LITERATURE REFERENCES:

NAME	1, trans-3-Dimethylcyclohexane	STRUCTURAL FORMULA

Structural formula:

$$\begin{array}{c} \text{CHCH}_3 \\ H_2C \qquad CH_2 \\ H_2C \qquad CHCH_3 \\ CH_2 \end{array}$$

Mole % Pur.	Ref.	Molecular Formula C_8H_{16}	Molecular Weight 112.208

		Ref.			Ref.				Ref.
F.P. °C	-90.108	2	dt/dP			f	to		
F.P. 100%			°C/mm			g	°K		
			25°C	1.0670	5	h			
B.P. °C			BP	0.04910	2				
760 mm	124.450	2	t_e	0.0370	5	f'	to		
100	62.549	2				g'	°K		
30	35.42	4	30 mm	0.6778	5	h'			
10	15.0	5	ΔHm cal/g			m	300 to	-0.0632	4
1	-19.5	5				n	600 °K	0.0015	4
			ΔHv cal/g			o		-0.0_640	4
Pressure			25°C	83.86	5				
mm 25°C	17.60	5	30 mm	82.96	5	m'	700 to	-0.0198	4
t_e	1095.	5	BP	72.1	2	n'	1000 °K	0.0014	4
			t_e	70.37	5	o'		-0.0_653	4
Density			t_e (d, e)	70.37	5	Surface tension			
g/ml 20°C	0.78472	2	$\Delta Hv/T_e$	19.17	5	dynes/cm. 20°C	24.48	5
d_4^t 25	0.78055	2	d 35 to	87.28	5	γ	30	23.45	5
30	0.77637	4	e 140 °C	0.1220	5		40	22.45	5
a	0.80139	4	d' 20 to	86.03	5				
b	-0.0_3829	4	e' 35 °C	0.0867	5	Parachor [P]		
Ref. Index			d_c g/ml	0.246	5	20°C		
n_D 20°C	1.43085	2	v_c ml/g	4.07	5	30		
25	1.42843	2	t_c °C	309.5	5	40		
30	1.42602	4	P_c mm	20187.	5	Sugd.	318.1	5
"C"	0.7290	4	PV/RT			Exp. L. l.%/wt.		
MR (Obs.)	37.002	2	25°C	1.0000	5	u.		
MR (Calc.)	36.944	5	30 mm	1.0000	5	Dispersion	97.1	2
(nD-d/2)	1.03849	2	BP	0.9656	5	Flash Point °C		
Dielectric	2.047	5	t_e	0.9556	5	Fire Point		
A 35 to	6.83866	2	t_c	0.254	5	M Spec.		
B 165 °C	1345.859	2	ΔHc kcal/m	1172.59	2	Ultra V.		
C	215.598	2	ΔHf	-51.57	2	X-Ray Dif.		
A* 35 to	1.24195	5	ΔFf	6.44	2	Infrared		
B* 150 °C	1254.9	5	Viscosity			Solubility in +		
K			centistokes			Acetone		
c			η °C			Carbon tet.		
t_k to						Benzene		
t_x °C						Ether		
A' 15 to	7.17644	5				n-Heptane		
B' 35 °C	1520.8	5				Ethanol		
C'	231.4	5	B^v to			Water		
A'* 20 to	1.57507	5	A^v °C			Water in		
B'* 35 °C	1422.8	5	(B^v) to					
Ac 165 to	7.25259	5	(A^v) °C					
Bc t_c °C	1678.3	5	c_p liq. °K					
Cc	259.9	5						
Cryos. A°	0.0354	2	c_p vap.300°K	0.33777	2			
consts. B°	0.0031	2	400	0.45540	2			
t_e °C	138.65	5	c_v vap.					

$T_R = 0.75\,T_c$ + grams/100 grams solvent

REFERENCES: 1-Dow   2-API   3-Lit.   4-Calc. from det. data   5-Calc. by formula

SOURCE:	API
PURIFICATION:	API
LITERATURE REFERENCES:	

TABLE XIX. CYCLOHEXANES

No. 9

NAME	1, cis-4-Dimethylcyclohexane	STRUCTURAL FORMULA

Structural formula:

$$H_2C \overset{CHCH_3}{\underset{CHCH_3}{\begin{array}{c} CH_2 \\ CH_2 \end{array}}} CH_2$$

Mole % Pur. 99.94	Ref. 2	Molecular Formula C_8H_{16}	Molecular Weight 112.208

		Ref.			Ref.					Ref.
F.P. °C	-87.436	2	dt/dP °C/mm			f		to °K		
F.P. 100%			25°C	1.0533	5	g		— — °K		
B.P. °C			BP	0.04921	2	h				
760 mm	124.321	2	t_e	0.0371	5	f'		to		
100	62.283	2	30 mm	0.6792	4	g'		— — °K		
30	35.10	4	ΔHm cal/g	19.820	2	h'				
10	14.4	5	ΔHv cal/g			m		300 to	-0.0632	4
1	-20.0	5	25°C	83.38	5	n		600 °K	0.0015	4
Pressure			30 mm	82.62	5	o			-0.0640	4
mm 25°C	17.93	5	BP	71.9	2	m'		700 to	-0.0198	4
t_e	1095.	5	t_e	70.19	5	n'		1000 °K	0.0014	4
Density			t_e (d, e)	70.19	5	o'			-0.0654	4
g/ml 20°C	0.78285	2	ΔHv/T_e	19.13	5	Surface tension				
d_4^t 25	0.77870	2	d 35 to	86.83	4	dynes/cm. 20°C		24.25		5
30	0.77454	4	e 140 °C	0.1201	4	γ 30		23.23		5
a	0.79944	4	d' 10 to	85.26	4	40		22.24		5
b	-0.0383	4	e' 35 °C	0.0752	4	Parachor [P]				
Ref. Index			d_c g/ml	0.244	5	20°C				
n_D 20°C	1.42966	2	v_c ml/g	4.10	5	30				
25	1.42731	2	t_c °C	309.	5	40				
30	1.42482	4	P_c mm	20030.	5	Sugd.		318.1		5
"C"	0.7289	4	PV/RT			Exp. L.1.%/wt.				
MR (Obs.)	37.001	2	25°C	1.0000	5	u.				
MR (Calc.)	36.944	5	30 mm	1.0000	5	Dispersion		97.1		2
(nD-d/2)	1.03796	2	BP	0.9658	4	Flash Point °C		16.0		5
Dielectric	2.044	5	t_e	0.9558	5	Fire Point				
A 35 to	6.83699	2	t_c	0.254	5	M. Spec.				
B 165 °C	1347.794	2	ΔHc kcal/m	1172.57	2	Ultra V.				
C	216.360	2	ΔHf	-51.55	2	X-Ray Dif.				
A* 35 to	1.23936	4	ΔFf	6.85	2	Infrared		Yes		2
B* 150 °C	1256.32	4	Viscosity			Solubility in +				
K			centistokes			Acetone		∞		
c			η °C			Carbon tet.		∞		
t_k to						Benzene		∞		
t_x °C						Ether		∞		
A' 0 to	7.2554	5				n-Heptane		∞		
B' 35 °C	1566.5	5				Ethanol		∞		
C'	236.	5	B^v to			Water				
A'* 15 to	1.64530	5	A^v °C			Water in				
B'* 35 °C	1464.5	5	(B^v) to							
Ac 165 to	7.2522	5	(A^v) °C							
Bc t_c °C	1681.8	5	c_p liq. °K							
Cc	260.8	5								
Cryos. A°	0.03245	2	c_p vap.300°K	0.33777	2					
consts. B°	0.00272	2	400	0.45540	2					
t_e °C	138.55	5	c_v vap.							

$T_R = 0.75 \, T_c$

+ grams/100 grams solvent

REFERENCES: 1-Dow 2-API 3-Lit. 4-Calc. from det. data 5-Calc. by formula

SOURCE: API

PURIFICATION: API

LITERATURE REFERENCES:

No. 10

NAME	1, trans-4-Dimethylcyclohexane					STRUCTURAL FORMULA

Structural formula:

$$H_2C \overset{CHCH_3}{\underset{CHCH_3}{\underset{\displaystyle |}{\overset{\displaystyle |}{C}}}} \overset{CH_2}{\underset{CH_2}{}}$$

Mole % Pur.	Ref.	Molecular Formula C_8H_{16}		Molecular Weight 112.208		

		Ref.			Ref.				Ref.
F.P. °C	-36.962	2	dt/dP			f		to	
F.P. 100%			°C/mm			g		°K	
B.P. °C			25°C	0.8929	5	h			
760 mm	119.351	2	BP	0.04903	2				
100	57.6	2	t_e	0.0373	5	f'		to	
30	30.54	4	30 mm	0.6753	4	g'		°K	
10	10.0	5	ΔHm cal/g	24.285	2	h'			
1	-24.2	5	ΔHv cal/g			m	300 to	-0.0891	4
Pressure			25°C	81.24	5	n	600 °K	0.0016	4
mm 25°C	22.69	5	30 mm	80.65	5	o		-0.0₆53	4
t_e	1081.	5	BP	70.4	2				
Density			t_e	68.80	5	m'	700 to	0.0123	4
g/ml 20°C	0.76255	2	t_e (d, e)	68.82	5	n'	1000 °K	0.0014	4
d_4^t 25	0.75835	2	ΔHv/T_e	19.00	5	o'		-0.0₆49	4
30	0.75414	4	d	30 to	84.17	5	Surface tension		
a	0.77934	4	e	135 °C	0.1154	5	dynes/cm. 20°C	21.83	5
b	-0.0₃83	4	d'	10 to	83.93	5	γ	30	20.87	5
Ref. Index			e'	30 °C	0.1076	5		40	19.94	5
n_D 20°C	1.42090	2	d_c g/ml	0.235	5	Parachor [P]		
25	1.41853	2	v_c ml/g	4.257	5	20°C		
30	1.41600	2	t_c °C	299.	5	30		
"C"	0.7338	4	P_c mm	18900.	5	40		
MR (Obs.)	37.308	2				Sugd.	318.1	5
MR (Calc.)	36.944	5	PV/RT			Exp. L.1.%/wt.		
(nD-d/2)	1.03963	2	25°C	1.0000	5	u.		
Dielectric	2.019	5	30 mm	1.0000	5	Dispersion	97.1	2
A 30 to	6.82180	2	BP	0.9663	4	Flash Point °C	12.	5
B 155 °C	1332.613	2	t_e	0.9568	5	Fire Point		
C	218.791	2	t_c	0.253	5	M Spec.		
A* 30 to	1.22667	4	ΔHc kcal/m	1170.67	2	Ultra V.		
B* 145 °C	1240.9	4	ΔHf	-53.18	2	X-Ray Dif.		
K			ΔFf	5.50	2	Infrared	Yes	1
c			Viscosity			Solubility in +		
t_k to			centistokes			Acetone	∞	
t_x °C			η °C			Carbon tet.	∞	
A' 10 to	7.1689	5				Benzene	∞	
B' 30 °C	1511.4	5				Ether	∞	
C'	235.	5	B^v to			n-Heptane	∞	
A'* 15 to	1.5652	5	A^v °C			Ethanol	∞	
B'* 30 °C	1411.5	5	(B^v) to			Water		
Ac 155 to	7.23940	5	(A^v) °C			Water in		
Bc t_c °C	1663.83	5						
Cc	262.8	5	c_p liq. °K					
Cryos. A°	0.02658	2	c_p vap.300°K	0.33866	2			
consts. B°	0.00296	2	400	0.45986	2			
t_e °C	133.02	5	c_v vap.					

$T_R = 0.75 T_c$

+ grams/100 grams solvent

REFERENCES: 1-Dow   2-API   3-Lit.   4-Calc. from det. data   5-Calc. by formula

SOURCE:	API
PURIFICATION:	API
LITERATURE REFERENCES:	

No. 11

| NAME | n-Propylcyclohexane | | | | | STRUCTURAL FORMULA | | | |

$$H_2C \overset{CHC_3H_7}{\underset{\underset{CH_2}{|}}{\overset{|}{\bigcirc}}} \overset{CH_2}{\underset{CH_2}{|}}$$

| Mole % Pur. | | Ref. | Molecular Formula C_9H_{18} | | Molecular Weight 126.234 | | | | |

		Ref.			Ref.				Ref.
F. P. °C	-94.900	2	dt/dP			f		to	
F. P. 100%			°C/mm			g		°K	
			25°C	3.896	5	h			
B. P. °C			BP	0.05200	2				
760 mm	156.724	2	t_e	0.0370	5	f'		to	
100	90.979	5				g'		°K	
30	62.05	5	30 mm	0.7236	5	h'			
10	40.13	5	ΔHm cal/g			m	300 to	-0.0611	4
1	4.024	5	ΔHv cal/g			n	600 °K	0.0015	4
Pressure			25°C	84.60	5	o		-0.0651	4
mm 25°C	4.247	5	30 mm	81.50	5	m'	700 to	0.0124	4
t_e	1178.4	5	BP	70.15	5	n'	1000 °K	0.0014	4
Density			t_e	68.02	5	o'		-0.0652	4
g/ml 20°C	0.79360	2	t_e (d, e)	67.97	5	Surface tension			
d_4^t 25	0.78977	2	ΔHv/T_e	19.16		dynes/cm. 20°C	25.40	5
30	0.78594	4	d 60 to	88.94	5	ɤ	30	24.43	5
a	0.8089	4	e 175 °C	0.1199	5		40	23.49	5
b	-0.03765	4	d' 20 to	86.69	5	Parachor [P]			
Ref. Index			e' 60 °C	0.0837	5		20°C		
n_D 20°C	1.43705	2	d_c g/ml	0.2623	5		30		
25	1.43478	2	v_c ml/g	3.813	5		40		
30	1.43250	4	t_c °C	346.0	5		Sugd.	357.1	5
"C"	0.7307	4	P_c mm	19098.	5	Exp. L. l.%/wt.			
MR (Obs.)	41.677	2	PV/RT				u.		
MR (Calc.)	41.562	5	25°C	1.0000	5	Dispersion	97.4	2
(nD-d/2)	1.04025	2	30 mm	1.0000	5	Flash Point °C			
Dielectric	2.065	5	BP	0.9580	5	Fire Point			
A 60 to	6.89968	4	t_e	0.9451	5	M. Spec.			
B 190°C	1469.8	4	t_c	0.238	5	Ultra V.			
C	209.0	4	ΔHc kcal/m	1320.44	2	X-Ray Dif.			
A* 60 to	1.33525	5	ΔHf	-56.98	2	Infrared			
B* 185 °C	1376.2	5	ΔFf	8.22	2	Solubility in +			
K			Viscosity			Acetone	∞	
c			centistokes			Carbon tet.	∞	
t_k to			η 20 °C	1.268	2	Benzene	∞	
t_x °C			40	0.976	2	Ether	∞	
A' 25 to	7.3199	5	60	0.787	2	n-Heptane	∞	
B' 60 °C	1706.4	5	80	0.66	2	Ethanol	∞	
C'	230.	5	B^v -30 to	563.14	4	Water		
A'* 25 to	1.7506	5	A^v 30 °C	$\bar{2}.18246$	4	Water in		
B'* 60 °C	1604.	5	(B^v) 30 to	469.11	4			
Ac 190 to	7.30759	5	(A^v) 90 °C	$\bar{2}.49136$	4			
Bc t_c °C	1814.5	5	c_p liq. °K					
Cc	253.5	5						
Cryos. A°			c_p vap.300°K	0.35109	2			
consts. B°			400	0.46818	2			
t_e °C	174.92	5	c_v vap.					

$T_R = 0.75 T_c$

+ grams/100 grams solvent

REFERENCES: 1-Dow 2-API 3-Lit. 4-Calc. from det. data 5-Calc. by formula

SOURCE: API

PURIFICATION: API

LITERATURE REFERENCES:

No. 12

NAME	Isopropylcyclohexane				STRUCTURAL FORMULA

$$CHCH(CH_3)_2$$
$$H_2C \quad CH_2$$
$$H_2C \quad CH_2$$
$$CH_2$$

| Mole % Pur. | | Ref. | Molecular Formula | C_9H_{18} | | Molecular Weight 126.234 |

		Ref.			Ref.					Ref.
F.P. °C	-89.8	3	dt/dP			f		to		
F.P. 100%			°C/mm			g		°K		
			25°C	3.555	5	h				
B.P. °C			BP	0.05179	4					
760 mm	154.50	3	t_e	0.03726	5	f'		to		
100	89.03	5				g'		°K		
30	60.23	5	30 mm	0.72045	5	h'				
10	38.28	5	ΔHm cal/g							
1	1.57	5	ΔHv cal/g			m		to		
Pressure			25°C	83.89	5	n		°K		
mm 25°C	4.694	5	30 mm	80.97	5	o				
t_e	1160.002	5	BP	69.12	4					
Density			t_e	67.03	5	m'		to		
g/ml 20°C	0.80232	3	t_e (d, e)	66.93	5	n'		°K		
d_4^t 25	0.79840	3	ΔHv/T_e	19.01	5	o'				
30	0.79448	4	d 60 to	88.54	5	Surface tension				
a	0.81799	4	e 170 °C	0.1257	5	dynes/cm. 20°C		26.53	5
b	-0.0₃79	4	d' 25 to	85.97	5	ɣ	30	25.51	5
Ref. Index			e' 60 °C	0.0829	5		40	24.51	5
n_D 20°C	1.44095	3	d_c g/ml	0.251	5	Parachor [P]				
25	1.43875	3	v_c ml/g	3.98	5		20°C			
30	1.43639	4	t_c °C	343.	5		30			
"C"	0.7287	4	P_c mm	19116.	5		40			
MR (Obs.)	41.5438	2	PV/RT				Sugd.	357.1	5
MR (Calc.)	41.562	5	25°C	1.0000	5	Exp. L.l. %/wt.				
(nD-d/2)	1.03979	2	30 mm	1.0000	5	u.				
Dielectric			BP	0.94997	5	Dispersion				
A 60 to	6.89690	4	t_e	0.93663	5	Flash Point °C				
B 185 °C	1461.86	4	t_c	0.25	5	Fire Point				
C	209.5	4	ΔHc kcal/m			M Spec.				
A* 60 to	1.34872	5	ΔHf			Ultra V.				
B* 180 °C	1372.46	5	ΔFf			X-Ray Dif.				
K			Viscosity			Infrared				
c			centistokes			Solubility in +				
t_k to			η °C			Acetone		∞		
t_x °C						Carbon tet.		∞		
A' 25 to	7.30882	5				Benzene		∞		
B' 60 °C	1692.52	5				Ether		∞		
C'	230.	5	B^V to			n-Heptane		∞		
A'* 25 to	1.74105	5	A^V °C			Ethanol		∞		
B'* 60 °C	1590.64	5	(B^V) to			Water				
Ac 185 to	7.30519	5	(A^V) °C			Water in				
Bc t_c °C	1805.47	5	c_p liq. °K							
Cc	254.	5								
Cryos. A°			c_p vap. °K							
consts. B°										
t_e °C	171.94	5	c_v vap.							

T_R = 0.75 T_c + grams/100 grams solvent

REFERENCES: 1-Dow 2-API 3-Lit. 4-Calc. from det. data 5-Calc. by formula

SOURCE: Lit.

PURIFICATION: Lit.

LITERATURE REFERENCES: 3 Receuil. Trav. Chim., 58, (1939)

TABLE XIX. CYCLOHEXANES 453

No. 13

NAME	n-Butylcyclohexane	STRUCTURAL FORMULA

Structural formula:
$$H_2C \overset{\displaystyle CH\ C_4H_9}{\underset{\displaystyle CH_2}{\underset{\displaystyle |}{|}}} CH_2$$
$$H_2C \qquad CH_2$$

Mole % Pur.	Ref.	Molecular Formula	$C_{10}H_{20}$	Molecular Weight 140.260

		Ref.			Ref.			Ref.
F. P. °C	-74.725	2	dt/dP °C/mm			f	to	
F. P. 100%			25°C	10.96	5	g	°K	
			BP	0.05412	2	h		
B. P. °C			t_e	0.03734	5	f'	to	
760 mm	180.947	2	30 mm	0.7585	5	g'	°K	
100	112.35	4	ΔHm cal/g			h'		
30	82.06	4						
10	58.96	5	ΔHv cal/g			m	to	
1	20.33	5	25°C	83.77	5	n	°K	
Pressure			30 mm	78.58	5	o		
mm 25°C	1.3725	5	BP	66.48	5			
t_e	1222.2	5	t_e	64.13	5	m'	to	
Density			t_e (d, e)	63.96	5	n'	°K	
g/ml 20°C	0.79918	2	ΔHv/T_e	18.95	5	o'		
d_4^t 25	0.79551	2				Surface tension		
30	0.79184	4	d 82 to	88.62	5	dynes/cm. 20°C	25.94	5
a	0.81386	4	e 210 °C	0.1224	5	ɣ 30	25.00	5
b	-0.0₃73	4	d' 20 to	86.05	5	40	24.09	5
Ref. Index			e' 82 °C	0.0910	5	Parachor [P]		
n_D 20°C	1.44075	2	d_c g/ml	0.259	5	20°C		
25	1.43855	2	v_c ml/g	3.860	5	30		
30	1.43647	4	t_c °C	372.6	5	40		
"C"	0.7313	4	P_c mm	18301.	5	Sugd.	396.1	5
MR (Obs.)	46.323	2	PV/RT			Exp. L.1.%/wt.		
MR (Calc.)	46.180	5	25°C	1.0000	5	u.		
(nD-d/2)	1.04116	2	30 mm	1.0000	5	Dispersion	97.0	2
Dielectric			BP	0.9413	5	Flash Point °C		
A 82 to	6.95572	4	t_e	0.9253	5	Fire Point		
B 240 °C	1572.7	4	t_c	0.24	5	M. Spec.		
C	205.	5	ΔHc kcal/m	1467.54	2	Ultra V.		
A* 82 to	1.44343	5	ΔHf	-62.91	2	X-Ray Dif.		
B* 215 °C	1482.6	5	ΔFf	9.69	2	Infrared		
K			Viscosity			Solubility in +		
c			centistokes			Acetone		
t_k to			η 10 °C	1.95	2	Carbon tet.		
t_x °C			30	1.406	2	Benzene		
A' 20 to	7.29925	5	50	1.069	2	Ether		
B' 82 °C	1776.1	5	70	0.863	2	n-Heptane		
C'	223.	5	B_v 30 to	551.5	4	Ethanol		
A'* 20 to	1.77024	5	A^v 80 °C	2.32906	4	Water		
B'* 82 °C	1675.3	5	(B^v) to			Water in		
Ac 240 to	7.58996	5	(A^v) °C					
Bc t_c °C	2187.8	5	c_p liq. °K					
Cc	285.	5						
Cryos. A°			c_p vap 300°K	0.35513	2			
consts. B°			400	0.47055	2			
t_e °C	201.53	5	c_v vap.					
$T_R = 0.80 T_c$						+ grams/100 grams solvent		

REFERENCES: 1-Dow 2-API 3-Lit. 4-Calc. from det. data 5-Calc. by formula

SOURCE: API

PURIFICATION: API

LITERATURE REFERENCES:

No. 14

NAME	n-Pentylcyclohexane		STRUCTURAL FORMULA

Structural formula:
$$H_2C\overset{\overset{\displaystyle CHC_5H_{11}}{|}}{\underset{\underset{\displaystyle CH_2}{|}}{C}}\overset{CH_2}{\underset{CH_2}{}}$$

Mole % Pur.	Ref.	Molecular Formula $C_{11}H_{22}$		Molecular Weight 154.286	

		Ref.				Ref.			Ref.
F.P. °C	-57.5	2	dt/dP °C/mm				f | to		
F.P. 100%			25°C	27.60	5		g | °K		
B.P. °C			BP	0.05656	4		h |		
760 mm	202.8	2	t_e	0.03773	5		f' | to		
100	131.1	4	30 mm	0.7932	5		g' | °K		
30	99.4	5	ΔHm cal/g				h' |		
10	75.3	5	ΔHv cal/g				m | to		
1	34.9	5	25°C	81.97	5		n | °K		
Pressure			30 mm	75.16	5		o |		
mm 25°C	0.5062	5	BP	63.18	5		m' | to		
t_e	1276.4	5	t_e	60.65	5		n' | °K		
Density			t_e (d, e)	60.45	5		o' |		
g/ml 20°C	0.8037	2	ΔHv/T_e	18.73	5		Surface tension		
d_4^t 25	0.8002	2	d | 99 to	86.68	5		dynes/cm. 20°C	26.39	5
30	0.7967	2	e | 226 °C	0.1159	5		γ 30	25.48	5
a	0.8177	4	d' | 20 to	84.26	5		40	24.60	5
b	-0.0₃70	4	e' | 99 °C	0.0916	5		Parachor [P]		
Ref. Index			d_c g/ml	0.257	5		20°C		
n_D 20°C	1.4437	2	v_c ml/g	3.893	5		30		
25	1.4416	2	t_c °C	394.	5		40		
30	1.4396	4	P_c mm	16556.	5		Sugd.	435.1	5
"C"	0.7318	4	PV/RT				Exp. L.1.%/wt.		
MR (Obs.)	50.96	2	25°C	1.0000	5		u.		
MR (Calc.)	50.798	5	30 mm	1.0000	5		Dispersion	98.	2
(nD-d/2)	1.0418	2	BP	0.9365	5		Flash Point °C		
Dielectric			t_e	0.9183	5		Fire Point		
A | 99 to	6.96030	4	t_c	0.239	5		M Spec.		
B | 260 °C	1647.3	4	ΔHc kcal/m	1614.47	2		Ultra V.		
C	201.	5	ΔHf				X-Ray Dif.		
A* | 99 to	1.47836	5	ΔFf				Infrared		
B* | 236 °C	1555.9	5	Viscosity				Solubility in +		
K			centistokes				Acetone		
c			η 10 °C	2.61	2		Carbon tet.		
t_k | to			30	1.779	2		Benzene		
t_x | °C			50	1.311	2		Ether		
A' | 20 to	7.28882	5	70	1.034	2		n-Heptane		
B' | 99 °C	1850.6	5	B^v | 5 to	714.66	4		Ethanol		
C'	219.	5	A^v | 40 °C	3̄.89312	4		Water		
A'* 20 to	1.79373	5	(B^v) | 40 to	571.69	4		Water in		
B'* 99 °C	1749.6	5	(A^v) | 80 °C	2̄.34876	4				
Ac | 260 to	7.62691	5	c_p liq. °K						
Bc | t_c °C	2319.2	5							
Cc	287.	5	c_p vap.300°K	0.35849	2				
Cryos. A°			400	0.47315	2				
consts. B°			c_v vap.						
t_e °C	226.39	5							

$T_R = 0.80 T_c$ + grams/100 grams solvent

REFERENCES: 1-Dow 2-API 3-Lit. 4-Calc. from det. data 5-Calc. by formula
SOURCE: API
PURIFICATION: API
LITERATURE REFERENCES:

TABLE XIX. CYCLOHEXANES 455

No. 15

NAME	n-Hexylcyclohexane			STRUCTURAL FORMULA
	1-Cyclohexylhexane			

Structural formula: CHC_6H_{13}, H_2C CH_2, H_2C CH_2, CH_2

Mole % Pur.		Ref.	Molecular Formula $C_{12}H_{24}$		Molecular Weight 168.312	

		Ref.			Ref.				Ref.
F.P. °C	-43.0	2	dt/dP			f		to	
F.P. 100%			°C/mm			g		°K	
B.P. °C			25°C	74.95	5	h			
760 mm	224.0	2	BP	0.05835	4				
100	149.9	4	t_e	0.03762	5	f'		to	
30	117.07	5	30 mm	0.8227	5	g'		°K	
10	92.00	5	ΔHm cal/g			h'			
1	50.06	5	ΔHv cal/g			m	300 to	-0.0362	4
Pressure			25°C	81.43	5	n	600 °K	0.0015	4
mm 25°C	0.1720	5	30 mm	72.86	5	o		-0.0₆48	4
t_e	1331.7	5	BP	61.07	5				
Density			t_e	58.38	5	m'	700 to	0.0258	4
g/ml 20°C	0.8076	2	t_e (d, e)	58.16	5	n'	1000 °K	0.0014	4
d_4^t 25	0.8041	2	ΔHv/T_e	18.76	5	o'		-0.0₆50	4
30	0.8006	4	d 117 to	85.77	5	Surface tension			
a	0.8216	4	e 250 °C	0.1103	5	dynes/cm. 20°C		26.78	5
b	-0.0₃70	4	d' 20 to	83.76	5	γ	30	25.86	5
Ref. Index			e' 117 °C	0.0931	5		40	24.97	5
n_D 20°C	1.4462	2	d_c g/ml	0.255	5	Parachor [P]			
25	1.4441	2	v_c ml/g	3.92	5		20°C		
30	1.4430	4	t_c °C	412.	5		30		
"C"	0.7321	4	P_c mm	15296.	5		40		
MR (Obs.)	55.60	2					Sugd.	474.1	5
MR (Calc.)	55.416	5	PV/RT			Exp. L.1.%/wt.			
(nD-d/2)	1.0424	2	25°C	1.0000	5	u.			
Dielectric			30 mm	1.0000	5	Dispersion		98.	2
			BP	0.9341	5	Flash Point °C			
A 117 to	7.00361	4	t_e	0.9141	5	Fire Point			
B 275 °C	1735.7	4	t_c	0.205	5	M. Spec.			
C	197.	5	ΔHc kcal/m	1761.40	2	Ultra V.			
A* 117 to	1.54590	5	ΔHf			X-Ray Dif.			
B* 260 °C	1642.2	5	ΔFf			Infrared			
K			Viscosity			Solubility in +			
c			centistokes			Acetone			
t_k to			η 10 °C	3.40	2	Carbon tet.			
t_x °C			30	2.25	2	Benzene			
A' 20 to	7.32035	5	50	1.611	2	Ether			
B' 117 °C	1940.4	5	70	1.240	2	n-Heptane			
C'	215.	5	B^v 5 to	769.79	4	Ethanol			
A'* 20 to	1.85557	5	A^v 40 °C	3.81329	4	Water			
B'* 117°C	1839.2	5	(B^v) 40 to	630.48	4	Water in			
Ac 275 to	7.66201	5	(A^v) 80 °C	2.25636	4				
Bc t_c °C	2412.9	5	c_p liq. °K						
Cc	282.	5							
Cryos. A°			c_p vap 300°K	0.36123	2				
consts. B°			400	0.47471	2				
t_e °C	250.44	5	c_v vap.						

$T_R = 0.80 T_c$ + grams/100 grams solvent

REFERENCES: 1-Dow 2-API 3-Lit. 4-Calc. from det. data 5-Calc. by formula

SOURCE: API

PURIFICATION: API

LITERATURE REFERENCES:

No. 16

NAME	n-Heptylcyclohexane	STRUCTURAL FORMULA
	1-Cyclohexylheptane	

Structural formula: H_2C $CH(C_7H_{15})$ CH_2 / H_2C CH_2 / CH_2

Mole % Pur.	Ref.	Molecular Formula $C_{13}H_{26}$	Molecular Weight 182.338

		Ref.				Ref.						Ref.
F.P. °C	-30.5	2	dt/dP				f			to		
F.P. 100%			°C/mm				g			°K		
			25°C	187.78	5		h					
B.P. °C			BP	0.06056	4							
760 mm	244.	2	t_e	0.03783	5		f'			to		
100	167.	4					g'			°K		
30	133.	5	30 mm	0.8539	5		h'					
10	107.	5	ΔHm cal/g									
1	64.	5	ΔHv cal/g				m		300 to	-0.0379	4
Pressure			25°C	80.39	5		n		600 °K	0.0015	4
mm 25°C	0.06420	5	30 mm	70.20	5		o			-0.0_652	4
t_e	1386.5	5	BP	58.70	5						
Density			t_e	55.87	5		m'		700 to	0.0689	4
g/ml 20°C	0.8109	2	t_e (d, e)	55.64	5		n'		1000 °K	0.0013	4
d_4^t 25	0.8074	2	ΔHv/T_e	18.63	5		o'			-0.0_644	4
30	0.8039	4	d 133 to	83.99	5		Surface tension				
a	0.8249	4	e 274 °C	0.1037	5		dynes/cm. 20°C		27.11	5
b	-0.0_370	4	d' 20 to	82.75	5		γ		30	26.19	5
Ref. Index			e' 133 °C	0.0943	5				40	25.29	5
n_D 20°C	1.4484	2	d_c g/ml	0.253	5		Parachor [P]				
25	1.4463	2	v_c ml/g	3.95	5		20°C				
30	1.4443	4	t_c °C	430.	5		30				
"C"	0.7325	4	P_c mm	13840.	5		40				
MR (Obs.)	60.24	2	PV/RT						Sugd. 513.1	5
MR (Calc.)	60.034	5	25°C	1.0000	5		Exp. L.1.%/wt.				
(nD-d/2)	1.0429	2	30 mm	1.0000	5		u.				
Dielectric			BP	0.9333	5		Dispersion		98.	2
A 133 to	7.00437	4	t_e	0.9115	5		Flash Point °C				
B 325 °C	1802.	4	t_c	0.227	5		Fire Point				
C	193.	5	ΔHc kcal/m	1908.32	2		M Spec.				
A* 133 to	1.56661	5	ΔHf				Ultra V.				
B* 284 °C	1705.8	5	ΔFf				X-Ray Dif.				
K			Viscosity				Infrared				
c			centistokes				Solubility in +				
t_k to			η 10 °C	4.35	2		Acetone				
t_x °C			30	2.79	2		Carbon tet.				
A' 20 to	7.30954	5	50	1.95	2		Benzene				
B' 133 °C	2006.5	5	70	1.468	2		Ether				
C'	211.	5	B^v 5 to	828.14	4		n-Heptane				
A'* 20 to	1.87344	5	A^v 40 °C	3.71427	4		Ethanol				
B'* 133 °C	1905.6	5	(B^v) 40 to	683.84	4		Water				
Ac 325 to	8.37928	5	(A^v) 80 °C	2.17419	4		Water in				
Bc t_c °C	3507.9	5	c_p liq. °K								
Cc	398.	5	c_p vap.300°K	0.36361	2						
Cryos. A°			400	0.47659	2						
consts. B°			c_v vap.								
t_e °C	273.54	5									

$T_R = 0.85 T_c$ + grams/100 grams solvent

REFERENCES: 1-Dow   2-API   3-Lit.   4-Calc. from det. data   5-Calc. by formula

SOURCE:	API
PURIFICATION:	API
LITERATURE REFERENCES:	

TABLE XIX. CYCLOHEXANES

NAME	n-Octylcyclohexane	STRUCTURAL FORMULA
	1-Cyclohexyloctane	

Mole % Pur.	Ref.	Molecular Formula $C_{14}H_{28}$	Molecular Weight 196.364

Structural formula:
$$CH \cdot C_8H_{17}$$
$$H_2C \quad CH_2$$
$$H_2C \quad CH_2$$
$$CH_2$$

		Ref.			Ref.				Ref.
F.P. °C	-19.7	2	dt/dP			f	to		
F.P. 100%			°C/mm			g	°K		
B.P. °C			25°C	487.90	5	h			
760 mm	264.	2	BP	0.06273	4				
100	184.3	4	t_e	0.03804	5	f'	to		
30	149.	5	30 mm	0.8849	5	g'	°K		
10	122.	5	ΔHm cal/g			h'			
1	77.	5							
Pressure			ΔHv cal/g			m	300 to	-0.0322	4
mm 25°C	0.02311	5	25°C	79.83	5	n	600 °K	0.0015	4
t_e	1440.7	5	30 mm	67.96	5	o		-0.0_651	4
Density			BP	56.68	5	m'	700 to	0.0738	4
g/ml 20°C	0.8138	2	t_e	53.71	5	n'	1000 °K	0.0013	4
d_4^t 25	0.8104	2	t_e (d, e)	53.47	5	o'		-0.0_643	4
30	0.8070	4	ΔHv/T_e	18.51	5				
a	0.8274	4	d | 149 to	82.57	5	Surface tension			
b	-0.0368	4	e | 297 °C	0.0981	5	dynes/cm. 20°C		27.41	5
Ref. Index			d' | 20 to	82.22	5	γ	30	26.50	5
n_D 20°C	1.4503	2	e' | 149 °C	0.0957	5		40	25.62	5
25	1.4483	2	d_c g/ml	0.252	5	Parachor [P]			
30	1.4462	4	v_c ml/g	3.972	5	20°C			
"C"	0.7328	4	t_c °C	449.	5	30			
MR (Obs.)	64.88	2	P_c mm	12718.	5	40			
MR (Calc.)	64.652	5	PV/RT			Sugd.		552.1	5
(nD-d/2)	1.0434	2	25°C	1.0000	5	Exp. L. 1.%/wt.			
Dielectric			30 mm	1.0000	5	u.			
A | 149 to	7.00707	4	BP	0.9322	5	Dispersion		98.	2
B | 340 °C	1869.2	4	t_e	0.9086	5	Flash Point °C			
C	189.	5	t_c	0.220	5	Fire Point			
A* | 149 to	1.58770	5	ΔHc kcal/m	2055.24	2	M. Spec.			
B* | 307 °C	1770.5	5	ΔHf			Ultra V.			
K			ΔFf			X-Ray Dif.			
c			Viscosity			Infrared			
t_k | to			centistokes			Solubility in +			
t_x | °C			η 50 °C	2.34	2	Acetone			
A' | 20 to	7.30155	5	70	1.72	2	Carbon tet.			
B' | 149 °C	2073.6	5	90	1.31	2	Benzene			
C'	207.	5	110	1.02	2	Ether			
A'* 20 to	1.89164	5	B^V | 40 to	741.46	4	n-Heptane			
B'* 149 °C	1973.0	5	A^V | 80 °C	$\bar{2}.07510$	4	Ethanol			
Ac | 340 to	8.33827	5	(B^V) | 80 to	756.22	4	Water			
Bc | t_c °C	3542.9	5	(A^V) | 120 °C	$\bar{2}.03517$	4	Water in			
Cc	388.	5	c_p liq. °K						
Cryos. A°			c_p vap.300°K	0.36560	2				
consts. B°			400	0.47768	2				
t_e °C	296.70	5	c_v vap.						

$T_R = 0.85 T_c$

+ grams/100 grams solvent

REFERENCES: 1-Dow 2-API 3-Lit. 4-Calc. from det. data 5-Calc. by formula

SOURCE: API

PURIFICATION: API

LITERATURE REFERENCES:

No. 18

NAME	n-Nonylcyclohexane	STRUCTURAL FORMULA
	1-Cyclohexylnonane	

$CH C_9H_{19}$
H_2C CH_2
H_2C CH_2
   CH_2

Mole % Pur.	Ref.	Molecular Formula $C_{15}H_{30}$	Molecular Weight 210.390

		Ref.			Ref.					Ref.
F.P. °C	-10.2	2	dt/dP			f		to		
F.P. 100%			°C/mm			g		°K		
B.P. °C			25°C	1211.62	5	h				
760 mm	282.	2	BP	0.06462	4					
100	200.	5	t_e	0.03825	5	f'		to		
30	164.	5	30 mm	0.9118	5	g'		°K		
10	136.	5	ΔHm cal/g			h'				
1	89.	5	ΔHv cal/g			m	300 to	-0.0242	4
Pressure			25°C	79.35	5	n	600 °K	0.0015	4
mm 25°C	0.00874	5	30 mm	65.86	5	o		-0.0$_6$48	4
t_e	1486.4	5	BP	54.70	5				
Density			t_e	51.61	5	m'	700 to	0.0644	4
g/ml 20°C	0.8163	2	t_e (d, e)	51.36	5	n'	1000 °K	0.0013	4
d_4^t 25	0.8129	2	ΔHv/T_e	18.39	5	o'		-0.0$_6$45	4
30	0.8095	4	d 164 to	81.26	5	Surface tension			
a	0.8299	4	e 317 °C	0.0942	5	dynes/cm. 20°C		27.67	5
b	-0.0$_3$68	4	d' 20 to	81.79	5	ɤ		30	26.76	5
Ref. Index			e' 164 °C	0.0974	5			40	25.87	5
n_D 20°C	1.4519	2	d_c g/ml	0.251	5	Parachor [P]			
25	1.4499	2	v_c ml/g	3.99	5	20°C			
30	1.4479	4	t_c °C	463.	5	30			
"C"	0.7330	4	P_c mm	11612.	5	40			
MR (Obs.)	69.52	2	PV/RT			Sugd.	591.1	5
MR (Calc.)	69.270	5	25°C	1.0000	5	Exp. L.1.%/wt.		
(nD-d/2)	1.0438	2	30 mm	1.0000	5	u.		
Dielectric			BP	0.9299	5	Dispersion	98.	2
A 164 to	7.01057	4	t_e	0.9045	5	Flash Point °C		
B 353 °C	1928.6	4	t_c	0.212	5	Fire Point		
C	185.	5	ΔHc kcal/m	2202.17	2	M Spec.		
A* 164 to	1.61199	5	ΔHf			Ultra V.		
B* 327 °C	1828.8	5	ΔFf			X-Ray Dif.		
K			Viscosity			Infrared		
c			centistokes			Solubility in +		
t_k to			η 50 °C	2.76	2	Acetone		
t_x °C			70	2.00	2	Carbon tet.		
A' 20 to	7.29634	5	90	1.49	2	Benzene		
B' 164 °C	2132.9	5	110	1.15	2	Ether		
C'	203.	5	B^v 40 to	775.79	4	n-Heptane		
A'* 20 to	1.91204	5	A^v 80 °C	$\bar{2}$.04057	4	Ethanol		
B'* 164 °C	2033.2	5	(B^v) 80 to	782.81	4	Water		
Ac 353 to	8.33828	5	(A^v) 120 °C	$\bar{2}$.01788	4	Water in		
Bc t_c °C	3621.8	5	c_p liq. °K					
Cc	384.	5	c_p vap 300 °K	0.36732	2			
Cryos. A°			400	0.47863	2			
consts. B°			c_v vap.					
t_e °C	317.45	5						

$T_R = 0.85 T_c$ + grams/100 grams solvent

REFERENCES: 1-Dow   2-API   3-Lit.   4-Calc. from det. data   5-Calc. by formula

SOURCE: API

PURIFICATION: API

LITERATURE REFERENCES:

TABLE XIX. CYCLOHEXANES

No. 19

NAME	n-Decylcyclohexane	STRUCTURAL FORMULA
	1-Cyclohexyldecane	

Structural formula:
$$\begin{array}{c} H_2C \overset{CH\ C_{10}H_{21}}{\underset{CH_2}{\diagup\diagdown}} CH_2 \\ H_2C \underset{CH_2}{\diagdown\diagup} CH_2 \end{array}$$

Mole % Pur.	Ref.	Molecular Formula	$C_{16}H_{32}$	Molecular Weight 224.416

		Ref.			Ref.				Ref.
F.P. °C	-1.726	2	dt/dP			f	to		
F.P. 100%			°C/mm			g	°K		
			25°C	2833.0	5	h			
B.P. °C			BP	0.06652	4				
760 mm	299.	2	t_e	0.03843	5	f'	to		
100	215.	4	30 mm	0.9389	5	g'	°K		
30	177.	5	ΔHm cal/g			h'			
10	148.	5	ΔHv cal/g			m	300 to	-0.0236	4
1	101.	5	25°C	78.50	5	n	600 °K	0.0015	4
Pressure			30 mm	63.73	5	o		-0.0_649	4
mm 25°C	0.00354	5	BP	52.85	5				
t_e	1533.6	5	t_e	49.71	5	m'	700 to	0.0849	4
Density			t_e (d, e)	49.43	5	n'	1000 °K	0.0012	4
g/ml 20°C	0.81858	2	ΔHv/T_e	18.27	5	o'		-0.0_642	4
d_4^t 25	0.81517	2	d 177 to	79.51	5	Surface tension			
30	0.81176	4	e 337 °C	0.0892	5	dynes/cm. 20°C		27.90	5
a	0.8322	4	d' 20 to	80.92	5	γ	30	26.99	5
b	-0.0_3682	4	e' 177 °C	0.0972	5		40	26.09	5
Ref. Index			d_c g/ml	0.240	5	Parachor [P]			
n_D 20°C	1.45338	2	v_c ml/g	4.17	5	20°C			
25	1.45141	2	t_c °C	477.	5	30			
30	1.44938	4	P_c mm	10200.	5	40			
"C"	0.7332	4	PV/RT			Sugd.		630.1	5
MR (Obs.)	74.154	2	25°C	1.0000	5	Exp. L.1.%/wt.			
MR (Calc.)	73.888	5	30 mm	1.0000	5	u.			
(nD-d/2)	1.04409	2	BP	0.9292	5	Dispersion		97.8	2
Dielectric			t_e	0.9029	5	Flash Point °C			
A 177 to	7.01282	4	t_c	0.204	5	Fire Point			
B 376 °C	1987.5	4	ΔHc kcal/m	2349.09	2	M. Spec.			
C	182.	5	ΔHf			Ultra V.			
A* 177 to	1.63076	5	ΔFf			X-Ray Dif.			
B* 347 °C	1885.3	5	Viscosity			Infrared			
K			centistokes			Solubility in +			
c			η 50 °C	3.24	2	Acetone			
t_k to			70	2.30	2	Carbon tet.			
t_x °C			90	1.69	2	Benzene			
A' 20 to	7.29035	5	110	1.28	2	Ether			
B' 177 °C	2191.8	5				n-Heptane			
C'	200.	5	B^v 40 to	825.4	4	Ethanol			
A'* 20 to	1.92825	5	A^v 80 °C	$\overline{3}.95681$	4	Water			
B'* 177 °C	2091.9	5	(B^v) 80 to	839.8	4	Water in			
Ac 376 to	7.58052	5	(A^v) 120 °C	$\overline{3}.91567$	4				
Bc t_c °C	2671.8	5	c_p liq. °K						
Cc	271.	5							
Cryos. A°			c_p vap300°K	0.36887	2				
consts. B°			c_p 400	0.47991	2				
t_e °C	337.32	5	c_v vap.						

$T_R = 0.90 T_C$

+ grams/100 grams solvent

REFERENCES: 1-Dow 2-API 3-Lit. 4-Calc. from det. data 5-Calc. by formula

SOURCE: API

PURIFICATION: API

LITERATURE REFERENCES:

No. 20

NAME	n-Undecylcyclohexane	STRUCTURAL FORMULA
	1-Cyclohexylundecane	

Structural formula:
$$CH_2C \underset{CH_2}{\overset{CH C_{11}H_{23}}{\big|}} CH_2$$
$$H_2C \quad CH_2$$
$$H_2C \quad CH_2$$
$$CH_2$$

Mole % Pur.		Ref.	Molecular Formula	$C_{17}H_{34}$	Molecular Weight 238.442	

		Ref.				Ref.					Ref.
F.P. °C	5.8	2	dt/dP °C/mm				f		to		
F.P. 100%			25°C	6854.8	5		g		°K		
B.P. °C			BP	0.06836	4		h				
760 mm	316.	2	t_e	0.03857	5		f'		to		
100	229.	4	30 mm	0.9656	5		g'		°K		
30	191.	5	ΔHm cal/g				h'				
10	161.	5	ΔHv cal/g				m		300 to	-0.0198	4
1	112.	5	25°C	77.99	5		n		600 °K	0.0015	4
Pressure			30 mm	61.89	5		o			-0.0₆49	4
mm 25°C	0.00139	5	BP	51.28	5						
t_e	1580.7	5	t_e	48.06	5		m'		700 to	0.0728	4
Density			t_e (d,e)	47.79	5		n'		1000 °K	0.0013	4
g/ml 20°C	0.8206	2	ΔHv/T_e	18.18	5		o'			-0.0₆44	4
d_4^t 25	0.8172	2	d 191 to	78.02	5		Surface tension				
30	0.8138	4	e 357 °C	0.0846	5		dynes/cm. 20°C			28.12	5
a	0.8342	4	d' 20 to	80.42	5		∮		30	27.20	5
b	-0.0₃68	4	e' 191 °C	0.0972	5				40	26.30	5
Ref. Index			d_c g/ml	0.239	5		Parachor [P]				
n_D 20°C	1.4547	2	v_c ml/g	4.18	5				20°C		
25	1.4527	2	t_c °C	491.	5				30		
30	1.4507	4	P_c mm	9427.	5				40		
"C"	0.7334	4	PV/RT						Sugd.	669.1	5
MR (Obs.)	78.80	2	25°C	1.0000	5		Exp. L.1.%/wt.				
MR (Calc.)	78.506	5	30 mm	1.0000	5		u.				
(nD-d/2)	1.0444	2	BP	0.9288	5		Dispersion			98.	2
Dielectric			t_e	0.9012	5		Flash Point °C				
A 191 to	7.01858	4	t_c	0.197	5		Fire Point				
B 491 °C	2048.2	4	ΔHc kcal/m	2496.01	2		M Spec.				
C	179.	5	ΔHf				Ultra V.				
A* 191 to	1.65109	5	ΔFf				X-Ray Dif.				
B* 367 °C	1943.4	5	Viscosity				Infrared				
K			centistokes				Solubility in	+			
c			η 50 °C	3.77	2		Acetone				
t_k to			70	2.63	2		Carbon tet.				
t_x °C			90	1.90	2		Benzene				
A' 20 to	7.28845	5	110	1.41	2		Ether				
B' 191 °C	2252.6	5					n-Heptane				
C'	197.	5	B^V 40 to	867.3	4		Ethanol				
A'* 20 to	1.94742	5	A^V 80 °C	3̄.89286	4		Water				
B'* 191 °C	2152.9	5	(B^V) 80 to	901.4	4		Water in				
Ac to			(A^V) 120 °C	3̄.79695	4						
Bc t_c °C			c_p liq. °K								
Cc			c_p vap.300°K	0.37019	2						
Cryos. A°			400	0.48062	2						
consts. B°			c_v vap.								
t_e °C	357.22	5									

+ grams/100 grams solvent

REFERENCES: 1-Dow 2-API 3-Lit. 4-Calc. from det. data 5-Calc. by formula

SOURCE: API

PURIFICATION: API

LITERATURE REFERENCES:

TABLE XIX. CYCLOHEXANES   461

No. 21

NAME	n-Dodecylcyclohexane	STRUCTURAL FORMULA
	1-Cyclohexyldodecane	

Structural formula:
$$H_2C \begin{array}{c} CH \cdot C_{12}H_{25} \\ CH_2 \\ CH_2 \end{array} CH_2$$
$$H_2C \quad CH_2$$

Mole % Pur.	Ref.	Molecular Formula	$C_{18}H_{36}$	Molecular Weight	252.468

		Ref.				Ref.					Ref.
F.P. °C	12.5	2	dt/dP				f		to		
F.P. 100%			°C/mm				g		°K		
B.P. °C			25°C	15324.	5		h				
760 mm	331.	2	BP	0.07003	4						
100	242.	5	t_e	0.03877	5		f'		to		
30	203.	5	30 mm	0.9891	5		g'		°K		
10	172.	5	ΔHm cal/g				h'				
1	122.	5	ΔHv cal/g				m		300 to	-0.0219	4
Pressure			25°C	77.34	5		n		600 °K	0.0015	4
mm 25°C	0.03591	5	30 mm	60.04	5		o			-0.0₆52	4
t_e	1619.8	5	BP	49.62	5		m'		700 to	0.1010	4
Density			t_e	46.35	5		n'		1000 °K	0.0012	4
g/ml 20°C	0.8223	2	t_e (d, e)	46.07	5		o'			-0.0₆40	4
d_4^t 25	0.8190	2	ΔHv/T_e	18.06	5		Surface tension				
30	0.8157	4	d	203 to	76.48	5	dynes/cm. 20°C			28.29	5
a	0.8355	4	e	375 °C	0.0811	5	γ		30	27.40	5
b	-0.0₃66	4	d'	20 to	79.78	5			40	26.52	5
Ref. Index			e'	203 °C	0.0974	5	Parachor [P]				
n_D 20°C	1.4559	2	d_c g/ml	0.239	5		20°C				
25	1.4539	2	v_c ml/g	4.19	5		30				
30	1.4523	4	t_c °C	503.	5		40				
"C"	0.7337	5	P_c mm	8743.	5		Sugd.		708.1	5
MR (Obs.)	83.44	2	PV/RT				Exp. L. l. %/wt.				
MR (Calc.)	83.124	5	25°C	1.0000	5		u.				
(nD-d/2)	1.0447	2	30 mm	1.0000	5		Dispersion		98.	2
Dielectric			BP	0.9274	5		Flash Point °C				
A 203 to	7.01789	4	t_e	0.8985	5		Fire Point				
B 425 °C	2097.5	4	t_c	0.191	5		M. Spec.				
C	176.	5	ΔHc kcal/m	2642.93	2		Ultra V.				
A* 203 to	1.66739	5	ΔHf				X-Ray Dif.				
B* 385 °C	1991.3	5	ΔFf				Infrared				
K			Viscosity				Solubility in +				
c			centistokes				Acetone				
t_k to			η 50 °C	4.35	2		Carbon tet.				
t_x °C			70	2.98	2		Benzene				
A' 20 to	7.28135	5	90	2.12	2		Ether				
B' 203 °C	2301.7	5	110	1.56	2		n-Heptane				
C'	194.	5	B^v 40 to	911.1	4		Ethanol				
A'* 20 to	1.96111	5	A^v 80 °C	3̄.81962	4		Water				
B'* 203 °C	2202.5	5	(B^v) 80 to	927.1	4		Water in				
Ac 425 to	8.31283	5	(A^v) 120 °C	3̄.77383	4						
Bc t_c °C	3942.8	5	c_p liq. °K								
Cc	399.	5	c_p vap.300°K	0.37141	2						
Cryos. A°			400	0.48165	2						
consts. B°			c_v vap.								
t_e °C	374.75	5									
T_R = 0.90 T_c							+ grams/100 grams solvent				

REFERENCES: 1-Dow 2-API 3-Lit. 4-Calc. from det. data 5-Calc. by formula

SOURCE:	API
PURIFICATION:	API
LITERATURE REFERENCES:	

No. 22

NAME	n-Tridecylcyclohexane				STRUCTURAL FORMULA

1-Cyclohexyltridecane

Mole % Pur.	Ref.	Molecular Formula $C_{19}H_{38}$		Molecular Weight 266.494	

		Ref.			Ref.					Ref.
F.P. °C	18.5	2	dt/dP			f		to		
F.P. 100%			°C/mm			g		°K		
			25°C	35356.	5	h				
B.P. °C			BP	0.07165	4					
760 mm	346.	2	t_e	0.03890	5	f'		to		
100	255.	5				g'		°K		
30	215.	5	30 mm	1.0122	5	h'				
10	184.	5	ΔHm cal/g							
1	132.	5	ΔHv cal/g			m		300 to	-0.0161	4
Pressure			25°C	76.98	5	n		600 °K	0.0014	4
mm 25°C	0.0_3244	5	30 mm	58.42	5	o			-0.0_650	4
t_e	1661.3	5	BP	48.22	5					
			t_e	44.89	5	m'		700 to	0.0925	4
Density			t_e (d,e)	44.62	5	n'		1000 °K	0.0012	4
g/ml 20°C	0.8239	2	ΔHv/T_e	17.97	5	o'			-0.0_641	4
d_4^t 25	0.8206	2	d	215 to	75.07	5	Surface tension			
30	0.8173	4	e	392 °C	0.0776	5	dynes/cm. 20°C	28.46	5
a	0.8371	4	d'	20 to	79.43	5	γ	30	27.56	5
b	-0.0_366	4	e'	215 °C	0.0979	5		40	26.68	5
Ref. Index			d_c g/ml	0.239	5	Parachor [P]			
n_D 20°C	1.4570	2	v_c ml/g	4.19	5	20°C			
25	1.4550	2	t_c °C	515.	5	30			
30	1.4531	4	P_c mm	8135.	5	40			
"C"	0.7340	4	PV/RT			Sugd. 747.1	5		
MR (Obs.)	88.08	2	25°C	1.0000	5	Exp. L.1.%/wt.			
MR (Calc.)	87.742	5	30 mm	1.0000	5	u.			
(nD-d/2)	1.0450	2	BP	0.9271	5	Dispersion	98.	2
Dielectric			t_e	0.8971	5	Flash Point °C			
			t_c	0.185	5	Fire Point			
A 215 to	7.01992	4	ΔHc kcal/m	2789.86	2	M Spec.			
B 436 °C	2148.2	4	ΔHf			Ultra V.			
C	173.	5	ΔFf			X-Ray Dif.			
A* 215 to	1.68318	5				Infrared			
B* 402 °C	2040.0	5	Viscosity			Solubility in +			
K			centistokes			Acetone			
c			η 50 °C	4.99	2	Carbon tet.			
t_k to			70	3.37	2	Benzene			
t_x °C			90	2.36	2	Ether			
A' 20 to	7.27735	5	110	1.71	2	n-Heptane			
B' 215 °C	2352.4	5	B^v 40 to	945.5	4	Ethanol			
C'	191.	5	A^v 80 °C	$\overline{3}.77282$	4	Water			
A'* 20 to	1.97641	5	$(B^{\overline{v}})$ 80 to	973.6	4	Water in			
B'* 215 °C	2253.6	5	(A^v) 120 °C	$\overline{3}.69224$	4				
Ac 436 to	8.30585	5	c_p liq. °K						
Bc t_c °C	3999.9	5							
Cc	395.	5	c_p vap.300°K	0.37247	2				
Cryos. A°			400	0.48219	2				
consts. B°			c_v vap.						
t_e °C	392.39	5							

T_R = 0.90 T_c + grams/100 grams solvent

REFERENCES: 1-Dow   2-API   3-Lit.   4-Calc. from det. data   5-Calc. by formula

SOURCE: API

PURIFICATION: API

LITERATURE REFERENCES:

TABLE XIX. CYCLOHEXANES

NAME	n-Tetradecylcyclohexane	STRUCTURAL FORMULA
	1-Cyclohexyltetradecane	

Mole % Pur.	Ref.	Molecular Formula $C_{20}H_{40}$	Molecular Weight 280.520

		Ref.			Ref.				Ref.
F.P. °C	24.0	2	dt/dP			f	| to		
F.P. 100%			°C/mm			g	|___ °K		
B.P. °C			25°C	74925.8	5	h	|		
760 mm	360.	2	BP	0.07326	4				
100	267.	5	t_e	0.03909	5	f'	| to		
30	226.	5	30 mm	1.03530	5	g'	|___ °K		
10	194.	5	ΔHm cal/g			h'	|		
1	141.	5				m	| 300 to	-0.0112	4
Pressure			ΔHv cal/g			n	|_600 °K	0.0014	4
mm 25°C	0.0_3110	5	25°C	76.12	5	o		-0.0$_6$47	4
t_e	1698.8	5	30 mm	56.74	5				
			BP	46.79	5	m'	| 700 to	0.0844	4
Density			t_e	43.43	5	n'	|_1000 °K	0.0012	4
g/ml 20°C	0.8254$^{\neq}$	2	t_e (d, e)	43.17	5	o'		-0.0$_6$43	4
d_4^t 25	0.8221	2	$\Delta Hv/T_e$	17.86	5				
30	0.8188	4				Surface tension			
a	0.8386	4	d | 226 to	73.45	5	dynes/cm. 20°C		28.62	5
b	-0.0$_3$66	4	e |_409 °C	0.0741	5	ȣ	30	27.72	5
			d' | 20 to	78.54	5		40	26.84	5
Ref. Index			e' | 226 °C	0.0966	5				
n_D 20°C	1.4579$^{\neq}$	2				Parachor [P]			
25	1.4559	2	d_c g/ml	0.238	5	20°C			
30	1.4545	4	v_c ml/g	4.206	5	30			
"C"	0.7340	4	t_c °C	525.	5	40			
			P_c mm	7509.	5		Sugd.	786.1	5
MR (Obs.)	92.72$^{\neq}$	2	PV/RT			Exp. L. 1.%/wt.			
MR (Calc.)	92.360	5	25°C	1.0000	5	u.			
(nD-d/2)	1.0452$^{\neq}$	2	30 mm	1.0000	5	Dispersion		98.	2
Dielectric			BP	0.9262	5	Flash Point °C			
A | 226 to	7.02261	5	t_e	0.8952	5	Fire Point			
B |_445 °C_	2199.3	5	t_c	0.178	5	M. Spec.			
C	171.	5	ΔHc kcal/m	2936.78	2	Ultra V.			
A*| 226 to	1.69987	5	ΔHf			X-Ray Dif.			
B*|_419 °C_	2089.1	5	ΔFf			Infrared			
K			Viscosity			Solubility in $^+$			
c			centistokes			Acetone			
t_k |‾ to ‾			η 50 °C	5.69	2	Carbon tet.			
t_x |_ °C _			70	3.78	2	Benzene			
A'| 20 to	7.27430	5	90	2.61	2	Ether			
B'|_226 °C_	2403.5	5	110	1.87	2	n-Heptane			
C'	189.	5	B^V | 40 to	985.1	4	Ethanol			
A'*| 20 to	1.99109	5	A^V | 80 °C	3.70715	4	Water			
B'*|_226 °C_	2304.7	5	(B^V)| 80 to	1007.7	4	Water in			
Ac| 445 to	8.30924	5	(A^V)|120 °C	3.64228	4				
Bc|_t_c °C_	4070.1	5							
Cc	393.	5	c_p liq. °K						
Cryos. A°			c_p vap.300°K	0.37341	2				
consts. B°			400	0.48268	2				
t_e °C	408.91	5	c_v vap.						

$T_R = 0.90 T_c$	$\neq$ for undercooled liquid	$^+$ grams/100 grams solvent

REFERENCES: 1-Dow 2-API 3-Lit. 4-Calc. from det. data 5-Calc. by formula

SOURCE:	API
PURIFICATION:	API

LITERATURE REFERENCES:

NAME	n-Pentadecylcyclohexane	STRUCTURAL FORMULA
	1-Cyclohexylpentadecane	

Mole % Pur.	Ref.	Molecular Formula $C_{21}H_{42}$	Molecular Weight 294.546	H_2C CH $C_{15}H_{31}$ / H_2C CH_2 / CH_2 CH_2

		Ref.			Ref.				Ref.
F.P. °C	29.0	2	dt/dP °C/mm			f	to °K		
F.P. 100%			25°C	165462.9	5	g			
B.P. °C			BP	0.07460	5	h			
760 mm	373.	2	t_e	0.03919	5	f'	to °K		
100	278.	5	30 mm	1.05452	5	g'			
30	236.	5	ΔHm cal/g			h'			
10	204.	5	ΔHv cal/g			m	300 to 600 °K	-0.0133	4
1	150.	5	25°C	75.90	5	n		0.0014	4
Pressure			30 mm	55.32	5	o		-0.0_650	4
mm 25°C	0.0_448	5	BP	45.52	5	m'	700 to 1000 °K	0.1086	4
t_e	1733.5	5	t_e	42.12	5	n'		0.0012	4
Density			t_e (d,e)	41.86	5	o'		-0.0_639	4
g/ml 20°C	$0.8267^{\neq}$	2	$\Delta Hv/T_e$	17.79	5	Surface tension			
d_4^t 25	$0.8234^{\neq}$	2	d 236 to	72.22	5	dynes/cm. 20°C		28.76	5
30	0.8201	4	e 424 °C	0.0716	5	γ 30		27.85	5
a	0.8399	4	d' 20 to	78.33	5	40		26.97	5
b	-0.0_366	4	e' 236 °C	0.0975	5	Parachor [P]			
Ref. Index			d_c g/ml	0.228	5	20°C			
n_D 20°C	$1.4588^{\neq}$	2	v_c ml/g	4.38	5	30			
25	$1.4568^{\neq}$	2	t_c °C	533.	5	40			
30	1.4545	4	P_c mm	6700.	5	Sugd.		825.1	5
"C"	0.7342	4	PV/RT			Exp. L.l.%/wt.			
MR (Obs.)	$97.36^{\neq}$	2	25°C	1.0000	5	u.			
MR (Calc.)	96.978	2	30 mm	1.0000	5	Dispersion		$98.^{\neq}$	2
(nD-d/2)	$1.0454^{\neq}$	2	BP	0.9255	5	Flash Point °C			
Dielectric			t_e	0.8934	5	Fire Point			
A 236 to	7.0248	5	t_c	0.172	5	M Spec.			
B 533 °C	2241.9	5	ΔHc kcal/m	3083.70	2	Ultra V.			
C	168.	5	ΔHf			X-Ray Dif.			
A* 236 to	1.71642	5	ΔFf			Infrared			
B* 434 °C	2130.5	5	Viscosity			Solubility in +			
K			centistokes			Acetone			
c			η 50 °C	6.44	2	Carbon tet.			
t_k to			70	4.22	2	Benzene			
t_x °C			90	2.88	2	Ether			
A' 20 to	7.27190	5	110	2.03	2	n-Heptane			
B' 236 °C	2446.1	5	B^v 40 to	1018.2	4	Ethanol			
C'	186.	5	A^v 80 °C	$\overline{3}.65865$	4	Water			
A'* 20 to	2.00685	5	(B^v) 80 to	1056.9	4	Water in			
B'* 236 °C	2348.0	5	(A^v) 120 °C	$\overline{3}.54918$	4				
Ac to			c_p liq. °K						
Bc t_c °C			c_p vap.300°K	0.37430	2				
Cc			400	0.48346	2				
Cryos. A°			c_v vap.						
consts. B°									
t_e °C	424.17	5							

$\neq$ for undercooled liquid
+ grams/100 grams solvent

REFERENCES: 1-Dow 2-API 3-Lit. 4-Calc. from det. data 5-Calc. by formula

SOURCE: API

PURIFICATION: API

LITERATURE REFERENCES:

TABLE XIX. CYCLOHEXANES

No. 25

NAME	n-Hexadecylcyclohexane	STRUCTURAL FORMULA
	1-Cyclohexylhexadecane	H_2C⟨$CH \cdot C_{16}H_{33}$⟩CH_2 / H_2C⟨ ⟩CH_2 / CH_2

Mole % Pur.	Ref.	Molecular Formula $C_{22}H_{44}$	Molecular Weight 308.572

		Ref.			Ref.				Ref.
F.P. °C	33.6	2	dt/dP			f	to		
F.P. 100%			°C/mm			g	°K		
			25°C	330428.	5	h			
B.P. °C			BP	0.07595	4				
760 mm	385.	2	t_e	0.03935	5	f'	to		
100	288.	5	30 mm	1.07382	5	g'	°K		
30	246.	5	ΔHm cal/g			h'			
10	213.	5	ΔHv cal/g			m	300 to	-0.0107	4
1	158.	5	25°C	75.12	5	n	600 °K	0.0014	4
Pressure			30 mm	53.81	5	o		-0.0₆50	4
mm 25°C	0.0₄23	5	BP	44.21	5	m'	700 to	0.0979	4
t_e	1764.7	5	t_e	40.78	5	n'	1000 °K	0.0012	4
Density			t_e (d, e)	40.54	5	o'		-0.0₆41	4
g/ml 20°C	0.8279#	2	ΔHv/T_e	17.69	5	Surface tension			
d_4^t 25	0.8246#	2	d 246 to	70.73	5	dynes/cm. 20°C	28.89	5
30	0.8213	4	e 438 °C	0.0689	5	δ 30	27.98	5
a	0.8411	4	d' 20 to	77.53	5	40	27.09	5
b	-0.0₃66	4	e' 246 °C	0.0966	5	Parachor [P]		
Ref. Index			d_c g/ml	0.235	5	20°C		
n_D 20°C	1.4596#	2	v_c ml/g	4.25	5	30		
25	1.4576#	2	t_c °C	541.	5	40		
30	1.4557	4	P_c mm	6432.	5	Sugd.	864.1	5
"C"	0.7343	4	PV/RT			Exp. L.1.%/wt.		
MR (Obs.)	102.00#	2	25°C	1.0000	5	u.		
MR (Calc.)	101.596	5	30 mm	1.0000	5	Dispersion	98.#	2
(nD-d/2)	1.0456#	2	BP	0.9244	5	Flash Point °C		
Dielectric			t_e	0.8914	5	Fire Point		
A 246 to	7.02636	5	t_c	0.166	5	M. Spec.		
B 460 °C	2284.2	5	ΔHc kcal/m	3230.63	2	Ultra V.		
C	166.	5	ΔHf			X-Ray Dif.		
A* 246 to	1.73216	5	ΔFf			Infrared		
B* 448 °C	2171.6	5	Viscosity			Solubility in +		
K			centistokes			Acetone		
c			η 50 °C	7.26	2	Carbon tet.		
t_k to			70	4.69	2	Benzene		
t_x °C			90	3.16	2	Ether		
A' 20 to	7.26902	5	110	2.20	2	n-Heptane		
B' 246 °C	2488.3	5	B^v 40 to	1052.5	4	Ethanol		
C'	184.	5	A^v 80 °C	3.60448	4	Water		
A'* 20 to	2.02061	5	(B^v) 80 to	1094.4	4	Water in		
B'* 246 °C	2390.5	5	(A^v) 120 °C	3.48640	4			
Ac 460 to	8.30856	5	c_p liq. °K					
Bc t_c °C	4171.7	5						
Cc	386.	5	c_p vap.300°K	0.37508	2			
Cryos. A°			400	0.48384	2			
consts. B°			c_v vap.					
t_e °C	438.33	5						

$T_R = 0.90 T_c$ # for undercooled liquid   + grams/100 grams solvent

REFERENCES: 1-Dow 2-API 3-Lit. 4-Calc. from det. data 5-Calc. by formula

SOURCE: API

PURIFICATION: API

LITERATURE REFERENCES:

No. 26

NAME	n-Heptadecylcyclohexane	STRUCTURAL FORMULA
	1-Cyclohexylheptadecane	

Structural formula: $CHC_{17}H_{35}$, H_2C CH_2, H_2C CH_2, CH_2

Mole % Pur. -	Ref.	Molecular Formula $C_{23}H_{46}$	Molecular Weight 322.598

		Ref.			Ref.				Ref.
F.P. °C	37.8	2	dt/dP			f	to		
F.P. 100%			°C/mm			g	°K		
B.P. °C			113°C	336.97	5	h			
760 mm	397.	2	BP	0.07729	4				
100	299.	5	t_e	0.03994	5	f'	to		
30	255.	5	30 mm	1.09304	5	g'	°K		
10	222.	5	ΔHm cal/g			h'			
1	166.	5	ΔHv cal/g			m	to		
Pressure			113°C	64.15	5	n	°K		
mm113°C	0.0425	5	30 mm	52.44	5	o			
t_e	1770.3	5	BP	42.55	5				
Density			t_e	39.08	5	m'	to		
g/ml 20°C	0.8290#	2	t_e (d, e)	38.75	5	n'	°K		
d_4^t 25	0.8257#	2	ΔHv/T_e	17.40	5	o'			
d_4^t 30	0.8224	4	d	255 to	70.23	5	Surface tension		
a	0.8422	4	e	450 °C	0.0697	5	dynes/cm. 20°C	29.01	5
b	-0.0366	4	d'	113 to	73.18	5	γ 30	28.10	5
Ref. Index			e'	255 °C	0.0825	5	40	27.20	5
n_D 20°C	1.4603#	2	d_c g/ml			Parachor [P]		
25	1.4583#	2	v_c ml/g			20°C		
30	1.4564	4	t_c °C	548.	5	30		
"C"	0.7343	4	P_c mm	5760.	5	40		
MR (Obs.)	106.64#	2	PV/RT				Sugd. 903.1	5
MR (Calc.)	106.214	5	113°C	1.0000	5	Exp. L.1.%/wt.		
(nD-d/2)	1.0458#	2	30 mm	1.0000	5	u.		
Dielectric			BP	0.9135	5	Dispersion	98.#	2
A 255 to	7.02840	5	t_e	0.8780	5	Flash Point °C		
B 548 °C	2326.8	5	t_c			Fire Point		
C	164.	5	ΔHc kcal/m			M Spec.		
A* 255 to	1.76616	5	ΔHf			Ultra V.		
B* 460 °C	2220.7	5	ΔFf			X-Ray Dif.		
K			Viscosity			Infrared		
c			centistokes			Solubility in +		
t_k to			η °C			Acetone		
t_x °C						Carbon tet.		
A' 113 to	7.63490	5				Benzene		
B' 255 °C	2674.9	5				Ether		
C'	184.	5	B^v to			n-Heptane		
A'* 113 to	2.14124	5	A^v °C			Ethanol		
B'* 255 °C	2490.6	5	(B^v) to			Water		
Ac to			(A^v) °C			Water in		
Bc t_c °C			c_p liq. °K					
Cc								
Cryos. A°			c_p vap. °K					
consts. B°								
t_e °C	451.50	5	c_v vap.					

for undercooled liquid.

+ grams/100 grams solvent

REFERENCES: 1-Dow 2-API 3-Lit. 4-Calc. from det. data 5-Calc. by formula

SOURCE:	API
PURIFICATION:	API
LITERATURE REFERENCES:	

TABLE XIX. CYCLOHEXANES

No. 27

NAME	n-Octadecylcyclohexane		STRUCTURAL FORMULA
	1-Cyclohexyloctadecane		

Structural formula:
$$H_2C \underset{CH_2}{\overset{CHC_{18}H_{37}}{\underset{CH_2}{C}}} CH_2$$
$$H_2C \quad CH_2$$

Mole % Pur.	Ref.	Molecular Formula	$C_{24}H_{48}$	Molecular Weight 336.624

		Ref.			Ref.				Ref.
F.P. °C	41.6	2	dt/dP			f	to		
F.P. 100%			°C/mm			g	°K		
			121°C	332.06	5	h			
B.P. °C			BP	0.07850	4				
760 mm	409.	2	t_e	0.04000	5	f'	to		
100	309.	4	30 mm	1.1103	5	g'	°K		
30	265.	5				h'			
10	231.	5	ΔHm cal/g						
1	175.	5	ΔHv cal/g			m	to		
Pressure			121°C	62.82	5	n	°K		
mm 121°C	0.04398	5	30 mm	51.32	5	o			
t_e	1802.5	5	BP	41.57	5				
Density				38.06	5	m'	to		
g/ml 20°C	0.8300‡	2	t_e (d, e)	37.74	5	n'	°K		
d_4^t 25	0.8267‡	2	ΔHv/T_e	17.34	5	o'			
30	0.8234	4	d 270 to	69.24	5	Surface tension			
a	0.8432	4	e 465 °C	0.0676	5	dynes/cm. 20°C	29.11	5
b	-0.0₃66	4	d' 121 to	72.48	5	ɣ 30	28.20	5
Ref. Index			e' 270 °C	0.0799	5	40	27.31	5
n_D 20°C	1.4610‡	2	d_c g/ml			Parachor [P]			
25	1.4590‡	2	v_c ml/g			20°C			
30	1.4573	4	t_c °C	555.	5	30			
"C"	0.7345	4	P_c mm	5332.	5	40 Sugd.	942.1	5
MR (Obs.)	111.28‡	2	PV/RT			Exp. L.1.%/wt.			
MR (Calc.)	110.832	5	121°C	1.0000	5	u.			
(nD-d/2)	1.0460‡	2	30 mm	1.0000	5	Dispersion	98.‡	2
Dielectric			BP	0.9132	5	Flash Point °C			
A 270 to	7.03010	5	t_e	0.8768	5	Fire Point			
B 555 °C	2365.1	5	t_c			M. Spec.			
C	161.	5	ΔHc kcal/m			Ultra V.			
A* 270 to	1.77983	5	ΔHf			X-Ray Dif.			
B* 475 °C	2257.9	5	ΔFf			Infrared			
K			Viscosity			Solubility in +			
c			centistokes			Acetone			
t_k to			η °C			Carbon tet.			
t_x °C						Benzene			
A' 121 to	7.62491	5				Ether			
B' 270 °C	2712.5	5				n-Heptane			
C'	181.	5	B^v to			Ethanol			
A'* 121 to	2.13806	5	A^v °C			Water			
B'* 270 °C	2524.2	5	(B^v) to			Water in			
Ac to			(A^v) °C						
Bc t_c °C			c_p liq. °K						
Cc									
Cryos. A°			c_p vap. °K						
consts. B°									
t_e °C	465.64	5	c_v vap.						

‡ for undercooled liquid   + grams/100 grams solvent

REFERENCES: 1-Dow 2-API 3-Lit. 4-Calc. from det. data 5-Calc. by formula

SOURCE: API

PURIFICATION: API

LITERATURE REFERENCES:

No. 28

NAME	n-Nonadecylcyclohexane	STRUCTURAL FORMULA
	1-Cyclohexylnonadecane	

H_2C — CH $C_{19}H_{39}$ / CH$_2$
H_2C — CH$_2$
CH_2

Mole % Pur.	Ref.	Molecular Formula $C_{25}H_{50}$	Molecular Weight 350.650

		Ref.			Ref.				Ref.
F.P. °C	45.2	2	dt/dP °C/mm			f	to		
F.P. 100%			124°C	374.1	5	g	°K		
B.P. °C			BP	0.08029	4	h			
760 mm	420.	2	t_e	0.03954	5	f'	to		
100	318.	4	30 mm	1.1289	5	g'	°K		
30	272.	5				h'			
10	237.	5	ΔHm cal/g						
1	180.	5	ΔHv cal/g			m	to		
Pressure			124°C	61.18	5	n	°K		
mm 124°C	0.03907	5	30 mm	49.70	5	o			
t_e	1881.9	5	BP	40.22	5	m'	to		
Density			t_e	37.59	5	n'	°K		
g/ml 20°C	0.8310#	2	t_e (d, e)	36.41	5	o'			
d_4^t 25	0.8277#	2	ΔHv/T_e	17.51	5	Surface tension			
30	0.8244	4				dynes/cm. 20°C	29.23	5
a	0.8442	4	d | 272 to	67.10	5	y 30	28.31	5
b	-0.0366	4	e | 480 °C	0.0640	5	40	27.41	5
Ref. Index			d' | 124 to	70.80	5			
n_D 20°C	1.4616#	2	e' | 272 °C	0.0776	5	Parachor [P]		
25	1.4596#	2	d_c g/ml			20°C		
30	1.4576	4	v_c ml/g			30		
"C"	0.7345	2	t_c °C	563.	5	40		
MR (Obs.)	115.93#	2	P_c mm	4977.	5	Sugd.	981.1	5
MR (Calc.)	115.450	5	PV/RT			Exp. L.1.%/wt.		
(nD-d/2)	1.0461#	2	124°C	1.0000	5	u.		
Dielectric			30 mm	1.0000	5	Dispersion	98.#	2
A | 272 to	7.00170	5	BP	0.9098	5	Flash Point °C		
B | 563 °C	2380.0	5	t_e	0.8985	5	Fire Point		
C	159.	5	t_c			M Spec.		
A* | 272 to	1.72697	5	ΔHc kcal/m			Ultra V.		
B* | 490 °C	2255.8	5	ΔHf			X-Ray Dif.		
K			ΔFf			Infrared		
c			Viscosity			Solubility in +		
t_k | to			centistokes			Acetone		
t_x | °C			η °C			Carbon tet.		
A' | 124 to	7.59604	5				Benzene		
B' | 272 °C	2728.3	5				Ether		
C'	179.	5	B^v | to			n-Heptane		
A'* | 124 to	2.11638	5	A^v | °C			Ethanol		
B'* 272 °C	2537.2	5	$(\overline{B^v})$ | to			Water		
Ac | to			$(\overline{A^v})$ | °C			Water in		
Bc | t_c °C								
Cc			c_p liq. °K					
Cryos. A°			c_p vap. °K					
consts. B°								
t_e °C	479.56	5	c_v vap.					

# for undercooled liquid	+ grams/100 grams solvent

REFERENCES: 1-Dow 2-API 3-Lit. 4-Calc. from det. data 5-Calc. by formula

SOURCE: API

PURIFICATION: API

LITERATURE REFERENCES:

TABLE XIX. CYCLOHEXANES
469

No. 29

NAME	n-Eicosylcyclohexane		STRUCTURAL FORMULA
	1-Cyclohexyleicosane		

STRUCTURAL FORMULA

$$CH C_{20}H_{41}$$
$$H_2C \quad CH_2$$
$$H_2C \quad CH_2$$
$$CH_2$$

Mole % Pur.		Ref.	Molecular Formula	$C_{26}H_{52}$	Molecular Weight 364.676		

		Ref.				Ref.				Ref.
F.P. °C	48.5	2	dt/dP				f		to	
F.P. 100%			°C/mm				g		°K	
			132°C	351.3	5		h			
B.P. °C			BP	0.08137	4					
760 mm	430.	2	t_e	0.04060	5		f'		to	
100	327.	5					g'		°K	
30	281.	5	30 mm	1.1471	5		h'			
10	246.	5	ΔHm cal/g							
1	188.	5					m		to	
			ΔHv cal/g				n		°K	
Pressure			132°C	59.69	5		o			
mm 132°C	0.04267	5	30 mm	48.61	5					
t_e	1855.7	5	BP	39.21	5		m'		to	
Density			t_e	35.67	5		n'		°K	
g/ml 20°C	0.8318≠	2	t_e (d, e)	35.37	5		o'			
d_4^t 25	0.8285≠	2	ΔHv/T_e	17.02	5					
30	0.8252	4					Surface tension			
a	0.8450	4	d 281 to	66.33	5		dynes/cm. 20°C		29.31	5
b	-0.0366	4	e 490 °C	0.0631	5		ɤ 30		28.39	5
Ref. Index			d' 132 to	69.51	5		40		27.49	5
n_D 20°C	1.4622≠	2	e' 281 °C	0.0744	5					
25	1.4602≠	2	d_c g/ml				Parachor [P]			
30	1.4582	4	v_c ml/g				20°C			
"C"	0.7346	4	t_c °C	568.	5		30			
MR (Obs.)	120.57≠	2	P_c mm	4629.	5		40			
MR (Calc.)	120.068	5	PV/RT						Sugd. 1020.1	5
(nD-d/2)	1.0463≠	2	132°C	1.0000	5		Exp. L.1.%/wt.			
Dielectric			30 mm	1.0000	5		u.			
A 281 to	7.00312	5	BP	0.9111	5		Dispersion		98.≠	2
B 568 °C	2419.8	5	t_e	0.8728	5		Flash Point °C			
C	157.	5	t_c				Fire Point			
A* 281 to	1.77812	5	ΔHc kcal/m				M. Spec.			
B* 500 °C	2311.0	5	ΔHf				Ultra V.			
K			ΔFf				X-Ray Dif.			
c			Viscosity				Infrared			
t_k to			centistokes				Solubility in +			
t_x °C			η °C				Acetone			
A' 132 to	7.58257	5					Carbon tet.			
B' 281 °C	2766.3	5					Benzene			
C'	177.	5	B^v to				Ether			
A'* 132 to	2.12278	5	A^v °C				n-Heptane			
B'* 281 °C	2575.0	5	(B^v) to				Ethanol			
Ac to			(A^v) °C				Water			
Bc t_c °C							Water in			
Cc			c_p liq. °K							
Cryos. A° consts. B°			c_p vap. °K							
t_e °C	490.94	5	c_v vap.							

≠ for undercooled liquid   + grams/100 grams solvent

REFERENCES: 1-Dow 2-API 3-Lit. 4-Calc. from det. data 5-Calc. by formula

SOURCE: API

PURIFICATION: API

LITERATURE REFERENCES:

No. 30

NAME	n-Heneicosylcyclohexane			STRUCTURAL FORMULA		
	1-Cyclohexylheneicosane					

Mole % Pur.	Ref.	Molecular Formula $C_{27}H_{54}$		Molecular Weight 378.702		

Structural formula: H_2C $CHC_{21}H_{43}$ / CH_2 / H_2C CH_2 / CH_2

		Ref.				Ref.				Ref.
F.P. °C	51.5	2	dt/dP °C/mm				f	to °K		
F.P. 100%			138°C	356.2	5		g			
B.P. °C			BP	0.08244	4		h			
760 mm	440.	2	t_e	0.04071	5		f'	to °K		
100	335.	5	30 mm	1.1625	5		g'			
30	289.	5	ΔHm cal/g				h'			
10	254.	5	ΔHv cal/g				m	to °K		
1	195.	5	138°C	58.40	5		n			
Pressure			30 mm	47.54	5		o			
mm 138°C	0.04265	5	BP	38.29	5		m'	to °K		
t_e	1880.9	5	t_e	34.75	5		n'			
Density			t_e (d, e)	34.45	5		o'			
g/ml 20°C	0.8326≠	2	ΔHv/T_e	16.96	5		Surface tension dynes/cm. 20°C	29.40	5	
d_4^t 25	0.8294≠	2	d | 289 to	65.23	5		γ			
30	0.8262	4	e | 503 °C	0.0612	5		30	28.50	5	
a	0.8454	4	d' | 138 to	68.32	5		40	27.63	5	
b	-0.0₃64	4	e' | 289 °C	0.0719	5		Parachor [P]			
Ref. Index			d_c g/ml				20°C			
n_D 20°C	1.4627≠	2	v_c ml/g				30			
25	1.4607≠	2	t_c °C	576.	5		40			
30	1.4588	4	P_c mm	4447.	5		Sugd.	1059.1	5	
"C"	0.7346	4	PV/RT				Exp. L.1.%/wt.			
MR (Obs.)	125.21≠	2	138°C	1.0000	5		u.			
MR (Calc.)	124.686	5	30 mm	1.0000	5		Dispersion	98.≠	2	
(nD-d/2)	1.0464≠	2	BP	0.9103	5		Flash Point °C			
Dielectric			t_e	0.8712	5		Fire Point			
A | 289 to	7.00501	5	t_c				M Spec.			
B | 576 °C	2453.9	5	ΔHc kcal/m				Ultra V.			
C	155.	5	ΔHf				X-Ray Dif.			
A* | 289 to	1.79203	5	ΔFf				Infrared			
B* | 513 °C	2344.5	5	Viscosity centistokes				Solubility in +			
K			η °C				Acetone			
c							Carbon tet.			
t_k | to							Benzene			
t_x | °C							Ether			
A' | 138 to	7.57669	5					n-Heptane			
B' | 289 °C	2800.3	5	B^v | to				Ethanol			
C'	175.	5	A^v | °C				Water			
A'* | 138 to	2.13093	5	(B^v) | to				Water in			
B'* 289 °C	2607.8	5	(A^v) | °C							
Ac | to			c_p liq. °K							
Bc | t_c °C										
Cc			c_p vap. °K							
Cryos. A° consts. B°										
t_e °C	502.77	5	c_v vap.							

≠ for undercooled liquid	+ grams/100 grams solvent

REFERENCES: 1-Dow 2-API 3-Lit. 4-Calc. from det. data 5-Calc. by formula

SOURCE:	API
PURIFICATION:	API
LITERATURE REFERENCES:	

TABLE XIX. CYCLOHEXANES

471

No. 31

NAME	n-Docosylcyclohexane		STRUCTURAL FORMULA	
	1-Cyclohexyldocosane			

Structural formula:

$$H_2C \begin{array}{c} CH\, C_{22}H_{45} \\ CH_2 \end{array}$$
$$H_2C \underset{CH_2}{} CH_2$$

Mole % Pur.	Ref.	Molecular Formula	$C_{28}H_{56}$	Molecular Weight 392.728

		Ref.				Ref.				Ref.
F.P. °C	54.4	2	dt/dP			f		to		
F.P. 100%			°C/mm			g		°K		
			143°C	360.8	5	h				
B.P. °C			BP	0.08352	4					
760 mm	449.	2	t_e	0.04083	5	f'		to		
100	343.	5	30 mm	1.1780	5	g'		°K		
30	296.	5	ΔHm cal/g			h'				
10	260.	5								
1	200.	5	ΔHv cal/g			m		to		
			143°C	56.92	5	n		°K		
Pressure			30 mm	46.38	5	o				
mm 143°C	0.04268	5	BP	37.34	5					
t_e	1905.4	5	t_e	33.79	5	m'		to		
			t_e (d, e)	33.53	5	n'		°K		
Density			$\Delta Hv/T_e$	16.87	5	o'				
g/ml 20°C	0.8334≠	2								
d_4^t 25	0.8301≠	2	d 296 to	63.84	5	Surface tension				
30	0.8268	4	e 514 °C	0.0590	5	dynes/cm. 20°C		29.49	5
			d' 143 to	66.77	5	γ		30	28.56	5
a	0.8466	4	e' 296 °C	0.0689	5			40	27.66	5
b	-0.0₃66	4								
			d_c g/ml			Parachor [P]				
Ref. Index			v_c ml/g					20°C		
n_D 20°C	1.4632≠	2	t_c °C	578.	5			30		
25	1.4612≠	2	P_c mm	4054.	5			40		
30	1.4592	4						Sugd.	1098.1	5
"C"	0.7347	4	PV/RT							
MR (Obs.)	129.85≠	2	143°C	1.0000	5	Exp. L.1.%/wt.				
MR (Calc.)	129.304	5	30 mm	1.0000	5	u.				
(nD-d/2)	1.0465≠	2	BP	0.9102	5	Dispersion		98.≠	2
Dielectric			t_e	0.8704	5					
			t_c			Flash Point °C				
A 296 to	7.00634	5				Fire Point				
B 578 °C	2487.7	5	ΔHc kcal/m							
C	154.	5	ΔHf			M. Spec.				
A* 296 to	1.80375	5	ΔFf			Ultra V.				
B* 524 °C	2376.8	5				X-Ray Dif.				
K			Viscosity			Infrared				
c			centistokes							
t_k to			η °C			Solubility in +				
t_x °C						Acetone				
						Carbon tet.				
A' 143 to	7.57039	5				Benzene				
B' 296 °C	2834.0	5				Ether				
C'	174.	5	B^v to			n-Heptane				
			A^v °C			Ethanol				
A'* 143 to	2.13816	5	(B^v) to			Water				
B'* 296 °C	2640.0	5	(A^v) °C			Water in				
Ac to										
Bc t_c °C			c_p liq. °K							
Cc										
Cryos. A°			c_p vap. °K							
consts. B°										
t_e °C	513.60	5	c_v vap.							

≠ for undercooled liquid + grams/100 grams solvent

REFERENCES: 1-Dow 2-API 3-Lit. 4-Calc. from det. data 5-Calc. by formula

SOURCE: API

PURIFICATION: API

LITERATURE REFERENCES:

NAME	n-Tricosylcyclohexane	STRUCTURAL FORMULA
	1-Cyclohexyltricosane	$H_2C \overset{CH\,C_{23}H_{47}}{\underset{CH_2}{\big|}} CH_2$ $H_2C \underset{CH_2}{\big|} CH_2$

Mole % Pur.	Ref.	Molecular Formula $C_{29}H_{58}$	Molecular Weight 406.754

		Ref.			Ref.				Ref.
F.P. °C	57.0	2	dt/dP			f	to		
F.P. 100%			°C/mm			g	°K		
B.P. °C			149°C	366.2	5	h			
760 mm	459.	2	BP	0.08458	4				
100	352.	5	t_e	0.04096	5	f'	to		
30	304.	5	30 mm	1.1932	5	g'	°K		
10	268.	5	ΔHm cal/g			h'			
1	207.	5							
			ΔHv cal/g			m	to		
Pressure			149°C	55.82	5	n	°K		
mm 149°C	0.04260	5	30 mm	45.46	5	o			
t_e	1928.9	5	BP	36.52	5				
Density			t_e	32.95	5	m'	to		
g/ml 20°C	0.8341‡	2	t_e (d, e)	32.69	5	n'	°K		
d_4^t 25	0.8308‡	2	ΔHv/T_e	16.78	5	o'			
30	0.8275	4				Surface tension			
a	0.8473	4	d | 304 to	62.99	5	dynes/cm. 20°C		29.56	5
b	-0.0₃66	4	e | 525 °C	0.0577	5	γ 30		28.64	5
Ref. Index			d' | 149 to	65.78	5	40		27.73	5
n_D 20°C	1.4637‡	2	e' | 304 °C	0.0668	5				
25	1.4617‡	2				Parachor [P]			
30	1.4598	4	d_c g/ml			20°C			
"C"	0.7350	4	v_c ml/g			30			
MR (Obs.)	134.49‡	2	t_c °C	584.	5	40			
MR (Calc.)	133.922	4	P_c mm	3819.	5	Sugd.		1137.1	5
(nD-d/2)	1.0466‡	2	PV/RT			Exp. L. 1.%/wt.			
Dielectric			149°C	1.0000	5	u.			
A | 304 to	7.00879	5	30 mm	1.0000	5	Dispersion		98.‡	2
B | 584 °C	2522.2	5	BP	0.9087	5				
C	152.	5	t_e	0.8681	5	Flash Point °C			
			t_c			Fire Point			
A* | 304 to	1.81836	5				M Spec.			
B* | 535 °C	2411.1	5	Δ'Hc kcal/m			Ultra V.			
K			ΔHf			X-Ray Dif			
c			ΔFf			Infrared			
t_k | to			Viscosity			Solubility in †			
t_x | °C			centistokes			Acetone			
A' | 149 to	7.56556	5	η °C			Carbon tet.			
B' | 304 °C	2868.5	5				Benzene			
C'	172.	5				Ether			
A'* 149 to	2.14637	5	B^v | to			n-Heptane			
B'* 304 °C	2673.3	5	A^v | °C			Ethanol			
Ac | to			(B^v) | to			Water			
Bc | t_c °C			(A^v) | °C			Water in			
Cc			c_p liq. °K						
Cryos. A°									
consts. B°			c_p vap. °K						
t_e °C	525.38	5	c_v vap.						

‡ for undercooled liquid   † grams/100 grams solvent

REFERENCES: 1-Dow 2-API 3-Lit. 4-Calc. from det. data 5-Calc. by formula

SOURCE:	API

PURIFICATION:	API

LITERATURE REFERENCES:

TABLE XIX. CYCLOHEXANES

NAME	n-Tetracosylcyclohexane	STRUCTURAL FORMULA
	1-Cyclohexyltetracosane	$CHC_{24}H_{49}$ H_2C CH_2 H_2C CH_2 CH_2

Mole % Pur.	Ref.	Molecular Formula $C_{30}H_{60}$		Molecular Weight 420.780		

		Ref.			Ref.			Ref.
F.P. °C	59.5	2	dt/dP			f	to	
F.P. 100%			°C/mm			g	°K	
			153°C	391.8	5	h		
B.P. °C			BP	0.08538	4			
760 mm	467.	2	t_e	0.04104	5	f'	to	
100	359.	5	30 mm	1.2047	5	g'	°K	
30	310.	5	ΔHm cal/g			h'		
10	274.	5	ΔHv cal/g			m	to	
1	213.	5	153°C	54.82	5	n	°K	
Pressure			30 mm	44.52	5	o		
mm 153°C	0.03994	5	BP	35.69	5			
t_e	1947.6	5	t_e	32.13	5	m'	to	
Density			t_e (d,e)	31.87	5	n'	°K	
g/ml 20°C	0.8347≠	2	ΔHv/T_e	16.73	5	o'		
d_4^t 25	0.8315≠	2	d 310 to	62.02	5	Surface tension		
30	0.8283	4	e 535 °C	0.0564	5	dynes/cm. 20°C	29.63	5
a	0.8475	4	d' 153 to	64.86	5	४ 30	28.73	5
b	-0.0364	4	e' 310 °C	0.0656	5	40	27.85	5
Ref. Index			d_c g/ml			Parachor [P]		
n_D 20°C	1.4641≠	2	v_c ml/g			20°C		
25	1.4621≠	2	t_c °C	590.	5	30		
30	1.4602	4	P_c mm	3692.	5	40		
"C"	0.7349	4				Sugd.	1176.1	5
MR (Obs.)	139.13≠	2	PV/RT			Exp. L. l.%/wt.		
MR (Calc.)	138.540	4	153°C	1.0000	5	u.		
(nD-d/2)	1.0467≠	2	30 mm	1.0000	5	Dispersion	98.≠	2
Dielectric			BP	0.9077	5	Flash Point °C		
A 310 to	7.0103	5	t_e	0.8664	5	Fire Point		
B 590 °C	2547.9	5	t_c			M. Spec.		
C	150.	5	ΔHc kcal/m			Ultra V.		
A* 310 to	1.83227	5	ΔHf			X-Ray Dif.		
B* 540 °C	2436.9	5	ΔFf			Infrared		
K			Viscosity			Solubility in +		
c			centistokes			Acetone		
t_k to			η °C			Carbon tet.		
t_x °C						Benzene		
A' 153 to	7.56534	5				Ether		
B' 310 °C	2895.4	5	B^v to			n-Heptane		
C'	170.	5	A^v °C			Ethanol		
A'* 153 to	2.17549	5	(B^v) to			Water		
B'*310 °C	2705.0	5	(A^v) °C			Water in		
Ac to			c_p liq. °K					
Bc t_c °C								
Cc			c_p vap. °K					
Cryos. A°								
consts. B°			c_v vap.					
t_e °C	534.77	5						

≠ for undercooled liquid   + grams/100 grams solvent

REFERENCES: 1-Dow 2-API 3-Lit. 4-Calc. from det. data 5-Calc. by formula

SOURCE: API

PURIFICATION: API

LITERATURE REFERENCES:

NAME	n-Pentacosylcyclohexane		STRUCTURAL FORMULA

1-Cyclohexylpentacosane

Structural formula:
$$H_2C \begin{array}{c} CH \, C_{25}H_{51} \\ CH_2 \end{array}$$
$$H_2C \begin{array}{c} CH_2 \\ CH_2 \end{array}$$

Mole % Pur.	Ref.	Molecular Formula	$C_{31}H_{62}$	Molecular Weight 434.806

		Ref.			Ref.			Ref.
F.P. °C	61.9	2	dt/dP °C/mm			f ⎪ ⎪ to		
F.P. 100%			158°C	396.8	5	g ⎪ ⎪ __ °K		
B.P. °C			BP	0.08645	4	h ⎪		
760 mm	476.	2	t_e	0.04117	5	f' ⎪ ⎪ to		
100	366.	5	30 mm	1.2201	5	g' ⎪ ⎪ __ °K		
30	317.	5	ΔHm cal/g			h' ⎪		
10	280.	5						
1	218.	5	ΔHv cal/g			m ⎪ ⎪ to		
Pressure			158°C	53.60	5	n ⎪ ⎪ __ °K		
mm158°C	0.03996	5	30 mm	43.57	5	o ⎪		
t_e	1971.0	5	BP	34.91	5			
Density			t_e	31.35	5	m' ⎪ ⎪ to		
g/ml 20°C	0.8353≠	2	t_e (d,e)	31.11	5	n' ⎪ ⎪ __ °K		
d_4^t 25	0.8321≠	2	$ΔHv/T_e$	16.65	5	o' ⎪		
30	0.8289	4				Surface tension		
a	0.8481	4	d ⎪ 317 to	60.90	5	dynes/cm. 20°C	29.69	5
b	-0.0₃64	4	e ⎪ 546 °C	0.0546	5	30	28.79	5
Ref. Index			d' ⎪ 158 to	63.57	5	40	27.91	5
n_D 20°C	1.4645≠	2	e' ⎪ 317 °C	0.0631	5	Parachor [P]		
25	1.4626≠	2	d_c g/ml			20°C		
30	1.4607	4	v_c ml/g			30		
"C"	0.7349	4	t_c °C	594.	5	40		
MR (Obs.)	143.77≠	2	P_c mm	3443.	5	Sugd.	1215.1	5
MR (Calc.)	143.158	4	PV/RT			Exp. L.1.%/wt.		
(nD-d/2)	1.0468≠	2	158°C	1.0000	5	u.		
Dielectric			30 mm	1.0000	5	Dispersion	98.≠	2
A ⎪317 to	7.01201	5	BP	0.9071	5	Flash Point °C		
B ⎪594 °C	2582.0	5	t_e	0.8652	5	Fire Point		
C	149.	5	t_c			M Spec.		
A*⎪317 to	1.84364	5	ΔHc kcal/m			Ultra V.		
B*⎪556 °C	2469.9	5	ΔHf			X-Ray Dif.		
K			ΔFf			Infrared		
c			Viscosity			Solubility in +		
t_k ⎪ to			centistokes			Acetone		
t_x ⎪ °C			η °C			Carbon tet.		
A'⎪158 to	7.55992	5				Benzene		
B'⎪317 °C	2929.4	5				Ether		
C'	169.	5	B^v ⎪ to			n-Heptane		
A'*158 to	2.18184	5	A^v ⎪ °C			Ethanol		
B'*317 °C	2737.5	5	(B^v)⎪ to			Water		
Ac⎪ to			(A^v)⎪ °C			Water in		
Bc⎪ t_c °C			c_p liq. °K					
Cc								
Cryos. A°			c_p vap. °K					
consts. B°								
t_e °C	545.59	5	c_v vap.					

≠ for undercooled liquid   + grams/100 grams solvent

REFERENCES: 1-Dow   2-API   3-Lit.   4-Calc. from det. data   5-Calc. by formula

SOURCE: API

PURIFICATION: API

LITERATURE REFERENCES:

TABLE XIX. CYCLOHEXANES

475

No. 35

NAME	n-Hexacosylcyclohexane	STRUCTURAL FORMULA
	1-Cyclohexylhexacosane	$CH\ C_{26}H_{53}$ $H_2C\ CH_2$ $H_2C\ CH_2$ CH_2

Mole % Pur.	Ref.	Molecular Formula $C_{32}H_{64}$	Molecular Weight 448.832

		Ref.			Ref.			Ref.
F.P. °C	64.0	2	dt/dP			f $\rvert$ to		
F.P. 100%			°C/mm			g $\rvert$ °K		
B.P. °C			164°C	378.9	5	h $\rvert$		
760 mm	484.	2	BP	0.08725	4			
100	373.	5	t_e	0.04123	5	f' $\rvert$ to		
30	324.	5	30 mm	1.2316	5	g' $\rvert$ °K		
10	287.	5	ΔHm cal/g			h' $\rvert$		
1	224.	5	ΔHv cal/g			m $\rvert$ to		
Pressure			164°C	52.54	5	n $\rvert$ °K		
mm164°C	0.04252	5	30 mm	42.74	5	o $\rvert$		
t_e	1990.9	5	BP	34.18	5			
Density			t_e	30.58	5	m' $\rvert$ to		
g/ml 20°C	0.8359$^{\neq}$	2	t_e (d, e)	30.38	5	n' $\rvert$ °K		
d_4^t 25	0.8326$^{\neq}$	2	ΔHv/T_e	16.57	5	o' $\rvert$		
30	0.8293	4				Surface tension		
a	0.8491	4	d $\rvert$ 324 to	60.07	5	dynes/cm. 20°C	29.76	5
b	-0.0366	4	e $\rvert$ 555 °C	0.0535	5	ɣ 30	28.83	5
Ref. Index			d' $\rvert$ 164 to	62.59	5	40	27.92	5
n_D 20°C	1.4649$^{\neq}$	2	e' $\rvert$ 324 °C	0.0613	5			
25	1.4629$^{\neq}$	2	d_c g/ml			Parachor [P]		
30	1.4609	4	v_c ml/g			20°C		
"C"	0.7350	4	t_c °C	595.	5	30		
MR (Obs.)	148.41$^{\neq}$	2	P_c mm	3155.	5	40		
MR (Calc.)	147.776	4	PV/RT			Sugd.	1254.1	5
(nD-d/2)	1.0469$^{\neq}$	2	164°C	1.0000	5	Exp. L.1.%/wt.		
Dielectric			30 mm	1.0000	5	u.		
A $\rvert$ 324 to	7.01345	5	BP	0.9065	5	Dispersion	98.$^{\neq}$	2
B $\rvert$ 595 °C	2607.7	5	t_e	0.8640	5	Flash Point °C		
C	147.	5	t_c			Fire Point		
A* $\rvert$ 324 to	1.85585	5	ΔHc kcal/m			M. Spec.		
B* $\rvert$ 565 °C	2495.3	5	ΔHf			Ultra V.		
K			ΔFf			X-Ray Dif.		
c			Viscosity			Infrared		
t_k $\rvert$ to			centistokes			Solubility in $^+$		
t_x $\rvert$ °C			η °C			Acetone		
A' $\rvert$ 164 to	7.55267	5				Carbon tet.		
B' $\rvert$ 324 °C	2953.9	5				Benzene		
C'	167.	5	B^v $\rvert$ to			Ether		
A'* 164 to	2.17073	5	A^v $\rvert$ °C			n-Heptane		
B'* 324 °C	2755.8	5	$(B^v)\rvert$ to			Ethanol		
Ac $\rvert$ to			$(A^v)\rvert$ °C			Water		
Bc $\rvert$ t_c °C						Water in		
Cc			c_p liq. °K					
Cryos. A°			c_p vap. °K					
consts. B°								
t_e °C	555.05	5	c_v vap.					

$\neq$ for undercooled liquid　　　　　　　　　　　　　　　　$^+$ grams/100 grams solvent

REFERENCES: 1-Dow 2-API 3-Lit. 4-Calc. from det. data 5-Calc. by formula

SOURCE: API

PURIFICATION: API

LITERATURE REFERENCES:

No. 36

NAME	n-Heptacosylcyclohexane	STRUCTURAL FORMULA
	1-Cyclohexylheptacosane	CH $C_{27}H_{55}$ / H_2C CH_2 / H_2C CH_2 / CH_2

Mole % Pur.	Ref.	Molecular Formula $C_{33}H_{66}$	Molecular Weight 462.858

		Ref.
F.P. °C	66.1	2
F.P. 100%		
B.P. °C		
760 mm	492.	2
100	380.	5·
30	330.	5
10	292.	5
1	229.	5
Pressure		
mm 168°C	0.04119	5
t_e	2011.8	5
Density		
g/ml 20°C	0.8365#	2
d_4^t 25	0.8332#	2
30	0.8299	4
a	0.8497	4
b	-0.0366	4
Ref. Index		
n_D 20°C	1.4653#	2
25	1.4633#	2
30	1.4613	2
"C"	0.7350	4
MR (Obs.)	153.05#	2
MR (Calc.)	152.394	4
(nD-d/2)	1.0470#	2
Dielectric		
A 330 to	7.01513	5
B 599 °C	2637.7	5
C	146.	5
A* 330 to	1.86691	5
B* 575 °C	2524.3	5
K		
c		
t_k to °C		
t_x		
A' 168 to	7.55018	5
B' 330 °C	2984.4	5
C'	166.	5
A'* 168 to	2.18799	5
B'* 330 °C	2788.0	5
Ac to		
Bc t_c °C		
Cc		
Cryos. A°		
consts. B°		
t_e °C	564.67	5

		Ref.
dt/dP °C/mm		
168°C	394.1	5
BP	0.08818	4
t_e	0.04133	5
30 mm	1.2450	5
ΔHm cal/g		
ΔHv cal/g		
168°C	51.48	5
30 mm	41.86	5
BP	33.46	5
t_e	29.86	5
t_e (d,e)	29.68	5
$ΔHv/T_e$	16.50	5
d 330 to	59.02	5
e 565 °C	0.0520	5
d' 168 to	61.46	5
e' 330 °C	0.0594	5
d_c g/ml		
v_c ml/g		
t_c °C	599.	5
P_c mm	2983.	5
PV/RT		
168°C	1.0000	5
30 mm	1.0000	5
BP	0.9061	5
t_e	0.8630	5
t_c		
ΔHc kcal/m		
ΔHf		
ΔFf		
Viscosity centistokes		
η °C		
B^v to		
A^v °C		
(B^v) to		
(A^v) °C		
c_p liq. °K		
c_p vap. °K		
c_v vap.		

			Ref.
f to			
g °K			
h			
f' to			
g' °K			
h'			
m to			
n °K			
o			
m' to			
n' °K			
o'			
Surface tension dynes/cm. 20°C		29.83	5
γ 30		28.90	5
40		27.99	5
Parachor [P]			
20°C			
30			
40			
Sugd.		1293.1	5
Exp. L.1.%/wt.			
u.			
Dispersion		98.#	2
Flash Point °C			
Fire Point			
M Spec.			
Ultra V.			
X-Ray Dif.			
Infrared			
Solubility in +			
Acetone			
Carbon tet.			
Benzene			
Ether			
n-Heptane			
Ethanol			
Water			
Water in			

for undercooled liquid   + grams/100 grams solvent

REFERENCES: 1-Dow 2-API 3-Lit. 4-Calc. from det. data 5-Calc. by formula

SOURCE: API

PURIFICATION: API

LITERATURE REFERENCES:

TABLE XIX. CYCLOHEXANES

477

No. 37

NAME	n-Octacosylcyclohexane		STRUCTURAL FORMULA
	1-Cyclohexyloctacosane		

Structural formula:
$$H_2C \begin{array}{c} CH \cdot C_{28}H_{57} \\ CH_2 \end{array}$$
$$H_2C \quad CH_2$$
$$CH_2$$

Mole, % Pur.	Ref.	Molecular Formula	$C_{34}H_{68}$	Molecular Weight	476.884

		Ref.			Ref.			Ref.
F.P. °C	68.0	2	dt/dP			f | to		
F.P. 100%			°C/mm			g | °K		
			173°C	386.4	5	h |		
B.P. °C			BP	0.08885	4			
760 mm	499.	2	t_e	0.04141	5	f' | to		
100	386.	5	30 mm	1.2546	5	g' | °K		
30	336.	5	ΔHm cal/g			h' |		
10	298.	5	ΔHv cal/g			m | to		
1	234.	5	173°C	50.55	5	n | °K		
Pressure			30 mm	41.09	5	o |		
mm 173°C	0.04247	5	BP	32.76	5			
t_e	2026.9	5	t_e	29.16	5	m' | to		
Density			t_e (d, e)	28.98	5	n' | °K		
g/ml 20°C	0.8370‡	2	ΔHv/T_e	16.43	5	o' |		
d_4^t 25	0.8337‡	2	d | 336 to	58.28	5	Surface tension		
30	0.8304	4	e | 573 °C	0.0511	5	dynes/cm. 20°C	29.88	5
a	0.8502	4	d' | 173 to	60.59	5	ɤ 30	28.95	5
b	-0.0₃66	4	e' | 336 °C	0.0580	5	40	28.04	5
Ref. Index			d_c g/ml			Parachor [P]		
n_D 20°C	1.4656‡	2	v_c ml/g			20°C		
25	1.4636‡	2	t_c °C	601.	5	30		
30	1.4616	4	P_c mm	2799.	5	40		
"C"	0.7350	4	PV/RT			Sugd.	1332.1	5
MR (Obs.)	157.69‡	2	173°C	1.0000	5	Exp. L. 1.%/wt.		
MR (Calc.)	157.012	4	30 mm	1.0000	5	u.		
(nD-d/2)	1.0471‡	2	BP	0.9048	5	Dispersion	98.‡	2
Dielectric			t_e	0.8611	5	Flash Point °C		
A | 336 to	7.01611	5	t_c			Fire Point		
B |601 °C	2659.0	5	ΔHc kcal/m			M. Spec.		
C	144.	5	ΔHf			Ultra V.		
A* | 336 to	1.87979	5	ΔFf			X-Ray Dif.		
B* |583 °C	2546.2	5				Infrared		
K			Viscosity			Solubility in +		
c			centistokes			Acetone		
t_k | to			η °C			Carbon tet.		
t_x | °C						Benzene		
A' |173 to	7.54532	5				Ether		
B' |336 °C	3005.1	5				n-Heptane		
C'	164.	5	B^v | to			Ethanol		
A'* 173 to	2.18668	5	A^v | °C			Water		
B'* 336 °C	2805.4	5	(B^v)| to			Water in		
Ac | to			(A^v)| °C					
Bc | t_c °C			c_p liq. °K					
Cc								
Cryos. A°			c_p vap. °K					
consts. B°								
t_e °C	572.85	5	c_v vap.					

‡ for undercooled liquid   + grams/100 grams solvent

REFERENCES: 1-Dow   2-API   3-Lit.   4-Calc. from det. data   5-Calc. by formula

SOURCE: API

PURIFICATION: API

LITERATURE REFERENCES:

No. 38

NAME	n-Nonacosylcyclohexane	STRUCTURAL FORMULA
	1-Cyclohexylnonacosane	$CH \ C_{29}H_{59}$
		$H_2C \quad CH_2$
		$H_2C \quad CH_2$
		CH_2

Mole % Pur.	Ref.	Molecular Formula	$C_{35}H_{70}$	Molecular Weight 490.910

		Ref.			Ref.				Ref.
F.P. °C	69.9	2	dt/dP			f | to			
F.P. 100%			°C/mm			g | °K			
			177°C	401.8	5	h |			
B.P. °C			BP	0.08978	4				
760 mm	507.	2	t_e	0.04153	5	f' | to			
100	393.	5	30 mm	1.2680	5	g' | °K			
30	342.	5	ΔHm cal/g			h' |			
10	304.	5							
1	239.	5	ΔHv cal/g			m | to			
Pressure			177°C	49.61	5	n | °K			
mm177°C	0.04116	5	30 mm	40.32	5	o |			
t_e	2046.7	5	BP	32.12	5				
Density			t_e	28.54	5	m' | to			
g/ml 20°C	0.8374‡	2	t_e (d, e)	28.36	5	n' | °K			
d_4^t 25	0.8342‡	2	ΔHv/T_e	16.37	5	o' |			
30	0.8310	4				Surface tension			
a	0.8502	4	d | 342 to	57.36	5	dynes/cm. 20°C	29.92	5
b	-0.0₃64	4	e | 592 °C	0.0498	5	ɤ 30	29.02	5
Ref. Index			d' | 177 to	59.58	5	40	28.13	5
n_D 20°C	1.4659‡	2	e' | 342 °C	0.0563	5	Parachor [P]		
25	1.4640‡	2	d_c g/ml			20°C		
30	1.4620	4	v_c ml/g			30		
"C"	0.7350	4	t_c °C	608.	5	40		
MR (Obs.)	162.33‡	2	P_c mm	2737.	5	Sugd.	1371.1	5
MR (Calc.)	161.630	4	PV/RT			Exp. L. 1.%/wt.		
(nD-d/2)	1.0472‡	2	177°C	1.0000	5	u.		
Dielectric			30 mm	1.0000	5	Dispersion	98.‡	2
A | 342 to	7.01788	5	BP	0.9041	5	Flash Point °C		
B | 608 °C	2689.1	5	t_e	0.8597	5	Fire Point		
C	143.	5	t_c			M Spec.		
A* | 342 to	1.89083	5	ΔHc kcal/m			Ultra V.		
B* | 592 °C	2575.6	5	ΔHf			X-Ray Dif.		
K			ΔFf			Infrared		
c			Viscosity			Solubility in +		
t_k | to			centistokes			Acetone		
t_x | °C			ɳ °C			Carbon tet.		
A' | 177 to	7.54310	5				Benzene		
B' | 342 °C	3035.7	5				Ether		
C'	163.	5	B^v | to			n-Heptane		
A'* 177 to	2.20299	5	A^v | °C			Ethanol		
B'* 342 °C	2837.6	5	(B^v) | to			Water		
Ac | to			(A^v) | °C			Water in		
Bc | t_c °C			c_p liq. °K					
Cc								
Cryos. A°			c_p vap. °K					
consts. B°								
t_e °C	582.45	5	c_v vap.					

‡ for undercooled liquid   + grams/100 grams solvent

REFERENCES: 1-Dow 2-API 3-Lit. 4-Calc. from det. data 5-Calc. by formula

SOURCE: API

PURIFICATION: API

LITERATURE REFERENCES:

NAME	n-Triacontylcyclohexane	STRUCTURAL FORMULA
	1-Cyclohexyltriacontane	

Structural formula: H_2C $CHC_{30}H_{61}$ CH_2 / H_2C CH_2 / CH_2

Mole % Pur.	Ref.	Molecular Formula $C_{36}H_{72}$	Molecular Weight 504.936	

		Ref.				Ref.					Ref.
F.P. °C	71.6	2	dt/dP				f $\vert$	to			
F.P. 100%			°C/mm				g $\vert$	°K			
B.P. °C			182°C	394.5	5		h $\vert$				
760 mm	514.	2	BP	0.09044	4		f' $\vert$	to			
100	399.	5	t_e	0.04157	5		g' $\vert$	°K			
30	348.	5	30 mm	1.2776	5		h' $\vert$				
10	309.	5	ΔHm cal/g				m $\vert$	to			
1	244.	5	ΔHv cal/g				n $\vert$	°K			
Pressure			182°C	48.79	5		o $\vert$				
mm182°C	0.04237	5	30 mm	39.64	5		m' $\vert$	to			
t_e	2063.6	5	BP	31.51	5		n' $\vert$	°K			
Density			t_e	27.89	5		o' $\vert$				
g/ml 20°C	0.8379≠	2	t_e (d, e)	27.75	5		Surface tension				
d_4^t 25	0.8346≠	2	ΔHv/T_e	16.30	5		dynes/cm. 20°C		29.98	5	
30	0.8313	4	d $\vert$ 348 to	56.69	5		γ 30		29.05	5	
a	0.8511	4	e $\vert$ 591 °C	0.0490	5		40		28.13	5	
b	-0.0₃66	4	d' $\vert$ 182 to	58.82	5		Parachor [P]				
Ref. Index			e' $\vert$ 348 °C	0.0551	5		20°C				
n_D 20°C	1.4662≠	2	d_c g/ml				30				
25	1.4643≠	2	v_c ml/g				40				
30	1.4622	4	t_c °C	617.	5		Sugd.		1410.1	5	
"C"	0.7350	4	P_c mm	2774.	5		Exp. L.1.%/wt.				
MR (Obs.)	166.97≠	2	PV/RT				u.				
MR (Calc.)	166.248	4	182°C	1.0000	5		Dispersion		98.≠	2	
(nD-d/2)	1.0473≠	2	30 mm	1.0000	5		Flash Point °C				
Dielectric			BP	0.9034	5		Fire Point				
A $\vert$ 348 to	7.01928	5	t_e	0.8586	5		M. Spec.				
B $\vert$ 617 °C	2710.7	5	t_c				Ultra V.				
C	141.	5	ΔHc kcal/m				X-Ray Dif.				
A* 348 to	1.90227	5	ΔHf				Infrared				
B* 600 °C	2597.2	5	ΔFf				Solubility in +				
K			Viscosity				Acetone				
c			centistokes				Carbon tet.				
t_k $\vert$ to			η °C				Benzene				
t_x $\vert$ °C							Ether				
A' 182 to	7.53892	5					n-Heptane				
B' 348 °C	3056.8	5	B^v $\vert$ to				Ethanol				
C'	161.	5	A^v $\vert$ °C				Water				
A'* 182 to	2.20219	5	$(B^v)\vert$ to				Water in				
B'* 348 °C	2855.5	5	$(A^v)\vert$ °C								
Ac $\vert$ to			c_p liq. °K								
Bc $\vert$ t_c °C											
Cc			c_p vap. °K								
Cryos. A°											
consts. B°			c_v vap.								
t_e °C	590.70	5									

≠ for undercooled liquid

+ grams/100 grams solvent

REFERENCES:	1-Dow	2-API	3-Lit.	4-Calc. from det. data	5-Calc. by formula
SOURCE:	API				
PURIFICATION:	API				
LITERATURE REFERENCES:					

No. 40

NAME	n-Hentriacontylcyclohexane		STRUCTURAL FORMULA
	1-Cyclohexylhentriacontane		$H_2C \overset{CH}{\underset{CH_2}{C}} \overset{C_{31}H_{63}}{\underset{CH_2}{CH_2}}$ $H_2C \underset{CH_2}{C} CH_2$
Mole % Pur.	Ref.	Molecular Formula $C_{37}H_{74}$	Molecular Weight 518.962

		Ref.			Ref.			Ref.
F.P. °C	73.3	2	dt/dP			f | to		
F.P. 100%			°C/mm			g | °K		
B.P. °C			186°C	387.2	5	h		
760 mm	520.	2	BP	0.09111	4			
100	404.	5	t_e	0.04164	5	f' | to		
30	353.	5	30 mm	1.2872	5	g' | °K		
10	314.	5	ΔHm cal/g			h' |		
1	248.	5	ΔHv cal/g			m | to		
Pressure			186°C	47.79	5	n | °K		
mm186°C	0.04363	5	30 mm	38.87	5	o |		
t_e	2078.8	5	BP	30.88	5			
Density			t_e	27.30	5	m' | to		
g/ml 20°C	0.8383‡	2	t_e (d,e)	27.16	5	n' | °K		
d_4^t 25	0.8351‡	2	ΔHv/T_e	16.26	5	o' |		
30	0.8319	4				Surface tension		
a	0.8511	4	d | 353 to	55.73	5	dynes/cm. 20°C	30.02	5
b	-0.0₃64	4	e | 598 °C	0.4779	5	γ 30	29.12	5
Ref. Index			d' | 186 to	57.72	5	40	28.23	5
n_D 20°C	1.4665‡	2	e' | 353 °C	0.0534	5			
25	1.4645‡	2	d_c g/ml			Parachor [P]		
30	1.426	4	v_c ml/g			20°C		
"C"	0.7351	4	t_c °C	622.	5	30		
MR (Obs.)	171.61‡	2	P_c mm	2722.	5	40		
MR (Calc.)	170.866	4	PV/RT			Sugd. 1449.1		5
(nD-d/2)	1.0473‡	2	186°C	1.0000	5	Exp. L.1.%/wt.		
Dielectric			30 mm	1.0000	5	u.		
A |353 to	7.02020	5	BP	0.9030	5	Dispersion	98.‡	2
B |622 °C	2732.0	5	t_e	0.8577	5	Flash Point °C		
C	140.	5	t_c			Fire Point		
A* |353 to	1.91253	5	ΔHc kcal/m			M Spec.		
B* |608 °C	2618.0	5	ΔHf			Ultra V.		
K			ΔFf			X-Ray Dif.		
c			Viscosity			Infrared		
t_k | to			centistokes			Solubility in +		
t_x | °C			η °C			Acetone		
A' |186 to	7.53433	5				Carbon tet.		
B' |353 °C	3077.5	5				Benzene		
C'	160.	5	B^v | to			Ether		
A'*186 to	2.20037	5	A^v | °C			n-Heptane		
B'*353 °C	2872.6	5	(B^v)| to			Ethanol		
Ac | to			(A^v)| °C			Water		
Bc | t_c °C						Water in		
Cc			c_p liq. °K					
Cryos. A° consts. B°			c_p vap. °K					
t_e °C	597.90	5	c_v vap.					

‡ for undercooled liquid   + grams/100 grams solvent

REFERENCES: 1-Dow 2-API 3-Lit. 4-Calc. from det. data 5-Calc. by formula

SOURCE: API

PURIFICATION: API

LITERATURE REFERENCES:

TABLE XIX. CYCLOHEXANES

No. 41

NAME	n-Dotriacontylcyclohexane	STRUCTURAL FORMULA
	1-Cyclohexyldotriacontane	$CH C_{32}H_{65}$

| Mole % Pur. | Ref. | Molecular Formula $C_{38}H_{76}$ | Molecular Weight 532.988 | H_2C CH_2 / H_2C CH_2 / CH_2 |

		Ref.			Ref.					Ref.
F.P. °C	74.8	2	dt/dP			f		to		
F.P. 100%			°C/mm			g		°K		
B.P. °C			189°C	412.2	5	h				
760 mm	527.	2	BP	0.09191	4					
100	410.	5	t_e	0.04172	5	f'		to		
30	358.	5	30 mm	1.2987	5	g'		°K		
10	319.	5				h'				
1	253.	5	ΔHm cal/g							
			ΔHv cal/g			m		to		
Pressure			189°C	47.01	5	n		°K		
mm 189°C	0.04110	5	30 mm	38.17	5	o				
t_e	2097.2	5	BP	30.30	5					
Density			t_e	26.68	5	m'		tc		
g/ml 20°C	0.8388≠	2	t_e (d, e)	26.59	5	n'		°K		
d_4^t 25	0.8355≠	2	ΔHv/T_e			o'				
30	0.8322	4		16.17	5	Surface tension				
a	0.8520	4	d 358 to	54.91	5	dynes/cm. 20°C		30.08	5
b	-0.0366	4	e 606 °C	0.0467	5	γ	30\	29.15	5
Ref. Index			d' 189 to	56.90	5		40	28.23	5
n_D 20°C	1.4668≠	2	e' 358 °C	0.0523	5	Parachor [P]				
25	1.4648≠	2	d_c g/ml				20°C		
30	1.4628	4	v_c ml/g				30		
"C"	0.7351	4	t_c °C	621.	5		40		
MR (Obs.)	176.25≠	2	P_c mm	2471.	5		Sugd.	1488.1	5
MR (Calc.)	175.484	4	PV/RT			Exp. L.1.%/wt.				
(nD-d/2)	1.0474≠	2	189°C	1.0000	5	u.				
Dielectric			30 mm	1.0000	5	Dispersion		98.≠	2
A 358 to	7.02150	5	BP	0.9027	5	Flash Point °C				
B 621 °C	2757.7	5	t_e	0.8570	5	Fire Point				
C	139.	5	t_c			M. Spec.				
A* 358 to	1.92198	5	ΔHc kcal/m			Ultra V.				
B* 616 °C	2642.9	5	ΔHf			X-Ray Dif.				
K			ΔFf			Infrared				
c			Viscosity			Solubility in +				
t_k to			centistokes			Acetone				
t_x °C			η °C			Carbon tet.				
A' 189 to	7.53416	5				Benzene				
B' 358 °C	3104.3	5				Ether				
C'	159.	5	B^v to			n-Heptane				
A'* 189 to	2.22516	5	A^v °C			Ethanol				
B'* 358 °C	2903.8	5	(B^v) to			Water				
Ac to			(A^v) °C			Water in				
Bc t_c °C			c_p liq. °K							
Cc										
Cryos. A°			c_p vap. °K							
consts. B°										
t_e °C	606.35	5	c_v vap.							

≠ for undercooled liquid

+ grams/100 grams solvent

REFERENCES:	1-Dow 2-API 3-Lit. 4-Calc. from det. data 5-Calc. by formula
SOURCE:	API
PURIFICATION:	API
LITERATURE REFERENCES:	

No. 42

NAME	n-Tritriacontylcyclohexane					STRUCTURAL FORMULA			
	1-Cyclohexyltritriacontane								

Structural formula:

$$CHC_{33}H_{67}$$
$$H_2C \quad CH_2$$
$$H_2C \quad CH_2$$
$$CH_2$$

Mole % Pur.	Ref.	Molecular Formula	$C_{39}H_{78}$	Molecular Weight 547.014	

		Ref.				Ref.				Ref.
F.P. °C	76.3	2	dt/dP				f	to		
F.P. 100%			°C/mm				g	°K		
			193°C	404.9	5		h			
B.P. °C			BP	0.09257	4					
760 mm	533.	2	t_e	0.04185	5		f'	to		
100	415.	5					g'	°K		
30	363.	5	30 mm	1.3082	5		h'			
10	323.	5	ΔHm cal/g							
1	257.	5					m	to		
			ΔHv cal/g				n	°K		
Pressure			193°C	46.12	5		o			
mm 193°C	0.04228	5	30 mm	37.48	5					
t_e	2107.9	5	BP	29.69	5		m'	to		
Density			t_e	26.11	5		n'	°K		
g/ml 20°C	0.8391#	2	t_e (d, e)	26.00	5		o'			
d_4^t 25	0.8359#	2	ΔHv/T_e	16.11	5		Surface tension			
30	0.8327	4					dynes/cm. 20°C		30.11	5
a	0.8519	4	d | 363 to	54.15	5		γ 30		29.20	5
b	-0.0364	4	e | 613 °C	0.0459	5		40		28.32	5
			d' | 193 to	55.93	5					
Ref. Index			e' | 363 °C	0.0508	5		Parachor [P]			
n_D 20°C	1.4670#	2	d_c g/ml				20°C			
25	1.4651#	2	v_c ml/g				30			
30	1.4631	4	t_c °C	626.	5		40			
"C"	0.7352	4	P_c mm	2427.	5		Sugd. 1527.1			5
MR (Obs.)	180.89#	2	PV/RT				Exp. L.1.%/wt.			
MR (Calc.)	180.102	4	193°C	1.0000	5		u.			
(nD-d/2)	1.0475#	2	30 mm	1.0000	5		Dispersion		98.#	2
Dielectric			BP	0.9009	5		Flash Point °C			
A |363 to	7.02283	5	t_e	0.8546	5		Fire Point			
B |626 °C	2779.3	5	t_c							
C	138.	5	ΔHc kcal/m				M Spec.			
			ΔHf				Ultra V.			
A* |363 to	1.93473	5	ΔFf				X-Ray Dif.			
B* |623 °C	2665.3	5					Infrared			
K			Viscosity							
c			centistokes				Solubility in +			
t_k | to			η °C				Acetone			
t_x | °C							Carbon tet.			
A' |193 to	7.53018	5					Benzene			
B' |363 °C	3125.3	5					Ether			
C'	158.	5	B^v | to				n-Heptane			
			A^v | °C				Ethanol			
A'*193 to	2.22396	5	(B^v)| to				Water			
B'*363 °C	2921.5	5	(A^v)| °C				Water in			
Ac | to										
Bc | t_c °C			c_p liq. °K							
Cc										
Cryos. A°			c_p vap. °K							
consts. B°										
t_e °C	613.37	5	c_v vap.							

\# for undercooled liquid

\+ grams/100 grams solvent

REFERENCES: 1-Dow 2-API 3-Lit. 4-Calc. from det. data 5-Calc. by formula

SOURCE:	API
PURIFICATION:	API

LITERATURE REFERENCES:

TABLE XIX. CYCLOHEXANES

No. 43

NAME	n-Tetratriacontylcyclohexane	STRUCTURAL FORMULA
	1-Cyclohexyltetratriacontane	$CHC_{34}H_{69}$ $H_2C\ CH_2$ $H_2C\ CH_2$ CH_2

Mole % Pur.	Ref.	Molecular Formula $C_{40}H_{80}$	Molecular Weight 561.040	

		Ref.				Ref.				Ref.
F.P. °C	77.7	2	dt/dP				f	to		
F.P. 100%			°C/mm				g	°K		
			198°C	397.9	5		h			
B.P. °C			BP	0.09323	4					
760 mm	540.	2	t_e	0.04189	5		f'	to		
100	421.	5	30 mm	1.3178	5		g'	°K		
30	369.	5	ΔHm cal/g				h'			
10	329.	5	ΔHv cal/g				m	to		
1	262.	5	198°C	45.46	5		n	°K		
Pressure			30 mm	36.94	5		o			
mm 198°C	0.04347	5	BP	29.21	5		m'	to		
t_e	2124.9	5	t_e	25.61	5		n'	°K		
Density			t_e (d, e)	25.52	5		o'			
g/ml 20°C	0.8395#	2	ΔHv/T_e	16.06	5		Surface tension			
d_4^t 25	0.8363#	2	d 369 to	53.62	5		dynes/cm. 20°C	30.16	5
30	0.8331	4	e 622 °C	0.0452	5		δ 30	29.25	5
a	0.8523	4	d' 198 to	55.32	5		40	28.36	5
b	-0.0364	4	e' 369 °C	0.0498	5		Parachor [P]		
Ref. Index			d_c g/ml				20°C		
n_D 20°C	1.4673#	2	v_c ml/g				30		
25	1.4653#	2	t_c °C	628.	5		40		
30	1.4634	4	P_c mm	2281.	5		Sugd.	1566.1	5
"C"	0.7354	4	PV/RT				Exp. L.1.%/wt.		
MR (Obs.)	185.53#	2	-198°C	1.0000	5		u.		
MR (Calc.)	184.720	4	30 mm	1.0000	5		Dispersion	98.#	2
(nD-d/2)	1.0475#	2	BP	0.9002	5		Flash Point °C		
Dielectric			t_e	0.8535	5		Fire Point		
A 369 to	7.02415	5	t_c				M. Spec.		
B 628 °C	2800.9	5	ΔHc kcal/m				Ultra V.		
C	136.	5	ΔHf				X-Ray Dif.		
A* 369 to	1.94482	5	ΔFf				Infrared		
B* 632 °C	2686.9	5	Viscosity				Solubility in +		
K			centistokes				Acetone		
c			η °C				Carbon tet.		
t_k to							Benzene		
t_x °C							Ether		
A' 198 to	7.52630	5					n-Heptane		
B' 369 °C	3146.4	5					Ethanol		
C'	156.	5	B^v to				Water		
A'* 198 to	2.22222	5	A^v °C				Water in		
B'* 369 °C	2939.3	5	(B^v) to						
Ac to			(A^v) °C						
Bc t_c °C									
Cc			c_p liq. °K						
Cryos. A°			c_p vap. °K						
consts. B°									
t_e °C	621.65	5	c_v vap.						

for undercooled liquid   + grams/100 grams solvent

REFERENCES: 1-Dow   2-API   3-Lit.   4-Calc. from det. data   5-Calc. by formula

SOURCE: API

PURIFICATION: API

LITERATURE REFERENCES:

No. 44

NAME	n-Pentatriacontylcyclohexane	STRUCTURAL FORMULA
	1-Cyclohexylpentatriacontane	

$H_2C\begin{smallmatrix}CHC_{35}H_{71}\\CH_2\end{smallmatrix}$
$H_2C\begin{smallmatrix}CH_2\\CH_2\end{smallmatrix}$

Mole % Pur.	Ref.	Molecular Formula $C_{41}H_{82}$	Molecular Weight 575.066

		Ref.			Ref.			Ref.
F.P. °C	79.1	2	dt/dP			f | to		
F.P. 100%			°C/mm			g | °K		
			202°C	391.1	5	h |		
B.P. °C			BP	0.09389	4			
760 mm	546.	2	t_e	0.04189	5	f' | to		
100	427.	5	30 mm	1.3273	5	g' | °K		
30	374.	5	ΔHm cal/g			h' |		
10	333.	5						
1	266.	5	ΔHv cal/g			m | to		
			202°C	44.65	5	n | °K		
Pressure			30 mm	36.32	5	o |		
mm 202°C	0.04468	5	BP	28.72	5			
t_e	2144.2	5	t_e	25.09	5	m' | to		
Density			t_e (d, e)	25.06	5	n' | °K		
g/ml 20°C	0.8399≠	2	ΔHv/T_e	15.99	5	o' |		
d_4^t 25	0.8366≠	2				Surface tension		
30	0.8333	4	d | 374 to	52.80	5	dynes/cm. 20°C	30.20	5
			e | 629 °C	0.0441	5	ɣ 30	29.26	5
a	0.8531	4	d' | 202 to	54.43	5	40	28.35	5
b	-0.0₃66	4	e' | 374 °C	0.0484	5			
Ref. Index			d_c g/ml			Parachor [P]		
n_D 20°C	1.4675≠	2	v_c ml/g			20°C		
25	1.4656≠	2	t_c °C	627.	5	30		
30	1.4637	4	P_c mm	2096.	5	40		
"C"	0.7353	4	PV/RT			Sugd.	1605.1	5
MR (Obs.)	190.17≠	2	202°C	1.0000	5	Exp. L.1.%/wt.		
MR (Calc.)	189.338	4	30 mm	1.0000	5	u.		
(nD-d/2)	1.0476≠	2	BP	0.9011	5	Dispersion	98.≠	2
Dielectric			t_e	0.8542	5	Flash Point °C		
A | 374 to	7.02545	5	t_c			Fire Point		
B | 627 °C	2822.5	5	ΔHc kcal/m			M Spec.		
C	135.	5	ΔHf			Ultra V.		
A* | 374 to	1.95188	5	ΔFf			X-Ray Dif.		
B* | 639 °C	2706.8	5				Infrared		
K			Viscosity			Solubility in +		
c			centistokes			Acetone		
t_k | to			η °C			Carbon tet.		
t_x | °C						Benzene		
A' | 202 to	7.52250	5				Ether		
B' | 374 °C	3167.5	5	B^v | to			n-Heptane		
C'	155.	5	A^v | °C			Ethanol		
A'* | 202 to	2.22064	5	(B^v) | to			Water		
B'* | 374 °C	2956.9	5	(A^v) | °C			Water in		
Ac | to								
Bc | t_c °C			c_p liq. °K					
Cc			c_p vap. °K					
Cryos. A°								
consts. B°			c_v vap.					
t_e °C	629.04	5						

≠ for undercooled liquid   + grams/100 grams solvent

REFERENCES: 1-Dow 2-API 3-Lit. 4-Calc. from det. data 5-Calc. by formula

SOURCE: API

PURIFICATION: API

LITERATURE REFERENCES:

TABLE XIX. CYCLOHEXANES

No. 45

NAME	n-Hexatriacontylcyclohexane	STRUCTURAL FORMULA
	1-Cyclohexylhexatriacontane	$CH_{C_{36}H_{73}}$ H_2C CH_2 H_2C CH_2 CH_2

Mole % Pur.	Ref.	Molecular Formula $C_{42}H_{84}$	Molecular Weight 589.092

		Ref.			Ref.			Ref.
F.P. °C	80.4	2	dt/dP			f | to		
F.P. 100%			°C/mm			g | °K		
B.P. °C			205°C	393.8	5	h |		
760 mm	551.	2	BP	0.09442	4			
100	431.	5	t_e	0.04198	5	f' | to		
30	378.	5	30 mm	1.3350	5	g' | °K		
10	337.	5	ΔHm cal/g			h' |		
1	269.	5						
			ΔHv cal/g			m | to		
Pressure			205°C	43.89	5	n | °K		
mm 205°C	0.04463	5	30 mm	35.69	5	o |		
t_e	2154.0	5	BP	28.18	5			
Density			t_e	24.59	5	m' | to		
g/ml 20°C	0.8402≠	2	t_e (d, e)	24.54	5	n' | °K		
d_4^t 25	0.8370≠	2	ΔHv/T_e	15.95	5	o' |		
30	0.8338	4				Surface tension		
a	0.8530	4	d | 378 to	52.06	5	dynes/cm. 20°C	30.24	5
b	-0.0₃64	4	e | 635 °C	0.0433	5	ɣ 30	29.32	5
Ref. Index			d' | 205 to	53.61	5	40	28.43	5
n_D 20°C	1.4678≠	2	e' | 378 °C	0.0474	5			
25	1.4658≠	2	d_c g/ml			Parachor [P]		
30	1.4644	4	v_c ml/g			20°C		
"C"	0.7356	4	t_c °C	631.	5	30		
MR (Obs.)	194.81≠	2	P_c mm	2062.	5	40		
MR (Calc.)	193.956	4				Sugd.	1644.1	5
(nD-d/2)	1.0476≠	2	PV/RT			Exp. L.1.%/wt.		
Dielectric			205°C	1.0000	5	u.		
			30 mm	1.0000	5	Dispersion	98.≠	2
A |378 to	7.02635	5	BP	0.8999	5	Flash Point °C		
B |631 °C	2839.7	5	t_e	0.8525	5	Fire Point		
C	134.	5	t_c			M. Spec.		
A*|378 to	1.96288	5	ΔHc kcal/m			Ultra V.		
B*|645 °C	2724.5	5	ΔHf			X-Ray Dif.		
K			ΔFf			Infrared		
c			Viscosity			Solubility in +		
t_k | to			centistokes			Acetone		
t_x | °C			η °C			Carbon tet.		
A' |205 to	7.52055	5				Benzene		
B' |378 °C	3184.7	5				Ether		
C'	154.	5	B^v | to			n-Heptane		
A'*205 to	2.22836	5	A^v | °C			Ethanol		
B'*378 °C	2973.6	5	(B^v)| to			Water		
Ac| to			(A^v)| °C			Water in		
Bc| t_c °C			c_p liq. °K					
Cc								
Cryos. A°			c_p vap. °K					
consts. B°								
t_e °C	634.92	5	c_v vap.					

≠ for undercooled liquid + grams/100 grams solvent

REFERENCES: 1-Dow 2-API 3-Lit. 4-Calc. from det. data 5-Calc. by formula

SOURCE:	API
PURIFICATION:	API

LITERATURE REFERENCES:

NAME	γ-Hexachlorocyclohexane				STRUCTURAL FORMULA

γ-Hexane

STRUCTURAL FORMULA

$$\begin{array}{c} CHCl \\ ClHC \quad CHCl \\ ClHC \quad CHCl \\ CHCl \end{array}$$

Mole % Pur. 99.84	Ref. 1	Molecular Formula $C_6H_6Cl_6$	Molecular Weight 290.850

		Ref.				Ref.			Ref.
F.P. °C	112.50	1	dt/dP				f | to		
F.P. 100%			°C/mm				g | °K		
B.P. °C			113°C	42.855	5		h |		
760 mm	323.4	4	BP	0.06551	4				
100	240.5	4	t_e	0.03746	5		f' | to		
30	204.0	4	30 mm	0.9143	4		g' | °K		
10	176.2	5	ΔHm cal/g	66.60	4		h' |		
1	130.	5	ΔHv cal/g				m | to		
Pressure			113°C	66.0	5		n | °K		
mm 113°C	0.3601	5	30 mm	56.71	5		o |		
t_e	1561.0	5	BP	44.75	5				
Density			t_e	41.65	5		m' | to		
g/ml 20°C			t_e (d, e)	40.85	5		n' | °K		
d_4^t 25			ΔHv/T_e	19.06	5		o' |		
30			d | 205 to	77.14	5		Surface tension		
a			e | 350 °C	0.1002	5		dynes/cm. 20°C		
b			d' | 113 to	77.54	5		γ 30		
Ref. Index			e' | 205 °C	0.1021	5		40		
n_D 20°C			d_c g/ml				Parachor [P]		
25			v_c ml/g				20°C		
30			t_c °C				30		
"C"			P_c mm				40		
MR (Obs.)			PV/RT				Sugd.	463.3	5
MR (Calc.)	56.908	5	113°C	1.0000	5		Exp. L.1.%/wt.		
(nD-d/2)			30 mm	1.0000	5		u.		
Dielectric			BP	0.9100	5		Dispersion		
A | 205 to	6.92309	4	t_e	0.8829	5		Flash Point °C		
B | 450 °C	1873.3	4	t_c				Fire Point		
C	140.	5	ΔHc kcal/m				M Spec.		
A* | 205 to	1.69095	5	ΔHf				Ultra V.		
B* | 380 °C	1797.0	5	ΔFf				X-Ray Dif.		
K			Viscosity				Infrared		
c			centistokes				Solubility in +		
t_k | to			η °C				Acetone		
t_x | °C							Carbon tet.		
A' | 113 to	7.23920	5					Benzene		
B' | 205 °C	2097.4	5					Ether		
C'	160.	5	B^v | to				n-Heptane		
A'* 113 to	1.54557	5	A^v | °C				Ethanol		
B'* 205 °C	1997.0	5	(B^v) | to				Water		
Ac | to			(A^v) | °C				Water in		
Bc | t_c °C			c_p liq. °K						
Cc									
Cryos. A°			c_p vap. °K						
consts. B°									
t_e °C	362.26	5	c_v vap.						

+ grams/100 grams solvent

REFERENCES: 1-Dow   2-API   3-Lit.   4-Calc. from det. data   5-Calc. by formula

SOURCE: Dow

PURIFICATION: Distillation, crystallization

LITERATURE REFERENCES:

TABLE XIX. CYCLOHEXANES

NAME	Bromocyclohexane	STRUCTURAL FORMULA

Structural formula:
$$\begin{array}{c} \text{CHBr} \\ \text{H}_2\text{C} \quad \text{CH}_2 \\ \text{H}_2\text{C} \quad \text{CH}_2 \\ \text{CH}_2 \end{array}$$

Mole % Pur. 99.86	Ref. 1	Molecular Formula $C_6H_{11}Br$	Molecular Weight 163.064

		Ref.			Ref.				Ref.
F.P. °C	-56.51	1	dt/dP			f | to			
F.P. 100%			°C/mm			g | °K			
B.P. °C			25°C	5.2211	5	h |			
760 mm	166.17	1	BP	0.05347	4				
100	98.33	4	t_e	0.03743	5	f' | to			
30	68.33	4	30 mm	0.7516	4	g' | °K			
10	45.51	5	ΔHm cal/g	12.75	4	h' |			
1	7.3	5	ΔHv cal/g			m | to			
Pressure			25°C	65.66	5	n | °K			
mm 25°C	3.161	5	30 mm	63.03	5	o |			
t_e	1198.0	5	BP	55.11	5				
Density			t_e	53.67	5	m' | to			
g/ml 20°C	1.33585	1	t_e (d,e)	53.54	5	n' | °K			
d_4^t 25	1.32976	1	$\Delta Hv/T_e$	19.07	5	o' |			
30	1.32253	4	d | 68 to	68.56	5	Surface tension			
a	1.35939	4	e | 190 °C	0.0809	5	dynes/cm. 20°C	34.02	1
b	-0.00123	4	d' | 15 to	67.18	5	ɤ 30	32.88	1
Ref. Index			e' | 68 °C	0.0607	5	40	31.81	1
n_D 20°C	1.49570	1	d_c g/ml			Parachor [P]			
25	1.49333	1	v_c ml/g			20°C	294.8	4
30	1.48165	1	t_c °C			30	295.25	4
"C"	0.4885	4	P_c mm			40	295.6	4
MR (Obs.)	35.646	4	PV/RT			Sugd.	291.0	5
MR (Calc.)	35.473	5	25°C	1.0000	5	Exp. L.1.%/wt.			
(nD-d/2)	0.82278	4	30 mm	1.0000	5	u.			
Dielectric	7.845	1	BP	0.9520	5	Dispersion			
A | 68 to	6.97980	4	t_e	0.9385	5	Flash Point °C			
B |260 °C	1572.19	4	t_c			Fire Point			
C	217.38	4	ΔHc kcal/m			M. Spec.			
A* | 68 to	1.51871	5	ΔHf			Ultra V.			
B* |205 °C	1473.57	5	ΔFf			X-Ray Dif.			
K			Viscosity			Infrared			
c			centistokes			Solubility in +			
t_k | to			η 20 °C	1.7008	1	Acetone	∞	
t_x | °C			40	1.2272	1	Carbon tet.	∞	
A' | 0 to	7.34139	5	60	0.9337	1	Benzene	∞	
B' | 68 °C	1778.81	5	80	0.7404	1	Ether		
C'	235.	5	B^v | 30 to	606.87	4	n-Heptane		
A'* | 0 to	1.87190	5	A^v | 90 °C	2.15127	4	Ethanol	∞	
B'* 68 °C	1671.58	5	(B^v)| to			Water		
Ac | to			(A^v)| °C			Water in	0.036	1
Bc | t_c °C			c_p liq. °K					
Cc |								
Cryos. A°	0.02092	1	c_p vap. °K					
consts. B°								
t_e °C	185.58	5	c_v vap.					

+ grams/100 grams solvent

REFERENCES: 1-Dow 2-API 3-Lit. 4-Calc. from det. data 5-Calc. by formula
SOURCE: Dow
PURIFICATION: Distillation
LITERATURE REFERENCES:

No. 48

NAME	(2-Bromoethyl)cyclohexane		STRUCTURAL FORMULA
	β-Bromoethylcyclohexane		

Structural formula:
$$H_2C-\overset{CH_2}{\underset{CH_2}{C}}CHCH_2CH_2Br$$
$$H_2C \quad CH_2$$
$$\overset{}{\underset{H_2}{C}}$$

Mole % Pur. 99.99	Ref. 1	Molecular Formula $C_8H_{15}Br$	Molecular Weight 191.116

		Ref.			Ref.				Ref.
F.P. °C	-57.28	1	dt/dP °C/mm			f	to		
F.P. 100%			25°C	37.459	5	g	°K		
B.P. °C			BP	0.05767	4	h			
760 mm	212.13	1	t_e	0.03736	5	f'	to		
100	138.83	4	30 mm	0.8150	4	g'	°K		
30	106.33	4	ΔHm cal/g			h'			
10	81.313	5	ΔHv cal/g			m	to		
1	39.60	5	25°C	66.51	5	n	°K		
Pressure			30 mm	61.26	5	o			
mm 25°C	0.3711	5	BP	52.95	5				
t_e	1322.0	5	t_e	51.12	5	m'	to		
Density			t_e (d, e)	50.93	5	n'	°K		
g/ml 20°C	1.23574	1	ΔHv/T_e	19.12	5	o'			
d_4^t 25	1.23049	1	d 105 to	69.61	5	Surface tension			
30	1.22724	4	e 240 °C	0.0785	5	dynes/cm. 20°C	33.96	1
a	1.25274	4	d' 10 to	68.12	5	γ 30	32.90	1
b	-0.0₃85	4	e' 105 °C	0.0645	5	40	31.88	1
Ref. Index			d_c g/ml			Parachor [P]			
n_D 20°C	1.48986	1	v_c ml/g			20°C	373.3	4
25	1.48777	1	t_c °C	437.0	5	30	373.0	4
30	1.47697	1	P_c mm			40	372.6	4
"C"	0.5223	4				Sugd.	369.0	4
MR (Obs.)	44.703	4	PV/RT			Exp. L.1.%/wt.		
MR (Calc.)	44.709	5	25°C	1.0000	5	u.		
(nD-d/2)	0.87200	4	30 mm	1.0000	5	Dispersion		
Dielectric			BP	0.9475	5	Flash Point °C		
A 105 to	7.02343	4	t_e	0.9297	5	Fire Point		
B 300 °C	1731.83	4	t_c					
C	205.92	4	ΔHc kcal/m			M Spec.		
A* 105 to	1.60197	5	ΔHf			Ultra V.		
B* 260 °C	1629.23	5	ΔFf			X-Ray Dif.		
K						Infrared		
c			Viscosity			Solubility in +		
t_k to			centistokes			Acetone		
t_x °C			η 20 °C	2.2721	1	Carbon tet.		
A' 10 to	7.22369	5	40	1.5878	1	Benzene		
B' 105 °C	1875.28	5	60	1.1852	1	Ether		
C'	220.	5	80	0.9292	1	n-Heptane		
A'* 10 to	1.81532	5	B^v 30 to	643.52	4	Ethanol		
B'* 105 °C	1772.32	5	A^v 90 °C	2.14614	4	Water		
Ac to			(B^v) to			Water in		
Bc t_c °C			(A^v) °C					
Cc			c_p liq. °K					
Cryos. A°	0.01412	1	c_p vap. °K					
consts. B°								
t_e °C	237.88	5	c_v vap.					

+ grams/100 grams solvent

REFERENCES: 1-Dow 2-API 3-Lit. 4-Calc. from det. data 5-Calc. by formula

SOURCE: Dow

PURIFICATION: Distillation

LITERATURE REFERENCES:

TABLE XX. CYCLOHEXENES

No. 1

NAME	Cyclohexene		STRUCTURAL FORMULA

H_2C $\overset{CH}{\underset{CH}{}}$
H_2C $\underset{CH_2}{CH_2}$

Mole % Pur.	Ref.	Molecular Formula C_6H_{10}	Molecular Weight 82.140	

		Ref.			Ref.					Ref.
F.P. °C	-103.512	2	dt/dP			f		to		
F.P. 100%			°C/mm			g		°K		
B.P. °C			25°C	0.2466	5	h				
760 mm	82.979	2	BP	0.04381	2					
100	27.62	4	t_e	0.03620	5	f'		to		
30	3.29	4	30 mm	0.6086	5	g'		°K		
10	-15.14	5	ΔHm cal/g	9.582	3'	h'				
1	-45.49	5	ΔHv cal/g			m	300 to	-0.1232	4
			25°C	96.83	5	n	600 °K	0.0017	4
Pressure			30 mm	101.30	5	o		-0.0₆74	4
mm 25°C	88.83	5	BP	88.47	5				
t_e	970.61	5	t_e	87.13	5	m'	700 to	0.0336	4
Density			t_e (d, e)	87.12	5	n'	1000 °K	0.0012	4
g/ml 20°C	0.81096	2	ΔHv/T_e	19.63	5	o'		-0.0₆44	4
d_4^t 25	0.80609	2	d 3 to	101.83	5	Surface tension			
30	0.80141	2	e 91 °C	0.1610	5	dynes/cm. 20°C	26.54	3'
a	0.8304	4	d' to			ð 30	25.22	3'
b	-0.0₃96	4	e' °C			40	23.98	3'
Ref. Index						Parachor [P]		
n_D 20°C	1.44654	2	d_c g/ml	0.288	5	20°C	229.9	4
25	1.44377	2	v_c ml/g	3.473	5	30	229.7	4
30	1.44100	2	t_c °C	286.	5	40	229.5	4
"C"	0.7295	4	P_c mm	31784.	5	Sugd.	229.1	5
MR (Obs.)	27.038	2	PV/RT			Exp. L.1.%/wt.		
MR (Calc.)	27.241	5	25°C	0.9866	5	u.		
(nD-d/2)	1.04106	2	30 mm	1.0000	5	Dispersion	117.1	2
Dielectric	2.220	3	BP	0.9635	5	Flash Point °C		
A 3 to	6.88617	2	t_e	0.9570	5	Fire Point		
B 146 °C	1229.973	2	t_c	0.260	5	M. Spec.	Yes	1
C	224.104	2	ΔHc kcal/m			Ultra V.		
A* 3 to	1.20240	5	ΔHf			X-Ray Dif.		
B* 101 °C	1147.7	5	ΔFf			Infrared	293.	1
K			Viscosity			Solubility in +		
c			centistokes			Acetone	∞	
t_k to			η °C			Carbon tet.	∞	
t_x °C						Benzene	∞	
A' to						Ether	∞	
B' °C						n-Heptane	∞	
C'			B^v to			Ethanol	∞	
A'* to			A^v °C			Water		
B'* °C			(B^v) to			Water in		
Ac 146 to	7.31379	5	(A^v) °C					
Bc t_c °C	1566.7	5	c_p liq. °K					
Cc	272.	5						
Cryos. A°			c_p vap 300°K	0.30777	2			
consts. B°			400	0.42172	2			
t_e °C	91.34	5	c_v vap.					

$T_R = 0.75\ T_c$ + grams/100 grams solvent

REFERENCES: 1-Dow 2-API 3-Lit. 4-Calc. from det. data 5-Calc. by formula

SOURCE: API

PURIFICATION: API

LITERATURE REFERENCES: 3 NBS 514; 3' Timmermans

No. 2

NAME	1-Methylcyclohexene	STRUCTURAL FORMULA

Structural formula:

$$H_2C\overset{CH_3}{\underset{H_2C\underset{CH_2}{\big|}}{\overset{\overset{C}{\big|}}{\big|}}}\overset{CH}{\underset{CH_2}{\big|}}$$

Mole % Pur.	Ref.	Molecular Formula C_7H_{12}	Molecular Weight 96.166

		Ref.			Ref.				Ref.
F.P. °C	-121.	2	dt/dP			f	to		
F.P. 100%			°C/mm			g	°K		
B.P. °C			25°C	0.6405	5	h			
760 mm	110.0	2	BP	0.0470	2				
100	50.66	4	t_e	0.03665	5	f'	to		
30	24.6	4	30 mm	0.6514	5	g'	°K		
10	4.88	5	ΔHm cal/g			h'			
1	-27.57	3							
			ΔHv cal/g			m	to		
Pressure			25°C	93.83	5	n	°K		
mm 25°C	30.61	5	30 mm	93.78	5	o			
t_e	1046.2	5	BP	81.27	5				
Density			t_e	79.57	5	m'	to		
g/ml 20°C	0.8102	2	t_e (d, e)	79.54	5	n'	°K		
d_4^t 25	0.8058	2	ΔHv/T_e	19.37	5	o'			
30	0.8014	4				Surface tension			
a	0.8278	4	d | 25 to	97.38	5	dynes/cm. 20°C	26.01	5
b	-0.0₃87	4	e | 130 °C	0.1465	5	γ	30	24.89	5
			d' | to				40	23.80	5
Ref. Index			e' | °C						
n_D 20°C	1.4503	2	d_c g/ml	0.272	5	Parachor [P]			
25	1.4478	2	v_c ml/g	3.679	5	20°C			
30	1.4459	4	t_c °C	311.	5	30			
"C"	0.7360	4	P_c mm	26771.	5	40			
MR (Obs.)	31.91	2	PV/RT			Sugd.	268.1	5
MR (Calc.)	31.859	5	25°C	1.0000	5	Exp. L.1.%/wt.			
(nD-d/2)	1.0452	2	30 mm	1.0000	5	u.			
Dielectric			BP	0.9600	5	Dispersion	120.	2
A | 25 to	6.86861	5	t_e	0.9519	5	Flash Point °C			
B | 165 °C	1308.0	5	t_c	0.260	5	Fire Point			
C	218.	5	ΔHc kcal/m			M Spec.			
A* | 25 to	1.22876	5	ΔHf			Ultra V.			
B* | 131 °C	1222.1	5	ΔFf			X-Ray Dif.			
K			Viscosity			Infrared			
c			centistokes			Solubility in +			
t_k | to			η °C			Acetone			
t_x | °C						Carbon tet.			
A' | to						Benzene			
B' | °C						Ether			
C'			B^v | to			n-Heptane			
A'* | to			A^v | °C			Ethanol			
B'* °C			(B^v) | to			Water			
Ac | 165 to	7.28846	5	(A^v) | °C			Water in			
Bc | t_c °C	1649.7	5	c_p liq. °K						
Cc	265.	5							
Cryos. A°			c_p vap. °K						
consts. B°									
t_e °C	121.83	5	c_v vap.						

T_R = 0.75 T_c + grams/100 grams solvent

REFERENCES: 1-Dow 2-API 3-Lit. 4-Calc. from det. data 5-Calc. by formula

SOURCE: API

PURIFICATION: API

LITERATURE REFERENCES:

TABLE XX. CYCLOHEXENES

No. 3

NAME	3-Methylcyclohexene	STRUCTURAL FORMULA

STRUCTURAL FORMULA

$$H_2C \overset{\overset{CH}{|}}{\underset{\underset{CH_2}{|}}{C}} \overset{CH}{\underset{CHCH_3}{C}}$$

Mole % Pur.	Ref.	Molecular Formula	C_7H_{12}	Molecular Weight	96.166

		Ref.			Ref.			Ref.
F.P. °C			dt/dP °C/mm			f | to		
F.P. 100%			25°C	0.5160	5	g | °K		
B.P. °C			BP	0.04630	2	h |		
760 mm	104.0	2	t_e	0.03655	5	f' | to		
100	45.55	4	30 mm	0.6416	5	g' | °K		
30	19.88	4	ΔHm cal/g			h' |		
10	0.46	5	ΔHv cal/g			m | to		
1	-31.50	5	25°C	91.50	5	n | °K		
Pressure			30 mm	92.22	5	o |		
mm 25°C	38.92	5	BP	80.01	5	m' | to		
t_e	1029.9	5	t_e	78.43	5	n' | °K		
Density			t_e (d, e)	78.40	5	o' |		
g/ml 20°C	0.8010	2	ΔHv/T_e	19.43	5	Surface tension		
d_4^t 25	0.7966	2	d | 20 to	95.11	5	dynes/cm. 20°C	24.85	5
30	0.7922	4	e | 115 °C	0.1451	5	ɤ 30	23.76	5
a	0.8186	4	d' | to			40	22.70	5
b	-0.0387	4	e' | °C			Parachor [P]		
Ref. Index			d_c g/ml	0.272	5	20°C		
n_D 20°C	1.4444	2	v_c ml/g	3.682	5	30		
25	1.4419	2	t_c °C	301.	5	40		
30	1.4392	4	P_c mm	26290.	5	Sugd.	268.1	5
"C"	0.7353	4	PV/RT			Exp. L.1.%/wt.		
MR (Obs.)	31.92	2	25°C	1.0003	5	u.		
MR (Calc.)	31.859	5	30 mm	1.0000	5	Dispersion		
(nD-d/2)	1.0439	2	BP	0.9619	5	Flash Point °C		
Dielectric			t_e	0.9534	5	Fire Point		
A | 20 to	6.86718	5	t_c	0.260	5	M. Spec.		
B |158 °C	1287.6	5	ΔHc kcal/m			Ultra V.		
C	219.	5	ΔHf			X-Ray Dif.		
A* | 20 to	1.23234	5	ΔFf			Infrared		
B* |125 °C	1202.6	5	Viscosity			Solubility in +		
K			centistokes			Acetone		
c			η °C			Carbon tet.		
t_k | to						Benzene		
t_x | °C						Ether		
A' | to						n-Heptane		
B' | °C			B^v | to			Ethanol		
C'			A^v | °C			Water		
A'* | to			{B^v} | to			Water in		
B'* °C			{A^v} °C					
Ac |158 to	7.28693	5	c_p liq. °K					
Bc | t_c °C	1622.9	5						
Cc	265.	5	c_p vap. °K					
Cryos. A°								
consts. B°								
t_e °C	115.06	5	c_v vap.					

$T_R = 0.75\ T_c$ + grams/100 grams solvent

REFERENCES: 1-Dow   2-API   3-Lit.   4-Calc. from det. data   5-Calc. by formula

SOURCE: API

PURIFICATION: API

LITERATURE REFERENCES:

No. 4

NAME	4-Methylcyclohexene	STRUCTURAL FORMULA

Structural formula:

$$H_2C \overset{CH}{\underset{CH_2}{\overset{\displaystyle CH}{\underset{\displaystyle CHCH_3}{}}}} $$

Mole % Pur.	Ref.	Molecular Formula	C_7H_{12}	Molecular Weight	96.166

		Ref.				Ref.					Ref.
F.P. °C	-115.5	2	dt/dP °C/mm				f		to		
F.P. 100%			25°C		0.4944	5	g	°K			
B.P. °C			BP		0.0461	2	h				
760 mm	102.74	2	t_e		0.03649	5	f'		to		
100	44.53	4	30 mm		0.6390	5	g'	°K			
30	18.98	4	ΔHm cal/g				h'				
10	-0.37	5	ΔHv cal/g				m		to		
1	-32.20	5	25°C		91.15	5	n	°K			
Pressure			30 mm		92.03	5	o				
mm 25°C	40.76	5	BP		79.83	5	m'		to		
t_e	1026.4	5	t_e		78.27	5	n'	°K			
Density			t_e (d, e)		78.25	5	o'				
g/ml 20°C	0.7991	2	$ΔHv/T_e$		19.46	5	Surface tension				
d_4^t 25	0.7947	2	d 19 to		94.79	5	dynes/cm. 20°C		24.61	5	
30	0.7902	4	e 114 °C		0.1456	5	γ 30		23.53	5	
a	0.8168	4	d' to				40		22.47	5	
b	-0.0388	4	e' °C				Parachor [P]				
Ref. Index			d_c g/ml		0.272	5	20°C				
n_D 20°C	1.4414	2	v_c ml/g		3.675	5	30				
25	1.4389	2	t_c °C		299.	5	40				
30	1.4362	4	P_c mm		26254.	5	Sugd.		268.1	5	
"C"	0.7324	4	PV/RT				Exp. L.1.%/wt.				
MR (Obs.)	31.80	2	25°C		1.0000	5	u.				
MR (Calc.)	31.859	5	30 mm		1.0000	5	Dispersion				
(nD-d/2)	1.0418	2	BP		0.9620	5	Flash Point °C				
Dielectric			t_e		0.9537	5	Fire Point				
A 19 to	6.86881	5	t_c		0.260	5	M Spec.				
B 156 °C	1283.1	5	ΔHc kcal/m				Ultra V.				
C	219.	5	ΔHf				X-Ray Dif.				
A* 19 to	1.23537	5	ΔFf				Infrared				
B* 124 °C	1198.4	5	Viscosity				Solubility in +				
K			centistokes				Acetone				
c			η °C				Carbon tet.				
t_k to							Benzene				
t_x °C							Ether				
A' to							n-Heptane				
B' °C			B^v to				Ethanol				
C'			A^v °C				Water				
A'* to			(B^v) to				Water in				
B'* °C			(A^v) °C								
Ac 156 to	7.28813	5	c_p liq. °K								
Bc t_c °C	1616.5	5									
Cc	265.	5	c_p vap. °K								
Cryos. A°											
consts. B°			c_v vap.								
t_e °C	113.62	5									

$T_R = 0.75 T_c$ + grams/100 grams solvent

REFERENCES: 1-Dow   2-API   3-Lit.   4-Calc. from det. data   5-Calc. by formula

SOURCE: API

PURIFICATION: API

LITERATURE REFERENCES:

TABLE XX. CYCLOHEXENES

NAME	1-Ethylcyclohexene	STRUCTURAL FORMULA

Mole % Pur. | Ref. | Molecular Formula C_8H_{14} | Molecular Weight 110.192

Structural formula:
$$H_2C\overset{C\cdot C_2H_5}{\underset{CH_2}{\overset{\text{}}{\big|}}}CH$$
$$H_2C\underset{CH_2}{\big|}CH_2$$

		Ref.			Ref.				Ref.
F.P. °C			dt/dP			f	to		
F.P. 100%			°C/mm			g	°K		
			25°C	1.7022	5	h			
B.P. °C			BP	0.04993	4				
760 mm	136.	2	t_e	0.03702	5	f'	to		
100	72.94	4	30 mm	0.6926	5	g'	°K		
30	45.25	4				h'			
10	24.16	5	ΔHm cal/g						
1	-11.03	5				m	to		
			ΔHv cal/g			n	°K		
Pressure			25°C	89.87	5	o			
mm 25°C	10.48	5	30 mm	88.02	5				
t_e	1116.5	5	BP	75.79	5	m'	to		
Density			t_e	73.81	5	n'	°K		
g/ml 20°C	0.823	2	t_e (d, e)	73.74	5	o'			
d_4^t 25	0.819	2	$\Delta Hv/T_e$	19.16	5				
30	0.815	4				Surface tension			
a	0.8390	4	d 45 to	94.11	5	dynes/cm. 20°C	27.67	5
b	-0.0380	4	e 151 °C	0.1347	5	γ 30	26.61	5
			d' 25 to	92.15	5	40	25.57	5
Ref. Index			e' 45 °C	0.0913	5				
n_D 20°C	1.4575	2				Parachor [P]			
25	1.4552	2	d_c g/ml	0.268	5	20°C			
30	1.4528	4	v_c ml/g	3.738	5	30			
"C"	0.7355	4	t_c °C	339.	5	40			
			P_c mm	23910.	5	Sugd.	307.1	5
MR (Obs.)	36.5	2							
MR (Calc.)	36.477	5	PV/RT			Exp. L.1.%/wt.			
(nD-d/2)	1.046	2	25°C	1.0000	5	u.			
Dielectric			30 mm	1.0000	5	Dispersion	117.	2
			BP	0.9569	5	Flash Point °C			
A 45 to	6.87507	4	t_e	0.9455	5	Fire Point			
B 186 °C	1394.0	4	t_c	0.258	5				
C	213.	5				M. Spec.			
			ΔHc kcal/m			Ultra V.			
A* 45 to	1.27409	5	ΔHf			X-Ray Dif.			
B* 161 °C	1304.9	5	ΔFf			Infrared			
K			Viscosity			Solubility in +			
c			centistokes			Acetone			
t_k to			η °C			Carbon tet.			
t_x °C						Benzene			
A' 25 to	7.25131	5				Ether			
B' 45 °C	1595.1	5				n-Heptane			
C'	231.	5	B^v to			Ethanol			
			A^v °C			Water			
A'* 25 to	1.63487	5	(B^v) to			Water in			
B'* 45 °C	1495.5	5	(A^v) °C						
Ac 186 to	7.29002	5							
Bc t_c °C	1744.7	5	c_p liq. °K						
Cc	260.	5							
Cryos. A°			c_p vap. °K						
consts. B°									
t_e °C	151.24	5	c_v vap.						

$T_R = 0.75\ T_c$ +grams/100 grams solvent

REFERENCES: 1-Dow 2-API 3-Lit. 4-Calc. from det. data 5-Calc. by formula

SOURCE: API

PURIFICATION: API

LITERATURE REFERENCES:

No. 6

NAME	3-Ethylcyclohexene		STRUCTURAL FORMULA

H_2C $\overset{CH}{\underset{}{}}$ CH
H_2C CH C_2H_5
CH_2

Mole % Pur.	Ref.	Molecular Formula C_8H_{14}	Molecular Weight 110.192

		Ref.			Ref.				Ref.
F.P. °C			dt/dP			f	to		
F.P. 100%			°C/mm			g		°K	
			25°C	1.5563	5	h			
B.P. °C			BP	0.04988	4				
760 mm	134.	2	t_e	0.03713	5	f'	to		
100	71.03	4				g'		°K	
30	43.38	4	30 mm	0.6912	5	h'			
10	22.34	5	ΔHm cal/g						
1	-12.77	5				m	to		
			ΔHv cal/g			n		°K	
Pressure			25°C	88.78	5	o			
mm 25°C	11.60	5	30 mm	87.16	5				
t_e	1111.0	5	BP	75.13	5	m'	to		
Density			t_e	73.20	5	n'		°K	
g/ml 20°C	0.814	2	t_e (d, e)	73.14	5	o'			
d_4^t 25	0.810	2	ΔHv/T_e	19.10	5				
30	0.806	4				Surface tension			
a	0.8300	4	d 43 to	92.92	5	dynes/cm. 20°C	26.48	5
b	-0.0₃80	4	e 149 °C	0.1328	5	7 30	25.45	5
			d' 25 to	90.99	5	40	24.44	5
Ref. Index			e' 43 °C	0.0883	5				
n_D 20°C	1.451	2	d_c g/ml	0.263	5	Parachor [P]		
25	1.449	2	v_c ml/g	3.809	5	20°C		
30	1.446	4	t_c °C	335.	5	30		
"C"	0.7337	4	P_c mm	23315.	5	40		
MR (Obs.)	36.5	2				Sugd.	307.1	5
MR (Calc.)	36.477	5	PV/RT			Exp. L.1.%/wt.		
(nD-d/2)	1.044	2	25°C	1.0000	5	u.		
Dielectric			30 mm	1.0000	5	Dispersion		
			BP	0.9570	5	Flash Point °C		
A 43 to	6.86759	4	t_e	0.9458	5	Fire Point		
B 183 °C	1387.4	4	t_c	0.258	5			
C	214.	5	ΔHc kcal/m			M Spec.		
			ΔHf			Ultra V.		
A* 43 to	1.26777	5	ΔFf			X-Ray Dif.		
B* 159 °C	1298.2	5				Infrared		
K			Viscosity			Solubility in +		
c			centistokes			Acetone		
t_k to			7 °C			Carbon tet.		
t_x °C						Benzene		
A' 25 to	7.24458	5				Ether		
B' 43 °C	1588.2	5				n-Heptane		
C'	232.	5	B^v to			Ethanol		
A'* 25 to	1.62837	5	A^v °C			Water		
B'* 43 °C	1488.3	5	(B^v) to			Water in		
Ac 183 to	7.28346	5	(A^v) °C					
Bc t_c °C	1736.9	5	c_p liq. °K					
Cc	261.	5						
Cryos. A°			c_p vap. °K					
consts. B°								
t_e °C	149.02	5	c_v vap.					

$T_R = 0.75 T_c$ + grams/100 grams solvent

REFERENCES: 1-Dow   2-API   3-Lit.   4-Calc. from det. data   5-Çalc. by formula

SOURCE: API

PURIFICATION: API

LITERATURE REFERENCES:

TABLE XX. CYCLOHEXENES

No. 7

NAME	4-Ethylcyclohexene	STRUCTURAL FORMULA

Structural formula:

$$H_2C-\overset{\displaystyle CH}{\underset{\displaystyle CH}{}}-CH$$

$$H_2C \underset{CH\ C_2H_5}{\overset{}{}} CH_2$$

Mole % Pur.	Ref.	Molecular Formula C_8H_{14}		Molecular Weight 110.192	

		Ref.			Ref.			Ref.
F.P. °C			dt/dP			f	to	
F.P. 100%			°C/mm			g	°K	
			25°C	1.51221	5	h		
B.P. °C			BP	0.04963	4			
760 mm	133.	2	t_e	0.03705	5	f'	to	
100	70.32	4	30 mm	0.6885	5	g'	°K	
30	42.78	4	ΔHm cal/g			h'		
10	21.82	5				m	to	
1	-13.16	5	ΔHv cal/g			n	°K	
			25°C	88.75	5	o		
Pressure			30 mm	87.17	5			
mm 25°C	11.95	5	BP	75.06	5	m'	to	
t_e	1106.7	5	t_e	73.14	5	n'	°K	
Density			t_e (d, e)	73.08	5	o'		
g/ml 20°C	0.810	2	ΔHv/T_e	19.14	5	Surface tension		
d_4^t 25	0.806	2				dynes/cm. 20°C	25.96	5
30	0.802	4	d 43 to	92.92	5	ℽ 30	24.95	5
a	0.8260	4	e 148 °C	0.1343	5	40	23.96	5
b	-0.0₃80	4	d' 25 to	90.96	5			
Ref. Index			e' 43 °C	0.0884	5	Parachor [P]		
n_D 20°C	1.449	2	d_c g/ml	0.264	5	20°C		
25	1.447	2	v_c ml/g	3.792	5	30		
30	1.444	2	t_c °C	332.	5	40		
"C"	0.7342	4	P_c mm	23306.	5	Sugd.	307.1	5
MR (Obs.)	36.5	2	PV/RT			Exp. L.l.%/wt.		
MR (Calc.)	36.477	5	25°C	1.0000	5	u.		
(nD-d/2)	1.044	2	30 mm	1.0000	5	Dispersion		
Dielectric			BP	0.9561	5	Flash Point °C		
A 43 to	6.87619	4	t_e	0.9449	5	Fire Point		
B 180 °C	1386.4	4	t_c	0.258	5	M. Spec.		
C	214.	5	ΔHc kcal/m			Ultra V.		
A* 43 to	1.27931	5	ΔHf			X-Ray Dif.		
B* 158 °C	1297.9	5	ΔFf			Infrared		
K			Viscosity			Solubility in +		
c			centistokes			Acetone		
t_k to			η °C			Carbon tet.		
t_x °C						Benzene		
A' 25 to	7.25465	5				Ether		
B' 43 °C	1587.6	5				n-Heptane		
C'	232.	5	B_v to			Ethanol		
A'* 25 to	1.63900	5	A_v °C			Water		
B'* 43 °C	1487.8	5	(B^v) to			Water in		
Ac 180 to	7.29156	5	(A^v) °C					
Bc t_c °C	1733.8	5	c_p liq. °K					
Cc	261.	5	c_p vap. °K					
Cryos. A° consts. B°								
t_e °C	147.78	5	c_v vap.					

$T_R = 0.75\,T_c$

+ grams/100 grams solvent

REFERENCES: 1-Dow 2-API 3-Lit. 4-Calc. from det. data 5-Calc. by formula

SOURCE:	API
PURIFICATION:	API
LITERATURE REFERENCES:	

No. 8

NAME	1,2-Dimethylcyclohexene					STRUCTURAL FORMULA		

Structural formula: H_2C CCH_3 / CCH_3 ; H_2C CH_2 / CH_2

Mole % Pur.	Ref.	Molecular Formula	C_8H_{14}		Molecular Weight 110.192			

			Ref.				Ref.				Ref.
F.P. °C				dt/dP °C/mm				f $\quad$	to		
F.P. 100%				25°C	1.7633	5		g $\quad$	°K		
B.P. °C				BP	0.05008	4		h			
760 mm	137.	2		t_e	0.03709	5		f' $\quad$	to		
100	73.76	4		30 mm	0.6946	5		g' $\quad$	°K		
30	45.98	4		ΔHm cal/g				h'			
10	24.83	5		ΔHv cal/g				m $\quad$	to		
1	-10.46	5		25°C	90.08	5		n $\quad$	°K		
Pressure				30 mm	88.16	5		o			
mm 25°C	10.10	5		BP	75.85	5		m' $\quad$	to		
t_e	1118.05	5		t_e	73.85	5		n' $\quad$	°K		
Density				t_e (d, e)	73.78	5		o'			
g/ml 20°C	0.8250	2		ΔHv/T_e	19.12	5		Surface tension			
d_4^t 25	0.8208	2		d $\mid$ 45 to	94.38	5		dynes/cm. 20°C	27.94	5
30	0.8166	4		e $\mid$ 152 °C	0.1353	5		γ $\qquad$ 30	26.82	5
a	0.8418	4		d' $\mid$ 25 to	92.36	5		40	25.72	5
b	-0.0384	4		e' $\mid$ 45 °C	0.0912	5		Parachor [P]		
Ref. Index				d_c g/ml	0.265	5		20°C		
n_D 20°C	1.4588	2		v_c ml/g	3.768	5		30		
25	1.4564	2		t_c °C	340.			40		
30	1.4540	4		P_c mm	23762.	5		Sugd.	307.1	5
"C"	0.7357	4		PV/RT				Exp. L.1.%/wt.		
MR (Obs.)	36.50	2		25°C	1.0000	5		u.		
MR (Calc.)	36.477	5		30 mm	1.0000	5		Dispersion	123.	2
(nD-d/2)	1.0463	2		BP	0.9559	5		Flash Point °C		
Dielectric				t_e	0.9443	5		Fire Point		
A $\mid$ 45 to	6.87452	4		t_c	0.258	5		M Spec.		
B $\lfloor$186 °C	1397.8	4		ΔHc kcal/m				Ultra V.		
C	213.	5		ΔHf				X-Ray Dif.		
A* $\mid$ 45 to	1.27411	5		ΔFf				Infrared		
B* $\lfloor$162 °C	1308.8	5		Viscosity				Solubility in $\quad$ +		
K				centistokes				Acetone		
c				η $\qquad$ °C				Carbon tet.		
t_k $\mid$ to								Benzene		
t_x $\mid$ °C								Ether		
A' $\mid$ 25 to	7.24966	5						n-Heptane		
B' $\lfloor$ 45 °C	1598.9	5		B^v $\mid$ to				Ethanol		
C'	231.	5		A^v $\mid$ °C				Water		
A'* 25 to	1.63262	5		(B^v) $\mid$ to				Water in		
B'* 45 °C	1499.1	5		(A^v) $\mid$ °C						
Ac $\mid$186 to	7.28962	5		c_p liq. °K						
Bc $\mid$ t_c °C	1749.3	5								
Cc	260.	5		c_p vap. °K						
Cryos. A° consts. B°				c_v vap.						
t_e °C	152.34	5								

$T_R = 0.75\, T_c$ + grams/100 grams solvent

REFERENCES: 1-Dow 2-API 3-Lit.   4-Calc. from det. data   5-Calc. by formula
SOURCE: API
PURIFICATION: API
LITERATURE REFERENCES:

TABLE XX. CYCLOHEXENES

No. 9

NAME	1,3-Dimethylcyclohexene	STRUCTURAL FORMULA

Structural formula:

H_2C — C — CCH_3
H_2C — CH — CH CH_3
     CH_2

Mole % Pur.	Ref.	Molecular Formula C_8H_{14}	Molecular Weight 110.192	

		Ref.				Ref.				Ref.
F.P. °C			dt/dP			f	to			
F.P. 100%			°C/mm			g	°K			
			25°C	1.7642	5	h				
B.P. °C			BP	0.05007	5					
760 mm	137.	2	t_e	0.03708	5	f'	to			
100	73.76	4	30 mm	0.6946	5	g'	°K			
30	45.99	4				h'				
10	24.84	5	ΔHm cal/g			m	to			
1	-10.45	5				n	°K			
			ΔHv cal/g			o				
Pressure			25°C	90.09	5					
mm 25°C	10.09	5	30 mm	88.17	5	m'	to			
t_e	1118.2	5	BP	75.86	5	n'	°K			
			t_e	73.85	5	o'				
Density			t_e (d, e)	73.78	5					
g/ml 20°C	0.802	2				Surface tension			
d_4^t 25	0.798	2	ΔHv/T_e	19.12	5	dynes/cm. 20°C	24.95	5
30	0.794	4	d 45 to	94.40	5	Y 30	23.97	5
a	0.8180	4	e 152 °C	0.1353	5	40	23.00	5
b	-0.0380	4	d' 25 to	92.37	5				
			e' 45 °C	0.0912	5	Parachor [P]			
Ref. Index						20°C			
n_D 20°C	1.445	2	d_c g/ml	0.262	5	30			
25	1.443	2	v_c ml/g	3.821	5	40			
30	1.440	4	t_c °C	337.	5	Sugd.	307.1	5
"C"	0.7354	4	P_c mm	23046.	5				
MR (Obs.)	36.6	2	PV/RT			Exp. L.1.%/wt.		
MR (Calc.)	36.477	5	25°C	1.0000	5	u.		
(nD-d/2)	1.044	2	30 mm	1.0000	5	Dispersion	120.	2
Dielectric			BP	0.9560	5	Flash Point °C		
A 45 to	6.87509	4	t_e	0.9445	5	Fire Point		
B 185 °C	1398.0	4	t_c	0.255	5	M. Spec.		
C	213.	5	ΔHc kcal/m			Ultra V.		
A* 45 to	1.27450	5	ΔHf			X-Ray Dif.		
B* 162 °C	1309.0	5	ΔFf			Infrared		
K			Viscosity			Solubility in +		
c			centistokes			Acetone		
t_k to			η °C			Carbon tet.		
t_x °C						Benzene		
A' 25 to	7.25026	5				Ether		
B' 45 °C	1599.1	5				n-Heptane		
C'	231.	5	B^v to			Ethanol		
A'* 25 to	1.63321	5	A^v °C			Water		
B'* 45 °C	1499.3	5	(B^v) to			Water in		
Ac 185 to	7.28951	5	(A^v) °C					
Bc t_c °C	1746.8	5						
Cc	260.	5	c_p liq. °K					
Cryos. A°			c_p vap. °K					
consts. B°								
t_e °C	152.34	5	c_v vap.					

$T_R = 0.75 T_C$ + grams/100 grams solvent

REFERENCES:	1-Dow	2-API	3-Lit.	4-Calc. from det. data	5-Calc. by formula
SOURCE:	API				
PURIFICATION:	API				

LITERATURE REFERENCES:

No. 10

NAME	1,4-Dimethylcyclohexene					STRUCTURAL FORMULA		

Structural formula:
H_2C—C—CCH_3
$\quad\quad$ CH
H_2C—CH_2
$\quad\quad$ $CHCH_3$

Mole % Pur.		Ref.	Molecular Formula	C_8H_{14}		Molecular Weight 110.192		

		Ref.			Ref.			Ref.
F.P. °C	-59.	2	dt/dP °C/mm			f | to		
F.P. 100%			25°C	1.25098	5	g | °K		
B.P. °C			BP	0.04906	4	h |		
760 mm	128.	2	t_e	0.03696	5	f' | to		
100	66.04	4	30 mm	0.6806	5	g' | °K		
30	38.82	4	ΔHm cal/g			h' |		
10	18.10	5	ΔHv cal/g			m | to		
1	-16.50	5	25°C	87.17	5	n | °K		
Pressure			30 mm	85.99	5	o |		
mm 25°C	14.70	5	BP	74.14	5	m' | to		
t_e	1093.5	5	t_e	72.32	5	n' | °K		
Density			t_e (d, e)	72.26	5	o' |		
g/ml 20°C	0.802	2	ΔHv/T_e	19.19	5	Surface tension		
d_4^t 25	0.798	2	d | 39 to	91.14	5	dynes/cm. 20°C	24.95	5
30	0.794	4	e | 155 °C	0.1328	5	γ 30	23.96	5
a	0.8180	4	d' | 25 to	89.30	5	40	23.00	5
b	-0.0₃80	4	e' | 39 °C	0.0855	5	Parachor [P]		
Ref. Index			d_c g/ml	0.266	5	20°C		
n_D 20°C	1.446	2	v_c ml/g	3.766	5	30		
25	1.444	2	t_c °C	323.	5	40		
30	1.441	4	P_c mm	22934.	5	Sugd.	307.1	5
"C"	0.7369	4	PV/RT			Exp. L.l.%/wt.		
MR (Obs.)	36.6	2	25°C	1.0000	5	u.		
MR (Calc.)	36.477	5	30 mm	1.0000	5	Dispersion	119.	2
(nD-d/2)	1.045	2	BP	0.9570	5	Flash Point °C		
Dielectric			t_e	0.9463	5	Fire Point		
A | 39 to	6.87585	4	t_c	0.256	5	M Spec.		
B | 174 °C	1370.3	4	ΔHc kcal/m			Ultra V.		
C	215.	5	ΔHf			X-Ray Dif.		
A* | 39 to	1.28236	5	ΔFf			Infrared		
B* | 152 °C	1282.3	5	Viscosity			Solubility in +		
K			centistokes			Acetone		
c			η °C			Carbon tet.		
t_k | to						Benzene		
t_x | °C						Ether		
A' | 25 to	7.25871	5	B^v | to			n-Heptane		
B' | 39 °C	1571.5	5	A^v | °C			Ethanol		
C'	233.	5	(B^v) | to			Water		
A'* 25 to	1.64691	5	(A^v) | °C			Water in		
B'* 39 °C	1472.4	5	c_p liq. °K					
Ac | 174 to	7.29137	5						
Bc | t_c °C	1712.9	5	c_p vap. °K					
Cc	261.	5						
Cryos. A°			c_v vap.					
consts. B°								
t_e °C	142.13	5						

T_R = 0.75 T_c $\qquad$ + grams/100 grams solvent

REFERENCES: 1-Dow 2-API 3-Lit. 4-Calc. from det. data 5-Calc. by formula
SOURCE: $\qquad$ API
PURIFICATION: $\qquad$ API
LITERATURE REFERENCES:

TABLE XX. CYCLOHEXENES   499

No. 11

NAME	1, 5-Dimethylcyclohexene	STRUCTURAL FORMULA
	2, 4-Dimethylcyclohexene	

| Mole % Pur. | Ref. | Molecular Formula C_8H_{14} | Molecular Weight 110.192 | |

Structural formula:
$$H_2C \overset{\displaystyle CCH_3}{\underset{\displaystyle CH_2}{\overset{|}{\underset{|}{C}}} } \quad H_3CHC \overset{CH}{\underset{CH_2}{}} CH_2$$

		Ref.			Ref.			Ref.
F.P. °C			dt/dP			f $\lfloor$ to		
F.P. 100%			°C/mm			g $\lfloor$ _ _ °K		
B.P. °C			25°C	1.2510	5	h $\lfloor$		
760 mm	128.	2	BP	0.04906	4			
100	66.04	4	t_e	0.03696	5	f' $\lfloor$ to		
30	38.82	4	30 mm	0.6806	5	g' $\lfloor$ _ _ °K		
10	18.10	5	ΔHm cal/g			h' $\lfloor$		
1	-16.50	5	ΔHv cal/g			m $\lfloor$ to		
Pressure			25°C	87.17	5	n $\lfloor$ °K		
mm 25°C	14.70	5	30 mm	85.99	5	o $\lfloor$		
t_e	1093.5	5	BP	74.14	5	m' $\lfloor$ to		
Density			t_e	72.31	5	n' $\lfloor$ °K		
g/ml 20°C	0.8051	.2	t_e (d, e)	72.26	5	o' $\lfloor$ _ _		
d_4^t 25	0.8009	2	ΔHv/T_e	19.19	5			
30	0.7967	4	d $\lfloor$ 39 to	91.14	5	Surface tension		
a	0.8219	4	e $\lfloor$ 155 °C	0.1328	5	dynes/cm. 20°C	25.34	5
b	-0.0384	4	d' $\lfloor$ 25 to	89.30	5	ɣ 30	24.29	5
Ref. Index			e' $\lfloor$ 39 °C	0.0855	5	40	23.27	5
n_D 20°C	1.448	2	d_c g/ml	0.265	5	Parachor [P]		
25	1.446	2	v_c ml/g	3.774	5	20°C		
30	1.443	4	t_c °C	323.	5	30		
"C"	0.7371	4	P_c mm	22887.	5	40		
MR (Obs.)	36.6	2	PV/RT			Sugd.	307.1	5
MR (Calc.)	36.477	5	25°C	1.0000	5	Exp. L. 1.%/wt.		
(nD-d/2)	1.045	2	30 mm	1.0000	5	u.		
Dielectric			BP	0.9570	5	Dispersion	119.	2
A $\lfloor$ 39 to	6.87585	4	t_e	0.9463	5	Flash Point °C		
B $\lfloor$ 174 °C	1370.3	4	t_c	0.256	5	Fire Point		
C	215.	5	ΔHc kcal/m			M. Spec.		
A* $\lfloor$ 39 to	1.28235	5	ΔHf			Ultra V.		
B* $\lfloor$ 152 °C	1282.3	5	ΔFf			X-Ray Dif.		
K			Viscosity			Infrared		
c			centistokes			Solubility in +		
t_k $\lfloor$ to			η °C			Acetone		
t_x $\lfloor$ °C						Carbon tet.		
A' $\lfloor$ 25 to	7.25871	5				Benzene		
B' $\lfloor$ 39 °C	1571.5	5				Ether		
C'	233.	5	B^V $\lfloor$ to			n-Heptane		
A'* 25 to	1.64691	5	A^V $\lfloor$ °C			Ethanol		
B'* 39 °C	1472.4	5	$(B^V)\lfloor$ to			Water		
Ac $\lfloor$ 174 to	7.29133	5	$(A^V)\lfloor$ °C			Water in		
Bc $\lfloor$ t_c °C	1712.8	5	c_p liq. °K					
Cc $\lfloor$ _ _	261.	5						
Cryos. A°			c_p vap. °K					
consts. B°								
t_e °C	142.13	5	c_v vap.					

T_R = 0.75 T_c + grams/100 grams solvent

REFERENCES: 1-Dow 2-API 3-Lit. 4-Calc. from det. data 5-Calc. by formula

SOURCE: API

PURIFICATION: API

LITERATURE REFERENCES:

No. 12

NAME	1, 6-Dimethylcyclohexene	STRUCTURAL FORMULA
	2, 3-Dimethylcyclohexene	

Structural formula:

$H_3CHC\overset{CCH_3}{\underset{}{}}CH$
$H_2C\quad CH_2$
CH_2

Mole % Pur.	Ref.	Molecular Formula C_8H_{14}		Molecular Weight 110.192	

		Ref.			Ref.				Ref.
F.P. °C			dt/dP			f	to		
F.P. 100%			°C/mm			g	└ ─ °K		
B.P. °C			25°C	1.5122	5	h			
760 mm	133.	2	BP	0.04963	4	f'	to		
100	70.32	4	t_e	0.03704	5	g'	└ ─ °K		
30	42.78	4	30 mm	0.6885	5	h'			
10	21.82	5	**ΔHm cal/g**						
1	-13.16	5	**ΔHv cal/g**			m	to		
Pressure			25°C	88.75	5	n	└ ─ °K		
mm 25°C	11.95	5	30 mm	87.17	5	o			
t_e	1107.2	5	BP	75.09	5	m'	to		
Density			t_e	73.17	5	n'	└ ─ °K		
g/ml 20°C	0.815	2	t_e (d, e)	73.11	5	o'			
d_4^t 25	0.811	2	**ΔHv/T_e**	19.15	5	**Surface tension**			
30	0.807	4	d 43 to	92.90	5	dynes/cm. 20°C	26.61	5
a	0.8310	4	e 155 °C	0.1339	5	γ 30	25.57	5
b	-0.0380	4	d' 25 to	90.96	5	40	24.57	5
Ref. Index			e' 43 °C	0.0884	5	**Parachor [P]**		
n_D 20°C	1.454	2	d_c g/ml	0.269	5	20°C		
25	1.452	2	v_c ml/g	3.721	5	30		
30	1.449	4	t_c °C	333.		40		
"C"	0.7373	4	P_c mm	23511.	5	Sugd.	307.1	5
MR (Obs.)	36.6	2	**PV/RT**			Exp. L.1.%/wt.		
MR (Calc.)	36.477	5	25°C	1.0000	5	u.		
(nD-d/2)	1.046	2	30 mm	1.0000	5	Dispersion		
Dielectric			BP	0.9564	5	**Flash Point °C**		
A 43 to	6.87619	4	t_e	0.9452	5	Fire Point		
B 180 °C	1386.4	4	t_c	0.255	5			
C	214.	5	**ΔHc kcal/m**			M Spec.		
A* 43 to	1.27870	5	**ΔHf**			Ultra V.		
B* 158 °C	1297.8	5	**ΔFf**			X-Ray Dif.		
K						Infrared		
c			**Viscosity**					
t_k to			centistokes			Solubility in +		
t_x °C			η °C			Acetone		
A' 25 to	7.25465	5				Carbon tet.		
B' 43 °C	1587.6	5				Benzene		
C'	232.	5	B^v to			Ether		
A'* 25 to	1.63900	5	A^v °C			n-Heptane		
B'* 43 °C	1487.8	5	(B^v) to			Ethanol		
Ac 182 to	7.29175	5	(A^v) °C			Water		
Bc t_c °C	1734.6	5				Water in		
Cc	261.	5	c_p liq. °K					
Cryos. A°			c_p vap. °K					
consts. B°								
t_e °C	147.80	5	c_v vap.					

$T_R = 0.75\, T_c$ + grams/100 grams solvent

REFERENCES: 1-Dow   2-API   3-Lit.   4-Calc. from det. data   5-Calc. by formula

SOURCE: API

PURIFICATION: API

LITERATURE REFERENCES:

TABLE XX. CYCLOHEXENES

No. 13

NAME	3,3-Dimethylcyclohexene	STRUCTURAL FORMULA

H_2C — CH — CH
H_2C — $C(CH_3)_2$
CH_2

Mole % Pur.	Ref.	Molecular Formula C_8H_{14}		Molecular Weight 110.192	

		Ref.				Ref.				Ref.
F.P. °C			dt/dP			f	to		
F.P. 100%			°C/mm			g	°K		
B.P. °C			25°C	0.8936	5	h			
760 mm	119.	2	BP	0.04804	5				
100	58.36	5	t_e	0.03689	5	f'	to		
30	31.73	5	30 mm	0.6655	5	g'	°K		
10	11.47	5	ΔHm cal/g			h'			
1	-22.35	5				m	to		
Pressure			ΔHv cal/g			n	°K		
mm 25°C	21.23	5	25°C	84.53	5	o			
t_e	1067.3	5	30 mm	83.98	5				
			BP	72.35	5	m'	to		
Density			t_e	70.68	5	n'	°K		
g/ml 20°C	0.804	2	t_e (d, e)	70.63	5	o'			
d_4^t 25	0.800	2	ΔHv/T_e	19.23	5	Surface tension			
30	0.796	4				dynes/cm. 20°C	25.20	5
a	0.8200	4	d 32 to	88.21	5	8	30	24.20	5
b	-0.0₃79	4	e 140 °C	0.1333	5		40	23.23	5
Ref. Index			d' 25 to	86.57	5				
n_D 20°C	1.445	2	e' 32 °C	0.0815	5	Parachor [P]			
25	1.443	2				20°C			
30	1.440	4	d_c g/ml	0.269	5	30			
"C"	0.7335	4	v_c ml/g	3.720	5	40			
MR (Obs.)	36.5	2	t_c °C	310.	5	Sugd.	307.1	5
MR (Calc.)	36.477	5	P_c mm	22801.	5				
(nD-d/2)	1.043	2	PV/RT			Exp. L.1.%/wt.			
Dielectric			25°C	1.0000	5	u.			
A 32 to	6.86558	4	30 mm	1.0000	5	Dispersion			
B 164 °C	1334.9	4	BP	0.9570	5	Flash Point °C			
C	216.	5	t_e	0.9470	5	Fire Point			
A* 32 to	1.28233	5	t_c	0.257	5	M. Spec.			
B* 142 °C	1249.1	5	ΔHc kcal/m			Ultra V.			
K			ΔHf			X-Ray Dif.			
c			ΔFf			Infrared			
t_k to			Viscosity			Solubility in +			
t_x °C			centistokes			Acetone			
A' 25 to	7.25710	5	η °C			Carbon tet.			
B' 32 °C	1535.9	5				Benzene			
C'	234.	5				Ether			
A'* 25 to	1.64711	5	B^v to			n-Heptane			
B'* 32	1436.8	5	A^v °C			Ethanol			
Ac 164 to	7.28069	5	(B^v) to			Water			
Bc t_c °C	1669.3	5	(A^v) °C			Water in			
Cc	261.	5	c_p liq. °K						
Cryos. A°			c_p vap. °K						
consts. B°									
t_e °C	131.87	5	c_v vap.						

T_R = 0.75 T_c

+ grams/100 grams solvent

REFERENCES: 1-Dow 2-API 3-Lit. 4-Calc. from det. data 5-Calc. by formula

SOURCE: API

PURIFICATION: API

LITERATURE REFERENCES:

No. 14

NAME	4,4-Dimethylcyclohexene		STRUCTURAL FORMULA

Mole % Pur.	Ref.	Molecular Formula C_8H_{14}	Molecular Weight 110.192

		Ref.			Ref.			Ref.
F.P. °C	-80.5	2	dt/dP °C/mm			f | to		
F.P. 100%			25°C	0.8280	5	g | °K		
B.P. °C			BP	0.04781	4	h		
760 mm	116.98	2	t_e	0.03686	5			
100	56.61	4	30 mm	0.6630	5	f' | to		
30	30.09	4	**ΔHm cal/g**			g' | °K		
10	9.91	5				h'		
1	-23.80	5	**ΔHv cal/g**					
Pressure			25°C	83.80	5	m | to		
mm 25°C	23.11	5	30 mm	83.41	5	n | °K		
t_e	1061.6	5	BP	71.96	5	o		
Density			t_e	70.34	5			
g/ml 20°C	0.7996	2	t_e (d, e)	70.30	5	m' | to		
d_4^t 25	0.7956	2	$ΔHv/T_e$	19.24	5	n' | °K		
30	0.7916	4				o'		
a	0.8156	4	d | 30 to	87.37	5	**Surface tension**		
b	-0.0$_3$79	4	e | 140 °C	0.1317	5	dynes/cm. 20°C	24.65	5
Ref. Index			d' | 15 to	85.76	5	$γ$ 30	23.67	5
n_D 20°C	1.4420	2	e' | 30 °C	0.0780	5	40	22.71	5
25	1.4396	2	d_c g/ml	0.269	5	**Parachor [P]**		
30	1.4373	4	v_c ml/g	3.719	5	20°C		
"C"	0.7329	4	t_c °C	306.	5	30		
			P_c mm	22652.	5	40		
MR (Obs.)	36.46	2	**PV/RT**			Sugd.	307.1	5
MR (Calc.)	36.477	5	25°C	1.0000	5	Exp. L.1.%/wt.		
(nD-d/2)	1.0422	2	30 mm	1.0000	5	u.		
Dielectric			BP	0.9571	5	Dispersion	115.	2
A | 30 to	6.87266	4	t_e	0.9473	5	**Flash Point °C**		
B |161 °C	1333.2	4	t_c	0.257	5	**Fire Point**		
C	217.	5	**ΔHc kcal/m**			**M Spec.**		
A* | 30 to	1.29067	5	**ΔHf**			**Ultra V.**		
B* |140 °C	1247.4	5	**ΔFf**			**X-Ray Dif.**		
K			**Viscosity**			**Infrared**		
c			centistokes			**Solubility in +**		
t_k | to			$η$ °C			Acetone		
t_x | °C						Carbon tet.		
A' | 15 to	7.26571	5				Benzene		
B' | 30 °C	1534.5	5	B^v | to			Ether		
C'	235.	5	A^v | °C			n-Heptane		
A'* | 15 to	1.65563	5	(B^v) | to			Ethanol		
B'* | 30 °C	1435.0	5	(A^v) | °C			Water		
Ac |161 to	7.28876	5	c_p liq. °K			Water in		
Bc | t_c °C	1666.8	5	c_p vap. °K					
Cc	262.	5	c_v vap.					
Cryos. A°								
consts. B°								
t_e °C	129.58	5						

$T_R = 0.75\, T_c$ + grams/100 grams solvent

REFERENCES: 1-Dow 2-API 3-Lit. 4-Calc. from det. data 5-Calc. by formula

SOURCE: API

PURIFICATION: API

LITERATURE REFERENCES:

TABLE XXI. THIACYCLOHEXANES 503

No. 1

NAME	Thiacyclohexane					STRUCTURAL FORMULA

Structural Formula:

$$H_2C \overset{\displaystyle S}{\underset{\displaystyle CH_2}{}} CH_2$$
$$H_2C \qquad CH_2$$
$$CH_2$$

Mole % Pur. 99.9	Ref. 3'	Molecular Formula $C_5H_{10}S$		Molecular Weight 102.196	

		Ref.			Ref.						Ref.
F.P. °C	19.09	3'	dt/dP			f		290 to	0.1712	4
F.P. 100%			°C/mm			g		350 °K	0.0366	4
B.P. °C			25°C	2.1809	5	h			0.0616	4
760 mm	141.75	3	BP	0.05019	5	f'		to		
100	78.28	3	t_e	0.03658	5	g'		°K		
30	50.34	3	30 mm	0.6989	5	h'				
10	29.08	5	ΔHm cal/g	5.73	3'	m		390 to	-0.1362	4
1	-6.3	5	ΔHv cal/g			n		500 °K	0.0015	4
Pressure			25°C	100.03	5	o			-0.0665	4
mm 25°C	7.9256	5	30 mm	97.08	5	m'		to		
t_e	1140.5	5	BP	84.14	3'	n'		°K		
Density			t_e	81.93	5	o'				
g/ml 20°C	0.9856	2	t_e (d, e)	81.85	5	Surface tension				
d_4^t 25	0.9810	2	ΔHv/T_e	19.42	5	dynes/cm. 20°C			34.94	5
30	0.9764	4	d 75 to	104.20	5	8		30	33.65	5
a	1.0040	4	e 160 °C	0.1415	5			40	32.39	5
b	-0.0392	4	d' 10 to	102.94	5	Parachor [P]				
Ref. Index			e' 75 °C	0.1164	5	20°C				
n_D 20°C	1.5067	2	d_c g/ml	0.332	5	30				
25	1.5041	2	v_c ml/g	3.011	5	40				
30	1.5016	4	t_c °C	379.	5	S = 51.		Sugd.	252.1	5
"C"	0.6759	4	P_c mm	33708.	5	Exp. L. 1.%/wt.				
MR (Obs.)	30.84	4	PV/RT			u.				
MR (Calc.)	30.780	5	25°C	1.0000	5	Dispersion			114.	2
(nD-d/2)	1.0139	4	30 mm	1.0000	5	Flash Point °C				
Dielectric			BP	0.9620	5	Fire Point				
A 50 to	6.90518	3	t_e	0.9508	5	M. Spec.				
B 210 °C	1422.470	3	t_c	0.255	5	Ultra V.				
C	211.718	3	ΔHc kcal/m	-930.26	3'	X-Ray Dif.				
A* 50 to	1.25671	5	ΔHf	25.18	3'	Infrared				
B* 175 °C	1329.9	5	ΔFf			Solubility in +				
K			Viscosity			Acetone				
c			centistokes			Carbon tet.				
t_k to			η °C			Benzene				
t_x °C						Ether				
A' 0 to	7.18029	5				n-Heptane				
B' 50 °C	1570.3	5				Ethanol				
C'	225.	5	B^v to			Water				
A'* 0 to	1.53543	5	A^v °C			Water in				
B'* 50 °C	1474.1	5	(B^v) to							
Ac 210 to	7.32621	5	(A^v) °C							
Bc t_c °C	1805.6	5	c_p liq.300 °K	0.38361	3'					
Cc	266.	5	350	0.42181	3'					
Cryos. A°	0.004	2	c_p vap400°K	0.35029	3'					
consts. B°			500	0.43916	3'					
t_e °C	157.94	5	c_v vap.							

T_R = 0.75 T_c + grams/100 grams solvent

REFERENCES: 1-Dow 2-API 3-Lit. 4-Calc. from det. data 5-Calc. by formula

SOURCE:	API
PURIFICATION:	API

LITERATURE REFERENCES: 3 Ind. Eng. Chem. **44**, 1430 (1952), P. T. White et al;
3' J.A.C.S. **76**, 2661 (1954) McCullough et al.

No. 2

NAME	2-Methylthiacyclohexane	STRUCTURAL FORMULA
	Tetrahydro-2-methyl-1-thiapyran	

Mole % Pur. 99.2	Ref. 3	Molecular Formula $C_6H_{12}S$	Molecular Weight 116.216

		Ref.			Ref.				Ref.
F.P. °C	-58.14	2	dt/dP °C/mm			f	to °K		
F.P. 100%			25°C	3.2182	5	g			
B.P. °C			BP	0.0521	2	h			
760 mm	153.04	3	t_e	0.03722	5	f'	to °K		
100	87.24	3	30 mm	0.7223	5	g'			
30	58.35	3	ΔHm cal/g			h'			
10	36.37	5	ΔHv cal/g			m	to °K		
1	-0.2694	5	25°C	89.88	5	n			
Pressure			30 mm	86.74	5	o			
mm 25°C	5.2566	5	BP	75.03	5				
t_e	1172.0	5	t_e	72.87	5	m'	to °K		
Density			t_e (d, e)	72.80	5	n'			
g/ml 20°C	0.9428	2	ΔHv/T_e	19.06	5	o'			
d_4^t 25	0.9381	2	d 58 to	93.95	5	Surface tension			
30	0.9334	4	e 171 °C	0.1236	5	dynes/cm. 20°C	29.92	5	
a	0.9616	4	d' 25 to	92.23	5	y 30	28.74	5	
b	-0.0₃938	4	e' 58 °C	0.0942	5	40	27.60	5	
Ref. Index			d_c g/ml	0.316	5	Parachor [P]			
n_D 20°C	1.4905	2	v_c ml/g	3.168	5	20°C			
25	1.4881	2	t_c °C	375.	5	30			
30	1.4853	4	P_c mm	26344.	5	40			
"C"	0.6854	4	PV/RT			Sugd.	288.3	5	
MR (Obs.)	35.67	2	25°C	1.0000	5	Exp. L.1.%/wt.			
MR (Calc.)	35.398	5	30 mm	1.0000	5	u.			
(nD-d/2)	1.0191	2	BP	0.9606	5	Dispersion	114.	2	
Dielectric			t_e	0.9482	5	Flash Point °C			
A 58 to	6.86962	3	t_c	0.255	5	Fire Point			
B ⌊213 °C	1450.987	3	ΔHc kcal/m			M Spec.			
C	210.727	3	ΔHf			Ultra V.			
A* 58 to	1.26718	5	ΔFf			X-Ray Dif.			
B* ⌊181 °C	1356.2	5	Viscosity			Infrared			
K			centistokes			Solubility in +			
c			η °C			Acetone			
t_k to						Carbon tet.			
t_x °C						Benzene			
A' 25 to	7.21579	5				Ether			
B' ⌊58 °C	1643.3	5				n-Heptane			
C'	228.	5	B^v to			Ethanol			
A'* 25 to	1.61631	5	A^v °C			Water			
B'* 58 °C	1543.2	5	(B^v) to			Water in			
Ac ⌊213 to	7.28726	5	(A^v) °C						
Bc ⌊t_c °C	1826.3	5	c_p liq. °K						
Cc	262.	5							
Cryos. A°			c_p vap. °K						
consts. B°									
t_e °C	171.04	5	c_v vap.						

T_R = 0.75 T_c + grams/100 grams solvent

REFERENCES: 1-Dow   2-API   3-Lit.   4-Calc. from det. data   5-Calc. by formula

SOURCE:	API
PURIFICATION:	API

LITERATURE REFERENCES: 3 Ind. Eng. Chem. 44, 1430 (1952), P. T. White et al.

TABLE XXI. THIACYCLOHEXANES

No. 3

NAME	3-Methylthiacyclohexane			STRUCTURAL FORMULA			
	Tetrahydro-3-methyl-1-thiapyran			H_2C CH_2 $CHCH_3$			
Mole % Pur. 99.8	Ref. 3	Molecular Formula $C_6H_{12}S$	Molecular Weight 116.216	H_2C CH_2 S			

		Ref.			Ref.				Ref.
F.P. °C	-60.17	2	dt/dP			f	to		
F.P. 100%			°C/mm			g	°K		
B.P. °C			25°C	3.9100	5	h			
760 mm	158.04	2	BP	0.0524	2				
100	91.66	2	t_e	0.03705	5	f'	to		
30	62.37	2				g'	°K		
10	40.03	5	30 mm	0.7336	5	h'			
1	2.69	5	ΔHm cal/g						
Pressure			ΔHv cal/g			m	to		
mm 25°C	4.2904	5	25°C	90.64	5	n	°K		
t_e	1183.7	5	30 mm	87.49	5	o			
Density			BP	76.26	5	m'	to		
g/ml 20°C	0.9473	2	t_e	74.12	5	n'	°K		
d_4^t 25	0.9430	2	t_e (d, e)	74.09	5	o'			
30	0.9387	4	ΔHv/T_e	19.15	5				
a	0.9645	4	d 62 to	94.81	5	Surface tension			
b	-0.0386	4	e 176 °C	0.1174	5	dynes/cm. 20°C	30.49	5
			d' 25 to	92.74	5	δ 30	29.40	5
Ref. Index			e' 62 °C	0.0843	5	40	28.33	5
n_D 20°C	1.4922	2							
25	1.4899	2	d_c g/ml	0.311	5	Parachor [P]			
30	1.4875	4	v_c ml/g	3.212	5	20°C			
"C"	0.6828	2	t_c °C	384.		30			
			P_c mm	27997.	5	40			
MR (Obs.)	35.61	2				Sugd.	288.3	5
MR (Calc.)	35.398	5	PV/RT			Exp. L.l.%/wt.			
(nD-d/2)	1.0186	2	25°C	1.0000	5	u.			
Dielectric			30 mm	1.0000	5	Dispersion	113.	2
A 62 to	6.95022	3	BP	0.9587	5	Flash Point °C			
B 220 °C	1517.984	3	t_e	0.9459	5	Fire Point			
C	214.985	3	t_c	0.255	5	M. Spec.			
A* 62 to	1.34142	5	ΔHc kcal/m			Ultra V.			
B* 186 °C	1420.0	5	ΔHf			X-Ray Dif.			
K			ΔFf			Infrared			
c			Viscosity			Solubility in +			
t_k to			centistokes			Acetone	∞	
t_x °C			η °C			Carbon tet.	∞	
A' 25 to	7.28598	5				Benzene	∞	
B' 62 °C	1710.0	5				Ether	∞	
C'	232.	5	B^v to			n-Heptane	∞	
A'* 25 to	1.67792	5	A^v °C			Ethanol	∞	
B'* 62 °C	1606.1	5	(B^v) to			Water		
Ac 220 to	7.37528	5	(A^v) °C			Water in		
Bc t_c °C	1910.3	5	c_p liq. °K					
Cc	268.	5						
Cryos. A°			c_p vap. °K					
consts. B°								
t_e °C	176.55	5	c_v vap.					

T_R = 0.75 T_c

+ grams/100 grams solvent

REFERENCES: 1-Dow 2-API 3-Lit. 4-Calc. from det. data 5-Calc. by formula

SOURCE: API

PURIFICATION: API

LITERATURE REFERENCES: 3 Ind. Eng. Chem. 44, 1430 (1952), P. T. White et al.

No. 4

NAME	4-Methylthiacyclohexane	STRUCTURAL FORMULA
	Tetrahydro-4-methyl-1-thiapyran	

Mole % Pur. 99.8	Ref. 3	Molecular Formula $C_6H_{12}S$	Molecular Weight 116.216

		Ref.			Ref.				Ref.
F.P. °C	-28.1	2	dt/dP °C/mm			f	to °K		
F.P. 100%			25°C	4.0139	5	g			
B.P. °C			BP	0.05270	5	h			
760 mm	158.64	2	t_e	0.03728	5	f'	to °K		
100	92.07	2	30 mm	0.7315	5	g'			
30	62.82	2	ΔHm cal/g			h'			
10	40.56	5	ΔHv cal/g						
1	3.43	5	25°C	91.55	5	m	to °K		
Pressure			30 mm	87.98	5	n			
mm 25°C	4.1375	5	BP	76.06	5	o			
t_e	1186.4	5	t_e	73.80	5				
Density			t_e (d, e)	73.73	5	m'	to °K		
g/ml 20°C	0.9471	2	ΔHv/T_e	19.04	5	n'			
d_4^t 25	0.9427	2				o'			
30	0.9383	4	d | 62 to	95.80	5	Surface tension			
a	0.9647	4	e | 177 °C	0.1244	5	dynes/cm. 20°C	30.47	5
b	-0.0₃88	4	d' | 25 to	93.91	5	ɣ 30	29.35	5
Ref. Index			e' | 62 °C	0.0944	5	40	28.26	5
n_D 20°C	1.4923	2	d_c g/ml	0.315	5	Parachor [P]		
25	1.4899	2	v_c ml/g	3.179	5	20°C		
30	1.4874	4	t_c °C	385.	5	30		
"C"	0.6846	4	P_c mm	27013.	5	40		
MR (Obs.)	35.62	2	PV/RT			Sugd.	288.3	5
MR (Calc.)	35.398	5	25°C	1.0000	5	Exp. L.1.%/wt.		
(nD-d/2)	1.0188	2	30 mm	1.0000	5	u.		
Dielectric			BP	0.9593	5	Dispersion	113.	2
A | 62 to	6.87976	3	t_e	0.9463	5	Flash Point °C		
B |220 °C	1474.821	3	t_c	0.252	5	Fire Point		
C	210.162	3	ΔHc kcal/m			M Spec.		
A* | 62 to	1.27377	5	ΔHf			Ultra V.		
B* |187 °C	1379.3	5	ΔFf			X-Ray Dif.		
K			Viscosity			Infrared		
c			centistokes			Solubility in +		
t_k | to			η °C			Acetone	∞	
t_x | °C						Carbon tet.	∞	
A' | 25 to	7.23280	5				Benzene	∞	
B' | 62 °C	1673.9	5				Ether	∞	
C'	228.	5	B^v | to			n-Heptane	∞	
A'* 25 to	1.62988	5	A^v | °C			Ethanol	∞	
B'* 62 °C	1573.0	5	(B^v) | to			Water		
Ac | 220 to	7.29810	5	(A^v) | °C			Water in		
Bc | t_c °C	1857.2	5						
Cc	263.	5	c_p liq. °K					
Cryos. A° consts. B°			c_p vap. °K					
t_e °C	177.38	5	c_v vap.					

$T_R = 0.75 T_C$ + grams/100 grams solvent

REFERENCES: 1-Dow   2-API   3-Lit.   4-Calc. from det. data   5-Calc. by formula

SOURCE: API

PURIFICATION: API

LITERATURE REFERENCES: 3 Ind. Eng. Chem. 44, 1430 (1952) P. T. White, et al.

TABLE XXII. MISCELLANEOUS

No. 1

NAME	m-Nitrobenzotrifluoride	STRUCTURAL FORMULA
	a,a,a-Trifluoro-m-nitrotoluene	

Mole % Pur.		Ref.	Molecular Formula $C_7H_4F_3NO_2$		Molecular Weight 191.110	

		Ref.				Ref.						Ref.
F.P. °C	-132.	3	dt/dP °C/mm				f	to				
F.P. 100%			25°C	45.28	5		g	°K				
			BP	0.0529	4		h					
B.P. °C			t_e	0.0350	5							
760 mm	202.75	3	30 mm	0.7614	4		f'	to				
100	135.10	4	ΔHm cal/g				g'	°K				
30	104.82	4					h'					
10	81.6	4	ΔHv cal/g				m	to				
1	42.	5	25°C	72.03	5		n	°K				
Pressure			30 mm	65.05	4		o					
mm 25°C	0.2835	5	BP	55.03	4							
t_e	1277.	5	t_e	52.94	5		m'	to				
Density			t_e (d,e)	52.78	5		n'	°K				
g/ml 20°C			ΔHv/T_e	20.23	5		o'					
d_4^t 25			d 105 to	75.78	5		Surface tension					
30			e 225 °C	0.1024	5		dynes/cm. 20°C					
a			d' 25 to	74.22	5		δ 30					
b			e' 105 °C	0.0874	5		40					
Ref. Index			d_c g/ml				Parachor [P]					
n_D 20°C	1.4719	3	v_c ml/g				20°C					
25	1.4697	4	t_c °C				30					
30	1.4675	3	P_c mm				40					
"C"							Sugd.	307.3	5			
MR (Obs.)			PV/RT				Exp. L.l.%/wt.					
MR (Calc.)			25°C	1.0000	5		u.					
(nD-d/2)			30 mm	1.0000	5		Dispersion					
Dielectric	30.17	3	BP	0.9389	4		Flash Point °C					
A 105 to	7.18025	3	t_e	0.9180	5		Fire Point					
B 320 °C	1710.60	2	t_c				M. Spec.					
C	195.12	3	ΔHc kcal/m				Ultra V.					
A* 105 to	1.79365	5	ΔHf				X-Ray Dif.					
B* 235 °C	1621.98	5	ΔFf				Infrared					
K			Viscosity				Solubility in +					
c			centistokes				Acetone					
t_k to			η °C				Carbon tet.					
t_x °C							Benzene					
A' 25 to	7.53955	5					Ether					
B' 105 °C	1932.93	5					n-Heptane					
C'	214.02	5					Ethanol					
A'* 25 to	2.13992	5	B^v to				Water					
B'* 105 °C	1834.57	5	A^v °C				Water in					
Ac to			(B^v) to									
Bc t_c °C			(A^v) °C									
Cc			c_p liq. °K									
Cryos. A°			c_p vap. °K									
consts. B°												
t_e °C	224.76	5	c_v vap.									

+ grams/100 grams solvent

REFERENCES: 1-Dow 2-API 3-Lit. 4-Calc. from det. data 5-Calc. by formula

SOURCE: Lit.

PURIFICATION: Lit.

LITERATURE REFERENCES: 3 J.A.C.S. 75, 1997 (1953) Kardon and Saylor

No. 2

NAME	2-Chloro-5-Nitrobenzotrifluoride	STRUCTURAL FORMULA
	2-Chloro-α,α,α-trifluoro-5-nitrotoluene	CF₃ / Cl / NO₂ (ring)

Mole % Pur.	Ref.	Molecular Formula $C_7H_3ClF_3NO_2$	Molecular Weight 225.559

		Ref.			Ref.			Ref.
F.P. °C	21.7	3	dt/dP °C/mm			f | to		
F.P. 100%			25°C	196.5	5	g | °K		
B.P. °C			BP	0.05570	4	h		
760 mm	231.88	3	t_e	0.03550	5	f' | to		
100	160.70	4	30 mm	0.7995	4	g' | °K		
30	128.89	4	ΔHm cal/g			h'		
10	104.40	5	ΔHv cal/g			m | to		
1	63.05	5	25°C	67.81	5	n | °K		
Pressure			30 mm	59.28	5	o		
mm 25°C	0.0588	5	BP	49.38	5	m' | to		
t_e	1343.2	5	t_e	47.32	5	n' | °K		
Density			t_e (d,e)	46.42	5	o'		
g/ml 20°C			$\Delta Hv/T_e$	20.11	5	Surface tension		
d_4^t 25 / 30	1.5043	3	d | 128 to	71.67	5	dynes/cm. 20°C	27.86	5
a			e | 250 °C	0.0961	5	γ 30		
b			d' | 20 to	69.86	5	40		
Ref. Index			e' | 128 °C	0.0821	5	Parachor [P]		
n_D 20°C / 25 / 30			d_c g/ml			20°C		
"C"			v_c ml/g			30		
MR (Obs.)			t_c °C			40		
MR (Calc.)	41.522	5	P_c mm			Sugd.	344.5	5
(nD-d/2)			PV/RT			Exp. L.1.%/wt.		
Dielectric			25°C	1.0000	5	u.		
A |128 to	7.15409	3	30 mm	1.0000	5	Dispersion		
B |310 °C	1779.91	3	BP	0.9300	5	Flash Point °C		
C	184.64	3	t_e	0.9097	5	Fire Point		
A* |128 to	1.83498	5	t_c			M Spec.		
B* |270 °C	1694.27	5	ΔHc kcal/m			Ultra V.		
K			ΔHf			X-Ray Dif.		
c			ΔFf			Infrared		
t_k | to			Viscosity			Solubility in +		
t_x | °C			centistokes			Acetone		
A' | 10 to	7.60270	5	η °C			Carbon tet.		
B' |128 °C	2075.9	5				Benzene		
C'	210.0	5	B^v | to			Ether		
A'* 20 to	2.26106	5	A^v | °C			n-Heptane		
B'* 128 °C	1975.7	5	(B^v)| to			Ethanol		
Ac | to			(A^v)| °C			Water		
Bc | t_c °C			c_p liq. °K			Water in		
Cc			c_p vap. °K					
Cryos. A°			c_v vap.					
consts. B°								
t_e °C	257.47	5				+ grams/100 grams solvent		

REFERENCES: 1-Dow 2-API 3-Lit. 4-Calc. from det. data 5-Calc. by formula

SOURCE: Lit.

PURIFICATION: Lit.

LITERATURE REFERENCES: 3 J.A.C.S. 75, 1997 (1953) Kardon and Saylor

TABLE XXII.   MISCELLANEOUS

No. 3

NAME	4-Chloro-3-nitrobenzotrifluoride	STRUCTURAL FORMULA
	4-Chloro-α, α, α-trifluoro-3-nitrotoluene	

Mole % Pur.	Ref.	Molecular Formula $C_7H_3F_3ClNO_2$	Molecular Weight 225.559	

		Ref.			Ref.			Ref.
F.P. °C	-2.54	3	dt/dP			f $\quad$ to		
F.P. 100%			°C/mm			g $\quad$ °K		
			25°C	142.51	4	h		
B.P. °C			BP	0.0543	4			
760 mm	222.58	3	t_e	0.0348	5	f' $\quad$ to		
100	153.15	4				g' $\quad$ °K		
30	122.13	4	30 mm	0.7800	4	h'		
10	98.30	4	ΔHm cal/g					
1	58.2	5				m $\quad$ to		
			ΔHv cal/g			n $\quad$ °K		
Pressure			25°C	68.04	5	o		
mm 25°C	0.0808	5	30 mm	58.84	5			
t_e	1334.3	5	BP	49.31	5	m' $\quad$ to		
			t_e	46.89	5	n' $\quad$ °K		
Density			t_e (d, e)	46.97	5	o'		
g/ml 20°C			ΔHv/T_e	21.33	5			
d_4^t $\quad$ 25						Surface tension		
$\quad$ 30			d $\quad$ 125 to	70.43	5	dynes/cm. 20°C		
a			e $\quad$ 255 °C	0.0949	5	γ $\quad$ 30		
b			d' $\quad$ 20 to	70.40	5	$\quad$ 40		
Ref. Index			e' $\quad$ 125 °C	0.0947	5			
n_D $\quad$ 20°C	1.4895	3				Parachor [P]		
$\quad$ 25	1.4874	4	d_c g/ml			$\quad$ 20°C		
$\quad$ 30	1.4852	3	v_c ml/g			$\quad$ 30		
"C"			t_c °C			$\quad$ 40		
			P_c mm			$\quad$ Sugd. 344.5	5	
MR (Obs.)			PV/RT			Exp. L.1.%/wt.		
MR (Calc.)			25°C	1.0000	5	$\quad$ u.		
(nD-d/2)			30 mm	1.0000	5	Dispersion		
Dielectric	12.8	3	BP	0.9400	4			
			t_e	0.9215	5	Flash Point °C		
A $\quad$ 122 to	7.15778	3	t_c			Fire Point		
B $\quad$ 360 °C	1738.71	3						
C	183.95	3	ΔHc kcal/m			M. Spec.		
			ΔHf			Ultra V.		
A* $\quad$ 122 to	1.82994	5	ΔFf			X-Ray Dif.		
B* $\quad$ 260 °C	1650.18	5				Infrared		
K			Viscosity			Solubility in +		
c			centistokes			$\quad$ Acetone		
t_k $\quad$ to			η $\quad$ °C			$\quad$ Carbon tet.		
t_x $\quad$ °C						$\quad$ Benzene		
A' $\quad$ 20 to	7.51566	5				$\quad$ Ether		
B' $\quad$ 122 °C	1964.69	5				$\quad$ n-Heptane		
C'	203.23	5	B^v $\quad$ to			$\quad$ Ethanol		
			A^v $\quad$ °C			$\quad$ Water		
A'* $\quad$ 20 to	2.19002	5	(B^v) $\quad$ to			$\quad$ Water in		
B'* $\quad$ 122 °C	1871.30	5	(A^v) $\quad$ °C					
Ac $\quad$ to			c_p liq. °K					
Bc $\quad$ t_c °C								
Cc			c_p vap. °K					
Cryos. A°								
consts. B°			c_v vap.					
t_e °C	247.22	5						

$\quad$ + grams/100 grams solvent

REFERENCES: 1-Dow 2-API 3-Lit. 4-Calc. from det. data 5-Calc. by formula
SOURCE: $\quad$ Lit.
PURIFICATION: $\quad$ Lit.
LITERATURE REFERENCES: 3 J.A.C.S. 75, 1997 (1953) Kardon and Saylor

No. 4

NAME	Phenylhydrazine		STRUCTURAL FORMULA

Structural formula: benzene ring with $NHNH_2$

Mole % Pur. 99.63	Ref. 1	Molecular Formula $C_6H_8N_2$	Molecular Weight 108.140

		Ref.			Ref.			Ref.
F.P. °C	19.60	1	dt/dP			f | to |		
F.P. 100%	19.79	1	°C/mm			g | |__ °K_		
B.P. °C			25°C	400.3	5	h |		
760 mm	243.09	1	BP	0.05500	5			
100	172.11	1	t_e	0.0345	5	f' | to		
30	139.9	5	30 mm	0.8122	5	g' | |__ °K_		
10	115.0	5				h' |		
1	72.8	5	ΔHm cal/g	31.04	4			
Pressure			ΔHv cal/g			m | to		
mm 25°C	0.0278	5	25°C	147.08	5	n | |__ °K_		
t_e	1358.1	5	30 mm	128.7	5	o |		
Density			BP	107.68	5			
g/ml 20°C	1.09859	1	t_e	103.15	5	m' | to		
d_4^t 25	1.09445	1	t_e (d, e)	102.44	5	n' | |__ °K_		
30	1.08056	1	ΔHv/T_e	20.58	5	o' |		
a	1.11515	4	d | 140 to	157.26	5	Surface tension		
b	-0.0₃828	4	e | 260 °C	0.2040	5	dynes/cm. 20°C	53.57	5
			d' | 25 to	151.08	5	30	51.97	5
Ref. Index			e' | 140 °C	0.1598	5	40	50.41	5
n_D 20°C	1.60837	1	d_c g/ml			Parachor [P]		
25	1.60604	1	v_c ml/g			20°C		
30	1.59455	1	t_c °C			30		
"C"	0.7900	4	P_c mm			40		
MR (Obs.)	34.054	4	PV/RT			N = 12.5 Sugd. 266.3		5
MR (Calc.)	33.447	5	25°C	1.0000	5	Exp. L.1.%/wt.		
(nD-d/2)	1.05908	4	30 mm	1.0000	5	u.		
Dielectric	7.106	1	BP	0.9218	5	Dispersion		
A | 140 to	7.41124	4	t_e	0.9007	5	Flash Point °C		
B |_335°C	1975.68	4	t_c			Fire Point		
C	193.	5	ΔHc kcal/m			M Spec.		
A* | 140 to	1.77454	5	ΔHf			Ultra V.		
B* |_280°C	1889.2	5	ΔFf			X-Ray Dif.		
K			Viscosity			Infrared		
c			centistokes			Solubility in +		
t_k | to			η 20 °C	13.393	1	Acetone		
t_x | °C			40	6.2138	1	Carbon tet.		
A' | 25 to	7.78509	5	60	dec.	1	Benzene		
B' |_140°C	2232.5	5				Ether		
C'	214.	5	B^v | to			n-Heptane		
A'* 25 to	2.11369	5	A^v | °C			Ethanol		
B'* 140 °C	2128.3	5	(B^v)| to			Water		
Ac | 335 to	7.8233	5	(A^v)| °C			Water in		
Bc|_t_c_°C_	2434.5	5	c_p liq. °K					
Cc	251.	5						
Cryos. A°	0.01972	1	c_p vap. °K					
consts. B°								
t_e °C	268.79	5	c_v vap.					

$T_R = 0.75 T_c$ + grams/100 grams solvent

REFERENCES: 1-Dow 2-API 3-Lit. 4-Calc. from det. data 5-Calc. by formula

SOURCE: Dow

PURIFICATION: Dow

LITERATURE REFERENCES:

TABLE XXII. MISCELLANEOUS 511

No. 5

NAME	p-Phenetidine		STRUCTURAL FORMULA

NH₂ structural formula shown: NH_2 benzene ring with OC_2H_5

Mole % Pur. 99.88	Ref. 1	Molecular Formula $C_8H_{11}NO$	Molecular Weight 137.176		

		Ref.			Ref.					Ref.
F.P. °C	4.65	1	dt/dP			f		to		
F.P. 100%			°C/mm			g		°K		
			25°C	1064.8	5	h				
B.P. °C			BP	0.05449	5					
760 mm	248.59	1	t_e	0.03405	5	f'		to		
100	178.92	1	30 mm	0.7832	4	g'		°K		
30	147.76	4	ΔHm cal/g	19.80	4	h'				
10	123.8	5								
1	83.1	5	ΔHv cal/g			m		to		
			25°C	131.35	5	n		°K		
Pressure			30 mm	109.25	5	o				
mm 25°C	0.0092	5	BP	88.09	5					
t_e	1377.2	5	t_e	83.79	5	m'		to		
			t_e (d, e)	82.35	5	n'		°K		
Density			ΔHv/T_e	20.97	5	o'				
g/ml 20°C	1.06117	1				Surface tension				
d_4^t 25	1.05680	1	d 148 to	140.24	5	dynes/cm. 20°C	40.2	1		
30	1.05243	4	e 260 °C	0.2098	5	γ 30	39.25	1		
a	1.07865	4	d' 20 to	135.85	5	40	38.25	1		
b	-0.0₃874	4	e' 148 °C	0.1800	5					
Ref. Index			d_c g/ml			Parachor [P]				
n_D 20°C	1.56101	1	v_c ml/g			20°C	325.5	4		
25	1.55856	1	t_c °C			30	326.2	4		
30	1.54660	1	P_c mm			40	326.5	4		
"C"	0.6905	4				O=20 N=12.5 Sugd.	334.7	5		
MR (Obs.)	41.860	4	PV/RT			Exp. L.l.%/wt.				
MR (Calc.)	41.496	5	25°C	1.0000	5	u.				
(nD-d/2)	1.03043	4	30 mm	1.0000	5	Dispersion				
Dielectric	7.431	1	BP	0.9259	5	Flash Point °C				
A 148 to	7.16534	4	t_e	0.9033	5	Fire Point				
B 300 °C	1750.62	4	t_c			M. Spec.				
C	160.0	4	ΔHc kcal/m			Ultra V.				
A* 148 to	1.64219	5	ΔHf			X-Ray Dif.				
B* 285 °C	1676.51	5	ΔFf			Infrared				
K			Viscosity			Solubility in +				
c			centistokes			Acetone				
t_k to			η 20 °C	13.532	1	Carbon tet.				
t_x °C			40	5.4381	1	Benzene				
A' 20 to	7.87653	5	60	2.9766	1	Ether				
B' 148 °C	2216.5	5	80	1.9206	1	n-Heptane				
C'	198.6	5	B^v to			Ethanol				
A'* 20 to	2.32186	5	A^v °C			Water				
B'* 148 °C	2122.0	5	(B^v) to			Water in				
Ac to			(A^v) °C							
Bc t_c °C			c_p liq. °K							
Cc										
Cryos. A°	0.01773	1	c_p vap. °K							
consts. B°										
t_e °C	274.79	5	c_v vap.							

+ grams/100 grams solvent

REFERENCES: 1-Dow 2-API 3-Lit. 4-Calc. from det. data 5-Calc. by formula

SOURCE: Dow

PURIFICATION: Dow Dist. Chromat.

LITERATURE REFERENCES:

No. 6

NAME	N-Butylacetanilide		STRUCTURAL FORMULA

$N(C_4H_9)COCH_3$

Mole % Pur. 99.74	Ref. 1	Molecular Formula $C_{12}H_{17}NO$	Molecular Weight 191.264

		Ref.			Ref.			Ref.
F.P. °C	24.47	1	dt/dP			f	to	
F.P. 100%	24.54	1	°C/mm			g	°K	
B.P. °C			25°C	2082.0	5	h		
760 mm	281.07	1	BP	0.06029	4			
100	203.40	1	t_e	0.0362	5	f'	to	
30	168.4	4	30 mm	0.8822	4	g'	°K	
10	141.4	5	ΔHm cal/g	22.07	4	h'		
1	95.7	1						
Pressure			ΔHv cal/g			m	to	
mm 25°C	0.00491	5	25°C	90.35	5	n	°K	
t_e	1439.	5	30 mm	76.55	5	o		
Density			BP	62.83	5	m'	to	
g/ml 20°C	0.99115	1	t_e	59.66	5	n'	°K	
d_4^t 25	0.98707	1	t_e (d, e)	59.04	5	o'		
30	0.98313	4	ΔHv/T_e	19.49	5	Surface tension		
a	1.00745	4	d 160 to	97.07	5	dynes/cm. 20°C	35.96	1
b	-0.0₃802	4	e 300 °C	0.1218	5	γ 30	34.96	1
Ref. Index			d' 25 to	92.76	5	40	33.88	1
n_D 20°C	1.51457	1	e' 160 °C	0.0962	5	Parachor [P]		
25	1.51246	1	d_c g/ml	0.311	5	20°C	472.6	4
30	1.50772	1	v_c ml/g	3.21	5	30	473.1	4
"C"			t_c °C	494.		40	473.2	4
MR (Obs.)	58.150	4	P_c mm	19880.	5	Sugd.	468.4	5
MR (Calc.)	58.336	5	PV/RT			Exp. L.l.%/wt.		
(nD-d/2)	1.01900	4	25°C	1.0000	5	u.		
Dielectric	11.66	1	30 mm	1.0000	5	Dispersion		
A 170 to	7.32668	1	BP	0.9073	5	Flash Point °C		
B 380 °C	2085.31	1	t_e	0.8836	5	Fire Point		
C	188.08	1	t_c	0.255	5	M Spec.		
A* 168 to	1.9292	5	ΔHc kcal/m			Ultra V.		
B* 320 °C	2000.0	5	ΔHf			X-Ray Dif.		
K			ΔFf			Infrared		
c			Viscosity			Solubility in +		
t_k to			centistokes			Acetone		
t_x °C			η 20 °C	16.2754	1	Carbon tet.		
A' 60 to	7.6952	5	40	6.6868	1	Benzene		
B' 170 °C	2356.3	5	60	3.6049	1	Ether		
C'	210.5	5	80	2.2885	1	n-Heptane		
A'* 60 to	2.2568	5	B^V to			Ethanol		
B'* 170 °C	2250.0	5	A^V °C			Water		
Ac 380 to	9.2820	5	(B^V) 55 to	1124.8	4	Water in		
Bc t_c °C	4975.	5	(A^V) 90 °C	3.18632	4			
Cc	504.3	5	c_p liq. °K					
Cryos. A°	0.02275	1	c_p vap. °K					
consts. B°								
t_e °C	312.16	5	c_v vap.					

T_R = 0.85 T_c

+ grams/100 grams solvent

REFERENCES: 1-Dow 2-API 3-Lit. 4-Calc. from det. data 5-Calc. by formula

SOURCE:	Dow
PURIFICATION:	Dow

LITERATURE REFERENCES:

TABLE XXII. MISCELLANEOUS

No. 7

NAME	Methyl anthranilate	STRUCTURAL FORMULA
	o-Amino methylbenzoate	NH_2 CO_2CH_3 (benzene ring)

Mole % Pur. 99.90	Ref. 1	Molecular Formula $C_8H_9NO_2$	Molecular Weight 151.160

		Ref.			Ref.				Ref.
F.P. °C	24.42	1	dt/dP °C/mm			f $\vert$	to °K		
F.P. 100%			25°C	646.0	5	g $\vert$			
B.P. °C			BP	0.05897	4	h $\vert$			
760 mm	259.82	1	t_e	0.03575	5	f' $\vert$	to °K		
100	184.19	1	30 mm	0.8551	4	g' $\vert$			
30	150.23	4	ΔHm cal/g	18.73	4	h' $\vert$			
10	124.20	5	ΔHv cal/g			m $\vert$	to °K		
1	80.0	5	25°C	107.08	5	n $\vert$			
Pressure			30 mm	91.90	5	o $\vert$			
mm 25°C	0.0169	5	BP	79.11	5	m' $\vert$	to °K		
t_e	1427.0	5	t_e	72.69	5	n' $\vert$			
Density			t_e (d,e)	74.45	5	o' $\vert$			
g/ml 20°C	1.16725	1	ΔHv/T_e	19.18	5	Surface tension			
d_4^t 25	1.16283	1	d $\vert$ 150 to	109.45	5	dynes/cm. 20°C	44.12	1
30	1.15841	4	e $\vert$ 270 °C	0.1167	5	ɤ 30	43.02	1
a	1.18493	4	d' $\vert$ 25 to	110.11	5	40	41.92	1
b	-0.0$_3$884	4	e' $\vert$ 150 °C	0.1212	5			
Ref. Index			d_c g/ml			Parachor [P]		
n_D 20°C	1.58327	1	v_c ml/g			20°C	333.76	4
25	1.58096	1	t_c °C			30	334.18	4
30	1.57856	4	P_c mm			40	334.6	4
"C"	0.6509	4	PV/RT			Sugd.	340.1	5
MR (Obs.)	43.30	4	25°C	1.0000	5	Exp. L.l.%/wt.		
MR (Calc.)	43.510#	5	30 mm	1.0000	5	u.		
(nD-d/2)	0.99965	4	BP	0.9325	5	Dispersion		
Dielectric	3.721	1	t_e	0.8949	5	Flash Point °C		
A $\vert$ 150 to	7.24299	4	t_c			Fire Point		
B $\vert$ 260 °C	1963.72	4	ΔHc kcal/m			M. Spec.		
C	190.35	4	ΔHf			Ultra V.		
A* $\vert$ 150 to	1.71345	5	ΔFf			X-Ray Dif.		
B* $\vert$ 320 °C	1865.73	5	Viscosity			Infrared		
K			centistokes			Solubility in +		
c			η 20 °C	7.1420	1	Acetone		
t_k $\vert$ to			40	4.5046	1	Carbon tet.		
t_x $\vert$ °C			60	2.6784	1	Benzene		
A' $\vert$ 20 to	7.57558	5	80	1.7855	1	Ether		
B' $\vert$ 150 °C	2196.85	5				n-Heptane		
C'	210.0	5	B^v $\vert$ 15 to	1533.4	4	Ethanol		
A'* 20 to	2.04652	5	A^v $\vert$ 45 °C	5.76095	4	Water	0.285	1
B'* 150 °C	2093.53	5	$(B^v)\vert$ 55 to	1036.3	4	Water in	1.128	1
Ac $\vert$ to			$(A^v)\vert$ 85 °C	3.31773	4			
Bc t_c °C			c_p liq. °K					
Cc								
Cryos. A°	0.01619	1	c_p vap. °K					
consts. B°								
t_e °C	299.95	5	c_v vap.					

≠ Taking C = O as double bond and conjugated   + grams/100 grams solvent

REFERENCES: 1-Dow 2-API 3-Lit. 4-Calc. from det. data 5-Calc. by formula

SOURCE: Dow

PURIFICATION: Distillation

LITERATURE REFERENCES:

No. 8

NAME	Ethyl anthranilate	STRUCTURAL FORMULA
	o-Amino ethyl Benzoate	NH_2 $CO_2C_2H_5$

Mole % Pur. 99.77	Ref.	Molecular Formula $C_9H_{11}NO_2$	Molecular Weight 165.186

		Ref.			Ref.					Ref.
F.P. °C	14.30	1	dt/dP °C/mm			f	to			
F.P. 100%	14.37	1	25°C	1895.3	5	g	°K			
B.P. °C			BP	0.0607	4	h				
760 mm	268.84	1	t_e	0.0379	5	f'	to			
100	192.8	4	30 mm	0.8473	5	g'	°K			
30	159.0	5	ΔHm cal/g	31.97	4	h'				
10	133.2	5								
1	90.1	5	ΔHv cal/g			m	to			
Pressure			25°C	115.18	5	n	°K			
mm 25°C	0.0049	5	30 mm	88.39	5	o				
t_e	1392.	5	BP	70.00	5	m'	to			
Density			t_e	64.74	5	n'	°K			
g/ml 20°C	1.11788	1	t_e (d,e)	64.86	5	o'				
d_4^t 25	1.11348	1	$\Delta Hv/T_e$	18.67	5					
30	1.10908	4	d 160 to	115.01	5	Surface tension				
a	1.13548	4	e 300 °C	0.1674	5	dynes/cm. 20°C	39.62	1		
b	-0.0₃88	4	d' 25 to	120.18	5	γ	30	38.75	1	
Ref. Index			e' 160 °C	0.1999	5		40	37.75	1	
n_D 20°C	1.56503	1	d_c g/ml			Parachor [P]				
25	1.56234	1	v_c ml/g				20°C	370.9	4	
30	1.55780	1	t_c °C				30	371.6	4	
"C"	0.6958	4	P_c mm				40	372.1	4	
MR (Obs.)	48.098	4	PV/RT				Sugd.	379.5	5	
MR (Calc.)	46.126	5	25°C	1.0000	5	Exp. L.l.%/wt.				
(nD-d/2)	1.00609	4	30 mm	1.0000	5	u.				
Dielectric	4.140	1	BP	0.9181	5	Dispersion				
A 160 to	6.92119	1	t_e	0.8736	5	Flash Point °C				
B 320 °C	1734.75	1	t_c			Fire Point				
C	159.67	1	ΔHc kcal/m			M Spec.				
A* 160 to	1.50060	5	ΔHf			Ultra V.				
B* 310 °C	1668.5	5	ΔFf			X-Ray Dif.				
K			Viscosity			Infrared				
c			centistokes			Solubility in +				
t_k to			η 20 °C	9.4307	1	Acetone				
t_x °C			40	4.5646	1	Carbon tet.				
A' 25 to	7.26417	5	60	2.7268	1	Benzene				
B' 160 °C	1960.2	5	100	1.8452	1	Ether				
C'	179.7	5	B^v 30 to	1087.83	4	n-Heptane				
A'* 25 to	1.80529	5	A^v 90 °C	3.18613	4	Ethanol				
B'* 160 °C	1876.8	5	(B^v) to			Water				
Ac to			(A^v) °C			Water in				
Bc t_c °C			c_p liq. °K							
Cc										
Cryos. A°	0.03218	1	c_p vap. °K							
consts. B°										
t_e °C	299.6	5	c_v vap.							

+ grams/100 grams solvent

REFERENCES: 1-Dow 2-API 3-Lit. 4-Calc. from det. data 5-Calc. by formula

SOURCE: Dow

PURIFICATION: Distillation

LITERATURE REFERENCES:

TABLE XXII. MISCELLANEOUS   515

No. 9

NAME	Morpholine	STRUCTURAL FORMULA
	Tetrahydro-p-isoxazine	

Structural formula:
$$H_2C \begin{array}{c} NH \\ \end{array} CH_2$$
$$H_2C \begin{array}{c} \\ O \end{array} CH_2$$

Mole % Pur. 99.71	Ref. 1	Molecular Formula C_4H_9NO	Molecular Weight 87.120

		Ref.			Ref.				Ref.
F.P. °C	-4.75	1	dt/dP			f	to		
F.P. 100%			°C/mm			g	_ _ °K		
			25°C	1.3945	5	h			
B.P. °C			BP	0.04517	4				
760 mm	128.29	1	t_e	0.03412	5	f'	to		
100	70.54	1	30 mm	0.6489	4	g'	_ _ °K		
30	44.73	4	ΔHm cal/g	39.77	4	h'			
10	24.86	4				m	to		
1	-37.0	5	ΔHv cal/g			n	_ _ °K		
			25°C	120.61	5	o			
Pressure			30 mm	118.44	5				
mm 25°C	10.08	5	BP	101.64	5	m'	to		
t_e	1082.6	5	t_e	99.51	5	n'	_ _ °K		
			t_e (d, e)	99.22	5	o'			
Density			$\Delta Hv/T_e$	20.935	5				
g/ml 20°C	1.00047	1				Surface tension			
d_4^t 25	0.99573	1	d 44 to	127.40	5	dynes/cm. 20°C	37.84	1
30	0.99084	4	e 135 °C	0.2010	5	γ 30	36.50	1
			d' 15 to	123.36	5	40	35.14	1
a	1.01970	4	e' 44 °C	0.1100	5			
b	-0.00096	4	d_c g/ml			Parachor [P]		
			v_c ml/g			20°C	216.0	4
Ref. Index			t_c °C			30	216.1	4
n_D 20°C	1.45480	1	P_c mm			N = 14.4 40	216.2	4
25	1.45265	1	PV/RT			O = 20 Sugd.	213.8	5
50	1.44158	1	25°C	1.0000	5	Exp. L.l.%/wt.		
"C"	0.5711	4	30 mm	1.0000	5	u.		
MR (Obs.)	23.617	4	BP	0.9500	5	Dispersion		
MR (Calc.)	23.685	5	t_e	0.9397	5	Flash Point °C		
(nD-d/2)	0.95457	4	t_c			Fire Point		
Dielectric	7.176	1	ΔHc kcal/m			M. Spec.		
A 44 to	7.16030	4	ΔHf			Ultra V.		
B 170 °C	1447.70	4	ΔFf			X-Ray Dif.		
C	210.0	4	Viscosity			Infrared		
A* 44 to	1.48270	5	centistokes			Solubility in +		
B* 160 °C	1366.046	5	η 20 °C	2.2900	1	Acetone		
K			40	1.5216	1	Carbon tet.		
c			60	1.1010	1	Benzene		
t_k to			80	0.8430	1	Ether		
t_x °C			B^v 30 to	709.3	4	n-Heptane		
A' 0 to	7.71813	5	A^v 90 °C	3.91761	4	Ethanol		
B' 44 °C	1745.8	5	(B^v) to			Water		
C'	235.0	5	(A^v) °C			Water in		
A'* 15 to	1.99494	5						
B'* 44 °C	1643.4	5	c_p liq. °K					
Ac to								
Bc t_c °C			c_p vap. °K					
Cc								
Cryos. A°	0.02421	1	c_v vap.					
consts. B°								
t_e °C	140.887	5						

+ grams/100 grams solvent

REFERENCES: 1-Dow 2-API 3-Lit. 4-Calc. from det. data 5-Calc. by formula

SOURCE:	Dow
PURIFICATION:	Distillation
LITERATURE REFERENCES:	

No. 10

NAME	Furan		STRUCTURAL FORMULA
	Furfurane		

Mole % Pur. 99.98	Ref. 3	Molecular Formula C_4H_4O	Molecular Weight 68.072

		Ref.			Ref.			Ref.
F.P. °C	-85.65	3	dt/dP °C/mm			f $\vert$ to		
F.P. 100%			25°C	0.04359	5	g $\vert$ °K		
B.P. °C			BP	0.04131	4	h $\vert$		
760 mm	31.360	3	t_e	0.03402	5	f' $\vert$ to		
100	-14.085	4	30 mm	0.5080	4	g' $\vert$ °K		
30	-35.14	4	ΔHm cal/g	13.35	3	h' $\vert$		
10	-50.20	4	ΔHv cal/g			m $\vert$ to		
1	-75.6	5	25°C	96.38	3	n $\vert$ °K		
Pressure			30 mm	108.52	5	o $\vert$		
mm 25°C	599.9	4	BP	95.105	3			
t_e	821.4	5	t_e	94.29	5	m' $\vert$ to		
Density			t_e (d,e)	94.63	5	n' $\vert$ °K		
g/ml 10°C	0.95144	3	ΔHv/T_e	20.93	5	o' $\vert$		
d_4^t 15	0.94467	3	d $\vert$ -35 to	101.43	5	Surface tension		
20	0.93781	3	e $\vert$ 35 °C	0.2017	5	dynes/cm. 20°C	22.34	5
a	0.97864	4	d' $\vert$ to			ɣ 30		
b	-0.00130	4	e' $\vert$ °C			40		
Ref. Index			d_c g/ml			Parachor [P]		
n_D 20°C	1.42140	3	v_c ml/g			20°C		
25			t_c °C			30		
30			P_c mm			40		
"C"	0.5973	4				Sugd.	162.5	5
MR (Obs.)	18.422	4	PV/RT			Exp. L. 1.%/wt.		
MR (Calc.)	19.181	5	25°C	0.9697	4	u.		
(nD-d/2)	0.94568	4	30 mm	1.0000	5	Dispersion		
Dielectric			BP	0.9655	4	Flash Point °C		
A $\vert$ -35 to	6.97523	3	t_e	0.9630	5	Fire Point		
B $\vert$ 90 °C	1060.851	3	t_c			M Spec.		
C	227.740	3	ΔHc kcal/m			Ultra V.		
A* $\vert$ -35 to	1.33663	5	ΔHf	14.90	3	X-Ray Dif.		
B* $\vert$ 40 °C	1006.9	5	ΔFf			Infrared		3
K			Viscosity			Solubility in +		
c			centistokes			Acetone		
t_k $\vert$ to			η °C			Carbon tet.		
t_x $\vert$ °C						Benzene		
A' $\vert$ to						Ether		
B' $\vert$ °C						n-Heptane		
C' $\vert$			B^v $\vert$ to			Ethanol		
A'* to			A^v $\vert$ °C			Water		
B'* °C			(B^v) $\vert$ to			Water in		
Ac $\vert$ to			(A^v) $\vert$ °C					
Bc $\vert$ t_c °C			c_p liq. 1.0 °K	0.3861	3			
Cc			21.6	0.4000	3			
Cryos. A°			c_p vap. °K					
consts. B°								
t_e °C	33.51	5	c_v vap.					

+ grams/100 grams solvent

REFERENCES:	1-Dow	2-API	3-Lit.	4-Calc. from det. data	5-Calc. by formula
SOURCE:	Lit.				
PURIFICATION:	Lit.				

LITERATURE REFERENCES: 3 J.A.C.S. 74, 4662, (1952) G. B. Guthrie et al.

TABLE XXII. MISCELLANEOUS

517

No. 11

NAME	Cyclooctatetraene					STRUCTURAL FORMULA

Structural formula:

HC–CH / HC–CH / HC–CH / HC–CH (octagon ring) CH

Mole % Pur. 99.9	Ref. 3	Molecular Formula	C_8H_8	Molecular Weight 104.144		

		Ref.			Ref.			Ref.
F.P. °C	-4.68	3	dt/dP			f	to	
F.P. 100%			°C/mm			g	°K	
			25°C	2.195	5	h		
B.P. °C			BP	0.04900	5			
760 mm	140.557	4	t_e	0.03598	5	f'	to	
100	78.163	3	30 mm	0.6962	4	g'	°K	
30	50.42	4				h'		
10	29.1	4	ΔHm cal/g	25.87	3			
1	-6.3	5				m	to	
			ΔHv cal/g			n	°K	
Pressure			25°C	98.24	5	o		
mm 25°C	7.87	5	30 mm	95.67	5			
t_e	1124.0	5	BP	83.60	5	m'	to	
Density			t_e	81.74	5	n'	°K	
g/ml 20°C			t_e (d, e)	81.57	5	o'		
d_4^t 25			ΔHv/T_e	19.85	5			
30								
a			d 50 to	102.42	5	Surface tension		
b			e 160 °C	0.1339	5	dynes/cm. 20°C		
			d' 0 to	100.77	5	γ 30		
Ref. Index			e' 50 °C	0.1011	5	40		
n_D 20°C								
25			d_c g/ml			Parachor [P]		
30			v_c ml/g			20°C		
"C"			t_c °C			30		
			P_c mm			40		
MR (Obs.)			PV/RT			Sugd.	268.0	5
MR (Calc.)	40.156	5	25°C	1.0000	5	Exp. L. l. %/wt.		
(nD-d/2)			30 mm	1.0000	5	u.		
Dielectric			BP	0.9530	5	Dispersion		
A 50 to	7.06926	3	t_e	0.9418	5	Flash Point °C		
B 210 °C	1504.036	3	t_c			Fire Point		
C	218.534	3	ΔHc kcal/m			M. Spec.		
A* 50 to	1.44012	5	ΔHf			Ultra V.		
B* 170 °C	1412.1	5	ΔFf			X-Ray Dif.		
K			Viscosity			Infrared		
c			centistokes			Solubility in +		
t_k to			η °C			Acetone		
t_x °C						Carbon tet.		
A' 0 to	7.30765	5				Benzene		
B' 50 °C	1635.0	5				Ether		
C'	230.	5	B^v to			n-Heptane		
A'* 0 to	1.66300	5	A^v °C			Ethanol		
B'* 50 °C	1534.8	5	(B^v) to			Water		
Ac to			(A^v) °C			Water in		
Bc t_c °C								
Cc			c_p liq. °K					
Cryos. A°			c_p vap. °K					
consts. B°								
t_e °C	155.730	5	c_v vap.					

+ grams/100 grams solvent

REFERENCES: 1-Dow 2-API 3-Lit. 4-Calc. from det. data 5-Calc. by formula

SOURCE: Lit.

PURIFICATION: Lit.

LITERATURE REFERENCES: 3 J.A.C.S. 71, 1634, (1949), D. W. Scott et al.

No. 12

NAME	Diphenylmethane	STRUCTURAL FORMULA

$\bigcirc$ CH_2 $\bigcirc$

Mole % Pur.	99.64	Ref. 1	Molecular Formula	$C_{13}H_{12}$	Molecular Weight	168.226

		Ref.				Ref.					Ref.
F.P. °C	25.21	1	dt/dP °C/mm				f	to			
F.P. 100%	25.35	1					g	°K			
B.P. °C			25°C	649.6	5		h				
760 mm	264.25	1	BP	0.06064	5						
100	186.73	1	t_e	0.03708	5		f'	to			
30	152.08	5	30 mm	0.8712	5		g'	°K			
10	125.5	5					h'				
1	80.6	5	ΔHm cal/g	25.98	4						
			ΔHv cal/g				m	to			
Pressure			25°C	94.97	5		n	°K			
mm 25°C	0.0170	5	30 mm	81.74	5		o				
t_e	1416.	5	BP	67.78	5						
Density			t_e	64.42	5		m'	to			
g/ml 20°C	1.00592	1	t_e (d, e)	63.97	5		n'	°K			
d_4^t 25	1.00192	1	$\Delta Hv/T_e$	19.08	5		o'				
30	0.99792	4	d 150 to	100.67	5		Surface tension				
a	1.02192	5	e 295 °C	0.1245	5		dynes/cm. 20°C	38.06	1		
b	-0.0380	5	d' 25 to	97.57	5		30	36.98	1		
Ref. Index			e' 150 °C	0.1041	5		40	35.99	1		
n_D 20°C	1.57527	1	d_c g/ml				Parachor [P]				
25	1.57074	1	v_c ml/g				20°C	415.4	4		
30	1.56390	1	t_c °C	494.4	5		30	415.7	4		
"C"	0.7456	4	P_c mm	22367.	5		40	416.2	4		
MR (Obs.)	55.284	4	PV/RT				Sugd.	419.0	5		
MR (Calc.)	55.032	5	25°C	1.0000	5		Exp. L.1.%/wt.				
(nD-d/2)	1.07409	4	30 mm	1.0000	5		u.				
Dielectric	2.541	1	BP	0.9203	5		Dispersion				
A 150 to	7.16125	4	t_e	0.8961	5		Flash Point °C				
B 310 °C	1944.42	4	t_c				Fire Point				
C	190.	5	ΔHc kcal/m				M Spec.				
A* 150 to	1.69830	5	ΔHf				Ultra V.				
B* 305 °C	1853.7	5	ΔFf				X-Ray Dif.				
K							Infrared				
c			Viscosity				Solubility in +				
t_k to			centistokes				Acetone				
t_x °C			η 20 °C	3.1807	1		Carbon tet.				
A' 25 to	7.51935	5	40	2.1351	1		Benzene				
B' 150 °C	2197.1	5	60	1.5499	1		Ether				
C'	211.6	5	80	1.1896	1		n-Heptane				
A'* 25 to	2.03468	5	B^v 30 to	702.51	4		Ethanol				
B'* 150 °C	2092.8	5	A^v 90 °C	2.08643	4		Water				
Ac 310 to	7.60249	5	(B^v) to				Water in				
Bc t_c °C	2410.9	5	(A^v) °C								
Cc	246.8	5	c_p liq. °K								
Cryos. A°	0.02472	1	c_p vap. °K								
consts. B°											
t_e °C	294.88	5	c_v vap.								

$T_R = 0.76 T_c$ + grams/100 grams solvent

REFERENCES: 1-Dow   2-API   3-Lit.   4-Calc. from det. data   5-Calc. by formula

SOURCE:	Dow
PURIFICATION:	Dow

LITERATURE REFERENCES:

TABLE XXII. MISCELLANEOUS

No. 13

NAME	Spiropentane		STRUCTURAL FORMULA

Mole % Pur. 99.87	Ref. 3	Molecular Formula C_5H_8	Molecular Weight 68.114

		Ref.			Ref.				Ref.
F.P. °C	-107.06	3	dt/dP °C/mm			f	to		
F.P. 100%			25°C	0.05709	4	g	°K		
B.P. °C			BP	0.03819	4	h			
760 mm	38.977	3	t_e	0.03529	5	f'	to		
100	-9.41	4	30 mm	0.5333	4	g'	°K		
30	-30.72	4	ΔHm cal/g	22.61	3	h'			
10	-46.9	5	ΔHv cal/g			m	to		
1	-73.4	5	25°C	96.485	3	n	°K		
Pressure			30 mm	106.63	4	o			
mm 25°C	457.7	4	BP	93.86	3	m'	to		
t_e	842.0	5	t_e	93.32	5	n'	°K		
Density			t_e (d, e)	93.31	5	o'			
g/ml 20°C	0.755	3'	$\Delta Hv/T_e$	20.14	5	Surface tension			
d_4^t 25 30			d -30 to	100.967	4	dynes/cm. 20°C			
a	0.7744	5	e 50 °C	0.1824	4	γ 30			
b	-0.0009	5	d' to			40			
Ref. Index			e' °C			Parachor [P]			
n_D 20°C 25 30	1.41200	3	d_c g/ml	0.220	5	20°C 30			
"C"			v_c ml/g	4.54	5	40			
MR (Obs.)	22.43	4	t_c °C	193.6	5	Sugd.			
MR (Calc.)	22.32	5	P_c mm	25000.	5	Exp. L.1.%/wt.			
(nD-d/2)	1.0345	4	PV/RT			u.			
Dielectric	2.016	5	25°C	0.9732	4	Dispersion			
A -30 to	6.91794	3	30 mm	1.0054	4	Flash Point °C			
B 100 °C	1090.589	3	BP	0.9625	4	Fire Point			
C	231.165	3	t_e	0.9602	5	M. Spec.			
A* -30 to	1.20119	4	t_c	0.265	5	Ultra V.			
B* 60 °C	1015.87	4	ΔHc kcal/m			X-Ray Dif.			
K			ΔHf			Infrared			
c			ΔFf			Solubility in +			
t_k to			Viscosity			Acetone	∞		
t_x °C			centistokes			Carbon tet.	∞		
A' to			η °C			Benzene	∞		
B' °C						Ether	∞		
C'						n-Heptane	∞		
A'* to			B^v to			Ethanol	∞		
B'* °C			A^v °C			Water			
Ac 100 to	8.06920	5	(B^v) to			Water in			
Bc t_c °C	1975.29	5	(A^v) °C						
Cc	344.44	5	c_p liq. °K						
Cryos. A° consts. B°			c_p vap. °K						
t_e °C	41.983	5	c_v vap.						

+ grams/100 grams solvent

REFERENCES: 1-Dow 2-API 3-Lit. 4-Calc. from det. data 5-Calc. by formula

SOURCE: Lit.

PURIFICATION: Lit.

LITERATURE REFERENCES: 3 J.A.C.S. 72, 4664 (1950) Scott, Finke, Hubbard,
McCullough, Gross, Williamson, Washington, and Huffman; 3' J.A.C.S. 66, 314 (1944)
Murray and Stevenson.

No. 14

NAME	Thiacyclobutane		STRUCTURAL FORMULA
	Trimethylene sulfide		$CH_2 - S$
			$CH_2 - CH_2$

Mole % Pur. 99.95	Ref. 3	Molecular Formula C_3H_6S	Molecular Weight 74.124

		Ref.			Ref.			Ref.
F.P. °C	-73.25	3	dt/dP			f | to		
F.P. 100%			°C/mm			g | °K		
			25°C	0.3889	4	h |		
B.P. °C			BP	0.04414	4			
760 mm	94.969	3	t_e	0.03536	5	f' | to		
100	38.875	3				g' | °K		
30	14.013	4	30 mm	0.6233	4	h' |		
10	-14.90	4	ΔHm cal/g					
1	-36.20	5				m | to		
			ΔHv cal/g			n | °K		
Pressure			25°C	115.48	3'	o |		
mm 25°C	52.61	4	30 mm	118.26	5			
t_e	1007.3	5	BP	104.28	5	m' | to		
			t_e	102.61	5	n' | °K		
Density			t_e (d, e)	102.60	5	o' |		
g/ml 20°C	1.02000	3	ΔHv/T_e	20.12	5			
d_4^t 25	1.01472	3				Surface tension		
30	1.00957	3	d | 10 to	120.68	5	dynes/cm. 20°C	36.3	3
			e | 115 °C	0.1727	5	γ 30	35.6	3
a	1.04097	4	d' | to			40	35.0	3
b	-0.00105	4	e' | °C					
Ref. Index			d_c g/ml			Parachor [P]		
n_D 20°C	1.51020	3	v_c ml/g			20°C	178.41	4
25	1.50738	3	t_c °C	302.0	5	30	178.47	4
30	1.50448	3	P_c mm			40	178.62	4
"C"	0.6572	4				Sugd.	176.8	5
MR (Obs.)	21.743	4	PV/RT			Exp. L.1.%/wt.		
MR (Calc.)	21.824	5	25°C	0.9999	5	u.		
(nD-d/2)	1.00020	4	30 mm	1.0000	5	Dispersion		
Dielectric			BP	0.9650	5	Flash Point °C		
A | -15 to	7.01667	3	t_e	0.9580	5	Fire Point		
B | 210 °C	1321.331	3	t_c			M Spec.		
C	224.513	3	ΔHc kcal/m			Ultra V.		
			ΔHf	25.87	3'	X-Ray Dif.		
A* | -15 to	1.26847	5	ΔFf	16.43	3'	Infrared		
B* | 115 °C	1234.26	5				Solubility in +		
K			Viscosity			Acetone		
c			centistokes			Carbon tet.		
t_k | to			η 20 °C	0.640	3	Benzene		
t_x | °C			25	0.609	3	Ether		
A' | to			30	0.578	3	n-Heptane		
B' | °C						Ethanol		
C'			B^v | 10 to	393.37	4	Water		
			A^v | 50 °C	2.46454	4	Water in		
A'* | to			(B^v) | to					
B'* | °C			(A^v) | °C					
Ac | to			c_p liq.298 °K	0.365	3			
Bc | t_c °C			308	0.3707	3			
Cc			c_p vap.328 °K	0.279	3'			
Cryos. A°	0.023	3	c_v vap.					
consts. B°								
t_e °C	104.707	5						
						+ grams/100 grams solvent		

REFERENCES: 1-Dow   2-API   3-Lit.   4-Calc. from det. data   5-Calc. by formula

SOURCE: API

PURIFICATION: API

LITERATURE REFERENCES: 3 API Res. Proj. 48; 3' ACS 75, 2795 (1953)

TABLE XXII. MISCELLANEOUS

NAME	Diphenyloxide	STRUCTURAL FORMULA
	Phenyl ether	

Mole % Pur. 99.86	Ref. 1	Molecular Formula $C_{12}H_{10}O$	Molecular Weight 170.200

		Ref.			Ref.			Ref.
F.P. °C	26.79	1	dt/dP			f	to	
F.P. 100%	26.84	1	°C/mm			g	°K	
			25°C	517.70	5	h		
B.P. °C			BP	0.06012	4			
760 mm	257.93	1	t_e	0.03711	5	f'	to	
100	181.3	1	30 mm	0.8574	4	g'	°K	
30	147.13	4				h'		
10	121.	5	ΔHm cal/g	22.90	4			
1	77.	5				m	to	
Pressure			ΔHv cal/g			n	°K	
mm 25°C	0.0213	5	25°C	94.10	5	o		
t_e	1402.6	5	30 mm	80.19	5			
			BP	66.16	5	m'	to	
Density			t_e	62.86	5	n'	°K	
g/ml 20°C	1.07480≠	1	t_e (d, e)	62.37	5	o'		
d_4^t 25	1.07043≠	1	ΔHv/T_e	19.07	5			
30	1.06608	4	d 145 to	98.83	5	Surface tension		
a	1.09228	4	e 290 °C	0.1267	5	dynes/cm. 20°C	40.05	1
b	-0.03874	4	d' 25 to	96.94	5	ɤ 30	38.82	1
			e' 145 °C	0.1138	5	40	37.73	1
Ref. Index								
n_D 25°C	1.57870	1	d_c g/ml	0.312	5	Parachor [P]		
45	1.56919	1	v_c ml/g	3.203	5	20°C	398.4	4
50	1.56681	1	t_c °C	492.5	5	30	398.5	4
"C"	0.7046	4	P_c mm	23380.	5	40	399.0	4
MR (Obs.)	52.818	4	PV/RT			Sugd.	398.0	5
MR (Calc.)	52.057	5	25°C	1.0000	5	Exp. L.1.%/wt.		
(nD-d/2)	1.04359	4	30 mm	1.0000	5	u.		
Dielectric	3.658	1	BP	0.9223	5	Dispersion		
A 145 to	7.09894	1	t_e	0.8985	5	Flash Point °C		
B 325 °C	1871.92	1	t_c	0.245	5	Fire Point		
C	185.84	1	ΔHc kcal/m			M. Spec.		
A* 145 to	1.6455	5	ΔHf			Ultra V.		
B* 300 °C	1783.4	5	ΔFf			X-Ray Dif.		
K						Infrared		
c			Viscosity			Solubility in +		
t_k to			centistokes			Acetone		
t_x °C			η 20 °C	3.9663	1	Carbon tet.		
A' 25 to	7.4531≠	5	40	2.4594	1	Benzene		
B' 147 °C	2115.2	5	60	1.7065	1	Ether		
C'	206.8	5	80	1.2716	1	n-Heptane		
A'* 25 to	1.9826≠	5	B^v 35 to	792.3	4	Ethanol		
B'*147 °C	2015.	5	A^v 85 °C	3.86114	4	Water		
Ac 325 to	7.6329	5	(B^v) to			Water in		
Bc t_c °C	2462.1	5	(A^v) °C					
Cc	260.9	5	c_p liq. °K					
Cryos. A°	0.02177	1						
consts. B°			c_p vap. °K					
t_e °C	287.82	4	c_v vap.					

$T_R = 0.78 T_c$	≠ Supercooled	+ grams/100 grams solvent

REFERENCES: 1-Dow   2-API   3-Lit.   4-Calc. from det. data   5-Calc. by formula

SOURCE: Dow

PURIFICATION: Distillation

LITERATURE REFERENCES:

No. 16

NAME	p-Bromo diphenyl oxide	STRUCTURAL FORMULA
	p-Bromophenyl phenyl ether	

Structural formula: Br ⬡ O ⬡

Mole % Pur. 99.60	Ref. 1	Molecular Formula $C_{12}H_9BrO$	Molecular Weight 249.108

		Ref.				Ref.					Ref.
F.P. °C	18.72	1	dt/dP				f		to		
F.P. 100%			°C/mm				g		°K		
B.P. °C			25°C	33388.	5		h				
760 mm	310.14	1	BP	0.0666	5						
100	226.78	4	t_e	0.03789	5		f'		to		
30	190.65	4	30 mm	0.9000	4		g'		°K		
10	163.	5	ΔHm cal/g	15.00	4		h'				
1	118.	5									
Pressure			ΔHv cal/g				m		to		
mm 25°C	0.0_3217	5	25°C	95.16	5		n		°K		
t_e	1594.5	5	30 mm	63.57	5		o				
Density			BP	50.4	5						
g/ml 20°C	1.42078	1	t_e	46.75	5		m'		to		
d_4^t 25	1.41555	1	t_e (d, e)	45.89	5		n'		°K		
30	1.41030	4	ΔHv/T_e	18.65	5		o'				
a	1.44170	4	d 190 to	84.58	5		Surface tension				
b	-0.00105	4	e 330 °C	0.1102	5		dynes/cm. 20°C	42.69		1
Ref. Index			d' to				30	41.49		1
n_D 20°C	1.60839	1	e' °C				40	40.47		1
25	1.60619	1	d_c g/ml				Parachor [P]			
50	1.60135	1	v_c ml/g				20°C	448.1		4
"C"			t_c °C				30	448.6		4
MR (Obs.)	60.658	4	P_c mm				40	448.4		4
MR (Calc.)	59.822	5	PV/RT				O = 18 Sugd.	448.8		5
(nD-d/2)	0.89800	4	25°C	1.0000	5		Exp. L.1.%/wt.			
Dielectric			30 mm	1.0000	5		u.			
A 190 to	6.68143	1	BP	0.9446	5		Dispersion			
B 400 °C	1683.84	1	t_e	0.9179	5		Flash Point °C			
C	132.90	1	t_c				Fire Point			
A* 190 to	1.3397	5	ΔHc kcal/m				M Spec.			
B* 360 °C	1594.3	5	ΔHf				Ultra V.			
K			ΔFf				X-Ray Dif.			
c			Viscosity				Infrared			
t_k to			centistokes				Solubility in +			
t_x °C			η 20 °C	5.7395	1		Acetone			
A' 25 to	7.0093	5	40	3.2605	1		Carbon tet.			
B' 190 °C	1902.7	5	60	2.1438	1		Benzene			
C'	153.3	5	80	1.5426	1		Ether			
A'* to			B^v to				n-Heptane			
B'* °C			A^v °C				Ethanol			
Ac to			(B^v) to				Water			
Bc t_c °C			(A^v) °C				Water in			
Cc			c_p liq. °K							
Cryos. A°	0.02210	1	c_p vap. °K							
consts. B°										
t_e °C	351.13	5	c_v vap.							

+ grams/100 grams solvent

REFERENCES: 1-Dow   2-API   3-Lit.   4-Calc. from det. data   5-Calc. by formula

SOURCE: Dow

PURIFICATION: Distillation

LITERATURE REFERENCES:

TABLE XXII. MISCELLANEOUS

No. 17

NAME	o-Chlorobenzaldehyde	STRUCTURAL FORMULA

Structural formula: CHO, Cl (benzene ring)

Mole % Pur. 99.61	Ref. 1	Molecular Formula C_7H_5ClO	Molecular Weight 141.567

		Ref.			Ref.			Ref.
F.P. °C	12.19	1	dt/dP			f ___ to °K		
F.P. 100%	12.39	1	°C/mm			g		
B.P. °C			25°C	48.61	5	h		
760 mm	211.89	1	BP	0.05615	4			
100	140.40	4	t_e	0.03665	5	f' ___ to °K		
30	108.63	5	30 mm	0.7974	5	g'		
10	84.31	5				h'		
1	43.53	5	ΔHm cal/g	22.67	4			
			ΔHv cal/g			m ___ to °K		
Pressure			25°C	94.47	5	n		
mm 25°C	0.2718	5	30 mm	85.55	5	o		
t_e	1307.6	5	BP	72.53	5			
Density			t_e	69.72	5	m' ___ to °K		
g/ml 20°C	1.24829	1	t_e (d, e)	69.43	5	n'		
d_4^t 25	1.24320	1	ΔHv/T_e	19.37	5	o'		
30	1.23811	4	d 109 to	99.25	5	Surface tension		
a	1.26865	4	e 236 °C	0.1261	5	dynes/cm. 20°C	31.70	5
b	-0.00102	4	d' 25 to	97.14	5	ɤ 30	30.68	5
Ref. Index			e' 109 °C	0.1067	5	40	29.68	5
n_D 20°C	1.56620	1	d_c g/ml					
25	1.56384	1	v_c ml/g			Parachor [P]		
30	1.56161	4	t_c °C			20°C		
"C"	0.59201	4	P_c mm			30		
MR (Obs.)	37.005	4				40		
MR (Calc.)	37.073	5	PV/RT			Sugd.	269.1	5
(nD-d/2)	0.94206	4	25°C	1.0000	5	Exp. L.1.%/wt.		
Dielectric			30 mm	1.0000	5	u.		
A 109 to	7.06216	1	BP	0.9405	5	Dispersion		
B 290 °C	1718.10	1	t_e	0.9222	5	Flash Point °C		
C	199.	1	t_c			Fire Point		
A* 109 to	1.52895	5	ΔHc kcal/m			M. Spec.		
B* 246 °C	1623.5	5	ΔHf			Ultra V.		
K			ΔFf			X-Ray Dif.		
c			Viscosity			Infrared		
t_k ⌐ to			centistokes			Solubility in +		
t_x ⌐ °C			η °C			Acetone		
A' 25 to	7.38896	5				Carbon tet.		
B' 109 °C	1925.0	5				Benzene		
C'	217.	1	B^v to			Ether		
A'* 25 to	1.85246	5	A^v °C			n-Heptane		
B'*109 °C	1823.9	5	(B^v) to			Ethanol		
Ac to			(A^v) °C			Water		
Bc ⌐t_c °C						Water in		
Cc ⌐			c_p liq. °K					
Cryos. A°	0.01986 ⧧	1	c_p vap. °K					
consts. B°								
t_e °C	236.44	5	c_v vap.					

⧧ purity 99.39 mole %   + grams/100 grams solvent

REFERENCES:	1-Dow 2-API 3-Lit. 4-Calc. from det. data 5-Calc. by formula
SOURCE:	Dow
PURIFICATION:	Distillation
LITERATURE REFERENCES:	

Index